ANNUAL REVIEW OF PHYSIOLOGY

EDITORIAL COMMITTEE

ANNUAL REVIEW OF PHYSIOLOGY

VICTOR E. HALL, *Editor*

University of California, Los Angeles

RALPH R. SONNENSCHEIN, *Associate Editor*

University of California, Los Angeles

ARTHUR C. GIESE, *Associate Editor*

Stanford University

VOLUME 25

1963

ANNUAL REVIEWS, INC.

PALO ALTO, CALIFORNIA, U.S.A.

ANNUAL REVIEWS, INC.
PALO ALTO, CALIFORNIA, U.S.A.

ⓒ 1963 by Annual Reviews, Inc.
All Rights Reserved

Library of Congress Catalogue Card Number: 39-15404

FOREIGN AGENCY

Maruzen Company, Limited
6, Tori-Nichome, Nihonbashi
Tokyo

PRINTED AND BOUND IN THE UNITED STATES OF AMERICA
BY GEORGE BANTA COMPANY, INC.

PREFACE

With the appearance of this, the twenty-fifth volume of the *Annual Review of Physiology*, we have come to feel that our publication has become a stable and mature part of the physiological establishment. Among those responsible for this happy state, we wish now to acknowledge the part played by the members of the Editorial Committee in the critical task of selection of topics and, even more importantly, of authors. The Committee has received, essentially without remuneration, the services of some twenty of the prominent American physiologists. The founding fathers were: A. J. Carlson, J. F. Fulton, M. H. Jacobs, and F. C. Mann, with Walter J. Meek as Chairman, all of whom served until 1945. Their successors, with years of appointment, have been: R. F. Pitts (1948), M. B. Visscher (1949), J. B. Baumberger (1952), J. Field (1952), W. F. Hamilton (1952), J. P. Quigley (1953), H. W. Magoun (1955), G. K. Moe (1955), H. D. Green (1956), J. M. Brookhart (1958), H. W. Davenport (1960), H. Hoagland (1960), R. L. Riley (1960), R. S. Alexander (1961), C. M. Szego (1961), R. Galambos (1962), and A. E. Wilhelmi (1962).

Meeting only once a year, they have brought to the deliberations a great corporate knowledge of the directions in which the various aspects of animal physiology were expanding, and a wealth of intimate personal acquaintance with potential authors as to their merit as investigators and as writers. They have critically reviewed the editorial policy and guided the work of the editorial staff. That their decisions have been predominantly wise appears from the useful role which the *Review* has come to play. We the Editors are confident that our readers will join us in heart-felt appreciation of their valued contribution.

And let us not forget to speak of our delight that Joann Huddleston continues as Assistant Editor to do the lion's share of the work regally, nor that our publisher, the George Banta Company, as ever, faithfully multiplies our words of wisdom in durable form.

V.E.H.
A.C.G.
R.R.S.

CONTENTS

C. HEYMANS, M.D.

A LOOK AT AN OLD BUT STILL CURRENT PROBLEM

By C. Heymans, M.D.

Emeritus Professor of Pharmacology, University of Ghent, Belgium

> *Science is the delight of the soul,*
> *as light is the joy of the eyes.*
> (Aristotle)

When the Editor of the *Annual Review of Physiology* invited me to write the prefatory chapter for Volume 25, I was very honoured and accepted with enthusiasm. Thinking over and over again which theme I was going to present in this chapter, I became more and more worried. Many excellent chapters regarding the history and philosophy of physiology have, indeed, already been written authoritatively for previous volumes, so that I decided not to handle this theme again; this also because I soon realized that my product would be a much weaker one. I also disliked writing an autobiographical sketch, because it would necessarily and embarrassingly extend to a frequent "I", and readers could, therefore, feel what Sacha Guitry said so humorously: "Etre sérieux visiblement, c'est visiblement se prendre au sérieux." I finally realized that the old Greek philosopher was right when advising: "Cobbler, stick to your last!" and I thus decided to write a short historical sketch and story which deals with respiration, my beloved "physiological last". The over-all objective of this modest contribution is the hope that it may prove of some value to the physiologically inclined student and give him at least the feeling that, as Scheele stated so nicely: "There is no delight like that which springs from a discovery, it is a joy that gladdens the heart." In writing this contribution I also wanted to serve my hobby, the background and historical development of a chapter of physiology, mainly because I agree with the statement of Auguste Comte that "to understand a science, it is necessary to know its history" and also with the statement of Goethe: "Die Geschichte einer Wissenschaft ist die Wissenschaft selbst."

The problem of the regulation of respiration is old, but still, we believe, fundamental for the physiology of pulmonary ventilation. All mammalian organisms are indeed dependent for their lives on an uninterrupted exchange of oxygen and carbon dioxide between their blood and the external environment.

1

Experimenting with his air pump, Robert Boyle (1627–91) first showed that a mouse or a bird could not live in a vacuum. If, however, the supply of air was renewed in time, the mouse or bird would recover. He concluded, therefore, that air was essential for life.

The problem of the interaction between air and blood was solved by Richard Lower (1631–91). John Mayow (1643–79) concluded from his observations that "some constituent of the air necessary to life enters into the blood in the act of breathing." Mayow had, in fact, discovered oxygen, though it did not acquire that name until the discovery of Joseph Priestley (1733–1804) more than a century later.

It was, however, Lavoisier (1743–94) who really discovered the nature of oxygen and its importance in respiration, and who proved that inspired air contained oxygen, while expired air contained carbon dioxide.

Pulmonary ventilation has to be very delicately adjusted to the changing requirements of the organism and is influenced by a series of factors and conditions in order to meet specific needs of the body. Such effective regulation of pulmonary ventilation requires an intricate and sensitive control mechanism, consisting of a co-ordinating centre, a receptor system, and an effector system.

Legallois showed, in 1812, that sections above the medulla do not interrupt respiration, while sections below the medulla induce arrest of the respiratory movements. Thus he located the respiratory centre in the area of the medulla.

It was shown by Flourens (1851) that injury or destruction of a limited area located in the medulla oblongata results in immediate and fatal cessation of respiration. Flourens called this area the *noeud vital*, or "vital centre". Various later experimental observations led, however, to the discovery of additional spinal, pontine, mesencephalic, and diencephalic, as well as cortical, nervous structures which also participate in respiratory initiation and regulation. Today it is customary to distinguish a primary respiratory centre in the reticular substance of the medulla and pons from superimposed or secondary respiratory centres in the mesencephalon and diencephalon, and also from spinal effector centres in the spinal cord. The bulbar respiratory centre represents, however, the minimal substrate through which an automatic, i.e., autorhythmic and regulatory activity of the respiration can be maintained. Explorations of the medulla and neighbouring pons have demonstrated the existence of several separate areas which also are essential for the maintenance and control of respiration. Thus alternating stimulation of an inspiratory centre and of an expiratory centre results in rhythmic respiration.

Ablation or section experiments [Lumsden (45)] have led to the assumption of two pontine respiratory centres. In the cranial part of the tegumentum pontis lies a nervous substrate inhibiting respiratory activity, which is called the pneumotaxic centre. A more extensive region in the middle and caudal pons is called the apneustic centre. The latter exerts a strong tonic effect on the bulbar inspiratory centre; therefore, apneustic respiration results when the inhibiting expiratory influence of the pneumotaxic centre is abolished. Concerning the location of the apneustic centre, uniform agreement has as yet not been reached. Probably the apneustic centre includes extensive areas of the lateral reticular substance in the pons. Recent experiments (61) suggest that a nervous structure necessary for the maintenance of respiration is located in the reticular formation, extending rostrally from the level of the obex and lying ventrolaterally of the rostral part of the hypoglossus nucleus. Destruction of this area arrested respiration and led to gasping, thus the area may represent the bulbar inspiratory centre. An excellent review of the anatomical localization of the respiratory centres has been presented recently by Oberholzer & Tofani (50).

As to the mechanisms leading to rhythmic respiration, several possibilities have been suggested. It is generally accepted that the inspiratory centre is tonically active and emits impulses continuously. This locally originating inspiratory tone would then be modulated through two or three inhibitory processes and thus transformed into a series of rhythmic events.

Rylant (57) presented a different interpretation. According to his experimental observations, the origin of inspiratory tonus is located in a pontine centre, the apneustic centre. The continuous activity of this centre would then be modulated, furthered or inhibited by the medullary centre.

Pitts (54) and Wyss (71) have developed, in their detailed review articles, their conceptions of the intrinsic neuronal mechanisms of respiration.

The autonomic activity of the bulbopontine respiratory centres can be furthered or inhibited by a variety of extrinsic nervous or chemical influences.

As to the physiological control of pulmonary ventilation, a century of investigations has gradually produced an impressive accumulation of experimental data. At each stage attempts have been made to organize the observations into a coherent theory on the regulation of pulmonary ventilation.

In earlier days it was customary to distinguish between a proprioceptive reflex and a central chemical regulation of the activities of the respiratory centres. More recent observations, however, have clearly shown that this distinction is no longer exact since a number of chemical regulatory processes also take place through reflex mechanisms. It is therefore better to differentiate between mechanisms regulating breathing on the basis of factors which are responsible for them rather than on the basis of the channels through which they are operative. We must distinguish between mechanical and chemical factors concerned with regulation of respiration.

The mechanical factors are the proprioceptive reflexes, mainly the Hering-Breuer reflexes. The mechanoreceptors involved are located in the airways, chiefly in the lungs, and are connected with the respiratory centres by means of the vagus nerves. The Hering-Breuer reflexes play an important role in regulating the amplitude of inspiratory and expiratory movements.

They also contribute to the maintenance of rhythmicity of the respiratory centres. It was generally accepted that the respiratory motoneurons of the spinal cord receive barrages solely of excitory impulses, the site of interaction being located in the respiratory centres. Recent experiments of Eccles *et al.* (9) showed, however, that the spinal respiratory motoneurons are also the sites of convergence for inhibitory and excitatory pathways of central and segmental reflex mechanisms. The presence and distribution of monosynaptic spinal reflexes also provide a possible basis for the effects of dorsal root section on the Hering-Breuer reflexes reported by Sears (60). Proprioceptive respiratory reflexes acting in the same way on respiration have also been located in the upper airways, the trachea, and the larynx, in the intercostal muscles and joints, and in the diaphragm. These mechanical proprioceptive reflexes contribute primarily to the integrated control of the respiratory cycle, but not to the pulmonary ventilation itself, which is mainly controlled by chemical factors.

As long ago as 1868, Pflüger (53) showed that an increase of carbon dioxide and a decrease of oxygen content in the inhaled air induce a stimulation of breathing and an increase in pulmonary ventilation. Paul Bert (1878) investigated the effects of low barometric pressure on respiration and showed that the respiratory effects produced by carbon dioxide and oxygen were traceable to the partial pressure of these gases in the air breathed. In 1882, Rosenthal (56) came to the conclusion that it is solely, or almost solely, by virtue of its varying oxygen content that the blood does or does not stimulate the respiratory centre. On the other hand, in 1885 Miescher-Rüsch (48) stated that under normal conditions at rest the chemical control of respiration is mainly related to the carbon dioxide percentage in the air of the lungs and less related to the oxygen percentage. Haldane & Smith (21) found that the hyperpnea caused by breathing air in a closed circuit was a result of the rise of partial pressure of carbon dioxide. Further, crossed-circulation experiments reported in 1901 by Léon Fredericq (12) showed that changes in activity of the respiratory centre are induced by variations of the carbon dioxide concentrations in the arterial blood supplying the perfused head.

The investigations of Haldane & Priestley (22) demonstrated more directly that an increase of about 0.01 per cent in the alveolar carbon dioxide concentration is sufficient to increase the resting pulmonary ventilation, whereas a diminution of 0.2 per cent may produce arrest of breathing. On the other hand, the respiration was found to remain practically unchanged until the alveolar oxygen was reduced to 8 per cent. At and under this concentration, respiration increased markedly. These experimental observations led to the conclusion that in normal conditions carbon dioxide acts specifically on the respiratory centre. The increased breathing during oxygen lack was also ascribed to a direct stimulation of the respiratory centre.

Experiments also showed that increase of acidity of the arterial blood stimulates respiration, while alkalinity inhibits breathing [Walter (62),

Araki (1)]. Later, Boycott & Haldane (6) advanced the theory that the hyperpnea of anoxia is caused by lactacidosis, lactic acid being supposed to act in the same way as does carbon dioxide. These authors stated that "the action on the respiratory centre of the circulating blood is due to what may be called its total acidity, including of course, that due to free CO_2." In 1911, Winterstein (63) advanced his first "reaction theory", according to which the activity of the respiratory centre is regulated in all physiological conditions, including oxygen lack, by the hydrogen-ion concentration in the arterial blood. Next, Hasselbach (23) proposed that the arterial pH is the respiratory stimulus, but that other factors may alter the sensitivity of the respiratory centre to this unique stimulus. Later experiments showed, however, that during acute hypoxemic hyperpnea the arterial blood shifts not to the acid but to the alkaline side [Winterstein (64)].

Experiments of Laqueur & Verzar (41); Hooker, Wilson & Connet (37); Scott (59); Haldane, Kellas & Kennaway (19, 20); Henderson & Haggard (25); Mellanby (47); and Ege & Henriques (10) also demonstrated that the adjustment of pulmonary ventilation by carbon dioxide is not always related to an increase in arterial hydrogen-ion concentration and that hyperventilation induced by oxygen deficiency does not always involve arterial acidosis. In 1921, Winterstein (65) advanced his second "reaction theory" and stated that the chemical regulation of the respiratory centre is dependent on the hydrogen-ion concentration within the centre itself and not on the hydrogen-ion concentration of the arterial blood. In 1923, Gesell (13, 14, 15) also advanced the "intracellular acidity theory" and stated that "the activity of the respiratory centre is fundamentally a function of its own acidity, as opposed to the acidity of the arterial blood, the specificity of CO_2 and the direct stimulating effect of lack of oxygen."

In accordance with his experimental observations, Nielsen (49) stated, however, that arterial pCO_2 acts as the unique and specific central stimulant of respiration and that pO_2, pH, and exercise are only sensitizers to carbon dioxide. There is, however, at present little reason to suppose that carbon dioxide exerts a specific action on the respiratory centre; it is undoubtedly a powerful respiratory stimulant, but it may well exert this central action solely by means of its ready diffusibility, thus acting as a rapid source of intracellular hydrogen ions.

The regulation of the pulmonary ventilation at rest thus seemed to be fairly well understood. The importance of carbon dioxide, oxygen lack, and increased acidity, and combinations thereof, as direct chemical stimuli to centrally located specialized neural structures seemed to be well accepted. From 1925 on, however, a change occurred and a new concept for the chemical regulation of respiration had to be considered. J. F. and C. Heymans (35, 36) showed, indeed, that chemoreceptors peripherally located in the aortic arch area act reflexly on the respiratory centre. Perfusing the isolated head of a recipient dog by means of a donor dog, the perfused head being connected with the body of the recipient by means of the vagus nerves only,

these investigators observed that asphyxia or anoxia of the body of the recipient induced a reflex stimulation of the respiratory centre of the perfused
head. Hyperventilation of the body induced, on the contrary, a reflex inhibition of the respiratory centre. Some pharmacological substances, such as
nicotine, injected into the circulation of the body of the recipient also provoked a reflex stimulation of the respiratory centre of the perfused head. By
means of several experimental methods, the origin of this chemoreflex stimulation of the respiratory centre was located in the area of the aortic arch,
the afferent pathways being situated in the vagus nerves. Chemoreceptors so
located, responding to increase or decrease of carbon dioxide and lack of
oxygen in the arterial blood and acting reflexly on the respiratory centre,
were thus discovered.

While investigating the pressoreceptors of the carotid sinus, C. Heymans
and co-workers (27 to 34) observed that this area is also provided with
chemoreceptors that respond to the same chemical stimuli as the aortic
chemoreceptors. These chemoreceptors act reflexly mainly on the respiratory
centre, but also on the cardiovascular centres. The afferent pathways of
these chemoreceptors are located in the carotid sinus nerves. Further experiments showed that the carotid sinus chemoreceptors are located in the carotid body or glomus caroticum, while the pressoreceptors of the carotid sinus
are situated in the arterial walls of this area. Later, Comroe & Schmidt (7)
showed that the chemoreceptors of the aortic arch area are located in the
aortic bodies.

The question has been asked several times: "How did you find these
chemoreceptors?" Here's the answer. The primary observations on the
chemoreceptors of the aortic arch area were made during performance of
experiments for other purposes with the use of the isolated perfused head of
a dog, connected with his body by means of the vagus nerves only. Arrest of
the artificial ventilation of the body of the recipient dog induced a reflex
stimulation of the respiratory centre of the perfused head. This astonishing
and unexpected observation started a series of planned experiments which
continued until the location and functions of the chemoreceptors in the
aortic arch area were identified.

The discovery of the chemoreceptors of the carotid sinus area occurred
in the following way. My father and best teacher always advised his pupils,
"Never kill an animal at the end of a planned experiment, if the animal may
still be used for any experimental purpose, and take profit of this animal to
perform any experimental trial, even if it looks foolish, but keep your eyes
well open in order to catch any unexpected event." One day, also bearing in
mind the statement of Darwin, "I like to perform foolish experiments," we
finished a planned experiment on the carotid sinus baroreceptors. One carotid
sinus area of the dog was denervated, the other being still innervated. Won-
dering for what experimental purpose this dog could still be used, we injected into the common carotid artery with normal carotid sinus innervation
some potassium cyanide solution, which was standing on the laboratory

desk. According to expectation, a marked hyperpnea occurred. When similar amounts of cyanide were next injected into the carotid artery, the carotid sinus of which was denervated, no hyperpnea occurred. The alternate injections were repeated several times and the same very unexpected respiratory responses were observed. Next morning a planned experiment was performed and gave the same results. This primary unplanned experiment, at first sight a very foolish-looking trial, also started a series of planned experiments, performed with several methods, which led to the identification of the chemoreceptors of the carotid body and their functions.

Good luck thus was of great help, but perhaps as Pasteur stated: "Dans le champs de l'observation, le hasard ne favorise que les esprits préparés." Investigators indeed have to be ready to catch an unexpected event, especially if this event is or seems to be in opposition to so-called classic opinions or theories. When, in 1927, we arrived in the department of Carl Wiggers, one of our best teachers, he asked us first of all which experiments we had performed recently? Answering this question, we explained carefully our observations concerning the baroreceptors regulating arterial pressure and the chemoreceptors acting on respiration. Carl Wiggers listened and then said: "Heymans, do you really believe what you said? Because I suppose you know that it is in full contradiction with all classic opinions. Now, let us not argue, but tomorrow we shall provide a dog and you are going to demonstrate what you said." Just as John Hunter said to Edward Jenner: "Why think? Why not try the experiment?" Next morning, then, we performed the demonstration while Carl Wiggers was looking at it very carefully. At the end of the experiment, he said: "Heymans, the dog is right, textbooks are wrong!" This behaviour of Carl Wiggers shows how open-minded he is and explains why he made so many very important and fundamental contributions to cardiovascular physiology. A free and open mind is fundamental in research, and as Claude Bernard advised: "L'expérimentateur doit douter, fuir les idées fixes et garder toujours sa liberté d'esprit." Too many investigators are, indeed, bound by hypotheses and theories, which soon become dogmatic and irreversible opinions. Laennec very correctly counseled: "Soyons prêts à abandonner une théorie dès qu'un fait lui résiste." The old Chinese philosopher Lao-Tseu also stated very nicely: "It is a very outstanding merit to realize that we are very ignorant, but to believe that we are very well informed is the disease of man." Let us also never forget the so true statement of Frederick Gowland Hopkins that "all dogmatic teaching about any aspect of the phenomena of life is apt to be checked by the ultimate discovery that the living cell is before all things a heretic."

The discovery of peripherally located chemoreceptors acting reflexly on respiration was, however, not accepted without much resistance coming from several sources and we also had to undergo what Claude Bernard predicted: "Quand vous avez trouvé quelque chose de nouveau, on commence par dire que ce n'est pas vrai, puis lorsque la vérité de ce que vous avez avancé devient absolument évidente, on dit que ce n'est pas vous qui l'avez trouvé." Investigators have to accept such situations in a philosophical way. Anyway, I may repeat what Léon Fredericq also felt when he said: "J'ai vécu des jours heureux. Il en est peu qui m'aient laissé des souvenirs plus vifs que ceux où le hasard favorable m'a mis sur la trace de quelque fait nouveau."

The anatomy and development of the aortic and carotid bodies have been investigated by a number of anatomists and histologists (34). Experiments showed that these structures are very sensitive to the oxygen tension in the arterial blood and that acute hypoxia induces stimulation of the respiratory centre by means of a reflex chemoreceptive drive only.

Recordings of the action potentials of the carotid body chemoreceptive fibres also showed increasing impulses with increasing hypoxemia. The great sensitivity of the chemoreceptors to changes in oxygen tension is attested, furthermore, by the fact that impulses from them could be recorded as soon as the oxygen saturation of the blood fell below 96 per cent, while increasing the oxygen saturation of the blood above 96 per cent decreases them. Recent experiments by Eyzaguirre & Lewin (11) on the cat's carotid body *in vitro* also showed that chemoreceptor discharge frequency is very low if the carotid body is bathed with saline equilibrated with 100 per cent oxygen, while the discharge is increased if the solution is replaced by another with 50 per cent oxygen, a maximum of discharge being attained with 20 per cent or 10 per cent oxygen. Experiments performed *in vivo* also showed that the carotid body chemoreceptors respond to a wide range of changes of oxygen tension in the plasma.

It was shown, furthermore, that in animals deprived of their aortic and carotid chemoreceptors, hypoxia or low barometric pressure induces respiratory depression, rather than hyperpnea. Hyperpnea produced by acute oxygen deficiency, which was considered previously as centrogenic, is therefore brought about by the chemoreceptor reflexogenic drive.

As to the role of the chemoreceptor reflex mechanism in the hyperventilation induced by prolonged and chronic oxygen want, experiments of Bjurstedt (5) stated that, while the initial effect of oxygen lack on respiration is exclusively attributable to the chemoreceptive reflex drive, the effect of prolonged hypoxemia results mainly from direct central impulses. In hypoxemia of long duration, the alkalinity of the blood caused by the hyperpnea progressively disappears. At the same time the chemoreflex drive becomes less active, and the central drive becomes more and more important, and finally controls respiration almost entirely. Winterstein (66, 67), however, pointed out that in spite of the reduction of the oxygen saturation of the blood during oxygen lack, the increase in arterial cH has induced an increase in oxygen tension of the blood, which might well be sufficient to explain the decrease in chemoreflex drive during prolonged hypoxemia. Experiments of Schmidt & Comroe (58) showed indeed that the oxygen tension, rather than the oxygen saturation in the arterial blood, is the main factor affecting the chemoreceptors.

In animals or patients with respiratory failure and acidemia, the chemo-receptive hypoxic drive seems not to be a major factor in the respiratory control. The level of the pH, the pCO_2, and pO_2 of the arterial blood and the interaction between these factors seem to be the major mechanism in regulating the pulmonary ventilation of these patients.

Numerous authors have observed a gradual and prolonged respiratory depression after the administration of oxygen to patients with respiratory failure. According to Penman (52) these effects of breathing oxygen coincide with a fall in levels of fixed acid in the blood. The potency of prolonged oxygen lack as a stimulus to respiration thus seems to be related to the pH of the arterial blood. The chemoreceptive and centrogenic drives are, however, related to the arterial pH. The chemoreceptors are also strongly stimulated by anemic hypoxia, evoked mainly by carotid occlusion or by a fall in arterial pressure and blood supply to the aortic and carotid bodies.

As to the role of the chemoreceptors in the regulation of respiration by arterial carbon dioxide, experiments (4, 34, 68, 69, 70) have indicated that the chemoreceptors are stimulated by a slight increase in arterial carbon dioxide. Recordings of action potentials of chemoreceptive fibres further showed that these fibres began to discharge as soon as the alveolar pCO_2 exceeded about 30 mm Hg and that the discharge increased in approximately linear relation to the alveolar pCO_2. The respiratory centre, however, deprived of its chemoreflex innervation, still responds to increased carbon dioxide in the inhaled air and in the arterial blood. The respiratory centre, therefore, also reacts directly to the arterial pCO_2.

The relative importance of the chemoreflexes and of the respiratory centre itself in the regulation of breathing by carbon dioxide has been much discussed. According to one viewpoint, the chemoreflex mechanism plays a significant part in the control of breathing by carbon dioxide, under all circumstances. A second viewpoint implies that the chemoreceptors are not active under normal conditions and only become so in unusual (emergency) circumstances typified by hypoxemia, by marked hypercarbia associated with severe respiratory depression, and by action of certain drugs.

The importance of the aortic and carotid chemoreflex component, as compared with that of the direct central drive, in the regulation of breathing by carbon dioxide in different physiological and pathological conditions, is still open for discussion. Under some conditions the former may, indeed, be the most important, while in other conditions the latter may be predominant. The regulation of respiration, therefore, must be considered in the light of the "multiple factor theory" of respiratory regulation as emphasized by Gray (16, 17, 18). Indeed, the interaction between the different factors regulating respiration controls the pulmonary ventilation under different physiological or physiopathological conditions. The mechanical reflexes of respiratory regulation may also interfere with the chemical centrogenic and chemoreceptive reflexogenic regulatory mechanisms of breathing. Thus, the importance of any factor regulating respiration may vary according to the activity level of other factors acting directly or reflexly on the respiratory centre. As stated a long time ago by Haldane & Priestley (22), "the evaluation of each factor in the regulation of breathing depends on its varying relation to the others."

The question arose as to the extent to which the "chemoreflex mechanism" of respiratory regulation requires modification of the "reaction theory" of the regulation of breathing. This problem has been examined mainly by Hesser (26) and Winterstein (67).

Heymans et al. (30, 33, 34) showed that acidity stimulates the chemoreceptors, while alkalinity acts in the opposite way. Euler et al. (34) presented evidence that the factor exciting the chemoreceptors during oxygen want and carbon dioxide excess is the cH within the chemoreceptive cells themselves. Winterstein (66, 67), after summarizing the results of the investigations performed by different authors, proposes the following picture of the chemical regulation of respiration: the activity of the respiratory centre is entirely parallel with the reaction of the blood and, as far as hematogenic regulation of breathing is concerned, agrees completely with the "reaction theory". The effect of oxygen lack is entirely reflex by way of the chemoreceptors, whose activity—again is complete agreement with the "reaction theory"—depends on the intracellular hydrogen-ion concentration in the glomi (chemoreceptive cells). The chemoreceptive regulation of respiration in hypoxia leads to an increase in the alkalinity of the blood as a result of the induced hyperpnea. This increase in alkalinity reduces the oxygen tension of the blood for the same oxygen saturation, and, thus, increases again the intracellular cH in the glomi (chemoreceptive cells) and consequently reinforces the hyperpnea by chemoreflex drive. The sensitivity of the respiratory centre and of the chemoreceptors to any variation in cH may therefore explain the changes in respiration induced by carbon dioxide and by hypoxemia.

In the opinion of Hesser (26) the experimental evidences speak in favour of the "intracentral acidity theory" for the chemical stimulation of the centre itself. The peripheral chemoreceptors probably respond more rapidly to changes in arterial cH than do the central chemosensitive cells of the respiratory centre.

Recently, Joels et al. (38, 39, 40) have used the isolated perfused carotid body of the cat to study the independent and combined effects of pCO_2, pH, and hypoxia on chemoreceptor impulse discharge. They found that the chemoreceptor response to the combination of hypoxia and hypercapnia greatly exceeded that which might have been expected from the arithmetic summation of the effects of either stimulus acting alone. At constant perfusate pH, they also detected a stimulus produced by the rising pCO_2, whether the pO_2 of the perfusate was high or low. The pH had a similar independent effect. The responses of the chemoreceptors to hypoxia were, however, weak if the pH was very alkaline. Experiments of Aström (3) also showed that the stimulation of respiration by carbon dioxide depends on the degree of oxygen saturation of the arterial blood.

A number of drugs also stimulate the chemoreceptors. Substances such as cyanide, acetylcholine, sulfide, nicotine, lobeline, and many others, which were long supposed to stimulate the respiratory centre directly, induce, on the contrary, hyperpnea reflexly by means of a stimulation of the chemo-receptors. The direct central effect of these compounds is indeed not a stimu-lation but an inhibition.

Several explanations have been proposed (34), concerning the mechanisms involved in the physiological or pharmacological stimulation of the aortic and carotid bodies' chemoreceptors. These explanations are, however, still open to further investigations.

Respiratory reflexes induced by chemical stimulation of receptors located in the cardiopulmonary circulation have been identified by several investi-gators. The pulmonary respiratory chemoreflexes may be elicited by several chemical stimulants such as ethylacetoacetate, amidines, guanidines, isothio-ureas, 5-hydroxytryptamine (serotonin), veratrum alkaloids, and ATP. Coronary chemoreflexes may also act on respiration and can be induced by a number of drugs. Adequate physiological chemical stimuli for these re-ceptors are less well known.

Recently Riley et al. (55) and Armstrong et al. (2) suggested the possi-bility of a pulmonary arterial carbon dioxide chemoreceptor mechanism acting reflexly on the respiratory centre. However, Cropp & Comroe (8) failed to observe any ventilatory effect by increasing the pulmonary arterial pCO_2 when the arterial pCO_2 was held constant. Direct evidence for the existence of venous or pulmonary arterial carbon dioxide receptors con-trolling respiration is not provided.

It was claimed by Héger (24) and Pagano (51), and more recently by others, that chemoreceptors acting on respiration are also present in many other vascular areas, mainly in the mesenteric area. It should be pointed out, however, that experimental evidence for the existence of specific chemo-receptors in these vascular areas is not very convincing. The reactions ob-tained seem, indeed, to be caused by nonspecific stimulation of other vas-cular or regional receptors by irritant drugs, noxious stimuli, ischemia, and pain. Differentiation between specific and nonspecific stimulations of re-ceptors is absolutely necessary. Many receptors, such as baroreceptors, stretch receptors, and pain receptors, may be stimulated by nonspecific agencies, mainly drugs, and induce reflex reactions. These reactions do not mean, however, that the receptors which were stimulated are true chemo-receptors.

Cerebrospinal fluid chemoreceptors acting on respiration and sensitive to pH, pCO_2, and drugs have been identified primarily by Leusen (42). The location of these receptors has not been settled. Loeschke (43) believes them to be located in the lateral recess of the fourth ventricle, whereas Massion *et al.* (46) placed them in the area postrema. Changes in pH or pCO_2 in the perfusates of the fourth ventricle may induce respiratory reactions. The transfer between blood and the spinal fluid is, however, relatively slow and thus may not be considered as responsible for the rapidly occurring responses of the respiratory centre to changes in pH, pCO_2, or pO_2 in the arterial blood. Changes in pH, pO_2, or pCO_2 in the spinal fluid could, nevertheless, be responsible for some slowly occurring respiratory responses, as in acclimatization to altitude and in some pathological conditions.

According to Loeschke (43, 44), there may be intracranial chemoreceptors which can reflexly affect the activity of the respiratory centre. More experimental evidence would, however, be needed to show that these receptors are true specific chemoreceptors, and not other intracranial receptors also sensitive to nonspecific stimulants.

Respiration may also be affected reflexly by means of the aortic and carotid sinus baroreceptors, stimulation of which by a rise of arterial pressure may reflexly inhibit the respiratory centre and even induce apnea, while a decrease may provoke hyperpnea.

The mechanisms of hyperpnea during muscular exercise and in high-altitude acclimatization are still open for discussion. At the Haldane Centenary Symposium on Respiration, held in Oxford (1961), different opinions have been presented, but obviously more work is needed here.

Coming at the end of this short and, we are afraid, very incomplete survey of some problems related to respiration, we are sure that the readers will also realize the truth of the answer of Broemser to the question of Frank, when Broemser came to work in his laboratory: "Young man, tell me what you know?" Broemser said: "Professor, it would be easier for me to answer if you would ask me what I do not know!" In the physiology of respiration, there also are still more unknown than known answers to many questions. But, to the young physiologically inclined investigators we would like to say with Renan: "Jeunes gens, faites de la science, c'est encore ce qu'il y a de plus sérieux"—"Young men, be interested in research, it is still the most thrilling activity in life!

LITERATURE CITED

Many detailed references in *Reflexogenic Areas of the Cardiovascular System* (Heymans, C., and Neil, E., Eds., J. & A. Churchill, Ltd., London, 1958)

1. Araki, T. Z., *Z. Physiol. Chem.*, **19**, 422 (1894)
2. Armstrong, B. W., Hunt, H. H., Blyde, R. W., and Workman, J. M., *Science*, **133**, 1897 (1961)
3. Aström, A., *Acta Physiol. Scand.*, **27**, Suppl. 98 (1952)
4. Bartels, H., and Witzleb, E., *Arch. Ges. Physiol.*, **262**, 466 (1956)
5. Bjurstedt, H., *Acta Physiol. Scand.*, **12**, Suppl. 38 (1946)
6. Boycott, A. E., and Haldane, J. S. *J. Physiol. (London)*, **37**, 355 (1908)
7. Comroe, J. H., and Schmidt, C. F., *Am. J. Physiol.*, **121**, 75 (1938)
8. Cropp, G., and Comroe, J. H., Jr., *The Physiologist*, **3**, 43 (1960)
9. Eccles, R. M., Sears, T. A., and Shealy, C. N., *Nature*, **193**, 844 (1962)
10. Ege, R., and Henriques, V., *Biochem. Z.*, **176**, 441 (1926)
11. Eyzaguirre, C., and Lewin, J., *J. Physiol. (London)*, **159**, 222 (1962)
12. Fredericq, L., *Arch. Biol. (Paris)*, **17**, 561 (1901)
13. Gesell, R., *Am. J. Physiol.*, **66**, (1923)
14. Gesell, R., *Physiol. Rev.*, **5**, 551 (1925)
15. Gesell, R., *Ergeb. Physiol.*, **43**, 477 (1940)
16. Gray, J. S., *Research Project AAF School Aviation Med.*, No. 386 (1945)
17. Gray, J. S., *Science*, **103**, 739 (1946)
18. Gray, J. S., *Pulmonary Ventilation and Its Physiological Regulation* (C C Thomas, Publ., Springfield, Ill., 1950)
19. Haldane, J. S., *Respiration* (Oxford, 1935)
20. Haldane, J. S., Kellas, A. M., and Kennaway, E. L., *J. Physiol. (London)*, **53**, 181 (1919)
21. Haldane, J. S., and Smith, J. L., *J. Pathol. Bacteriol.*, **1**, 168, 318 (1893)
22. Haldane, J. S., and Priestley, J. G., *J. Physiol. (London)*, **32**, 225 (1905)
23. Hasselbach, K., *Biochem. Z.*, **46**, 403 (1912)
24. Héger, P., *Beitr. Physiol.*, Ludwig gewidmet, p. 193 (1887)
25. Henderson, Y., and Haggard, H. W., *J. Biol. Chem.*, **33**, 333, 345, 355
26. Hesser, C. M., *Acta Physiol. Scand.*, **18**, Suppl. 64 (1949)
27. Heymans, C., "Action of Drugs on Carotid Body and Sinus," *Pharmacol. Rev.*, **7**, 119 (1955) (With detailed literature)
28. Heymans, C., and Bouckaert, J. J., *Compt. Rend. Soc. Biol.*, **103**, 498 (1930)
29. Heymans, C., and Bouckaert, J. J., *J. Physiol. (London)*, **69**, 13P (1930)
30. Heymans, C., and Bouckaert, J. J., *La sensibilité réflexogène des vaisseaux aux excitants chimiques* (Hermann et Cie, Paris, 1934)
31. Heymans, C., Bouckaert, J. J., and Dautrebande, L., *Arch. Intern. Pharmacodynamie*, **39**, 400 (1930)
32. Heymans, C., Bouckaert, J. J., von Euler, U. S., and Dautrebande, L., *Arch. Intern. Pharmacodynamie*, **43**, 86 (1932)
33. Heymans, C., Bouckaert, J. J., and Regniers, P., *Le sinus carotidien* (Doin et Cie, Paris, 1933)
34. Heymans, C., and Neil, E., *Reflexogenic Areas of the Cardiovascular System* (J. & A. Churchill, Ltd., London, 1958) (With detailed literature)
35. Heymans, J. F., and Heymans, C., *Compt. Rend. Soc. Biol.*, **92**, 1335 (1925); **94**, 1255 (1926); **95**, 1118 (1926)
36. Heymans, J. F., and Heymans, C., *Arch. Intern. Pharmacodynamie*, **32**, 9 (1926); **33**, 273 (1927)
37. Hooker, D. R., Wilson, D. W., and Connet, H., *Am. J. Physiol.*, **43**, 351 (1917)
38. Joels, N., and Neil, E., *J. Physiol. (London)*, **154**, 7P (1960)
39. Joels, N., and Neil, E., *J. Physiol. (London)*, **155**, 45P (1961)
40. Joels, N., Neil, E., and Vaughan Hudson, B., *J. Physiol. (London)*, **155**, 30P (1961)
41. Laqueur, E., and Verzar, F., *Arch. Ges. Physiol.*, **143**, 395 (1912)
42. Leusen, I., *Arch. Intern. Physiol.*, **58**, 115 (1950); *Arch. Intern. Pharmacodynamie*, **87**, 248 (1951)
43. Loeschke, H. H., Katsaros, B., and Lerche, D., *Arch. Ges. Physiol.*, **270**, 461 (1960)
44. Loeschke, H. H., Koepchen, H. P., and Gentz, K. H., *Arch. Ges. Physiol.*, **266**, 569 (1958)
45. Lumsden, T., *J. Physiol. (London)*, **57**, 153, 354 (1923); **58**, 81, 111 (1923/24)
46. Massion, W. H., Mitchell, R. A., and Severinghaus, J. W., *Anesthesiology*, **22**, 137 (1961)

47. Mellanby, J., *J. Physiol. (London)*, **56**, 38 (1922)
48. Miescher-Rüsch, F., *Arch. f. Physiol.*, 355 (1885)
49. Nielsen, M., *Skand. Arch. Physiol.*, **74**, Suppl. 10 (1936)
50. Oberholzer, R. J. H., and Tofani, W. O., *Handbook of Physiology*, **2**, 111 (1961)
51. Pagano, G., *Arch. Ital. Physiol.*, **33**, 1 (1900)
52. Penman, R. W. B., *Clin. Sci.*, **22**, 155 (1962)
53. Pflüger, E. F. W., *Arch. Ges. Physiol.*, **1**, 61 (1868)
54. Pitts, R. F., *Physiol. Rev.*, **26**, 609 (1946)
55. Riley, R. L., Ross, R. S., and Armstrong, B., *Federation Proc.*, **20**, 431 (1961)
56. Rosenthal, J., *Hermann's Handb. Physiol.*, **4**, 157 (1882)
57. Rylant, P., *Mém. Acad. Roy. Méd. Belg.*, **1**, 1 (1942)
58. Schmidt, C. F., and Comroe, J. H., *Physiol. Rev.*, **20**, 115 (1940)
59. Scott, W. R., *Am. J. Physiol.*, **47**, 43 (1918)
60. Sears, T. A., *J. Physiol. (London)*, **142**, 35P (1958)
61. Vassella, T., *Helv. Physiol. Pharmacol. Acta*, 19, 166 (1961)
62. Walter, F., *Arch. Exptl. Pathol. Pharmakol.*, **7**, 148 (1877)
63. Winterstein, H., *Arch. Ges. Physiol.*, **138**, 167 (1911)
64. Winterstein, H., *Biochem. Z.*, **70**, 45 (1915)
65. Winterstein, H., *Arch. Ges. Physiol.*, **187**, 293 (1921)
66. Winterstein, H., *Arch. Intern. Pharmacodynamie*, **83**, 80 (1950)
67. Winterstein, H., *Ergeb. Physiol.*, **48**, 328 (1955)
68. Witzleb, E., *Arch. Ges. Physiol.*, **256**, 234 (1952); **257**, 244 (1953)
69. Witzleb, E., *Arch. Ges. Physiol.*, **269**, 439, 471 (1959)
70. Witzleb, E., Bartels, H., Budde, H., and Mochizucki, M., *Arch. Ges. Physiol.*, **261**, 211 (1955)
71. Wyss, O. A. M., *Helv. Physiol. Pharmacol. Acta*, **12**, Suppl. 10 (1954)

PROTOPLASM: ENDOPLASMIC RETICULUM AND MICROSOMES AND THEIR PROPERTIES[1,2]

By Philip Siekevitz

The Rockefeller Institute

Introduction

In recent years, much biological interest has been evinced in the structure and function of the intracellular membranes. This review has been written because of this, and not because we have a great deal of definite knowledge concerning these membranes. However, I do think a partial summing at this time is in order. Most of these membranes can be isolated, from cells which contain them, in a fraction which has been called microsomes. This name is unfortunate because it merely denotes a procedure, the high-speed pellet obtained from a mitochondrial supernatant, and hence the identity of the structures in the microsome fraction will depend on the intracellular structure of the cells from which the fractions were obtained. This is brought out more fully in a recent article (1), which also contains some methods for obtaining mammalian microsomes. In the past ten years some review articles have contained information concerning microsomes, both from a biochemical (2 to 10) and a morphological viewpoint (11 to 16a). The latter articles reported observations on the endoplasmic reticulum, and since in most cases, assuredly that of liver (17) and pancreas (18), the microsome fraction is the isolated fragmented reticulum, I will use the term "microsome" as denoting the isolated intracellular membrane fraction. Since, in some cases it has been shown (17, 18) that the fraction is heterogeneous, containing both membranes and particles, and since the literature on the role of the particles in protein synthesis is by this time voluminous, I have omitted references to protein synthesis. This review will then discuss the isolation of microsomes from various tissues, the identity of the fraction in certain cases, the enzymes which have been found contained therein, and various theoretical musings on the functionings of the intracellular membranes. In addition, since it is thought (cf. 11, 13) that the intracellular membranes are in certain instances in continuity with the cell membrane, some relevant experiments concerning the latter will also be cited.

Isolation

The systematic isolation of, and biochemical work on, microsomes began with Claude (cf. 19) and was continued by Schneider & Hogeboom (cf. 2, 3),

---

[1] The survey of literature pertaining to this review was concluded in August 1962.

[2] Abbreviations used are: ATP, ATPase (adenosine triphosphate and triphosphatase); CDP, CTP (cytidine di- and triphosphate); CoA (coenzyme A); CoQ (coenzyme Q); GDP (guanosine diphosphate); NAD, NADP, NADH, NADPH (nicotinamide adenine dinucleotide, nicotinamide adenine dinucleotide phosphate, and their respective reduced forms); RNA (ribonucleic acid); UDP, UMP, and UTP (uridine di-, mono-, and triphosphate).

until by now it has embraced many cell types and different tissues. The technique of simple differential centrifugation in a medium of single density was used by the early workers (cf. 4), and indeed it still is the popular one. But lately, other techniques have been used to isolate the membranous components of the cell. Gradient differential centrifugation, isopycnic centrifugation, and isopycnic gradient centrifugation (cf. 20) have all been used to separate light membranous components from heavier elements, or to separate membranes without particles from membranes with particles attached to them. Thomson and his co-workers (21, 22) have used a gradient method to fractionate microsomes from liver, while Kuff and his collaborators (23, 24, 25) have not only fractionated microsomes from whole homogenate by gradient techniques, but have isolated Golgi membranes (25) by similar methods. Lately, microsomes from brain (26) and smooth-surfaced membranes (those without attached particles) from liver (27) have been isolated by isopycnic centrifugation. A novel scheme of fractionation in a two-phase liquid system has been adopted by Albertsson et al. to separate brain microsomes (28).

Microsomes, that is, a high-speed particle preparation, have been isolated, using mostly differential centrifugation methods, from such tissues as adrenal cortex (29), testicles (30, 31), brain (26, 32, 33, 34), mammary gland and milk (35), and various plant organs (36 to 43). The latter work is significant in that electron micrographs of microsomes from onion roots (41) or beet petioles and wheat roots (40) showed the same predominant structure, membranes lined with particles, such as the microsomes isolated by similar methods from liver (17) and pancreas (18).

If one looks at various cells *in situ*, one is struck by the morphological differences among the various membranous structures in the cell; the most obvious is that some membranes have ribonucleoprotein particles, or ribosomes, on them and some do not. In addition, there are the membranes of the Golgi complex (44), the fine membranous network of the sarcoplasmic reticulum (45), and the small vesicles associated with the glycogen areas in liver (46). Attempts have been made to isolate all these different membranes, the procedures being controlled by electron microscopy. Kuff & Dalton (25) have isolated Golgi membranes from epithelial cells. Luck (47) has isolated the membranes associated with the glycogen areas in liver, while smooth membranes, devoid of particles, have been isolated from liver by Rothschild (27) and by Moulé and co-workers (48, 49). The isolation of the membranes of the sarcoplasmic reticulum is a special problem in that, if one works with heart, one has to contend with the fragility of heart mitochondria. During the homogenization or fractionation, or both, some of the mitochondria break up and the fragments end up in the microsome fraction (1, 50). Since these fragments resemble sarcoplasmic reticulum fragments of the heart, the only way of determining the contamination is by enzymatic analyses (1, 50). Whether the difficulty in isolating muscle cell microsomes is true only of heart is not known, but frog skeletal muscle microsomes can be prepared practically free of mitochondrial contamination (51). Rat myometrium microsomes have also been isolated (52, 53), but again, electron-microscopic evidence and enzymatic assays indicate some mitochondrial contamination. Recent interest has been evinced in the so-called "relaxing factor" of muscle (cf. 54); this now seems to be in reality a preparation of the isolated fragments of the sarcoplasmic reticulum (55). Once again the problem arises as to whether the presence of "relaxing factor" in the microsomes is caused by mitochondrial contamination, but evidence having to do with the presence of a distinctive ATPase activity (51, 56) makes one think that the factor is truly a microsomal component. I will come back to this later.

CHEMICAL COMPOSITION

It has been known for a long time that the microsomes of certain tissues, such as liver, are concentrations of phospholipid and RNA (19). Indeed a good deal of the RNA of the liver and pancreas cell seems to be concentrated in this fraction, and we now know that the RNA is mostly in the ribosomal particles attached to the membranes (17, 18). However, since not all of the RNA in the microsomal fraction can be isolated in the form of ribosomal particles, the question of whether or not there is some RNA in the membrane has arisen. This question is difficult to answer, because the small quantities involved raise the possibility of contamination of membranes by ribosomes. However, there is some indication that the membranes of the microsome fraction do contain a small, but significant, amount of RNA. Thus Kuff & Dalton (25) found that the Golgi membranes from the epithelial cells of the epididymis contained about 10 per cent of the RNA of the whole homogenate, and electron micrographs of the preparation indicated that the possible contamination of the preparation by ribosomes could not be high enough to account for the relatively large amount of RNA. Also membranes associated with the glycogen fraction of liver (47), though containing very few ribosomes in the preparation, had an RNA-to-protein ratio identical with that of whole liver microsomes, indicating some RNA in this type of membrane. Again, the smooth membranes from liver, as isolated, contain a significant amount of RNA (27, 48, 49). The form or function of this RNA is unknown. It may be different from ribosomal RNA since there seem to be differences in turnover among the RNA of microsomal subfractions (57 to 61); whether these differences come from different kinds of RNA in the ribosomes, or differences between ribosomal and "membrane" RNA, or both, is not known.

The amount of total lipid in the microsomes has been estimated to be from 30 to 50 per cent (19, 35, 37, 62, 63, 64), with not too much variation among different tissues. Of these total lipids, one half to two-thirds are reported to be phospholipids (19, 35, 37, 63), though one report gives a lower amount of phospholipids in the microsomes from various tissues (65). The presence of phospholipids in microsomes is not surprising, considering the membrane origin of the fraction. Values which can be calculated, from the data, for the ratio of phospholipid to protein in isolated microsomes have ranged from 0.2 for castor bean (43), 0.3 for milk (35) and liver (62), 0.4 for myometrium (53) and the membranes of the liver glycogen fraction (47), 0.5

for silver beet (37) and liver (47), and 0.6 for liver (17, 49), to 0.9 for beef adrenal cortex (29). These values are for whole microsome preparations or for isolated membranes devoid of particles; the variations among the values may illustrate that some of the microsomal preparations have particles and some do not, or that there may be great differences in the protein content of the vesicles (cf. 66). In pancreas microsomes, a value of 0.05 was found (18), but this may reflect a possible difficulty of extracting phospholipids in this tissue.

Of the total phospholipids, from 50 to 90 per cent is in the form of lecithin and cephalin, about equally divided among the two; this holds for liver, heart, and brain microsomes (62, 63, 64, 67 to 71). Phosphatidylserine is low in amount, and this holds for mitochondrial phospholipids also. The rest of the phospholipid content is spread over the minor components (62, 64, 68, 69, 71); it is of interest that microsomes have only very small amounts of cardiolipin (64, 68, 71), a phospholipid peculiar to mitochondria. On the other hand there is more lecithin in microsomes than in any other cell fraction; in fact a good deal of the lecithin of the liver cell is concentrated in the microsome fraction (64). Also, the microsome fraction from brain contains a goodly quantity of the gangliosides in this tissue (72). A complex amino phospholipid has been found in microsomes, and not in mitochondria, of liver (69). There also seems to be a difference in the relative amounts of lecithin and cephalin in microsomes and mitochondria; the ratio of lecithin to cephalin is from 1.5 to 2.5 times higher in the microsomes from various tissues than in the mitochondria of the same tissues (cf. 64). Otherwise, no great difference has been found between microsomal and mitochondrial phospholipid composition (cf. 63, 64). A similar situation holds for the fatty acid composition of microsomal and mitochondrial lipids, though the mitochondrial fatty acids appear in general to be more unsaturated (63, 64, 73). Of the steroid components, free cholesterol and cholesterol esters have been examined. There is more free and total cholesterol in microsomes than in any other fraction, derived from various tissues (29, 74, 75), though the percentage amount of cholesterol in mitochondrial and microsomal lipids is about the same in liver (62, 63), but higher in the microsomes of heart (71) and adrenal cortex (29). All in all, it appears that there is not too much difference in the gross steroid and lipid chemistry of mitochondria and microsomes. Any differences which might prove to be significant will have to await both the distinctive isolation of mitochondrial and microsomal membranes, not of whole fractions, and better fractionations of steroids and fats.

Sialic acid has been found to be concentrated in the microsomal fraction of rat liver, probably in the membranes (76). Of the acid-soluble components not much work has been done. The only acidic ultraviolet-absorbing components present are inosine, in liver (77) and pancreas microsomes (unpublished, P.S.), and cytidylic 3′-phosphate in pancreas microsomes (unpublished, P.S.), the latter probably caused by RNase action on microsomal RNA. The amount of liver NAD plus NADH, and NADP plus NADPH, is much lower in the microsomes than in the mitochondria (78), while CoQ, though mainly in mitochondria, has also been found in liver and adrenal microsomes (79).

FATTY ACID METABOLISM

The microsome fraction of various tissues is involved in fat and steroid metabolism; but the actual extent of the involvement, the actual localization in the cell of the various enzymes concerned, is far from having been worked out. In the metabolism of fatty acids, it appears that it is the mitochondria which contain all the enzymes needed for fatty acid oxidation, and nearly all the enzymes needed for fatty acid synthesis from acetate (cf. 80). This is probably also true of plant systems (cf. 81), though in peanuts there is an additional microsomal alpha-oxidase knocking off carbon dioxide from higher fatty acids (82). Enzymes so far specifically localized in microsomes have been those involved in the reductive synthesis of short-chain fatty acids, catalyzing, for example, the conversion of crotonyl CoA to butyryl CoA (83, 83a), though this has been disputed (86a) on the basis that the microsomal activity is brought about by fragmented mitochondria. However, intestinal mucosa microsomes have a long-chain fatty acid thiokinase, synthesizing fatty acyl CoA derivatives with CoA and adenosine triphosphate (87a). Rat brain microsomes have also been found to synthesize the derived fatty acid, sphingosine, from palmityl CoA, serine, and NADPH (84). The systems synthesizing fatty acids, in contradistinction to the mitochondrial oxidation system, have not been fully worked out; but it appears that there are two systems, both starting from acetate: one in the mitochondria which is primarily a reversal of the oxidation system, and one in the supernatant which is not (cf. 85). However, there is a report of the conversion of stearic acid to oleic acid by liver microsomes, using NADPH (85a). The involvement of the microsomes in the supernatant system, outside of the need to control the generation of NADPH for reductive synthesis (86), is not clear. Some authors have obtained no effect *in vitro* by the addition of microsomes on fatty acid synthesis from acetate catalyzed by mammary gland or liver supernatant enzymes (cf. 80), while others have obtained an effect by adding mammary gland microsomes (87, 88) or liver microsomes (89, 90); the discrepancy can be explained by the narrow concentration range of the microsomes (90) necessary for the effect. To explain the requirement for microsomes there has been postulated the existence of a transcarboxylase between citrate and acetyl CoA to give malonyl CoA (90). A fraction of microsomes from yeast has been found to have the same effect as liver microsomes (90), but we know nothing about the morphological identity of the yeast microsome fraction. Finally, it is clear that the enzyme complex responsible for the synthesis of fatty acids involving malonyl CoA exists in the final supernatant fraction of many tissues, obtained by the conventional centrifugation methods (91). However, it is conceivable that the enzyme system involved is still part of membrane structures which are very small and very light and might therefore take a longer sedimentation time to bring down. Lynen (92) speaks of a fatty acid synthetase multi-enzyme complex existing in the supernatant, but this could still be part of a membrane structure. It is instructive that the pentose cycle enzymes of liver could not be sedimented in two hours, but did sediment after sixteen hours at high speed (93). Whether both of these systems are complexes of protein molecules or proteins complexed to lipid and forming a membrane structure is a question for future work.

PHOSPHOLIPID METABOLISM

In plants the situation regarding the localization of phospholipid and triglyceride synthesis is confused. Both mitochondria (cf. 81) and microsomes (93a) seem to play a role, the former probably being involved in phosphatidic acid synthesis (94a), while the latter is instrumental in synthesizing triglycerides (93a). In animal tissues the microsome fraction plays a predominant part. Rat liver microsomes contain an enzyme synthesizing neutral glycerides from palmitate and alpha-glycerophosphate (94). A similar enzyme has been noted in intestinal mucosa mitochondria (95), but the condensation of monoglycerides plus palmityl CoA has been ascribed to the microsomes of the same tissue (95a). In addition, brain microsomes catalyze a synthesis of phosphatidic acid from monoglycerides and adenosine triphosphate (96). It was first thought that there were two morphological sites for lecithin synthesis, one a cytidine triphosphate-dependent choline incorporation taking place in mitochondria (97), and the other involving the methylation of phosphatidylaminoethanol, presumably by adenosyl methionine, and taking place in microsomes (98, 99, 100). However, we now know that the synthesis of phosphatidylcholine from cytidine diphosphate choline is a microsomal event as well (101, cf. 102). Also, the acylation of glycerophosphate to phosphatidic acid takes place in microsomes (103), as well as an enzyme which can acylate lysolecithin using the thioester of CoA (104). The decarboxylation of phosphatidylserine to phosphatidylethanolamine occurs in liver microsomes (105), but this enzyme has also been found in a preparation of liver mitochondria (106). In addition, a phosphatidic acid phosphatase has been localized in kidney microsomes (107), and in the mitochondria and microsomes of intestinal mucosa (108) and of liver (109). This enzyme has also been found in the microsomes and nuclear fraction of the albatross salt gland (110), as well as a diglyceride kinase, the latter enzyme synthesizing phosphatidic acid from diglycerides. Also, an α-glycerophosphate phosphatase was located in adipose tissue microsomal and supernatant fractions (111). At present it would appear that the metabolic route for phospholipid syntheses involving cytidine diphosphate-choline is in the microsomes, while those involving cytidine diphosphate-ethanolamine and cytidine diphosphate-diglycerides reside in both mitochondria and microsomes (101). Thus the microsomes, those from liver having been particularly studied, have all the enzymes necessary to synthesize phosphatidic acids from L-α-glycerophosphates or from D-α,β-diglycerides, and then to use these substrates to make lecithin. Also, it would appear that specific phospholipid synthesis in microsomes, via the methylation and deacylation reactions, produces not only a net synthesis of the specific phospholipids but also a distribution of the phospholipids among phosphatidylcholine, phosphatidylethanolamine, and phosphatidylserine. It is intriguing that perhaps the properties of the membranes of the endoplasmic reticulum depend on the relative amounts of these three different phosphatides, and the microsomal enzymes have as one of their purposes a redistribution, under certain conditions, of the relative amounts of the phosphatides in the membranes, thus perhaps conferring different properties on the membrane. For the interchange of serine, ethanolamine, and choline in the phosphatides seems to take place while these compounds are part of the lipid. Finally, from the sparse amount of work so far, involving experiments in which incomplete fractionation has been performed with no enzyme recovery data, we cannot say very much more about membrane synthesis in mitochondria and microsomes. From the limited results, we cannot tell whether each of these fractions makes its own membranes or not.

The P^{32} turnover of the phospholipid fractions of liver, brain, and pancreas microsomes is similar to that of the mitochondria from the same tissues (112, 113, 114). However, the turnover *in vitro* of brain microsomal phosphatides was increased by acetylcholine (113, 115) while that of the mitochondria was not (113), and the turnover *in vivo* of pancreas microsomal phospholipid was increased much more than was the turnover of pancreas mitochondrial phospholipid by inducing secretion by the pancreas (114). The meaning of these latter observations will be discussed below.

Steroid Metabolism

The situation is quite similar with regard to steroids, for one of the distinctive features of the microsomal fraction is its involvement in steroid metabolism. Bucher & McGarrahan (116) first showed that liver microsomes, and probably the membranous component of it, could synthesize cholesterol from acetate, with the aid of the glycolytic components and the acetate-activating enzyme in the supernatant fraction. Later it was found that both the microsomes and the soluble fractions are involved in the conversion of mevalonic acid to squalene (117, 118), and of squalene to sterol (117, 119), though the soluble fraction by itself (117, 120) can synthesize squalene from mevalonic acid at a reduced rate; here again one wonders if all the microsome material were spun down. Acetate is a precursor of mevalonic acid, but this reaction apparently needs both the microsome and soluble fractions (121). However, a need for mitochondria is also seen in that the conversion of acetyl CoA to hydroxymethylglutarate takes place there (122). The need for liver microsomes seems to arise in the reduction of hydroxymethylglutarate to mevalonate (116, 122), and in the step, farnesyl pyrophosphate to squalene (123, 124), since the soluble fraction alone can take mevalonate to farnesyl pyrophosphate (125). The cyclization of squalene to lanosterol is reported to be in the supernatant fraction (126), while the conversion of lanosterol to cholesterol is a microsomal function (126). This shifting back and forth of intermediates between the microsomal and supernatant fractions is rather strange, and might reflect differences in methods of fractionation between the laboratories and also inadequate sedimentation of all the microsomes from the mitochondrial supernatant. In most cases, recovery and specific activity data were not given, and without these it is impossible to say anything about the adequacy of the fractionations. Just this point has been raised by Gosselin *et al.* (118) who, by altering the components of the fractionation media and of the speeds of sedimentation, obtained varying results, possibly because of the leaching out of some of the enzymes, and also because of the heterogeneity of the common liver microsome fraction, containing membranes with and without particles and possibly also some of the Golgi and glycogen-area membranes. It could also be that there is differentiation among these morphological types of membranes with regard to the individual steps of sterol synthesis.

The microsome fraction is also greatly involved in the intraconversions and degradations of the sterols. The conversion of Δ^7-cholestenol to cholesterol requires both liver microsomes and supernatant (127), but enzymes oxidizing the terminal methyl group of cholesterol to carbon dioxide occur in liver mitochondria (128). While the Δ^4-5-α-dehydrogenases of liver are in the microsomes (129, 130), the Δ^4-5-β hydrogenases seem to be soluble enzymes (129, 130, 131). Other microsomal enzymes are the liver 3-β-hydroxysteroid dehydrogenases (132), the 17-β hydroxysteroid NAD-specific (133) dehydrogenase of liver, but not the NAD-specific enzyme of placenta (134) nor the NADP-specific enzyme of liver (135), both of which seem to be soluble enzymes. The microsomes are the source also of the 11-β-hydroxysteroid dehydrogenases of liver (136) and kidney (137), a 20-cortisone reductase of kidney (137), a liver enzyme degrading the side chain of cortisone (138), a 20-β-hydroxysteroid dehydrogenase (139), and a liver 6-β-hydroxysteroid dehydrogenase (140). However, other enzymes seem to be soluble, for instance, the liver steroid isomerases (141), a 17-β-estradiol dehydrogenase (134), and a 4,5-cortisone reductase (142).

OXIDATION-REDUCTION REACTIONS

Involved in steroid metabolism is a whole series of hydroxylases. All these enzymes seem to be peculiar to microsomes except for the 11-β-hydroxylase of adrenal mitochondria (143). The rest, a 17-α-hydroxylase, a 17-α-hydroxysteroid hydroxylase, and particularly an adrenal 21-hydroxylase have been found to be microsomal in origin (144). In addition to having sterols as substrates, liver microsomes have been found capable of binding and hydroxylating certain carcinogenic azo dyes (145 to 152), and a large variety of various compounds (145, 153, 154, 155) including acetanilide (156 to 160), various aromatic carcinogens (161 to 165), estradiol (166), and various other aromatic compounds like phenols and aromatic acids (cf. 159). Related to these enzymes are microsomal N-demethylation enzymes (154, 167 to 171) and N-deacylases in kidney (172) and liver (173). Both the hydroxylation and N-demethylation steps seem to require both microsomes and soluble fractions, but the need for the soluble fraction seems to be only to generate NADPH. It is interesting that the addition of cytochrome c inhibits the N-demethylation reaction (170) and the addition of ascorbic acid inhibits the 21-hydroxylation reaction (173a), probably in both cases by setting up competitive conditions for the available NADPH. Another interesting feature of these enzymes is that, in addition to the requirement for NADPH, there is also one for oxygen; the possible mechanism of such a reaction will be discussed below. Possibly also related to these hydroxylases is the deiodinating activity towards thyroxine, and the mono-, di-, and triiodotryosines, carried out by liver, brain, and thyroid microsomes plus supernatant fractions, the latter possibly donating the NADPH (174 to 177).

The existence of an electron transport system in microsomes has been known for a long time. Besides a mitochondrial localization, NADH-cytochrome c reductase has been found in microsomes of the liver of various species (17, 178 to 186), as well as in the microsomal fractions of spleen (187), mammary gland (188), silver beet (36), intestinal mucosa (189), Novikoff hepatoma ascites cells (190), brain (191, 192, 193), nerve (194), adrenal medulla (195), adrenal cortex (196), and chick embryonic heart (197). The difficulty in making heart microsomes free of mitochondrial contamination (1, 50) makes the finding of this enzyme in heart microsomal preparations not quite so certain (1, 50); the reason for the lack of enzyme in pancreatic microsomes is not known (18). A NADPH-cytochrome c reductase has also been found in the microsomal preparations from liver (180, 184, 186, 198, 199), brain (193), adrenal medulla (195) and cortex (196), and silver beet (36). In addition, there has been reported a liver microsome pyridine nucleotide unspecific diaphorase (200, 201) and a NADP-diaphorase (202).

The existence of a peculiar microsomal cytochrome, cytochrome b_5, has been known for a long time, although there is a report that liver mitochondria also contain this cytochrome (203). This cytochrome has been reported to occur in the microsomes prepared from liver (17, 181, 182, 204 to 207), from mammary gland (189), from silver beet (36), from hog adrenal (208, 209), but not from beef adrenal (195, 196). Indeed, a new cytochrome has been reported in beef adrenal medulla microsomes (195, 196, 210), this new cytochrome being similar in spectral properties to one named cytochrome b_3 which has been found in some plant tissue microsomes (211). The relationship of cytochrome b_5 to microsomal pyridine nucleotide reduction is not clear, even though the two seem to appear together, but what evidence there is indicates that the b_5 acts as an acceptor of electrons from NADH and NADPH and as a donor of electrons to added cytochrome c (182). Some properties of the electron transport segment of microsomes have been determined (181 to 186, 199 to 202, 204, 205, 206, 212 to 215a). The NADH-linked enzyme seems to be tightly bound to the membranes, while the NADPH-linked enzyme is either loosely bound or not bound at all to the membranes (209). Very little free NAD, NADP, or the reduced forms have been found in microsomal extracts (178).

The reason for the existence of this segment of the electron transport chain in microsomes, especially since there is thought to be no cytochrome c in microsomes, has been a mystery ever since it was unearthed. Since there is a need for reductive synthesis of fatty acids in the soluble phase and of steroids in the microsomes, it has been postulated that the NADH and NADPH reductases of liver microsomes act as a regulatory device in these synthetic reactions. These enzymes could also act in the same capacity in the hydroxylation reactions mentioned above. Another possibility is that we are isolating an electron transport segment of a longer chain of enzymatic reactions, and thus the biological receptor(s) of hydrogens is still unknown. It was noted with regard to the hydroxylation reactions that in addition to NADPH, oxygen was a necessary component of the microsomal system (156), and that NADPH oxidation generates hydrogen peroxide (145). This would imply that NADPH reduces some unknown cofactor which then reacts with oxygen (cf. 141); when we add cytochrome c to the system, it could take the place of the cofactor and be reduced instead. A third possibility is that this electron transport fragment doubles as a membrane anion transport mechanism.

Transport and Transmission Functions

An adenosine triphosphatase can be found in the nonmitochondrial cytoplasmic fraction of striated muscle, the so-called Kielley-Meyerhof ATPase (216). This fraction has been since found (217, 218) to be probably identical to the relaxing fraction of Marsh (219) which is "granular" in nature (220), and which has the properties of preventing contraction and inhibiting ATPase. This relaxing factor preparation is derived (51, 221 to 223a) from the sarcoplasmic reticulum of muscle (223), which is the counterpart of the endoplasmic reticulum in other types of cells, but without attached ribosomes. This membrane fraction has Ca^{++}-binding activity (224) but only in the presence of ATP, and this binding correlates with the property of this fraction to inhibit and reverse the contraction of muscle. The role of this membrane fraction in muscle contraction and relaxation has been recently reviewed (225, 226).

In other tissues, there is a liver microsomal ATPase (215, 227 to 230), which is a membrane enzyme (215) and has different properties from the liver mitochondrial ATPase (215), while myometrium microsomes have a cation-stimulated, non-dinitrophenol-stimulated ATPase (231).

Another probable function of the intracellular membranes has been uncovered by researchers working with nervous tissue. Acetylcholine and choline acetylase were first thought to be localized in mitochondria from brain, either rat or pigeon, and to be less in the microsomes from these tissues (232). However, by fractionation in a density gradient (233), the mitochondrial fraction was resolved into two fractions, only one of which had acetylation activity. This latter fraction was thought to represent the synaptic vesicles of nerve; and, indeed, electron micrographs of a brain mitochondria fraction showed it to be heavily contaminated with these vesicles (233, 234). Recently, these synaptic vesicles have been isolated virtually free of mitochondria (235, 236, 237). A more clear-cut picture was obtained when cholinesterase was studied. Most of the cholinesterase of the cell was found in the microsomal fraction of rat brain (32, 33, 238, 239) and of electric tissue of *Torpedo* (240). Most of the cholinesterase activity found in mitochondria is probably a contamination by synaptic vesicles. These findings of bound acetylcholine and cholinesterase in synaptic vesicles have some relevance for the theory of chemical transmission at nerve endings (240a). It is interesting in this regard that microsome fractions from liver (241, 242), muscle (243), and adrenal medulla (244) also contain cholinesterase.

In recent years, there has been described a microsomal Mg^{++}-activated ATPase which will be further stimulated by the addition of Na^+ plus K^+ (245, 246, 247). This activity seemed to reside in high-speed particles (245), and indeed it seems to reside in red blood cell membranes (248, 248a) and, more intriguing, in the microsome fraction of brain tissue (249 to 250a), and in the neuron cell membrane (251a). Moreover, the brain microsome fraction has a Na^+-binding capacity which is dependent on the addition of ATP (251), and has some other properties, including inhibition of the Na^+, K^+-stimulated ATPase by ouabain, a transport inhibitor, which have suggested the notion that the ATPase activity is an expression of some sort of Na^+ transport mechanism in these membranes (246, 248a, 250a, 251a, 252, 252a). The possible relationships between the cholinesterase activity, the Na^+, K^+-activated ATPase activity, the polarization of the membrane, and the conduction of the nerve impulse along the synaptic membranes of brain and nervous tissue are a ripe field for membrane research. However, the same sort of Na^+ and K^+-activated ATPase has been found in kidney and in frog skin (246); thus it appears that this kind of ATPase is not peculiar to nervous tissue, but may be involved in Na^+ transport in many kinds of cells.

GLUCOSE-6-PHOSPHATASE

Liver glucose-6-phosphatase is exclusively a microsomal enzyme (227, 253, 254, 255). In fact, the enzyme seems to be a tightly bound membrane enzyme, not found in the ribosomes or in the contents of the vesicles (215, 256, 257, 258). Some properties of this enzyme have been elucidated (215, 257, 259 to 261a), and the possible relationship between its intracellular localization and the glucose-secreting function of the liver cell has been outlined (262). It is also found in the microsome fraction of the kidney (254) and the adrenal cortex (262a) and in that of guinea pig intestine (263).

ESTERASES

The isolated microsomal fraction of various tissues has been found to have a variety of enzymes. In most cases, it was not determined how much of the total cellular enzymatic activity was localized in the microsomal fraction, so that it is not known whether these various enzymes are peculiar to the microsomes or even whether their existence in the microsomal fraction is traceable to contaminants. However, nonspecific esterases are enzymes which seem to be specifically localized in microsomes of liver or brain (242, 264 to 268) as, for example, enzymes acting on the esters of butyric acid (238, 269, 270, 271), ethanol (268), naphthol (242, 264, 272), indoxyl (242), cholesterol

(75, 268), vitamin A (268, 273), and enzymes also having an arylsulfatase-C activity (274, 275, 276). The liver vitamin-A esterases and cholesterol esterases are found in mitochondria also, but the microsomes have the larger amounts (268). However, the possibility of artifáctual solution and adsorption of these esterases has been raised, so that they might really be lysosomal rather than microsomal enzymes (277, 278). The invertase, maltase, and trehalase activities of intestinal mucosa are all concentrated in the microsomal fraction (279). Liver microsomes have a glutamine synthetase (280) and also have enzymes which can synthesize taurocholic acid (281 to 285) and glycocholic acid (286) by mechanisms utilizing a supernatant fraction which supplies cholyl-CoA. Whether this amide-bond formation is a function of the ribosomes of the membranes or of both is not known, though the glutamine synthetase can be extracted with deoxycholate (280), indicating nonribosomal origin.

Uridine-Linked Transferases and Ascorbic Acid Synthesis

Liver microsomes specifically have some of the enzymes involved in glucuronide metabolism. The enzyme making UDP-glucose from UTP and glucose-1-phosphate seems to be a supernatant enzyme (287), while the location of the UDP-glucose dehydrogenase is probably soluble (288). But the microsomes do have glucosyl transferase activities for glucosyl residues from UDP-glucose to phenols, carboxylic acids, and amines (288 to 292). In addition, they are able to break down, eventually, UDP-glucuronic acid with a specific phosphatase to glucuronic acid and UMP (292), and also to break down glucuronides with a β-glucuronidase to glucuronic acid (180, 292). The glucuronic acid produced in these latter cases can be used by liver microsomal enzymes for the synthesis of ascorbic acid (209, 293 to 301a), with the possible exception that one of the enzymes involved, glucuronic acid dehydrogenase, is soluble (293, 297). However, since the UDP-glucose transferase, like phosphorylase, has been found to be bound to liver glycogen (47, 302, 303), and since liver glycogen fractions contain vesicular structures (47), it is possible that the enzymes mentioned above as being membranous bound are really glycogen bound. This is probably unlikely because one of the enzymes, glucosyl transferase, can be solubilized by snake venom (291). In addition to the above enzymes, a brain enzyme transferring galactose from UDP-galactose to sphingosine to form psychosine is also microsomal in extent (304). Brain microsomes also have a high rate of incorporation of glucose and galactose into glycolipids (305). A particulate fraction from mammary glands containing both mitochondria and microsomes has the capacity to transfer galactose from UDP-galactose to glucose to form lactose (305a).

Nucleotide Metabolism

While an inorganic pyrophosphatase has been described as being soluble (306), it may really be particulate (307) [microsomal, precisely (284)], and may have been solubilized during the fractionation. But, in many tissues the enzyme seems to be in the soluble phase (308 to 311). Liver microsomal enzymes have been described which break down the nucleoside triphosphates, releasing inorganic pyrophosphate (312). In addition, the microsomes also seem to contain enzymes which specifically break down the nucleoside diphosphates, in nerve (313) and liver (314, 315); in the latter case the GDPase and UDPase, and not the ADPase and CDPase, can be activated by treatments which solubilize the microsomes (315). A 5'-nucleotidase activity, which acts mostly on adenylic acid-5', has been found to be associated with both the nuclear and microsomal fractions of liver (264, 316, 317, 318), brain (309, 319), placenta (310, 320), and Novikoff hepatoma (311, 321). Enzymes attacking NAD, NADH, and NADP, either by splitting at the nicotinamide ribose bond or at the pyrophosphate link, have a diffuse distribution; they are found in all cell fractions, but with the microsome fraction of liver, kidney, brain, and tumor cells having very high NAD and NADH pyrophosphatase activities (322 to 326), while liver and kidney microsomes have high NADase activities (325). Although the deaminase attacking adenylic acid-5' is microsomal in nerve (313), adenosine, adenine, and guanosine deaminases are all supernatant enzymes in brain (327) and liver (328). Dehydrogenases for xanthine and hypoxanthine were found in mammary gland microsomes (36, 188).

MISCELLANEOUS ENZYMES

Of miscellaneous enzymes, there is a tightly bound microsomal L-α-amino acid oxidase, a part of which is also found in the supernatant (329); oxygen was needed in the reaction and H_2O_2 was an end product, indicating that the enzyme is a flavoprotein and linking it to the aromatic hydroxylations discussed above. Cystine reductase has been reported to be a wholly microsomal enzyme in liver and kidney (330), while sulfite-cytochrome c reductase (331) and cysteine desulferase (332) are predominantly microsomal enzymes in liver. Arginase activity has been found in both nuclear and microsomal fractions (272, 333).

A γ-glutamyl transpeptidase has been localized in rat and pig kidney microsomes (334, 335, 336) but was found, curiously enough, in the rabbit liver nuclear fraction (337). Kidney microsomes have a cysteinyl-glycine dipeptidase (335), while ox thyroid microsomes can split a number of di- and tripeptides at alkaline pH (337a). Liver microsomes can activate a large variety of organophosphates with NADH, the activated product being inhibitory for cholinesterase (338). Kidney microsomes have been found to contain triacetic acid lactonase (339).

Other than nucleoside triphosphatases, an alkaline phosphatase is found in both the nuclear and microsomal fractions (340, 341), while the acid phosphatase is probably a lysosomal enzyme (342).

MISCELLANEOUS PROPERTIES

Various azo dyes, including carcinogens, have been found to be rather specifically bound by liver microsomes *in vivo* (146 to 152). The distribution of K^+ (343), Na^+, Ca^+, and Mg^{++} (344, 345) and other metals (345) among liver fractions has been studied. While isolated microsomes have been found to bind Na$^+$ and K$^+$ (346), the nature of the binding is not known. Microsomal fractions are quite good binders in other respects, but it is not known whether the binding is done by the membranes or the particles. For example, hemoglobin from broken red blood cells probably accounts for the pink color of the liver microsome fraction (347, 348), but the ribosomes could be the source of the binding (349). Thyroid mitochondria (350) and microsomes (351) bind iodide *in vitro*, but the mitochondrial activity is probably caused by contaminating microsomes (351). Testicular microsomes have also been found to adsorb *in vitro* various compounds including proteins, steroids, phosphates, and other ions (30), while liver microsomes can bind soluble lactic dehydrogenase from a medium of low ionic strength (351a). Epinephrine and norephinephrine have been found in heart and salivary gland microsomes, not in mitochondria, while only norepinephrine was in adrenal medulla microsomes (352). The distribution of various proteins, tested antigenically, has been investigated by Perlmann and his co-workers, with some of them being localized in the microsome fractions of various tissues (353 to 356).

The isolated microsomes, being vesicular structures, have been tested for with regard to their swelling properties. Their addition to mitochondrial suspensions does seem to have an effect on mitochondrial swelling (357, 358). The microsomes themselves, while adsorbing cytochrome c, are also aggregated by it at the same time (359). There is some doubt whether isolated microsomes can respond to osmotic changes in the bathing medium; the sucrose and carboxypolyglucose space was determined (360), in view of the finding that isolated microsomes do not swell in hypotonic sucrose solutions (360); this finding is the reverse of an earlier one on the finding of microsomal swelling in hypotonic media (361).

CORRELATIONS; SUMMARY

What do all these findings mean in relation to the functions of these intracellular membranes? First, what is their significance in regard to the presence or absence in the microsomes of enzymes catalyzing the various major metabolic pathways? Microsomes seem to have none of the enzymes having to do with glycolysis, all of them being soluble, except the ancillary enzyme, glucose-6-phosphatase. Glycogen synthesis also involves supernatant enzymes. Likewise, the pentose-phosphate oxidation cycle enzymes are all in the final supernatant, with the possible reservation mentioned earlier. The tricarboxylic acid cycle is predominantly a mitochondrial one, but individual enzymes do appear in the final supernatant. Oxidative phosphorylation linked to electron transport is an exclusively mitochondrial function. The information is scanty regarding the localization of enzymes which are involved in amino acid breakdown and synthesis, but again the microsomes seem to play little role in these events, with one possible exception, the catabolism of sulfur-containing amino acids and of sulfur itself. Protein synthesis is of course a ribosomal event, and cannot be considered a microsomal function if one regards microsomes as also having membranes, Again, in nucleic acid metabolism, we know too little regarding the localization of individual enzymatic steps involved in purine and pyrimidine breakdown and synthesis to say more than that it appears unlikely that the microsome fraction has much to do with these events. Fatty acid metabolism takes place both in the mitochondria and cell sap. Thus, the only major pathway in which the microsomes seem to be involved is that having to do with lipid and steroid metabolism, but even here, some of the enzymes do not seem to be microsomal in origin. It could be that many of the enzymes involved in phospholipid and steroid metabolism are lipoprotein complexes, being a part of the membrane, and before the substrates can be attacked, they must be "solubilized" in the lipidal part of the endoplasmic reticulum membranes (362).

However, much of the data upon which the evidence for intracellular localization of enzymes is based is extremely sketchy; thus what we nowadays would call a microsomal function might turn out to be one uniformly distributed in the cell, while other enzymes might turn out to be microsomal after all. To be sure of enzyme localization, one has to fractionate the cell in such a way that the ensuing fractions have their known morphological counterparts and are reasonably pure, and that complete recovery of enzymatic activity is obtained, in order to guard against inactivation or activation in some fractions and not in others. In many of the references cited above this has not been done, and what is true today might turn out to be false tomorrow. In spite of this, the general properties of the microsome fraction, as given in the preceding paragraph, are probably true, and are relevant to our thinking about the functioning of this fraction.

Thus, the microsomes seem to have within them most of the enzymes necessary for the synthesis of the lipoidal part of their membranes; whether these enzymes can and do synthesize all the cellular membrane components, such as the mitochondrial membranes, is a moot question at present. The metabolism of the protein constituents of the membranes is at present completely unknown, but it is likely that they are synthesized by the ribosomes of the cytoplasm. However, there appears to be no doubt that these membranes are involved in some sort of transport phenomena, as has been postulated above for cation transport. Also, in muscle, the sarcoplasmic reticulum (cf. 45) has been implicated in muscle contraction and relaxation (cf. 225, 226), and has been postulated to be the vehicle for the intracellular transmission of excitation (363, 364). A somewhat similar ion transport and excitation flow has been postulated with regards to phosphoprotein metabolism in nervous tissue (365).

The membranes coming down in the microsome fraction are probably akin to the cell membrane material, and this possible identity has given rise to a theory of membrane continuity between these structures (366). This might also be the case with plant cell-wall material, in that there is some cytological evidence that the endoplasmic reticulum functions in the laying down of the cell wall (367). This theory has been strengthened by the finding of the phenomena of micropinocytosis as a mechanism for the uptake of certain materials in *Amoeba* (368, 369) and in other cells as well (370). The membranes seem to have also some connection to the membrane surrounding the nucleus; in fact, the outer nuclear membrane seems to be in continuity with the membranes of the endoplasmic reticulum (371). The extrusion of materials, secretory or excretory, could possibly occur by a process of membrane movement, in which packets of membrane-enclosed material are brought to the plasma membrane, fuse with it, and then are discharged from the cell (cf. 372); a special instance of this has been observed in the case of pancreatic zymogen granule secretion (373), and has been implicated in albumin discharge by the liver (374). Some supporting evidence has been given by Hokin & Hokin with biochemical experiments, in which phospholipid turnover in microsome fractions has been stimulated by cholinergic drugs, in brain (113, 115) and pancreas (114). These endoplasmic reticulum membranes are involved in a similar movement in bringing material from one side of the cell to the other. This has been beautifully shown in the case of the endothelial cells of blood capillaries, where pinocytotic vesicles move material from the plasma to the pericapillary spaces of the interstitial fluid (374a).

The idea has thus come about that many specialized membranes, such as that surrounding the nucleus, those surrounding the Golgi spaces, the plasma membrane, and those bounding various secretory or storage vesicles, are all part of one endoplasmic reticulum system (cf. 13). In fact, the membranes appear to divide the cell into two compartments: one inside, containing any excretory or secretory, or pinocytotic material, dependent on the cell type, and also containing the nucleus with its own membrane; and a space outside, in which are situated the mitochondria, ribosomes, and various cellular inclusions. Thus we can guess, and only guess at present, that these membranes have a regulatory role, regulating metabolism directly by acting as a selective barrier for certain materials, and indirectly by containing bound enzymes whose substrates or products can regulate the flow of metabolism.

It would appear that of all the intracellular structures and enzymes, those of the endoplasmic reticulum membranes are the ones involved in the exchange of materials between cell and environment. The membrane is not only instrumental in excretory and secretory processes but also in getting substances into cells. The enzymes on the membranes, thinking of these membranes as being in continuity with the plasma membrane, are the first ones in position to attack certain substrates and other compounds coming into the cell. This is particularly shown in the case of the "detoxifying" enzymes found in liver microsomes. Of course, it could be that these enzymes are really on the plasma membrane. However, it has been found that these foreign compounds, including certain carcinogens, drugs like phenobarbital, and various aromatic polycyclic hydrocarbons, all cause increases in protein synthesis by the liver, these proteins being either the enzymes metabolizing the drugs (162, 375 to 384), or microsomal enzymes involved in ascorbic acid biosynthesis (379, 385), or amino acid incorporating activity into microsomal proteins (386); this effect seems to be a direct one on the liver microsomes themselves, and not indirect through the adrenals (375, 384, 387). Thus the hydrocarbons do seem to act on the membranes of the endoplasmic reticulum, for it is these membranes which carry the protein-synthesizing ribosomes. What the relationship is between the membranes and the ribosomes is completely unknown at present, though there is some evidence that the drugs are metabolized by the membranous component of the microsomes (388), and the lipoidal solubility of the drugs is directly proportional to their susceptibility to being destroyed (362), as if the compounds in question have to be "fixed" in the lipophilic part of the membranes before they can be metabolized. Thus, it could be that hormones, particularly the steroids, have their effects by reacting with membrane components. In this regard, it would be instructive to know if there is any biochemical differentiation among the extramitochondrial membranes of the cell, particularly the plasma membrane and the endoplasmic reticulum membranes (cf. 389, 390). For this reason, it would be good to work out a fractionation scheme which will unequivocally separate the two membrane components.

Changes in the structure of the endoplasmic reticulum or isolated microsomes have been noticed, in treatments with hormones (318, 391 to 394), or various other compounds (395), or starvation (396), and these have included studies *in vitro* on various metabolic functions of microsomes (31, 365, 394, 397). The lability of some of these microsomal enzymes to environmental changes *in vivo* or *in vitro* is marked (184, 215, 262a). Alterations have also been noticed in microsomal function during germination of pea-seedling roots (42). Finally, genetic changes produce variations in microsomal enzymes, both in function, as in the case of glucosyl transfer (398), and in localization within the cell, as in the case of β-glucuronidase (399).

Since the microsomes, as isolated from most mammalian cells, constitute a heterogenous fraction, attempts have been made to subfractionate it, particularly to separate and obtain pure ribosomes and pure membranes. The separation of these two components has been attempted (24, 27, 42, 48, 49, 247, 388, 400), while attempts have also been made to differentiate between enzymes localized on membranes with ribosomes and membranes without ribosomes (24, 49, 388). In addition, Golgi membranes have been isolated (25) while membranes have been isolated free of particles from a mixture of membranes with and without bound ribosomes (215). Cell membrane isolations have been attempted, from liver cells (401), from epithelial brush border of small intestine (402), and from skeletal muscle (403, 404); and in fact there is some speculation (389) that the ATPase found in the microsomal fraction comes from a contamination of microsomes by cell membrane material, for a cell membrane ATPase has been recently identified (390). I should also mention some recent work on the localization of enzymes on bacterial cell wall and membrane (cf. 405): invertase (406, 407), succinic dehydrogenase (408), polynucleotide phosphorylase (409), ATPase (410), as well as phosphate turnover studies with bacterial membrane preparations *in vitro* (411).

Ideas having to do with the relationship of the endoplasmic reticulum to the rest of the cell have been voiced with respect to mitochondrial function (262, 412, 413, 414), to enzymes in the soluble phase (262, 413, 414), and to protein synthesis (373, 415 to 418). In the former two cases, the relationship has to do with the presence of a segment of the electron transport chain in the microsomes. Since this is a ubiquitous occurrence, being found in the microsomes of all tissues so far examined, it does seem to be a truly distinctive feature of microsomal function. There really is no evidence for any theory which has been brought forth regarding the functions of the NADH and NADPH reductases in the microsomal membranes (cf. 413). A solution to this problem will tell us quite a bit regarding the function of those intracellular membranes which we call the isolated microsome fraction. Outside of what has been written and cited above, there is no need for me to go into the possible regulatory functionings of these membranes, with regard to the rest of the cell; there are already some ideas concerning this (cf. 262, 373, 412 to 418) and I would just be repeating them. What is needed is more work.

LITERATURE CITED

1. Siekevitz, P., in *Methods in Enzymology*, **V**, 61 (Colowick, S. P., and Kaplan, N. O., Eds., Academic, New York, 1962)
2. Schneider, W. C., and Hogeboom, G. H., *Cancer Res.*, **11**, 1 (1951)
3. Hogeboom, G. H., Schneider, W. C., and Striebich, M. J., *Cancer Res.*, **13**, 617 (1953)
4. de Duve, C., and Berthet, J., *Intern. Rev. Cytol.*, **3**, 225 (1954)
5. Lindberg, O., and Ernster, L., *Protoplasmatologia*, **III** (A4) (Springer-Verlag, Vienna, 1954)
6. Hogeboom, G. H., and Schneider, W. C., in *Nucleic Acids*, **II**, 199 (Chargaff, E., and Davidson, J. N., Eds., Academic, New York, 1955)
7. Howatson, A. F., and Ham, A. W., *Can. J. Biochem. Physiol.*, **35**, 549 (1957)
8. Rossiter, R. J., *Can. J. Biochem. Physiol.*, **35**, 579 (1957)
9. Allfrey, V., in *The Cell*, **I**, p. 193 (Brachet, J. and Mirsky, A. E., Eds., Academic, New York, 1959)
10. Hultin, T., *Biochem. Pharmacol.*, **5**, 359 (1961)
11. Porter, K. R., *Harvey Lectures*, **LI**, 175 (1955–56)
12. Novikoff, A. B., *Science*, **124**, 969 (1956)
13. Palade, G. E., *J. Biophys. Biochem. Cytol.*, Suppl. 2, 85 (1956)
14. Sjöstrand, F. S., *Intern. Rev. Cytol.*, **5**, 546 (1956)
15. Jackson, S. F., and Randall, J. T., *Proc. Roy. Soc. (London), B*, **148**, 290 (1958)
16. Haguenau, F., *Intern. Rev. Cytol.*, **7**, 425 (1958)
16a. Porter, K. R., in *The Cell*, **II**, 621 (Academic, New York, 1961)
17. Palade, G. E., and Siekevitz, P., *J. Biophys. Biochem. Cytol.*, **2**, 171 (1956)
18. Palade, G. E., and Siekevitz, P., *J. Biophys. Biochem. Cytol.*, **2**, 671 (1956)
19. Claude, A., *Harvey Lectures*, **XLIII**, 121 (1947–48)
20. Anderson, N. G., *Exptl. Cell. Res.*, **9**, 446 (1955)
21. Thomson, J. F., and Mikuta, E. T., *Arch. Biochem. Biophys.*, **51**, 487 (1954)
22. Thomson, J. F., and Klipfel, F. J., *Arch. Biochem. Biophys.*, **70**, 224 (1957)
23. Kuff, E. L., and Schneider, W. C., *J. Biol. Chem.*, **206**, 677 (1954)
24. Kuff, E. L., Hogeboom, G. H., and Dalton, A. J., *J. Biophys. Biochem. Cytol.*, **2**, 33 (1956)
25. Kuff, E. L., and Dalton, A. J., in *Subcellular Particles*, 114 (Hayashi, T., Ed., Ronald Press, New York, 1959)
26. Hanzon, V., and Toschi, G., *Exptl. Cell Res.*, **21**, 332 (1960)
27. Rothschild, J. A., *Federation Proc.*, **20**, 145 (1961)
28. Albertsson, P. A., *J. Ultrastruct. Res.*, **2**, 366 (1959)
29. Schultz, R. L., and Meyer, R. K., *J. Biophys. Biochem. Cytol.*, **4**, 23 (1958)
30. Lynn, W. S., Jr., Brown, R. H., and Mullins, J., *J. Biol. Chem.*, **232**, 995 (1958)
31. Lynn, W. S., Jr., and Brown, R. H., *J. Biol. Chem.*, **232**, 1005 (1958)
32. Toschi, G., *Exptl. Cell Res.*, **16**, 232 (1959)

33. Hanzon, V., and Toschi, G., *Exptl. Cell Res.*, **2**, 256 (1959)
34. Wolfe, L. S., *Biochem. J.*, **79**, 348 (1961)
35. Bailie, M. J., and Morton, R. K., *Biochem. J.*, **69**, 44 (1958)
36. Martin, E. M., and Morton, R. K., *Biochem. J.*, **62**, 696 (1956)
37. Martin, E. M., and Morton, R. K., *Biochem. J.*, **64**, 221 (1956)
38. Martin, E. M., and Morton, R. K., *Biochem. J.*, **64**, 687 (1956)
39. Martin, E. M., and Morton, R. K., *Biochem. J.*, **65**, 404 (1957)
40. Hodge, A. J., Martin, E. M., and Morton, R. K., *J. Biophys. Biochem. Cytol.*, **3**, 61 (1957)
41. Szarkowski, J. W., Buttrose, M. S., Mühlethaler, K., and Frey-Wyssling, A., *J. Ultrastruct. Res.*, **4**, 222 (1960)
42. Loening, U. E., *Biochem. J.*, **81**, 254 (1961)
43. Akazawa, T., and Beevers, H., *Biochem. J.*, **67**, 110 (1957)
44. Dalton, A. J., and Felix, M. D., *Symp. Soc. Exptl. Biol.*, **10**, 148 (1957)
45. Porter, K. R., *J. Biophys. Biochem. Cytol.*, **10**, Suppl., 219 (1961)
46. Porter, K. R., and Bruni, C., *Cancer Res.*, **19**, 997 (1959)
47. Luck, D. J. L., *J. Biophys. Biochem. Cytol.*, **10**, 195 (1961)
48. Moulè, Y., Rouiller, C., and Chauveau, J., *J. Biophys. Biochem. Cytol.*, **7**, 547 (1960)
49. Chauveau, J., Moulè, Y., Rouiller, C., and Schneebeli, J., *J. Cell Biol.*, **12**, 17 (1962)
50. Hulsmans, H. A. M., *Biochim. Biophys. Acta*, **54**, 1 (1961)
51. Muscatello, U., Andersson-Cedergren, E., Azzone, G. F., and von der Decken, A., *J. Biophys. Biochem. Cytol.*, **10**, Suppl., 201 (1961)
52. Wakid, N. W., *Biochem. J.*, **76**, 88 (1960)
53. Wakid, N. W., and Needham, D. M., *Biochem. J.*, **76**, 95 (1960)
54. Ebashi, S., *Progr. Theoret. Phys.*, **17**, 35 (1961)
55. Ebashi, S., and Lipmann, F., *J. Cell Biol.*, **14**, 389 (1962)
56. Ebashi, S., *Arch. Biochem. Biophys.*, **76**, 410 (1958)
57. Shiguera, H. T., and Chargaff, E., *J. Biol. Chem.*, **233**, 197 (1958)
58. Takanami, M., *J. Histochem. Cytochem.*, **7**, 126 (1959)
59. Reid, E., *Biochim. Biophys. Acta*, **49**, 218 (1961)
60. Bhargava, P. M., Simkin, J. L., and Work, T. S., *Biochem. J.*, **68**, 265 (1958)
61. Goswami, P., Barr, G. C., and Munro, H. N., *Biochim. Biophys. Acta*, **55**, 408 (1962)
62. Spiro, M. J., and McKibbin, J. M., *J. Biol. Chem.*, **219**, 643 (1956)
63. Biran, A., and Bartley, W., *Biochem. J.*, **79**, 159 (1961)
64. Getz, G. S., Bartley, W., Stirpe, F., Notton, B. M., and Renshaw, A., *Biochem. J.*, **83**, 181 (1962)
65. Biezenski, J. J., and Spalt, T. H., *Biochim. Biophys. Acta*, **51**, 221 (1961)
66. Siekevitz, P., and Palade, G. E., *J. Biophys. Biochem. Cytol.*, **4**, 401 (1958)
67. Strickland, E. H., and Benson, A. A., *Arch. Biochem. Biophys.*, **88**, 344 (1960)
68. Macfarlane, M. G., Gray, G. M., and Wheeldon, L. W., *Biochem. J.*, **77**, 626 (1960)
69. Collins, F. D., and Shotlander, V. L., *Biochem. J.*, **79**, 321 (1961)
70. Peterson V. P., and Schou, M., *Acta Physiol. Scand.*, **33**, 309 (1955)
71. Marinetti, G. V., Erbland, J., and Stotz, E., *J. Biol. Chem.*, **233**, 562 (1958)
72. Wolfe, L. S., *Biochem. J.*, **79**, 348 (1961)
73. Getz, G. S., and Bartley, W., *Biochem. J.*, **78**, 307 (1961)
74. Kritchevsky, D., Langan, J., and Whitehouse, M. W., *Experientia*, **16**, 452 (1960)
75. Schotz, M. C., Rice, L. I., and Alfin-Slater, R. B., *J. Biol. Chem.*, **204**, 19 (1953)
76. Patterson, M. K., Jr., and Touster, O., *Biochim. Biophys. Acta*, **56**, 626 (1962)
77. Siekevitz, P., *J. Biophys. Biochem. Cytol.*, **1**, 447 (1955)
78. Glock, G. E., and McLean, P., *Exptl. Cell Res.*, **11**, 234 (1956)
79. Leonhäuser, S., Leybold, K., Krisch, K., Staudinger, H., Gale, P. H., Page, A. C., Jr., and Folkers, K., *Arch. Biochem. Biophys.*, **96**, 580 (1962)
80. Hele, P. *Brit. Med. Bull.*, **14**, 201 (1958)
81. Stumpf, P. K., *Nature*, **194**, 1158 (1962)
82. Humphreys, T. E., and Stumpf, P. K., *J. Biol. Chem.*, **213**, 941 (1955)
83. Lachance, J. P., Popjak, G., and de Waard, A. *Biochem. J.*, **68**, 7P (1958)
83a. Matthes, K. J., Abraham, S., and Chaikoff, I. L., *Biochim. Biophys. Acta*, **37**, 180 (1960)

84. Brady, R. O., and Koval, G. J., *J. Biol. Chem.*, **233**, 26 (1958)
85. Green, D. E., and Gibson, D. M., in *Metabolic Pathways*, **I**, 301 (Academic, New York, 1960)
85a. Marsh, J. B., and James, A. T., *Biochim. Biophys. Acta*, **60**, 320 (1962)
86. Langdon, R. G., *J. Biol. Chem.*, **226**, 615 (1957)
86a. Hülsman, W. C., *Biochim. Biophys. Acta*, **58**, 417 (1962)
87. Popjak, G., and Tietz, A., *Biochem. J.*, **60**, 147 (1955)
87a. Senior, J. R., and Isselbacher, K. J., *Biochim. Biophys. Acta*, **44**, 399 (1960)
88. Abraham, S., Matthes, K. J., and Chaikoff, I. L., *Biochim. Biophys. Acta*, **36**, 556 (1959)
89. Matthes, K. J., Abraham, S., and Chaikoff, I. L., *J. Biol. Chem.*, **235**, 2560 (1960)
90. Abraham, S., Chaikoff, I. L., Bortz, W. M., Klein, H. P., and Den, H., *Nature*, **192**, 1287 (1961)
91. Ganguly, J., *Biochim. Biophys. Acta*, **40**, 110 (1960)
92. Lynen, F., *Federation Proc.*, **20**, 941 (1961)
93. Newburgh, R. W., and Cheldelin, V. H., *J. Biol. Chem.*, **218**, 89 (1956)
93a. Barron, E. J., and Stumpf, P. K., *Biochim. Biophys. Acta*, **60**, 329 (1962)
94. Stein, Y., and Shapiro, B., *Biochim. Biophys. Acta*, **30**, 271 (1958)
94a. Bradbeer, C., and Stumpf, P. K., *J. Lipid Res.*, **1**, 214 (1960)
95. Clark, B., and Hübscher, G., *Biochim. Biophys. Acta*, **46**, 479 (1961)
95a. Senior, J. R., and Isselbacher, K. J., *J. Biol. Chem.*, **237**, 1454 (1962)
96. Pierenger, R. A., and Hokin, L. E., *J. Biol. Chem.*, **237**, 653 (1962)
97. Kennedy, E. P., and Weiss, S. B., *J. Biol. Chem.*, **222**, 193 (1956)
98. Bremer, J., and Greenberg, D. M., *Biochim. Biophys. Acta*, **37**, 173 (1960)
99. Gibson, K. D., Wilson, J. D., and Udenfriend, S., *J. Biol. Chem.*, **236**, 673 (1961)
100. Bremer, J., and Greenberg, D. M., *Biochim. Biophys. Acta*, **46**, 205 (1961)
101. Wilgram, G., and Kennedy, E. P., *J. Biol. Chem.* (Submitted)
102. Dils, R. R., and Hübscher, G., *Biochim. Biophys. Acta*, **46**, 505 (1961)
103. Kornberg, A., and Pricer, W. E., Jr., *J. Biol. Chem.*, **204**, 345 (1953)
104. Lands, W. E. M., *J. Biol. Chem.*, **235**, 2233 (1960)
105. Wilson, J. D., Gibson, K. D., and Udenfriend, S., *J. Biol. Chem.*, **235**, 3539 (1960)
106. Borkenhagen, L. F., Kennedy, E. P., and Fielding, L., *J. Biol. Chem.*, **236**, PC28 (1961)
107. Coleman, R., and Hübscher, G., *Biochim. Biophys. Acta*, **56**, 479 (1962)
108. Johnston, J. M., and Bearden, J. H., *Biochim. Biophys. Acta*, **56**, 365 (1962)
109. Smith, S. W., Weiss, S. B., and Kennedy, E. P., *J. Biol. Chem.*, **228**, 915 (1957)
110. Hokin, L. E., and Hokin, M. R., *J. Gen. Physiol.*, **44**, 61 (1960)
111. Margolis, S., and Vaughan, M., *J. Biol. Chem.*, **237**, 44 (1962)
112. Levin, E., Johnson, R. M., and Albert, S., *Arch. Biochem. Biophys.*, **73**, 247 (1958)
113. Hokin, L. E., and Hokin, M. R., *J. Biol. Chem.*, **233**, 822 (1958)
114. Redman, C. M., and Hokin, L. E., *J. Biophys. Biochem. Cytol.*, **6**, 207 (1959)
115. Hokin, L. E., and Hokin, M. R., *J. Biol. Chem.*, **234**, 1387 (1959)
116. Bucher, N. L. R., and McGarrahan, K., *J. Biol. Chem.*, **222**, 1 (1956)
117. Popjak, G., Gosselin, L., Gore, I. Y., and Gould, R. G., *Biochem. J.*, **69**, 238 (1958)
118. Gosselin, L., Podber-Wagner, E., and Waltregny, A., *Nature*, **193**, 252 (1962)
119. Goodman, D. S., *J. Biol. Chem.*, **236**, 2429 (1961)
120. Witting, L. A., and Porter, J. W., *J. Biol. Chem.*, **234**, 2841 (1959)
121. Knauss, H. J., Porter, J. W., and Wasson, G., *J. Biol. Chem.*, **234**, 2835 (1959)
122. Bucher, N. L. R., Overath, P., and Lynen, F., *Biochim. Biophys. Acta*, **40**, 491 (1960)
123. Goodman, D. S., and Popjak, G., *J. Lipid Res.*, **1**, 286 (1960)
124. Anderson, D. G., Rice, M. S., and Porter, J. W., *Biochem. Biophys. Res. Commun.*, **3**, 591 (1960)
125. Popjak, G., Goodman, D. S., Cornfurth, J. W., Cornfurth, R. H., and Ryhage, R., *J. Biol. Chem.*, **236**, 1934 (1961)
126. Tchen, T. T., and Bloch, K., *J. Am. Chem. Soc.*, **77**, 6085 (1955)
127. Frantz, I. D., Davidson, A. G., Dubit, E., and Mobberly, M. L., *J. Biol. Chem.*, **234**, 2290 (1959)

128. Anfinsen, C. B., and Horning, M. G., *J. Am. Chem. Soc.*, **75**, 1511 (1953)
129. Forchielli, E., and Dorfman, R. I., *J. Biol. Chem.*, **223**, 443 (1956)
130. McGuire, J. S., Jr., and Tomkins, G. M., *Arch. Biochem. Biophys.*, **82**, 476 (1959)
131. McGuire, J. S., Jr., Hollis, V. W., Jr., and Tomkins, G. M., *J. Biol. Chem.*, **235**, 3112 (1960)
132. Beyer, K. F., and Samuels, L. T., *J. Biol. Chem.*, **219**, 69 (1956)
133. Endahl, G. L., Kochakian, C. D., and Hamm, D., *J. Biol. Chem.*, **235**, 2792 (1960)
134. Ryan, K. J., *J. Biol. Chem.*, **234**, 268 (1959)
135. Villee, C. A., and Spencer, J. M., *J. Biol. Chem.*, **235**, 3615 (1960)
136. Hurlock, B., and Talalay, P., *Arch. Biochem. Biophys.*, **80**, 468 (1959)
137. Mahesh, V. B., and Ulrich, F., *J. Biol. Chem.*, **235**, 356 (1960)
138. Recknagel, R. O., and Glenn, E. M., *Proc. Soc. Exptl. Biol. Med.*, **89**, 156 (1955)
139. Recknagel, R. O., *J. Biol. Chem.*, **227**, 273 (1957)
140. Mueller, G. C., and Rumney, G., *J. Am. Chem. Soc.*, **79**, 1004 (1957)
141. Talalay, P., *Physiol. Rev.*, **37**, 362 (1957)
142. McGuire, J. S., Jr., and Tomkins, G. M., *Nature*, **182**, 261 (1958)
143. Sweat, M. L., *J. Am. Chem. Soc.*, **73**, 4056 (1951)
144. Ryan, K. J., and Engel, L. L., *J. Am. Chem. Soc.*, **78**, 2654 (1956)
145. Brodie, B. B., Axelrod, J., Cooper, J. R., Gaudette, L., LaDu, B. N., Jr., Mitoma, C., and Udenfriend, S., *Science*, **121**, 603 (1955)
146. Mueller, G. C., and Miller, J. A., *J. Biol. Chem.*, **180**, 1125 (1949)
147. Mueller, G. C., and Miller, J. A., *J. Biol. Chem.*, **185**, 145 (1950)
148. Mueller, G. C., and Miller, J. A., *J. Biol. Chem.*, **202**, 579 (1953)
149. Hultin, T., *Exptl. Cell Res.*, **10**, 71 (1956)
150. Hultin, T., *Exptl. Cell Res.*, **10**, 697 (1956)
151. Hultin, T., and von der Decken, A., *Acta Chem. Scand.*, **12**, 596 (1958)
152. Hecker, E., and Mueller, G. C., *J. Biol. Chem.*, **233**, 991 (1958)
153. Axelrod, J., *J. Biol. Chem.*, **214**, 753 (1955)
154. Brodie, B. B., *J. Pharm. Pharmacol.*, **8**, 1 (1956)
155. Cooper, J. R., and Brodie, B. B., *J. Pharmacol. Exptl. Therap.*, **114**, 409 (1955)
156. Mitoma, C., Posner, H. S., Reitz, H. C., and Udenfriend, S., *Arch. Biochem. Biophys.*, **61**, 431 (1956)
157. Krisch, K., and Staudinger, H., *Biochem. Z.*, **334**, 312 (1961)
158. Krisch, K., and Staudinger, H., *Biochem. Biophys. Res. Commun.*, **4**, 118 (1961)
159. Posner, H. S., Mitoma, C., and Udenfriend, S., *Arch. Biochem. Biophys.*, **94**, 269 (1961)
160. Posner, H. S., Mitoma, C., Rothberg, S., and Udenfriend, S., *Arch. Biochem. Biophys.*, **94**, 280 (1961)
161. Seal, U. S., and Gutman, H. R., *J. Biol. Chem.*, **234**, 648 (1959)
162. Conney, A. H., Miller, E. C., and Miller, J. A., *J. Biol. Chem.*, **228**, 753 (1957)
163. Hultin, T., *Exptl. Cell Res.*, **13**, 47 (1957)
164. Hultin, T., *Exptl. Cell Res.*, **18**, 112 (1959)
165. Booth, J., and Boyland, E., *Biochem. J.*, **70**, 681 (1958)
166. Mueller, G. C., and Rumney, G., *J. Am. Chem. Soc.*, **79**, 1004 (1957)
167. Axelrod, J., *J. Pharmacol. Exptl. Therap.*, **117**, 322 (1956)
168. Mueller, G. C., and Miller, J. A., *J. Biol. Chem.*, **202**, 579 (1953)
169. LaDu, B. N., Jr., Gaudette, L. E., Trousof, N., and Brodie, B. B., *J. Biol. Chem.*, **214**, 741 (1955)
170. Gaudette, L. E., and Brodie, B. B., *Biochem. Pharmacol.*, **2**, 89 (1959)
171. Conney, A. H., Brown, R. R., Miller, J. A., and Miller, E. C., *Cancer Res.*, **17**, 628 (1957)
172. Nimmo-Smith, R. H., *Biochem. J.*, **75**, 284 (1960)
173. Seal, U. S., and Gutmann, H. R., *J. Biol. Chem.*, **234**, 648 (1959)
173a. Cooper, D. Y., and Rosenthal, O., *Arch. Biochem. Biophys.*, **96**, 331 (1962)
174. Stanbury, J. B., *J. Biol. Chem.*, **228**, 801 (1957)
175. Stanbury, J. B., and Morris, M. L., *J. Biol. Chem.*, **233**, 106 (1958)
176. Tata, J. R., *Biochim. Biophys. Acta*, **28**, 95 (1958)
177. Yamazaki, E., and Slingerland, D. W., *Endocrinology*, **64**, 126 (1959)
178. Hogeboom, G. H., *J. Biol. Chem.*, **177**, 847 (1949)
179. Hogeboom, G. H., and Schneider, W. C., *J. Natl. Cancer Inst.*, **10**, 983 (1950)
180. de Duve, C., Pressman, B. C., Gianetto, R., Wattiaux, R., and Appelmans, F., *Biochem. J.*, **60**, 604 (1955)

181. Strittmatter, C. F., and Ball, E. G., *J. Cellular Comp. Physiol.*, **43**, 57 (1954)

182. Strittmatter, P., and Velick, S. F., *J. Biol. Chem.*, **221**, 277 (1956)

183. Garfinkel, D., *Arch. Biochem. Biophys.*, **71**, 100 (1957)

184. Ernster, L., *Acta Chem. Scand.*, **12**, 600 (1958)

185. Penn, N., and Mackler, B., *Biochim. Biophys. Acta*, **27**, 539 (1958)

186. Reynafarje, B., and Potter, V. R., *Cancer Res.*, **17**, 1112 (1957)

187. Eichel, H. J., *J. Biophys. Biochem. Cytol.*, **3**, 397 (1957)

188. Bailie, M. J., and Morton, R. K., *Biochem. J.*, **69**, 35 (1958)

189. Bailie, M. J., and Morton, R. K., *Nature*, **176**, 111 (1955)

190. Novikoff, A. B., in *Cell Physiology of Neoplasia*, 219 (Univ. Texas Press, Austin, Texas, 1960)

191. Abood, L. G., Gerard, R. W., Banks, J., and Tschugi, R. D., *Am. J. Physiol.*, **168**, 728 (1952)

192. Brody, T. M., Wang, R. E. H., and Bain, J. A., *J. Biol. Chem.*, **198**, 821 (1952)

193. Giuditta, A., and Strecker, H. J., *J. Neurochem.*, **5**, 50 (1959)

194. Abood, L. G., and Gerard, R. W., *J. Cellular Comp. Physiol.*, **43**, 379 (1954)

195. Spiro, M. J., and Ball, E. G., *J. Biol. Chem.*, **236**, 225 (1961)

196. Spiro, M. J., and Ball, E. G., *J. Biol. Chem.*, **236**, 231 (1961)

197. Brand, L., and Mahler, H. R., *J. Biol. Chem.*, **234**, 1615 (1959)

198. Hogeboom, G. H., and Schneider, W. C., *J. Biol. Chem.*, **186**, 417 (1950)

199. Williams, C. H., Jr., and Kamin, H., *J. Biol. Chem.*, **237**, 587 (1962)

200. Ernster, L., Ljunggren, M., and Danielson, L., *Biochem. Biophys. Res. Commun.*, **2**, 88 (1960)

201. Danielson, L., Ernster, L., and Ljunggren, M., *Acta Chem. Scand.*, **14**, 1837 (1960)

202. Williams, C. H., Jr., Gibbs, R. H., and Kamin, H., *Biochim. Biophys. Acta*, **32**, 568 (1959)

203. Mahler, H. R., Raw, I., Molinari, R., and Do Amaral, D. F., *J. Biol. Chem.*, **233**, 230 (1958)

204. Strittmatter, P., and Velick, S. F., *J. Biol. Chem.*, **221**, 253 (1956)

205. Garfinkel, D., *Arch. Biochem. Biophys.*, **71**, 111 (1957)

206. Chance, B., and Williams, G. R., *J. Biol. Chem.*, **209**, 945 (1954)

207. Klingenberg, M., *Arch. Biochem. Biophys.*, **75**, 376 (1958)

208. Krisch, K., and Staudinger, H., *Biochem. Z.*, **331**, 37 (1959)

209. Krisch, K., and Staudinger, H., *Biochem. Z.*, **331**, 195 (1959)

210. Krisch, K., *Nature*, **193**, 982 (1962)

211. Martin, E. M., and Morton, R. K., *Nature*, **176**, 115 (1955)

212. Strittmatter, P., *J. Biol. Chem.*, **233**, 748 (1958)

213. Packer, L., *Nature*, **193**, 880 (1962)

214. Garfinkel, D., *Arch. Biochem. Biophys.*, **77**, 493 (1958)

215. Ernster, L., Siekevitz, P., and Palade, G. E., *J. Cell Biol.* (In press)

215a. Stirpe, F., and Schwarz, K., *Arch. Biochem. Biophys.*, **96**, 672 (1962)

216. Kielley, W. W., and Meyerhof, O., *J. Biol. Chem.*, **176**, 591 (1948)

217. Ebashi, S., *Arch. Biochem. Biophys.*, **76**, 410 (1958)

218. Ebashi, S., *J. Biochem. (Japan)*, **48**, 150 (1960)

219. Marsh, B. B., *Nature*, **167**, 1065 (1951)

220. Portzehl, A., *Biochim. Biophys. Acta*, **24**, 474 (1957)

221. Ebashi, S., and Lipmann, F., *J. Cell Biol.*, **14**, 389 (1962)

222. Nagai, T., Makinose, M., and Hasselbach, W., *Biochim. Biophys. Acta*, **43**, 223 (1960)

222a. Berne, R. M., *Biochem. J.*, **83**, 364 (1962)

223. Porter, K. R., and Palade, G. E., *J. Biophys. Biochem. Cytol.*, **3**, 269 (1957)

223a. Stam, A. C., Jr., and Honig, C. L., *Biochim. Biophys. Acta*, **60**, 259 (1962)

224. Ebashi, S., *J. Biochem. (Japan)*, **50**, 236 (1961)

225. Ebashi, S., *Progr. Theoret. Phys.*, Suppl. 17, 35 (1961)

226. Azzone, G. F., in *Symposium 11, Intern. Congr. Biochem., 5th, Moscow, 1961* (Pergamon, London)

227. Reid, E., O'Neal, M. A., and Lewin, I., *Biochem. J.*, **64**, 730 (1956)

228. Schneider, W. C., *Cancer Res.*, **6**, 685 (1946)

229. Schneider, W. C., Hogeboom, G. H., and Ross, H. E., *J. Natl. Cancer Inst.*, **10**, 977 (1950)

230. Abood, L. G., and Romanchek, L., *Exptl. Cell Res.*, **8**, 459 (1955)

231. Wakid, N. W., *Biochem. J.*, **76**, 88 (1960)

232. Bellamy, D., *Biochem. J.*, **72**, 165 (1959)

233. Whittaker, V. P., *Biochem. J.*, **72**, 694 (1959)

234. De Robertis, E., De Iraldi, A. P.,

Rodriguez, G., and Gomez, C. J., *J. Biophys. Biochem. Cytol.*, **9**, 229 (1961)

235. Gray, E. G., and Whittaker, V. P., *J. Physiol. (London)*, **153**, 2 (1960)

236. De Robertis, E., De Iraldi, A. P., Rodriguez, G., and Salganicoff, L., *J. Neurochem.*, **9**, 23 (1962)

237. De Robertis, E., Rodriguez, G., and De Iraldi, A. P., *Nature*, **194**, 794 (1962)

238. Aldridge, W. N., and Johnson, M. K., *Biochem. J.*, **73**, 270 (1959)

239. Parmar, S. S., Sutter, M. C., and Nickerson, M., *Can. J. Biochem. Physiol.*, **39**, 1335 (1961)

240. Frontali, M., and Toschi, G., *Exptl. Cell Res.*, **15**, 446 (1958)

240a. Whittaker, V. P., *Biochem. Pharmacol.*, **5**, 392 (1961)

241. Goutier, R., and Goutier-Pirotte, M., *Biochim. Biophys. Acta*, **16**, 361 (1955)

242. Underhay, E., Holt, S. J., Beaufay, H., and de Duve, C., *J. Biophys. Biochem. Cytol.*, **2**, 635 (1956)

243. Smith J. C., Foldes, V., and Foldes, F. F., *Federation Proc.*, **19**, 260 (1960)

244. Hagen, P., *J. Physiol. (London)*, **129**, 50 (1955)

245. Skou, J. C., *Biochim. Biophys. Acta*, **23**, 394 (1957)

246. Skou, J. C., *Biochim. Biophys. Acta*, **42**, 6 (1960)

247. Skou, J. C., *Biochim. Biophys. Acta*, **58**, 314 (1962)

248. Post, R. L., Merritt, C. R., Kinsolving, C. R., and Albright, C. D., *J. Biol. Chem.*, **235**, 1796 (1960)

248a. Whittam, R., *Biochem. J.*, **84**, 110 (1962)

249. Järnefelt, J., *Biochim. Biophys. Acta*, **48**, 104 (1961)

249a. Järnefelt, J., *Biochim. Biophys. Acta*, **59**, 643 (1962)

250. Järnefelt, J., *Exptl. Cell Res.*, **21**, 214 (1960)

250a. Aldridge, W. N., *Biochem. J.*, **83**, 527 (1962)

251. Järnefelt, J., *Biochem. Biophys. Res. Commun.*, **6**, 285 (1961)

251a. Cummins, J., and Hydén, H., *Biochim. Biophys. Acta*, **60**, 277 (1962)

252. Järnefelt, J., *Biochim. Biophys. Acta*, **48**, 111 (1961)

252a. Järnefelt, J., *Biochim. Biophys. Acta*, **59**, 655 (1962)

253. Hers, H. G., and de Duve, C., *Bull. Soc. Chim. Biol.*, **32**, 20 (1950)

254. Hers, H. G., Berthet, J., Berthet, L., and de Duve, C., *Bull. Soc. Chim. Biol.*, **33**, 21 (1951)

255. Beaufay, H., Bendall, D. S., Baudhuin, P., and de Duve, C., *Biochem. J.*, **73**, 623 (1959)

256. Hultin, T., *Exptl. Cell Res.*, **12**, 290 (1957)

257. Segal, H. L., and Washko, M. E., *J. Biol. Chem.*, **234**, 1937 (1957)

258. Busch, S., Weill, J. D., and Mandel, P., *Compt. Rend. Soc. Biol.*, **154**, 798 (1960)

259. Beaufay, H., and de Duve, C., *Bull. Soc. Chim. Biol.*, **36**, 1551 (1954)

260. Beaufay, H., Hers, H. G., Berthet, J. and de Duve, C., *Bull. Soc. Chim. Biol.*, **36**, 1539 (1954)

261. Ashmore, J., and Nesbett, F. B., *Proc. Soc. Exptl. Biol. Med.*, **89**, 78 (1955)

261a. Görlich, M., and Heise, E., *Nature*, **194**, 376 (1962)

262. Siekevitz, P., in *Ciba Found. Symp. Metabolic Regulation*, 17 (Churchill, London, 1958)

262a. Hilf, R., Breuer, C., and Borman, A., *Nature*, **194**, 897 (1962)

263. Ginsburg, V., and Hers, H. G., *Biochim. Biophys. Acta*, **38**, 427 (1960)

264. Novikoff, A., Podber, E., Ryan, J., and Noe, E., *J. Histochem. Cytochem.*, **1**, 27 (1953)

265. Omachi, A., Barnum, C. P., and Glick, D., *Proc. Soc. Exptl. Biol. Med.*, **67**, 133 (1948)

266. Carruthers, C., Woernley, D. L., Baumler, A., and Lilga, K., *Arch. Biochem. Biophys.*, **87**, 266 (1960)

267. Carruthers, C., and Baumler, A., *Arch. Biochem. Biophys.*, **94**, 351 (1961)

268. Krishnamurthy, S., Sastry, P. S., and Ganguly, J., *Arch. Biochem. Biophys.*, **75**, 6 (1958)

269. Heller, L., and Bargoni, N., *Arkiv Kemi*, **1**, 447 (1950)

270. Markert, C. L., and Hunter, R. L., *J. Histochem. Cytochem.*, **7**, 42 (1959)

271. Omachi, A., Barnum, C. P., and Glick, D., *Proc. Soc. Exptl. Biol. Med.*, **67**, 133 (1948)

272. Ludewig, S., and Chanutin, A., *Arch. Biochem.*, **29**, 441 (1950)

273. Ganguly, J., *Arch. Biochem. Biophys.*, **52**, 187 (1954)

274. Dodgson, K. S., Spencer, B., and Thomas, J., *Biochem. J.*, **59**, 29 (1955)

275. Gianetto, R., and Viala, R., *Science*, **121**, 801 (1955)

276. Roy, A. B., *Biochem. J.*, **68**, 519 (1958)

277. de Duve, C., *Nature*, **187**, 836 (1960)

278. Novikoff, A. B., in *The Cell*, **II** (Academic, New York, 1961)
279. Borgström, B., and Dahlqvist, A., *Acta Chem. Scand.*, **12**, 1997 (1958)
280. Wu, C., *Federation Proc.*, **20**, 218 (1961)
281. Bremer, J., *Acta Chem. Scand.*, **10**, 56 (1956)
282. Elliott, W. H., *Biochem. J.*, **62**, 427 (1956)
283. Elliott, W. H., *Biochem. J.*, **62**, 433 (1956)
284. Elliott, W. H., *Biochem. J.*, **65**, 315 (1957)
285. Bremer, J., and Gloor, V., *Acta Chem. Scand.*, **9**, 689 (1955)
286. Bremer, J., *Acta Chem. Scand.*, **9**, 268 (1955)
287. Villar-Palasi, C., and Larner, J., *Arch. Biochem. Biophys.*, **86**, 270 (1960)
288. Strominger, J. L., Maxwell, E. S., Axelrod, J., and Kalckar, H. M., *J. Biol. Chem.*, **224**, 79 (1957)
289. Axelrod, J., Inscoe, J. K., and Tomkins, G. M., *J. Biol. Chem.*, **232**, 835 (1958)
290. Dutton, G. J., and Storey, I. D. E., *Biochem. J.*, **57**, 275 (1954)
291. Isselbacher, K. J., *Biochem. Biophys. Res. Commun.*, **5**, 243 (1961)
292. Pogell, B. M., and Leloir, L. F., *J. Biol. Chem.*, **236**, 293 (1961)
293. ul Hassan, M., and Lehninger, A. L., *J. Biol. Chem.*, **223**, 123 (1956)
294. Burns, J. J., Peyser, P., and Moltz, A., *Science*, **124**, 1148 (1956)
295. Winkelman, J., and Lehninger, A. L., *J. Biol. Chem.*, **233**, 794 (1958)
296. Bublitz, C., and Lehninger, A. L., *Biochim. Biophys. Acta*, **32**, 290 (1959)
297. Mano, Y., Yamada, K., Suzuki, K., and Shimazono, N., *Biochim. Biophys. Acta*, **34**, 563 (1959)
298. Chatterjee, I. B., Chatterjee, C. G., Ghosh, N. C., Ghosh, J. J., and Guha, B. C., *Biochem. J.*, **76**, 279 (1960)
299. Chatterjee, I. B., Ghosh, J. J., Ghosh, N. C., and Guha, B. C., *Naturwissenschaften*, **46**, 580 (1959)
300. Isherwood, F. A., Mapson, L. W., and Chen, Y. T., *Biochem. J.*, **76**, 157 (1960)
301. Kanfer, J., Burns, J. J., and Ashwell, G., *Biochim. Biophys. Acta*, **31**, 556 (1959)
301a. Kar, N. C., Chatterjee, I. B., Ghosh, N. C., and Guha, B. C., *Biochem J.*, **184**, 16 (1962)
302. Halac, E., and Frank, S., *Biochem.*

303. Leloir, L. F., and Goldemberg, S. H., *J. Biol. Chem.*, **235**, 919 (1960)
304. Cleland, W. W., and Kennedy, E. P., *J. Biol. Chem.*, **235**, 45 (1960)
305. Burton, R. M., Sodd, M. A., and Brady, R. O., *J. Biol. Chem.*, **233**, 1053 (1958)
305a. Hassid, W. Z., and Watkins, W. M., *J. Biol. Chem.*, **237**, 1432 (1962)
306. Nordlie, R. C., and Lardy, H. A., *Biochim. Biophys. Acta*, **50**, 189 (1961)
307. Dianzani, M. U., *Biochim. Biophys. Acta*, **14**, 514 (1954)
308. Sacktor, B., *J. Gen. Physiol.*, **36**, 371 (1953)
309. Waked, N., and Kerr, S. E., *J. Histochem. Cytochem.*, **3**, 75 (1955)
310. Ahmed, Z., and King, E. J., *Biochim. Biophys. Acta*, **34**, 313 (1959)
311. Novikoff, A. B., *Cancer Res.*, **17**, 1010 (1957)
312. Kenney, F. T., Colowick, S. P., and Barbehenn, E., *Arch. Biochem. Biophys.*, **69**, 617 (1957)
313. Abood, L. G., and Gerard, R. W., *J. Cellular Comp. Physiol.*, **43**, 379 (1954)
314. Jones, L. C., and Ernster, L., *Acta Chem. Scand.*, **14**, 1839 (1960)
315. Ernster, L., and Jones, L. C., *J. Cell Biol.* (In press)
316. Goodlad, G. A. J., and Mills, G. T., *Biochem. J.*, **66**, 346 (1957)
317. de Lamirande, G., Allard, C., and Cantero, A., *J. Biophys. Biochem Cytol.*, **4**, 373 (1958)
318. Segal, H. L., and Brenner, B. M., *J. Biol. Chem.*, **235**, 471 (1962)
319. Giuditta, A., and Strecker, H. J., *J. Neurochem.*, **5**, 50 (1959)
320. Cerletti, P., Fronticelli, C., and Zichella, L., *Clin. Chim. Acta*, **5**, 439 (1960)
321. de Lamirande, G. Allard C., and Cantero, A., *Cancer Res.*, **18**, 952 (1958)
322. Kun, E., Talalay, P., and Williams-Ashman, H. G., *Cancer Res.*, **11**, 855 (1951)
323. Bojarski, T. B., and Wynne, A. M., *Can. Cancer Conf.*, **2**, 95 (1957)
324. Sung, S., and Williams, J. N., Jr., *J. Biol. Chem.*, **197**, 175 (1952)
325. Jacobson, K. B., and Kaplan, N. O., *J. Biophys. Biochem. Cytol.*, **3**, 31 (1957)
326. Dianzani, M. U., *Biochim. Biophys. Acta*, **17**, 391 (1955)
327. Jordan, W. K., March, K., Boyd,

O. H., and Popp E., *J. Neurochem.*, **4**, 170 (1959)

328. de Lamirande, G., Allard, C., and Cantero, A., *Cancer Res.*, **18**, 952 (1958)

329. Struck, J., and Sizer, I. W., *Arch. Biochem. Biophys.*, **90**, 22 (1960)

330. Meyers, L. T., and Worthen, H. G., *Federation Proc.*, **20**, 218 (1961)

331. Macleod, R. M., Farkas, W., Fridovitch, I., and Handler, P., *J. Biol. Chem.*, **236**, 1841 (1961)

332. Johnson, R. M., Albert, S.. and Reeves, A., *Proc. Soc. Exptl. Biol. Med.*, **88**, 594 (1955)

333. Rosenthal, O., Gottlieb, B., Gorez, J. D., and Vars, H. M., *J. Biol. Chem.*, **223**, 469 (1956)

334. Avi-Dor, Y., *Biochem. J.*, **76**, 370 (1960)

335. Binkley, F., *J. Biol. Chem.*, **236**, 1075 (1961)

336. Binkley, F., Davenport, J., and Eastall, F., *Biochem. Biophys. Res. Commun.*, **1**, 206 (1959)

337. Cliffe, E. E., and Waley, S. G., *Biochem. J.*, **79**, 118 (1961)

337a. Weiss, B., *J. Biol. Chem.*, **205**, 193 (1953)

338. O'Brien, R. D., *Nature*, **183**, 121 (1959)

339. Meister, A., *Science*, **115**, 521 (1952)

340. Allard, C., de Lamirande, G., Farin, H., and Cantero, A., *Can. J. Biochem. Physiol.*, **32**, 383 (1954)

341. Allard, C., de Lamirande, G., and Cantero, A., *Cancer Res.*, **17**, 862 (1957)

342. Appelmans, F., Wattiaux, R., and de Duve, C., *Biochem. J.*, **59**, 438 (1955)

343. Berger, M., *Biochim. Biophys. Acta*, **23**, 504 (1957)

344. Griswold, R. L., and Pace, N., *Exptl. Cell Res.* **11**, 362 (1956)

345. Thiers, R. E., and Vallee, B. L., *J. Biol. Chem.*, **226**, 911 (1957)

346. Sanui, H., and Pace, N., *J. Gen. Physiol.*, **42**, 1325 (1959)

347. Paigen, K., *Biochim. Biophys. Acta*, **19**, 297 (1956)

348. Garfinkel, D., *Arch. Biochem. Biophys.*, **77**, 493 (1958)

349. Petermann, M. L., and Pavlovec, A., *J. Biol. Chem.*, **236**, 3235 (1961)

350. DeGroot, L. J., and Carvalho, E., *J. Biol. Chem.*, **235**, 1390 (1960)

351. Ekholm, R., *J. Ultrastruct. Res.*, **5**, 575 (1961)

351a. Paigen, K., and Wenner, C. E., *Arch. Biochem. Biophys.*, **97**, 213 (1962)

352. Potter, L. T., and Axelrod, J., *Nature*, **194**, 581 (1962)

353. Perlmann, P., and D'Amelio, V., *Nature*, **181**, 491 (1958)

354. D'Amelio, V., and Perlmann, P., *Exptl. Cell Res.*, **19**, 383 (1960)

355. Morgan, W. S., Perlmann, P., and Hultin, T., *J. Biophys. Biochem. Cytol.*, **10**, 411 (1960)

356. Perlmann, P., and de Vincentiis, M., *Exptl. Cell Res.*, **23**, 612 (1961)

357. Pressman, B. C., and Lardy, H. A., *Biochim. Biophys. Acta.*, **21**, 458 (1956)

358. Avi-Dor, Y., *Biochim. Biophys. Acta*, **39**, 53 (1960)

359. Gamble, J. L., Jr., *Biochim. Biophys. Acta*, **23**, 311 (1957)

360. Share, L., and Hansrote, R. W., *J. Biophys. Biochem. Cytol.*, **7**, 239 (1960)

361. Arcos, J. C., and Arcos, M., *Biochim. Biophys. Acta*, **28**, 9 (1958)

362. Gaudette, L. E., and Brodie, B. B., *Biochem. Pharmacol.*, **2**, 89 (1959)

363. Ruska, H., Edwards, G. A., and Caesar, R., *Experientia*, **14**, 117 (1958)

364. Peachey, L. D., and Porter, K. R., *Science*, **129**, 721 (1959)

365. Heald, P. J., *Nature*, **193**, 451 (1962)

366. Bennett, H. S., *J. Biophys. Biochem. Cytol.*, **2**, Suppl., 99 (1956)

367. Porter, K. R., and Machado, R. D., *J. Biophys. Biochem. Cytol.*, **7**, 167 (1960)

368. Holter, H., and Marshall, J. M., Jr., *Compt. Rend. Lab. Carlsberg*, **29**, 7 (1959)

369. Holter, H., *Ann. N.Y. Acad. Sci.*, **78**, 524 (1959)

370. Holter, H., and Holtzer, S., *Compt. Rend. Lab. Carlsberg*, **31**, 373 (1960)

371. Porter, K. R., *Intern. Kongr. Elektronmikroscopie*, **4**, *Berlin, 1958*, 186 (1960)

372. Palay, S. L., in *Frontiers in Cytology*, 303 (Paley, S. L., Ed., Yale Univ. Press, New Haven, Conn., 1958)

373. Palade, G. E., Siekevitz, P., and Caro, L. G., *Ciba Found. Symp.*, *Exocrine Pancreas* (Churchill, London, 1962)

374. Peters, T., Jr., *J. Biol. Chem.*, **237**, 1181, 1186 (1962)

374a. Palade, G. E., *Circulation*, **XXIV**, 368 (1961)

375. Conney, A. H., Miller, E. C., and Miller, J. A., *Cancer Res.*, **16**, 450 (1956)

376. Conney, A. H., Gillette, J. K., Inscoe, J. K., Trams, E. R., and Posner, H. S., *Science*, **130**, 1478 (1959)

377. Cramer, J. W., Miller, J. A., and Miller, E. C., *J. Biol. Chem.*, **235**, 200 (1960)

378. Arcos, J. C., Conney, A. H., and Buu-Hoi, N. P., *J. Biol. Chem.*, **236**, 1291 (1961)

379. Conney, A. H., and Burns, J. J., *Nature*, **184**, 363 (1959)

380. Brown, R. R., Miller, J. A., and Miller, E. C., *J. Biol. Chem.*, **209**, 211 (1954)

381. Murphy, S. D., and DuBois, K., *J. Pharmacol. Exptl. Therap.*, **124**, 194 (1958)

382. Conney, A. H., Davison, C., Gastel, R., and Burns, J. J., *J. Pharmacol. Exptl. Therap.*, **130**, 1 (1960)

383. Conney, A. H., Brown, R. R., Miller, J. A., and Miller, E. C., *Cancer Res.*, **17**, 628 (1957)

384. Remmer, H., *Arch. Exptl. Pathol. Pharmakol.*, **235**, 279 (1959)

385. Burns, J. J., Conney, A. H., Dayton, P. G., Evans, C., Martin, G. R., and Taller, D., *J. Pharmacol. Exptl. Therap.*, **129**, 132 (1960)

386. von der Decken, A., and Hultin, T., *Arch. Biochem. Biophys.*, **90**, 201 (1960)

387. Burns, J. J., Evans, C., and Trousof, N., *J. Biol. Chem.*, **227**, 785 (1957)

388. Fouts, J. R., *Biochem. Biophys. Res. Commun.*, **6**, 373 (1961)

389. Wallach, D. F. H., and Ullrey, D., *Cancer Res.*, **22**, 228 (1962)

390. Emmelot, P., and Bos, C. J., *Biochim. Biophys. Acta*, **58**, 374 (1962)

391. Barrnett, R. J., and Ball, E. G., *J. Biophys. Biochem. Cytol.*, **8**, 83 (1960)

392. Harkin, J. C., *Endocrinology*, **60**, 185 (1957)

393. Deane, H. W., and Porter, K. R., *J. Histochem. Cytochem.*, **7**, 315 (1959)

394. Groth, D. P., and Brandes, D., *J. Ultrastruct. Res.*, **4**, 166 (1960)

395. Emmelot, P., and Benedetti, E. L., *J. Biophys. Biochem. Cytol.*, **7**, 393 (1960)

396. Dixon, R. L., Shultice, R. W., and Fouts, J. R., *Proc. Soc. Exptl. Biol. Med.*, **103**, 333 (1960)

397. Brouwers, J. A. J., and Emmelot, P., *Exptl. Cell Res.*, **19**, 467 (1960)

398. Arias, I. M., *J. Histochem. Cytochem.*, **7**, 250 (1959)

399. Paigen, K., *Exptl. Cell Res.*, **25**, 286 (1961)

400. Hultin, T., *Exptl. Cell Res.*, **12**, 290 (1957)

401. Neville, D. M., Jr., *J. Biophys. Biochem. Cytol.*, **8**, 413 (1960)

402. Miller, D., and Crane, R. K., *Anal. Biochem.*, **2**, 284 (1961)

403. Kono, T., and Colowick, S. P., *Arch. Biochem. Biophys.*, **93**, 520 (1961)

404. McCollester, D. L., *Biochim. Biophys. Acta*, **57**, 427 (1962)

405. McQuillen, K., in *The Bacteria*, **I**, 249 (Gunsalus, I. E., and Stanier, R. Y., Eds., Academic, New York, 1960)

406. Friis, J., and Ottolenghi, P., *Compt. Rend. Lab. Carlsberg*, **31**, 259 (1959)

407. Burger, M., Bacon, E. E., and Bacon, J. S. D., *Biochem. J.*, **78**, 504 (1961)

408. Lukoianova, M. A., Gelman, N. J., and Biriusova, V. I., *Biokhimiya*, **26**, 916 (1961)*

409. Abrams, A., and McNamara, P., *J. Biol. Chem.*, **237**, 170 (1962)

410. Abrams, A., McNamara, P., and Johnson, F. B., *J. Biol. Chem.*, **235**, 3654 (1960)

411. Hill, P. B., *Biochim. Biophys. Acta*, **57**, 386 (1962)

412. Bernhard, W., and Rouiller, C., *J. Biophys. Biochem. Cytol.*, **2**, 73 (1956)

413. Siekevitz, P., *Symposium 11, Intern. Congr. Biochem., 5th, Moscow* (Pergamon, London, 1961)

414. Siekevitz, P., in Allen, J. M., Ed., *Molecular Control of Cellular Activity*, 143 (McGraw-Hill, New York, 1962)

415. Hultin, T., *Biochem. Pharmacol.*, **5**, 359 (1961)

416. Hunter, G. D., and Godson, G. N., *Nature*, **189**, 140 (1961)

417. Birbeck, M. S. C., and Mercer, E. H., *Nature*, **189**, 558 (1961)

418. Hendler, R. W., *Nature*, **193**, 821 (1962)

* English translation will be announced in *Technical Translations*, issued by the Office of Technical Services, U. S. Department of Commerce, and will be made available by the Photoduplication Service, Library of Congress, and by the SLA Translation Center at the John Crerar Library, Chicago, Illinois.

CONNECTIVE TISSUE[1]

By G. Asboe-Hansen

Connective Tissue Research Laboratory, Rigshospital,
University of Copenhagen, Denmark

Connective tissues are ubiquitous and participate in vital processes of mammalian physiology. It is scarcely possible to discuss the pathogenesis of any disease in man without regarding the role of connective tissue elements. Mesenchymal cells and extracellular material undergo more or less specific changes during growth, regeneration and repair, aging, arteriosclerosis, fertility and reproduction, development and growth of tumors, inflammation and immunity, infection, avitaminosis, and poisoning of various kinds. It is an exciting fact, however, that these processes can be influenced, reversed, or stimulated by drugs active on connective tissue. The hormonal control of connective tissues is in the foreground of interest in clinical medicine as well as in research laboratories in most parts of the world.

The last four years covered by this review have brought to our knowledge important results from laboratories utilizing modern biochemical and physical methods. Morphologic research into the submicroscopic area has approached chemical and physical research fields on molecular structures and behavior. Actually, in the year of 1962 the narrow margin between morphology and chemistry is under constant exploration.

Cells

Fibroblasts.—By histological methods the fibroblast can not be made quite as interesting as many other cells. However, modern methods partly overcome this drawback, and recent years have yielded important information concerning the structure and function of the fibroblast. The cells which histologists name "fibroblasts" may well be mesenchymal cells with widely different functions and tasks in the tissues. When several authors have mentioned transformation of fibroblasts into mast cells, they did not take into consideration the possibility that such "fibroblasts" might well be potential mast cells without metachromatic granules (18). Not until later, when the cells become granulated, are the criteria of mast cells fulfilled. These authors did not consider the possibility of environmental conditioning of cell functions either. The term "fibroblast" signifies the ability to form fibrils. Fibrillogenesis has been a matter of intensive research in many laboratories, and there seems to be no doubt that the fibroblast is the site of origin of collagen. There is disagreement, however, concerning the site and the mode of synthesis and release. From electron-microscopic studies of ultrathin tissue sections, Policard *et al.* (125), Nemetschek (119), and others concluded

[1] The survey of literature pertaining to this review was concluded in September 1962.

that fiber formation takes place in the extracellular compartment exclusively. Fitton-Jackson (52) studied the fetal tendon through the electron microscope and advocated the view that fibril formation takes place intra- as well as extracellularly. She also observed parallel filaments in the cytoplasm of fowl osteoblasts grown in tissue culture (51). Porter & Pappas (126) concluded from their observations that collagen fibrils are formed in the cell membrane or on the surface of the cell. They could never demonstrate intracellular fibril formation. On the basis of electron optical findings, Gieseking (57) believed that the synthesis of micellar precursors of fibril material and the formation of primary fibrils take place within the endoplasmic reticulum of the fibroblasts. The elimination of the primary fibrils has to do with the disintegration and disappearance of the peripheral cytoplasmic zone. From evidence obtained using electron microscopy of normal human granulation tissue, Merker (99) also considered the endoplasmic reticulum responsible for collagen synthesis. Moreover, tropocollagen molecules (15 A by 2800 A) were demonstrated on the outside of the cell membrane. Costero (33) found intracellular fibrils which are transformed into mature collagenous substance outside the fibroblast. He admits that collagen fibers can also form extracellularly.

In the absence of cells, Wolff (172) demonstrated formation of collagen fibrils *in vitro* in the semiliquid material from the cavities of arytenoid cartilage of cattle.

There is considerable information on the nuclear structure, mitochondria, and the membrane systems of fibroblasts, chondrocytes, and osteocytes. Motion pictures have revealed the mobility of the intact or cultivated cell and of its membranes and all its structures. The phenomenon of pinocytosis (68) has been clearly demonstrated and elucidated, and its biological importance is generally accepted. Fibroblastic cells may also attain the property of phagocytosis.

Smith & Fitton-Jackson (148) demonstrated a rapid uptake of proline into granular components of the fibroblast. Green & Lowther (61) isolated collagen from microsomal particles of fibroblasts in carageenin granulomas. *In vitro*, collagenase inhibits the growth of fibroblasts from bone marrow while hemic cells are not affected (48).

Fibroblasts have been reported to be influenced during lathyrism. Mager *et al.* (95) demonstrated a cytotoxic effect of the lathyrogen aminoacetonitrile on chick and mouse fibroblasts *in vitro*. The toxic influence was strongest on young, proliferating cells. It was accelerated by triiodothyronine, whereas amino acids exerted a protective action. While fibroblasts have been reported to proliferate in experimental lathyrism, this could not be demonstrated by Enzinger & Warner (47) in connective tissue formed in a polyvinyl sponge.

Fibroblasts are subject to hormonal influence [see Asboe-Hansen (7)]. Although there is some disagreement, it is still generally believed that adrenal steroids inhibit and growth hormone stimulates fibroblast activity.

Mast cells.—Mast cells are mesenchymal cells containing coarse cytoplasmic granules. During the last few years a series of electron-microscopic studies on mast cells have been published. The cells studied originated mostly from mastocytosis, from mastocytomas, or from peritoneal fluid. Orfanos & Stüttgen (121) described mast cells from the skin of a patient with diffuse mastocytosis as rounded or oval cells, the outline of which was characterized by numerous fine cytoplasmic protrusions. The nucleus was oval with increased chromatin density along the periphery. One or two nucleoli and a circumnuclear cisterne between the karyoplasmic and cytoplasmic nuclear membranes were observed. Mitochondria were described, whereas the mastocytosis cells did not show distinct granules specific of mast cells. The cytoplasm was fine granular, sometimes filamentous, and vacuoles were demonstrated. An endoplasmic reticulum was also seen, but it appeared blurred and indistinct. Bloom (25) studied mast cells of a dog mastocytoma and described them as surrounded by a distinct cell membrane with a thickness of about 50 to 60 A. He also found cytoplasmic protrusions, with a length of 0.3 to 0.7 μ and a width of 0.06 to 0.08 μ. They might be straight, curved, branched, or forming loops. The granules were rather uniform in size, their diameter averaging 0.6 μ. When fixed in an aqueous osmium tetroxide solution, the granules were found in various stages of dissolution. In the granules, Bloom demonstrated a granular and diffuse filamentous pattern or even a lamellar structure. A distinct Golgi apparatus and typical mitochondria were regularly found. In peritoneal mast cells of the rat and mouse, a Golgi apparatus was rarely observed, and the cellular protrusions were not as conspicuous as in the mastocytoma cells.

Hagen *et al.* (64) combined electron-microscopic studies with biochemical and bioassay procedures on centrifuged material. In cells of a mouse mastocytoma these authors demonstrated heparin, histamine, and 5-hydroxytryptamine within specific granules which were clearly separated from mitochondria and other intracellular organelles.

Bloom (25), as well as Schiller & Dorfman (141), demonstrated heparin as the main mucopolysaccharide component in rat and mouse peritoneal mast cells. From dog mastocytomas Bloom & Ringertz (25, 130, 131) extracted heparin, chondroitin, and hyaluronic acid.

Synthesis, content, and release of heparin (55, 72) and hyaluronic acid (2, 16, 83, 167) by mast cells were demonstrated from the thirties through the fifties of this century and has been confirmed repeatedly during recent years. Recently, using electrophoresis and infrared spectrophotometry on the urine of a one-year-old patient with bullous, diffuse mastocytosis, Asboe-Hansen (12) demonstrated urinary excretion of hyaluronic acid while no trace of sulfomucopolysaccharides could be demonstrated. In an adult patient with mastocytosis (urticaria pigmentosa), hyaluronic acid and chondroitin sulfuric acid B were demonstrated in the urine and blood serum by similar methods (14). Histamine has been demonstrated in large amounts in the skin (146, 178) and urine (41). No 5-hydroxytryptamine has been found in mast cells of human skin or in body fluids of patients with mastocytosis.

Histamine was regarded by Bloom (25) as a mast cell agent that blocks the anticoagulant properties of heparin. Evidently, heparin did not influence the effect of histamine. Histamine has also been shown to form a complex *in vitro* with heparin, and the morphological characters and staining properties of the complex to resemble those of naturally occurring mast cell granules (137). Smith (147) found evidence that histamine can be released by mast cells independent of heparin release. Uvnäs and co-workers (49, 162) have studied the mechanism of histamine release from isolated rat mast cells. Polymeric amines, e.g. compound 48/80, extracts of *Ascaris suis* and *Cyanea capillata*, and antigen-antibody reactions cause morphologic changes in the cells and release of histamine and 5-hydroxytryptamine. The influence of pH, ionic milieu, temperature, and enzyme inhibitors indicated to the authors a participation of enzymic mechanisms in these processes, while the influence of metabolic inhibitors, anoxia, and glucose protection suggested that the release processes require energy. During the release process, biologically active acid lipids are formed in the mast cells. Phosphatidase A and chymotrypsin disrupt mast cells *in vitro* (49, 76). Histidine decarboxylase has been demonstrated in mast cells of mastocytoma of the mouse, of urticaria pigmentosa in man, and of rat skin (23, 65, 139).

Sensitized mast cells are damaged by antigen when an anaphylactic release of histamine is produced in actively sensitized rats, mice, and guinea pigs (115, 116). In the guinea pig, anaphylatoxin produced mast cell damage similar to that produced by antigen-antibody reaction, but different from that produced by chemical histamine liberators. Tokuda & Weiser (161) found no morphologic changes in mast cells in tissues of mice following anaphylactic death. Rat peritoneal mast cells fix human gamma-globulin and, upon addition of antigen, undergo degranulation at 37°C. This can be inhibited by calcium deficiency and by measures inducing a decrease in complement activity (77).

Ascorbic acid deficiency may induce morphologic changes in tissue mast cells. In scorbutic guinea pigs, Pettersson (124) found partial or complete disappearance of the cytoplasmic granules, and the production of granules seemed to be arrested. Larsen (81, 82) found degranulation and vacuolization of the cytoplasm in 12 out of 14 scorbutic animals, and their uptake of ^{35}S was inhibited.

Mast cells are subject to hormonal influence. Since in 1950–1952 it was shown that cortisone and corticotropin (ACTH) induce morphologic changes in mast cells, and that simultaneously a suppressive effect on mast cell activity could be demonstrated (3, 5, 163), this has been confirmed by numerous investigators. Bloom (24) found vacuolization and disruption of mast cells and release of cytoplasmic granules as well as an increase in the number of binucleated and multinucleated cells after treatment with cortisone. Larsen (81) found similar changes in mast cells of the uveal tract of rabbits, and Cronberg (36) demonstrated a decrease in the number of peritoneal mast cells after intraperitoneal administration of hydrocortisone and prednisolone. Hydrocortisone and prednisolone did not prevent the disruption of mast cells following intraperitoneal injection of the histamine releaser 48/80 (37). In the gastric mucosa of rats, prednisolone has been found to induce degranulation of mast cells. It was suggested by Räsänen (134) that, in the lamina propria of the gastrointestinal tract, glucocorticoids conjugate with the polysaccharides of the mast granules and that the tissue eosinophils eliminate the histamine and 5-hydroxytryptamine liberated. Hill & Pospisil (67) found that extravascular mast cells degranulated and disintegrated, perivascular cells vacuolized and lost granule stainability as a response to hydrocortisone. Discussing these findings, the authors considered the reaction of mast cells a morphologic manifestation of the secretion of mucopolysaccharides of the hyaluronic acid type. The reaction was believed to be brought about by a change in the physicochemical properties of the extracellular ground substance. Csaba & Mold (38) found an increase in the number of mast cells of the thymus during cortisone treatment. Such an increase is known also from other experiments where involution of parenchymatous organs and reactive proliferation of connective tissue take place. Evidently, in rats the regeneration process in connective tissue can go on while the thymus tissue yields to cortisone influence. In accordance with the results reported above, Telford & West (158) reported that intramuscular injections of cortisone, prednisolone, triamcinolone, dexamethasone, fluorocortisone, and 2-methylfluorocortisone markedly reduced the content of histamine and 5-hydroxytryptamine (serotonin) in skin and small intestine of rats.

In the uterus of spayed mice, testosterone and estradiol significantly decrease the number of mast cells (71). After prolonged treatment with estrogenic hormone the mast cells in the vagina of mice increase significantly (169).

In the human oral mucosa, Schiff & Burn (140) found an increase in the total count as well as in the granule content of mast cells after administration of estrogen.

Thyrotropic hormone increases the number of mast cells in connective tissues and stimulates the synthesis of mucopolysaccharides as well as the release to the extracellular ground substance, producing a myxedema. Thyroxine has the reverse effect (10, 17, 20, 81, 83, 166).

Although lathyrogenic agents are known to induce severe changes in connective tissues of various animals, Wegelius et al. (168) found no changes in mast cells of hamsters treated with aminoacetonitrile. The authors concluded that the impairment of regeneration demonstrated in healing wounds was not mediated by changes in the mast cells.

INTERCELLULAR SUBSTANCES

The composition of the extracellular mass varies to some extent in various organs and areas of the body. Generally the constituents are as follows: collagen, elastin, acid mucopolysaccharides (mostly in complexes with non-collagenous protein), heteropolysaccharides, lipids, salts, and water.

Collagen is a fibrous protein characterized chemically by its high content of hydroxyproline and hydroxylysine and, besides, a considerable content of proline and glycine (46). Native collagen fibrils give a typical X-ray fiber diagram (21). There is an axial periodicity of 640 A, a spacing which is highly characteristic in the electron microscope (22), and the diameters of the fibrils vary from 100 to 1000 A in various tissues. The collagenous fibrils are inextensible and can be converted into gelatin. The latest years have brought detailed information on the molecular structure of collagen. Collagen has a helical structure. The polypeptide chains are linked together by hydrogen bonds forming a coil. There is no complete agreement concerning the amino acid composition and sequence along their length [see Fitton-Jackson (53)]. Tropocollagen is the monomeric unit of collagen (62) which has a length of 2800 A. Collagen fibrils can be brought into solution and can reaggregate without the presence of cells. The rate of precipitation varies with ionic strength and pH [Wood & Keech (174)]. During synthesis of collagen, Fitton-Jackson & Smith (54) found proline to be the major precursor of hydroxyproline in tissue culture. Similar findings have been made in the live animal [Stetten (155)]. Immediately after synthesis, the precollagen macromolecule contains both proline and hydroxyproline. The latter is the most characteristic component of collagen. In studies with tritium-labeled proline in guinea pig granuloma, Stone & Meister (156) demonstrated that two types of proline are involved in collagen synthesis. One becomes collagen proline, whereas the other is oxidized to a hydroxyproline-containing intermediate which is not yet in peptide linkage. Evidently vitamin C is active in this oxidation.

Peterkofsky & Udenfriend (123), in a cell-free system from chick embryo, found proline-^{14}C to be converted into peptide-bound hydroxyproline-^{14}C. They concluded that proline is a far better precursor than hydroxyproline itself. Free hydroxylysine can not be incorporated in collagen lysine or hydroxylysine. The last-mentioned amino acid orginates from hydroxylation of lysine during formation of collagen (145).

Elastin.—Partridge & Davis (122) demonstrated that glycine constitutes a part of the total amino acid pool which is equivalent to that of collagen. The content of hydroxyproline is very low. On the other hand, the amount of valine is about seven times that in collagen. Elastic fibrils are thinner than collagen fibrils or about 70 A in diameter. There is no axial periodicity (128). Elastin can not be converted into gelatin, and is highly elastic.

Acid mucopolysaccharides are polysaccharides containing hexosamine and usually uronic acid. This group of compounds is characteristic of the ground substance in connective tissue. Such polysaccharides are formed by the local mesenchymal cells and they occur in various concentrations and proportions in different mesenchymal tissues. Two main groups are generally considered: (*a*) the sulfomucopolysaccharides, and (*b*) the nonsulfated mucopolysaccharides. The first consists of chondroitin sulfate A, B, and C, composed of equimolar concentrations of N-acetylgalactosamine, hexuronic acid, and sulfate. While the hexuronic acid of the A and C types is glucuronic acid, it is iduronic acid in the B variety. Heparitin sulfate contains glucosamine, uronic acid, and sulfate. Keratosulfate is the only acid mucopolysaccharide that does not contain uronic acid. It is composed of N-acetyl-glucosamine, galactose, and sulfate.

Suzuki & Strominger (157) have shown that the hen oviduct contains enzymes which can transfer inorganic sulfate to preformed polysaccharides, such as sulfated and desulfated chondroitin sulfate A, B, and C. Rabbit skin seems to contain similar enzymes (40).

Heparin has never been demonstrated in extracellular ground substance. In several species, among them some of the usual laboratory animals, this acid mucopolysaccharide is contained in connective tissues, but only in proportions that correspond to the amount of mast cells.

The nonsulfated mucopolysaccharides are hyaluronic acid, composed of N-acetylglucosamine and glucuronic acid, and chondroitin. The latter has the same components as chondroitin sulfate, lacking only sulfate (102, 117).

Dorfman (44) showed that glucose is a direct precursor of both the glucosamine and the glucuronic acid of the hyaluronic acid molecule. Hyaluronic acid occurs in loose complexes to noncollagen protein. However, in mesenchymal tissues the sulfomucopolysaccharides exist as firmly bound complexes with noncollagen protein. By specific labeling, the rates of turnover of the protein and the mucopolysaccharide moieties have been found to be equal (63). The turnover of hyaluronic acid is relatively rapid, the biological half life being about two days. The biological half life of the sulfomucopolysaccharides of skin and cartilage is several times longer (27, 28, 43). Collagen, once deposited, is probably a metabolically inert substance (120).

The acid mucopolysaccharides lend to the ground substances certain of their most important physicochemical properties, e.g. their viscosity, gelatinous character, and water-binding capacity.

Neutral mucopolysaccharides or heteropolysaccharides do not contain hexuronic acid or sulfate (42). They are present in extracellular substances, but their functional significance is unknown. They can be distinguished from the plasma proteins.

In the interstitial fluid are low molecular weight substances, e.g., amino acids, peptides, nucleotides, plasma proteins, simple sugars, and free electrolytes. The interstitial fluid occurs in colloid suspension, and probably never in the free fluid state (53).

Ascorbic acid.—The extracellular substances are subject to changes in the control of cell functions by vitamin deficiency, hormones, and stimuli of various kinds. Lack of ascorbic acid leads to accumulation of hyaluronic acid in repair tissue (132). The maintenance of preformed collagen does not require ascorbic acid. Although not definitely blocked, collagen synthesis is markedly restricted in scurvy. Despite the presence of a large number of fibroblasts in tissues, ascorbic acid deficiency may result in a loss of collagen. Ascorbic acid acts on the fibroblasts in granulation tissue as well as in other tissue. Robertson believes that ascorbic acid is concerned with hydroxylation of proline before the peptide chain is synthesized. This author has found no evidence that, in scurvy, a nonfibrous hydroxyproline-poor protein precursor of collagen accumulates.

Gould (60) presented evidence that ascorbic acid is involved in the formation of growth collagen, but at a concentration that is extremely low in comparison with that for repair collagen. He distinguishes between ascorbic acid-independent and ascorbic acid-dependent collagen-forming mechanisms. In the guinea pig, ascorbic acid has been found to accumulate in skin wounds during the period shortly following incision and before collagen is formed (1). In his studies of the inhibition of wound healing by thyroxine, Moltke (104, 108) found that ascorbic acid alters the level but not the character of the dose-response curve of thyroxine. He also found that, in scurvy, there was only slight incorporation of ^{35}S-labeled sulfate into wounds as well as into intact skin. However, the activity in the wounds was relatively higher than in the skin, the activity ratio in the scorbutic guinea pig being higher than in the groups of thyroxine-treated and intact guinea pigs. Martin *et al.* (97) demonstrated a decrease of hydroxyproline in scurvy and an increase in lathyrism as well as in aging.

Lathyrism.—Merkow (100) suggested that the lathyrogenic substance β-aminopropionitrile acts by disrupting the cross-links within mesenchymal scleroprotein units. Using ^{14}C-glycine incorporation into collagen subunits, Martin *et al.* (96) concluded from their experiments on rats that there is a defect at the molecular level in the maturation of collagen in lathyritic animals. The failure to produce chain pairs by intramolecular cross-linking results in a high proportion of collagen in acid extracts similar to young collagen in the normal animal. In fracture callus of lathyrogenic rats, Bolognani (26) found a decreased hexosamine content while there was no change in the hydroxyproline concentration. Dasler *et al.* (39) believed that the effect of lathyrogens on collagen is indirect. They suggest that there is a change in ionic environment, and that the mode of action may be through the formation of chelates.

Hormonal influence.—The effect of hormones on the intercellular substances has been further elucidated by recent experiments. Because of the importance of adrenal steroids in clinical therapy of connective tissue disorders, the fundamental mechanism of action of the glucocorticoids is still in the center of interest. Carsten *et al.* (29) found experimental evidence that adrenocortical hormones do not act directly on collagen fibers of skin, but have some effect on the mucopolysaccharides of the ground substance. This effect was thought to be responsible for changes in diameter and in silver staining of the collagenous fibrils, which were observed after adrenalectomy and cortisone. These observations are in agreement with earlier findings indicating a steroid effect on mast cells while the effect on fibroblasts was dubious [see Asboe-Hansen (6)]. In contrast to steroids, thyrotropic hormone brings about an increase in the ground substance content of acid mucopolysaccharides (9, 11, 20).

AGING OF CONNECTIVE TISSUE

With advancing age various changes in the structure and function of connective tissues have been demonstrated. The research within this field seems to follow the need of the modern communities for information concerning diseases of old age. The turgor and thickness of skin are reduced with age, and the dermis appears more fibrous and dry in old individuals than in young. Kirk & Dyrbye (78, 79) found no qualitative variations in the content of mucopolysaccharides in human thoracic aorta from the neonatal stage to the age of 60 years. After this, the relative content decreased considerably. The authors demonstrated an increasing galactosamine-to-glucosamine ratio in the fraction of aortic mucopolysaccharides and, thus, a qualitative change in old age. Dyrbye (45) found evidence of lowered metabolic activity of the sulfomucopolysaccharides in human aorta with aging and with the development of arteriosclerosis.

Sobel and co-workers (149 to 153) have shown that the gel-to-fiber ratio decreases with aging in the skin of the rat, guinea pig, squab, rabbit, and man, in the femur of the rat, and in the lung tissue of the rabbit. The same group of investigators believes that corticoid-androgen antagonism is the only hormonal influence on connective tissues in aging. During growth, anabolic influences predominate, and the fibrillar components grow at a faster rate than the soluble ground substance. During maturity there is nitrogen equilibrium, and the ground substance mantains a constant composition while the fibrillar phase grows slowly. In aging, the antianabolic influences predominate. The fibrillar component is stable or relatively increasing.

Clausen (31, 32) determined the age variations in the extracellular substance of thoracic aorta, myocardium, and skin of 35 normal human fetuses aged 11 to 19 weeks. He also studied the same tissues in autopsy material of 87 persons aged 4 months to 86 years who had met with sudden death, i.e., by accident, suicide, poisoning, cerebral hemorrhage, or coronary occlusion. In all three organs, the connective tissue of which by gross examination appeared normal, Clausen could demonstrate a significant and steady decrease in the hexosamine-to-hydroxyproline and the hexuronic acid-to-hydroxyproline ratios with advancing age. The results indicate a decrease in the gel-to-fiber ratio or a steady increase in the fibrous components in relation to ground substance. Martin *et al.* (96) found an increased urinary excretion of hydroxyproline in aging.

In 1947, Hellström & Holmgren (66) had found a decrease in the number of mast cells in skin and myocardium with advancing age from birth to 83 years. Taken together, these investigations indicate a reduced capacity of acid mucopolysaccharide formation in connective tissues with advancing age.

Collagen fibers undergo morphological changes during aging. With the electron microscope, Wolff (173) demonstrated an increase in fibrillar thickness in early fetal life. Maximum thickness and periodic silver stainability were noted in the second half of the prenatal period. The thickness decreased without loss of silver stainability in the postnatal life, and a medium thickness was maintained till about 60 years. In old age a decrease in thickness was demonstrated.

ARTERIOSCLEROSIS

As a response to injury to the arterial wall, one of the earliest observable changes is an accumulation of metachromatic unstructured ground substance. This may or may not be accompanied by necrosis and calcification. Accumulation of acid mucopolysaccharides occurs after damage of widely different kinds. Pyridoxine deficiency (129), toxic doses of vitamin D (58), lathyrism (59, 101), treatment with adrenocorticotropic hormone (170, 171) or with epinephrine or thyroid hormone or both (88) have been reported to induce such changes in the arterial wall.

Lorenzen (87 to 94) demonstrated in a series of experiments that the acid mucopolysaccharides of the arterial wall participate actively in the arteriosclerotic process. Administration of epinephrine, norepinephrine, or thyroxine (or all three), both the D- and L-isomer, induced severe changes in the media and also intimal thickening. After two weeks of daily intravenous administration of epinephrine to rabbits, a rise in the hexosamine-to-hydroxyproline and the hexuronic acid-to-hydroxyproline ratios could be observed. Simultaneously, the uptake of ^{35}S-labeled sulfate and the content of water were increased. These biochemical changes were significant before any morphologic change could be demonstrated. Evidently the age of the lesions determined the biochemical pattern, which explains the dissociation in relation to the microscopic lesions. After three to four weeks the changes mentioned above were reversed: the collagen content was now increasing, and the incorporation of radiosulfate decreasing. These processes took place independently of lipid deposition. It was believed that, somehow, the acid mucopolysaccharides prepare the tissues for lipid accumulation. Thyroidectomy protected against the above-mentioned lesions. Thyrotropic hormone seemed not to influence the arterial wall, and the thyroxines did not act by way of pituitary inhibition. The sequence of changes is recognized from the healing process of skin wounds, and presumably the arteriosclerotic process is to be considered the result of a series of healing processes as responses to injurious attacks of some kind, most probably repeated anoxic damage to the arterial wall or minor variations in blood pressure. Hypercholesterolemia, endocrine influence, age, nutrition, and other factors may, by themselves, induce damage and, secondarily, repair processes in the arterial wall. As Waters (165) maintained, the response of the arterial wall seems to be qualitatively the same, regardless of the type of damage inflicted on it. Quantitatively, on the other hand, there are differences depending on the type, intensity, and duration of the injury.

These investigations immediately release serious reflections on the pathogenesis of human arteriosclerosis, because they suggest a hitherto "missing link" between psychologic stress and strain and vascular damage. Release of epinephrine may well be one important noxious agent and thyroid function a conditioning factor. At present, the endocrine control of arteriosclerosis is the subject of intensive research in laboratories all over the world.

Cox *et al.* (34), by a freezing technique, produced local aseptic necroses in the aorta, skeletal muscle, liver, spleen, and kidney, and incision wounds in skin and muscle. When the serum cholesterol was below the level of 250 mg per 100 ml there was no accumulation of lipoproteins in the areas of arterial damage. In case of higher cholesterol level, an accumulation of lipids could be demonstrated in arterial scars. When the level exceeded 1100 mg per cent, lipids accumulated as xanthomatous lesions in the experimental wounds of the liver, spleen, kidney, muscle, and skin. Such lipid accumulation interfered with the healing. It is known from clinical observations that in hypercholesterolemic individuals lipid deposition takes place in various areas with degenerated connective tissue, e.g. eyelids and striae gravidarum. Eruptive xanthomatosis or discrete xanthomas, as well as atheromatosis of the arteries, are not extraordinary in such patients (8).

REGENERATION, GROWTH, AND REPAIR

The variation in structure and functions of connective tissues from early embryonic life to old age is immediately recognized in the processes of regeneration, growth, and repair (11, 13). These processes are characterized primarily by edema, secondarily by mucinous and fibrous organization of the water. The processes have been studied in the normal growing and aging organism, in healing wounds and fractures, during the development of serosal adhesions, in acute and chronic edemas of human patients and in induced edemas in man and laboratory animals, in inflammation, and in responses of connective tissue to tumor growth. Cells of mesenchymal origin produce the overwhelming amount of extracellular substance, determining to a large extent the growth process.

In fresh edemas of the dermis, as it occurs in an acute urticarial wheal, mast cells are degranulated and hardly demonstrable. The extracellular ground substance contains acid mucopolysaccharides of the nonsulfated type, predominantly hyaluronic acid. A few minutes after intradermal injection of Tyrode's fluid, similar phenomena can be observed. In chronic edemas of the legs because of venous stasis, the number of mast cells is increased, the ground substance is ample and contains considerable amounts of nonsulfated as well as sulfated mucopolysaccharides. In this phase there is evidence of fibrosis, the fibroblasts are numerous, and the thickness of the dermis is increased. In edemas experimentally induced in hamster cheek pouches, increased vascular permeability, mast cell degranulation, and hyaluronic acid increase in the extracellular compartment, followed by chondroitin sulfate increase, and collagen fibrillogenesis have been observed. The mucinous organization of the extracellular water takes place within minutes while the sulfate uptake is significant by the second day (15). The presence of chondroitin sulfate is probably essential to primary fibril aggregation, while there is no close correlation between chondroitin sulfate and the fibrillar system of the resultant mature fibers (118). Chondroitin sulfate is lacking in normal synovia and in the humors of the eye and labyrinth. This may explain the lack of fibrosis in these sites.

Histamine, which like acid mucopolysaccharides is a product of mast cells, induces increase of vascular permeability and, thus, tissue edema. Histamine can be released without simultaneous release of mucopolysaccharides (147), and this may be part of the very first response of the tissues to injury. Hyaluronic acid changes the water into a viscous gel, which forms a matrix for collagen deposition, for example.

5-Hydroxytryptamine is another edema-producing substance and may be an important stimulus of repair and fibrosis (19).

The processes mentioned above depend on a well-regulated control system. Hormones exert a continuous influence and control. The main and most sensitive target seems to be the mucinous system of connective tissue. The reason behind this is the faster turnover of hyaluronic acid and the other acid mucopolysaccharides compared with the relatively inert collagen.

Moltke (107), Kasavina et al. (75), and others have confirmed that, at an early point of the wound healing process, hyaluronic acid is increased. Later on, the amounts of chondroitin sulfate and collagen increase.

In scorbutic guinea pigs, hydroxyproline in the skin is below normal, and hexosamine and tyrosine above the normal level. Two days after vitamin C supplementation the values approach the normal level (135). Hughes & Kodicek (69) found evidence that there is little or no galactosamine in granulation tissue of scorbutic guinea pigs. It appeared that there is impaired formation, not associated with inanition, of chondroitin-containing mucopolysaccharides in scorbutic granulation tissue. Ross & Benditt (133) believe that interference with protein synthesis is the major defect in the scorbutic fibroblast.

Various hormones have been reported to influence the wound healing process. The 13-year-old finding by Ragan et al. (127) that cortisone exerts an inhibition has been corroborated several times. In 1961, Zaaijer (175) found therapeutic doses of hydrocortisone to have an unmistakable effect on the resistance and tensile strength of gastric and intestinal sutured wounds in rabbits. He concluded that the inhibition by corticosteroids should be taken into account in postoperative treatment and that distention of the intestine should be avoided.

In alloxan diabetes, wound healing and granulation tissue formation are inhibited in rats (86). The adrenals of the diabetic animals were found enlarged. The average weight of the new granulation tissue was 24 per cent below the weight of the controls. Hexosamine remained unchanged, glycogen was increased, and water was somewhat lowered.

The tensile strength of skin and wounds depends mainly upon the content of collagenous fibrils in the tissue. The formation of these fibers is conditioned not only by cellular activity, but also by the quantity and composition of the mucinous interfibrillar ground substance, primarily the acid mucopolysaccharides. Moltke and co-workers (103 to 113) carried out tensile strength measurements *in situ* on live, adult guinea pigs. In thyroidectomized as well as in intact guinea pigs, D,L-thyroxine reduced the tensile strength of healing incision wounds. Thyrotropic hormone reduced the tensile strength in intact, but not significantly in thyroidectomized, guinea pigs. Upon administration of thyroxine together with a dehalogenase inhibitor, wound healing was restricted and retarded even more than during treatment with thyroxine alone. While L-thyroxine reduced the tensile strength, D-thyroxine was found to increase it. Incorporation of ^{35}S-labeled sulfate into wound tissue of intact animals increased in a rectilinear way from the third to the seventh day, decreasing thereafter. This increase coincided with the increase of tensile strength of the wounds. While thyroxine reduced the uptake of ^{35}S-sulfate into wound tissue, no change was found in intact skin. Ascorbic acid deficiency involved a reduction of ^{35}S-sulfate incorporation into intact skin and a somewhat slighter reduction of the uptake into wound tissue. Moltke concluded that D,L-thyroxine inhibits the formation of collagen fibrils. This inhibition is exerted on a target situated in the wound tissue, a target different from that of ascorbic acid. Both targets are essential to the formation of sulfated mucopolysaccharides and collagen fibrils.

In the hands of Hvidberg *et al.* (70), depletion of histamine in granulation tissue did not induce changes in the hexosamine and hydroxyproline concentrations. In the skin of the rat the level of histidine-decarboxylase activity may be adaptively increased by giving repeated injections of one of the histamine liberators 48/80 and polymyxin B (139). At the peak of histamine-forming capacity in skin, i.e., the stage in which the histamine content is low, the rate of healing of incision wounds has been significantly accelerated. Polymyxin B has the same effect (73, 74). High histamine-forming capacity and low histamine have been found in embryonic and other rapidly growing tissue. Kahlson suggested differences in function between nonmast-cell and mast-cell histamine, because "binding sites" to accommodate the histamine formed were absent in growing tissues in contrast to tissues rich in mast cells. Skin burns and other injurious influences brought about an increase in histidine decarboxylase. Schayer (138) suggested that the new "induced histamine" was instrumental in the control of the microcirculation in the region of damage. Between the third and the ninth day of healing, while the skin level of histidine-decarboxylase was high, the rate of collagen formation, as evidenced by the hydroxyproline content, exceeded that of untreated controls by 50 per cent (136). From their experiments Kahlson and his group concluded that a certain connection exists between rate of repair and rate of histamine formation in connective tissues. The results and the theories of the Lund group are in full accordance with the above-mentioned notion of the Copenhagen group that tissue edema initiates any process of repair, regeneration, or growth of connective tissue.

Considering the possibility of an influence of histamine and 5-hydroxy-tryptamine on connective tissue repair, Fiore-Donati & Moltke (50) measured the tensile strength of healing incision wounds in rats influenced by 5-hydroxytryptamine (serotonin) and the serotonin-liberator substance reserpine. Polymyxin B, a potent histamine-releaser substance, was also tested. Reserpine and 5-hydroxytryptamine caused a significant decrease in the tensile strength of the wounds. The animals treated with polymyxin B showed no significant change. No morphologic changes in mast cells were observed after reserpine and 5-hydroxytryptamine, whereas polymyxin B caused severe changes in these cells. The authors concluded that the effect of reserpine and 5-hydroxytryptamine was probably not mediated by the mast cells of the granulation tissue.

In lathyritic hamsters wound healing is significantly inhibited. As a response to the lathyritic agent aminoacetonitrile, Wegelius et al. (167) found the healing of incision wounds impaired. There was no change in the uptake of ^{35}S-labeled sulfate in the wound tissue, nor in the concentration of hydroxy-proline or hexosamine in the aortas. In lathyritic rats, after administration of β-aminopropionitrile, Kowalewski & Emery (80) found a decreased uptake of ^{35}S-sulfate into fractured humeri. They also found fracture healing promoted by the anabolic steroid 17-ethyl-19-nortestosterone.

INFLAMMATION AND IMMUNITY

Menkin (98) defined inflammation as a complex vascular, lymphatic, and local tissue reaction elicited in higher animals by the presence of viable or nonviable irritants. It is a reaction to injury, which takes aim at localizing and destroying the offender. The development of immunity is related to the cell reactions characterizing chronic phases of inflammation. Increased vascular permeability allows the passage of plasma protein, and fibrinogen comes to the extracellular compartment of the injured area. A network of fibrin is laid down. Formation of acid mucopolysaccharides from mesenchymal cells takes place and, at last, collagen formation, fibrosis, and healing. The plasma cell is considered the major source of antibody. Wagner (164) presented evidence relating the activity of adenosine deaminase to lymphocytosis—lymphocytolysis in antibody—producing lymph nodes. He pointed out the stimulating effects of certain purines on oxidative phosphorylation in vitro. He also advanced the hypothesis that lymphocytes may supply key intermediates, purines, nucleotides, and nucleosides, to the local metabolic pool, which serve to influence protein synthesis. The amino groups released by the deaminase may serve as building blocks in amino acid synthesis. The first morphologic evidence of immunity is the perivascular accumulation of mononuclear cells. At least some of these cells are macrophages. This perivascular reaction may be protective to the vessel wall against the damaging effect of antibody-antigen reactions (56).

The inflammatory reaction is influenced by hormones controlling vascular permeability, extracellular water, synthesis of ground-substance mucopolysaccharides and of collagen, i.e. regeneration, and, besides, antibody production, phagocytosis, enzymic activity, etc. (11).

INFECTION

When hyaluronidase-producing bacteria invade connective tissue, they break down the hyaluronate of the ground substance, reducing its viscosity. Thus, bacteria as well as toxins are allowed to spread in the tissues of the host. Some of the degradation products may counteract the enzyme, reducing the permeability of the connective tissue, while others seem to promote it (4, 30, 143, 154). This is a highly important field for research, inasmuch it concerns the rather vague concept of resistance against infection. This resistance, depending on the conditions of the tissues, may vary with stress of life and the hormonal influence on connective tissues. Any change in the condition of the connective tissue alters the inflammatory process and the balance between the noxious agent and the host.

TUMORS

The condition of the connective tissue stroma of various tumors in man and laboratory animals seems, to some extent, to control the integrity, development, growth, and spreading of the neoplasms. The finding by Cramer & Simpson (35) that mast cells accumulate in precancerous papillomas induced in mice by painting the back skin with carcinogenic hydrocarbons has been confirmed later by several authors. In 1962, Simpson (144) reported on significant correlations between the thickness of the carcinogen-painted epidermis and the number of mast cells in the dermis. Concurrent changes in the mesentery were found to be the inverse of the dermal changes. It was maintained that inferences may be drawn concerning the presence of increased mast cell counts adjacent to hyperplastic epithelium of human cervix and pylorus as one of the marks of a preneoplastic transformation of the tissue. The precise role of the mast cell in neoplastic tissue is still obscure. Ground-substance formation and changes in the permeability of the matrix of the tumor may be highly important to the ability of the neoplasm to spread and develop further. In the connective tissue of squamous and basal cell carcinoma, Moore & Schoenberg (114) found changes similar to those observed in the development cycle and repair process of connective tissue. The authors found no relation to either the aggressiveness of the neoplasm or to the capacity of the host to resist it.

Zachariae & Asboe-Hansen (179) treated pre-existing carcinogen-induced squamous cell carcinomas in mice with local injections of hydrocortisone acetate. During the first 8 to 11 weeks this resulted in regression of the

tumors which decreased in size or disappeared entirely. After the eleventh
week, however, the tumors resumed growing and finally killed a large proportion of the mice.

FERTILITY AND REPRODUCTION

Zachariae (176), in a thesis on the mechanism of ovulation, studied the
role of the acid mucopolysaccharides in the female genital tract of the
rabbit and the cow. He stated that these mucinous substances are under
constant hormonal influence and control. The individual components of
bovine follicular fluid were studied by histochemical, autoradiographic, and
physicochemical techniques. The acid mucopolysaccharides hyaluronic acid
and chondroitin sulfuric acid were isolated. In small follicles the concentration
of hyaluronic acid was high, whereas in the less viscous fluid of the larger
follicles chondroitin sulfate was the predominating mucopolysaccharide.
After sexual stimulation or injection of gonadotropin to rabbits, ^{35}S-sulfate
was not incorporated in the fluid of the ovarian follicles. An enzyme with the
characteristics of hyaluronidase brought about preovulatory depolymerization, as a result of which the colloid-osmotic pressure of the mucopolysaccharides tripled. This is believed to explain follicular growth and rupture.
An increase in the permeability of the blood-follicular fluid barrier facilitating endosmosis was demonstrated. Under the influence of estrogens, the
Fallopian tube, cervix, and vagina secrete acid mucopolysaccharides. As far
as the cervix is concerned, keratosulfate is probably the only mucopolysaccharide present. During estrogen stimulation an accumulation of sulfomucopolysaccharides was demonstrated in the extracellular substance. Their
biological half life was estimated to be about three days. Progesterone
blocked their formation. Hyaluronidase was unable to denude the ovum,
while, on the other hand, a fibrinolytic factor effected complete release of the
cumulus from the ovum. The observation was made (177) that basophil
leucocytes accumulate around recently ovulated follicles. It was suggested
that these mucopolysaccharide-containing blood cells may take over functions that, in tissues, are generally covered by mast cells.

Fertilization, i.e., fusion of the sperm cell with the ovum, is thought to
take place only if the hyaluronidase of the sperm is allowed access to the
hyaluronate of the mucinous mass surrounding the egg after release from the
ovary. The production of this hyaluronate is presumed to be subject to
hormonal control [see Asboe-Hansen (7)]. Most research within this field has
been histochemical and needs biochemical verification. The latest years have
brought little new information concerning the interrelationship between
connective tissue components and fertility.

Thorsøe (159, 160), investigating the influence of thyroid hormone on
ovarian mucopolysaccharides and fertility, demonstrated that, in the rabbit,
thyroidectomy leads to increased ovarian weight and a tendency towards
development of polycystic ovaries. This process is preceded by an increase in
the ovarian content of acid mucopolysaccharides. Fifty days after radical

thyroidectomy five out of ten rabbits had enormously enlarged polycystic ovaries. The synthesis of sulfomucopolysaccharides was reduced, while the hexosamine content was still increased. Dextro- and levo-thyroxine did not influence the mucopolysaccharides, nor did the ovarian weight change, and ovulation took place uninhibited. As in rabbits, the decreased fertility of hypothyroid women is caused by a defect in the mechanism of ovulation and altered function of corpora lutea (84, 85, 142). It has also been shown that hypothyroid women may develop ovarian cysts (84).

LITERATURE CITED

1. Abt, A. F., and Schuching, S. von, *Ann. N. Y. Acad. Sci.*, **92**, 148 (1961)
2. Asboe-Hansen, G., *Ann. Rheumatic Diseases*, **9**, 149 (1950)
3. Asboe-Hansen, G., *Scand. J. Clin. Lab. Invest.*, **2**, 271 (1950)
4. Asboe-Hansen, G., *Acta Endocrinol.*, **9**, 29 (1952)
5. Asboe-Hansen, G., *Proc. Soc. Exptl. Biol. Med.*, **80**, 677 (1952)
6. Asboe-Hansen, G., *Physiol. Rev.*, **38**, 446 (1958)
7. Asboe-Hansen, G., *Am. J. Med.*, **26**, 470 (1959)
8. Asboe-Hansen, G., *Acta Dermato Venereol.*, **39**, 344 (1959)
9. Asboe-Hansen, G., *Arch. Dermatol.*, **82**, 32 (1960)
10. Asboe-Hansen, G., in *Endocrinologiae progressus*, 29 (Canadell, J., Barcelona, 1961)
11. Asboe-Hansen, G., in *Inflammation and Diseases of Connective Tissue*, 38 (Saunders, Philadelphia, 1961)
12. Asboe-Hansen, G., *Acta Dermato-Venereol.*, **42**, 211 (1962)
13. Asboe-Hansen, G., *Intern. Symp. Injury, Inflammation and Immunity* (Miles Lab., Inc., 1962)
14. Asboe-Hansen, G., and Clausen, J., *Acta Dermato-Venereol.* (In press)
15. Asboe-Hansen, G., Dyrbye, M. O., Moltke, E., and Wegelius, O., *J. Invest. Dermatol.*, **32**, 505 (1959)
16. Asboe-Hansen, G., and Glick, D., *Proc. Soc. Exptl. Biol. Med.*, **98**, 458 (1958)
17. Asboe-Hansen, G., and Iversen, K., *Acta Endocrinol.*, **8**, 90 (1951)
18. Asboe-Hansen, G., and Levi, H., *Acta Pathol. Microbiol. Scand.* (In press)
19. Asboe-Hansen, G., and Wegelius, O., *Nature*, **178**, 262 (1956)
20. Asboe-Hansen, G., and Wegelius, O., *Acta Endocrinol.*, **33**, 287 (1960)
21. Astbury, W. T., *Proc. Roy. Soc. (London)*, **134**, 303 (1947)
22. Baer, R. S., *Advances Protein Chem.*, **7**, 69 (1952)
23. Birt, A. R., Hagen, P., and Zebrowski, E., *J. Invest. Dermatol.*, **37**, 273 (1961)
24. Bloom, G., *Acta Morphol. Neerl.-Scand.*, **1**, 331 (1958)
25. Bloom, G., *Studies on the Cytology, Cytochemistry and Pathology of the Mast Cell* (Stockholm, 1960)
26. Bolognani, L., *Proc. Soc. Exptl. Biol. Med.*, **108**, 70 (1961)
27. Boström, H., *J. Biol. Chem.*, **196**, 477 (1952)
28. Boström, H., in *Connective Tissue in Health and Disease*, 97 (Munksgaard, Copenhagen, 1954)
29. Carsten, P. M., Merker, H. J., and Günther, T., *Z. Naturforsch.*, **16b**, 680 (1961)
30. Cavallero, C., in *Connective Tissue in Health and Disease*, 214 (Munksgaard, Copenhagen, 1954)
31. Clausen, B., *Lab. Invest.*, **11**, 229 (1962)
32. Clausen, B., *Lab. Invest.* (In press)
33. Costero, I., *Arch. "de Vecchi" Anat. Patol. Med. Clin.*, **31**, 39 (1960)
34. Cox, C. E., Nelson, L. G., Taylor, C. B., and Davis, C. B., *Aerospace Med.*, **32**, 25 (1961)
35. Cramer, W., and Simpson, W. L., *Cancer Res.*, **4**, 601 (1944)
36. Cronberg, S., *Acta Rheumatol. Scand.*, **7**, 156 (1961)
37. Cronberg, S., *Acta Rheumatol. Scand.*, **7**, 174 (1961)
38. Csaba, G., and Mold, K., *Z. Mikroskop-Anat. Forsch.*, **68**, 163 (1962)
39. Dasler, W., Stoner, R. E., and Milliser, R. V., *Metabolism, Clin. Exptl.*, **10**, 883 (1961)
40. Davidson, E. A., *Federation Proc.*, **19**, 146 (1960)
41. Demis, D. J., Walton, M. D., and Higdon, R. S., *Arch. Dermatol.*, **83**, 127 (1961)
42. Dische, Z., Danilczenko, A., and

Zelmanis, G., *Ciba Found. Symp.*, *Chem. Biol. Mucopolysaccharides*, *1958*, 116

43. Dorfman, A., in *Connective Tissue in Health and Disease*, 81 (Munksgaard, Copenhagen, 1954)

44. Dorfman, A., *Pharmacol. Rev.*, **7**, 1 (1955)

45. Dyrbye, M. O., *Ageing of Human Arterial Tissue. Biochemical Studies of the Acid Mucopolysaccharides* (Munksgaard, Copenhagen, 1959)

46. Eastoe, J. E., in *The Biochemistry and Physiology of Bone*, 81 (Academic, New York, 1956)

47. Enzinger, F. M., and Warner, E. D., *Arch. Pathol.*, **69**, 333 (1960)

48. Farnes, P., and Trobaugh, F. E., *Exptl. Cell. Res.*, **24**, 612 (1961)

49. Fernö, O., Högberg, B., and Uvnäs, B., *Acta Pharmacol. Toxicol.*, **17**, 18 (1960)

50. Fiore-Donati, L., and Moltke, E., *Acta Endocrinol.*, **34**, 430 (1960)

51. Fitton-Jackson, S., *Proc. Roy. Soc.* (*London*), **142**, 536 (1954)

52. Fitton-Jackson, S., *Proc. Roy. Soc.* (*London*), **144**, 556 (1956)

53. Fitton-Jackson, S., in *Inflammation and Diseases of Connective Tissue*, 6 (Saunders, Philadelphia, 1961)

54. Fitton-Jackson, S., and Smith, R. H., *J. Biophys. Biochem. Cytol.*, **3**, 897 (1957)

55. Friberg, W., Graf, W., and Aberg, B., *Acta Pathol. Microbiol. Scand.*, **29**, 198 (1951)

56. Gell, P. G. H., in *Cellular and Humoral Aspects of the Hypersensitive States* (Hoeber, New York, 1959)

57. Gieseking, R., in *Struktur und Stoffwechsel des Bindegewebes* (Thieme, Stuttgart, 1960)

58. Gillman, T., and Hathorn, M., *J. Mt. Sinai Hosp.*, **24**, 857 (1957)

59. Gillman, T., and Hathorn, M., *J. Embryol. Exptl. Morphol.*, **6**, 270 (1958)

60. Gould, B. S., *Ann. N. Y. Acad. Sci.*, **92**, 168 (1961)

61. Green, N. M., and Lowther, D. A., *Biochem. J.* (*London*), **71**, 55 (1959)

62. Gross, J., Highberger, J. H., and Schmitt, F. O., *Proc. Natl. Acad. Sci. US*, **40**, 679 (1954)

63. Gross, J., Mathews, M. B., and Dorfman, A., *J. Biol. Chem.*, **235**, 2889 (1960)

64. Hagen, P., Barnett, R. J., and Lee, F. L., *J. Pharmacol. Exptl. Therap.*, **126**, 91 (1959)

65. Hagen, P., Weiner, N., Ono, S., and

Fu-Li, L., *J. Pharmacol. Exptl. Therap.*, **130**, 9 (1960)

66. Hellström, B., and Holmgren, G., *Svenska Lakartidn.*, **11**, 1 (1947)

67. Hill, M., and Pospisil, M., *Arch. Intern. Pharmacodynamie*, **124**, 139 (1960)

68. Holter, H., *Intern. Rev. Cytol.*, **8**, 481 (1959)

69. Hughes, R. E., and Kodicek, E., *Biochem. J.*, **77**, 3P (1960)

70. Hvidberg, E., Jørgensen, O., Schmidt, A., and Schou, J., *Acta Pharmacol. Toxicol.*, **18**, 313 (1961)

71. Johansson, H., and Westin, B., *Acta Pathol. Microbiol. Scand.*, **11**, 413 (1957)

72. Jorpes, E., Holmgren, H., and Wilander, O., *Z. Mikroskop.-Anat. Forsch.* **42**, 279 (1937)

73. Kahlson, G., *Perspectives Biol. Med.*, **5**, 179 (1962)

74. Kahlson, G., Nilsson, K., Rosengren, E., and Zederfeldt, B., *Lancet*, **II**, 230 (1960)

75. Kasavina, B. S., Lirtsman, V. M., and Muzykant, L. S., *Eksptl. Khir*, **4**, 12 (1959)*

76. Keller, R., *Pathol. Microbiol.*, **24**, 932 (1961)

77. Keller, R., and Schwarz-Speck, M., *Intern. Arch. Allergy*, **19**, 202 (1961)

78. Kirk, J. E., and Dyrbye, M. O., *J. Gerontol.*, **11**, 273 (1956)

79. Kirk, J. E., and Dyrbye, M. O., *J. Gerontol.*, **12**, 23 (1957)

80. Kowalewski, K., and Emery, M. A., *Acta Endocrinol.*, **34**, 317 (1960)

81. Larsen, G., *Am. J. Ophthalmol.*, Part II, **47**, 509 (1959)

82. Larsen, G., *Am. J. Ophthalmol.*, Part II, **47**, 519 (1959)

83. Larsen, G., *Experimental Studies on the Influence of Hormones, Avitaminosis-C and Sensitization on Ocular Mesenchymal Tissues* (Munksgaard, Copenhagen, 1962)

84. Leathem, J. H., *Anat. Records*, **131**, 487 (1958)

85. Lederer, J., de Meyer, R., and Mersseman, F., *Helv. Med. Acta*, **24**, 174 (1957)

86. Lindner, A., and Rudas, B., *Arch. Exptl. Pathol. Pharmakol.*, **242**, 576 (1962)

87. Lorenzen, I., *Proc. Soc. Exptl. Biol. Med.*, **102**, 440 (1959)

88. Lorenzen, I., *Acta Endocrinol.*, **36**, 197 (1961)

89. Lorenzen, I., *Acta Endocrinol.*, **37**, 183 (1961)

90. Lorenzen, I., *Acta Endocrinol.*, **37**, 191 (1961)
91. Lorenzen, I., *Proc. Soc. Exptl. Biol. Med.*, **108**, 325 (1961)
92. Lorenzen, I., *Acta Endocrinol.*, **39**, 605 (1962)
93. Lorenzen, I., *Acta Endocrinol.*, **39**, 615 (1962)
94. Lorenzen, I., *Experimental Arteriosclerosis. Biochemical and Morphological Changes Induced by Adrenaline and Thyroxine* (Copenhagen, 1962)
95. Mager, J., Fuchs, Z., Halvey, S., and Sciaky, J., *Nature*, **192**, 170 (1961)
96. Martin, G. R., Gross, J., Piez, K. A., and Lewis, M. S., *Biochim. Biophys. Acta*, **53**, 599)1961)
97. Martin, G. R., Mergenhagen, S. E. and Prockop, D. J., *Nature*, **191**, 1008 (1961)
98. Menkin, V., in *Inflammation and Diseases of Connective Issues*, 53 (Saunders, Philadelphia, 1961)
99. Merker, H. J., *Arch. Klin. Chir.*, **297**, 411 (1961)
100. Merkow, A. P., *Dissertation Abstr.*, **22**, 1130 (1961)
101. Merkow, L. P., Lalich, J. J., and Angevine, D. M., *Arch. Pathol.*, **71**, 654 (1961)
102. Meyer, K., Hoffman, P., and Linker, A., in *Connective Tissue*, 86 (CIOMS, Blackwell, Oxford, 1957)
103. Moltke, E., *Proc. Soc. Exptl. Biol. Med.*, **88**, 596 (1955)
104. Moltke, E., *Acta Endocrinol.*, **23**, 105 (1956)
105. Moltke, E., *Acta Endocrinol.*, **24**, 226 (1957)
106. Moltke, E., *Acta Endocrinol.*, **24**, 229 (1957)
107. Moltke, E., *Acta Endocrinol.*, **25**, 179 (1957)
108. Moltke, E., *Experimental Studies on the Influence of Thyroxine on Wound Healing* (Munksgaard, Copenhagen, 1958)
109. Moltke, E., *Acta Endocrinol.*, **29**, 421 (1958)
110. Moltke, E., *Endocrinology*, **93**, 931 (1958)
111. Moltke, E., *Acta Endocrinol.*, **37**, 450 (1961)
112. Moltke, E., and Ebbesen, I., *Acta Endocrinol.*, **24**, 220 (1957)
113. Moltke, E., and Lorenzen, I., *Acta Endocrinol.*, **34**, 407 (1960)
114. Moore, R. E., and Schoenberg, M. D., *Am. J. Clin. Pathol.*, **34**, 125 (1960)
115. Mota, I., *Nature*, **192**, 1201 (1961)
116. Mota, I., and da Silva, W. D., *Nature*, **186**, 245 (1960)
117. Muir, H., in *Inflammation and Diseases of Connective Tissue*, 14 (Saunders, Philadelphia, 1961)
118. Nemeth-Csaka, M., *Acta Histochem.*, **12**, 255 (1961)
119. Nemetschek, T., *Z. Naturforsch.*, **13b** 255 (1958)
120. Neuberger A., Perrone, J. C., and Slack, H. G. B., *Biochem. J.*, **49**, 199 (1951)
121. Orfanos, C., and Stüttgen, G., *Arch. Klin. Exptl. Dermatol.*, **214**, 521 (1962)
122. Partridge, S. M., and Davis, H. F., *Biochem. J.*, **61**, 21 (1955)
123. Peterkofsky, B., and Udenfriend, S., *Biochem. Biophys. Res. Commun.*, **6**, 184 (1961)
124. Pettersson, T., *Acta Pathol. Microbiol. Scand.*, **45**, 32 (1959)
125. Policard, A., Collet, A., Pregermain, S., and Ronet, C., *Bull. Microscop. Appl.*, **7**, 73 (1957)
126. Porter, K. R, and Pappas, G. D., *J. Biophys. .Biochem. Cytol.*, **5**, 153 (1959)
127. Ragan, C., Howes, E. L., Plotz, C. M., Meyer, K., and Blunt, J. W., *Proc. Soc. Exptl. Biol. Med.*, **72**, 718 (1949)
128. Rhodin, J., and Dalhamn, T., *Exptl. Cell Res.*, **9**, 371 (1955)
129. Rinehart, J. F., and Greenberg, L. D., *Arch. Pathol.*, **51**, 12 (1951)
130. Ringertz, N. R., *Acid Polysaccharides of Mast Cell Tumors* (Stockholm, 1960)
131. Ringertz, N. R., and Bloom, G., *Arkiv Kemi*, **16**, 57 (1960)
132. Robertson, W. van B., *Ann. N. Y. Acad. Sci.*, **92**, 159 (1961)
133. Ross, R., and Benditt, E. P., *J. Cell Biol.*, **12**, 533 (1962)
134. Räsänen, T., *Acta Endocrinol.*, **37**, 153 (1961)
135. Sakata, R., *Kumamoto Med. J.*, **13**, 54 (1960)
136. Sandberg, N., *Nature* (In press) (Cited by Kahlson, 1962)
137. Sanyal, R. K., and West, G. B., *J. Pharm. Pharmacol.*, **11**, 548 (1959)
138. Schayer, R. W., *Science*, **131**, 336 (1960)
139. Schayer, R. W., Rothschild, Z., and Bizoni, P.. *Am. J. Physiol.*, **196**, 295 (1959)
140. Schiff, M., and Burn, H. F., *The Laryngoscope*, **71**, 765 (1961)
141. Schiller, S., and Dorfman, A., *Biochim. Biophys. Acta*, **31**, 278 (1959)

142. Schneeberg, N. G., *Clin. Obstet. Gynecol.*, **2**, 826 (1959)
143. Seifter, J., and Baeder, D. H., *Proc. Soc. Exptl. Biol. Med.*, **85**, 160 (1954)
144. Simpson, W., *Mast Cells and Basophils* (N. Y. Acad. Sci., 1962).
145. Sinex, F. M., van Slyke, D. D., and Christman, D. R., *J. Biol. Chem.*, **234**, 918 (1959)
146. Sjoerdsma, A., Waalkes, T. P., and Weissbach, H., *Science*, **125**, 1202 (1957)
147. Smith, D. E., *Science*, **128**, 207 (1958)
148. Smith, R. H., and Fitton-Jackson, S., *J. Biophys. Biochem. Cytol.*, **3**, 913 (1957)
149. Sobel, H., Gabay, S., Johnson, C., and Hassan, B., *Metabolism, Clin. Exptl.*, **8**, 180 (1959)
150. Sobel, H., and Marmorston, J., *J. Gerontol.*, **11**, 2, (1956)
151. Sobel, H., and Marmorston, J., *Recent Progr. Hormone Res.*, **14**, 457 (1958)
152. Sobel, H., Marmorston, J., and Moore, F., *Proc. Soc. Exptl. Biol. Med.*, **87**, 346 (1954)
153. Sobel, H., Zutrauen, H. H., and Marmorston, J., *Arch. Biochem. Biophys.*, **46**, 221 (1953)
154. Sprunt, D. H., in *Connective Tissue in Health and Diseases*, 208 (Munksgaard, Copenhagen, 1954)
155. Stetten, M. R., *J. Biol. Chem.*, **181**, 31 (1949)
156. Stone, N., and Meister, A., *Nature*, **194**, 555 (1962)
157. Suzuki, S., and Strominger, J. L., *J. Biol. Chem.*, **235**, 257 (1960)
158. Telford, J. M., and West, G. B., *Brit. J. Pharmacol.*, **15**, 532 (1960)
159. Thorsøe, H., *Acta Endocrinol.*, **40**, 161 (1962)
160. Thorsøe, H., *Thyroid Influence on Ovarian Mucopolysaccharides and Fertility* (Copenhagen, 1962)

161. Tokuda S., and Weiser, R. S., *J. Immunol.*, **86**, 292 (1961)
162. Uvnäs, B., *Chemotherapia*, **3**, 137 (1961)
163. Videbæk, Aa., Asboe-Hansen, G., Astrup, P., Faber, V., Hamburger, C., Schmith, K., Sprechler, M., and Brøchner-Mortensen, K., *Acta Endocrinol.*, **4**, 245 (1950)
164. Wagner, B. M., in *Inflammation and Diseases of Connective Tissue*, 103 (Saunders, Philadelphia, 1961)
165. Waters, L. L., in *Symp. Atherosclerosis* (Natl. Acad. Sci., Natl. Res. Council, Washington, 1954)
166. Wegelius, O., and Asboe-Hansen, G., *Acta Endocrinol.*, **22**, 157 (1956)
167. Wegelius, O., and Asboe-Hansen, G., *Exptl. Cell. Res.*, **11**, 437 (1956)
168. Wegelius, O., Moltke, E., and Dyrbye, M. O., *Experientia*, **15**, 349 (1959)
169. Westin, B., *Exptl. Cell Res.*, **10**, 558 (1956)
170. Wexler, B. C., Brown, T. E., and Miller, B. F., *Circulation Res.*, **8**, 278 (1960)
171. Wexler, B. C., and Miller, B. F., *Science*, **127**, 590 (1958)
172. Wolff, J., *Rev. Tech. Ind. Cuir.*, **51**, 243 (1959)
173. Wolff, J., *Z. Rheumaforsch.*, **20**, 175 (1961)
174. Wood, G. C., and Keech, M. K., *Biochem. J.*, **175**, 588 (1960)
175. Zaaijer, J., *Arch. Chir. Neerl.*, **13**, 207 (1961)
176. Zachariae, F., *Acid Mucopolysaccharides in the Female Genital System and Their Role in the Mechanism of Ovulation* (Periodica, Copenhagen, 1959)
177. Zachariae, F., Asboe-Hansen, G., and Boseila, A. W. A., *Acta Endocrinol.*, **28**, 547 (1958)
178. Zachariae, H., *Acta Dermato-Venereol.* (In press)
179. Zachariae, L., and Asboe-Hansen, G., *Cancer Res.*, **18**, 822 (1958)

* English translation will be announced in *Technical Translations*, issued by the Office of Technical Services, U. S. Department of Commerce, and will be made available by the Photoduplication Service, Library of Congress, and by the SLA Translation Center at the John Crerar Library, Chicago, Illinois.

SMOOTH MUSCLE: AUTONOMIC NERVE TRANSMISSION[1]

By G. Burnstock and M. E. Holman

Departments of Zoology and Physiology, University of Melbourne, Victoria, Australia

INTRODUCTION

Most reviews on physiology of smooth muscle have been mainly concerned with its mechanical and pharmacological properties (1 to 5). During the past ten to fifteen years, the application of electrophysiological methods to smooth muscle has shed new light on many of the old problems. Early work with external electrode methods was reviewed by Bozler (6) and Rosenblueth (7). More recently the advances resulting from the use of microelectrode and sucrose gap techniques have been reviewed from specialized aspects. Examples include the following: interfibre conduction (8, 9); action of drugs and hormones at the membrane level (10 to 15); ions and permeability (13, 16, 17). More comprehensive reviews of smooth muscle physiology for comparison with those on skeletal and heart muscle are also available (18, 19). For this review, we have selected one aspect of smooth muscle electrophysiology, namely, the mechanism of transmission of excitation from autonomic nerves to smooth muscle, which has not been dealt with since Rosenblueth's review in 1950 (7) when only external electrode recording from smooth muscle was possible on stimulation of the extrinsic nerve supply. Records from pilomotor and nictitating membrane muscles in the cat consisted of complex wave forms including both fast and slow components. Interpretation of these results was difficult and has been discussed fully elsewhere (2, 7, 20, 21). We intend to discuss findings in this field since the introduction of microelectrode and sucrose gap recording from smooth muscle, comparing these with the electrophysiology and electron microscopy of the better known transmission process at the skeletal neuromuscular junction (22, 23, 24). There has been a revival of interest in the organization of the autonomic nervous system as conceived by Elliot (25), Langley (26), and Dale (27) because of the large number of exceptions to their classification into adrenergic sympathetic and cholinergic parasympathetic divisions (see 28, 29). Other aspects of the autonomic transmission process which have received attention during the last few years include: (*a*) morphology of the innervation of smooth muscle (30, 31); (*b*) the effects of stimulus parameters on the physiology and pharmacology of the responses of isolated organs to nerve stimulation (7, 28, 32 to 50); (*c*) the action of reserpine (51, 52) and its relation to the theory of Burn & Rand (53) concerning the cholinergic nature of sympathetic nerves (54 to 64); (*d*) evolutionary aspects of the autonomic nervous system in nonmammalian forms (43, 44, 65 to 74); (*e*) synthesis, storage, release, and destruction of autonomic trans-

---

[1] The survey of literature pertaining to this review was concluded in April 1962.

mitters (64, 75 to 82). Only those approaches which have a bearing on the interpretation of electrophysiological results will be discussed.

Morphology of Autonomic Nerve-Smooth Muscle Junctions

The general form and interrelationships of smooth muscle cells will be discussed first, since these are important to understanding of the innervation. Despite the many previous studies of the structure of vertebrate smooth muscle using the light microscope, it is only recently, with the introduction of the electron microscope, that any real progress has been made (83).

Smooth muscle cells are spindle shaped. The thick middle portion of the cell, which contains the nucleus, lies adjacent to the long tapering ends of surrounding cells. Most fibres are 4 to 8μ in diameter in the central region, and 50 to 200 μ long, depending upon the degree of stretch. There are several exceptions: arterial smooth muscle cells are smaller (2 to 3 μ in diameter; 20 to 50 μ long) with irregularly shaped branched processes (84 to 87); the cells of pregnant uterus show considerable hypertrophy, being up to 500 μ long and 9 to 14μ in diameter (88). Most smooth muscle coats are composed of cylindrical bundles of closely packed fibres. The bundles are usually 40 μ to 100 μ in diameter and contain 10 to 75 cells in cross section (86). Single bundles are fairly uniform in diameter but rarely extend more than a few millimeters longitudinally before branching. The cells of the longitudinal muscle layer of the cat intestine (86) and of the circular layer of the rat uterus (89) are not arranged in bundles but form a continuous sheet of loosely arranged fibres. It is unlikely that the bundles are functional units in terms of electrical excitability and conduction; they are more likely to have a mechanical significance.

Individual cells have clearly defined membranes reported to have a thickness of about 150 A in the rat uterus (89) and 250 A in the rat ureter (90). Caesar, Edwards & Ruska (91) differentiated the membrane into three regions: an opaque basement membrane (90 to 250 A); an interspace (90 to 130 A); a dense plasma membrane (70 to 110 A). The smooth muscle membrane shows several characteristics not usually associated with those of the striated muscle membrane. Plasma and, in particular, basement membranes vary greatly in thickness (86, 91). Dense thickenings alternate with thin regions where pinocytotic activity is indicated. The thickenings often lie at corresponding regions in adjacent cells. The significance of these local thickenings is unknown, but they may play some role in intercellular transmission of excitation (91), or they may be "attachment devices" joining the system of myofilaments to the cell surface (92). Since they are seen in both stretched and contracted portions of the cells, they cannot be a consequence of contraction. While in some muscles, for example the cat intestine and the guinea pig taenia coli and ureter, the membranes of neighbouring cells lie approximately parallel, in others, such as the dog retractor penis and the muscularis mucosae of the pig esophagus, the membranes are extremely convoluted and irregular (even when stretched) and form complicated relationships with each other (86).

The most distinctive feature of visceral smooth muscles as seen with the electron microscope is the abundance of vesiclelike structures. Two main types have been distinguished: (a) large vacuolar vesicles with a wide range of shape and size 1000 to 4000 A (86, 87, 91, 93, 94); (b) small ovoid vesicles with more darkly staining contents and of a more specific size (100 to 600 A). They are usually arranged in a single or double row in the granular matrix just beneath the plasma membrane and may well be pinocytotic (84, 86, 89, 92, 94 to 97). A mixture of large and small vesicles lies in longitudinal ridges protruding from the surface of the muscles (86). There are 15 to 20 ridges of vesicles per cell, the rows being about 0.5 μ apart. Mitochondria are always abundant behind the region directly populated with vesicles.

The question of the relationships of individual smooth muscle cells to one another is of great functional importance and has occupied considerable attention from smooth muscle morphologists. Is there a true syncytium, i.e., protoplasmic continuity between fibres? If not, what is the nature of the cell interrelationship, which allows the whole muscle to act as a "functional syncytium"? Unfortunately, even with the use of the electron microscope the answers to these questions still remain somewhat ambiguous.

The term "intercellular bridge" was first used to describe the connections between smooth muscle cells as seen with the light microscope (98, 99, 100) and implied a continuity of protoplasm between the cells. Recent electron microscope studies have established that intercellular processes do exist. The point of disagreement is whether there is complete protoplasmic continuity across these processes (89, 97, 101) or whether the processes (or bridges) are spanned by intact membranes (86, 90, 102). Moore & Ruska (103), working with smooth muscles of heart arteries; Yamamoto (93), working with human vermiform appendix; Caesar, Edwards & Ruska (91), working with mouse urinary bladder and uterus, failed to find intercellular bridges of any kind, but did see areas of close contact between membranes of adjacent cells. The general dimensions of the intercellular bridges, whether seen with or without cross membranes, are similar (approximately 0.1 to 0.5 μ long and 0.2 to 0.7 μ wide). The bridges described by Bergman (90) are 2 to 3 μ long, but there is good reason to believe that this is an error brought about by excessive shrinkage of his material during fixation. What is the explanation of these contradictory observations concerning the existence of membranes spanning these bridges? Both Mark (89)and Thaemert (97) occasionally observed incomplete membranes across bridges. Thaemert suggests that these, and the membranes seen by Bergman, might represent either disintegrating remnants of plasma membranes between the cells or stages in their reformation. Further support of this idea comes from observations that evaginations of opposed smooth muscle cells often seem to project towards each other, and sometimes form very close contact (86, 91).

What emerges, then, is a concept of the plastic nature of the interrelationships between smooth muscle cells with active formation and retraction of living intercellular bridges. Lewis (104), using tissue culture methods, observed that intercellular bridges would withdraw on slight provocation (e.g., treatment with glycerine). Such a withdrawal reaction from irritated cells may account for the failure of some investigators to find intercellular bridges.

Thaemert (97) found the dimensions of the intercellular bridges to be similar regardless of the plane of section and concluded that the bridges were tubular or cylindrical. He found them to lie primarily between the sides rather than the ends of cells. The exact number of bridges associated with each cell is not easily determined, but Bergman (90) concluded that each muscle cell is likely to have several intercellular bridges with adjacent cells. Whereas Bergman (90) described vesicles and granular components on one side only of the intercellular bridge region, Prosser, Burnstock & Kahn (86) observed aggregations of large and small vesicles on both sides of the membranes. Thaemert (97) also described vesicles in protoplasmic bridges.

Burnstock, Prosser & Barr (105) did not consider the presence or absence of membranes across the bridge of great significance in the conduction process. They argue that the resistance across such a narrow bridge even in the absence of membranes would be so high (about 10^8 ohms) that it is unlikely to be the electrical pathway between adjacent cells. They suggest that intercellular bridges may serve a mechanical function and that it is the area of close contact of adjacent cell membranes that may be more significant in terms of conduction of excitation. In faster conducting muscles (e.g. pig esophagus muscularis mucosa, guinea pig taenia coli) the fibres are more closely packed than in the slower or nonconducting muscles (e.g. dog retractor penis, pig arteries) (86).

An account of the innervation of smooth muscle will follow, emphasis being on recent electron microscope studies. Although the ganglion cells of the autonomic nervous system have been classified morphologically and a good deal is known of their physiology, little is known about the peripheral extensions of their axons (29, 31, 106). Physiological evidence suggests that the axon must branch extensively before finally terminating (29, 107), but it is not clear whether this branching occurs entirely at the periphery or along the course of the postganglionic nerve trunk. It is generally accepted that the postganglionic fibres of mammals are predominantly nonmyelinated —one exception being the short postganglionic fibres supplying the ciliary muscle of the cat. The classification of autonomic fibres on functional and morphological grounds has been discussed by Hillarp (29).

There are many difficulties involved in working out the course, distribution, and ending of individual postganglionic axons by either morphological or physiological methods. The vast literature describing the morphology of autonomic nerve endings as seen from silver and methylene blue staining is reviewed by Clara (108), Hillarp (29, 30), and Richardson

(31). Recent studies with the electron microscope, notably those by Caesar, Edwards & Ruska (91), Richardson (106), Yamamoto (93), Lever & Esterhuizen (109), and Burnstock, Holman & Merrillees (94, 110), are beginning to solve some of these difficulties.

It is generally agreed that there exists a fine meshed plexus of nonmyelinated nerves [0.1 to 1.7 μ diameter (91, 106)] enveloped by a Schwann syncytium and distributed throughout the muscle layers. This plexus has been called variously an "autonomic ground plexus" (30), "Schwann plasmodium" (111), "sympathetic ground plexus" (112), and "terminal reticulum" (113, 114). An "interstitial cell network" is also distributed throughout the muscle. Recent work with light microscopy as well as electron micrography (31, 91, 106) has shown that the interstitial cell network is quite distinct from the autonomic ground plexus and is not formed of Schwann cells. This evidence supports the view that the network is formed of connective tissue, probably fibroblasts, rather than of primitive nerve cells. It has been suggested that it forms a link between the autonomic nerve endings and the muscle fibres (115) but there is little evidence to support this view (30, 106).

The nature of the relation between the smallest branches of the plexus and the muscle cells is becoming clearer (91, 94, 106, 109, 110, 116). Most commonly, bundles of two to eight nerve fibres can be seen to run between the muscle cells. The nerve fibres within the bundles are for the most part enclosed in Schwann sheath, but frequently parts of a nerve fibre are left uncovered. Many of the nerve fibres, especially in those regions incompletely covered by Schwann sheath, are packed with vesicles (350 to 450 A) and mitochondria. More rarely, fine nerve processes, free of Schwann sheath and rich with vesicles and mitochondria, are found in close apposition to the muscle membrane, often in shallow indentations in the muscle surface. The space between nerve and muscle plasma membranes in these regions is about 200 to 300 A, a separation comparable with that observed at other synapses. There is no evidence for any specialization of the postjunctional smooth muscle membrane comparable with that of the skeletal neuromuscular junction. As we have seen, the surface of a smooth muscle cell consists of a fairly uniform arrangement of small protuberances, indentations, and vesicles; these do not appear to be exaggerated or reduced in regions where axons approximate the muscle membrane.

Occasionally, profiles resembling axons have been seen "inside" smooth muscle cells (93, 94). These intracellular "profiles" do not always contain vesicles. Coupland (117) has made the same observation with nerve endings on chromaffin cells, but he was able to trace their course more closely. A minority of nerve fibres invaginate the plasma membrane of the chromaffin cell before terminating a variable distance from the cell centre in a typical synapselike ending. During its "intracellular" course the nerve fibre is surrounded by a tubular invagination of the chromaffin cell plasma membrane. No protoplasmic continuity between nerve and muscle has been observed. This unusual arrangement probably accounts for the so-called "intracellular nerve endings" described by some earlier workers (118, 119). There is a possibility also that some of these "intracellular profiles" may consist of invaginations of processes from neighbouring smooth muscle cells. No investigations have been reported on the effects of cutting the dorsal roots on the various axon profiles described. Thus some of them may well be afferent endings.

Most workers have found a striking paucity of nerve fibres in smooth muscle sections; "synaptic junctions" were even rarer (85, 86, 90, 106). This led Richardson (106) to conclude from his observations on the small intestine of the rabbit that " . . . it is most improbable that each muscle fibre receives an ending. . . . " On the other hand, Caesar, Edwards & Ruska (91), working with the urinary bladder, uterus, and gall bladder of the mouse, concluded " . . . that each and every muscle cell shows a close relationship to the axon at a well defined locus." In the vas deferens of the guinea pig, the innervation is dense and widely distributed (94, 110, 120). None of these authors excludes the possibility that axons passing close to muscle fibres may not possess discrete endings at all, but may release transmitter substances at intervals along their length.

It may well become apparent after further investigations on more tissues that there is a spectrum of smooth muscles with different densities of innervation. For example there is some indication that the muscles of the nictitating membrane, iris, and arteries are richly supplied with nerves, while those of the gut and uterus are more sparsely innervated (6, 86, 121). The proximal region of the dog retractor penis is more densely innervated than the distal region (122).

The suggestion has been put forward for the skeletal neuromuscular junction that acetylcholine is parcelled up in minute secretory granules (123) associated with the small vesicles which have been seen in the presynaptic nerve terminals with the electron microscope (24, 124, 125). Vesicles of about the same dimensions (350 to 450 A) as those seen in the presynaptic terminals of skeletal muscle have been observed in autonomic nerve endings in smooth muscle (91, 94, 106, 109, 110, 126). Recently Burnstock, Holman & Merrillees (94, 110) demonstrated a marked reduction in the number of these vesicles in the axons of the sympathetic nerves supplying the vas deferens of guinea pigs whose local stores of norepinephrine had been depleted by chronic reserpine treatment. Depletion of presynaptic vesicles has also been demonstrated in sympathetic nerve endings in the adrenal medulla after prolonged stimulation of the splanchnic nerve (126).

Autonomic nerve bundles and endings of similar form to those described which innervate smooth muscle cells have also been observed for nerve endings on the rat pineal gland (127), on axillary sweat glands (128), on rat salivary and lacrimal glands (129), and on chromaffin cells in the rat adrenal medulla (117).

A specific active agent in a protein or protein-bound particle has been discovered in mouse sarcomas, snake venom, mouse submaxillary glands, and mammalian sympathetic nerve cells, which possesses the striking property of enhancing the growth potentialities of sympathetic and sensory ganglia of the chick embryo, and of producing excessive and abnormal innervation of the embryonic viscera (130). Furthermore, an antiserum to the purified salivary gland protein selectively destroys nearly all the sympathetic nerve cells in the adult animal. No adverse effects are observed in other organs or structures, besides a slight volume increase in the spinal ganglia. It would be of considerable interest to observe the electrophysiological and electron-microscopical changes in sympathetically innervated smooth muscle under both these conditions of hypertrophy and atrophy.

Electrophysiology of Transmission from Nerve to Smooth Muscle

Microelectrode studies of the membrane potential changes associated with transmission from nerve to smooth muscle are still in their early stages. Progress has been slow, largely because there are many technical difficulties involved in recording from single smooth muscle cells: the individual cells are small; many types of visceral smooth muscle show spontaneous electrical and mechanical activity; individual smooth muscle cells are intimately mixed with collagen fibres, and many organs are surrounded by tough connective tissue sheaths. Some uncertainty always exists as to the degree of damage caused by the microelectrode.

In spite of these difficulties, the characteristics of the spontaneous electrical activity of visceral smooth muscle have been established mainly by Bülbring and her co-workers for the taenia coli of the guinea pig (131, 132, 133), and by Marshall (134) and Kuriyama (15) for the uterus. In the taenia coli the "resting" membrane potential is unstable and fluctuates about a level of 50 to 60 mv in the form of "slow waves". If sufficient depolarization is generated by the slow wave, an action potential (spike) is initiated. All the smooth muscle cells of the guinea pig taenia coli probably have the capacity to generate slow waves but one cell or a small group of cells usually becomes the pacemaker for neighbouring cells. The site of the pacemaker varies from time to time. Thus, records from individual cells in moderately stretched preparations show a mixture of locally generated and conducted activity. The slow waves appear to be myogenic in origin since spontaneous activity continues after anatomical and pharmacological "denervation" (132). In the estrogen-dominated uterus, pacemaker cells may be localized and intracellular records show a predominance of conducted spikes. Under the influence of progesterone, however, the spontaneous activity resembles more closely that of the taenia coli. Pacemakers can arise at any point and conduction from cell to cell may be partially blocked (15, 134, 135). The action potentials characteristic of a number of other smooth muscles appear to be essentially similar to those of the uterus and taenia coli. These potentials include various smooth muscles of the gastrointestinal tract (121, 136, 137), blood vessels (138), retractor penis (121) and bladder (139). The ureter of a number of species (121, 140, 141), the vascular smooth muscle of the turtle (142, 143) and the chick amnion (144), however, generate action potentials of the plateau type.

These preparations either are spontaneously active or generate action potentials in response to electrical pulses which are assumed to stimulate the smooth muscle directly. In all these cases interfibre conduction has been demonstrated. However, the ease with which a conducted response can be set up and the distance that it is propagated differ from one muscle to another (121); ease of conduction may be correlated with the degree of innervation (6). Interaction between neighbouring fibres may be greatest in muscles having the least dense innervation.

The effects of nerve stimulation as opposed to direct stimulation have only been analysed, so far, for the longitudinal muscle of the rabbit colon by Gillespie (137, 145), for the rabbit bladder by Ursillo (139), for the vas deferens of the guinea pig by Burnstock & Holman (110, 146 to 150), and for the retractor penis of the dog by Orlov (122). The results of these investigations will be described in some detail.

The spontaneous electrical activity of the rabbit colon is essentially similar to that of the guinea pig taenia coli. The slow waves in the rabbit colon, however, are of longer duration and give rise to bursts of spikes. As in other smooth muscles, spiking is associated with contraction. Stretching the preparation prolongs the duration of each burst until eventually a continuous discharge is produced at a frequency of about one per second. Gillespie (137) has studied the membrane potential responses to stimulation of both parasympathetic and sympathetic nerves in the doubly innervated colon preparation (28). Single stimuli to the parasympathetic nerve give rise to a depolarization, the excitatory junction potential, of some 600 msec duration which if large enough can give rise to a spike and contraction. Repetitive stimulation at about one per second "drives" the preparation so that each stimulus to the nerve is associated with a spike and an increment in tension. Stimulation at higher rates causes maintained depolarization similar to the effects of large doses of Ach on the longitudinal intestinal muscle of the cat (151). During these periods of depolarization the tension remains at maximum. The excitatory junction potentials in response to low-frequency parasympathetic stimulation have an extremely long latency (average 400 msec) which cannot be explained by a single ganglionic relay.

Excitatory junction potentials have also been recorded in the smooth muscle of the urinary bladder by Ursillo (139). Ursillo's preparation consists of an isolated strip of detrusor muscle from the rabbit bladder which is removed together with the nerves which accompany the blood vessels. This smooth muscle is also spontaneously active. Spikes occur either singly or in groups of two to five and are associated with slow waves of depolarization. Stretch and carbachol produce depolarization and an increase in tension. Single stimuli to the nerve give rise to junction potentials which may be of sufficient amplitude to generate one or more spikes. If spiking does not occur, the junction potential consists of a relatively rapid phase of depolarization for about 50 msec and is followed by a slow depolarization of several hundered milliseconds duration. The latencies of these responses vary and do not depend on the area of the muscle from which the recording is made. Junction potentials in response to successive stimuli at about ten per second sum with each other to produce depolarization and repetitive spiking.

A more detailed study of the transmission of excitation from sympathetic nerve to smooth muscle has been carried out using the guinea pig vas deferens supplied by the hypogastric nerve (146 to 150). This smooth muscle is not spontaneously active. Slow waves and spontaneous firing can be induced by small doses of norepinephrine but under normal conditions the resting potential is stable and lies between 60 and 70 mv. Stimuli to the hypogastric nerve give rise to junction potentials in all the smooth muscle cells of the longitudinal layer. Junction potentials in response to single maximal stimuli are usually too small to initiate a spike. In general, two or three stimuli are required and these must be given within a few seconds of each other. When the depolarization reaches threshold (about −40 mv), a spike is initiated and contraction occurs. In contrast to the spontaneously active smooth muscles, the membrane potential at which the spike is initiated is relatively constant. This suggests that the spikes recorded in most cells are probably caused by depolarization of that particular cell. If transmission is partially blocked by reserpine, and occasionally in a normal preparation, spikes may take off from a membrane potential of −60 mv or more. It seems probable that spikes such as these are conducted. If a small dose of norepinephrine is added to the isolated organ bath in the presence of a sympathetic blocking agent such as bretylium, rhythmic co-ordinated spontaneous activity appears suggesting that some form of interaction occurs between cells similar to that postulated for the taenia coli (132). The spikes recorded in the vas deferens are similar to those seen in most other visceral smooth muscles. They are up to 95 mv in amplitude (the majority being between 65 and 85 mv) and therefore "overshoot" by 10 to 15 mv. Their duration at half the total height is from 5 to 10 msec. The depolarization phase of the spike always brings the membrane potential back towards or occasionally beyond the original resting potential.

If the hypogastric nerve is stimulated at low frequencies (less than one per second) the form of the junction potentials can be examined without the complication of spiking and contraction. The configuration of individual junction potentials and their latency vary from cell to cell. Latencies from 20 to 70 msec can be recorded in cells less than 2 mm apart. These times include conduction down the nerve trunk and through the ramifications of the ground plexus. The amplitudes of the junction potentials in different cells are of the same order of magnitude provided the stimulus strength is well above threshold. This suggests that each axon in the hypogastric nerve must be able to influence the membrane potential of many different smooth muscle cells. The influence could be a result of extensive branching, or the liberation by one axon branch of its transmitter on or in the vicinity of many different cells, or a combination of these mechanisms. Somewhat similar conclusions about the distribution of postganglionic axons were reached by Lundberg (152) from his studies on the electrophysiology of salivary glands. One of the interesting features of transmission in the vas deferens is the way in which successive junction potentials are facilitated with stimulus intervals up to five seconds. If a rested preparation is stimulated at about one per second, the first six to ten junction potentials increase progressively severalfold in amplitude.

Rosenblueth and his co-workers (7) found that, on a number of effector organs, the effects of varying the frequency or strength of stimulation were quantitatively interchangeable. Both the amplitude and rate of rise of the junction potentials in the vas deferens increase as the strength of stimulation is increased. This leads to greater depolarization and frequency of firing and to an increased contractile response. Similarly, as the frequency of stimulation is increased, the rate of depolarization is increased so that the threshold for spike initiation is reached more quickly and there is an increase in spike frequency. At frequencies of stimulation exceeding 50 per second, the contractile response falls off before maximum tension is reached, probably as a result of failure of conduction in the nerve fibres. The shortest interval between the spikes in the vas deferens, at the beginning of a train of high-frequency stimuli, is 40 to 45 msec (22 per second). Since the contractile response associated with this frequency of firing is very vigorous, it has not been possible to maintain the impalement for longer than the first four to six spikes. It is possible, however, that prolonged periods of depolarization similar to those described by Gillespie (137) can also be induced in this preparation. Prolonged stimulation at low frequencies (about one per second) leads to an irregularity in shape and a reduction in the amplitude of the junction potentials which is exaggerated if the frequency is increased.

In the absence of nerve stimulation, the resting membrane potential of the vas deferens is interrupted at intervals by small potentials, unassociated with development of tension or shortening, which appear to be analogous to the miniature potentials recorded at other neuroeffector junctions (147, 149). This discharge can be recorded in all cells impaled satisfactorily, as judged by the stability of the resting potential and the amplitude of the action potential recorded in the same cell. The small potentials are not abolished by an increase in calcium concentration of up to six times normal. They are unaffected by atropine (10^{-4}) but are abolished by sympathetic blocking agents such as yohimbine. The amplitude and time course of the individual spontaneous potentials vary greatly. In general the larger potentials of 4 mv or more consist of depolarization followed by a slower repolarization. The smaller potentials may be more complex in shape. The mean frequency of the discharge (about 20 per minute) remains fairly constant throughout impalements lasting up to 50 minutes. The pattern of the discharge is remarkably constant from cell to cell. The smaller potentials recorded from any one cell occur much more frequently than do the larger ones. Calculation of the mean amplitude for any cell is arbitrary, since this is determined by the amplitude of the smallest potentials which can be resolved from the noise level of the baseline. The shape of the amplitude distribution curve is similar to that obtained for muscles where the microelectrode is recording simultaneously the activity of many different nerve endings at different distances from the point of impalement. Thus, records from the vas deferens resemble those of "slow fibres" in the frog and chick (153, 154) and of crustacean muscle fibres (155). They are in marked contrast to the "miniatures" recorded in the localized "end plate" of frog, chick, and mammalian "twitch" fibres (23, 24).

Although the passive electrical properties of smooth muscle have yet to be fully analysed, some sort of electrical coupling apparently exists between neighbouring cells (9, 132). Thus it is possible that the larger potentials recorded in the vas deferens may originate in a cell close to the point of impalement whereas the smaller potentials arise in more distant cells. However, a discharge with very similar characteristics has been recorded at the end plate of frog "twitch" fibres after denervation by Birks, Katz & Miledi (156). These authors concluded that the spontaneous potentials in this case were traceable to the release of transmitter from the Schwann cells which replace the nerve terminals after they degenerate and make intimate contact with the muscle membrane in the end plate region. This discharge resembles that of smooth muscle since neither is markedly increased in frequency when the tonicity of the bathing solution is increased by sucrose. It is well known that frequency of the miniatures at "twitch" fibre end plates is markedly increased under hypertonic conditions, and Furshpan (157) has shown that this response depends on the permeability of the presynaptic membrane. Only a transient response to sucrose has been observed in the vas deferens. It may be that the sympathetic C fibres are permeable to sucrose. Nevertheless, the possibility remains that the discharge may have originated in the Schwann cell network which surrounds the terminal branches of the C fibres or even from the so-called "interstitial cell network".

There may be another explanation for the shape of the amplitude distribution curve. If the transmitter is released at varying distances from the smooth muscle membrane, the largest potentials might be caused by release from nerve terminals in close contact with the membrane whereas the slower smaller potentials could be caused by release from bare axons of the ground plexus situated one or more micra away. It should be possible to test this hypothesis by studying the relationship between the potentials recorded simultaneously in two cells a known distance apart. The fine structure of this preparation (see Section on Morphology) suggests that such an arrangement might easily be the case.

Amplitude distribution curves for the small potentials in the vas deferens are characteristically uneven. Potentials of 3 to 7 mv often show a tendency to fall into groups of preferred values. It is tempting to suggest that such groups represent the release of transmitter from the same region of the ground plexus. Distribution curves also show a scattering of potentials of a much larger magnitude. Several of these "giant" potentials of 15 mv or more are usually observed in the course of a 20-minute impalement. It is unlikely that they could be caused by the random coincidence of smaller potentials. The frequency of potentials in the 3 to 8 mv range is low, and the probability of a triple coincidence of these potentials would be much too remote to account for the appearance of the giants. They might be caused by the release of a particularly large packet of transmitter and therefore be similar in origin to the "multiquantal" giants observed by Liley (158) in rat diaphragm.

The average amplitude of the individual potentials in the vas deferens is a good deal larger than that recorded in other muscles. This may be a result of the small diameter of the smooth muscle cells. Katz & Thesleff (159) calculated the mean amplitude for miniature end plate potentials in frog twitch fibres as a function of the input resistance of the film and, hence, its diameter. For a fibre of 10 μ, having an input resistance of 10 megohm, the mean value of the prostigmine-treated miniature end plate potentials was estimated to be 5 to 6 mv. The maximum diameter of the smooth muscle cell is much less than 10 μ, and the values that have been quoted for input resistance greatly exceed 10 megohm (105, 160). It would not therefore seem necessary to postulate that the packets of transmitter causing the spontaneous discharge in the vas deferens are any more effective in causing depolarization than those in other tissues.

Calculation of the mean interval between potentials or of the mean frequency is also arbitrary since this depends on the resolution permitted by base-line noise and the speed of recording. If successive intervals are plotted as a histogram, this closely approximates the theoretical exponential curve for a random process, i.e., the probability of occurrence of a potential does not appear to be related to the occurrence of the previous potential. (It should be emphasized that this test for randomness is only applicable to a single process. If the discharge in the vas deferens is made up of several different processes, for example, release of transmitter at several different points, this test gives no information about the degree of randomness of the individual processes.)

The depolarization phase of the larger potentials usually lasts from 30 to 50 msec. This is followed by an exponential repolarization which is complete in about 100 msec. The maximum rate of depolarization of the larger potentials (those of 5 mv or more) varies from cell to cell. The maximum rates obtained so far are up to 0.5 v per second with the majority of potentials showing rates between 0.15 v per second and 0.30 v per second. These values are somewhat higher than the depolarization associated with many of the junction potentials in response to low-frequency nerve stimulation. However, in experiments in which the nerve was stimulated at a high frequency, over-all rates of depolarization of up to 1.5 v per second were obtained (the small potentials arising in these cells were not measured simultaneously). At this stage it seems likely that the over-all depolarization induced by nerve stimulation is of the same order of magnitude as that of the largest "spontaneous" potentials. No "spontaneous" potentials have been observed with a faster rate of depolarization than that induced by high-frequency nerve stimulation.

After the first 10 to 15 msec, the repolarization phase of the small potentials is exponential with a single time constant. Time constants for the larger potentials are constant for any one cell and vary from 25 to 50 msec. This may represent the time constant for the smooth muscle membrane. It is well known that the duration of transmitter action at many synapses is brief (22) and that the latter part of the junction potential represents the passive decay of an imposed depolarization. This may also be the case at this junction. On the other hand, repolarization may be determined by the time course of inactivation of transmitter. Brown & Gillespie (161) calculated that the norepinephrine released during sympathetic stimulation of cat spleen is destroyed in about 100 msec.

The duration of transmitter action at the skeletal neuromuscular junction has been estimated from an analysis of the interaction between the muscle action potential and the end plate potential (24). Interaction between spikes and junction potentials in the vas deferens has not been fully clarified, once again because of technical difficulties involving movement artifacts. However, it seems likely that the spike "wipes out" some, but not all, of the depolarization associated with the junction potential. The repolarization phase of the junction potential is often irregular and usually considerably longer than that of the small potentials. It may well be that all the transmitter which is released on nerve stimulation is not liberated at the same instant. Release from different axons in the ground plexus in the vicinity of any one smooth muscle cell may occur after a variable latent period. The marked variation in the latency of onset of the junction potentials in different cells may be related to this problem.

The junction potentials in response to submaximal stimuli are often very flat and slow and could well be compounded of the smaller, more common spontaneous potentials. When the strength of stimulation is increased, junction potentials arise whose amplitude greatly exceeds that of the majority of small potentials. Occasionally a cell is encountered whose junction potentials have a configuration which strongly suggests that they are compounded of the small potentials characteristic in that cell. Since the small potentials vary in amplitude and shape over such a wide range, it is impossible to prove statistically whether or not the junction potentials are composed solely of small potentials. This is also the case for other muscles where the innervation is distributed. Dudel & Kuffler (155) solved this problem for crustacean striated muscle by recording from a single nerve ending with an extracellular microelectrode. Present attempts to identify such potentials in the vas deferens have not been successful.

The nature of the spontaneous discharge does not permit conclusions as to whether or not the transmitter is released in a quantal fashion—i.e., whether the same amount of transmitter is released at all the endings, or whether different amounts can be released by the same ending at different times. However, a quantal mechanism might account for the observation that the junction potentials themselves vary in a stepwise fashion and in this respect the vas deferens is somewhat similar to the calcium-deficient, magnesium-poisoned skeletal muscle end plate (162). The junction potentials in response to successive stimuli vary in shape. If the stimulus strength is low, only a fraction of the stimuli may lead to detectable junction potentials. The increase in amplitude produced by an increase in stimulus strength is also of a stepwise nature. During facilitation, successive junction potentials usually build up in a series of definite jumps rather than continuously.

Further evidence for this hypothesis has come from effects of reserpine treatment and from denervation studies (110, 148, 150). Preparations were taken from guinea pigs whose hypogastric nerves had been sectioned ten days before the experiment. Stimulation of the stump of the hypogastric nerve usually gives rise to some contraction in these preparations, though the threshold frequency is markedly increased and maximal contractions are often much weaker than under normal conditions. The presence of ganglion cells has been demonstrated in the pelvic plexus of the guinea pig, and this may be the reason why it has only been possible to obtain partial denervation. Records of the spontaneous discharge in these preparations show a marked reduction in the frequency of the potentials, although their configuration is identical with those from normal animals. Amplitude histograms for individual cells from partially denervated preparations vary markedly in shape. The junction potentials in partially denervated preparations are always smaller than normal, and facilitation is often irregular. The contributions of individual small potentials to the junction potentials can easily be recognized in these preparations. Both the spontaneous discharge and the junction potentials are reduced in cells from chronically reserpinized guinea pigs. This fact suggests that the transmitter substance is located in the nerves themselves rather than being stored or synthesized outside the nerves in tissue such as chromaffin cells. Recent histochemical studies on the localisation of catecholamines in sympathetically innervated structures are in accordance with this view (196).

A microelectrode study has been made of the response of single smooth muscle cells of the retractor penis of dogs under morphine-urethane anaesthesia upon stimulation of the motor sympathetic nerve supply (122). The results are essentially similar to those described for the isolated vas deferens-hypogastric nerve preparation of the guinea pig. Single stimuli to the nerve give rise to depolarization of the smooth muscle membrane. Repetitive nerve stimulation leads to summation of postsynaptic potentials (junction potentials) until a membrane potential is reached (19 to 22 mv) when an action potential is initiated and a contraction occurs. The rate of depolarization to the threshold firing level depends on the frequency of nerve stimulation. One pulse per second was usually the minimum pulse frequency required to produce sufficient summation depolarization for a spike to be initiated, although occasionally a single stimulus was enough to produce a response. Pulse frequencies of 50 per second, or more, often failed to lead to a spike and contraction. No "miniature" potentials have been observed in the absence of nerve stimulation, but this is probably because extremely critical conditions for good microelectrode penetration are required for their recording.

Unlike the vas deferens preparation, a consistent difference in the form and latency of the junction potentials is observed in different regions of the retractor penis. The junction potentials in the proximal muscle region are characterized by short latency and fast rate of rise, whereas those in the distal region have longer latencies and slower rates of rise. This suggests that the distal region might be less densely innervated. On resting preparations, epinephrine (10^{-6}) produces very little membrane depolarization of the retractor muscle cells. However, the same epinephrine concentration produces marked depolarization accompanied by a burst of spike potentials on a retractor penis supplied by a sympathetic nerve which had been stimulated submaximally for three minutes. Experiments with the retractor penis taken from dogs, seven to nine days after adrenalectomy, reveal a reduced sensitivity to the nerve-mediated response; i.e., higher-frequency stimulation is required to produce a response, and the time for the membrane to reach threshold depolarization is increased. Orlov explains these results in terms of an increase in resting potential resulting from interference with the synthesis of sympathetic mediator. Injection of epinephrine into adrenalectomized dogs re-established the sensitivity of the transmission process to its normal level.

The only study of the membrane potentials associated with inhibition of smooth muscle by nerve stimulation is that of Gillespie (137) on the doubly innervated colon of the rabbit. Here, stimulation of the sympathetic supply at frequencies greater than ten per second causes complete inhibition of mechanical activity. During this period the membrane potential remains at the maximum level observed during spontaneous electrical activity, both the slow waves and spikes being suppressed. The membrane is not hyperpolarized. Stimulation at lower frequencies reduces the rate of depolarization of the slow waves so that longer intervals occur between bursts of spikes. The activity in different parts of the preparation probably becomes asynchronous since tension is no longer correlated with the spiking in individual cells. If the preparation is stretched so that the membrane potential is reduced and continuous spiking occurs, sympathetic stimulation produces some hyperpolarization. Gillespie suggests that the action of the sympathetic transmitter is to stabilize the membrane. This may interfere with the process of conduction between cells before it suppresses all spontaneous activity in individual cells (137, 163). The mechanism by which the sympathetic transmitter is able to stabilize this smooth muscle membrane is not yet clear.

EFFECT OF AUTONOMIC TRANSMITTERS AT THE MEMBRANE LEVEL

Smooth muscle cells are small and often spontaneously active. For this reason it is not easy to impale them with microelectrodes; in particular, it is extremely difficult to record continuous changes in resting potential in the presence of stimulating drugs, because, with contraction, the microelectrode tip is often either broken or dislodged.

The sucrose gap technique, introduced to smooth muscle by Burnstock & Straub (164), is particularly suitable for studying the effects of drugs and ions on smooth muscle since continuous recording of changes in membrane potential is possible for periods of over an hour. This method enables the potential difference between two ends of a strip of smooth muscle to be measured extracellularly while one end is bathed in a test solution, short-circuiting between the electrodes being minimized by a continuous stream of high-resistance isotonic sucrose solution (165). The sucrose gap chamber has been further adapted to allow the simultaneous measurement of tension during both spontaneous and electrically induced activity (166, 167).

Values for differences in membrane potential across a strip of smooth muscle, one end of which was bathed in isotonic K_2SO_4, approximated those found with intracellular electrodes (54 to 60 mv compared with 40 to 70 mv recorded intracellularly for the taenia coli of the guinea pig). Although slow membrane potential changes can be measured fairly accurately with the sucrose gap method, spike potentials are usually considerably smaller than those recorded intracellularly. Attempts have been made to devise very small sucrose gaps, but even here one cannot find the true time course of action potentials because of temporal dispersion among the population of fibres in contact with the electrode. The question naturally arises, how can one record from smooth muscle with electrodes 7 to 10 mm apart, when the muscle between the electrodes is bathed in a high-resistance sucrose solution? As the length of a single smooth muscle fibre is only from about 50 to 200 μ, the recording electrodes are separated by a large number of muscle fibres. One possibility is that the sucrose solution fails to replace all the ions lying in the interfibre spaces. A more likely explanation is that there is some kind of relatively low-resistance connection between individual fibres. Artifacts caused by junction potentials are not likely to be significant in most sucrose gap experiments for reasons discussed in detail elsewhere (164, 168).

Acetylcholine (Ach).—Acetylcholine increases the excitability of most smooth muscles and usually causes contraction. These effects are always associated with depolarization of the smooth muscle membrane and initiation or increase in spike frequency. This was first shown with external electrodes on the cat nictitating membrane, bladder, uterus, and vas deferens (169) and on the toad stomach (170). More recently it has been measured with microelectrodes and with the sucrose gap technique in the guinea pig taenia coli (131, 164, 167, 171, 172); in the rabbit iris (173); in the rat uterus (15, 134); in the cat longitudinal intestinal muscle (151); in muscularis mucosae of the pig esophagus (174); and in the chick amnion (144).

Spike potentials seen in muscles just exposed to Ach are characterized by steeper "prepotentials" which tend to merge smoothly into the spike proper (134, 166). Later, after three minutes or more in Ach, the spike shows a marked reduction in the rate of decay and an absence of the normally prominent after-hyperpolarization (134, 166, 172). In cat longitudinal intestinal muscle, Ach 10^{-6} produces intermittent prolonged depolarizations lasting up to 7 seconds, with spikes appearing on the crest (151). Sometimes multiple spikes on the crests of shorter depolarizations lasting up to 0.7 seconds are seen in the taenia coli in the presence of Ach (172).

Burnstock (166) postulated that Ach (and probably other stimulating drugs) depolarizes smooth muscle by simultaneously increasing the permeability to Na, K, and probably to other free ions present, in the same way that Ach has been shown to act at the skeletal motor end plate (175). Radioactive tracer studies showing increase in K^+ and Ca^{++} flux in the presence of Ach, histamine, pilocarpine, and carbachol support this view (176 to 181). Under abnormal conditions, Ach contraction of smooth muscle can be produced by a mechanism that does not involve depolarization of the excitable membrane; i.e., Ach will still cause contraction of smooth muscle which is bathed in isotonic K_2SO_4 (182). It is suggested further that, even in depolarized smooth muscle, Ach causes increased membrane permeability, so that some substance, probably Ca^{++}, can still diffuse through the membrane and directly or indirectly activate contraction (183, 184).

The rates of depolarization produced by equi-active concentrations of Ach, histamine, and 5-hydroxytryptamine (in terms of the amplitude of contraction) decrease in that order (167). Furthermore, with a hundredfold increase in concentration the average rate of depolarization caused by Ach is increased four times, whereas the rate of depolarization caused by histamine is only increased one-and-a-half times. Depolarization of the taenia coli by Ach is abolished by atropine 10^{-6}, but persists in the presence of hexamethonium 10^{-4}, nicotine 10^{-4}, and cocaine 5×10^{-5} (171).

Epinephrine.—The action of epinephrine varies considerably among different preparations and animals. In those preparations in which epinephrine causes relaxation and loss of tone, this effect is associated with hyperpolarization of the smooth muscle membrane and reduction or cessation of spike activity (15, 134, 171, 172, 185, 186). Those spikes which do appear in the presence of weak concentrations of epinephrine are characterized by their large size, short duration, slow prepotentials, fast rate of decay, and prominent after-hyperpolarization (134, 172, 185). In preparations in which epinephrine causes contraction, there is a depolarization of the membrane accompanied by increase of initiation of spike activity (21, 169, 174). The configuration of the spikes seen during epinephrine contraction of the muscularis mucosae is indistinguishable from that of the spikes seen during Ach contraction (174). There is a diphasic action of epinephrine, i.e., initial relaxation associated with hyperpolarization, followed by contraction associated with depolarization in the toad stomach (170) and in the dog stomach (187, 188). These results suggest that epinephrine normally acts via a membrane system where depolarization and initiation of spike activity result in contraction, and hyperpolarization in relaxation.

Burnstock (185) has postulated that when epinephrine causes inhibition it acts by stimulating a sodium pump involving the electrogenic extrusion of sodium, thus raising the resting potential. Support for this hypothesis comes from radioactive tracer studies where, during epinephrine relaxation, an increase in both sodium efflux and potassium influx has been observed (176, 189). Furthermore, during the inhibiting action of epinephrine there is a marked increase in phosphorylase activity (190). Additional evidence that some active process is involved in the mechanism of epinephrine relaxation is that an effect indistinguishable from that of epinephrine can be produced through increasing the metabolic rate by raising the temperature $10°C$ (191). If lithium is substituted for the sodium in Krebs solution, tension is abolished, but action potentials are still present (192). Under these conditions epinephrine fails to abolish excitability (191). The decrease in excitability caused by epinephrine is not entirely explicable in terms of increase in resting potential, since spike activity is abolished before the membrane becomes hyperpolarized, while, on recovery, large spikes appear before the membrane potential returns to its initial value. Furthermore, spike activity is abolished by epinephrine even in muscles which have been partially depolarized by high potassium levels (185). It may be that epinephrine can inhibit the "carrier" for sodium or some other ion which is responsible for the rising phase of the action potential.

Epinephrine contraction, however, cannot be explained by the same mechanism. Potassium is extruded (193) and the configuration of the spikes accompanying depolarization is similar to that seen in the presence of Ach (174).

This has led Bülbring (189) to postulate that every observed response of smooth muscle to epinephrine should be regarded as the result of two opposing actions: depolarization (and contraction) caused by the production of a passive increase in membrane permeability; hyperpolarization (and relaxation) caused by the stimulation of an active process. Epinephrine fails to hyperpolarize the taenia coli in glucose-free medium; indeed after several hours exposure it depolarizes and excites the muscle (191). Thus the passive excitatory action of epinephrine is exposed when it is no longer masked by the inhibitory metabolic action. This concept of the double action of epinephrine is further supported by the following experiments. During the early stages of dinitrophenol poisoning, epinephrine has a transient stimulatory action (185). The action of iodoacetate in causing the abolition of excitability can be reversed by epinephrine. Moreover, the increased rate of sodium extrusion caused by epinephrine is not seen in the presence of iodoacetate (189). Bülbring and co-workers (189) found that epinephrine, norepinephrine, and isoprenaline have qualitatively the same effect on excitability of taenia coli and on rate of loss of radioactive sodium. Shuba (194) has shown recently that epinephrine reduces the physical electrotonus of the circular smooth muscle of the frog stomach; the reduction of the anelectronic potential is considerably greater than of the catelectronic. He interprets this result as indicating that epinephrine acts by increasing the permeability of the membrane mainly to cations.

THE RELATION OF ELECTROPHYSIOLOGICAL EXPERIMENTS TO RECENT ADVANCES IN SOME OTHER FIELDS

It is clear that the mechanism of transmission from autonomic nerve to smooth muscle cannot be understood from electrophysiological studies alone, although these may provide a means of integrating morphological and biochemical studies at the cellular level. Although no attempt will be made to review the many recent advances in our understanding of the synthesis, storage, release, and inactivation of autonomic transmitters, it may be useful to mention a few aspects of this work which could help to clarify the electrophysiological results discussed in the previous sections.

Most of the biochemical studies on autonomic transmitters have been carried out for Ach on brain preparations (76) and for catecholamines on the adrenal medulla (80). There seems no reason to suppose that in these situations different biochemical pathways operate from those in autonomic nerves. In the adrenal medulla, however, the amines consist mainly of epinephrine and norepinephrine while only a trace of dopamine is present. In most sympathetic nerves, about 50 per cent of the amine is dopamine and 50 per cent norepinephrine (195). It is likely that the autonomic transmitters are concentrated in large amounts in the terminal parts of the nerve fibres. Hillarp (29) has pointed out that the amounts of transmitter found in autonomic effector organs are so high that it seems necessary to "postulate that the individual endings, each constituting a transmitting junctional structure cannot be tiny knobs, but must have considerable length."

This idea has been confirmed recently for several sympathetically innervated structures by use of highly sensitive fluorescent methods for the detection of catecholamines (196). Fluorescence develops over the whole of the ground plexus with small intense enlargements dispersed at irregular intervals. The structures so far examined by this technique include the dilator muscle of the iris, blood vessels (197), and the guinea pig vas deferens (Falck, personal communication). The occurrence of "presynaptic" vesicles throughout the axons of the ground plexus (see section on Morphology) is consistent with this view. The importance of these vesicles in synaptic transmission has been discussed by Eccles (22) and by De Robertis et al. (198);

their role as a store and possible site of synthesis of Ach is indicated by the studies of Hebb & Whittaker and by De Robertis and his co-workers on particulate fractions of nervous tissue prepared by differential centrifugation (198, 199). Electron-microscopic examination of this material suggests that it consists largely of dendritic endings loaded with vesicles (198, 200, 201). Further support for this view has come from the work of De Robertis & Ferreira (126), who were able to deplete the vesicles present in nerve terminals in the adrenal medulla by prolonged high-frequency stimulation of the splanchnic nerve. They suggest that this depletion is associated with an "impairment in the activity of the nerve endings".

At the skeletal neuromuscular junction Katz and his co-workers have shown that Ach is released from the nerve terminals in a quantal fashion— i.e., in packets of uniform size (162). Since these nerve endings are loaded with vesicles, the majority having a uniform size, it is tempting to consider that each vesicle contains a quantum of Ach. Comparison of the effects of the ionophoretic application of Ach at the skeletal neuromuscular junction with the size and time course of miniature end plate potentials has been used to indicate the maximum number of Ach molecules contained in a single vesicle—some 10^5 (202). It is difficult to imagine how such a large number of molecules could be packed into a vesicle of about 450 A diameter but Miledi has emphasized that this estimate is probably much too generous. Attempts to deplete the store of transmitter at the skeletal neuromuscular junction by treatment with potassium and hypertonic media did not produce any dramatic changes in the appearance or number of vesicles. Although a reduction in number was seen on some occasions, this was unconvincing because of the wide range in number observed normally (203). The identification of the vesicles with individual quanta of Ach still requires decisive proof.

Nothing is known of the mechanism of storage or synthesis of Ach by parasympathetic nerve terminals. The parasympathetic nerves visualized so far with the electron microscope also contain typical vesicles in which the transmitter might be stored. It is likely that synthesis is similar to that established for other cholinergic junctions, i.e., the acetylation of choline involves two steps: first, the formation of acetyl coenzyme A by a number of metabolic pathways and second, the transfer of the active acetyl group to choline by means of choline acetylase (76). Studies of the Ach content of parasympathetically innervated structures are complicated by the possibility of Ach synthesis by nonnervous elements in the tissue. Some organs considered to be predominantly innervated by sympathetic nerves also contain a large amount of Ach, for example, cat spleen (204). It is possible to place many different interpretations on the results of experiments on the production of Ach by the alimentary tract (205).

The synthesis of catecholamines has received much attention during the last few years. In the adrenal medulla the amines are found in high concentrations in granules which can be readily separated by centrifugation and studied *in vitro*. It seems most likely that the mechanism of synthesis involves the passage of dopa into the cell or its synthesis from tyrosine. Dopa is converted to dopamine in the "cytoplasmic sap". Dopamine is then taken up by the granules where it is converted to norepinephrine. Methylation of norepinephrine occurs outside the granules. The storage mechanism is probably nonspecific and the epinephrine so produced may be stored on the same sites as those which bind norepinephrine (206, 207). Details of the cytoplasmic location of the enzymes involved have yet to be worked out. It may be that the storage granules are contained in some vesiclelike structure. The high lipid content of preparations of catecholamine-containing granules from the adrenal medulla suggests that these granules may be surrounded by a membranelike structure (208).

A number of electron microscope studies of adrenal chromaffin tissue have demonstrated the existence of granules of an irregular size (from 0.05 to 0.15 μ in ox adrenals) usually located within local dilatations of the endoplasmic reticulum. The granules prepared by differential centrifugation are essentially similar to those of intact chromaffin cells. In fact, granules can be seen surrounded by membranes together with debrislike material, probably from fragmented or partly dissolved granules (209). Storage granules have been prepared from sympathetic nerve fibres by Schumann (210) and von Euler (211). The latter found that only about 20 per cent of the amines are associated with the granular fraction, the remainder being present in the supernatant. The granules are somewhat smaller than those of the adrenal (ranging from 0.02 to 0.1 μ). Recently, Potter & Axelrod (212) have also identified small particles with a high norepinephrine content in the microsomal fraction sedimented from a number of different sympathetically innervated structures.

In most electron microscope preparations, the majority of the vesicles seen in the autonomic nerves appear to be empty. Nevertheless, in sections of the guinea pig vas deferens prepared by Richardson (personal communication) some of the vesicles appear to contain small, strongly osmiophilic granules. Similar granules have been observed in secretory cells from the pineal body and also within nerve endings found near large blood vessels in the pineal (127). The latter have been tentatively considered to be adrenergic endings. Lever & Esterhuizen (109) have demonstrated darkly staining material within the vesicles of adrenergic terminals in animals treated with Co^{++} salts; perhaps this finding is related to Hillarp's observation that metal ions form insoluble precipitates with the intragranular proteins (208).

Pharmacological and biochemical studies suggest that the storage of catecholamines in nerve terminals involves at least two compartments—a labile, or free, compartment and a fixed, or bound, compartment (213). The norepinephrine which is released in response to nerve stimulation or by tyramine may originate largely from the labile compartment (214, 215, 216).

Axelrod (217) found, by use of tritiated norepinephrine, a marked increase in the amine output from cat spleen in response to stimulation of the splenic nerve. He found that bretylium causes a transient suppression followed by a maintained increase in the rate of spontaneous output, although the nerve-induced increase was completely blocked (Axelrod, personal communication). These findings are exactly parallel with those of Burnstock & Holman (148), who observed that the miniature junction potentials in the vas deferens were suppressed at first by the bretylium but reappeared at an increased frequency, although there was no response to nerve stimulation at this time.

The way in which activation of the nerve might lead to release of transmitter remains obscure. It has been demonstrated for the skeletal neuromuscular junction that the amplitude of the presynaptic action potential determines how much transmitter is released (218). It is hard to imagine how a change in membrane potential alone could cause transmitter release, but perhaps the entry of calcium ions, which has been shown to accompany the action potential in skeletal muscle (219), may be important in the release mechanism. Schumann has shown that calcium ions release amines from both nerve and adrenal granules (220). Brown and his co-workers (221, 222) have attempted to follow the output of transmitter from sympathetic nerve terminals in cat spleen by measuring the overflow of pressor amines in the venous effluent during splenic nerve stimulation. They found that after dibenyline or other sympatholytic agents are given, the overflow per impulse at low frequencies increases until it equals the maximum output at higher frequencies (about 30 per sec). They suggest that sympatholytics prevent the uptake or inactivation of the liberated transmitter by the postjunctional receptors. After neuronal rest, produced by decentralization (preganglionic section) or by ganglion-blocking agents, the overflow of transmitter is reduced by half, but in the presence of sympatholytics is nearly doubled (223). Brown, Davies & Ferry conclude from these experiments that periods of inactivity of postganglionic neurons can cause an increased capacity for the uptake of transmitter by the postjunctional receptors as well as an accumulation of transmitter in the nerve terminals.

It has already been pointed out that the junction potentials accompanying the transmission of excitation in the pelvic viscera (colon, bladder, retractor penis, and vas deferens) are very similar although, according to the classical view, the excitatory transmitter for the colon is acetylcholine and norepinephrine is liberated by the hypogastric nerve. The characteristics of postjunctional excitatory responses may turn out to be determined by the nature of the junctional membrane rather than by the nature of the transmitter. It is clear that the nature of the membrane potential response to nerve stimulation can give no information regarding the identity of the transmitter.

Some of the actions of Ach and epinephrine on the membrane potential of visceral smooth muscle have already been discussed. Smooth muscle is particularly advantageous for these studies since the "receptors" which interact with the applied drugs are not localized but are probably widely distributed over the surface of many if not all of the smooth muscle cells of the organ. It remains to be shown whether or not the receptors involved in the response to the transmitter when it is added to the over-all environment of the tissue are the same as those which react with the transmitter which is liberated from nerve terminals.

Electrophysiological methods at the skeletal neuromuscular junction have already provided some information regarding the receptors on the post-junctional muscle membrane. The effects of the ionophoretic application of Ach suggest that the gradient of Ach sensitivity in the vicinity of an end plate is related to the density of receptors, and not to the efficiency of individual receptors which are probably uniformly active in bringing out depolarization (202). The depolarization produced by Ach is transient, partly because of the destruction of the transmitter by cholinesterase and partly because of diffusion away from the receptor site. However, other depolarizing drugs which are not destroyed by cholinesterase also cause only a transient increase in permeability. After the action of Ach or any other depolarizer, the membrane's electrical characteristics return to normal but it will no longer respond to a further dose of Ach. Studies by Katz & Thesleff (224) of this "desensitization" process have led to the idea that the receptor might exist in two forms, effective A and refractory B. The depolarizing drug S (Ach, carbachol, etc.) combines rapidly and reversibly with both forms, but S has a greater affinity for B than for A. Hence a small depolarization may be associated with a considerable amount of desensitization. Once SA is formed, this reverts relatively slowly to SB. Reconstitution of the effective receptor A from B also takes time. Such a concept of transmitter-receptor interaction may well be applicable to other junctions. The duration of action of the transmitter from hypogastric nerve terminals in the vas deferens may be brief. No enzyme with the properties of cholinesterase has been demonstrated to occur in the vicinity of sympathetic nerve endings. Thus it seems possible that the time course of the excitatory junction potentials in smooth muscle may be due to the reactions transmitter+receptor →depolarization→desensitized receptor rather than to the actual destruction of transmitter by a highly specific enzyme.

Paton (225) has recently drawn attention to the possibility that the effect of each molecule of transmitter may be produced at the moment it combines with the receptor, and that the transmitter itself may then remain in combination with the receptor for some appreciable time so that the receptor is effectively blocked. Thus the action produced by a drug is dependent on the rates of association and dissociation of the interaction between drug and receptor rather than the amount of drug actually combined. This theory, that the receptors may be blocked by the transmitter itself, or by any other drug mimicking the transmitter action, provides an attractive explanation for tachyphylaxis and for the supersensitivity which occurs after the degeneration of the efferent nerve supply or depletion of transmitter by reserpine. Electrophysiological studies on smooth muscle, particularly the ionophoretic application of transmitters, may help to provide the same pointers to the solution of this problem as those already established for the skeletal neuromuscular junction.

SUMMARY

(a) Transmission of excitation from autonomic nerves to smooth muscle is essentially similar to that found at other neuromuscular junctions. Supporting evidence includes the following:

Junction potentials have been recorded from single smooth muscle cells upon stimulation of the autonomic nerves, which facilitate and sum with each other until, at a critical threshold depolarization, one or more action potentials are initiated and a contraction occurs. Miniature junction potentials, probably representing the spontaneous release of transmitter from the nerve, have also been recorded.

Electron micrographs have revealed axon profiles, packed with vesicles (350 to 450 A) and mitochondria, between the smooth muscle cells. The minimum separation of nerve and muscle membranes is of the order of 200 to 300 A.

(b) It is possible that, unlike other known neuroeffector junctions, the axons passing close to muscle fibres release transmitter substances at intervals along their length and do not possess many discrete endings at all. This could account for the diffuse influence of autonomic nerve fibres on smooth muscle and the apparent density of its innervation. Supporting evidence:

Junction potentials and miniature junction potentials can be recorded from every smooth muscle cell.

Quantitative assay of transmitter substances in sympathetically innervated organs reveals amounts which are so high that it is unlikely the transmitter would be confined solely to discrete end-knobs.

Fluorescent histochemical staining methods for catecholamines have demonstrated fluorescence over the whole of the autonomic ground plexus with small intensely fluorescent enlargements dispersed at irregular intervals.

Electron micrographs reveal that not only the axon profiles in close apposition to the muscle membrane, but also the bundles of axons more or less enclosed in Schwann sheath running between the smooth muscle cells, are packed with vesicles and mitochondria.

(c) Electrophysiological observations of the action of transmitter substances at the membrane level suggest that the smooth muscle membrane has many properties in common with the end plate regions of skeletal muscle; for example, Ach increases the permeability of the membrane to sodium, potassium, and probably other ions.

(*d*) It is suggested that a combination of quantitative assay, electron microscopy, fluorescent staining of catecholamines, differential isolation of transmitters, and microelectrode studies on autonomic nerve-smooth muscle preparations is beginning, and will continue, to clarify the nature of the autonomic transmission process which has for so long remained a mystery.

LITERATURE CITED

1. Evans, C. L., *Physiol. Rev.*, **6**, 358 (1926)
2. Fischer, E., *Physiol. Rev.*, **24**, 467 (1944)
3. Vaughan-Williams, E. M., *Pharmacol. Rev.*, **6**, 159 (1954)
4. Furchgott, R. F., *Pharmacol. Rev.*, **7**, 183 (1955)
5. Csapo, A., in *Structure and Function of Muscle*, **I**, 229 (Academic Press, Inc., New York, 1960)
6. Bozler, E., *Experientia*, **4**, 213 (1948)
7. Rosenblueth, A., in *The Transmission of Nerve Impulses at Neuro-Effector Junctions and Peripheral Synapses* (Technology Press and John Wiley & Sons, New York and London, 1950)
8. Prosser, C. L., in *Structure and Function of Muscle*, **II** (Academic Press, Inc., New York, 1960)
9. Prosser, C. L., *Physiol. Rev.* (In press, 1962)
10. Bülbring, E., *Congr. intern. physiol.*, *20^e*, Brussels, 230 (1956)
11. Bülbring, E., *Lecture on the Scientific Basis of Medicine*, **7**, 374 (1958)
12. Bübring, E., *Arch. Ges. Physiol.*, **273**, 1 (1961)
13. Bülbring, E., *Physiol. Rev.* (In press, 1962)
14. Thesleff, S., in *The Structure and Function of Muscle*, **III**, 1 (Academic Press, Inc., New York, 1960)
15. Kuriyama, H., *CIBA Foundation Symposium. Progesterone and the Defence Mechanism of Pregnancy*, 51 (1961)
16. Bozler, E., *Physiol. Rev.* (In press, 1962)
17. Marshall, J., *Physiol. Rev.* (In press, 1962)
18. Goto, M., and Tamai, T., in *Modern Aspects of the Electrophysiology of Involuntary Muscles* (Kinpodo Pub. Co. Ltd., Tokyo, 1960)
19. Burnstock, G., Holman, M. E., and Prosser, C. L., *Physiol. Rev.* (In press, 1962)
20. Eccles, J. C., and Magladery, J. W., *J. Physiol. (London)*, **90**, 31 (1937)
21. Eccles, J. C., and Magladery, J. W., *J. Physiol. (London)*, **90**, 68 (1937)
22. Eccles, J. C., *Ergeb. Physiol.*, **51**, 299 (1961)
23. Terzuolo, C. A., and Edwards, C., *Ann. Rev. Physiol.*, **24**, 325 (1962)
24. Katz, B., *Proc. Roy. Soc. London, B*, **155**, 455 (1962)
25. Elliott, T. R., *J. Physiol. (London)*, **31**, 20 (1904)
26. Langley, J. N., in *The Autonomic Nervous System* (W. Heffer & Sons, Cambridge, 1921)
27. Dale, H. H., *J. Physiol. (London)*, **80**, 10 (1933)
28. Garry, R. C., and Gillespie, J. S., *J. Physiol. (London)*, **128**, 557 (1955)
29. Hillarp, N. A., *Handbook of Physiology. Neurophysiology*, **2**, 979 (Am. Physiol. Soc., Washington, D.C., 1960)
30. Hillarp, N. A., *Acta Physiol. Scand.*, **46**, 1 (1959)
31. Richardson, K. C., *J. Anat.*, **94**, 457 (1960)
32. McSwiney, B. A., *Physiol. Rev.*, **11**, 478 (1931)
33. Gruber, C. M., *Physicl. Rev.*, **13**, 497 (1933)
34. Cannon, W. B., and Rosenblueth, A., *Exptl. Biol. Monograph* (McMillan, New York, 1949)
35. Garry, R. C., *Advan. Sci.*, **9**, 197 (1953)
36. Munro, A. F., *J. Physiol. (London)*, **120**, 41 (1953)
37. Ambache, N., *Pharmacol. Rev.*, **7**, 467 (1955)
38. Edge, N. D., *J. Physiol. (London)*, **127**, 54 (1955)
39. Paton, W. D. M., *J. Physiol. (London)*, **127**, 40 (1955)
40. Semba, T., *Japan. J. Physiol.*, **6**, 321 (1956)
41. Varagić, V., *J. Physiol. (London)*, **132**, 92 (1956)
42. Varagić, V., *Arch. Intern. Pharmacodynamie*, **106**, 141 (1956)
43. Burnstock, G., *J. Physiol. (London)*, **141**, 35 (1958)
44. Burnstock, G., *Brit. J. Pharmacol.*, **13**, 216 (1958)
45. Thompson, J. W., *J. Physiol. (London)*, **141**, 46 (1958)
46. Carpenter, F. G., and Tankersley, J. C., *Am. J. Physiol.*, **196**, 1185 (1959)
47. Lee, C. Y., *J. Physiol. (London)*, **152**, 405 (1960)
48. Huković, S., *Brit. J. Pharmacol.*, **16**, 188 (1961)
49. Gyermek, L., *Am. J. Physiol.*, **201**, 325 (1961)
50. Ursillo, R. C., *J. Pharmacol. Exptl. Therap.*, **131**, 231 (1961)
51. Bertler, A., Carlsson, A., and Rosen-

gren, E., *Naturwissenschaften*, **43**, 521 (1956)

52. Burn, J. H., and Rand, M. J., *J. Physiol. (London)*, **144**, 314 (1958)

53. Burn, J. H., and Rand, M. J., *Nature*, **184**, 163 (1959)

54. Burn, J. H., and Rand, M. J., *J. Physiol. (London)*, **147**, 135 (1959)

55. Burn, J. H., Leach, E. H., Rand, M. J., and Thompson, J. W., *J. Physiol. (London)*, **148**, 332 (1959)

56. Chang, V., and Rand, M. J., *Brit. J. Pharmacol.*, **15**, 588 (1960)

57. Gillespie, J. S., and Mackenna, B. R., *J. Physiol. (London)*, **147**, 31 (1959)

58. Gillespie, J. S., and Mackenna, B. R., *J. Physiol. (London)*, **152**, 191 (1960)

59. Gillespie, J. S., and Mackenna, B. R., *J. Physiol. (London)*, **156**, 17 (1961)

60. Burn, J. H., *Brit. Med. J.*, **II**, 1523 (1961)

61. Day, M. D., and Rand, M. J., *Brit. J. Pharmacol.*, **17**, 245 (1961)

62. Brandon, K. W., and Boyd, H., *Nature*, **192**, 880 (1961)

63. Gardener, J. E., and Thompson, J. W., *Nature*, **191**, 86 (1961)

64. *CIBA Foundation Symposium. Adrenergic Mechanism* (Churchill, London, 1960)

65. Young, J. Z., *Quart. J. Microscop. Sci.*, **75**, 571 (1933)

66. Young, J. Z., *Proc. Roy. Soc. London, B*, **120**, 303 (1936)

67. Babkin, B. P., *Roy. Soc. Can., Proc. & Trans.*, **40**, 1 (1946)

68. Burnstock, G., *Quart. J. Microscop. Sci.*, **15**, 611 (1959)

69. Nicol, J. A. C., *Biol. Rev., Cambridge Phil. Soc.*, **27**, 1 (1952)

70. Pick, J., *J. Comp. Neurol.*, **107**, 169 (1957)

71. Burnstock, G., Wood, M., and O'Shea, J., *Australian J. Sci.*, **24**, 192 (1961)

72. Boyd, H., Burnstock, G., Campbell, G., Jowett, A., and Wood, M., *Australian J. Sci.* (In press, 1962)

73. Campbell, G., and Burnstock, G., *Australian J. Sci.* (In press, 1962)

74. Burnstock, G., O'Shea, J., and Wood, M., *J. Physiol. (London)* (Submitted) (1962)

75. Burn, J. H., *Functions of Autonomic Transmitters* (Williams & Wilkins, Baltimore, 1956)

76. Hebb, C. O., *Physiol. Rev.*, **37**, 196 (1957)

77. Blaschko, H., *Pharmacol. Rev.*, **11**, 307 (1959)

78. von Euler, U. S. , *Recent Progr. Hormone Research*, **14**, 483 (1958)

79. von Euler, U. S., in *Handbook of Physiology. Neurophysiology*, **1**, 215 (Am. Physiol. Soc., Washington, D.C., 1959)

80. von Euler, U. S., in *Harvey Lectures*, **55**, 43 (1961)

81. Axelrod, J., *Physiol. Rev.*, **39**, 751 (1959)

82. Florey, E., *Ann. Rev. Physiol.*, **23**, 501 (1961)

83. Rhodin, J. A. G., *Physiol. Rev.* (In press, 1962)

84. Keech, M. K., *J. Biophys. Biochem. Cytol.*, **7**, 533 (1960)

85. Pease, D. C., and Paule, W. J., *J. Ultrastruct. Res.*, **3**, 469 (1960)

86. Prosser, C. L., Burnstock, G., and Kahn, J., *Am. J. Physiol.*, **199**, 545 (1960)

87. Karrer, H. E., *J. Ultrastruct. Res.*, **5**, 1 (1961)

88. Woodbury, J. W., and McIntyre, D. M., *Am. J. Physiol.*, **177**, 355 (1954)

89. Mark, J. S. T., *Anat. Record*, **125**, 473 (1956)

90. Bergman, R. A., *Bull. Johns Hopkins Hosp.*, **102**, 195 (1958)

91. Caesar, R., Edwards, G., and Ruska, H., *J. Biophys. Biochem. Cytol.*, **3**, 867 (1957)

92. Pease, D. C., and Molinari, S., *J. Ultrastruct. Res.*, **3**, 447 (1960)

93. Yamamoto, T., *Acta Neuroveget. (Vienna)*, **21**, 406 (1960)

94. Burnstock, G., Holman, M. E., and Merrillees, N., *J. Cellular Biol.* (submitted) (1962)

95. Kawaguti, S., and Ikemoto, N., *Biol. J. Okayama Univ.*, **3**, 159 (1957)

96. Schoenberg, C. F., *J. Biophys. Biochem. Cytol.*, **4**, 609 (1958)

97. Thaemert, J. C., *J. Biophys. Biochem. Cytol.*, **6**, 67 (1959)

98. Barfurth, D., *Arch. Mikroskop. Anat.*, **38**, 38 (1891)

99. McGill, C., *Am. J. Anat.*, **9**, 493 (1909)

100. Aunap, E., *Z. Mikroskop. Anat. Forsch.*, **40**, 587 (1936)

101. Häggqvist, G., in *Handbuch der mikroskopischen Anatomie des Menschen*, 2 (Springer-Verlag, Berlin, 1956)

102. Bergman, R. A., in *First European Regional Conference on Electron Microscopy, Stockholm* (Academic Press, New York, 1957)

103. Moore, D. H., and Ruska, H., *J. Biophys. Biochem. Cytol.*, **3**, 457 (1957)

104. Lewis, M., *Carnegie Inst., Contrib. Embryol.*, 9, 191 (1920)
105. Burnstock, G., Prosser, C. L., and Barr, L. M., *Federation Proc.*, 18, 21 (1959)
106. Richardson, K. C., *Am. J. Anat.*, 103, 99 (1958)
107. Lundberg, A., *Physiol. Rev.*, 38, 21 (1958)
108. Clara, M., *Acta Neuroveget. (Vienna)*, Suppl. 5, 1 (1955)
109. Lever, J. D., and Esterhuizen, A. C., *Nature*, 192, 566 (1961)
110. Burnstock, G., Holman, M. E., and Merrillees, N., *Australian J. Sci.* (In press, 1962)
111. Lawrentjew, B. J., *Z. Mikroscop. Anat. Forsch.*, 36, 651 (1934)
112. Boeke, J., *Acta Anat.*, 8, 18 (1949)
113. Nonidez, J. F., *Anat. Anz.*, 82, 348 (1936)
114. Stöhr, P., Jr., *Acta Neuroveget. (Vienna)*, 10, 21 (1954)
115. Meyling, H. A., *J. Comp. Neurol.*, 99, 495 (1953)
116. Gansler, H., *Acta Neuroveget. (Vienna)*, 3, 192 (1961)
117. Coupland, R. E., *Nature*, 194, 310 (1962)
118. Fusari, R., *Arch. Ital. Biol.*, 16, 262 (1891)
119. Alpert, L. K., *Anat. Record*, 50, 221 (1931)
120. Burnstock, G., and Holman, M. E., *J. Physiol. (London)*, 155, 115 (1961)
121. Burnstock, G., and Prosser, C. L., *Am. J. Physiol.*, 199, 553 (1960)
122. Orlov, R. S., *Sechenov Physiol. J. USSR*, 48, 342 (1962)*
123. Feldberg, W., *Physiol. Rev.*, 25, 596 (1945)
124. De Robertis, E. D. P., and Bennett, H. S., *Federation Proc.*, 13, 35 (1954)
125. Robertson, J. D., *J. Biophys. Biochim. Cytol.*, 2, 381 (1956)
126. De Robertis, E., and Ferreira, A. V., *J. Biophys. Biochem. Cytol.*, 3, 611 (1957)
127. De Robertis, E., and Pellegrino de Iraldi, A. P., *J. Biophys. Biochem. Cytol.*, 10, 361 (1961a)
128. Yamada, H., and Miyake, S., *Z. Zell-forsch. Mikroskop. Anat.*, 52, 129 (1960)
129. Scott, B. L., and Pease, D. C., *Am. J. Anat.*, 104, 115 (1959)
130. Levi-Montalcini, R., and Angeletti, P., *Quart. Rev. Biol.*, 36, 99 (1961)
131. Bülbring, E., *J. Physiol. (London)*, 128, 200 (1955)

132. Bülbring, E., Burnstock, G., and Holman, M. E., *J. Physiol. (London)*, 142, 420 (1958)
133. Holman, M. E., *J. Physiol. (London)*, 141, 464 (1958)
134. Marshall, J. M., *Am. J. Physiol.*, 197, 935 (1959)
135. Kuriyama, H., *J. Physiol. (London)*, 159, 26 (1961)
136. Daniel, E. E., and Singh, H., *Can. J. Biochem. Physiol.*, 36, 959 (1958)
137. Gillespie, J. S., *J. Physiol. (London)*, 155, 59P (1961)
138. Funaki, S., *Proc. Japan Acad.*, 34, 534 (1958)
139. Ursillo, R. C., *Am. J. Physiol.*, 201, 408 (1961)
140. Bennett, M., Burnstock, G., Holman, M. E., and Walker, J. W., *J. Physiol. (London)* (In press, 1962)
141. Irisawa, H., and Kobayashi, M., *Proc. Japan Acad.*, 38, 171 (1962)
142. Roddie, I. C., and Kirk, S., *Science*, 134, 736 (1961)
143. Roddie, I. C., *J. Physiol. (London)*, 161, 20 (1962)
144. Cuthbert, A. W., *Nature*, 193, 488 (1962)
145. Gillespie, J. S., *J. Physiol. (London)*, 156, 32 (1961)
146. Burnstock, G., and Holman, M. E., *Nature*, 187, 951 (1960)
147. Burnstock, G., and Holman, M. E., *J. Physiol. (London)*, 155, 115 (1961)
148. Burnstock, G., and Holman, M. E., *Australian J. Sci.*, 24, 190 (1961)
149. Burnstock, G. and Holman, M. E., *J. Physiol. (London)*, 160, 446 (1962)
150. Burnstock, G., and Holman, M. E., *J. Physiol. (London)*, 160, 461 (1962)
151. Burnstock, G., and Prosser, C. L., *Proc. Soc. Exptl. Biol. Med.*, 103, 269 (1960)
152. Lundberg, A., *Physiol. Rev.*, 38, 21 (1958)
153. Burke, W., *J. Physiol. (London)*, 135, 511 (1957)
154. Ginsborg, B. L., *J. Physiol. (London)*, 150, 707 (1960)
155. Dudel, J., and Kuffler, S. W., *J. Physiol. (London)*, 155, 514 (1961)
156. Birks, R., Katz, B., and Miledi, R., *J. Physiol. (London)*, 150, 145 (1960)
157. Furshpan, E. J., *J. Physiol. (London)*, 134, 689 (1956)
158. Liley, A. W., *J. Physiol. (London)*, 136, 595 (1957)

159. Katz, B., and Thesleff, S., *J. Physiol.* (*London*), **137,** 267 (1957)
160. Barr, L., *Am. J. Physiol.*, **200,** 251 (1961)
161. Brown, G. L., and Gillespie, J. S., *J. Physiol.* (*London*), **138,** 81 (1957)
162. Del Castillo, J., and Katz, B., *Progr. Biophys. Biophys. Chem.*, **6,** 121 (1956)
163. Bozler, E., *Am. J. Physiol.*, **130,** 627 (1940)
164. Burnstock, G., and Straub, R. W., *J. Physiol.* (*London*), **140,** 156 (1958)
165. Stämpfli, R., *Experientia*, **10,** 500 (1954)
166. Burnstock, G., *J. Physiol.* (*London*), **143,** 165 (1958)
167. Bülbring, E., and Burnstock, G., *Brit. J. Pharmacol.*, **15,** 611 (1960)
168. Marshall, J. M., and Csapo, A., *Endocrinology*, **68,** 1026 (1961)
169. Bacq, Z. M., and Monnier, A. M., *Arch. Intern. Physiol.*, **40,** 467 (1935)
170. Sato, A., *Japan. J. Physiol.*, **10,** 359 (1960)
171. Bülbring, E., *J. Physiol.* (*London*), **125,** 302 (1954)
172. Bülbring, E., *J. Physiol.* (*London*), **135,** 412 (1957)
173. Bülbring, E., and Hooton, I. N., *J. Physiol.* (*London*), **125,** 292 (1954)
174. Burnstock, G., *Nature*, **186,** 727 (1960)
175. Del Castillo, J., and Katz, B., *J. Physiol.* (*London*), **128,** 396 (1955)
176. Born, G. V. R., and Bülbring, E., *J. Physiol.* (*London*), **131,** 690 (1956)
177. Lembeck, F., and Strobach, R., *Arch. Exptl. Pathol. Pharmakol.*, **228,** 130 (1955)
178. Durbin, R. P., and Jenkinson, D. H., *J. Physiol.* (*London*), **157,** 74 (1961)
179. Hurwitz, L., Tinsley, B., and Battle, F., *Am. J. Physiol.*, **199,** 107 (1960)
180. Weiss, G. B., Coalson, R. E., and Hurwitz, L., *Am. J. Physiol.*, **200,** 789 (1961)
181. Schatzmann, H. J., *Arch. Ges. Physiol.*, **274,** 295 (1961)
182. Evans, D. H. L., Schild, H. O., and Thesleff, S., *J. Physiol.* (*London*), **143,** 474 (1958)
183. Edman, K. A. P., and Schild, H. O., *Nature*, **190,** 350 (1961)
184. Durbin, R. P., and Jenkinson, D. H., *J. Physiol.* (*London*), **157,** 90 (1961)
185. Burnstock, G., *J. Physiol.* (*London*), **143,** 183 (1958)
186. Sperelakis, N., and Prosser, C. L., *Am. J. Physiol.*, **196,** 850 (1959)
187. Bozler, E., *Am. J. Physiol.*, **144,** 693 (1945)
188. Ichikawa, S., and Bozler, E., *Am. J. Physiol.*, **182,** 92 (1955)
189. Bülbring, E., *CIBA Foundation Symposium Adrenergic Mechanism*, 275 (1960)
190. Axelsson, J., Bueding, E., and Bülbring, E., *J. Physiol.* (*London*), **156,** 357 (1961)
191. Axelsson, J., and Bülbring, E., *J. Physiol.* (*London*), **156,** 344 (1961)
192. Axelsson, J., *J. Physiol.* (*London*), **158,** 381 (1961)
193. Ellis, S., *Pharmacol. Rev.*, **11,** 469 (1959)
194. Shuba, M. F., *Sechenov Physiol. J. USSR*, **47,** 1169 (1961)*
195. Schumann, H. J., *CIBA Foundation Symposium. Adrenergic Mechanisms*, 10 (1960)
196. Carlsson, A., Falck, B., Hillarp, N. A., Thieme, G., and Torp, A., *Med. Exptl.*, **4,** 123 (1961)
197. Falck, B., and Torp, A., *Med. Exptl.*, **6,** 169 (1962)
198. de Robertis, E., Pellegrino De Iraldi, A., Rodriguez, G., Arnaiz, G., and Salganicoff, L. *J. Neurochem.*, **7,** 922 (1962)
199. Hebb, C. O., and Whittaker, V. P., *J. Physiol.* (*London*), **142,** 187 (1958)
200. Gray, E. G., and Whittaker, V. P., *J. Anat.*, **96,** 79 (1962)
201. De Robertis, E., Pellegrino De Iraldi, A., Rodriguez, G., and Gomez, C. J. *J. Biophys. Biochem. Cytol.*, **9,** 229 (1961)
202. Miledi, R., *Discovery*, 442 (October issue, 1961)
203. Birks, R., Huxley, H. E., and Katz, B., *J. Physiol.* (*London*), **150,** 134 (1960)
204. Brandon, K. W., and Rand, M. J., *J. Physiol.* (*London*), **157,** 18 (1961)
205. Feldberg, W., and Lin, R. C. Y., *J. Physiol.* (*London*), **111,** 96 (1950)
206. Gaddum, J. H., *CIBA Foundation Symposium. Adrenergic Mechanisms*, 588 (1960)
207. Bertler, A., Hillarp, N. A., and Rosengren, E., *Acta Physiol. Scand.*, **50,** 124 (1960)
208. Hillarp, N. A., *CIBA Foundation Symposium. Adrenergic Mechanisms*, 481 (1960)
209. Hagen, P., and Barrnett, R. J., *CIBA Foundation Symposium. Adrenergic Mechanisms*, 83, (1960)
210. Schumann, H. J., *Arch. Exptl. Pathol. Pharmakol.*, **233,** 296 (1958)

211. von Euler, U. S., *CIBA Foundation Symposium. Adrenergic Mechanisms*, 492 (1960)
212. Potter, L. T., and Axelrod, J., *Nature*, 194, 581 (1962)
213. Trendelenburg, U., *J. Pharmacol. Exptl. Therap.*, 134, 8 (1961)
214. Crout, J. R., *Federation Proc.*, 21, 332 (1962)
215. Potter, L. T., Axelrod, J., and Kopin, I. J., *Federation Proc.*, 21, 177 (1962)
216. Hertting, G., Kopin, I. J., and Gordon, E., *Federation Proc.*, 21, 331 (1962)
217. Hertting, G., and Axelrod, J., *Nature*, 192, 172 (1961)
218. Hubbard, J. E., and Willis, W. D., *Nature*, 193, 1294 (1962)
219. Bianchi, C. P., and Shanes, A. M., *J. Gen. Physiol.*, 42, 803 (1959)
220. Schumann, H. J., and Philippu, A., *Experientia*, 18, 138 (1962)
221. Brown, G. L., Davies, B. N., and Gillespie, J. S., *J. Physiol. (London)*, 143, 41 (1958)
222. Brown, G. L., and Gillespie, J. S., *J. Physiol. (London)*, 138, 81 (1957)
223. Brown, G. L., Davies, B. N., and Ferry, C. B., *J. Physiol. (London)*, 159, 365 (1961)
224. Katz, B., and Thesleff, S., *J. Physiol. (London)*, 138, 63 (1957)
225. Paton, W. D. M., *Proc. Roy. Soc. London, B*, 154, 21 (1961)

* English translation will be announced in *Technical Translations*, issued by the Office of Technical Services, U. S. Department of Commerce, and will be made available by the Photoduplication Service, Library of Congress, and by the SLA Translation Center at the John Crerar Library, Chicago, Illinois.

KIDNEY, WATER, AND ELECTROLYTE METABOLISM[1,2]

By Karl J. Ullrich and Donald J. Marsh[3]

Physiologisches Institut der Freien Universität, Berlin

INTRODUCTION

A number of excellent monographs, review articles, and symposia have appeared in the period of the present survey and have proved highly useful in its preparation. These have dealt with the fields of renal physiology (1, 2, 3), membrane transport (4, 5), ontogenetic development of homeostatic mechanisms (6), endocrinological regulation of salt and water metabolism (7 to 10), and clinical disturbances of fluid and electrolyte metabolism and renal function (12, 13, 14).

MORPHOLOGY

Glomerulus.—Three structural layers separate the capillary lumen from the glomerular lumen. Recent attention has been directed to the fine structure of the middle layer, or basement membrane, where no porous structure had been demonstrable, although the endothelial lining had been shown to have pores of 400 to 1000 A diameter, and the epithelial lining to have pores of 250 to 300 A diameter. It has now been possible to demonstrate the presence of a fibrillar structure with interspaces of 30 to 75 A in the basement membrane, which is thus thought to represent the barrier for filtration of large molecules (15). Bohle & Sitte (16) consider the basement membrane to to be a gelfilter membrane whose permeability can be increased by swelling which occurs in certain pathological conditions. Farquhar (17) has shown that, although the endothelium is freely penetrated by ferritin, only a few particles appear within the basement membrane and glomerular epithelium, indicating very poor penetration of these structures. The parenteral injection of a variety of macromolecules resulted in certain characteristic morphologic changes in the glomeruli which are interpreted as secondary to the pinocytotic uptake of the molecules by the glomerular endothelium (18 to 21). Prolonged infusion of albumin into rats caused swelling and vacuolization of the glomerular epithelium, and focal fusion of foot processes; albumin molecules were taken up by the glomerular epithelium and albuminuria was observed. The changes noted in these experiments were qualitatively similar to those found in nephrosis, which was taken as evidence that the ultrastructural changes were the result rather than the cause of the albuminuria.

[1] The survey of the literature was concluded in June 1962.

[2] Abbreviations used in this chapter include: ACTH (adrenocorticotropic hormone); ADH (antidiuretic hormone); DOC (deoxycorticosterone acetate); GFR (glomerular filtration rate); PAH (*p*-aminohippurate); RPF (renal plasma flow).

[3] Fellow, National Institutes of Health. Present address: Department of Physiology, New York University, School of Medicine.

91

Kurtz & Feldman (22) labeled the glomerular basement membrane with deposits of AgNO₃ by addition of the salt to the drinking water. After AgNO₃ ingestion was discontinued, new increments of deposit-free basement membrane appeared on the epithelial side, indicating that the basement membrane is a product of the epithelial cells. The observed persistence of the argyric granules after long periods free of exposure to AgNO₃ led the authors to suggest that the basement membrane is not in a constant state of structural replacement.

Electron-microscopic studies of the juxtaglomerular apparatus and macula densa have been published (23, 24). The basement membrane of the macula densa cells is unique in that it is continuous with the material in which the juxtaglomerular cells are imbedded. If, as discussed in the section on regulation of aldosterone secretion, the juxtaglomerular cells, within the context of their operation as volume receptors, are sensitive to changes of external Na⁺ concentration, the author's suggestion that the macula densa is favorably structured for the transmission of information to the juxtaglomerular apparatus has its attractions. It has been suggested that the juxtaglomerular apparatus is sensitive to changes on the blood side only, but a sensory mechanism located on the tubular side just proximal to the locus of action of aldosterone, and able to transmit information about the Na⁺ load being delivered to this site, would be in a highly favorable position to integrate the fine regulation of aldosterone activity.

Tubular cells.—The ultramicroscopic structure of the tubular cells has been described by Rhodin (25) and Thoenes (26, 27). Particular attention was directed to the tubular and capillary structures within the medulla. When compared with the pars convoluta, the cells of the pars recta of the proximal tubule contained fewer mitochondria, had a smaller brush border, and had almost no basal invaginations. These structural features are thought to reflect less activity on the part of these cells.

The flat, simply structured cells of the thin descending and ascending limbs of Henle's loops contain only a few small mitochondria, and morphologists do not concede these structures much chance to perform active transport. The two types of capillaries, characterized by the presence or absence of pores, which had been described by Longley et al. (28) in the outer medulla, were also found in the inner medulla (27). Often these two types run in close contact with each other over relatively long distances. Capillaries which border on the tubules are usually porous and only rarely nonporous. It is not clear from these studies whether this differentiation merely represents a structural transition from arterial to venous vessels, or also has functional implications for the countercurrent system. It is of interest that similar differences have been found in the vessels of the *rete mirabile* of the fish swim bladder, which is quite clearly only a countercurrent exchanger. The uptake and breakdown of protein droplets by the proximal convoluted tubule have been investigated by Brewer & Eguren (29). They found that both hemoglobin and egg white were taken up from the tubular lumen by a pinocytotic process in which the cell membrane underwent an invagination between microvilli at the base of the brush border. Droplets arose by an infolding of membrane at the base of these invaginations and could be distinguished from mitochondria by their single enveloping membrane. These droplets disappeared within a few hours, probably after breakdown of the protein.

Dark intercalated cells were found in the distal parts of the distal convolution and in the collecting ducts in the cortex and outer medulla, and seem to contain many mitochondria, RNA particles, and other enzyme-rich organelles (30). A marked increase in the number of these dark cells occurred in experimentally induced potassium deficiency (31). As discussed later, present data implicate this location as the site of K^+ secretion.

Dimensions of tubular lumen and tubular cells changed rapidly and variably after biopsy removal of a specimen from a functioning kidney (32). In view of the complex interactions involved and variable results obtained, functional inferences drawn from histological measurements of tubular dimensions should be interpreted with the greatest caution. The claim of morphologists that post mortem dimensional changes are constant from one group of experimental animals to another, or even from one animal to the next in the same group, is particularly suspect (33).

A number of papers have dealt with morphological aspects of the renal medullary circulation (34, 35, 36). According to Ljungqvist & Lagergren (34), the human medulla is supplied chiefly by postglomerular *arteriolae rectae spuriae. Arteriolae rectae verae* with no interposition of glomeruli were also found, their number increasing with age; they are thought to represent an established continuity between afferent and efferent arterioles of degenerated juxtamedullary glomeruli. Hammersen & Staubesand (35) found *arteriolae rectae* of human kidneys coming directly from the plexus perivascularis of the large intrarenal vessels. These vessels were insufficient to maintain the medullary blood supply under normal conditions; but after interruption of renal arterial flow, a collateral circulation developed from ureteral and renal pelvic arteries through the plexus perivascularis to the renal medulla. Adebahr (37) has suggested that epithelioid cells found in the walls of the juxtamedullary vasa afferentia and efferentia may regulate the medullary blood flow.

RENAL CIRCULATION

Interest in renal circulation has been focused on three main subjects: autoregulation, participation of the kidney in general hemodynamic regulation with special reference to effects of vasoactive drugs, and renal medullary circulation. The third subject is discussed in the section on renal concentrating mechanisms.

Autoregulation.—Autoregulation is a phenomenon demonstrable not only in the renal circulation (38 to 42); recent findings in vascular beds of skeletal muscle shed new light on the problem of renal autoregulation and are therefore reviewed here. After sudden alteration of the perfusion pressure, skeletal muscle blood flow did not move immediately to a new steady state value but instead underwent a complex initial transient phase which bears a qualitative similarity to the results of similar experiments in the intestine (38), brain (42), and kidney (43 to 46). The imposition of a sudden increase in perfusion pressure caused a sudden augmentation of flow and dilatation of vessels. Since the return toward the original flow level occurred even though the increased internal pressure was maintained, it is concluded that active contraction of vascular smooth muscle occurred. In addition, the initial transient phase lasted for 1 to 2 min in resting muscle, but only 20 sec in contracting muscle, a contrast which points to a metabolic link in the reaction sequence. To explain these findings, Stainsby (41) offers the hypothesis that the vascular bed of muscle has a humorally or myogenically conditioned constrictor tone which is opposed by the action of vasodilating metabolites produced locally; the effective concentration of these metabolites is proportional to their rate of formation and inversely related to the local blood flow. Strong evidence for a similar myogenic origin of autoregulation in the kidney was found by Thurau & Kramer (43, 47). More recently Thurau & Wober (48) made direct measurements of renal capillary and proximal intratubular pressures in rats and found that these pressures remained unchanged in normal kidneys when the arterial blood pressure was varied within the autoregulation range, but increased parallel with arterial pressure when the vascular smooth musculature had been paralyzed by injection of papaverin. These data, and the observation of autoregulation of the GFR, point to the preglomerular renal arterioles as the site of regulatory vasomotion.

During perfusion of isolated kidneys, renal interstitial pressure increased with arterial pressure within the autoregulation range (44). This augmented interstitial pressure leads to an increased resistance in some intrarenal venous segments. Hinshaw (49) proposed that such a passive increase of the venous resistance is the fundamental cause of autoregulation, but the unusually low perfusion rates in his experiments indicate abnormal vasoconstriction. One therefore questions the viability of his preparation, and the applicability of his data to other situations in which flow rates are higher. Langston et al. (50), who previously found no autoregulation in normal kidneys perfused at unusually low flows, repeated their experiments with dogs rendered areflexic by total spinal anesthesia. They found, like others before them, a more or less marked autoregulation in a range of perfusion pressure between 80 and 200 mm Hg; the degree of renal autoregulation does not exceed that found in other organs. Finally, the isolated perfused frog kidney preparation autoregulated through an arterial pressure range between 20 to 40 mm Hg (51).

Responses of the renal circulation.—Infusion of less than 0.6 μg per kg per min of norepinephrine into dogs made areflexic by spinal anesthesia induced an increase in renal blood flow attributable to an increased arterial pressure (52). When perfusion pressure was maintained constant, renal vasoconstriction could be demonstrated with norepinephrine infusion rates as low as 0.1 μg per kg per min; this vasoconstriction overcame the effects of increasing arterial pressure when the infusion rate exceeded 0.6 μg per kg per min. The enormous sensitivity of the renal vascular bed to catecholamines was confirmed by Voudoukis & Boucek (54) who showed that the arteriogram of the renal vessels remained altered for more than 3 hr after the arterial pressure had returned to control levels following administration of catecholamines. Renal resistance increased more than femoral resistance following single injections of norepinephrine or angiotensin, indicating that direct humoral stimuli elicit a more intense reaction from the renal circulation (53). In contrast, chemoreceptor(anoxia)- and baroreceptor(common carotid occlusion)-mediated reflex activity had greater effects on femoral than on renal resistance. Increased intracranial pressure resulted in a strong renal vasoconstriction which was partly mediated through nervous stimuli, since chemical sympathectomy with bretylium reduced the renal constrictor response.

Several papers have compared the reactivity of the renal circulation with that of other vascular beds. Bleeding produced little change in the calculated renal resistance until more than 10 ml per kg had been removed; after withdrawal had exceeded 20 ml per kg, a sharp increase in renal resistance was observed (55). In contrast, the mesenteric and iliac resistance increased from the onset of hemorrhage. Reduction of cardiac output by orthostasis or by constriction of the pulmonary artery elicited smaller increases in renal resistance than in other areas (56). Similar vasomotor patterns, i.e., intense vasoconstriction in skeletal muscle beds and somewhat less vasoconstriction in the kidney were also observed after electrical stimulation of some hypothalamic areas (57). It is of further interest that the increase in renal resistance and decrease in blood flow observed after a bleeding of 15–30 ml per kg could be prevented by gastric administration of 20 ml per kg of isotonic saline 3 hr before the blood withdrawal, but not by the same volume of tap water (58). Also, in dogs made hyperthermic by increased environmental temperature, the kidneys initially did not play a role in the maintenance of arterial pressure, as indicated by renal resistances lower than control values. Later, with decreasing blood pressure, intrarenal resistance rose (59). Infusion of plasma expanders at a rate of 3 to 9 ml per min per kg led to a 20 per cent increase of renal plasma flow in normal subjects and in patients (60). While this effect could conceivably have come from decreased blood viscosity, the authors held it to be more likely a result of vasodilatation. This conclusion is supported by Dieter (51), who has shown that the vascular resistance of the innervated but isolated perfused frog kidney varies inversely with the degree of filling of heart and cerebral vessels.

Renal hypoxia has been widely accepted as the cause of tubular damage during reduced blood flow. However, Munck *et al.* (61) found that 80 per cent cortical oxygen saturation was maintained during hemorrhagic shock until mean arterial blood pressure fell below 60 mm Hg, while even with arterial pressures as low as 40 mm Hg, oxygen saturation remained in the range 40–75 per cent. These data cast serious doubt on the theory that acute tubular necrosis following hemorrhagic shock is caused by hypoxia.

CONCENTRATION AND DILUTION OF THE URINE

The mechanisms involved in the formation of dilute and concentrated urine have been reviewed by Berliner (62). Kuhn, who originally proposed that the urine concentration might result from the operation of a counter-current system, extended his previous theoretical considerations to include a model, composed of many loops of different lengths, in which the inflow and outflow channels were not in direct contact with each other (63). Gottschalk and co-workers (64) continued their micropuncture studies on the tubules in the hamster papilla and found that twice the Na^+ concentration accounts for 70 per cent of the osmolality of the Henle's loop fluid, while urea comprises an additional 10 to 20 per cent. In plasma taken from capillaries at the tip of the papilla, Na^+ concentration is approximately the same as in fluid from Henle's loop (65), while the accompanying anion was shown to be Cl^- exclusively. In the collecting duct, however, where the osmolality of the tubular urine is identical to that found in fluid from adjacent Henle's loops, more than 50 per cent of the solute present is urea, and the Na^+ fraction is small and variable.

The important question of the active participation in the concentrating process of the thin ascending limb of loops of Henle located in the inner medulla was studied with a variety of experimental techniques. Schmidt-Nielsen & O'Dell (66) measured tissue Na^+ concentrations at different levels in the medulla and found a pronounced increase through the inner zone to the tip of the papilla. They contend that active Na^+ transport, which has been demonstrated in the thick ascending limb of Henle's loop, also occurs in a similar manner in the thin ascending limb. Further evidence for this has been furnished by micropuncture studies (64), in which a progressive increase in osmolality towards the tip of the papilla was found in fluid collected from the thin limb of Henle's loop. Although the concept of active Na^+ transport in the inner zone loops of Henle may be compatible with the original Kuhn-Wirz hypothesis, direct experimental verification of such transport in elec-trochemical terms, already given for the proximal and distal tubules and collecting ducts, is still lacking. If it is found that the thin limbs do not perform active transport, the cause for longitudinal osmotic and NaCl gradients in the inner medullary zone must be sought in other mechanisms. some of which may be briefly described. For example, from theoretical con-siderations it is conceivable that hydrostatic pressure differences between the two loops of Henle might operate in the manner originally described by Hargitay & Kuhn (67). These authors calculated that hydrostatic pressures of several hundred mm Hg would be necessary to produce the osmolalities usually measured in concentrated urine. However, it is fairly evident that the major part of the osmolality increase in the outer zone of the medulla can be attributed to active transport of NaCl from the thick ascending limbs of Henle's loops. Thus, if only the inner medulla is considered, the equations of Hargitay & Kuhn can show that physiological pressures are sufficient to produce a considerable fraction of the further increase in osmolality and NaCl concentration found in this region. A further possibility for inner zone gradient production arises from the observation that the collecting ducts accomplish active net solute reabsorption. Reabsorption of Na^+ from these structures has been demonstrated, and it has also been calculated that a considerable fraction of this reabsorbed Na^+ is accompanied by Cl^-, rather than being exchanged for other cations (68). It has been argued that such NaCl reabsorption from the collecting ducts would not serve to increase medullary interstitial osmolality since water would be expected to accompany the transported solute, but this conclusion it not warranted since it can be shown from irreversible thermodynamics that active solute transport with codiffusion of water can give rise to distinct reabsorbate anisotonicity. In fact, reasonable models of collecting duct behavior can be described from which the necessary concentration effects are obtainable, but such formulations await the availability of the necessary data for proper evaluation. Finally, it is to be expected that concentration effects arising from several sources could complement one another, so that no single mechanism need be responsible for the production of the entire gradient in the medulla.

Certain discrepancies have appeared with respect to the increase in protein concentration in vasa recta plasma. Gottschalk *et al.* (69) and Thurau *et al.* (70) injected I^{131}-labeled human albumin and found the radioactivity of collected vasa recta plasma to be as high as three times that of systemic plasma. Ullrich *et al.* (65), using two different chemical methods, found the maximum plasma protein ratio (vasa recta: systemic plasma) to be 1.4, with a mean of 1.26. The finding that as much as 4 per cent of the albumin passing through the kidney is broken down (71), when considered with the observation that very steep longitudinal gradients for inorganic I^{131} can be established in the renal papilla (72, 73, 74), indicates that some of the measured radioactivity in vasa recta plasma might be accounted for by inorganic I^{131}. This difference in experimental results urgently requires clarification, since a knowledge of plasma protein concentration of vasa recta plasma is necessary for the evaluation of water and electrolyte fluxes in the vascular countercurrent system.

Countercurrent diffusion influences the distribution of all substances metabolized in the kidney medulla. A mathematical treatment of countercurrent diffusion in a simplified system has been developed by Günzler (75), and is pertinent to the experimental data available for O_2 (76, 77, 78), glucose, and lactic acid (79). Ruiz-Guinazu *et al.* (79) used this approach and questioned whether glycolysis is the principal source of energy in the inner medulla, as previously postulated.

Considerable interest has been expressed in the relationships between flow in the vasa recta and the maintenance of longitudinal osmotic gradients in the renal medulla. In the model of Günzler (75), the concentration of a given solute at the bend of the loop was seen to vary inversely with a power function of the flow through the loop system. Thus it could be predicted that in the presence of increased vasa recta flow, all other factors being equal, urine osmolality should decrease. That this conclusion is correct was shown by Thurau & Deetjen (80) who took advantage of the fact that the medullary circulation does not autoregulate and found that urine osmolality varied inversely with arterial blood pressure in the autoregulation range while GFR remained constant. Plasma skimming in the kidney has been discussed considerably since the papers of Pappenheimer & Kinter (81). Until recently, no compelling evidence for such a process in the cortex was available. The recent finding of Ulfendahl (82), however, that the hematocrit of blood taken from a subcapsular vein of cat kidneys was 8 to 10 per cent greater than the systemic blood hematocrit indicates at least minimal cortical cell separation. However, the low hematocrit (40 to 60 per cent of the systemic value) of blood in the renal papilla points to the operation of a much more efficient cell separation mechanism in the renal medulla (83, 84). Medullary cell separation certainly restricts the availability of oxygen in this tissue and may act to decrease blood viscosity. To date, however, no significance can be assigned to such cortical cell separation as may occur.

In order to evaluate the behavior of the medullary countercurrent system during water diuresis, Gottschalk *et al.* (85) punctured Henle's loops and vasa recta of hamsters with diabetes insipidus and found that both fluids had identical osmolalities amounting to about 500 mosm per kg H_2O, while in the adjacent collecting ducts the tubular urine osmolality was less than 100 mosm per kg H_2O. In other experiments (86), the composition of tissue slices from the medulla of dogs undergoing a water diuresis was analyzed and yielded essentially the same result as the micropuncture work. It may thus be concluded that operation of the countercurrent system as such is not involved in the dilution process. In a micropuncture study, Gertz *et al.* (87) observed that in water diuresis the inulin TF:P ratio in the distal convolution was the same as in antidiuretic rats, which indicates that solute and water transport in more proximal segments of the nephron is not materially affected by the diuretic state of the animal, and that changes in tubular characteristics necessary for diminution of water reabsorption occur more distally. The production and maintenance of a hypotonic fluid are functions of the distal nephron (including collecting duct and thick ascending limb), and are brought about by reabsorption of solutes from the tubular lumen while outward movement of water is simultaneously impeded. It is of interest that species lacking distal tubules, e.g., marine fishes, cannot produce a hypotonic urine (88).

The impaired concentrating ability caused by K^+ depletion has been extensively investigated. Rubini (89) observed a total loss of concentrating ability in man after three weeks of K^+ depletion. Vasopressin resistance, an additional feature of this syndrome noted also by other investigators (90), did not always closely parallel the development of the concentrating defect. Maximal water reabsorption during osmotic diuresis ($T_{M C H_2 O}$) fell abruptly as K^+ was withdrawn from the diet, while the minimum osmolality which could be achieved during water diuresis was altered only after prolonged depletion.

In an electron-microscopic study of tubules from K^+-depleted rats, MacDonald et al. (91) found that in the early stages of the syndrome the basement membrane of the thin segment of the loop of Henle and of the pars recta of the proximal tubule becomes thicker and fibrillar in appearance. In later stages granulation, hyperplasia, and degeneration of the cells of the collecting duct were seen. Sialic acid-containing and neutral mucopolysaccharides found in the granules were thought to enter the collecting duct cells from the tubular fluid after having been filtered from the plasma at the glomerulus (92). The functional and morphological lesions of K^+ depletion are as complex as the countercurrent system itself, and sufficient information is not yet available to permit confident deductions about the interactions involved.

The findings in Mg^{++}-deficient rats are even more complex and controversial. Smith et al. (93) found a significant reduction of maximal urinary concentration in Mg^{++} depletion, while Manitius & Epstein (94) found that maximum urinary concentration was not decreased by Mg^{++} depletion despite a concomitant K^+ depletion.

The maximal concentrating ability in response to exogenous Pituitrin decreased after the third day of forced water diuresis (95), possibly, the authors suggest, because of the development by the tubules of a relative refractoriness to ADH. This may have its structural equivalent in the observation of MacDonald et al. (91) that the basement membrane of the thin segment of the loop of Henle becomes thicker in hydrated animals.

In a study which confirmed earlier findings (96), Herms, Abbrecht & Malvin (97) have shown that the low urine osmolality of dogs in mannitol diuresis increased progressively with a reduction of GFR, the maximum being attained when GFR was 30 per cent of the control level. With further reduction of GFR, the urine osmolality decreased again, while at any given level of GFR, simultaneous reduction of RPF led to a decrease in urine osmolality; a change in Na load had no influence on these correlations (114). The authors conclude that changes in renal plasma flow have an effect on urine osmolality independent of glomerular filtration rate.

Antidiuretic Hormone

Many recent investigations have sought a better understanding of the fundamental mechanisms underlying neurohypophyseal hormonal influences on water permeability and sodium transport. Direct measurements with renal tubules have not yet been made, and reference is therefore made to pertinent findings in other organ systems (98).

Effects of antidiuretic hormone have been found in many tissues. In addition to producing an augmentation of the water permeability of toad skin (99) and toad bladder (100, 101, 102), the hormone increases water reabsorption through the gut (103), and leads to an increased water content of rat gastrocnemius (104) and kidney mitochondria (105). Hays & Leaf (106, 107) measured the activation energy for diffusion of tritiated water through the toad bladder and concluded that in the absence of ADH, membrane pore water exists in a highly structured state. Application of the hormone leads to increased pore size and reduction of the degree of water structuring, so that hydraulic flow now prevails when osmotic gradients are present. When viewed in the framework of this concept, the observation that the water permeability of the toad bladder can be influenced by the osmolality of test solutions is not surprising (108).

The increase of net transmembrane Na^+ transport after application of ADH is thought to be due to an increased Na^+ permeability of the mucosal barrier (109, 110, 111) which leads to an increased intracellular Na^+ concentration, as a result of which more Na^+ is made available to the transport mechanism located at the serosal side. Calcium antagonizes the action of ADH on Na^+ transport by reducing the Na^+ permeability of the mucosal barrier (109 to 112). In an excellent study Frazier *et al.* (109) have shown that the transfer of Na^+ across the mucosal surface does not occur by free diffusion alone, but involves considerable interaction with the barrier, since saturation kinetics for this process could be shown. In addition, the interesting findings of Orloff & Handler (112, 113) provide strong evidence that the action of ADH on the toad bladder is mediated through cyclic adenosine-3',5'-phosphate.

The renal actions of antidiuretic hormone.—The findings from work on frog skin and other anuran epithelia, skeletal muscle, and kidney mitochondria allow ample speculation about the natriuretic action of ADH (114). Because of the increase in Na^+ permeability, not only the active transport of Na^+ in one direction but also the passive Na^+ fluxes in one or both directions may be augmented by the action of ADH in presence of suitable concentration gradients. These considerations suggest that a passive influx of Na^+ down an electrochemical gradient from the renal medullary interstitium into the collecting duct urine could be responsible for the natriuretic action of ADH when administered during a water diuresis. This natriuretic response may be of such magnitude as to obscure the antidiuretic response, a relationship which is demonstrable in the rat when NaCl is infused simultaneously with administration of ADH, or simply by increasing the dose of ADH. Under these circumstances, a close correlation exists between Na^+ and water output (115, 116). This proposal is clearly not applicable to chronic experiments, where more complex interactions with other hormone systems are important (117).

With respect to the action of ADH on the tubules, Ginetzinsky (118, 119) has hypothesized that the hormone activates hyaluronidase which then breaks down hyaluronic acid located in the basement membrane of the distal tubule and collecting ducts and in the interstitium of the renal pyramids, with a consequent increase in water permeability of the tubular structures. It is further postulated that hyaluronidase is liberated by apocrine secretion from collecting duct cells (118); the hyaluronidase excreted in the urine represents the amount of enzyme not utilized in the tubular walls. Dicker & Eggleton (120) support these views with the suggestion that after injection of vasopressin the concentration of hyaluronidase in the urine is quantitatively related to the degree of antidiuresis produced. Unfortunately, their data seem rather to indicate that hyaluronidase excretion is constant, and not influenced by the diuretic state. The marked increase of Ca^{++} excretion following vasopressin infusion is considered to result from liberation during the depolymerization of hyaluronic acid. In patients with diabetes insipidus no urinary excretion of hyaluronidase is observed (121), and, in further support of the Ginetzinsky hypothesis, stop-flow experiments indicated that the locus of secretion of hyaluronidase corresponds exactly to the distal site of maximum Na^+ reabsorption (122). Additionally, it was found that intraperitoneal injection of ascorbic acid or heparin, which are *in vitro* hyaluronidase inhibitors, led to increased urine flow (123). Not all evidence favors Ginetzinsky's proposal, since attempts to confirm the histological evidence of apocrine secretion have yielded conflicting results (118, 124, 125). However, that secretion products of tubular cells do appear in the urine was indicated by the finding that urinary uromucoid did not come from plasma but seemed rather to be a product of the tubular cells (126).

Čapek & Heller (127) studied the ontogenetic development of the concentrating mechanism in rats and puppies and found a gradual increase of the Na^+ concentration in the papillary tissue with the gradual lengthening of the loops of Henle. Although no antidiuretic activity in plasma is demonstrable in the early postnatal period, dehydration results in an increased Na^+ concentration gradient in the renal medulla (128). Ginetzinsky (119) found that the physiological and morphological characteristics of the hyaluronidase system appear only after the twentieth day of life in rats.

The release and breakdown of antidiuretic hormone.—The disappearance of H^3- or I^{131}-labeled arginine vasopressin from the plasma was studied in man and dogs (129); the half-value disappearance time is 2 to 7 min in both species. Using rat bioassay methods, Chaudhury *et al.* (130) found a half-value disappearance time of 3.4 min in monkeys, a value not changed by severe liver damage. Furthermore, data from cirrhotic patients contradict the view that the breakdown of ADH in patients with liver damage is low and that, as a consequence thereof, the plasma ADH is high.

Additional data dealing with the ontogenetic appearance of ADH were obtained by the group in Prague (131, 132). Before birth, dog fetuses have the same high plasma ADH level as their mothers. At birth, plasma ADH activity in the puppy drops to zero, but reappears after the tenth neonatal day in normally hydrated animals. However, puppies younger than ten days respond to dehydration with a transient increase of plasma ADH to measurable levels and a decreased ADH content of the posterior pituitary. In dogs older than ten days, dehydration leads not only to an increased plasma ADH level but also to an increased ADH content of the posterior pituitary. Children can also respond to an osmotic stress before the age of five months, at which time plasma ADH activity normally becomes demonstrable.

The site of secretion of ADH, the related neuronal interconnections in the hypothalamic nuclei, and procedures which induce liberation of ADH are dealt with in another review in this volume. However, of particular interest to renal physiologists are the excellent studies of Brooks et al. (133) who used extracellularly placed microelectrodes to record the discharge pattterns of neurons within or near the supraoptic nuclei. Intracarotid injection of isotonic saline had no effect on neuron discharge, but addition of low concentrations of glucose to the saline augmented neuron firing, as did hypertonic NaCl. Distilled water injection generally reduced neuron activity, while stimulation of muscular or vagal efferents produced either inhibition or augmentation of supraoptic nucleus neuron activity. The recorded activity changes during these different procedures coincide with their known effects on ADH secretion.

ELECTROLYTE TRANSPORT

The handling of electrolytes by the proximal tubule was investigated by evaluation of the influence of various ionic substitutions on the transtubular electric profile in *Necturus maculosus* (134, 135, 136). Proceeding from these data, and the finding that the K^+ concentration in the tubular fluid is 1.8 times that of the interstitial fluid (137), Giebisch (134) and Whittembury et al. (136) proposed the following model to describe the more important events in the transport of alkali metal ions and Cl^- across this epithelium. An active Na^+ transport mechanism, located at the peritubular surface of the tubular cell, effects the movement of Na^+ from the cell into the adjacent interstitium in exchange for K^+ which is transported into the cell. The membrane potential at the peritubular surface is 70 mv, cell negative, and at the luminal surface, 50 mv, cell negative, with a net transtubular potential of 20 mv, lumen negative. Both membrane potentials are thought to be chiefly K^+ diffusion potentials, modified to slight but differing extents by Na^+ diffusion. Reabsorptive Cl^- movement is thought to be passive, along electrochemical gradients established by operations on the cations.

For several reasons, however, this model is not entirely applicable to the proximal tubule of the rat. Thus, after perfusion of single nephrons with a solution of 100 mM NaCl and 100 mM raffinose, a very slowly permeating trisaccharide, net water flux from this injected fluid column is negligible and ions for which no active transport mechanisms exist should be expected to come rapidly into thermodynamic equilibrium with the interstitium. In this state the transtubular potential remains 20 mv, lumen negative. If Cl^- were transported only passively, $[Cl^-]_{lumen}/[Cl^-]_{plasma}$ should become 0.5, but it remains 1.0 (138). Similarly, if both membrane potentials were simply K^+ diffusion potentials, $[K^+]_{lumen}/[K^+]_{plasma}$ should become 2.0; instead it is 0.9

(139). An additional feature of the *Necturus* model which conflicts with data from the rat is that Na^+ simply diffuses from the lumen into the cell down an electrochemical gradient. This suggestion implies that Na^+ should come into equilibrium across the luminal membrane during the raffinose experiments, a condition whose fulfillment would require either that the intracellular Na^+ concentration rise to several hundred meq per liter, in which case the condition of iso-osmolality could not be fulfilled, or that the cell potential lie within 30 mv of the interstitium, which it does not. From the available data, then, it would appear that (a) the reabsorption of Cl^- normally found under free flow conditions is accomplished against an active movement of Cl^- into the lumen, (b) active transport of K^+ out of the lumen displaces K^+ from its equilibrium position so that it cannot yet be said with certainty that the two cell membranes are K^+ electrodes, and (c) the movement of Na^+ across the luminal membrane is influenced by an active mechanism operating at that membrane.

Transtubular water and NaCl fluxes as a function of the Na^+ concentration of tubular fluid were measured with different methods by Windhager & Giebisch (140) and by Gertz (141). The luminal Na^+ concentration at which the sum of all active and passive Na^+ fluxes is zero was found to be 88 meq per liter by the former (140) and 104 meq per liter by the latter (138, 141). The question arises, however, whether at a given intraluminal Na^+ concentration the net Na^+ flux density is the same under free-flow and stop-flow conditions, since the injection of paraffin oil during the stop-flow perfusion experiments produced an increase of the inner tubular diameter from the normal 16 μ (142) to 30 μ. The calculations of Gertz do indicate that net Na^+ flux per unit luminal surface area is constant at a given Na^+ concentration, a conclusion with important implications for the concept of glomerulotubular balance.

Windhager & Giebisch (140, 143) measured the short-circuit current across the proximal tubular epithelium. When expressed as net univalent ion transport, their values exceed by 38 per cent net Na^+ flux measured under non-short-circuited conditions. This difference may be attributed to at least three factors whose relative contribution cannot yet be assessed. These are: (a) from theoretical considerations (144), the rate of net Na^+ transport would be expected to be greater in the presence of the zero electrochemical gradient prevailing in the short-circuit experiments than when the opposing potential is 20 mv; (b) the active transport of anions into the lumen (138) would enhance the short-circuit current oriented in the opposite direction; and (c) active transport of K^+ in the reabsorptive direction would be expected to contribute to the short circuit current.

Using micropuncture methods, Giebisch *et al.* (145) found that the percentages of filtered Na^+ and water reabsorbed by the proximal tubule remain constant when plasma Na^+ concentration was increased by infusion of 4 or 8 per cent NaCl. From these data it is concluded that net proximal NaCl reabsorption is increased when higher plasma concentrations lead to increased filtered loads of Na^+; no transfer maximum for Na^+ in the proximal tubule could be observed. A fundamental problem here is the observed failure of the proximal tubule to achieve complete reabsorption of the glomerular filtrate when GFR is diminished by more than 50 per cent. Tentative answers to this question have invoked a humoral mechanism (146) or simple distention of the tubules (141), but at present no clear explanation is available. If, therefore, we are not in a position to describe such fundamental processes as the regulation of proximal Na^+ and water reabsorption, speculations about the influence of the filtered load on the countercurrent system and on distal tubular and collecting duct Na^+ reabsorption must be viewed with the strongest reservations.

Gertz (141) and Kashgarian & Stöckle (138) have also applied their microperfusion techniques to the distal tubule. With an initial tubular fluid NaCl concentration of 150 mmol per liter, the net transfer of NaCl proceeded at only one third of the rate found in the proximal tubule. The limiting internal Na^+ concentration at which net transport is zero was found to be in the range of 30 meq per liter for the distal tubule. The free-flow ratio $[K^+]_{lumen}/[K^+]_{plasma}$ along the length of the distal tubule was found to be 0.7, which indicates that this epithelium effects a reabsorption of K^+ against an electrochemical gradient and that more distal sites in the nephron are responsible for secretion (139).

Opinion differs as to the mechanism of Cl^- transport across the distal tubular epithelium. In normal rats, Kashgarian & Stöckle (138) measured the Cl^- concentration in stop-flow microperfusates from the distal tubule. As noted above, this technique permits an evaluation of the electrochemical gradient when net flux approximates zero. It was found that the Cl^- concentration under these conditions was only occasionally different from the value which would be expected if Cl^- were transported passively. Rector & Clapp (147) measured the Cl^- concentration in distal tubular fluid collected during free flow from normal and salt-depleted rats undergoing a strong sodium sulfate diuresis, and found a Cl^- concentration ratio smaller than would be expected if Cl^- were transported passively. These data suggested an active mechanism which transports Cl^- out of the lumen. A possible approach to the resolution of this apparent discrepancy is suggested from the experimental designs derived by Schlögl (144) from thermodynamic considerations. In this treatment, unidirectional flux ratios are expressed as functions of the electrochemical gradient, which permits evaluation of single file or exchange diffusion interactions, solvent drag effects are considered, and a more rigid definition of the forces acting to transport a given ion species is thus possible.

Clapp *et al.* (148) have shown that the proximal transtubular potential remained uninfluenced by the infusion of Na^+ salts, the anions of which have different mobilities in the membranes, whereas the distal transtubular potential increased considerably after the infusion of sodium sulfate or sodium ferricyanide. Measurements of transtubular potentials are available from several laboratories; the agreement of the measured proximal values is good, but Clapp *et al.* (148) have found somewhat higher values for the distal tubule than have others (138, 149).

Hierholzer (150, 151) used microcatheterization methods in golden hamsters infused with KCl, Na₂SO₄, or acetazolamide, and found that K⁺ was secreted into collecting ducts of the inner medulla. He inferred that the upper third of the collecting duct which is not accessible to microcatheterization is also capable of K⁺ secretion, and confirmed that urine acidification occurs in more proximal segments of the nephron as well as in the terminal collecting ducts.

The distal nephron is the domain of the stop-flow experiment because good indications about electrolyte transport in this area can be obtained, and most other studies dealing with K⁺ secretion have utilized this technique. Vander's (152) results indicate that K⁺ reabsorption occurs in more proximal segments of the distal nephron; this seems to coincide with the K⁺ reabsorption site found by Marsh & Rumrich (139) in the distal convolute. More distal areas of stop-flow patterns indicate K⁺ secretion, but the distal K⁺ maximum disappears during "slow flow", since fluid with a reduced Na⁺ concentration is thus brought into contact with the K⁺-secreting site. The distal K⁺ maximum also disappears after prolonged stop flow, which is probably analogous to the slow-flow experiment since it can be shown that mannitol penetrates the tubular epithelium and is therefore able to diffuse out of the tubule down a concentration gradient (141). This mannitol escape should result in a continuous slow movement of the "stopped flow" fluid column. The disappearance of the distal K⁺ maximum as described, and the prevention of this disappearance by infusion of 10 per cent NaCl, supports the hypothesis that K⁺ secretion in the collecting duct is Na⁺ dependent. Sullivan (153) reached a similar conclusion from his observation of a correlation between the magnitude of the K⁺ maximum and the Na⁺ concentration at the same location. He also found that NaCl infusion increased the magnitude of the distal K⁺ minimum which is located more proximally. Sodium sulfate infusion shifted the K⁺ maximum to a more proximal location, which was tentatively attributed to the increased transtubular potential (148) to be expected under such circumstances, rather than to an increased Na⁺ concentration. However, the assumption that sulfate concentrations in the tubule remain the same under stop-flow and free-flow conditions should be experimentally verified.

Toussaint & Vereerstraeten (154) showed that K⁺ secretion increases proportionally with increasing plasma concentration. No K⁺ was excreted below a plasma level of 2 meq per liter. Although K⁺ excretion parallels increases and decreases in plasma concentrations, it does not follow that the filtered K⁺ is responsible for the observed changes in excretion; much evidence indicates that intracellular K⁺ concentrations of tubular cells are more likely responsible. Potassium excretion was augmented by increase of blood pH. The authors discuss this finding in connection with the well-known observation that migration of K^+ into the cells of the body as a whole increases markedly from acidosis to alkalosis; this again implies that tubular K^+ secretion is dependent upon intracellular K^+ concentration in the tubular cells. Similarly, infusion of NH_4^+ salts can inhibit K^+ secretion, presumably by diminishing intracellular K^+ concentration (155). That NH_4^+ can replace intracellular K^+ has been shown in kidney slices and erythrocytes (156).

Distal reabsorption of Na^+ is indicated by the presence of low Na^+ concentrations, approching zero, in distal specimens from stop-flow experiments (157). Adrenalectomy, administration of the aldosterone-inhibiting agent spirolactone, or administration of ouabain leads to significant increases of Na^+ concentration in the distal minimum. Goldsmith *et al.* (158) observed that during mannitol diuresis the Na^+ excretion in urine from dogs made acutely hyponatremic did not differ from that of normal dogs, while animals which had been chronically hyponatremic excreted much less Na^+. The authors suggest that chronic hyponatremia has a direct influence on the Na^+ transport mechanism, which is not simply an effect of the diminished filtered load of Na^+. However, the location at which the regulation of Na^+ excretion occurs is uncertain. The authors conclude that their observation was due largely to increased proximal Na^+ reabsorption, and exclude the participation of more distal areas because K^+ excretion was not increased. As mentioned above, however, significant Cl^- reabsorption may also occur in distal areas, either in the distal tubule, as suggested by the authors themselves (148), or in the collecting ducts (66), so that augmented Na^+ reabsorption in distal segments not involving cation exchange mechanisms need not be excluded. As noted elsewhere in this review, the maintenance of Na^+ and Cl^- concentration gradients across the collecting ducts is subject to the operation of many variables which influences the composition of the interstitium as well as the transport capacity of the epithelium itself. In fact, compelling evidence that the collecting ducts can be made to vary their ion transport functions is available, while direct evidence for such variability in the proximal tubules has yet to be advanced, and it is the reviewers' opinion that it is in the collecting ducts that most, if not all, of the final regulation of Na^+ excretion is accomplished.

Renal mechanisms of calcium, magnesium, and phosphate excretion.— Experiments by Walser (159) showed that in the absence of hypocalcemia, the renal tubules operated to maintain a constant ratio of Na^+ to ionized Ca^{++} in the tubular fluid. Micropuncture experiments by Lassiter *et al.* (160) provided direct confirmation. Calcium excretion is also modified by the presence of complexing anions which determines the excretion of additional Ca in bound form. The clearances of [85]Sr and Mg^{++} not only parallel Ca^{++} clearance but exceed it (161, 162). If due account is taken of changes in alkali-earth metal excretion induced by complexing anions, or in Na^+ excretion induced by mineralocorticoids, the above data seem best explained by the hypothesis that alkali-earth metal ions share a common reabsorptive transport mechanism linked to Na^+ transport. In the reviewers' opinion, K^+

should also be included in this group at least insofar as its reabsorption is concerned.

The excretion pattern of a single injected dose of ^{24}Mg, in contrast to that of Ca^{++}, is similar to the pattern of simultaneously injected creatinine, and it is concluded that the greatest fraction of excreted ^{24}Mg enters the tubule at the glomerulus and not through the tubular cell (163). Robinson & Portwood (164) reached the same conclusion from their results with unilateral portal vein infusion of ^{24}Mg in chickens which did not lead to increased unilateral ^{24}Mg excretion. It may therefore be concluded that Mg^{++} excretion is the result of glomerular filtration and tubular reabsorption, but of neither secretion nor significant unidirectional transtubular fluxes. However, care should be taken in interpretation of experiments where transient movements of labeled Mg or PO_4 are used as indicators of tubular permeability since the relatively large cellular pool of these ions may act to trap the tracer. As with Ca^{++}, Mg^{++} excretion is influenced by the presence of complexing agents in the tubular urine, which would explain the parallel increase of Mg^{++} excretion with lactate excretion following administration of alcohol (165).

Much said here regarding the transtubular movement of Mg^{++} may also apply to inorganic phosphate. Bronner & Thompson (163) have shown that the excretion pattern of a single injected dose of $^{32}PO_4$ into the renal artery is congruent with the excretion pattern of simultaneously injected creatinine. Furthermore, Handler (166) failed, despite vigorous attempts, to elicit net phosphate secretion; his manipulations included loading with inorganic phosphate, infusions of PAH, mannitol, or glucose, and parathyroid extract administration. Thus unequivocal evidence of net phosphate secretion in mammals is not yet available. Nevertheless, Carrasquer & Brodsky (167) continued their measurements of phosphate and creatinine transients and found that the calculated phosphate secretion previously reported was critically pH dependent. Since secretion was demonstrable following transient injection of NaH_2PO_4 in the presence of systemic acidosis induced by NaH_2PO_4 loading, the authors suggest that the secretory flux of inorganic phosphate indicates transport of $H_2PO_4^-$ from interstitium to lumen, but this conclusion conflicts with other findings. In experiments with chickens in which net tubular secretion of phosphate was unequivocally shown (168), unilateral renal portal vein infusion of phosphate produced equal bilateral increases of renal phosphate excretion; this indicates that inorganic phosphate did not penetrate the peritubular membrane as such. The findings of Bronner & Thompson (163) suggest that mammalian tubules are similar in this respect.

Parathyroid hormone and renal handling of calcium.—In the past year a small number of papers in this general area have appeared, of possible interest to renal physiologists. With respect to Ca^{++}, the effects of parathyroid hormone appear not to be restricted to bone-mobilizing activity. Widrow & Levinsky (169) observed a striking decrease of Ca^{++} excretion following parathyroid hormone administration, despite a simultaneous increase in filtered Ca^{++}. Direct infusion of blood with a high Ca^{++} concentration into the arterial supply of the parathyroid gland led to a depression of plasma Ca^{++} with a time course too rapid to be explained by simple inhibition of parathyroid hormone. The authors therefore suggested a second parathyroid hormone, named calcitonin (170), whose release is stimulated by hypercalcemia and whose end effect is the reduction of plasma Ca^{++}.

Electrolyte transport and metabolism at the cellular and subcellular level.— Ulrich (171) found that addition of ATP and an oxidizable substrate caused a significant decrease in the rate of K^+ loss from isolated mitochondria of kidney cortex, but much less decrease from mitochondria isolated from the renal medulla. Another interesting finding from this work is that K^+ seems to compete with H^+ for sites on the membrane, much as the intracellular K^+ and H^+ contents are inversely correlated, as indicated by accelerated K^+ loss from the mitochondria following increase in the acidity of the medium.

Kidney mitochondria take up sulfate from low concentrations to create concentration ratios of several hundredfold, a process similar to the uptake of sulfate by kidney cortex slices (172). Post & Rosenthal (173) extended their studies on the possible participation of a membrane ATPase in the Na^+-K^+-coupled active transport mechanisms to kidney preparations. The data indicated that posphorylation by this system, which leads to the formation of an intermediate high-energy phosphate compound, is Na^+ dependent, while the dephosphorylation step is K^+ dependent. Since ouabain stimulated the formation of this intermediate, it was concluded that the Na^+ transport-inhibiting activity of the glycoside operates elsewhere in the transport sequence. The data of Whittam & Wheeler (174) indicate that ouabain may interfere with the dephosphorylation step.

Sodium transport and oxygen consumption.—Deetjen & Kramer (175) studied the factors which determine renal O_2 consumption, and found that the consumption increment above a basal level of 0.44 meq per 100 g per min could be related linearly to the rate of Na^+ reabsorption. The quantitative relationship was 7 eq Na^+ reabsorbed per eq O_2 consumed, and remained constant despite large changes in the filtered load of Na^+ or reduction of Na^+ reabsorption by administration of mercurials or mannitol. Kiil *et al.* (176) confirmed these findings in dogs infused with hypertonic saline or 2 per cent glycine, but found that excessive loading with mannitol disturbed the relationship, since the expected decrease in O_2 consumption was not observed as the rate of Na^+ reabsorption was reduced. As discussed by the authors, however, these results, obtained after infusion of 20 per cent mannitol at 0.8–1.0 ml per kg per min, need not necessarily invalidate the concept that renal O_2 consumption is related primarily to Na^+ reabsorption.

Effects of ouabain on sodium excretion.—The ability of ouabain to inhibit Na^+ transport was demonstrated in experiments with dogs *in vivo* (177, 178). A series of digitalis glycosides was found to inhibit Ca^{++} reabsorption to the same extent as Na^+ reabsorption, a result which fits well with what is known of the relationship between Na^+ and Ca^{++} reabsorption in mammals discussed above (179).

VOLUME REGULATION—ALDOSTERONE

Homeostasis of the extracellular fluid volume is achieved by the regulation of ingestion and output of water and NaCl. The findings of Gauer et al. (180) show that the state of filling of the low-pressure vascular system, and in particular of the left atrium, influences the urine output. Share (181) has now provided direct evidence that ADH is involved in this type of "volume regulation". Reduction of the extracellular fluid volume by peritoneal lavage with hypertonic solutions produced a fourfold increase in the blood titer of ADH within 20 min, while expansion of vascular volume by intravenous infusion of isotonic dextran solutions led to a 50 per cent reduction in the blood level of ADH. In connection with the role of ADH in volume regulation it is useful to note that, in addition to its water-conserving properties, ADH has a natriuretic effect which might point to a participation of this hormone in salt regulation.

The hormones which directly regulate Na^+ excretion seem more important in terms of volume regulation; this subject has been reviewed comprehensively by Davis (182, 183). Of this group, aldosterone and the factors governing its secretion and mode of action require the most detailed examination. The problem of control of aldosterone secretion consists in identifying the various components of the receptor-effector system. The first of two main hypotheses states that peripheral nervous receptors, possibly located in the upper arterial tree (184), serve as the afferent limb of a reflex arc whose effector is a neurohormone or a pineal hormone (185). The second hypothesis holds that a peripheral receptor effects the release of renin from the juxtaglomerular apparatus in the kidney. Operating through previously well-defined pathways, renin leads to the liberation of angiotensin which in turn stimulates aldosterone secretion (186 to 189). Experiments designed to differentiate between the two proposals have, in general, been made with classical endocrinological methods and have thus taken the form of attempts to interrupt the chain by which vena cava constriction, Na^+ depletion, or bleeding induces increased aldosterone secretion.

Evidence contradicting the theory that the afferent reflex arc for aldosterone secretion begins in the upper arterial tree was offered by Carpenter et al. (190). Neither denervation of the cervical carotid and aortic arch nor bilateral vagotomy and splanchnic nerve section could completely prevent Na^+ retention produced in dogs either by thoracic vena cava constriction or by bleeding. To the extent that any consistent pattern emerges from the presently available data, the brainstem apparently does not play a key role in the regulation of aldosterone secretion. Taylor & Farrell (185) repeated and extended earlier studies (191) and found that the induction of small lesions around the central gray substance in the rostral midbrain led to a reduced aldosterone secretion. However, certain other lesions, particularly those involving the habenulopineal complex, obscured the effects of the discrete rostral and brain lesions, even to the extent of producing increased steroidogenesis in some cases. Pinealectomy or destruction of the subcommissural organ was found by some authors to lead to decreased Na^+ excretion (192, 193), while another author obtained the diametrically opposed result from pinealectomy (194). Further evidence against the importance of any pineal-adrenal relationship is found in the observation that the weight and histological appearance of the adrenals were not altered by pinealectomy (195, 196). Perhaps the most compelling argument against the first hypothesis is the fact that complete midbrain transection, which interrupts transmission from lower neural afferents, failed to diminish the increased aldosterone secretion response to either acute blood loss or to chronic thoracic caval obstruction (197). Pinealectomy itself also failed in this respect (194). Finally, pinealectomy did not prevent the enlargement of the adrenal zona glomerulosa induced by a low-salt diet.

With the appearance of evidence arguing against the importance of a pineal-adrenal relationship, data have simultaneously been accumulated which underscore the essential role of the renin-angiotensin system. After laparatomy, anesthetized dogs showed high secretion rates of corticosterone, a response attributed to a stress-induced ACTH release which also stimulated aldosterone secretion. Hypophysectomy usually caused an 80 to 90 per cent fall in aldosterone production from the elevated level induced by this stress (198). When aldosterone secretion was stimulated by thoracic caval constriction, subsequent hypophysectomy led to a reduction of aldosterone output from 0.135 μg per min to 0.033 μg per min. After these dogs had been nephrectomized, aldosterone production fell in every case; the postnephrectomy mean secretion rate was 0.006 μg per min which is indeed very low (186). A similar striking decrease in aldosterone secretion followed nephrectomy in Na^+-depleted hypophysectomized dogs. Ganong & Mulrow obtained similar results (199); they found that aldosterone secretion following hemorrhage of hypophysectomized dogs increased from 0.011 to 0.019 μg per min, but that this increase could be prevented by prior nephrectomy. Both groups (186, 199) demonstrated that injection of saline extracts of kidneys produced a tenfold or greater increase of aldosterone secretion and a small increase of 17-hydroxycorticoid and corticosterone secretion. These findings are consistent with the hypothesis that a renal mechanism, probably the renin-angiotensin system, is chiefly responsible for the increase in aldosterone secretion following hemorrhage, Na^+ depletion, or vena cava constriction in hypophysectomized dogs.

In conscious dogs, an eight- to thirtyfold increase in aldosterone secretion occurred following thoracic caval constriction although no appreciable increase in ACTH output was found (200). These findings led to the suggestion that ACTH supports the synthesis of aldosterone at a very high level, while the humoral material from the kidney provides the immediate stimulus to aldosterone secretion in dogs with vena caval constriction. Davis *et al.* (188) and Mulrow *et al.* (189) tested extracts of dog kidneys and found that pressor activity was closely associated with aldosterone-stimulating activity. Both the extracts and synthetic angiotensin II stimulated aldosterone secretion in hypophysectomized nephrectomized dogs; a slight increase in corticosterone secretion was simultaneously observed. Administration of ACTH, in small doses, stimulated only 17-hydroxycorticoid and corticosterone production, but not aldosterone. Injection of angiotensin II into the arterial blood supplying the adrenal gland elicited a greater stimulation of aldosterone production than did infusion into the jugular vein. This strongly suggests that the aldosterone-stimulating factor in dog kidney is renin, which, by action on angiotensinogen, leads to the liberation of angiotensin I which in turn is hydrolyzed to yield angiotensin II (201). Kaplan & Bartter (202) concluded from studies on slices of adrenal cortex that both ACTH and angiotensin II can influence the reaction sequence of steroidogenesis at the level of cholesterol. Angiotensin II potentiated the effect of ACTH on corticosterone production (203, 204).

Procedures which influence the granulation and renin content of the juxta-glomerular cells.—Evidence that the site of renin formation within the kidney lies in the granules of the cells of the juxtaglomerular apparatus was obtained from a demonstration of the coupling of fluorescein-stained renin antiserum to the granules (205), and from bioassay of microdissected juxtaglomerular areas (206). Hypergranulation of the juxtaglomerular cells and a high renin content were found in animals which had been Na^+-depleted or placed on a Na^+-deficient diet (187, 205, 207 to 210), in dogs with thoracic caval constriction (188), or in hypophysectomized dogs undergoing aortic constriction above the renal arteries. All these procedures are known to increase aldosterone secretion. Furthermore, a parallelism between the granulation of the cells of the juxtaglomerular apparatus and the width of the zona glomerulosa could be shown (187). Conversely, a high-Na^+ diet (187, 211) or hypertension (187, 210, 211) led to a reduction of granularity and of renin content. Since an inverse relationship between renal renin content and mineralocorticoid level seems to exist (209, 211), the presence of a feedback mechanism is indicated, although the complex intermediate pathways require clarification.

Because the idea fits well into the current framework of hypotheses, it is tacitly assumed that the renin content or its histological equivalent, the granularity of the cells of the juxtaglomerular apparatus, is proportional to the secretory rate. It may be difficult or even impossible to measure the secretory rate of renin-angiotensin even when suitable methods are available (212, 213) because of the high renal blood flow and the small arteriovenous differences which would be predicted as a consequence thereof; Lever & Peart (214) have suggested that higher values might be found in renal lymph.

The question of a mechanism whereby Na^+ depletion or reduced perfusion pressure induces increased renin secretion can only be discussed tentatively. An interesting speculation is that the extracellular-intracellular Na^+

gradient of vascular smooth muscle may be important in conditioning renin secretion (207). This gradient probably is higher in animals fed a low-salt diet, and lower in the face of increased arterial pressure, but the data are inconclusive since no attempt has been made to measure the volume of extracellular fluid in the vessels which have been analyzed.

The historical interest in the renin-angiotensin system deserves mention because of the very extensive investigation of its participation in the pathogenesis of arterial hypertension which took place before the importance of this system for aldosterone regulation became apparent. Despite a vast bibliography dealing with the subject, the relationship of renin to this disease remains to be clarified (215, 216).

Angiotensin may possibly have a direct action on the tubules as well. Schröder (217) found a time course for the changes in urinary $Na^+:K^+$ ratio after infusion of angiotensin which was different from that observed after infusion of aldosterone; angiotensin induced an almost instantaneous change in this parameter, whereas aldosterone acted only after a latent period of one hour. Since this effect of angiotensin could be seen after administration of spirolactone, which blocks aldosterone activity at the tubular level, and after additional blockage of aldosterone synthesis by metapirone, a direct action of angiotensin on the tubules was postulated. However, angiotensin also increases the secretion of other steroids, as yet only incompletely defined, which may also be involved in the regulation of Na^+ metabolism (218).

Additional renal factors, not directly related to renin, seem to influence the formation of angiotensin, although the mechanisms are not clear. When added to plasma of nephrectomized rats, a given amount of renin resulted in the liberation of four times as much angiotension as that obtained by addition to normal rat plasma. Since a change in converting enzyme and angiotensinase concentration could be excluded, another factor is postulated which is thought to alter the equilibrium conditions in the reaction sequence leading to angiotensin formation (219).

Other factors influencing aldosterone secretion.—Laragh & Stoerck (220) had shown in 1957 that K^+ influenced the secretion rate of aldosterone. Gann *et al.* (221) observed an increase of aldosterone secretion only when K^+ was infused into the carotid artery. Urquhart *et al.* (222), however, produced an increase of both aldosterone and corticosterone secretion rates by increasing the plasma K^+ concentration *per se* or by infusion of KCl into the adrenals of hypophysectomized nephrectomized dogs. If K^+ stimulates aldosterone secretion by reducing the ratio $[K^+]_{cell}/[K^+]_{plasma}$, one can explain the observation by Koczorek *et al.* (223) of an increased aldosterone secretion stimulated by metabolic acidosis induced with NH_4Cl, since it is now well known that acidosis leads to a decreased, intracellular K^+ concentration by exchange of K^+ for H^+. The problems of measuring aldosterone secretion and factors influencing aldosterone secretion in man were reviewed by Mills (224) and by Wright (225).

End organ responses to aldosterone.—The net effects of aldosterone on the kidney have been fairly well defined. Present evidence indicates that the hormone acts chiefly distally, presumably at the site of final Na^+ reabsorption and K^+ secretion in the collecting ducts. Since aldosterone enhances the urine concentration in man to a small but definite extent, it is assumed that the hormone increases Na^+ reabsorption somewhere in the countercurrent system (226). In stop-flow experiments Greene & Wilde (227) have shown that the inhibition of distal Na^+ reabsorption by ouabain could be blocked by aldosterone. These data indicate that both agents act at a distal site, but do not exclude an additional action.

Luetscher *et al.* (228) compared the effects of *d*- and *l*-aldosterone on Na^+ and K^+ excretion by adrenalectomized rats and found only the *d*-isomer to be biologically active. The biological properties of aldosterone have been reviewed by Ross (229) and the extrarenal actions by Gross (230). According to French & Manery (231), the $K^+:Na^+$ ratios in serum, muscle, and kidney cortex increased following adrenalectomy, but were maintained at normal values by aldosterone administration. These findings have led to the belief that aldosterone influences Na^+ and K^+ distribution in general, rather than having a specific action on Na^+ reabsorption in the kidney. However, it is not clear whether the cellular Na^+ and water loss which follows adrenalectomy results from augmented renal Na^+ and water excretion alone or from the removal of a direct aldosterone action on cellular Na^+ transport in tissues generally. That the alterations following adrenalectomy are secondary to changes in renal Na^+ and water excretion can be argued from the findings of Streeten & Spach (232) who measured *in vitro* ^{24}Na fluxes in erythrocytes from adrenalectomized dogs. They found that aldosterone strikingly inhibited Na^+ movement into cells and led to a decreased intracellular Na^+ concentration. Inasmuch as the findings *in vitro* conflict with studies *in vivo*, it can be concluded that the changes measured *in vivo* result primarily from increased renal excretion.

The normal rate of aqueous humor formation induced by Na^+ transport across the ciliary epithelium seems to be at least partially dependent upon endogenous aldosterone, since aldosterone antagonists reduce its formation by 40 to 45 per cent (233). The response to adrenal hormones of birds which supplement renal salt excretion with nasal gland secretion is quite interesting. In Na^+-loaded domestic ducks, aldosterone injection leads to reduced renal excretion of Na^+, but increases extrarenal excretion. Thus it would appear that aldosterone enhances transcellular Na^+ transport in both the kidney and nasal gland (234). Normally, however, glucocorticoids seem to be primarily responsible for the increase in nasal gland salt excretion which follows salt loading. The latter procedure results in decreased aldosterone secretion and increased ACTH and glucocorticoid output in these birds, a response similar to that found in mammals (235). Furthermore, adrenalectomized birds could respond with nasal gland secretion to NaCl administration only after glucocorticoids had been given; aldosterone had no effect

(236). The glucocorticoids act only to increase extrarenal NaCl excretion without changing renal output, and thereby lead to an increased total salt excretion. Crabbé observed increased Na^+ transport across the toad bladder in the presence of aldosterone (237, 238). Bladders from toads which previously had had a high level of endogenous aldosterone, or to whom exogenous aldosterone had been administered a day before the bladder was tested, did not exhibit further augmentation of Na^+ transport from the hormone, however. Aldosterone did not disturb the Na^+ transport-stimulating effects of ADH.

To summarize these effects of aldosterone, it enhances transcellular Na^+ transport in the kidney, ciliary epithelium, nasal gland, and toad bladder. The effects of aldosterone on the Na^+ transport mechanism at the cell membrane of muscle and erythrocytes remain to be clarified. It is suggested that aldosterone inhibits Na^+ influx across the membrane at which the transport site is located, and thereby contributes to an increased transport efficiency. This hypothesis would also explain the ability of both aldosterone and ADH to stimulate toad bladder Na^+ transport independently and in concert, in that it is suggested that ADH increases mucosal entry of Na^+ which leads to increased availability of Na^+ to the transport mechanism at the serosal side, while aldosterone inhibits the back flux of Na^+ at the serosal side.

The consensus of the many papers dealing with the subject is that the key to the regulation of Na^+ homeostasis is aldosterone. That this conclusion may be in error is dramatically indicated by the recent study of Davis *et al.* (239), in which dogs were subjected to adrenalectomy with deoxycorticosterone maintenance, and to unilateral nephrectomy with transplantation of the second kidney to the neck. Under these conditions constriction of the vena cava induced Na^+ retention and ascites, both of which disappeared following removal of the caval constriction. These experiments point clearly to the operation of other humoral factors which induce the change in renal function.

THE EXCRETION OF ORGANIC COMPOUNDS

WEAK ELECTROLYTES

The investigation of the renal handling of weak electrolytes has proceeded from calculations of over-all tubular transport rates to more detailed considerations. In the last few years it has become increasingly apparent that not only active transport, with its dependence on metabolism and possibilities for competitive inhibition, but also passive diffusion processes, either simple or involving membrane interactions, may participate in the transtubular transport of weak electrolytes. Even simple diffusion is highly dependent on such factors as lipid solubility and pK of the compound, and on pH of the tubular fluid. As a rule the nonionic or nondissociated forms, and compounds with higher lipid solubility, diffuse more rapidly across renal epithelia.

Transmembrane flux may be enhanced in a number of ways. Coupled nonionic diffusion, in which a weak acid and weak base diffuse together, may increase transmembrane movement. An example of the last-named case which has recently been studied is the transfer of NH_4HCO_3 as CO_2 and NH_3 across the dog bladder (240). Passive transport with membrane interactions may have the characteristics of facilitated diffusion, in which the transmembrane transport down a concentration gradient is accelerated, or may take the form of exchange diffusion, in which both unidirectional fluxes of a molecular species are enhanced. Carrier models have frequently been used in an attempt to understand the operation of such mechanisms. Thus it has been suggested that in exchange diffusion a carrier molecule traverses the membrane more easily in combination with the transported ion than it can when uncombined, so that carriers are brought into position more frequently at a given side of the membrane for attachment with the ion species to be transported. Competition is possible at either side of membrane, i.e., for inward or outward transport, of which one may be against an electrochemical gradient. An attractive and simplifying hypothesis is that the exchange carrier is the carrier which mediates active uphill transport. Very good evidence for the operation of these hypothetical processes is presented by Kinter & Cline (241).

With such complexity it may be extremely difficult to obtain reliable information about transport mechanisms from standard clearance experiments. Nevertheless, helpful indications may be obtained if certain techniques are used, as discussed by Toretti *et al.* (242) who have shown that certain organic bases show competitive inhibition. Since mutual inhibition is demonstrable for both amine and onium compounds, it is inferred that both types of compound are secreted as charged particles by the same transport system. However, separate systems exist for both bases and acids as indicated by competition studies (243) and by the observation that the two systems develop independently in the fetal and newborn puppy (244). In studies designed to evaluate the pH dependence of mecamylamine excretion, the clearance during alkalosis, when most of the compound is in the nonionic state, was only 25 per cent of that found during acidosis (245). Furthermore, with stop-flow techniques it could be shown that, in the presence of an acid urine, tubular secretion of mecamylamine occurred in proximal areas of the nephron, whereas tubular reabsorption could be demonstrated distally when the urine was alkaline (246). The best unifying explanation for these data is that the organic bases are secreted in the proximal tubule and undergo a back diffusion in more distal segments. For bases totally dissociated at physiological pH's, e.g. N-1-methylnicotinamide, no dependence of excretion on urinary pH is demonstrable, while rate of urine flow is of considerable importance in conditioning excretion. Although, as noted, N-1-methylnicotinamide is largely dissociated, considerable reabsorption also occurs, presumably by back diffusion at a point distal to the secreting area (247). Clarification of the mechanism of the renal handling of choline is somewhat more difficult (248), since both secretion, which could be inhibited by cyanine 863, and reabsorption occurred in the same proximal segment. It is not altogether surprising, therefore, that the excretion of this substance was not influenced either by urinary pH changes or by urine flow changes, both of which presumably act on back diffusion at distal sites.

Weak acids are secreted in the proximal tubule and also undergo back diffusion, presumably nonionic, which is dependent on urine pH and lipid solubility of the compound (245 to 252). As with the dissociated bases, tubular excretion of p-aminohippuric acid is independent of urinary pH (253). Furthermore, PAH seems to have little tendency toward back diffusion. Certain weak acids, as for example N-methyl-pyridinium-2-aldoxine, are not blocked by probenecid, indicating that they are not secreted by the usual weak acid mechanisms. Since this compound contains a quarternary nitrogen, it is possible that the organic base-transporting system is responsible for the observed secretion. In fact, amphoteric behavior of this compound could underlie the observation of good tubular penetration at high pH and accumulation in acid urine (253). Despopoulos (254) has proposed a unifying hypothesis in an attempt to define the molecular structural similarities of organic acids actively transported by the kidney. All compounds transported by the hippurate system contain an unsaturated oxygen group $(C:O$ or $S:O)$ in addition to a carboxylic or sulfonic acid group. Sulfonamides are compatible with this scheme, since in such compounds N and O have similar electron negativities.

Amino acids.—The problem of renal amino acid excretion has received renewed attention. As pointed out by Webber *et al.* (255), the infusion of a single amino acid may influence both the plasma level and transport rate of a number of other amino acids. For this reason conclusions about transport maxima and mutual inhibition which were derived from measurements of total urinary α-amino nitrogen deserve re-examination. As other tissues do, kidney slices take up amino acids from the medium against chemical gradients (256, 257, 258). This uptake could be inhibited by anaerobic conditions, by cyanide and by dinitrophenol. Mutual inhibition of arginine and lysine reabsorption was also observed with clearance methods (259); specificity of the shared mechanism for these two amino acids is suggested by the lack of inhibition by other amino acids tested. Stop-flow experiments have shown that the three dibasic amino acids have congruent reabsorption minima in the same area as the PAH secretory maximum, while the reabsorption minima of other amino acids tested (histidine, glycine, and aspartic and glutamic acids) were found more distally (260). In clearance experiments with dogs, in which the excretion of glycine, histidine, glutamic acid, lysine, leucine, arginine, and creatine were studied, a reabsorptive Tm could be demonstrated only for arginine (259, 261). The data suggest that passive back diffusion supplements the active transport mechanism so that there is nearly complete reabsorption of the amino acids even at excessively high plasma concentrations.

In rat kidney slices cystine did not share the transport mechanism common to the basic amino acids (258). This finding is in agreement with the suggestion of Frimpter *et al.* (262) that in cystinuria the excretion of the basic amino acids (lysine, arginine, and ornithine), together with cystine, is not due to a simple block of a common tubular reabsorption mechanism but rather to a metabolic defect which causes large cellular and intraluminal cystine concentrations with secondarily augmented excretion of the basic amino acids. L-Tyrosine and its monosubstituted (3-I-; 3-NH$_2$-*o*-methyl) derivatives were reabsorbed by the renal tubules, while several disubstituted derivatives were secreted into the tubular lumen against a concentration gradient. This secretion could compete effectively with the tubular transport of PAH and could be inhibited by probenecid (263). It was also shown that the disubstituted compounds have a reabsorptive flux, which presumably takes the form of a back diffusion, since it is augmented when the urine is acid. In addition, triiodothyronine and thyroxine depressed PAH uptake by kidney slices which indicates competition in the organic acid transport system (264).

The entire spectrum of complex interactions involved in the renal handling of weak electrolytes appears in the data relating to uric acid excretion. Stop-flow patterns presented by Yü *et al.* (265) indicate proximal secretion with U:P's as high as two in the Dalmatian coach hound, and of proximal reabsorption (which could have been passive) in the mongrel dog. Distal secretion of uric acid is suggested although not proved by the data, since distal stop-flow concentrations do not exceed the free-flow values appreciably. However, even in mongrel dogs tubular secretion of uric acid, indicated by a uric acid clearance ratio greater than 1.0, was observed in the presence of osmotic diuresis and increased plasma uric acid concentration (266). Rapid infusion of uric acid in man (normals and patients with gout) led to a flattening of the reabsorption curve at higher levels, but no uric acid reabsorptive *Tm* could be clearly demonstrated (267). Inhibition of secretion may explain the finding that some compounds, such as salicylate (268), chlorothiazide (269, 270), lactate (271), acetazolamide (272), and pyrazinamide (265), when present in low concentrations, diminish uric acid excretion. The mechanism of this inhibition may also be related to complex metabolic interactions (272). This problem is made somewhat more complicated, however, by the observation that high doses of certain of these compounds (salicylate, chlorothiazide, lactate) enhance uric acid excretion, as does probenecid (273). These dose-dependent relationships were also seen with another system by Kinter & Cline (241) who found that PAH at low levels enhanced the efflux of iodopyracet from kidney slices, possibly by supplying substrate for an exchange diffusion carrier, while at higher PAH concentrations iodopyracet efflux was inhibited, presumably by competitive inhibition. The pattern of uric acid transport as discussed may reflect similar interactions.

Citrate excretion also depends upon the factors outlined above. In normal subjects it was found to be increased when the urine was alkaline and

decreased when the urine was acid (274). Stop-flow experiments indicated
that citrate is reabsorbed from the proximal tubule (275) and that the reabsorption could be completely blocked by malate and succinate (276), but it
is not clear whether this inhibition is competitive in the ordinary sense or is
the result of increased intracellular citrate concentrations secondary to mass
action shifts in the tricarboxylic acid cycle. In other experiments, an inverse
relationship between the intracellular citrate content of kidney cells and the
renal excretion of Ca^{++} was found (277), which suggests that the combination
of intratubular citrate with filtered Ca^{++} facilitates the reabsorption of the
latter.

The behavior of l-malic acid, another compound which participates in the
tricarboxylic acid cycle, is also quite interesting. l-Malate was shown to be
reabsorbed in the proximal tubule (278). For reasons not immediately
apparent, infusion of fumarate led to increased reabsorption of malate,
whereas succinate infusion resulted in net secretion, as interpreted from stop-
flow patterns. The authors suggested that the reversal of transport direction
was caused by an increased intracellular concentration of l-malate beyond a
certain level; the hypothesis was supported with data from tissue analyses
and by the observation that the ability of succinate to abolish l-malate
secretion was in turn abolished by application of malonate, a succinoxidase
inhibitor. These data seem to establish that the operation of the tricarboxylic
acid cycle is directly involved in the l-malic acid transport system.

Studies in dogs (279) indicate that oxalate excretion is the resultant of
filtration, proximal tubular secretion which can be inhibited by caronamide,
probenecid, or PAH, and passive back diffusion. The latter could be inhibited
by production of a mannitol diuresis, but was not pH dependent. Inasmuch
as oxalic acid has a pK_1 of 1.2, virtually none of the compound will be present
in the nondissociated form even at the most acid urine pH's, and a pH
dependence of back diffusion would therefore not be expected.

When renal tubular transport of weak acids and bases is studied in
clearance experiments, plasma binding must always be considered (280, 281).
A useful list of 20 acids and bases with pK values, plasma protein binding,
and displacing activity was published by Anton (280), with a discussion of
certain structural and physiochemical properties of acids which displace
sulfonamides.

NONELECTROLYTES

Many features of urea excretion have yet to be explained satisfactorily.
O'Dell & Schmidt-Nielsen (282) found a urea slice-to-medium concentration
difference of 2.9 mmol per liter with kidney cortex, 3.17 mmol per liter with
tissue from the outer medulla, and 1.48 with slices of inner medulla. Additionally, this concentration difference was independent of the urea concentration in the medium, whereas no concentration difference for ^{14}C-labeled urea
added to the medium could be achieved. The most consistent explanation for
this comes from Carlisky et al. (283) who suggest that differences in urea

concentrations between renal slice and medium are the result of urea synthesis. The authors found urea synthesis to the extent of 4 to 8 μeq per kg per hr in tissue homogenates from cortical and subcortical areas of dog kidney suspended in media without added substrate or urea. Significant *in vivo* renal synthesis of urea would have many implications with respect to the role of urea within the countercurrent system and the influence of a low-protein diet on urea excretion (284).

Oliver *et al.* (285, 286) attempted to correlate the splay in the glucose titration curve with glomerulotubular structural balance and found that the larger splay from human experiments correlated with the greater variability of the structural dimensions of the human kidney compared with the dog kidney. The latter showed better structural glomerulotubular balance and only minimal splay. Studies such as these, however, cannot exclude a contribution to splay from kinetic factors.

The first accurate measurements of mammalian tubular permeability for nonelectrolytes made with micropuncture techniques have been published (141). The permeability for sorbose of the proximal convolution was three times as great as that of the distal convolution under antidiuretic conditions. In addition, the permeability coefficients of these structures for raffinose and mannitol did not differ significantly from the values for sorbose. Also of interest is the finding that even large molecules such as α and γ cyclodextrins, with molecular diameters as great as 10 A, can penetrate the tubular epithelium. Malvin & Fritz (287) confirmed that the tubule is permeable to sugars by the observation that parenterally administered fructose or arabinose can be found in the urine of aglomerular fishes.

Studies of pathologic proteinuria revealed that smaller protein molecules escaped more readily into the urine than did larger ones and that such a selective proteinuria could be reproduced *in vitro* with artificial membranes with average pore diameters of 20 to 30 mμ (288). The structure of the glomerulus suggests that it might be the site of such a membrane, and it was therefore somewhat surprising that the protein loss into normal urine was considerably less selective (289, 290). Lowenstein *et al.* (291) found that hemoglobin excretion in humans increased *pari passu* with the concentration of free hemoglobin in the plasma when the blood level of free hemoglobin was greater than 25 mg per cent; it was concluded that the hemoglobinuria resulted from saturation of the reabsorptive mechanism. The clearance of free hemoglobin was approximately 5 per cent of the inulin clearance under normal circumstances. Intravenous infusion of hemoglobin caused renal vasoconstriction which could be prevented if the hemoglobin first passed through the liver (292), from which it was inferred that the liver induces changes in the structure of the hemoglobin molecule. This protective function of the liver was seen to operate only with homologous and not with heterologous hemoglobin. An extensive study of the excretion of hemoglobin and myoglobin in high-voltage accidents was published by Schaefer *et al.* (293).

THE REGULATION OF ACID BASE BALANCE

THE ROLE OF BICARBONATE

Bicarbonate reabsorption increased with increasing filtered bicarbonate until a Tm was attained. This $Tm_{HCO_3^-}$ was found to be increased in respiratory acidosis, whereas administration of acetazolamide led to a reduction of Tm (294). Similar changes in $Tm_{HCO_3^-}$ can be seen from the curves of Toussaint & Vereerstraeten (295) although these authors plotted plasma Cl^- against HCO_3^- reabsorption. Infusion of Na_2SO_4 had no effect on $Tm_{HCO_3^-}$ in dogs, but led to increased reabsorption at loads less than Tm (decreased splay). This effect was especially pronounced in acetazolamide-treated animals (294). Rector & Seldin conclude that poorly reabsorbed anions facilitate H^+ secretion and HCO_3^- reabsorption by augmenting the distal transtubular potential. Analysis of the influence of pCO_2 and carbonic anhydrase inhibitors on HCO_3^- reabsorption led to the hypothesis that two distinct tubular H^+ secretory mechanisms are operating, one pCO_2 dependent and carbonic anhydrase independent, and another dependent upon the presence of carbonic anhydrase and independent of pCO_2 (296). Increased plasma K^+ led to a depression of the pCO_2-dependent—carbonic anhydrase-independent system (297). The authors analyzed their data in terms of Michaelis-Menten kinetics and concluded that the action of K^+ on H^+ secretion may be mediated by a process of noncompetitive inhibition or by a competitive process in which intracellular alkalinization plays a significant role. To ensure that the filtered HCO_3^- load exceeded Tm in these experiments, large amounts of HCO_3^- were infused. Giovannetti (298) approached the problem of H^+ secretion somewhat differently; he induced metabolic acidosis and simultaneously infused inorganic phosphate. When sufficient phosphate was present, free acid excretion increased as plasma HCO_3^- concentration fell, until a maximal level of free acid excretion was attained. These findings indicate a maximal capacity to secrete H^+ (Tm_{H^+}) which varies as a function of pCO_2, and are in accord with the conclusions of the HCO_3^- reabsorption experiments of Rector et al. (296, 297). However, these various data indicate that no matter how high the plasma pCO_2 is raised, an increased $Tm_{HCO_3^-}$ can always be demonstrated. This relationship indicates that it is the availability of CO_2, and not the H^+ transport system, which limits the rate of H^+ secretion, which in turn implies that measured HCO_3^- reabsorption is limited by local equilibrium conditions in various tubular segments, and not by any transfer maxima exclusively.

Simmons (299) has shown that acid excretion in metabolic acidosis is not influenced by compensatory changes in pCO_2. Bicarbonate excretion in metabolic alkalosis was also independent of such compensatory changes. The important implication of these observations is that the rate of H^+ excretion is determined primarily by the filtered load of HCO_3^- or other base, which is consistent with the view that local equilibrium conditions condition the net rate of H^+ movement.

Stop-flow studies by Hoagland & Solomon (300) indicated that urine acidification occurred at a distal site and continued even during the formation of an alkaline urine resulting from metabolic alkalosis. Patients with renal tubular acidosis were unable to acidify the urine below pH 6.2 when given acid (301, 302), while the loss of HCO_3^- and the failure to secrete NH_3 were secondary. Dedmon & Wrong (274) have proposed that a deficiency of some enzyme essential for the normal functioning of the Krebs cycle might be responsible for the tubular failure to secrete H^+ ions against a concentration gradient, as well as for the reduced excretion of citrate observed in this disease. Because of the diminished citrate excretion, binding of Ca^{++} to form a soluble calcium citrate complex is diminished, and calcium salts precipitate to form calculi within the urinary tract.

Balagura & Pitts (303) found that NH_4^+ injected rapidly into the renal artery during acidosis appeared in the urine earlier than simultaneously injected creatinine. In alkalosis, however, NH_3 excretion was abolished. These data support the hypothesis that ammonia diffuses as NH_3 and is distributed among the tubular urine, tubular cells, and peritubular blood in accordance with the respective pH's. Reduction of NH_3 excretion after administration of acetazolamide has long been attributed to the resultant alkalinization of the urine, but it has now been shown that this agent also leads to inhibition of renal phosphate activated glutaminase in the rat (304).

Adaptive processes in respiratory acidosis and alkalosis.—Buffer base from muscle and bone participated in the compensation to metabolic acidosis. In respiratory acidosis, however, bone buffer contributed little since the bone contained no salts of acids weaker than carbonic acid. During breathing of 8 per cent CO_2, muscle gave off buffer base previously bound to cellular proteins into the extracellular space in exchange for H^+. In normal rats, this buffer base was K^+, but in K^+-depleted rats it was Na^+. The extent of K^+ release from muscle seemed to be influenced by the removal of K^+ from the extracellular fluid by the kidneys, since in nephrectomized rats the muscle K^+ did not decrease (305). In dogs, tissue buffers also were of primary importance in the initial response to respiratory acidosis as indicated by the fact that very frequently no increase in renal acid excretion occurred, while plasma HCO_3^- rose sharply during the first day of exposure to 11 to 13 per cent CO_2. Subsequently, however, a considerable increase in net acid excretion, including NH_4^+, was observed and resulted in a saving of fixed base so large as to be accounted for only by restoration of cellular buffer base (306). During recovery from 6 to 75 days of chronic hypercapnia, the elevated HCO_3^- promptly returned to normal if sufficient Cl^- was available to correct the hypochloremia. The fall in plasma HCO_3^- occurred without a significant urinary excretion of HCO_3^-; this is attributed in part to a migration of H^+ from the cells into the extracellular space and in part to a transient suppression of renal acid excretion (307). Chloride also played a critical role in permitting the elevated plasma HCO_3^- concentration to return to normal levels following chronic metabolic alkalosis (308). Even in the first minutes of hypercapnia, changes in the blood buffer base occur, as indicated by change in CO_2 dissociation curves from *in vitro* curves (309). Sustained hypocapnia produced by mechanical hyperventilation induced a progressive true HCO_3^- deficit caused primarily by increased blood lactic acid and pyruvic acid levels, and only to an insignificant extent by a compensatory renal HCO_3^- loss. In experiments on dogs, an average of 74 per cent of the true HCO_3^- deficit could be attributed to the increased lactic and pyruvic acid levels (310), which in turn were secondary only to hypocapnia, and not to hyperventilation *per se*, pH changes, or a superadded hypoxia. This response to respiratory alkalosis may be sufficient to result in metabolic acidosis. In addition to the increase in blood lactic and pyruvic acid levels found in respiratory alkalosis, citric acid concentrations were elevated and inorganic phosphate concentrations decreased in the plasma in this condition (311). Since Ca^{++} and citrate form a nonionized complex, the increase in plasma citric acid concentrations and the fall in ionized Ca^{++} concentration, as manifested by tetanic symptoms, seem to be interrelated. In the compensation of respiratory alkalosis, cell buffers are also involved. A potassium shift from the extracellular space into the cells was described some time ago by Giebisch *et al.* (312) and recently confirmed by Gold *et al.* (313).

EXTRACELLULAR FLUID

EXTRARENAL WATER AND ELECTROLYTE METABOLISM

The turnover of tritiated water was measured in mouse, rat, kangaroo rat, rabbit, dog, man, and horse by Richmond *et al.* (314). An interspecies correlation of the power function type ($Y = ax^b$) between daily water turnover (Y, ml per day) and body weight (x in grams) was found for all species except the kangaroo rat. The value for a was 0.49, for b, 0.8. A similar value for b had previously been found by Adolph (315) who correlated water intake with urinary output and body weight. That the findings from the kangaroo did not correlate with those from other species is taken to indicate the existence of special water-conserving mechanisms which help to ensure survival in extremely arid environments. However, the degree of tissue hydration is quite normal in the kangaroo rat, as shown by the good correlation between body solids and body water for all seven species.

Von Bubnoff & Riecker (316) studied the water content of red cells as a function of serum osmolality. Following salt deprivation, both serum osmolality and cell water content decreased, while the opposite effects were seen after infusion of glucose. In both cases water flux followed solute flux. In contrast, after water drinking or infusion of hypertonic saline, water flux without solute flux was responsible for the shifts which maintained erythrocyte osmotic balance. During metabolic acidosis the inorganic cation content of red cells decreased while the anion and water contents increased. The change in cellular water and electrolyte content during acidosis came from a reduced dissociation of the cell proteins with a concomitant change in the Donnan equilibrium.

Intracellular Ion Composition

When the plasma K^+ concentration fell during K^+ depletion of rats, the skeletal muscle K^+ content was also reduced. However, this change could not be reproduced *in vitro* if no amino acids were present in the incubation medium (317). The cationic amino acids can replace intracellular K^+; the neutral amino acids produced a similar but much less marked effect, while anionic amino acids could not replace the K^+ (318). From these data, the extracellular concentration of cationic amino acids seems to be an important factor influencing the K^+ equilibrium of rat skeletal muscle. Furthermore, changes in K^+ concentration were regularly found in the presence of pH changes. Ordinarily, acidosis results in an increased plasma K^+ as a result of cellular K^+-H^+ exchange, but this relationship was disturbed during infusion of certain organic acids and bases because the compounds which were infused diffuse intracellularly in the nondissociated form and therefore do not result in K^+-H^+ exchange (319). In this connection, a paper by Joseph *et al.* (320) which deals with the behavior of Na^+ and K^+ in colloid-rich phases deserves special comment. Because of the lower hydration energy of K^+, the fraction of nonhydrated ions in any phase would be much greater for K^+ than for Na^+, and K^+ could therefore neutralize fixed charges more easily. The previous demonstration by the authors that application of respiratory inhibitors lowered colloidal charge is consistent with this view. The suggestion of Joseph *et al.* is also compatible with the following findings: The ratio of Na^+:K^+ in cytoplasm is 6:100 while in liver nuclei the ratio was found to be 72:146 (321). Since the sum of cations in nucleus water is more than twice that in cytoplasmic water, it was concluded that the activity coefficient of intranuclear alkali metal ions must be significantly lower than unity, as it is unlikely that the osmolalities of the two compartments differ. With respect to the relatively high nuclear sodium concentrations it is of interest that Na^+ is required for the uptake of alanine, adenine, and thymidine by isolated nuclei (321a). Furthermore, intranuclear Na^+ may not be exchangeable for K^+. This suggestion, as well as several others, is advanced by Susat & Vanatta (322) to explain their finding that rat skeletal muscle, which had been extracted for up to 14 days in 50 glycerol followed by a 5-hr extraction in 80 mmol KCl, still had a Na^+ content of 0.3 meq per kg.

Reduction of the Extracellular Fluid Volume

Acute reduction of extracellular fluid volume by hemorrhage or peritoneal dialysis caused rats to drink more water (323). If 30 per cent of the blood volume was removed, the animals drank amounts of water equal to the total blood and urine loss. The mechanisms responsible for the induction of water drinking by isotonic depletion of body fluids are obscure, but may be related to those responsible for the fact that a sharp reduction of plasma volume induced by Na^+ deficiency caused sheep to drink NaCl solutions in preference to water (324). This preference was independent of plasma Na^+ concentration. Share (325) observed that a reduction of extracellular fluid volume by 10 to 20 per cent increases the ADH concentration in jugular venous blood which is indicative of neurohypophyseal stimulation of ADH secretion. The effects of extracellular fluid volume reduction on aldosterone secretion are discussed in the section on that hormone.

Water and electrolyte changes during development were discussed in several papers. The amount of Na^+ retained per kilogram of weight gain (83 meq) by pregnant rats was the same as that found per kilogram of gravid uterus and products of gestation. In addition, the absolute amounts of Na^+ retained by the pregnant dams differed significantly from the total amount of Na^+ in the fetal tissues, and calculations indicated no net accumulation of Na^+ in the maternal tissues during pregnancy (326). Embryos proved to be highly sensitive to osmotic stress. When pregnant rats or guinea pigs were deprived of water for three days, all fetuses died. During this period, Na^+ concentration in maternal and fetal plasma and in amniotic fluid increased 10 per cent while K^+ concentrations in the same fluids increased 15 per cent. The dams appeared not to be permanently damaged by the water deprivation (327). The changes of body water compartments from the period of intrauterine life through childhood and adolescence are treated by Friis-Hansen (328). Total body water during the second month of fetal life is about 94 per cent, at birth 78 per cent, and at one year of life 60 per cent; it decreases little during further development. Extracellular volume is 62 per cent in the fifth fetal month, 45 per cent at birth, and 27 per cent at one year, while intracellular water increases during the first three postnatal months from 34 per cent to 43 per cent and decreases again to about 35 per cent at one year. Corresponding changes in cellular water were also observed in young rats (329). Simultaneously, intracellular K^+ concentration decreased. Similar developmental changes occurred in red-cell K^+ concentrations in that strain of sheep in which adult erythrocytes are high in Na^+ and low in K^+. During the first two months after birth the fetal relationship is reversed, so that the intracellular concentrations become 90 meq per liter Na^+ and 15 meq per liter K^+. The factors responsible for the changeover are not clear (330), but Tosteson & Hoffman (331) have shown that the difference between sheep high K^+ low Na^+ and low K^+ high Na^+ erythrocytes could be related to greater cation active transport and greater relative passive permeability for Na^+ in the former cell type.

Sodium and Vasomotor Tone

Considerable attention has been directed to the Na^+ and K^+ content of the walls of arteries and arterioles, since it has been supposed that changes in electrolyte composition could be related to vascular tonus and possibly therefrom to the pathogenesis of arterial hypertension. In rats with renal hypertension, Tobian *et al.* (332) found that mesenteric arterioles contained 27.3 meq Na$^+$ per 100 g dry tissue, as compared to 22.1 meq Na$^+$ per 100 g in normal animals and 23.5 meq Na$^+$ per 100 g in rats cured of hypertension by removal of the clip on the renal artery. No significant changes of arteriolar K$^+$ content were found. Water content was calculated to be 10 per cent higher in the arterioles of hypertensive rats. An inverse relationship between Na$^+$ content of the aortic wall and the arterial pressure was also found in acute experiments (333). Recently, Jamieson & Friedman (334) monitored femoral venous blood continuously with Na$^+$- and K$^+$-sensitive glass electrodes and found small decreases of blood Na$^+$ after injection of pressor agents such as epinephrine, 5-hydroxytryptamine, angiotensin, and vasopressin into the femoral artery. A simultaneous increase in K$^+$ concentration was sometimes found. The opposite changes in blood Na$^+$ and K$^+$ concentrations were seen to occur after the injection of vasodilating agents such as isoproterenol, acetylcholine, or histamine. The authors discuss the possibility that the blood cation concentration changes reflect converse changes in vascular tissue and suppose that ionic exchanges are related to vascular smooth muscle tension. Feeding rats for more than a year with a synthetic diet which contained 8 per cent NaCl led to increased Na$^+$, K$^+$, and Cl$^-$ contents of the aortic wall, but not to the development of hypertension (335). With the same diet, however, Dahl (336) was able to produce a self-sustaining hypertension which would seem therefore to indicate that a high Na$^+$ content of vascular tissue is not linked with hypertension under all circumstances. In hypertensive patients there was, however, a direct temporal relationship between salt loss and arterial pressure decrease, while neither was correlated to the decrease of extracellular fluid volume (337). These relationships indicated that an elevated intracellular Na$^+$ concentration somewhere is responsible for vascular tone. The complex influence of Na$^+$ on smooth muscle activity was indicated by the studies of Takagi *et al.* (338) in which rats made hyponatremic and hypovolemic by peritoneal dialysis showed an increased sympathetic vasomotor tone which seemed more dependent on intravascular volume than on extracellular Na$^+$ concentration.

Ion binding.—Peterson *et al.* (339, 340) studied the effects of pH on the dissociation of calcium proteinate in rabbit serum and purified bovine serum albumin. The published nomograms permit the determination of ionized Ca^{++} when pH, total Ca, and protein concentration are known. In the bones of rats, the Na$^+$ content of the crystal phase increased with age from 50 meq per kg on the 20th day to 183 meq per kg on the 90th day (341). Sodium content of the crystal phase was not altered by profound hypo- or hypernatremia and all changes could be ascribed entirely to the fraction of Na$^+$ within the fluid phase of bone. Although no crystal phase Na$^+$ change was observed in these acute experiments, experiments of longer duration might well give different results, particularly if such procedures as induction of acidosis or adrenalectomy were employed.

That Na$^+$ can be accumulated and retained for long periods in an osmotically inactive form is suggested by the finding that obese patients retain large quantities of Na^+ without water (342). By measuring colloidal charge in relation to pH, Engel *et al.* (343) constructed titration curves of connective tissue colloids in normal states and in the presence of a series of anions. The results led the authors to suggest that metabolically produced anions, in particular the di- and tricarboxylic acids, may be bound to extracellular substances thereby affecting the distribution of all other ions.

METABOLISM OF THE KIDNEY

Further efforts were made to study the over-all metabolism of the kidney, without special reference to its functional organization. With this intention, Levy (344) measured the uptake of lactate and pyruvate from the dog kidney *in vivo*, and found lactate arteriovenous differences equal to 10 per cent of the arterial level which could account for 22 per cent of the O_2 consumption if the lactate had been completely oxidized. Infusion of lactate led to increased blood levels and a progressive increase in the rate of lactate uptake. Under control conditions the net consumption of pyruvate was negligible. Under similar conditions Ochwadt *et al.* (345) found a renal lactate arteriovenous difference of 12 per cent which, in his experiments, could account for 62 per cent of the total O_2 consumption. Furthermore, an 8 per cent extraction of fatty acids was observed which alone would account for 99 per cent of O_2 consumption. These findings indicate the need for further investigation of the sources of renal metabolic energy. With respect to glucose, however, negative arteriovenous differences were found, indicating net glucose synthesis by the kidney (346). This renal gluconeogenesis was confirmed by the observation that kidney slices incubated in Ringer amino acid media synthesized considerable amounts of glucose, especially from *l*-proline (347).

The high levels of anaerobic glycolysis found in experiments *in vitro* suggest that the metabolism of the renal medulla is largely anaerobic (348), but calculations by Ruiz-Guinazu *et al.* (79) from direct measurements of glucose and lactic acid concentrations in vasa recta plasma show that the decrease in glucose concentration is four times greater than could be accounted for by lactic acid formation. From these data it may be concluded that, in contrast to the whole kidney, the renal medulla utilizes glucose and furthermore, if this glucose is not diverted through pathways other than those related to oxidative metabolism, that glycolysis does not yield a major fraction of the medullary energy, under "normal" conditions.

Several studies describe enzyme patterns within the kidney, but enzyme activity need not necessarily reflect metabolic activity, since such studies give no information about rate-limiting factors in a given reaction sequence. Weber (349) compared the enzymes of gluconeogensis, glycogenesis, glycolysis, and direct oxidation in rat kidney homogenates with those of liver homogenates, and concluded that in kidney cortex, the enzyme capacity for channeling glucose-6-phosphate into glycolysis and glucose production markedly predominates over enzymes involved in channeling this hexose ester into glycogenesis or pentose production, or into direct oxidative pathways. Quantitative histochemical studies showed that the enzymes necessary for pentose production and direct oxidative pathways (glucose-6-phosphate dehydrogenase and 6-phosphogluconic dehydrogenase) have a higher activity in the pars recta than in the pars convoluta of the proximal tubule (350).

Histochemical demonstration of glutaminase I activity proved very useful in explaining discrepancies concerning the site of NH_3 secretion (351). Normal rats had a moderate to low glutaminase concentration in all medullary tubular structures, in agreement with earlier findings (352, 353). In acidotic animals a general increase was observed, so that even in the proximal tubule, high values could be found. In contrast to the findings with rats, an extremely intense reaction for glutaminase I was found in collecting ducts of golden hamsters, where ammonia excretion has been directly measured with microcatheterization methods (354). In golden hamsters, however, the strong glutaminase activity can also be shown in the proximal tubule. These data indicate that large species differences exist, and that it is indeed possible that all parts of the nephron are capable of ammonia formation, which results in ammonia secretion, if acidification takes place at the particular nephron segment. Persijn et al. (355) have published impressive electron-microscopic pictures which demonstrate the localization of ATPase at the basal infolding and brush border of proximal tubular cells.

The effects of ischemia or anoxia on renal metabolite concentration and restitution during recovery are described in several papers. After the renal artery had been clamped for 5 sec, 20 per cent of the ATP had been split, after 15 sec more than 40 per cent, and after 10 min, 85 per cent (356). Simultaneously, some tri- and dinucleotides were degraded to nucleosides, purines, and pyrimidines (357). The restitution of metabolic concentrations after periods of renal ischemia lasting up to 120 min was carefully studied by Thorn & Liemann (358). Kidney slices from very young animals maintained their integrity under anaerobic conditions, but with increasing age, sensitivity to O_2 lack increased concomitantly with a decreased capacity for anaerobic glycolysis (359). These findings help explain why immature animals tolerate anoxia for much longer periods than adults.

DIURETICS

Excellent comprehensive reviews on diuretics have been published (360, 361). In addition, the contributions to a round table conference on diuretics (362), a monograph (363), and short reviews (364) giving special emphasis to clinical applications (365) or chemical pharmacology (366) have appeared.

Chlorothiazide, saluretic sulfonamides, and related compounds.—Current hypotheses about these compounds are in two categories:

(a) The two-action hypothesis—inhibition of carbonic anhydrase plus chloruretic effects.

(b) The one-action hypothesis—inhibition of carbonic anhydrase alone, with resultant diminution of Na^+-H^+ exchange. Reabsorption of HCO_3^- is depressed because of the failure of H^+ to gain access to the tubular lumen, and Cl^- reabsorption is decreased because of reduction of the electrical gradient (361).

Each hypothesis considers that kaliuresis is secondary and caused by the enhanced delivery of Na^+ to the site of Na^+-K^+ exchange. *In vitro*, the carbonic anhydrase inhibition of the saluretic sulfonamides does not coincide with their chloruretic effect (367). However, Beyer & Baer (361) argue that data concerning carbonic anhydrase inhibition from experiments *in vitro* may not be of value for predicting the order of *in vivo* inhibition.

The data of Beyer & Baer (368) indicate that the intracellular accumulation of chlorothiazide derivatives may be responsible for their chloruretic effects (367). Compounds which are secreted proximally and subsequently reabsorbed, possibly by back diffusion more distally, are more active at the distal site of Na^+-H^+ exchange, and lead to increased urinary pH and to increased HCO_3^- and K^+ excretion. An example of this type is acetazolamide. In contrast, compounds which are easily accumulated in the proximal tubular cells have small renal clearances, act in relatively small doses, are primarily saluretic, and probably act proximally. At higher doses, however, these compounds may also reach effective concentrations in the distal tubular cells (369) and thereby increase HCO_3^- and K^+ excretion. Many data fit into this framework, for example, the observation that the more potent diuretics of this group are more concentrated within the tubular cells (369). Also consistent with this view are the findings that good natriuretic and chloruretic effects were obtained with relatively small doses of benzthiazide, while higher doses produced no additional increase in these parameters although HCO_3^- and K^+ excretion did rise (370). Gertz & Ullrich (371), using micromethods, observed an inhibition of proximal Na^+ reabsorption by these compounds, but their method was found unsuitable for distal measurements because of greater variability in control measurements in this segment. However, results of stop-flow experiments do indicate an effect on the distal Na^+ minimum from the high-potency compounds (372). Although these data tend to support the views of Beyer & Baer, and despite any attractions which this hypothesis might hold, present knowledge of the intrarenal handling of Na^+ does not permit the *a priori* exclusion of the collecting ducts as the main site of action of these compounds.

It has been proposed that increased aldosterone secretion is responsible for the increased distal K^+ secretion which follows administration of saluretic sulfonamides, since spirolactones inhibit the K^+ loss and enhance the natriuresis induced by these drugs (373). These relationships were also found in adrenalectomized animals receiving maintenance doses of deoxycorticosterone (374). Furthermore, rats treated chronically with chlorothiazide had increased granularity of the cells of the juxtaglomerular apparatus (374). Evidence that other steroids can influence the action of saluretic sulfonamides is found in the work of Senft (375a). Rats with nucleoside nephrosis do not respond to hydrochlorothiazide, but will show saluresis without change in GFR if a small dose of the glucocorticoid Triamcinolon is given.

The antidiuretic action of thiazides in both rats and patients with diabetes insipidus is not easily explained (376, 377). Administration of chlorothiazide to patients with diabetes insipidus resulted in a reduction of GFR which occurred concomitantly with antidiuresis (378, 379, 380). Both effects could be prevented by administration of prednisolone (378). The GFR begins to decrease in artificially perfused cat kidneys after chlorothizaide is added, but only when the perfusion blood has been taken from a headless donor (381); and some causal connection between chlorothiazide, lack of neurohypophyseal hormones, decreased GFR, and antidiuretic action seems likely. In addition, hyponatremia was found to reduce free-water clearance (382) and might therefore be responsible for the persistence of the antidiuretic action of chlorothiazide in dogs with diabetes insipidus which was found when the initially depressed GFR returned to normal levels (383).

Mercurial diuretics.—Strong evidence exists for the hypothesis of Mudge & Weiner (384) that Hg^{++} is liberated from diuretic organomercurials following rupture of the C–Hg bond in the presence of thiol groups. This reaction is strikingly pH dependent. In an acid medium, Hg^{++} is rapidly liberated, and it is suggested that this could explain the enhanced diuretic activity of organic mercurials in acidosis. If the diuretically active form of mercurials is Hg^{++}, it follows that two-point attachment at the receptor site is a prerequisite for diuresis. It is further proposed that the lack of diuretic action of certain mercurial compounds (*p*-chloromercuribenzoate and *p*-chloromercuriphenylsulfonate) results from the availability of only a single mercury valence, but that the ability of these last named agents to prevent or even to reverse the diuretic effect of diuretically active mercurials arises from competition for sulfhydryl groups at the receptor (385). The binding of these compounds, whether diuretic or not, causes swelling of kidney cortex slices (386). Furthermore, the presence of 0.6 mM HgCl in the incubation fluid led to increased Na^+ and urea permeability, but unfortunately no indication is given that the action of nondiuretic mercurials was studied in this regard. However, an additional effect of $HgCl_2$, that of producing an increased loss of ^{45}Ca from kidney slices, may have a parallel in the diminished Ca^{++} concentration in kidneys found 4 hr after administration of mercurials (4 mg Hg^{++} per kg). This effect was seen only with compounds having diuretic potency (387). In this connection, Wesson (388) has found that Ca^{++} and Mg^{++} excretion increase considerably after injection of Mercurin indicating that changes in Ca^{++} binding may be important in the diuretic action of mercurials.

The inhibitory effects of mercurials on the dehydrogenases of α-ketoglutarate (389), succinate, and isocitrate (390) are produced only with high doses and therefore are thought not to be correlated with the diuretic effect, particularly since the onset of inhibition of these enzymes is immediate, while the onset of diuresis is delayed (387). Furthermore, the changes in renal vascular resistance (391) after intravenous injection of mercurials are probably independent of the diuretic action since both diuretic and nondiuretic mercurials elicit this effect.

Experiments with systems such as the frog skin and toad bladder have not clarified the diuretic action of mercurials, but do provide interesting data on electrolyte permeability when thiol groups are blocked by mercurials. Application of p-chloromercuribenzoate (nondiuretic) or chlormerodrin (diuretic) at concentrations of 0.1 mM or greater led to a fall in transmembrane potential, short-circuit current, and DC resistance (392, 393), while lower concentrations increased the membrane potential, particularly at the outer membrane. The latter is attributed by the author to a diminished Cl$^-$ permeability resulting from a steric hindrance block of thiol groups in anion permeable pores; it is suggested that cation permeable pores are larger. The etiology of the reduction of membrane resistance with higher concentrations of mercurials is not, however, discussed.

Antialdosterones.—Since the spirolactones reverse all of the effects of mineralocorticoids on electrolyte excretion, since they are effective only in the presence of mineralocorticoids, and since the inhibitory activity can be overcome by the administration of additional amounts of mineralocorticoids, it seems reasonable that the spirolactones act as competitive inhibitors of mineralocorticoids (394). The spirolactones apparently have no direct effect upon aldosterone secretion, metabolism, or excretion, although the salt depletion induced by these agents may lead secondarily to an increased aldosterone output (395). The study of Davidson & DeVenuto (396) is of interest with respect to the molecular interactions underlying aldosterone antagonism by the spirolactones. They used protein binding of steroids as a model to study the behavior of possible membrane receptor sites, and found that aldosterone bound to serum albumin could be displaced by addition of large amounts of spirolactone to the reaction mixture. Progesterone and cortisol were even more effective than spirolactones in accomplishing the displacement, and a parallelism to the competitive actions of these steroids at the tubular level would seem to exist. Because some spirolactones decrease water, Na$^+$, K$^+$, and Cl$^-$ excretion in adrenalectomized rats (397), it would seem that at least some of their activity is not related to aldosterone antagonism, although the exact nature of this additional activity is not specified. It is also of interest that aldactone protects against some of the cardiovascular-renal changes normally produced by an ischemic or endocrine kidney, and also against the manifestations of DOC overdosage (398).

Another inhibitor of aldosterone is 2,4,7-triamino-6-phenylpteridin (399 to 404), whose administration induced natriuresis and depressed K$^+$ excretion. Failure of this agent to alter the excretion rates of other adrenal corticoids suggests that its antimineralocorticoid activity takes place at the renal tubular level (402). Herken & Senft (405) tested this substance in adrenalectomized rats and found that the effects of aldosterone could be blocked completely. When 2,4,7-triamino-6-phenylpteridin was administered alone to saline-infused adrenalectomized rats, no change in Na$^+$ excretion was observed, although K$^+$ excretion decreased. When given to patients with Addison's disease, this compound led to an augmentation of urinary excretion of Na^+ and Cl^-, and to a reduction of the excretion of K^+, titratable acidity, and ammonia (394). Since this compound retains all of its aldosterone-inhibiting effects when no aldosterone or other mineralocorticoids are present, and since it acts synergistically with spirolactone, it is concluded that the aldosterone antagonism of this drug is nonspecific.

Lenzi *et al.* (406) have suggested that the escape from prolonged aldosterone administration which is manifested by a return to normal rates of Na^+ excretion can be related to an increased rate of glucocorticoid excretion, since they observed a 100 per cent increase in the rate of urinary glucocorticoid excretion in normal man subjected to protracted treatment with aldosterone. Steroids which increase Na^+ excretion are possibly responsible for the natriuresis observed after prolonged saline infusions. Under these circumstances, Herken (407) found a urinary steroid which is probably identical with 6-β-OH-corticosterone. A comprehensive discussion of the clinical applications of aldosterone antagonists is given in a series of papers edited by Krück, Koczorek & Betzien (408).

Other diuretic drugs.—Theophylline has been recently restudied, and found to increase renal plasma flow (409) and GFR (410). Buchborn *et al.* (409) observed that Tc_{H_2O} decreased almost to zero after intravenous injection of 0.24 to 0.48 g aminophylline. They concluded that the function of the medullary countercurrent system must have been disturbed by administration of this agent, and supposed that an increased medullary blood flow had served to reduce the longitudinal osmotic gradient normally present in antidiuresis and to a lesser extent in water diuresis. However, their data might also be explained by a direct tubular action similar to that of ADH, since Orloff & Handler (112) have found that both theophylline and ADH act on the frog skin through adenosine-3′-5′-monophosphate. Furthermore, infusion of theophylline into one leg vein of the chicken produced a unilateral diuresis which also suggests a tubular action, although an influence on the renal vascular system could not be absolutely excluded (411).

Antithyroid drugs cannot be considered as real diuretics, but they do cause a moderate diuresis (412, 413). Animals treated with these compounds have a diminished concentrating ability and excrete a given amount of solute in a greater volume of water. Furthermore, they drink isotonic saline preferentially (414) and cannot excrete a urea load by increasing the urine osmolality (413).

MISCELLANEOUS

DIURNAL RHYTHM

The excretion of water, Na^+, K^+, and ketogenic steroids, and the creatinine clearance, are all greater during the day than at night. Two days after reversal of day-night activity, diurnal patterns of these parameters were not altered, while after four days, the rhythm for water and Na^+ excretion and for creatinine clearance had reversed. The reversal of the creatinine clearance pattern did not occur simultaneously with that of Na^+ and water, however, and the rhythmicity of ketogenic steroid excretion remained unchanged altogether. Because of the observed dissociation of patterns it was concluded that neither ketogenic steroids nor GFR exerted any dominant control over the other excretory rhythms (415). Similarly, aldosterone seems to be unimportant for the diurnal pattern of Na^+ excretion, since the low nocturnal Na^+ excretion coincided with a period of reduced aldosterone excretion (416). Procedures such as chronic water loading with simultaneous ADH administration, salt depletion, or deoxycorticosterone administration affected only the amplitude of the rhythmic changes, not their frequency (417). It must be concluded that the renal causal factors responsible for renal diurnal rhythm are still unknown.

TROPHIC FUNCTIONS

Nephrectomy induced a rapid disappearance of erythroblasts from bone marrow and a decrease of the turnover of plasma iron to one tenth of the normal value. The resulting anemia could be corrected by injection of extracts from normal kidneys (418). In addition, erythropoiesis induced by bleeding occurred only when the kidneys were present (419). Conversely, erythropoietic activity was increased in patients with renal tumors (420). Occlusion of both ureters had at most only a slight stimulating effect on erythropoiesis (418, 420), and constriction of one renal artery failed to induce a significant increase in ^{59}Fe uptake (421). All of these data strongly indicate that the kidney plays a role in the control of erythropoietic activity. Localization of the site of liberation of erythropoietin to the renal cortex was accomplished by differential ablation of various areas of the kidneys (422).

The mechanisms regulating compensatory hypertrophy after partial organ removal are obscure. It is clear, however, that an increased work load on the remaining kidney after unilateral nephrectomy is not responsible for stimulating cell division (423), whereas high-protein diets under such circumstances did increase the extent of hypertrophy (424). A trophic influence of the hypophysis on the kidney was indicated by the finding that hypophysectomy induced a 50 per cent decrease of GFR in otherwise normal animals; the suggestion is supported by the observation that unilateral nephrectomy in hypophysectomized rats led to a decrease in the weight of the remaining kidney, rather than to the compensatory hypertrophy normally seen (425). Evidence that the phenomenon of compensatory renal hypertrophy may be related to the presence of an organ-specific substance which stimulates mitosis is found in the observation that serum from unilaterally nephrectomized rats stimulates mitosis in cultures of renal medullary tissue (426).

ACKNOWLEDGMENTS

The authors wish to express their appreciation to Drs. Gerhard Giebisch, Donald Seldin, and Sidney Solomon for critical review of this manuscript, and to Mrs. Sarah Marsh for editorial assistance.

LITERATURE CITED

1. Richet, G., Ed., *Compt. Rend. Congr. Intern. Nephrol., Geneva Evian, 1st, 1960* (1961)
2. Friedberg, C. K., Ed., *Heart, Kidney and Electrolytes* (Grune & Stratton, New York-London, 1962)
3. O'Connor, W. J., *Renal Function* (Arnold, London 1962)
4. *Colloq. Ges. Physiol. Chem., 1961* (Springer, Berlin-Göttingen-Heidelberg, 1961)
5. Kleinzeller, A., and Kotyk, A., Eds., *Membrane Transport and Metabolism, Proceedings of a Symposium, Praha, 1960* (Czech. Acad. Sci., Prague, 1961)
6. *The Development of Homeostasis with Special Reference to Factors of the Environment. Proc. Symp. Liblice near Prague, September 15–17, 1960* (Czech. Acad. Sci., Prague, 1961)
7. Dorfman, R. I., Gaunt, R., and Chart, J. J., *Handbuch der experimentellen Pharmakologie*, 14 (Eichler, O., and Farah, A., Eds., 1962)
8. Leaf A., and Hays, R. M., *Recent Progr. Hormone Res.*, 17, 488 (1961)
9. Deane, H. W., Gaunt, R., and Chart, J. J., *Handbuch der experimentellen Pharmakologie*, 14 (Eichler, O., and Farah, A., Eds., 1962)
10. Davis, J. O., *Recent Progr. Hormone Res.*, 17, 335 (1961)
11. *Symposium on Angiotensin*, 165–270 (Am. Heart Assoc. Monograph No. 3, 1962)
12. Maxwell, M. H., and Kleeman, C. R., *Clinical Disorders of Fluid and Electrolyte Metabolism* (McGraw-Hill, New York-Toronto-London, 1962)
13. Mertz, D. P., *Die extrazelluläre Flüssigkeit* (Weitzel, G., Tübingen, and Zöllner, N., München, Eds., Thieme-Verlag, 1962)
14. Black, D. A. K., *Renal Disease* (Blackwell, Oxford, 1962)
15. Bergstrand, A., *Compt. Rend. Congr. Intern. Nephrol., Geneva Evian, 1st, 1960*, 357 (1961)
16. Bohle, A., and Sitte, H., *Internationales Nierensymposion Würzburg-Glumeruläre und Tubuläre Nierenerkrankungen*, 205 (Georg Thieme, Stuttgart, 1962)
17. Farquhar M., *Compt. Rend. Congr. Intern. Nephrol., Geneva Evian, 1st, 1960*, 386 (1961)
18. James, J. A., and Ashworth, C. T., *Am. J. Pathol.*, 38, 515 (1961)
19. Ashworth, C. T., and James, J. A., *Am. J. Pathol.*, 39, 307 (1961)
20. Fisher, E. R., and Hellstrom, H. R., *Federation Proc.*, 21, 426 (1962)
21. Bohle, A., Miller, F., Sitte, H., and Yolac, A., *I Internationales Symposion Basel/Seelisberg 1958*, 70 (Schwabe, Basel, 1959)
22. Kurtz, S. M., and Feldman, J. D., *J. Ultrastruct. Res.*, 6, 19 (1962)
23. Reale, E., and Bucher, O., *Experientia*, 17, 430 (1961)
24. Thoenes, W., *Z. Zellforsch. Mikroskop. Anat.*, 55, 486 (1961)
25. Rhodin, J. A. G., *Internationales Nierensymposion Würzburg-Glomeruläre und Tubuläre Nierenerkrankungen*, 92 (Georg Thieme, Stuttgart, 1962)
26. Thoenes, W., *Klin. Wochschr.*, 39, 504 (1961)
27. Thoenes W. *Klin. Wochschr.* 39, 827 (1961)
28. Longley J. B., Banfield, W. G., and Brindley, D. C., *J. Biophys. Biochem. Cytol.*, 7, 103 (1960)
29. Brewer, D. B., and Eguren, L. M., *J. Pathol. Bacteriol.*, 83, 107 (1962)
30. Wachstein, M., and Bradshaw, M., *Nature*, 194, 299 (1962)
31. Oliver, J., MacDowell, M., Welt, L. G., Holiday, M. A., Hollander, W., Jr., Winters, R. W., Williams, T. F., and Seyar, W. E., *J. Exptl. Pathol.*, 106, 353 (1957)
32. Jahnecke, J., Kommerell, B., and Bohle, A., *Klin. Wochschr.*, 40, 227 (1962)
33. Sarre, H., and Rother, K., *I Symposion der Gesellschaft für Nephrologie*, 18 (Thieme Verlag, 1962)
34. Ljungqvist, A., and Lagergren, C., *J. Anat.*, 96, 285 (1962)
35. Hammersen, F., and Staubesand, J., *Z. Anat. Entwicklungsgeschichte*, 122, 349 (1961)
36. Passarge, E., *Z. Anat. Entwicklungsgeschichte*, 122, 86 (1960)
37. Adebahr, G., *Z. Zellforsch. Mikroskop. Anat.*, 68, 48 (1962)
38. Johnson, P. C., *Am. J. Physiol.*, 199, 311 (1960)
39. Stainsby, W. N., and Renkin, E. M., *Am. J. Physiol.*, 201, 117 (1961)
40. Stainsby, W. N., and Renkin, E. M., *Am. J. Cardiol.*, 8, 741 (1961)
41. Stainsby, W. N., *Am. J. Physiol.*, 202, 273 (1962)

42. Machowicz, P. P., Sabo, G., Lin, G., Rapela, C. E., and Green, H. D., *Physiologist*, **4,** 68 (1961)

43. Thurau, K., and Kramer, K., *Arch. Ges. Physiol.*, **268,** 188 (1959)

44. Waugh, W. H., and Shanks, R. G., *Circulation Res.*, **8,** 871 (1960)

45. Waugh, W. H., *Circulation Res.*, **6,** 363 (1958)

46. Schmid, H. E., Jr., and Spencer, M. P., *J. Appl. Physiol.*, **17,** 201 (1962)

47. Thurau, K., Kramer, K., and Brechtelsbauer, H., *Arch. Ges. Physiol.*, **269,** 77 (1959)

48. Thurau, K., and Wober, E., *Arch. Ges. Physiol.*, **274,** 553 (1962)

49. Hinshaw, L. B., and Worthen, D. M., *Circulation Res.*, **9,** 1156 (1961)

50. Langston, J. B., Guyton, A. C., Hull, C. C., and Armstrong, G. G., *Am. J. Physiol.*, **201,** 495 (1961)

51. Dieter, E., *Arch. Ges. Physiol.*, **274,** 69 (1961)

52. Langston, J. B., Guyton, A. C., DePoyster, J. H., and Armstrong, G. G., Jr., *Am. J. Physiol.*, **202,** 893 (1962)

53. McGiff, J. C., and Aviado, D. M., *Circulation Res.*, **9,** 1327 (1961)

54. Voudoukis, I. J., and Boucek, R. J., *Am. J. Physiol.*, **202,** 888 (1962)

55. Abel, F. L., and Murphy, Q. R., *Am. J. Physiol.*, **202,** 978 (1962)

56. Berne, R. M., and Levy, M. N., *J. Clin. Invest.*, **29,** 444 (1950)

57. Feigl, E., Johansson, B., and Löfving, B., *Proc. Intern. Congr. Physiol. Sci.*, *22nd, Free Commun.*, 232 (1962)

58. Pabst, K., and Gauer, O. H., *Arch. Ges. Physiol.*, **274,** 213 (1961)

59. Kanter, G. S., *Am. J. Physiol.*, **201,** 791 (1961)

60. Mertz, D. P., *Arzneim. Forsch. (Drug Res.)*, **12,** 489 (1962)

61. Munck, O., Lassen, N. A., Deetjen, P., and Kramer, K., *Arch. Ges. Physiol.*, **274,** 356 (1962)

62. Berliner, R. W., *Compt. Rend. Congr. Intern. Nephrol.*, *Geneva Evian, 1st, 1960,* 5 (1961)

63. Kuhn, H., *Internationales Nierensymposion Würzburg-Glomeruläre und Tubuläre Nierenerkrankungen*, 3 (1960)

64. Gottschalk, C. W., Lassiter, W. E., Mylle, M., Ullrich, K. J., Schmidt-Nielsen, B., Pehling, G. and O'Dell, R., *Compt Rend. Congr. Intern. Nephrol.*, *Geneva Evian, 1st, 1960,* 12 (1961)

65. Ullrich, K. J., Pehling, G., and Espinar-Lafuente, M., *Arch. Ges. Physiol.*, **273,** 562 (1961)

66. Schmidt-Nielsen, B., and O'Dell, R., *Am. J. Physiol.*, **200,** 1119 (1961)

67. Hargitay, B., and Kuhn, W., *Z. Electrochem.*, **55,** 539 (1951)

68. Ullrich, K. J., Kramer, K., and Boyland, J. W., *Renal Disease*, 49 (Black, D. A. K., Ed., 1962)

69. Gottschalk, C. W., Lassiter, W. E., and Mylle, M., *Proc. Intern. Congr. Physiol. Sci.*, *22nd,* **I,** 375 (1962)

70. Thurau, K., Sugiura, T., and Lilienfield, L. S., *Clin. Res.*, **8,** 383 (1960)

71. Harms, W. S., Blitch, P. G., Johnson, A. C., Jr., and Findley, T. J., *Metab. Clin. Exptl.*, **11,** 542 (1962)

72. Ochwadt, B., *Arch. Ges. Physiol.*, **262,** 207 (1956)

73. Ulfendahl, H. R., *Acta Physiol. Scand.*, **56,** 42 (1962)

74. Schück, O., Andrysek, O., and Andryskovà, J., *Experientia*, **18,** 8 (1962)

75. Thurau, K., and Deetjen, P., *Arch. Ges. Physiol.*, **274,** 567 (1962)

76. Kramer, K., Deetjen, P., and Brechtelsbauer, H., *Arch. Ges. Physiol.*, **274,** 63 (1961)

77. Aukland, K., and Krog, J., *Acta Physiol. Scand.*, **52,** 350 (1961)

78. Ulfendahl, H. R., *Acta Soc. Med. Upsalien.*, **67,** 95 (1962)

79. Ruiz-Guinazu, A., Pehling, G., Rumrich, G., and Ullrich, K. J., *Arch. Ges. Physiol.*, **274,** 311 (1961)

80. Thurau, K., Deetjen, P., and Kramer, K., *Arch. Ges. Physiol.*, **270,** 270 (1960)

81. Pappenheimer, J. R., and Kinter, W. B., *Am. J. Physiol.*, **185,** 377 (1956)

82. Ulfendahl, H. R., *Acta Physiol. Scand.*, **56,** 61 (1962)

83. Ullrich, K. J., Pehling, G., and Stöckle, H., *Arch. Ges. Physiol.*, **273,** 573 (1961)

84. Kramer, K., Thurau, K., and Deetjen, P., *Arch. Ges. Physiol.*, **270,** 251 (1960)

85. Gottschalk, C. W., Mylle, M., Lassiter, W. E., and Crawford, J. D., *Compt. Rend. Congr. Intern. Nephrol.*, *Geneva Evian, 1st, 1960,* 12 (1961)

86. Levitin, H., Goodman, A., Pigeon, G., and Epstein, F. H., *J. Clin. Invest.*, **41,** 1145 (1962)

87. Gertz, K. H., Kennedy, G. C., and Ullrich, K. J., *Proc. Intern. Congr. Physiol. Sci.*, *22nd,* **II,** 254 (1962)

88. Schmidt-Nielsen, B., *Am. Heart J.*, 62, 579 (1961)
89. Rubini, M. E., *J. Clin. Invest.*, 40, 2215 (1961)
90. Buchborn, E., and Anastasakis, S., *Der Internist*, 2, 611 (1961)
91. MacDonald, M. K., Sabour, M. S., Lambie, A. T., and Robson, J. S., *Quart. J. Exptl. Physiol.*, 47, 262 (1962)
92. Gasic, G., and Morrison, A. B., *Federation Proc.*, 21, 428 (1962)
93. Smith, W. O., Baxter, D. J., Lindner, A., and Ginn, H. E., *J. Lab. Clin. Med.*, 59, 211 (1962)
94. Manitius, A., and Epstein, F. H., *Federation Proc.*, 21, 309 (1962)
95. Yoon, M. C., and Hong, S. K., *J. Appl. Physiol.*, 16, 815 (1961)
96. Abbrecht, P. H., and Malvin, R. L., *Am. J. Physiol.*, 201, 754 (1961)
97. Herms, W., Abbrecht, P. H., and Malvin, R. L., *Federation Proc.*, 21, 427 (1962)
98. Leaf, A., and Frazier, H. S., *Progr. Cardiovascular Disease* 4, 47 (1961)
99. Andersen, B., and Ussing, H. H., *Acta Physiol. Scand.*, 39, 228 (1957)
100. Leaf, A., and Hays, R. M., *Recent Progr. Hormone Res.* (1960)
101. Hays, R. M., and Leaf, A., *J. Gen. Physiol.*, 45, 905 (1962)
102. Petersen, M. J., and Edelman, I. S., *Federation Proc.*, 21, 146 (1962)
103. Dombrádi, G. A., Krizsa, F., Jancsó, T., and Obál, F., *Acta Physiol. Hung.*, 18, 203 (1961)
104. Friedman, S. M., and Sréter, F. A., *Endocrinology*, 69, 386 (1961)
105. Brown, J. H. U., and Petkas, A. A., *Endocrinology*, 69, 182 (1961)
106. Hays, R. M., and Leaf, A., *J. Gen. Physiol.*, 45, 602A (1962)
107. Hays, R. M., and Leaf, A., *J. Gen. Physiol.*, 45, 933 (1962)
108. Earley, L. E., Sidel, V. W. and Orloff, J., *Federation Proc.*, 21, 145 (1962)
109. Frazier, H. S., Dempsey, E. F., and Leaf, A., *J. Gen Physiol.*, 45, 529 (1962)
110. Curran, P. F., Herrera, F. C., and Flanigan, W. J., *Federation Proc.*, 21, 145 (1962)
111. Herrera, F. C., and Curran, P. F., *J. Gen. Physiol.*, 45, 602A (1962)
112. Orloff, J., and Handler, J. S., *Biochem. Biophys. Res. Commun.*, 5, 63 (1961)
113. Orloff, J., and Handler, J. S., *J. Clin. Invest.*, 41, 702 (1962)
114. Gale, C. C., Taleisnik, S., and McCann,

S. M., *Am. J. Physiol.*, 201, 811 (1961)
115. Witte, E., Reineck, H., and Gauer, O. H., *Arch. Ges. Physiol.*, 274, 262 (1961)
116. Schroeder, R., and Nietmann, E., *Klin. Wochschr.*, 39, 246 (1961)
117. Carter, N. W., Rector, F. C., Jr., and Seldin, D. W., *New Engl. J. Med.*, 264, 67 (1961)
118. Ginetzinsky, A. G., and Krestinskaya, T. V., *Physiol. Bohemoslov.*, 11, 1 (1962)
119. Ginetzinsky, A., *Symp. Czech. Acad. Sci. Prague*, 63–76 (1960)
120. Dicker, S. E., and Eggleton, M. G., *J. Physiol. (London)*, 157, 351 (1961)
121. Dicker, S. E., and Eggleton, M. G., *Compt. Rend. Congr. Intern. Nephrol., Geneva Evian, 1st, 1960*, 609 (1961)
122. Ginetzinsky, A. G., Vasilyeva, V. F., and Natochin, Y. V., *Doklady Akad. Nauk SSSR*, 141, 502 (1961)*
123. Ginetsinskii, A. G., and Vasil'eva, V. F., *Bull. Exptl. Biol. Med.*, 52, 747 (1961)*
124. Breddy, P., Cooper, G., and Boss, J., *Nature*, 192, 76 (1961)
125. Heller, J., and Lojda, Z., *Physiol. Bohemoslov.*, 9, 504 (1960)
126. Boyce, W. H., King, J. S., Jr., and Fielden, M. L., *J. Clin. Invest.*, 40, 1453 (1961)
127. Čapek, K., and Heller, J., *Nature* (In print)
128. Levinsky, N. G., Davidson, D. G., and Berliner, R. W., *J. Clin. Invest.*, 38, 730 (1959)
129. LaBella, F. S., Beaulieu, G., and Reifenstein, R. J., *Nature*, 193, 173 (1962)
130. Chaudhury, R. R., Chuttani, H. K., and Ramalingaswami, V., *Clin. Sci.*, 21, 199 (1961)
131. Čapek, K., and Heller, J., *Physiol. Bohemoslov.*, 10, 522 (1961)
132. Janovský, M., Martínek, J., and Stanincová, V., *Cesk. Fysiol.*, 10, 251 (1961)
133. Brooks, C. McC., Ushiyama, J., and Lange, G., *Am. J. Physiol.*, 202, 487 (1962)
134. Giebisch, G., *J. Gen. Physiol.*, 44, 659 (1961)
135. Whittembury, G., and Windhager, E. E., *J. Gen. Physiol.*, 44, 679 (1961)
136. Whittembury, G., Sugino, N., and Solomon, A. K., *J. Gen. Physiol.*, 44, 689 (1961)

137. Oken, D. E., and Solomon, A. K., *Compt. Rend. Congr. Intern. Nephrol., Geneva Evian, 1st, 1960*, 52 (1961)

138. Kashgarian, M., and Stöckle, H., *Proc. Intern. Congr. Physiol. Sci., 22nd, Free Commun.*, 253 (1962)

139. Marsh, D., and Rumrich, G., *Proc. Intern. Congr. Physiol. Sci., 22nd, Free Commun.*, 251 (1962)

140. Windhager, E. E., and Giebisch, G., *Nature*, **191**, 1205 (1961)

141. Gertz, K. H., *Proc. Intern. Congr. Physiol. Sci., 22nd*, **I**, 370 (1962)

142. Thurau, K., and Deetjen, P., *Nach. Akad. Wiss. Göttingen, II. Math. Physik. Kl.*, **2**, 27 (1961)

143. Giebisch, G., and Windhager, E. E., *Proc. Intern. Congr. Physiol., 22nd*, **I**, 362 (1962)

144. Schlögl, R., *Zum Materietransport durch Porenmembranen. Neuere theoretische und experimentelle Untersuchungen Habil. Schrift Göttingen 1957*

145. Giebisch, G., Klose, R. M., and Windhager, E. E., *Federation Proc.*, **21**, 432 (1962)

146. Leyssac, P. P., Lassen, U. V., and Thaysen, J. H., *Biochem. Biophys. Acta*, **48**, 602 (1961)

147. Rector, F. C., Jr., and Clapp, J. R., *J. Clin. Invest.*, **41**, 101 (1962)

148. Clapp, J. R., Rector, F. C., Jr., and Seldin, D. W., *Am. J. Physiol.*, **202**, 781 (1962)

149. Solomon, S., *J. Cellular Comp. Physiol.*, **49**, 351 (1957)

150. Hierholzer, K., *Am. J. Physiol.*, **201**, 318 (1961)

151. Hierholzer, K., *Klin. Wochschr.*, **39**, 773 (1961)

152. Vander, A. J., *Am. J. Physiol.*, **201**, 505 (1961)

153. Sullivan, L. P., *Am. J. Physiol.*, **201**, 774 (1961)

154. Toussaint, C., and Vereerstraeten, P., *Am. J. Physiol.*, **202**, 768 (1962)

155. Orloff, J., Kahn, M., and Brenes, L., *Am. J. Physiol.*, **201**, 747 (1961)

156. Post, R. L., and Jolly, P. C., *Biochem. Biophys. Acta*, **25**, 118 (1957)

157. Lambert, P. P., *Compt. Rend. Congr. Intern. Nephrol. Geneva Evian, 1st, 1960*, 402 (1961)

158. Goldsmith, C., Rector, F. C., Jr., and Seldin, D. W., *J. Clin. Invest.*, **41**, 850 (1962)

159. Walser, M., *Am. J. Physiol.*, **201**, 769 (1961)

160. Lassiter, W. E., Gottschalk, C. W., and Mylle, M., *Federation Proc.*, **21**, 435 (1962)

161. Samachson, J., and Spencer-Laszlo, H., *J. Appl. Physiol.*, **17**, 525 (1962)

162. Robinson, B. H. B., Marsh, E. B., Jr., Duckett, J. W., Jr., and Walser, M., *Proc. Intern. Congr. Physiol. Sci., 22nd, Free Commun.*, 248 (1962)

163. Bronner, F., and Thompson, D. D., *J. Physiol. (London)*, **157**, 232 (1961)

164. Robinson, R. R., and Portwood, R. M., *Am. J. Physiol.*, **202**, 309 (1962)

165. Kalbfleisch, J. M., Lindeman, R. D., and Smith, W. O., *J. Lab. Clin. Med.*, **58**, 833 (1961)

166. Handler, J. S., *Am. J. Physiol.*, **202**, 787 (1962)

167. Carrasquer, G., and Brodsky, W. A., *Am. J. Physiol.*, **201**, 499 (1961)

168. Levinsky, N. G., and Davidson, D. G., *Am. J. Physiol.*, **191**, 530 (1957)

169. Widrow, S. H., and Levinsky, N. G., *Federation Proc.*, **21**, 435 (1962)

170. Copp, D. H., Cameron, E. C., Cheney, B. A., Davidson, A. G. F., and Henze, K. G., *Endocrinology*, **70**, 638 (1962)

171. Ulrich, F., *Biochem. J.*, **80**, 532 (1961)

172. Davies, R. E., Delluva, A. M. Deyrup, I. J., and Winters, R. W., *Membrane Transport and Metabolism. Proc. Symp. Praha, 1960*, 285 (1961) (Kleinzeller, A., and Kotyk, A., Eds., Czechoslov. Acad. Sci., Prague, 1961)

173. Post, R. L., and Rosenthal, A. S., *J. Gen. Physiol.*, **45**, 614A (1962)

174. Whittam, R., and Wheeler, K. P., *Biochim. Biophys. Acta*, **51**, 622 (1961)

175. Deetjen, P., and Kramer, K., *Arch. Ges. Physiol.*, **273**, 636 (1961)

176. Kiil, F., Aukland, K., and Refsum, H. E., *Am. J. Physiol.*, **201**, 511 (1961)

177. Tanabe, T., Tsunemi, I., Abiko, Y., and Dazai, H., *Arch. Intern. Pharmocodynamie*, **133**, 452 (1961)

178. Tsunemi, I., *Japan. J. Pharmacol.*, **11**, 11 (1961)

179. Vogel, G., Buchheim, S., and Lehmann, H. D., *Arch. Ges. Physiol.*, **275**, 12 (1962)

180. Gauer, O. H., Henry, J. P., and Sieker, H. O., *Heart, Kidney and Electrolytes*, 217 (Friedberg, C. K., Ed., Grune & Stratton, New York-London, 1962)

181. Share, L., *Am. J. Physiol.*, **202**, 791 (1962)
182. Davis, J. O., *Progr. Cardiovascular Diseases*, **4**, 27 (1961)
183. Davis, J. O., *The Physiologist*, **5**, 65 (1962)
184. Bartter, F. C., *Compt. Rend. Congr. Intern. Nephrol., Geneva Evian, 1st, 1960*, 58 (1961)
185. Taylor, A. N., and Farrell, G., *Endocrinology*, **70**, 556 (1962)
186. Davis, J. O., Ayers, C. R., and Carpenter, C. C. J., *J. Clin. Invest.*, **40**, 1466 (1961)
187. Hartroft, W. S., and Hartroft, P. M., *Federation Proc.*, **20**, 845 (1961)
188. Davis, J. O., Hartroft, P. M., Titus, E. O., Carpenter, C. C. J., Ayers, C. R., and Spiegel, H. E., *J. Clin. Invest.*, **41**, 378 (1962)
189. Mulrow, P. J., Ganong, W. F., Cera, G., and Kuljian, A., *J. Clin. Invest.*, **41**, 505 (1962)
190. Carpenter, C. C. J., Davis, J. O., and Ayers, C. R., *J. Clin. Invest.*, **40**, 1160 (1961)
191. Newman, A. E., Redgate, E. S., and Farrell, G., *Endocrinology*, **63**, 723 (1958)
192. Tanner, W. D., and Hungerford, G. F., *Proc. Soc. Exptl. Biol. Med.*, **109**, 388 (1962)
193. Upton, P. D., Dunihue, F. W., and Chambers, W. F., *Am. J. Physiol.*, **201**, 711 (1961)
194. Keeler, R., *J. Physiol. (London)*, **159**, 78P (1961)
195. Panagiotis, N. M., and Hungerford, G. F., *Endocrinology*, **69**, 217 (1961)
196. Yamada, T., *Endocrinology*, **69**, 706 (1961)
197. Davis, J. O., Anderson, E., Carpenter, C. C. J., Ayers, C. R., Haymaker, W., and Spence, W. T., *Am. J. Physiol.*, **200**, 437 (1961)
198. Davis, J. O., *Recent Progr. Hormone Res.*, **17**, 293 (1961)
199. Ganong, W. F., and Mulrow, P. J., *Endocrinology*, **70**, 182 (1962)
200. Davis, J. O., Ayers, C. R., and Carpenter, C. C. J., *J. Clin. Invest.*, **40**, 1466 (1961)
201. Ganong, W. F., Mulrow, P. J., Boryczka, A., and Cera, G., *Proc. Soc. Exptl. Biol. Med.*, **109**, 381 (1962)
202. Kaplan, N. M., and Bartter, F. C., *J. Clin. Invest.*, **41**, 715 (1962)
203. Goldman, J. K., and Cahill, G. F., Jr., *Federation Proc.*, **21**, 185 (1962)
204. Gann, D. S., Kingsbury, B., Drucker, W. R., and Travis, R. H., *Proc. Soc. Exptl. Biol. Med.*, **108**, 99 (1961)
205. Edelman, R., and Hartroft, P. M., *Circulation Res.*, **9**, 1069 (1961)
206. Bing, J. and Kazimierczak, J., *Compt. Rend. Congr. Intern. Nephrol., Geneva Evian, 1st, 1960*, 641 (1961)
207. Tobian, L., Janecek, J., and Tomboulian, A., *Proc. Soc. Exptl. Biol. Med.*, **100**, 94 (1959)
208. Tobian, L., Perry, S., and Mork, J., *J. Lab. Clin. Med.*, **58**, 963 (1961)
209. Dunihue, F. W., Bloomfield, M., and Robertson, W. Van B., *Endocrinology*, **69**, 934 (1961)
210. Tobian, L., *Compt. Rend. Congr. Intern. Nephrol., Geneva Evian, 1st, 1960*, 675 (1961)
211. Demopoulos, H., Kaley, G., and Zweifach, B. W., *Circulation Res.*, **9**, 845 (1961)
212. Scornik, O. A., and Paladini, A. C., *Am. J. Physiol.*, **201**, 526 (1961)
213. Boucher, R., Biron, P. and Genest, J., *Can. J. Biochem. Physiol.*, **39**, 581 (1961)
214. Lever, A. F., and Peart, W. S., *J. Physiol. (London)*, **160**, 548 (1962)
215. Peart, W. S., Robertson, J. I. S., and Grahame-Smith, D. G., *Circulation Res.*, **9**, 1171 (1961)
216. Merrill, J. P., Giordano, C., and Heetderks, D. R., *Am. J. Med.*, **31**, 931 (1961)
217. Schröder, R., *Klin. Wochschr.*, **40**, 752 (1962)
218. Nowaczynski, W., Koiw, E., Biron, P., Chrétien, M., and Genest, J., *Can. J. Biochem. Physiol.*, **40**, 727 (1962)
219. Regoli, D., Brunner, H., and Gross, F., *Helv. Physiol. Pharmacol. Acta*, **19**, C101 (1961)
220. Laragh, J. H. and Stoerck, H. C., *J. Clin. Invest.*, **36**, 383 (1957)
221. Gann, D. S., Cruz, J. F., Casper, A. G. T., and Bartter, F. C., *J. Clin. Invest.*, **202**, 991 (1962)
222. Urquhart, J., Davis, J. O., and Higgins, J. T., Jr., *Federation Proc.*, **21**, 186 (1962)
223. Koczorek, K. R., von Bubnoff, M., and Riecker, G., *Klin. Wochschr.*, **40**, 113 (1962)
224. Mills, J. N., *Brit. Med. Bull.*, **18**, 170 (1962)
225. Wright, R. D., *Brit. Med. Bull.*, **18**, 159 (1962)
226. Crabbé, J., *Nature*, **191**, 817 (1961)
227. Greene, J. A., and Wilde, W. S., *Federation Proc.*, **21**, 431 (1962)
228. Luetscher, J. A., Dowdy, A., Lew, W.,

and Callaghan, A. M., *Endocrinology*, **70**, 445 (1962)

229. Ross, E. J., *Brit. Med. Bull.*, **18**, 164 (1962)

230. Gross, F., *Deut. Med. Wochschr.*, **86**, 1989 (1961)

231. French, I. W., and Manery, J. F., *Federation Proc.*, **21**, 186 (1962)

232. Streeten, D. H. P., and Spach, C., *J. Clin. Invest.*, **41**, 1403 (1962)

233. Cole, D. F., *J. Endocrinol.*, **24**, vii (1962)

234. Holmes, W. N., Phillips, J. G., and Butler, D. G., *Endocrinology*, **69**, 483 (1961)

235. Phillips, J. G., Holmes, W. N., and Butler, D. G., *Endocrinology*, **69**, 958 (1961)

236. Phillips, J. G., and Bellamy, D., *J. Endocrinol.*, **24**, vi (1962)

237. Crabbé, J., *J. Clin. Invest.*, **40**, 2103 (1961)

238. Crabbé, J., *Endocrinol.*, **69**, 673 (1961)

239. Davis, J. O., Holman, J. E., Carpenter, C. C. J., Urquhart, J., and Higgins, J. T., Jr., *Proc. Intern. Congr. Physiol. Sci.*, *22nd, Free Commun.*, 247 (1962)

240. Rosenfeld, J. B., and Schwartz, W. B., *J. Clin. Invest.*, **41**, 1395 (1962)

241. Kinter, W. B., and Cline, A. L., *Am. J. Physiol.*, **201**, 309 (1961)

242. Torretti, J., Weiner, I. M., and Mudge, G. H., *J. Clin. Invest.*, **41**, 793 (1962)

243. Peters, L., *Pharmacol. Rev.*, **12**, 1 (1960)

244. Rennick B., Hamilton, B., and Evans, R., *Am. J. Physiol.*, **201**, 743 (1961)

245. Edwards, K. D. G., Crawford, M. A., Dempster, W. J., Milne, M. D., and Sicinski, A., *Clin. Sci.*, **21**, 175 (1961)

246. Pilkington, L. A., and Keyl, M. J., *Federation Proc.*, **21**, 434, (1962)

247. Farah, A., and Frazer, M., *J. Pharmacol. Exptl. Therap.*, **134**, 245 (1961)

248. Vander, A. J., *Am. J. Physiol.*, **202**, 319 (1962)

249. Knoefel, P. K., Huang, K. C., and Jarboe, C. H., *J. Pharmacol. Exptl. Therap.*, **134**, 266 (1961)

250. Huang, K. C., *Federation Proc.*, **21**, 433 (1962)

251. Knoefel, P. K., *Proc. Soc. Exptl. Biol. Med.*, **109**, 148 (1962)

252. Dayton, P. G., Yü, T. F., Chen, W., Berger, L., West, L. A., and Gutman, A. B., *Federation Proc.*, **21**, 426 (1962)

253. Berglund, F., Elwin, C. E., and Sundwall, A., *Biochem. Pharmacol.*, **11**, 383 (1962)

254. Despopoulos, A., *Compt. Rend. Congr. Intern. Nephrol.*, *Geneva Evian, 1st*, *1960*, 706 (1961)

255. Webber, W. A., Brown, J. L., and Pitts, R. F., *Am. J. Physiol.*, **200**, 380 (1961)

256. Neame, K. D., *J. Physiol. (London)*, **162**, 1 (1962)

257. Rosenberg, L. E., Blair, A., and Segal, S., *Biochim. Biophys. Acta*, **54**, 479 (1961)

258. Rosenberg, L. E., and Segal, S., *J. Clin. Invest.*, **41**, 1394 (1962)

259. Gerok, W., and Gayer, J., *Compt. Rend. Congr. Intern. Nephrol.*, *Geneva Evian, 1st*, *1960*, 720 (1961)

260. Gayer, J., and Gerok, W., *Klin. Wochschr.*, **39**, 1054 (1961)

261. Gayer, J., and Kreutz, F., *Klin. Wochschr.*, **40**, 289 (1962)

262. Frimpter, G. W., Horwith, M., Furth, E., Fellows, R. E., and Thompson, D. D., *J. Clin. Invest.*, **41**, 281 (1962)

263. Huang, K. C., *J. Pharmacol. Exptl. Therap.*, **134**, 257 (1961)

264. Nepomuceno, C., and Little, J. M., *Federation Proc.*, **21**, 150 (1962)

265. Yü, T. F., Berger, L., and Gutman, A. B., *Proc. Soc. Exptl. Biol. Med.*, **107**, 905 (1961)

266. Yü, T. F., Berger, L., Kupfer, S., and Gutman, A. B., *Am. J. Physiol.*, **199**, 1199 (1960)

267. Berger, L., Yü, T. F., and Gutman, A. B., *Federation Proc.*, **21**, 434 (1962)

268. Yü, T. F., and Gutman, A. B., *J. Clin. Invest.*, **38**, 1298 (1959)

269. Demartini, F. E., Wheaton, E. A., Healey, L. A., and Laragh, J. H., *Am. J. Med.*, **32**, 572 (1962)

270. Nash, H. L., and Kirkendall, W. M., *Federation Proc.*, **21**, 435 (1962)

271. Möller, J. V., *Acta Physiol. Scand.*, **54**, 30 (1962)

272. Ayvazian, J. H., and Ayvazian, L. F., *J. Clin. Invest.*, **40**, 1961 (1961)

273. Haagensen, N. R., and Nielsen, B., *Acta Pharmacol. Toxicol.*, **18**, 175 (1961)

274. Dedmon, R. E., and Wrong, O., *Clin. Sci.*, **22**, 19 (1962)

275. Grollman, A. P., Walker, W. G., Harrison, H. C., and Harrison, H. E., *Federation Proc.*, **21**, 436 (1962)

276. Grollman, A. P., Harrison, H. C., and

Harrison, H. E., *J. Clin. Invest.*, **40**, 1290 (1961)

277. Karam, J., Harrison, M. T., Hartog, M., and Frazer, R., *Clin. Sci.*, **21**, 265 (1961)

278. Vishwakarma, P., *Am. J. Physiol.*, **202**, 572 (1962)

279. Cattell, W. R., Spencer, A. G., Taylor, G. W., and Watts, R. W. E., *Clin. Sci.*, **22**, 43 (1962)

280. Anton, A. H., *J. Pharmacol. Exptl. Therap.*, **134**, 291 (1961)

281. Portwich, F., and Büttner, H., *Helv. Physiol. Pharmacol. Acta*, **19**, C99 (1961)

282. O'Dell, R. M., and Schmidt-Nielsen, B., *J. Cellular Comp. Physiol.*, **57**, 211 (1961)

283. Carlisky, N. J., Brodsky, W. A., and Huang, K. C., *Federation Proc.*, **21**, 427 (1962)

284. Gärtner, K., *Arch. Exptl. Pathol. Pharmakol.*, **243**, 113 (1962)

285. Oliver, J., and MacDowell, M., *J. Clin. Invest.*, **40**, 1093 (1961)

286. Bradley, S. E., Laragh, J. H., Wheeler, J. W., MacDowell, M., and Oliver, J., *J. Clin. Invest.*, **40**, 1113 (1961)

287. Malvin, R. L., and Fritz, I. B., *J. Cellular Comp. Physiol.*, **59**, 111 (1962)

288. Rowe, D. S., *Biochem. J.*, **67**, 435 (1957)

289. Rowe, D. S., and Soothill, J. F., *Clin. Sci.*, **21**, 75 (1961)

290. Rowe, D. S., and Soothill, J. F., *Clin. Sci.*, **21**, 87 (1961)

291. Lowenstein, J., Faulstick, D. A., Yiengst, M. J., and Shock, N. W., *J. Clin. Invest.*, **40**, 1172, (1961)

292. DeMaria, W. J. A., *Proc. Soc. Exptl. Biol. Med.*, **108**, 122 (1961)

293. Schaefer, H., Hieronymi, G., König, K., Steinhausen, M., Blömer, A., Günther, M., and Weiss, F., *Z. Ges. Exptl. Med.*, **135**, 83 (1961)

294. Rector, F. C., Jr., and Seldin, D. W., *Am. J. Physiol.*, **202**, 313 (1962)

295. Toussaint, C., and Vereerstraeten, P., *Experientia*, **17**, 80 (1961)

296. Rector, F. C., Jr., Seldin, D. W., Roberts, A. D., Jr., and Smith, J. S., *J. Clin. Invest.*, **39**, 1706 (1960)

297. Rector, F. C., Jr., Buttram, H., and Seldin, D. W., *J. Clin. Invest.*, **41**, 611 (1962)

298. Giovannetti, S., *Minerva Nefrol.*, **9**, 19 (1962)

299. Simmons, D. H., *Compt. Rend. Congr. Intern. Nephrol., Geneva Evian, 1st, 1960*, 709 (1961)

300. Hoagland, H. C., and Solomon, S., *Experientia*, **18**, 228 (1962)

301. Seldin, D. W., Rector, F. C., Jr., Portwood, R., and Carter, N., *Compt. Rend. Congr. Intern. Nephrol., Geneva Evian, 1st, 1960*, 725 (1961)

302. Hall, P. W. III, *J. Lab. Clin. Med.*, **58**, 823 (1961)

303. Balagura, S., and Pitts, R. F., *Federation Proc.*, **21**, 434 (1962)

304. Beaton, J. R., *Can. J. Biochem. Physiol.*, **39**, 663 (1961)

305. Levitin, H., Amick, C. J., and Epstein, F. H., *Am. J. Physiol.*, **200**, 1151 (1961)

306. Polak, A., Haynie, G. D., Hays, R. M., and Schwartz, W. B., *J. Clin. Invest.*, **40**, 1223 (1961)

307. Schwartz, W. B., Hays, R. M., Polak, A., and Haynie, G. D., *J. Clin. Invest.*, **40**, 1238 (1961)

308. Atkins, E. L., and Schwartz, W. B., *J. Clin. Invest.*, **41**, 218 (1962)

309. Cunningham, D. J. C., Lloyd, B. B., and Michel, C. C., *J. Physiol. (London)*, **161**, 26P (1961)

310. Eichenholz A., Mulhausen, R. O., Anderson, W. E., and MacDonald, F. M., *J. Appl. Physiol.*, **17**, 283 (1962)

311. Axelrod, D. R., *J. Appl. Physiol.*, **16**, 709 (1961)

312. Giebisch, G., Berger, L., and Pitts, R. F., *J. Clin. Invest.*, **34**, 231 (1955)

313. Gold, A. J., Barry, J. Q., and Ferguson, F. P., *J. Appl. Physiol.*, **16**, 837 (1961)

314. Richmond, C. R., Langham, W. H., and Trujillo, T. T., *J. Cellular Comp. Physiol.*, **59**, 45 (1962)

315. Adolph, E. F., *Physiological Regulations* (Jaques Cattell Press, Lancaster, Pa., 1943)

316. von Bubnoff, M., and Riecker, G., *Klin. Wochschr.*, **39**, 724 (1961)

317. Relman, A. S., Gorham, G. W., and Levinsky, N. G., *J. Clin. Invest.*, **40**, 386 (1961)

318. Levinsky, N. G., Tyson, I., Miller, R. B., and Relman, A. S., *J. Clin. Invest.*, **41**, 480 (1962)

319. Simmons, D. H., *Federation Proc.*, **21**, 309 (1962)

320. Joseph, N. R., Engel, M. B., and Catchpole, H. R., *Nature*, **191**, 1175 (1961)

321. Langendorf, H., Siebert, G., Lorenz, I., Hannover, R., and Beyer, R., *Biochem. Z.*, **335**, 273 (1961)

321a. Allfrey, V. G., Hopkins, J. W.,

Frenster, I. H., and Mirsky, A. E., *Ann. N. Y. Acad. Sci.*, **88,** 122 (1960)

322. Susat, R., and Vanatta, J. C., *Proc. Soc. Exptl. Biol. Med.*, **109,** 317 (1962)

323. Fitzsimons, J. T., *J. Physiol. (London)*, **159,** 297 (1961)

324. Denton, D. A., and Sabine, J. R., *J. Physiol. (London)*, **157,** 97 (1961)

325. Share, L., *Endocrinology*, **69,** 925 (1961)

326. Lichton, I. J., *Am. J. Physiol.*, **201,** 765 (1961)

327. Winkler, H., Goetze, E., and Meinerzhagen, K., *Acta Biol. Med. Ger.*, **7,** 349 (1961)

328. Friis-Hansen, B., *Pediatrics*, **28,** 169 (1961)

329. Jelínek, J., Martínek, J., and Stanincová, V., *Natl. Congr. Czechoslov. Physiol. Soc., 5th, Karlovy Vary, June 13–16, 1961* (In press)

330. Blechner, J. N., *Am. J. Physiol.*, **201,** 85 (1961)

331. Tosteson, D. C., and Hoffman, J. F., *J. Gen. Physiol.*, **44,** 169 (1960)

332. Tobian, L., Janecek, J., Tomboulian, A., and Ferreira, D., *J. Clin. Invest.*, **40,** 1922 (1961)

333. Daniel, E. E., Dodd, A., and Hunt, J., *Arch. Intern. Pharmacodynamie*, **119,** 43 (1959)

334. Jamieson, J. D., and Friedman, S. M., *Circulation Res.*, **9,** 996 (1961)

335. Haight, A. S., and Weller, J. M., *Proc. Soc. Exptl. Biol. Med.*, **108,** 209 (1961)

336. Dahl, L. K., *J. Exptl. Med.*, **114,** 231 (1961)

337. Mertz, D. P., and Keine, H., *Klin. Wochschr.*, **39,** 1123 (1961)

338. Takagi, H., Dustan, H. P., and Page, I. H., *Circulation Res.*, **9,** 1233 (1961)

339. Peterson, N. A., Feigen, G. A., and Crismon, J. M., *Am. J. Physiol.*, **201,** 386 (1961)

340. Peterson, N. A., and Crismon, J. M., *J. Appl. Physiol.*, **16,** 1103 (1961)

341. Forbes, G. B., and Breibart, S., *Proc. Soc. Exptl. Biol. Med.*, **108,** 697 (1961)

342. Elsbach, P., and Schwartz, I. L., *Metab. Clin. Exptl.*, **10,** 595 (1961)

343. Engel, M. B., Joseph, N. R., Laskin, D. M., and Catchpole, H. R., *Am. J. Physiol.*, **201,** 621 (1961)

344. Levy, M. N., *Am. J. Physiol.*, **202,** 302 (1962)

345. Ochwadt, B., Bethge, H., and Weber, R., *Arch. Ges. Physiol.*, **274,** 66 (1961)

346. McCann, W. P., and Jude, J. R., *Bull. Johns Hopkins Hosp.*, **103,** 77 (1958)

347. Hanson, R. W., Lindsay, R. H., and Barker, S. B., *Endocrinology*, **69,** 883 (1961)

348. Kean, E. L., Adams, P. H., Winters, R. W., and Davies, R. E., *Biochim. Biophys. Acta*, **54,** 474 (1961)

349. Weber, G., *Proc. Soc. Exptl. Biol. Med.*, **108,** 631 (1961)

350. Kissane, J. M., *J. Histochem. Cytochem.*, **9,** 578 (1961)

351. Karnovsky, M. J., and Himmelhoch, S. R., *Am. J. Physiol.*, **201,** 786 (1961)

352. Rector, F. C., and Orloff, J., *J. Clin. Invest.*, **38,** 366 (1959)

353. Weiss, M. B., and Longley, J. B., *Am. J. Physiol.*, **198,** 223 (1960)

354. Ullrich, K. J., Hilger, H. H., and Klümper, J. D., *Arch. Ges. Physiol.*, **267,** 244 (1958)

355. Persijn, J. P., *Histochemie*, **2,** 372 (1961)

356. Gerlach, E., Bader, W., and Schwoerer, W., *Arch. Ges. Physiol.*, **272,** 407 (1961)

357. Gerlach, E., Dreisbach, R. H., and Deuticke, B., *Naturwissenschaften*, **49,** 87 (1962)

358. Thorn, W., and Liemann, F., *Arch. Ges. Physiol.*, **273,** 528 (1961)

359. Whittam, R., *Biochim. Biophys. Acta*, **54,** 574 (1961)

360. Orloff, J., and Berliner, R. W., *Ann. Rev. Pharmacol.*, **1,** 287 (1961)

361. Beyer, K. H., and Baer, J. E., *Pharmacol. Rev.*, **13,** 517 (1961)

362. Bradley, S., *Compt. Rend. Congr. Intern. Nephrol., Geneva Evian, 1st, 1960,* 433 (1961)

363. Malizia, E., Giocovazzo, M., and Isidori, A., *Pensiero Scientifico Editore* (Rome, July 10, 1961)

364. Herken, H., *Deut. Med. Wochschr.*, **86,** 2091 (1961)

365. Modell, W., *Clin. Pharmacol. Therap.*, **2,** 567 (1961)

366. Fried, R., *Arzneimittelforschung*, **11,** 106 (1961)

367. Maren, T. H., and Wiley, C. E., *Federation Proc.*, **21,** 430 (1962)

368. Beyer, K. H., and Baer, J. E., *Ciba Found. Symp., Enzymes Drug Action* (1961)

369. Essig, A., *Am. J. Physiol.*, **201,** 303 (1961)

370. Scriabine, A., P'an, S. Y., Rowland,

D., and Bertrand, C., *J. Pharmacol. Exptl. Therap.*, **133**, 351 (1961)

371. Gertz, K. H., and Ullrich, K. J., *Arch. Ges. Physiol.*, **274**, 61 (1961)

372. Ross, C., and Cafruny, E. J., *Federation Proc.*, **21**, 426 (1962)

373. Stenger, E. G., *Experientia*, **17**, 322 (1961)

374. Kagawa, C. M., and Drill, V. A., *Arch. Intern. Pharmacodynamie*, **136**, 283 (1962)

375. Tobian, L., Janecek J., Foker, J., and Ferreira, D., *Am. J. Physiol.*, **202**, 905 (1962)

375a. Senft, G. (Personal communication)

376. Crawford, J. D., and Kennedy, G. C., *Nature*, **183**, 891 (1959)

377. Kennedy, G. C., and Crawford, J. D., *Lancet*, **I**, 866 (1959)

378. Havard, C. W. H., and Wood, P. H. N., *Clin. Sci.*, **21**, 321 (1961)

379. de los Reyes, M. P., Gómez, R., and Bradford, I., *Lancet*, **I**, 650 (1960)

380. Dávid, M. A., Lászlo, F. A., and Kovács, K., *Lancet*, **II**, 210 (1960)

381. DeLima, T., and Lockett, M. F., *J. Physiol.* (*London*), **157**, 454 (1961)

382. Takasu, T., and Hutcheon, D. E., *Compt. Rend. Congr. Intern. Nephrol.*, *Geneva Evian, 1st, 1960*, 702 (1961)

383. Gillenwater, J. Y., *Federation Proc.*, **21**, 427 (1962)

384. Mudge, G., and Weiner, I., *Ann. N. Y. Acad. Sci.*, **71**, 344 (1958)

385. Miller, T. B., and Farah, A. E., *J. Pharmacol. Exptl. Therap.*, **135**, 102 (1962)

386. Kleinzeller, A., and Cort, J. H., *Physiol. Bohemoslov.*, **10**, 349 (1961)

387. Dzúrik, R., and Krajči-Lazáry, B., *Arch. Intern. Pharmacodynamie*, **135**, 1 (1962)

388. Wesson, L. G., *J. Lab. Clin. Med.*, **59**, 630 (1962)

389. Shore, V., and Shore, B., *Am. J. Physiol.*, **198**, 187 (1960)

390. Mustakallio, K. K., Pitkänen, E., and Nikkilä, E. A., *Compt. Rend. Congr. Intern. Nephrol.*, *Geneva Evian, 1st, 1960*, 645 (1961)

391. Vargas, R., and Cafruny, E. J., *J. Pharmacol. Exptl. Therap.*, **135**, 112 (1962)

392. Jamison, R. L., *J. Pharmacol. Exptl. Therap.*, **133**, 1 (1961)

393. Janaček, K., *Biochim. Biophys. Acta*, **56**, 42 (1962)

394. Liddle, G. W., *Metab. Clin. Exptl.*, **10**, 1021 (1961)

395. Davidson, E. T., Coppage, W. S., Jr.,

Island, D., and Liddle, G. W., *J. Lab. Clin. Med.*, **58**, 505 (1961)

396. Davidson, E. T., and DeVenuto, F., *Federation Proc.*, **21**, 188 (1962)

397. Farmer, J. B., and Petch, B., *Nature*, **191**, 1308 (1961)

398. Nadasdi, M., *Endocrinology*, **69**, 246 (1961)

399. Wiebelhaus, V. D., Weinstock, J., Brennan, F. T., Sosnowski, G., and Larsen, T. J., *Federation Proc.*, **20**, 409 (1961)

400. Laragh, J. H., Reilly, E. B., Stites, T. B., and Angers, M., *Federation Proc.*, **20**, 410 (1961)

401. Crosley, A. P., Jr., Ronquillo, L., and Alexander, F., *Federation Proc.*, **20**, 410 (1961)

402. Crosley, A. P., Jr., Ronquillo, L., and Alexander, F., *Clin. Res.*, **9**, 178 (1961)

403. Krück, F., and Hild, R., *Klin. Wochschr.*, **39**, 1300 (1961)

404. Donnelly, R. J., Turner, P., and Sowry, G. S. C., *Lancet*, **I**, 245 (1962)

405. Herken, H., and Senft, G., *Klin. Wochschr.*, **39**, 1205 (1961)

406. Lenzi, S., Agnoli, G. C., Cariani, A., Lodi, A., and Pinelli, G., *Excerpta Med.*, **51**, 226 (1962)

407. Herken, H., *Deut. Med. Wochschr.*, **86**, 2091 (1961)

408. Koczorek, K. R., *Klinische Anwendung der Aldosteron-Antagonisten*, **2** (1962) (Thieme, Verlag-Stuttgart, 1962)

409. Buchborn, E., Anastasakis, S., and Edel, H., *Klin. Wochschr.*, **39**, 784 (1961)

410. Nielsen, O. E., *Acta Pharmacol. Toxicol.*, **18**, 23 (1961)

411. Nechay, B. R., and Sanner, E., *Acta Pharmacol. Toxicol.*, **18**, 329 (1961)

412. Fregley, M. J., *J. Pharmacol. Exptl. Therap.*, **134**, 69 (1961)

413. Stephan, F., Jahn, H., Reville, P., and Urban, M., *Compt. Rend. Acad. Sci.*, **254**, 571 (1962)

414. Fregley, M. J., Galindo, O., and Cook, K. M., *Endocrinology*, **69**, 1060 (1961)

415. Martel, P. J., Sharp, G. W. G., Slorach, S. A., and Vipond, H. J., *J. Endocrinol.*, **24**, 159 (1962)

416. Muller, A. F., Veyrat, R., Manning, E. L., and Riondel, A. M., *Compt. Rend. Congr. Intern. Nephrol.*, *Geneva Evian, 1st, 1960*, 78 (1961)

417. Wesson, L. G., Jr., and Lauler, D. P., *J. Clin. Invest.*, **40**, 1967 (1961)

418. Naets, J. P., *Compt. Rend. Congr. Intern. Nephrol.*, *Geneva Evian, 1st, 1960*, 547 (1961)
419. Naets, J. P., and Heuse, A. F. J., *J. Lab. Clin. Med.*, **58**, 946 (1961)
420. Keller, H. M., Khalifa, K., and Reubi, F., *Compt. Rend. Congr. Intern. Nephrol.*, *Geneva Evian, 1st, 1960.* 550 (1961)
421. Cooper, G. W., and Nocenti, M. R., *Proc. Soc. Exptl. Biol. Med.*, **108**, 546 (1961)

422. Sokabe, H., and Grollman, A., *Federation Proc.*, **21**, 425 (1962)
423. Simpson, D. P., *Am. J. Physiol.*, **201**, 517 (1961)
424. Konishi, F., and Brauer, R. W., *Am. J. Physiol.*, **202**, 88 (1962)
425. Astarabadi, T., *Quart. J. Exptl. Physiol.*, **47**, 93 (1962)
426. Ogawa, K., and Nowinski, W. W., *Proc. Soc. Exptl. Biol. Med.*, **99**, 350 (1958)

* English translation will be announced in *Technical Translations*, issued by the Office of Technical Services, U. S. Department of Commerce, and will be made available by the Photoduplication Service, Library of Congress, and by the SLA Translation Center at the John Crerar Library, Chicago, Illinois.

RESPIRATION[1]

By Oscar A. M. Wyss

Physiologisches Institut der Universität Zürich, Zürich, Switzerland

Space limitation does not permit a comprehensive review embracing the whole field of the physiology of respiration. Since chemical control, pulmonary gas exchange, and lung circulation were reviewed in detail in last year's article (1), restriction to respiratory mechanics and the nervous control of breathing, in which pertinent contributions were made in the last few years, seems justified. Lung dynamics have been reviewed up to 1961 by Mead (2) and Petit (3); for the nervous control of respiration, an extensive review article is about to appear (4).

RESPIRATORY MECHANICS

Alveolar surface tension.—During the past ten years increasing interest, theoretical as well as practical, has been devoted to alveolar surface phenomena as related to the elastic properties of the lungs. In his sixth Bowditch Lecture, Clements (5) gave a comprehensive review of the problem, including history and prospects. The basic statement was set forth by von Neergaard (6) as early as 1929, with the experimental proof that more than two thirds of the elastic recoil of the lungs was caused by alveolar surface tension. Von Neergaard even thought that the latter might be decreased physiologically by accumulation of surface-active material, but his attempt to extract such material from lungs proved unsuccessful. After a surprisingly long delay of 25 years, renewed attention was paid to the Neergaard principle. It was confirmed experimentally, and the conclusions drawn were considerably extended (2, 7, 8). The original assumption of a comparatively high alveolar surface tension which would approach that of serum and would remain constant and independent of lung volume, i.e., alveolar area, logically led to the conclusion that the alveolar system of the lungs is unstable physically on account of negative compliance (9). This would mean that physical forces acting alone, i.e., air bubble contraction as primary phenomenon, with consequent gas diffusion into the liquid as secondary phenomenon, induce atelectasis. Without the diffusion component, negative compliance caused by surface tension alone may also account for alveolar instability, in particular when aggregations of smaller alveoli empty into aggregations of larger ones, as occurs between communicating air bubbles of different size; and thus atelectasis may combine reciprocally with some early stage of functional emphysema. Since myriads of alveoli can be ventilated in parallel in the normal lung, they are in a stable state; i.e., their compliance, which would be negative on purely physical grounds, must be made positive by physiological factors. This conversion can only be achieved if the surface tension in the

[1] The survey of literature pertaining to this review was concluded June 30, 1962.

alveoli, besides being kept below that of serum, decreases as a function of decreasing lung volume, that is, of decreasing alveolar area. Thus the stability of the pulmonary alveolar structures must depend on the presence of an intrinsic surface-active material, which may be called the physiological "surfactant" (5). The latter, however, cannot be a soluble detergent, but must act as an insoluble film which covers the wet alveolar surface and, by virtue of its film pressure, depresses surface tension progressively, the smaller the area occupied by a given amount of surfactant.

The Neergaard principle was reinvestigated by Pierce et al. (10) on lungs that were excised from anesthetized dogs and subjected to static pressure-volume measurements. Air, saline, or mercury metal filling was used. The elastic properties were studied before and after treatment with elastase. Surface forces were shown to be dominant. Surface area was estimated from surface work recovered while air or mercury metal was removed from the lungs, and good agreement was found between values obtained from lungs treated with elastase and filled with air and those obtained from nontreated lungs filled with mercury metal. Loss of tissue elasticity was demonstrated on saline-filled lungs after treatment with elastase; but in lungs filled with air, passive collapse showed no appreciable difference before and after treatment with elastase. The authors, therefore, concluded "that elastic fibers are not essential for normal elastic performance on inflation with air."

Clements et al. (11) determined the pressure-volume diagrams of isolated human and rat lungs filled with air or with physiological salt solution, and examined the extracts obtained from these lungs for surface film-forming activity. They found a positive correlation between the aeration of alveolar space at functional residual pressure and the surface activity of the extracts, thus corroborating the view that alveolar stability must depend on the presence of physiological surfactant. Gruenwald et al. (12) made pressure-volume measurements on lungs of newborn infants which had died either of respiratory distress (congestive atelectasis) or of nonpulmonary causes, and compared these measurements with the tension-area diagrams obtained on saline extracts of these lungs. The surface activity of the extracts was found to be well correlated with the alveolar stability of the lungs, both indices being low in the atelectatic group and high in the group without pulmonary disease. These findings confirm the important role of physiological pulmonary surfactant in determining the initial expansion of the lungs after birth.

Recent progress in the chemical and physicochemical characterization of pulmonary surfactant material continued with the physical and chemical analyses of dried pulmonary edema foam obtained by different procedures. Pattle & Thomas (13) found that the infrared absorption spectrum of such material is similar to that of a mixture of 95 per cent lecithin and 5 per cent gelatin. Klaus et al. (14) obtained a 70 per cent lipid fraction, the remaining fraction probably containing protein; neither fraction, however, exhibited activity, although the crude powder was stated to be highly surface active. On separation through silicic acid columns, the lipid fraction yielded 74 per cent phospholipids, 8 per cent cholesterol, 10 per cent triglycerides, 8 per cent fatty acids, but no cholesterol esters. According to Siakotos (15), the phospholipid fraction contains about 40 per cent lecithin and several other phosphatides in smaller amounts. Klaus (16) succeeded in tracing the high surface activity to the phospholipid fraction, and made the important statement that the latter disappeared within several hours under air or oxygen, whereas it remained under nitrogen. This statement may help to explain the toxic effect of inhaled oxygen on the lung. From all these observations Clements (5) summarizes our present-day knowledge by indicating "that pulmonary surfactant is a complex of at least eight components in fairly definitive proportions. These fall into three major categories and a function can be tentatively assigned to each: unsaturated phospholipid to give low tensions; nonphosphated lipid to protect the phospholipids against oxidation; and proteins as the skeleton which holds the lipid body together."

Clements further concluded, from experiments of Tierney & Johnson (17), that the activity of pulmonary surfactant may be inhibited by the accumulation of excess free lipid in the alveolar membranes and that such inhibition may produce atelectasis. In a similar way, the congestive atelectasis reported by Tooley et al. (18) to follow the use of extracorporeal circuit procedures, in patients as well as in experimental animals, must be explained by the liberation in the plasma of the pumped blood of material which, according to Tooley et al., can inhibit the pulmonary surfactant activity.

The chemical identification of pulmonary surfactant was completed by Brown (19), who found that the active material contains choline, thus indicating that the physiological surfactant is an alpha lecithin. Klaus et al. (20) prepared guinea pig lungs for electron microscopy of alveolar epithelial cells several hours after bilateral vagotomy, a procedure associated with loss of pulmonary surfactant, and compared these lungs with those of control guinea pigs. Few mitochondria and lamellar transformations were found in the vagotomized lungs in accordance with the hypothesis that the surface-active material in the alveoli is produced by processes which result in lamellar transformations in the mitochondria of the alveolar epithelial cells. The same authors also prepared cell fractions from rabbit lungs by ultracentrifugation and found that the washed mitochondria and supernate fraction were highly surface active.

Miller & Bondurant (21) showed that only the extracts of mammalian lungs with true alveolar structure manifest a decrease in surface tension with decrease in surface area. Other vertebrate lung extracts, including those of birds, do not differ in this respect from most biological fluids. The surface activity of the lung extracts and the anatomy of the inflated lungs were studied in amphibians, reptiles, birds, and mammals. This allowed correlation of comparative anatomy, respiratory mechanics, and the surface characteristics of lung extracts.

In order to examine whether alveolar surface tension may play a role in determining pulmonary vascular resistance, Thomas et al. (22, 23) perfused isolated lungs of dogs with fresh dog's blood and subjected them to negative-pressure inflation. No significant difference was found in the course of vascular resistance, whether the lungs were filled with air or with dextran solution. Volume changes, therefore, appeared to be the primary factor in determining vascular resistance. Butler *et al.* (24), on the other hand, using a similar technique, showed that a pulmonary artery pressure, kept 2 to 3 cm H_2O below the airway pressure, can maintain blood flow through the lung, if the lung is inflated with air; it must be higher than the airway pressure after partial deflation and higher at any lung volume, if the lung is filled with fluid. It can thus be concluded that alveolar surface tension decreases pulmonary vascular resistance.

Mechanical characteristics of lung and thorax.—From comparative measurements carried out on 500 anesthetized rabbits of different body weights, functional residual capacities, and tidal volumes, Bucher (25) obtained a significant increase of lung elastance with decreasing tidal volume. The difference between the inspiratory and expiratory transpulmonary pressures. however, was found to remain constant over a threefold individual variation of tidal volume, and was therefore considered the preferred functional parameter for characterizing the species (rabbit) with regard to lung mechanics. In the anesthetized dog hyperventilated with oxygen (and possibly apneic), Verstraeten (26) measured transpulmonary pressure between esophageal balloon and tracheal catheter at different lung volumes. Pulmonary elastance was found to be considerably increased if a lobar or peripheral bronchus was occluded by an intrabronchial balloon. Occlusion of lower bronchus was more effective than that of upper bronchus. No difference was observed between left and right lung.

Daly & Bondurant (27) determined pulmonary compliance on seated normal male subjects using either the direct intrapleural pressure or the esophageal balloon technique. With local bubble pneumothorax, compliance was found considerably higher than with esophageal balloon, whereas with large (200 ml) pneumothorax the values did not differ significantly. Respiratory changes of intrapleural pressure were stated to be greater in the lower than in the upper chest, and only with a large pneumothorax are the pressure changes similar in the pleural space and in the esophagus.

During pressure breathing, lung compliance was measured by Kaufman (28) on six healthy male subjects by the endesophageal balloon technique. Compared with normal breathing, there was no change observed during positive-pressure breathing, whereas pulmonary compliance was reduced during negative-pressure breathing. Decrease of vital capacity in the latter condition and concurrent decrease in forearm volume led to the conclusion that the decrease in compliance was caused by pulmonary engorgement.

From records of air flow velocity, tidal volume, and transpulmonary pressure, Ting & Balos (29) determined the total resistance and dynamic lung compliance of normal male subjects breathing through tubes of various diameters. With external resistances which are no more negligible with regard to lung and airway resistance, dynamic compliance decreased and became dependent on the rate of breathing, thus demonstrating a prolonged time constant of respiratory mechanics.

Hull & Long (30) using a whole-body respirator measured pressure variations in right atrium and thoracic esophagus of dogs during artificial ventilation at frequencies between 1 and 17 cps. With sinusoidal pressure variations of 18 to 28 cm H_2O at frequencies up to 8 cps, similar amplitudes were recorded at the two sites, whereas with higher frequencies, smaller variations were obtained in the esophagus than in the right atrium. According to Crawford (30a), the panting frequency of unanesthetized dogs tallies almost exactly with the resonant frequency of the respiratory system, i.e., 5.33 ± 0.7 cps as compared with 5.28 ± 0.3 cps. From driving pressure and volume displacement, Long et $al.$ (31) obtained an increase in energy dissipated by airway resistance per liter of air displaced, with increasing frequency of forced ventilation, because of turbulence and changing airway geometry. Dynamic impedance (dP/dV) was determined at 10-degree intervals during the respiratory cycle, at different frequencies, and airway resistance was found to be a "non-ohmic" dependent variable which changes in magnitude throughout the respiratory cycle.

Petit et $al.$ (32) recorded transpulmonary pressure (by esophageal balloon) and lung volume changes concurrently with airflow and electrical activity of diaphragm (by esophageal electrode) and abdominal muscles, in healthy human subjects. Recovery from forced inspiration and forced expiration is represented in a pressure-volume diagram with a view to interpreting the individual respiratory behavior as to pulmonary elastance, hysteresis, and mode of innervation of the respiratory muscles. Pulmonary elastance was stated by Peslin et $al.$ (33) to increase with increasing rate of breathing, measuring 4.37 and 11 cm H_2O per liter at less than 10 and over 30 breaths per minute respectively. On the contrary, Petit et $al.$ (34) found no change of pulmonary elastance in the healthy human subject between 10 and 100 breaths per minute.

Cavagna et $al.$ (35) determined pulmonary hysteresis in man by plotting the area of the endothoracic pressure vs. tidal volume loops obtained at different ventilations, against the ventilation, and by extrapolating to zero ventilation. Calculated mean pressure was plotted against calculated mean flow. The curve thus obtained led at zero flow to a positive-pressure value of 0.5 to 0.9 cm H_2O, which is almost equal to the pressure necessary to overcome airway resistance and lung viscosity during respiration at rest.

According to Avery & Cook (36) the lungs of fetal goats are twice as heavy as those of animals which had lived a few hours. This finding suggests that the fetal lung contains a large amount of fluid which is absorbed rather rapidly after birth with the onset of breathing. In this connection, the intrapleural pressure was found to be atmospheric in the fetus and to become more and more negative with extrauterine growth, whereas the air content of the excised lungs measured at pressures above 5 cm H_2O showed a progressive increase with age. From pressure-volume characteristics determined in paralyzed anesthetized animals, pulmonary compliance was said to increase and that of the thorax to decrease from the newborn to the adult state. Wagner *et al.* (37) perfused isolated lung lobes of anesthetized heparinized dogs with fresh dog's blood and measured increase of weight as an index of edema formation. At physiological perfusion pressures, lobe weight soon reached a steady state. Abnormally high perfusion pressures caused a continuous increase of weight in collapsed as well as in inflated lungs. Only 10 per cent of the weight increase was traceable to blood accumulation. The slope of weight gain was not decreased by increasing the static airway pressure. The latter, however, did prevent discharge of transudate from the airways.

Dunne & Bernstein (38) studied the intrapulmonary pressure changes during sustained inflation and deflation of the intact lung-thorax of the anesthetized curarized rabbit. From the time course of the pressure decay during inflation and its reversal during deflation, and from the time course of the adaptation elicited at smaller volumes following inflation with a large volume, it was concluded that the pressure decay is caused by viscoelastic deformation of the tissues of the lung or thorax and that the adaptation to inflation results from alveolar recruitment.

To clarify the obvious relation which exists between the rate of breathing and the mechanical characteristics of lungs and thorax, Crosfill & Widdicombe (39) measured lung and chest-wall compliance as well as lung resistance in mouse, rat, guinea pig, rabbit, monkey, cat, and dog. The values were expressed in terms of unit lung volume at the expiratory level, and the time constants (compliance multiplied by resistance) were calculated. The latter were found to be closely related to the rate of breathing observed in the different species, thus corroborating the view that optimal rates are adopted by these animals with regard to the work of breathing. Relative pulmonary compliance showed little interspecific difference, except that it was greater in the rabbit than in the other species. Relative lung resistance tended to increase with body size, except that it was found to be low in the dog. Relative chest-wall compliance was very high in the four smaller as compared with the three larger animals, as was functional residual capacity expressed per unit lung volume.

Respiration was studied by Donoso & Cohn (40) in unanesthetized geese. Pressures were recorded in abdominal or thoracic air sacs simultaneously with airflow or tidal volume. Pressure changes, which were −1 mm Hg to +1 mm Hg during quiet breathing, both increased when resistance to airflow was introduced. Expiration was always of longer duration than inspiration, and expiratory flow rates were lower than inspiratory. Calculated airway resistance was greater during expiration. The rate of quiet breathing ranged from 10 to 19 per minute, the tidal volume from 210 to 155 ml.

Agostoni (41) investigated the thoracoabdominal mechanics during the breathing cycle in two male subjects trained in respiratory experiments. The lung volume was plotted against the intrathoracic and the intra-abdominal pressures. Static intrathoracic pressure exerted by the elastic recoil of the lungs was measured by the esophageal balloon technique at different lung volumes when the airways were open and airflow was nil. Static intrathoracic pressure exerted by the elasticity of the thoracic cage and the abdominal mass was measured by the same technique at different lung volumes during voluntary relaxation, the airways being closed. Dynamic intrathoracic pressure was recorded from the esophageal balloon during the breathing cycle, and the dynamic intra-abdominal pressure was obtained by simultaneously recording from an intragastric balloon and subtracting from the gastric pressure values the difference between the gastric and the intrathoracic pressure determined at the end of a normal expiration. The diagrams represent the two static intrathoracic pressure curves, the crossing point of which corresponds to the resting volume and the pressure prevailing at the end of expiration.

Airways.—Accurate measurements of dimensions and distribution of the airways and alveolar sacs in the human lungs were carried out by Weibel & Gomez (42) using plastic casts, histological sections, and bronchograms. From a simplified assumption of regular dichotomy and average length and diameter of the branches in each dichotomic generation, over-all aerodynamic considerations can be developed; and by taking into account the regional variations of the dimensions of airway elements and of the number of generations, the problem of air distribution in the human lungs can be studied on a sounder anatomical basis than hereto.

D'Silva & Lewis (43) calculated the mean bronchiolar caliber from simultaneous measurements of lung elastance and airflow resistance. The calculations were based on a simplified model closely representing the lung and yielding a linear relationship between lung elastance and flow resistance. This linear relation was confirmed in experiments on atropinized guinea pigs, rabbits, and cats in which lung inflation volume was progressively increased. Elastance and resistance were then measured during bronchoconstriction induced by histamine and methacholine, and an index of lower airway caliber was determined. Critical closing caliber was reached in the guinea pig, but not in the cat and rabbit, because in these animals the large doses of bronchoconstrictor drugs that were needed affected the heart. Lower airway stability was further investigated by Lewis (44) on anesthetized thoracotomized rabbits. Changes in total resistance appeared to be traceable to airway closure alone and there was no evidence of change in airway caliber prior to complete closure.

Collateral ventilation was shown by Martin (45) to occur not through alveolar pores but through larger channels, i.e., through respiratory bronchioles connecting one segment with another across the intersegmental plane. Experimentally, a relatively low pressure was adequate to start collateral ventilation in the excised lung of the dog; polystyrene spheres up to 100 μ in diameter were passed through the pathway of collateral ventilation, and when these pathways had been colored with aerosolizing dye solutions they were identified as respiratory bronchioles.

Airway resistance and the air volume of the lungs were measured by Polgar (46) in newborn infants, with the plethysmograph method of DuBois. From the data obtained it was suggested that with regard to the total lung volume the airway cross-section area is relatively larger in newborn than in older children or in adults. To what extent distensibility of the airways and geometrical factors are involved will perhaps be discussed in the full length paper.

Turino *et al.* (47) studied the pressure-volume characteristics of tracheal segments of young rabbits before and after treatment with pancreatic elastase. From the results obtained, it was concluded that the elastic tissue is necessary for maintaining the patency of the trachea at high intrapleural pressure. From determining the critical velocity at which turbulence appears during air flow through plastic casts of human trachea, Dekker (48) concluded that air flow in the trachea of most individuals is probably turbulent during the greater part of the normal respiratory cycle. This was confirmed by Dekker *et al.* (49) who succeeded in simultaneously recording airflow and tracheal breath sounds on 50 healthy human subjects. Critical "velocity" (ml per sec) was found to be higher in inspiration than in expiration, higher in men than in women, and higher in women than in children.

Hyatt & Wilcox (50) investigated the intra- and extrathoracic components of the airway resistance in unanesthetized human subjects during mouth breathing. Intrathoracic pressure drop was measured between esophageal balloon and intratracheal needle, upper airway pressure drop between the latter and a similar needle in mouthpiece tube distal to the lips. From the curves relating pressure-drop to airflow curves, it was concluded that the upper airway accounts for almost one half of the total airway resistance in the normal, and for approximately one fifth in the emphysematous human subject. More recently, Hyatt & Wilcox (51) determined the velocity profile of the air stream in the upper trachea of man with a specially designed needle Pitot tube. As the profile was found to be blunt under all conditions studied, the instantaneous flow velocity was concluded to be approximately equal to respiratory flow divided by tracheal cross section, measured radiographically. From the velocity of the tracheal air stream, a curve showing flow vs. convective acceleration pressure-drop was calculated from Bernoulli's equation, and the difference between this curve and that of the total pressure drop from alveolus to upper trachea yielded the pressure drop caused by frictional losses in the intrathoracic airway. West & Hugh-Jones (52) recorded rapid changes of bronchial airflow during bronchoscopic examination of patients with normal bronchial tree, using an argon-jet deflection flowmeter. Pulsatile flow caused by the heart beat was stated to produce volume displacements up to 5 ml between different parts of the lungs, as well as flow rates up to 2.5 liters per minute. These pulsations may even promote mixing of dead-space air with alveolar air.

McIlreath *et al.* (53) measured the airway resistance of unanesthetized dogs with exteriorized trachea. Pressure-flow relation showed considerable variations from day to day, which probably were caused by physiological changes in bronchial tonus. No evidence was found that, with the bronchioles constricted by histamine or carbamylcholine, expiratory resistance was greater than inspiratory. In rabbits and guinea pigs premedicated with reserpine, the bronchoconstrictor effect of 5-hydroxytryptamine, studied bronchographically by Jänkälä & Virtama (54), was found weak in the rabbit, strong in the guinea pig. Künzler (55) studied the effect of afferent vagal stimulation on airway resistance in the anesthetized rabbit. Reflex bronchodilatation was obtained with high stimulus strength, suggesting that afferent fibers of relatively high threshold were involved, i.e., fibers concerned with the strong inspiratory reaction or with a general nociceptive reflex.

Copp & Baker (56) recorded pressure changes occurring within endotracheal balloons in anesthetized dogs. Among the earlier findings that were confirmed, the inspiratory increase and expiratory decrease of pressure as well as the decreased pressure during distention of the lungs deserve particular attention. These effects should not be explained as "passive responses to respiratory movements", but as reflex changes of the tracheomotor tonus which increases with inspiration and decreases not only with expiration, but also with the inspiratory inhibition induced by lung distention (57). Some of the additional observations follow: the tracheal dilatation, elicited by painful stimuli and by the constrictive response to noxious stimuli which persists after vagal denervation, reflects the general behavior of bronchomotor tonus (58); the paradoxical effects produced by carbon dioxide and the extreme sensitivity of tracheal tonus to very slight changes in pulmonary ventilation can, however, only be discussed when the completed paper has appeared. Nadel & Widdicombe (59) measured simultaneously volume changes of trachea and changes of lung resistance to airflow (using an intrapleural catheter) in anesthetized dogs subjected to hypoxia, hypercapnia, or increase in carotid sinus perfusion pressure. Chemoreceptor stimulation decreased tracheal volume and increased airway resistance, whereas pressoreceptor stimulation only caused a small increase in tracheal volume. Dependent on intact vagal and glossopharyngeal nerves, the responses appeared to be reflex changes in airway smooth muscle tone.

Airway resistance was measured by Nadel & Tierney (60) at functional residual capacity in healthy adult subjects. It was not altered by previous deep inspiration in the normal state, but was always reduced following deep inspiration for one to two minutes when bronchoconstriction (induced by cigarette smoke, sulfur dioxide, or by histamine or methacholine aerosols) was present. No change of lung compliance was associated with the decrease of airway resistance; whether local mechanical forces or reflex effects were involved remains undetermined. The phenomenon bears a strong resemblance to the galvanic skin reflex elicited by deep inspiration. It may be caused by sympathetic inhibition of bronchomotor tonus and may only become apparent against a sufficient bronchoconstrictor background. Nadel & Comroe (61) studied the acute increase of airway resistance caused by inhalation of cigarette smoke and suggested that the response came from bronchiolar constriction rather than from vascular congestion, and that it was mediated reflexly. It did not, however, appear to be related to inhalation of nicotine or nitrogen oxides, but rather to that of inert particles less than a micron in diameter.

Work of breathing.—The frictional work done on the lungs during inspiration and expiration was determined by Cooper (62) from pressure-volume loops recorded with an esophageal balloon and spirometer in healthy males accustomed to breathing with apparatus. With increasing exertion on a treadmill, frictional work rose somewhat more than with the square of the minute volume, and the fraction accomplished in expiration which at low minute volumes was found to be less than that in inspiration became more than that in inspiration at higher minute volumes. The total work of respiration is larger than the work of ventilating the lungs, but only by a few per cent, because the work done on the chest wall is known to be negligibly small at rest. This does not apply to heavy exertion. Much of the work done against elastic forces during inspiration may be utilized in overcoming frictional resistance during expiration.

Milic-Emili *et al.* (63) determined the mechanical work of breathing from simultaneous recordings of respiratory volume and intrathoracic pressure (esophageal balloon) on five normal human subjects. Comparative measurements were made during muscular work at different levels and during rebreathing (probably starting with pure oxygen) up to the maximum tolerated. The curve relating respiratory work to pulmonary ventilation was found to be identical for both types of respiratory activation. It showed a progressively increasing slope up to the highest values, attained in a representative case at nearly 160 liters per minute for muscular work, and towards 200 liters per minute for rebreathing. The latter value, when obtained by voluntary activation (maximum breathing capacity), required more than double the mechanical work necessary for maximal rebreathing. The authors recommend the rebreathing procedure as equivalent to the ergometer test for respiratory fitness. The same authors (64) compared the mechanical work of breathing in trained and in untrained subjects exercising on a bicycle ergometer. With regard to pulmonary ventilation, mechanical work of breathing was the same for trained and untrained subjects, whereas with regard to oxygen uptake, pulmonary ventilation and, accordingly, mechanical work of breathing were smaller in the trained than in the untrained.

McGregor & Becklake (65) determined the oxygen cost per unit mechanical respiratory work on five normal subjects, during two forms of increased inspiratory activity, i.e., unobstructed "hyperventilation" and breathing against high airway resistance. Work done on the lungs was obtained from the pressure difference between esophageal balloon and mouthpiece, and ventilation volume. Relative oxygen cost was greater for resistance breathing than for hyperventilation. When related to force instead of work, oxygen cost was, however, higher for hyperventilation. Allowance had to be made for the force necessary to deflect the chest wall, in order to obtain similar relation between force and oxygen cost for both forms of respiratory activity. Force was therefore declared to be a more logical parameter to compare with energy consumption than is mechanical work.

Millahn & Eckermann (66) measured the additional consumption of oxygen caused by maximum voluntary hyperpnea in 15 healthy men and found that it ranged between 120 and 170 liters per minute. Between these values, the oxygen consumption for maximum respiratory work was stated to be related to the additional ventilation, as shown by a curve with a slope probably increasing exponentially. At 150 liters per minute, the maximum uptake of oxygen of 4 to 5 liters per minute was found to be concerned with the mere work of breathing, thus confirming a previous statement by Attinger (67). From 18 untrained women examined in the same way, Eckermann & Millahn (68) obtained significantly higher values for the oxygen consumption caused by the maximum work of breathing. Higher airflow resistance in the narrower tracheobronchial tubes was thought to be the primarily responsible factor.

Nervous Control of Respiration

Respiratory center.—Vassella (69) was the first to demonstrate the exact anatomical localization of Flourens' (70) *noeud vital* in the medulla oblongata, the selective destruction of which is immediately followed by primary and definitive respiratory paralysis. Flourens' original concept of a single point lying in the midline had already been refuted by Schiff (71) in 1858, on the basis of experiments in which the medulla was sectioned in the medial plane without serious damage to respiration, either half of the bulb at this level sufficing to ensure respiratory activity. The bilateral representation of the primary respiratory center in the medulla oblongata, to which Flourens (72) himself agreed in 1858, was fully confirmed by Vassella's experiments in the rabbit. Bilateral lesions caused an immediate and complete cessation of respiration, and the area common to all these lesions was found to be restricted to the reticular formation at the level of the obex, covering a transition zone that extends approximately two millimeters from the cranial part of the ventral reticular nucleus into the caudal portion of the nucleus gigantocellularis of Messen & Olszewski (73), which measures one millimeter in transverse as well as in dorsoventral extent. In 16 cases, bilateral lesions caused an almost complete loss of respiration; the area of destruction common to all these lesions, although invading the region just described, spared some part of it. In 48 cases, bilateral lesions did not affect respiration, and in these "negative" cases the area common to the 30 "positive" cases was left partially intact or was spared. Since primary respiratory paralysis means loss of inspiratory activity, the bulbar structure delimited by Vassella's experiments can be regarded as the primary inspiratory center. Its fundamental significance for respiration may also be inferred from the fact that, in all these experiments of primary loss of respiration, the breathing movements were simultaneously arrested with regard to their costodiaphragmatic as well as to their nasal component. The primary respiratory neurons, to be qualified as inspiratory, appear thus to be located in the portion of the bulbar reticular formation delimited by Vassella, where they form the inspiratory center responsible for respiratory autonomy, in accordance with the functional array of the respiratory center as proposed by Wyss (74) in 1954. However, in these experiments which were carried out on the rabbit, the bulbar inspiratory center lies lateral to the radix hypoglossi; the precise anatomical localization may perhaps be dissimilar in other species, such as the cat.

Continuing and completing earlier work of von Baumgarten (75) on respiratory potentials recorded from inspiratory and expiratory neurons of the rhombencephalon of the cat, Salmoiraghi & von Baumgarten (76) succeeded in leading off intracellular potentials from seven inspiratory neurons and one expiratory neuron, the net result of 51 experiments. The inspiratory neurons were identified by their firing during diaphragmatic activity; the expiratory neuron could be recognized by the onset of its firing when diaphragmatic activity ceased. Since bilateral pneumothorax combined with positive-pressure respiration was employed, but no statement made concerning bilateral vagotomy, the question whether respiration was reflex or spontaneous remains open. The main interest of these findings resides in the mode of action of central neurons and their possible interplay. The neurons investigated probably belong to the "inspiratory nucleus" discovered by von Baumgarten et al. (77, 78) in the medulla oblongata of the cat, a nucleus situated beneath the solitary tract system. Whether these cells are involved in the rhythm-producing processes of the respiratory center and would thus be responsible for its automaticity, or whether they generate primary inspiratory activity and would thus be responsible for its autonomy, cannot, however, be inferred by recording the activity of single neurons.

The concept of "pacemaker" neurons does not necessarily imply an autonomous property of a neuronic system, any more than does the authors' concept of "starter" neurons. No means have been found so far of recognizing, from the interior of a nerve cell, whether its slow membrane and superposed spike activity is spontaneous or evoked by synaptic excitatory activation. It has been shown in the rabbit that the solitary tract and surrounding region can be destroyed on both sides without affecting spontaneous respiratory activity, findings confirmed in the cat by Vassella (79) with bilateral destruction of the solitary system, including the "inspiratory nucleus" of von Baumgarten. It is clear, therefore, that the latter nucleus does not represent the primary inspiratory center, as conceived and located anatomically by Vassella (69) in the rabbit, which is still to be delimited in the cat. Many other neurons of bulbar structures that take part in the respiratory act, and even motoneurons such as those of the ambiguous or hypoglossal nuclei, would probably exhibit the same types of unitary responses if investigated along the same lines.

There are, however, several points in the discussion of Salmoiraghi & von Baumgarten's paper which may add to understanding of the central mechanism of respiratory rhythmicity. Three mechanisms, it is suggested, cooperate in producing rhythmic activity.

(a) "Self-reexciting circuits within the inspiratory and the expiratory networks of neurons provide for the maintenance of activity within the network." This may be illustrated by the depolarizing shift of the membrane potential of an inspiratory neuron in the course of its firing period, if this neuron be regarded as a primary one, or as depending on a primary inspiratory neuron. Self-reexcitation would occur not only within the confines of the primary inspiratory center located in the reticular formation (see above), but would also extend to bulbar and suprabulbar facilitatory structures, the latter being the well-known low-pontine "apneustic center".

(b) "Self-limiting systems tend to bring about a finite duration of activity of individual neurons." This also may be illustrated by the depolarizing shift of the firing level during inspiration, if one admits (with Salmoiraghi & von Baumgarten) that the shift of the firing level towards depolarization is the expression of a lowering of responsiveness of the neuron to the self-reexciting activation. This lowering of excitability, however, can not have its origin in the self-reexcitation; i.e., the self-limiting system has at its disposal at least one new link which can only be an inspiratory-inhibitory, viz. an expiratory one. This interpretation probably is not in accordance with the opinion of Salmoiraghi & von Baumgarten, who apparently ascribe the faculty of terminating the discharge to the self-reexciting mechanism proper. Whether a first expiratory link is represented by inspiratory-inhibitory neurons lying in the region of the primary inspiratory center itself or whether these first-order expiratory neurons are those of the bulbar expiratory center depends on whether the bulbar inspiratory and expiratory neurons are located in distinctly separate areas of the bulbar reticular formation or overlap. The self-limiting system also extends to suprabulbar inspiratory-inhibitory structures, representing the second-order expiratory link, which is well known as the high-pontine "pneumotaxic center".

(c) "Reciprocal innervation between the two networks brings about inhibition in the one when the other is active." This statement somewhat arbitrarily applies Sherrington's concept reserved for the innervation of antagonistic muscles to central interaction between inspiratory and expiratory neurons. The motor outflow of the respiratory center, both the inspiratory and the expiratory, may comprise internuncial neurons that subserve the antagonistic respiratory motoneurons reciprocally. The central interaction responsible for respiratory rhythmicity, however, takes place at a higher level and, by being essentially a temporal phenomenon, differs from the reciprocal innervation which depends mainly on the spatial array of synaptic connections. Moreover, reciprocal innervation is displayed symmetrically, whereas in central respiratory interaction, the inspiratory component is primary and fundamental, representing autonomous activity, and the expiratory component is secondary because it is elicited by the former, on which it acts in turn as an inspiration-inhibiting component.

Consequently, the mechanism of secondary inhibition of primary inspiratory activity is already included in the concept of the "self-limiting systems" mentioned above and there is no reason to postulate a third mechanism of "reciprocal innervation". Only self-reexciting circuits and self-limiting systems thus remain, both basic principles which suffice to provide a plausible explanation for the mechanism of respiratory rhythmicity. As pointed out by Wyss (80) in 1950, both processes are performed not only centrally in two stages of interaction, one at a bulbar and the other at a suprabulbar level, but also reflexly by the vagal control of the respiratory movements, a control which at decreased lung volume is inspiratory-excitatory, i.e., "self-reexciting", and with increasing lung volume becomes inspiratory-inhibiting, i.e., "self-limiting".

Manni & Cassiano (81) attempted to localize the pneumotaxic center in the unanesthetized guinea pig. From inspiratory spasms evoked in the doubly vagotomized animal either by transcollicular decerebration or by making a lesion localized bilaterally in the ventromedial portion of the mesencephalic tegmentum, they concluded that a pneumotaxic center is located in the rostral tegmentum of the midbrain. After lesions in the isthmus region, involving the lateral lemniscus, its dorsal nucleus, and the adjacent reticular formation of both sides, bilateral vagotomy also produced apneusis, thus yielding a gross localization of the "pontine" pneumotaxic center. It is, however, doubtful whether real apneusis was observed in all these experiments, for the pneumographic records do not show sustained inspiratory tonus and the authors were probably not aware that nonanesthetized guinea pigs, even without central lesions, may respond to bilateral vagotomy with a drastic fall of respiratory rate and with long and lethal periods of standstill of breathing in expiration (82). Use of this animal, therefore, in which inspiratory drive apparently depends on vagal afferents, may not be particularly suitable for confirmation or disproval of conclusions drawn from experiments made on cats or dogs. Fink *et al*. (83) claim to have demonstrated "suprapontine mechanisms in regulation of respiration" by showing that supracollicular decerebration in cats after initial ether anesthesia induces a high rate of breathing not liable to hypocapnic apnea, whereas subsequent intercollicular transection causes a marked fall of respiratory rate, and makes the preparation again responsive to hypocapnic apnea. The authors may be right in concluding "that a tonic facilitatory effect on respiration originates . . . in the reticular activating system". This conclusion can also be drawn from experiments conducted by Cohen & Hugelin (84) on preparations which on electrical stimulation of the mesencephalic tegmentum and the posterolateral hypothalamus, i.e, on stimulation of the "reticular activating system", showed a marked increase of the respiratory discharges in the phrenic nerve. This increase consisted in enhanced amplitude or sustained inspiratory activity, in acceleration or slowing of respiration, thus demonstrating a rather nonspecific facilitation of respiratory motor activity.

Innervation of diaphragm.—The method introduced by Hartmann & Wyss (85), consisting of double bipolar leading off of individual impulses from among the naturally occurring action currents of whole nerve, was applied by Yasargil (86) to a systematic investigation of the efferent and afferent innervation of the diaphragm in the cat. Efferent and afferent impulses were recorded simultaneously from the nonsevered branches of both phrenic nerves; they were distinguished from each other by spike polarity; their rate of conduction was determined from the time-difference of appearance of primary negativity—at both central and both peripheral leads respectively— of the two pairs of electrodes, and the length of the nerve measured between the corresponding leads.

The motor innervation to the diaphragm of the cat, as studied during spontaneous, eupneic breathing, was shown by Yasargil (87) to be mediated by phrenic fibers with highest conduction velocity ranging at body temperature between 45 and 60 m per sec. From a comparison with the motor innervation of the limb muscles of the same animal, it was concluded that the innervation of the diaphragm of the cat is provided by tonic alpha motoneurons. Whether gamma fibers are included in the low-velocity end of the distribution curve has not yet been ascertained. However, owing to the scarcity of diaphragmatic proprioceptors (see below), their number is expected to be small. For the motor fibers subserving the diaphragm of the rabbit, Yasargil *et al.* (88) found conduction velocities ranging at body temperature between 40 and 55 m per sec, which suggested conditions of motor innervation similar to those prevailing in the cat. It was further shown in the rabbit that with increased inspiratory activity, the velocity distribution curve of the active units is shifted to higher velocity values, i.e., that faster conducting motoneurons are recruited with the higher inspiratory effort.

The sensory innervation of the diaphragm, long since demonstrated anatomically (89, 90), was not recognized functionally until Cardin (91) succeeded in recording afferent impulses of respiratory rhythm from the peripheral end of the cut phrenic nerve in the rabbit. Cardin's findings were confirmed recently by Cuénod (92) insofar as slowly adapting discharges were found to originate in the peripheral phrenic nerve of the rabbit during passive stretch of the diaphragm.

Yasargil (87, 93) was the first to discover and to analyze the naturally occurring afferent impulses in the two cervical branches (C5, C6) of both phrenic nerves of the cat. The total number of slowly adapting afferent units which were found to be active during the different phases of spontaneous, eupneic respiration, varied between 0 and almost 40, with an average of about 20. These units were almost equally distributed between the two phrenics, less equally between the two branches (C5, C6) of each side. Two main groups of slowly adapting afferent units could be distinguished according to their changing state of activation with regard to the respiratory cycle, and this before and after complete motor denervation of the diaphragm.

The units of the first group exhibit highest activity during expiration with intact motor innervation, and appear to be unloaded during inspiration; after motor denervation, their state of activity is highest during (costal) inspiration, because with the changed respiratory mechanics the diaphragm is stretched passively during costal inspiration, more so than during (costal) expiration. These units apparently belong to the "parallel" muscle receptors (comparable to muscle spindles); they constitute the major part ($\frac{3}{4}$) of all slowly adapting units. This first group, however, is not a homogeneous one. It contains afferent fibers with high impulse amplitude and high conduction velocity (80 to 90 m per sec), and others with low impulse amplitude and low conduction velocity (below 70 m per sec). The receptors of the former fibers are particularly sensitive to passive stretch of the diaphragm and, after motor denervation, cease discharging almost entirely during expiration. The receptors of the latter fibers are much less sensitive to passive stretch and, after motor denervation, enter a steady state of discharge which is little modified by the remaining respiratory movements of the chest.

The units of the second group show highest activity during inspiration (up to almost 100 impulses per sec), as long as the motor innervation is preserved. After motor denervation, the discharge drops to low impulse rates and may even cease entirely. These units undoubtedly belong to the "series" tendon receptors (comparable with the Golgi organs); they constitute the minor part ($\frac{1}{4}$) of all slowly adapting units. This second group is uniformly made up of afferent fibers conducting at velocities above 70 m per sec; the corresponding receptors, however, are much less sensitive to passive stretch of the diaphragm than are those of the first group.

From this investigation of the slowly adapting afferent units of the diaphragm of the cat, Yasargil (87) concluded that the proprioceptive innervation of the diaphragm is similar to that of the skeletal muscle, i.e., that the units described correspond *seriatim* to group Ia, group II, and group Ib afferent fibers, although their absolute number is considerably smaller in the phrenic nerves than in the motor nerves of the limb muscles.

Besides these slowly adapting afferent units, others which adapt rapidly and respond to passive stretch of the diaphragm were found in relatively large numbers in all four branches of the phrenic nerves.

Because of the relatively small number of diaphragmatic tension receptors, as demonstrated by Yasargil for the cat, the physiological role of diaphragmatic proprioceptors cannot be convincingly demonstrated by experiments such as those conducted by Sant'Ambrogio *et al.* (94) on anesthetized or decerebrate cats. If, after vagotomy, the electromyographic activity of the diaphragm still increases on abdominal compression, and if this effect persists after complete somatic deafferentation, one may assume that the latter was not complete or that the leading off from the diaphragm was facilitated mechanically.

Pulmonary stretch receptors.—Widdicombe (95) measured the activity of pulmonary stretch receptors by recording from single fibers of the peripheral vagus nerve in cats and rabbits, anesthetized with pentobarbital sodium. The responsiveness to graded lung inflation was determined by establishing curves relating lung volume to fiber discharge-frequency before, during, and after production of pulmonary edema (by intravenous isotonic saline in the cats, and epinephrine in the rabbits), lung collapse, bronchoconstriction (by histamine aerosols), or inspiratory efforts (by tracheal occlusion). After each of these procedures, three-quarters of the receptors examined exhibited a significant increase of the discharge frequency at all lung volumes, and consequently showed a marked lowering of their firing threshold. From these findings the author concluded that the apparent sensitization of the stretch receptors is caused by changes in lung mechanics, i.e., that the receptors are located in the air passages and are sensitive to circumferential stretch.

Using a similar technique for recording the activity of pulmonary stretch receptors, Holmes & Troquet (96) studied the immediate respiratory effects shown by rabbits and rats, anesthetized with urethane, when suddenly exposed to high concentrations of ozone. In the rabbit, the activity of the stretch receptors increased considerably within a few minutes, thus yielding a plausible explanation for the initial tachypnea observed in this animal as soon as it is exposed to ozone inhalation. The rat, on the contrary, responds with a bradypnea or with apnea, and its pulmonary stretch receptors sometimes show a decrease in activity during inspiration, whereas a tonic activity appears during expiration. The apnea obtained may represent a tonic inspiratory reaction not essentially different from the tachypnea observed in the rabbit. More detailed information, however, should be available before a satisfactory explanation of these findings can be given. The final conclusion that a tonic effect, exerted by ozone on the pulmonary stretch receptors, may be responsible for their sensitization remains open; the possibility exists that ozone, by destroying pulmonary surfactant (see p. 144), induces atelectasis which in turn, as recently proposed by Widdicombe (see above), enhances the responsiveness of the pulmonary stretch receptors by changing lung mechanics.

Reflex control of breathing movements.—A comparative investigation of the Hering-Breuer reflexes was carried out by Widdicombe (97) on mouse, rat, guinea pig, rabbit, cat, dog, monkey, and man. Transpulmonary pressure and lung volume were recorded during inflation or deflation of the lungs and thorax. In conscious or anesthetized human subjects, comparatively weak responses were obtained, as shown by the duration of respiratory arrest (called "apnea") consequent to sudden inflation. It is certain that in man also the reaction to inflation is expiratory; whether the reaction to deflation is inspiratory is not known.

The immediate effects of a sudden increase of resistance to inspiration and expiration, as obtained by rebreathing against intermittently applied volume-pressure loads, were investigated by Campbell *et al.* (98) on conscious or anesthetized human subjects. All responded to the sudden elastic loading with an increased end-inspiratory muscle tension and with a slight fall in the end-expiratory level. These effects, however, did not appear immediately with the first loaded breath, but developed progressively during the five breaths exposed to the added load. Reflex action, rather than simple mechanical effects (including chest wall, properties of muscle, or changes in thoracic blood volume), was considered to be the real cause of these findings. The authors, however, do not believe that Hering-Breuer reflexes are involved, although this would seem to be very plausible. Their reasons are: the response requires five breaths to develop; the rate of breathing does not change; in the rabbit a similar progressive increase of tidal volume occurs in response to elastic loading and persists after vagotomy. They therefore conclude that the observed effects come from "a somatic reflex not necessarily involving afferents from the lungs". This view is not supported by Dejours *et al.* (99) who studied the same phenomenon in the rabbit, anesthetized or not, and showed it to depend on vagal afferents originating in the thorax, as well as on afferents from arterial chemoreceptors. Further, Campbell *et al.* (100, 101), in conscious or anesthetized human subjects, studied the effects exerted on breathing by imposing expiratory or inspiratory "threshold" loads, i.e., by ensuring a given pressure before air begins to flow, either during the expiratory or the inspiratory phase of respiration. Expiratory loading led to increased end-inspiratory and end-expiratory lung volumes, implying development of greater tension by the inspiratory muscles. This increased tension reappeared with each inspiration, as long as the expiratory load was maintained, and disappeared immediately after the first unloaded expiration. Inspiratory loading, on the other hand, led to a reduction of the end-inspiratory lung volume and to a slight reduction of the end-expiratory lung volume. There was evidence of increased tension developed by the inspiratory muscles during inspiration, so that in the conscious subjects, tidal volume recovered within a few breaths, whereas in the anesthetized subjects, reduced tidal volume was sustained during the inspiratory load and, on removal of this load, immediately returned to its previous value. From these observations, the authors concluded that reflex mechanisms are involved, and from the absence of any change of the rate of breathing as well as from comparative experiments conducted on vagotomized dogs, corroborated their earlier findings, i.e., that Hering-Breuer reflexes are weak in adult man. With regard to their conclusion that the reflex inspiratory contraction consequent upon expiratory loading is caused by "the increased elastic load the distended thorax imposes on the inspiratory muscles", it may perhaps be more accurate to ascribe the increased elastic load of the inspiratory muscles to the sudden unloading of the previously distended thorax.

Hypothermia may provide a new means of investigating the reflex control of respiratory movements in the intact animal. Hall & Salzano (102) studied the influence of graded tracheal obstruction on breathing movement and arterial blood oxygenation of anesthetized normothermic (37°C) and hypothermic (28°C) dogs. Over ten minutes after the onset of obstruction, respiratory rate was increased and tidal volume decreased in the former condition, whereas in the latter, rate was decreased and tidal volume increased. Since impaired arterial oxygenation under the imposed tracheal obstruction appeared in the normothermic, but not in the hypothermic state, the absence of chemical drive in the latter may thus disclose the pure reflex effect of tracheal obstruction, i.e., the slowing and deepening of respiration.

Dejours *et al.* (103) studied the immediate effect of external airway obstruction in man during natural sleep. Sudden obstruction at the end of expiration resulted in a shorter and weaker inspiration; sudden obstruction at the end of inspiration, in lengthening or shortening of the following phase of inspiratory relaxation, with consequent shortening of the next inspiration. From this it was concluded that pulmonary proprioceptive reflexes in man differ from the Hering-Breuer reflexes in the animal.

LITERATURE CITED

1. Severinghaus, J. W., *Ann. Rev. Physiol.*, **24**, 421–70 (1962)
2. Mead, J., *Physiol. Rev.*, **41**, 281–330 (1961)
3. Petit, J. M., *La dynamique pulmonaire* (1961)
4. Wyss, O. A. M., *Ergeb. Physiol.*, **52** (In preparation)
5. Clements, J. A., *The Physiologist*, **5**, No. 1, 11–28 (1962)
6. von Neergaard, K. *Z. Ges. Exptl. Med.*, **66**, 373–94 (1929)
7. Radford, E. P., Jr., *Tissue Elasticity*, 177 (Am. Physiol. Soc., Washington, 1957)
8. Mead, J., Whittenberger, J. L., and Radford, E. P., Jr., *J. Appl. Physiol.*, **10**, 191–96 (1957)
9. Radford, E. P., Jr., Lefcoe, N., and Mead, J., *Federation Proc.*, **13**, 114–15 (1954)
10. Pierce J., Hocott, J., and Hefley, B., *J. Clin. Invest.*, **40**, 1515–24 (1961)
11. Clements, J. A., Hustead, R. F., Johnson, R. P., and Gribetz, I., *J. Appl. Physiol.*, **16**, 444–50 (1961)
12. Gruenwald, P., Johnson, R. P., Hustead, R. F., quoted by Clements (5)
13. Pattle, R. E., and Thomas, L. C., *Nature*, **189**, 844 (1961)
14. Klaus, M., Reiss, O., Tooley, W. H., and Piel, C., *Federation Proc.*, **21**, No. 2, 445 (1962)
15. Siakotos, A., quoted by Clements (5)
16. Klaus, M., quoted by Clements (5)
17. Tierney, D. F., and Johnson, R. P., *The Physiologist*, **4**, No. 3, 122 (1961)
18. Tooley, W. H., Finley, T. N., and Gardner, R., *The Physiologist*, **4**, No. 3, 124 (1961)
19. Brown, E. S., *Federation Proc.*, **21**, No. 2, 438 (1962)
20. Klaus, M., Clements, J. A., and Havel, R. J., *Program Abstr.*, *71st Ann. Meeting Am. Pediat. Soc.*, 28 (May 2–5, 1961)
21. Miller, D. A., and Bondurant, St., *J. Appl. Physiol.*, **16**, 1075–77 (1961)
22. Thomas, L. J., Jr., Griffo, Z. J., and Roos, A., *J. Appl. Physiol.*, **16**, 451–56 (1961)
23. Thomas, L. J., Jr., Roos, A., and Griffo, Z. J., *J. Appl. Physiol.*, **16**, 457–62 (1961)
24. Butler, J., Bruderman, I., Hamilton, W. K., and Tooley, W. H., *Federation Proc.*, **21**, No. 2, 445 (1962)
25. Bucher, K., *Helv. Physiol. Acta*, **19**, C59–C60 (1961)
26. Verstraeten, J. M., *Rev. Franç. Etudes. Clin. Biol.*, **6**, 64–66 (1961)
27. Daly, W. J., and Bondurant, St., *Federation Proc.*, **21**, No. 2, 447 (1962)
28. Kaufman, W. C., *Federation Proc.*, **21**, No. 2, 446 (1962)
29. Ting, E. Y., and Balos, K. M., *Federation Proc.*, **21**, No. 2, 438 (1962)
30. Hull, W. E., and Long, E. C., *The Physiologist*, **4**, No. 3, 50 (1961)
30a. Crawford, E. C., Jr., *J. Appl. Physiol.*, **17**, 249–51 (1962)
31. Long, E. C., Hull, W. E., and Gebel, E. L., *Federation Proc.*, **21**, No. 2, 446 (1962)
32. Petit, J. M., Damoiseau, J., Troquet, J., Delhez, L., Deroanne, R., and Rousseau, M., *Arch. Intern. Physiol. Biochim.*, **69**, 409–12 (1961)
33. Peslin, R., Saunier, C., Lacoste, J., and Sadoul, P., *Compt. Rend. Soc. Biol.*, **155**, 1106–9 (1961)
34. Petit, J. M., Troquet, J., Damoiseau, J., Boccar, M., and Belge, G., *J. Physiol.* (*Paris*), **54**, 395 (1962)
35. Cavagna, G., Brandi, G., Saibene, F., and Torelli, G., *J. Appl. Physiol.*, **17**, 51–53 (1962)
36. Avery, M. E., and Cook, Ch. D., *J. Appl. Physiol.*, **16**, 1034–38 (1961)
37. Wagner, E., Rieben, P. A., Katsuhara, K., and Salisbury, P. F., *Circulation Res.*, **9**, 382–86 (1961)
38. Dunne, J. F., and Bernstein, L., *Federation Proc.*, **21**, No. 2, 447 (1962)
39. Crosfill, M. L., and Widdicombe, J. G., *J. Physiol.* (*London*), **158**, 1–14 (1961)
40. Donoso, H., and Cohn, J. E., *Federation Proc.*, **21**, No. 2, 440 (1962)
41. Agostoni, E., *J. Appl. Physiol.*, **16**, 1055–59 (1961)
42. Weibel, E., and Gomez, D., *Federation Proc.*, **21**, 439 (1962)
43. D'Silva, J. L., and Lewis, A. F., *J. Physiol.* (*London*), **157**, 611–22 (1961)
44. Lewis, A. F., *J. Physiol.* (*London*), **161**, 46P–47P (1962)
45. Martin, H. B., *Federation Proc.*, **21**, No. 2, 445 (1962)
46. Polgar, G., *The Physiologist*, **4**, No. 3, 88 (1961)
47. Turino, G. M., Lourenso, R. V., and

McCracken, G. H., *Federation Proc.*, **21**, No. 2, 446 (1962)

48. Dekker, E., *J. Appl. Physiol.*, **16**, 1060–64 (1961)

49. Dekker, E., van Vollenhoven, E., and During, J., *Schweiz. Med. Wochschr.*, **91**, 630–32 (1961)

50. Hyatt, R. E., and Wilcox, R. E., *J. Appl. Physiol.*, **16**, 326–30 (1961)

51. Hyatt, R. E., and Wilcox, R. E., *Federation Proc.*, **21**, No. 2, 444 (1962)

52. West, J. B., and Hugh-Jones, P., *J. Appl. Physiol.*, **16**, 697–702 (1961)

53. McIlreath, F. J., Jr., Craig, A. B., Jr., and Anzalone, A. J., *J. Appl. Physiol.*, **16**, 463–64 (1961)

54. Jänkälä, E. O., and Virtama, P., *J. Physiol. (London)*, **159**, 381–83 (1961)

55. Künzler, D., *Helv. Physiol. Acta*, **20**, 25–38 (1962)

56. Copp, D. B., and Baker, R. D., *Federation Proc.*, **21**, No. 2, 446 (1962)

57. Wyss, O. A. M., *Schweiz. Med. Wochschr.*, **82**, 988–90 (1952)

58. Wyss, O. A. M., *Les Bronches*, **2**, 101–51 (1952)

59. Nadel, J. A., and Widdicombe, J. G., *J. Physiol. (London)*, **161**, 43P–44P (1962)

60. Nadel, J. A., and Tierney, D. F., *J. Appl. Physiol.*, **16**, 717–19 (1961)

61. Nadel, J. A., and Comroe, J. H., Jr., *J. Appl. Physiol.*, **16**, 713–16 (1961)

62. Cooper, E. A., *Quart. J. Exptl. Physiol.*, **46**, 13–21 (1961)

63. Milic-Emili, G., Petit, J. M., and Deroanne, R., *Arch. Sci. Biol.*, **45**, 141–53 (1961)

64. Milic-Emili, G., Petit, J. M., and Deroanne, R., *J. Appl. Physiol.*, **17**, 43–46 (1962)

65. McGregor, M., and Becklake, M. R., *J. Clin. Invest.*, **40**, 971–80 (1961)

66. Millahn, H. P., and Eckermann, P., *Arbeitsphysiologie.*, **19**, 120–125 (1961)

67. Attinger, E. O., *Deutsch. Med. Wochschr.*, **86**, 157–60 (1961)

68. Eckermann, P., and Millahn, H. P., *Arbeitsphysiologie*, **19**, 168–72 (1962)

69. Vassella, F., *Helv. Physiol. Acta*, **19**, 166–82 (1961)

70. Flourens, P., *Recherches expérimentales sur les propriétés et les fonctions du système nerveux dans les animaux vertébrés*, 2nd ed. (J. B. Baillière, Paris, 1842)

71. Schiff, J. M., *Lehrbuch der Muskel- und Nervenphysiologie*, 323 (M. Schauenburg, Lahr, Germany, 1858–59)

72. Flourens, P., *Compt. Rend. Acad. Sci.*, **47**, 803–6 (1858)

73. Meessen, H., and Olszewski, J., *Cytoarchitektonischer Atlas des Rautenhirns des Kaninchens* (S. Karger, Basel, Switzerland, 1949)

74. Wyss, O. A. M., *Helv. Physiol. Acta*, **12**, Suppl. X, 5–25 (1954)

75. von Baumgarten, R., *Arch. Ges. Physiol.*, **262**, 573–94 (1956)

76. Salmoiraghi, G. C., and von Baumgarten, R., *J. Neurophysiol.*, **24**, 203–18 (1961)

77. von Baumgarten, R., von Baumgarten, A., and Schaefer, K. P., *Arch. Ges. Physiol.*, **264**, 217–27 (1957)

78. von Baumgarten, R., Balthasar, K., and Koepchen, H. P., *Arch. Ges. Physiol.* **270**, 504–28 (1960)

79. Vassella, F. (Unpublished)

80. Wyss, O. A. M., *Arch. Intern. Stud. Neurol.*, **1** (2), 1–25 (1950)

81. Manni, E., and Cassiano, O., *Arch. Sci. Biol.*, **45**, 389–400 (1961)

82. Oberholzer, R. J. H., and Schlegel, H., *Helv. Physiol. Acta*, **15**, 63–82 (1957)

83. Fink, B. R., Katz, R., Reinhold, H., and Schoolman, A., *Am. J. Physiol.*, **202**, 217–20 (1962)

84. Cohen, M. I., and Hugelin, A., *J. Physiol. (Paris)*, **53**, 303–4 (1961)

85. Hartmann, I., and Wyss, O. A. M., *Helv. Physiol. Acta*, **11**, C39–C41 (1953)

86. Yasargil, G. M., *Arch. Ges. Physiol.*, **274**, 92 (1961)

87. Yasargil, G. M., *Helv. Physiol. Acta*, **20**, 39–58 (1962)

88. Yasargil, G. M., Koller, E. A., and Bugajski, J., *Helv. Physiol. Acta*, **20**, C41–C42 (1962)

89. Dogiel, A. S., *Arch. Mikroshop. Anat.*, **59**, 1–31 (1902)

90. Hinsey, J. C., Hare, K., and Phillips, R. A., *Proc. Soc. Exptl. Biol. Med.*, **41**, 411–14 (1939)

91. Cardin, A., *Arch. Sci. Biol.*, **30**, 9–22 (1944)

92. Cuénod, M., *Helv. Physiol. Acta*, **19**, 360–72 (1961)

93. Yasargil, G. M., *Helv. Physiol. Acta*, **19**, C36–C38 (1961)

94. Sant'Ambrogio, G., Wilson, M. F., and Frazier, D. T., *The Physiologist*, **4**, No. 3, 100 (1961)

95. Widdicombe, J. G., *J. Physiol.* (*London*), **159**, 436–50 (1961)
96. Holmes, O., and Troquet, J., *J. Physiol.* (*Paris*), **53**, 364–65 (1961)
97. Widdicombe, J. G., *Clin. Sci.*, **21**, 163–70 (1961)
98. Campbell, E. J. M., Dinnick, O. P., and Howell, J. B. L., *J. Physiol.* (*London*), **156**, 260–73 (1961)
99. Dejours, P., Lefrançois, R., and Gautier, H., *J. Physiol.* (*Paris*), **54**, 319–20 (1962)
100. Campbell, E. J. M., Dickinson, C. J., Dinnick, O. P., and Howell, J. B. L., *J. Physiol.* (*London*), **156**, 27P–28P (1961)
101. Campbell, E. J. M., Dickinson, C. J., Dinnick, O. P., and Howell, J. B. L., *Clin. Sci.*, **21**, 309–20 (1961)
102. Hall, F. G., and Salzano, J., *J. Appl. Physiol.*, **16**, 1019–22 (1961)
103. Dejours, P., Raynaud, J., Monzein, P., and Bechtel, Y., *J. Physiol.* (*Paris*), **54**, 320–21 (1962)

THE DIGESTIVE SYSTEM[1]

By Morton I. Grossman

Veterans Administration Center and University of California Medical Center,
Los Angeles

In the dozen years since this reviewer last wrote this section of the *Annual Review of Physiology*, many a hydrogen ion has come tumbling down the intracellular canaliculi. Trying to epitomize the changes brought by these years, one is tempted to say "plus ça change, plus c'est la même chose". But this is not so. While there is much that is familiar, indeed repetitious, there are also whole new areas that have come into being. Many of these new areas do not fit easily under the rubrics that are traditionally used for reviews such as this, and so we are tempted to put them aside and say that they really belong to some other, unspecified, discipline. There are those who believe that organ physiology is dying and that in the future we shall all march under the banner of molecular biology. While admitting that molecular biology is likely to be the most fruitful contributor to further advances, I do not believe that it will replace organ physiology. Rather it will require the development of a new breed who can translate and apply the new concepts to organ physiology. Until that new breed evolves, reviews such as this one will deal with these important new seminal areas haltingly and obliquely.

HUNGER AND THIRST

This topic, long the province of the gastrointestinal physiologist by reason of preoccupation with gastric hunger contractions as a heritage of the Cannon-Carlson school, has now become the domain of the neurophysiologist and the physiological psychologist under whose hegemony rapid advances have been made. There are still enough gastrointestinal physiologists who retain an interest in this subject and the gastrointestinal factors play a sufficiently large role in the over-all regulatory process to justify continuing to devote some space to hunger and thirst in a review of the digestive system.

Anand (1) has provided a good exposition of modern concepts of hunger, viewing it as a problem in the nervous regulation of food intake. Centers in the brain facilitate or inhibit reflexes that comprise feeding behavior. The principal centers are in the hypothalamus where there is a feeding center located laterally and a satiety center located medially. A variety of factors, including temperature, blood levels of nutrients such as glucose, and signals arising from the gastrointestinal tract, play upon the hypothalamic centers to accomplish regulation of food intake.

Morgane (2, 3) interprets his recent evidence on discretely located lesions of the hypothalamus of rats to indicate that the lateral hypothalamic feeding "center" is not a collection of nuclei but a convergence site for critical fiber

[1] The survey of literature pertaining to this review was concluded in May 1962.

systems. He believes that the lateral hypothalamic area can be fractionated into a more medial component, important in motivation to eat, and far-lateral elements, destruction of which produces not only irreversible aphagia but also a metabolic defect interfering with the use of food. Animals with the latter lesion lose weight and die even when they are tube-fed. Electrical stimulation of the far-lateral hypothalamus provoked feeding in satiated rats and caused them to cross electrical barriers to get food. Midlateral hypothalamic stimulation led sated animals to feed but did not cause them to cross the electric grid.

Grossman (4) introduced minute amounts of crystalline chemicals into the "feeding area" of the lateral hypothalamus of rats through permanently implanted cannulas. Adrenergic agents, norepinephrine and epinephrine, caused satiated rats to eat, whereas cholinergic agents, acetylcholine or carbachol, resulted in a large drinking response. Grossman concluded that neural structures regulating eating and drinking occupied the same anatomical locus in the lateral hypothalamus but were strikingly different in their ability to be stimulated by specific drugs. Using a similar technique, Epstein (5) showed that introduction of procaine bilaterally into the ventromedial regions elicited feeding behavior in satiated animals whereas injections of hypertonic saline into the same areas suppressed eating in hungry animals. The converse effects occurred when the injections were made into the lateral hypothalamus; hypertonic saline elicited eating and procaine suppressed eating. Epstein thus showed that procaine produced the same effect as ablation of the neural area and that hypertonic saline gave an effect like electrical stimulation.

In these same studies Epstein (5) found that injection of glucose into the ventromedial nucleus did not suppress eating, contrary to what would be predicted on the basis of the glucostatic hypothesis. Quadde (6) determined the arteriovenous difference in glucose concentration of blood from the brain in human subjects and failed to find a correlation with hunger or satiety. On the other hand, a number of recent studies support the glucostatic hypothesis. Anand and co-workers (7) found that they could correlate the electrical activity of the satiety center with the level of peripheral glucose utilization. Other studies from Anand's laboratory (8) showed that the oxygen and glucose consumption of the satiety center, measured in excised tissue *in vitro*, was higher than that of the feeding center in fed monkeys and that the reverse relations occurred in the starving state. Debons *et al.* (9) used neutron activation to localize gold in the hypothalamus of mice treated with gold thioglucose. Although several areas of the hypothalamus took up gold, the most intense accumulation was in the region of the ventromedial nucleus. All hyperphagic animals showed this localization of gold whereas it was not seen in any of the mice that received gold thioglucose but did not become obese. The glucostatic hypothesis remains an enigma. The neurophysiological side of the story is convincing, but the behavioral aspect is not; administration of glucose increases electrical activity of the ventromedial nucleus, but it does not suppress eating.

Gastric distention caused an increase in the electrical activity of the satiety center in the studies of Sharma *et al.* (10). Andersson & Larsson (11) performed ingenious experiments in which they were able to heat or cool discrete areas of the hypothalamus in unanesthetized goats. Local cooling of the preoptic area and the rostral hypothalamus induced eating in fed goats and inhibited drinking in thirsted animals; local warming inhibited eating and stimulated drinking. These findings give support to Brobeck's hypothesis that there is a thermostatic component in the regulation of food intake. They also supplement the studies of Grossman (4), cited above, in showing that stimulation of a single area of the hypothalamus may have opposite effects on eating and drinking.

The quest for the site of action of amphetamine in reducing food intake has not been fruitful in recent studies (12, 13).

It is widely appreciated that areas of the brain other than the two hypothalamic regions which have been so extensively studied probably are concerned in the regulation of food intake, but there is little substantive evidence on this. Anand *et al.* (14) found that bilateral destructive lesions restricted to the neocortex did not alter food intake in cats or monkeys but that lesions of the head of the caudate nuclei resulted in significant decreases in food intake. Robinson & Mishkin (15) systematically explored the entire forebrain of the monkey with stimulating electrodes and found many sites that facilitated or inhibited feeding.

Rozin & Mayer (16) trained goldfish to press a lever for food and recorded their pattern of eating. Hollifield & Parson (17) found that rats given access to food for only two hours daily increased their food intake and became obese. The protein-depleted rats of Sanahuja & Harper (18) chose a protein-free diet in preference to a diet with amino acid imbalance. Durnin (19) found that most human subjects do not balance their energy expenditure with an equal intake of calories on a day-to-day basis even though they do accomplish such balance over longer periods.

Fitzsimons (20) used hemorrhage or peritoneal dialysis to deplete rats of body fluid without an associated increase in osmotic pressure. In both circumstances the rats drank more water. This demonstrates that there are mechanisms other than the well-known osmotic ones which can initiate drinking. The parallelism between food intake and water intake in rabbits was well documented in an extensive study by Cizek (21).

ELECTRIC ACTIVITY OF VISCERAL SMOOTH MUSCLE

Although it has been known for many years that visceral smooth muscle generates electric currents, clear conceptions of how these are related to contractile activity are only recently beginning to emerge. Notable recent contributions have been made by Barr (22) and Bortoff (23, 24) in Prosser's laboratory at the University of Illinois. Barr (22) studied the resistance across the cell membrane of individual smooth muscle cells of ganglion-free circular muscle of the small intestine of the cat. He found that this cell membrane had a resistance comparable to that of heart and striated muscle cells. From measurements of the resistance between two cell interiors less than 0.5 mm apart, he concluded that no low-resistance pathways between cells exist. Thus the intercellular connections that have recently been demonstrated by electron microscopy probably do not function as low-resistance electrical pathways. Bortoff (23) provided convincing evidence that the well-known slow waves of potential variation which can be recorded from the surface of the small intestine have their origin in the muscle cells of the longitudinal muscle layer. The propagation of slow waves is considered to be brought about by a process of modulation in which cells having a higher natural frequency of discharge ("pacemaker" cells) alter the activity of adjacent cells having a lower natural frequency ("follower" cells). Bortoff (24) also studied the effects of certain autonomic and metabolic drugs on the electrical activity of the small intestine. Epinephrine inhibited spike activity and increased membrane potential whereas acetylcholine had the reverse effect. Bortoff suggests that during normal peristaltic activity the longitudinal muscle contracts first because it can be activated by lower concentrations of acetylcholine and that the tension on the circular muscle produced by the contraction of the longitudinal layer decreases its threshold for activation by acetylcholine.

Sperelakis (25) applied electrical fields to strips of circular muscle of cat intestine that had been depolarized by bathing in high concentrations of potassium. Since he found that muscular contraction could be induced under such circumstances, he concluded that this smooth muscle could be activated by a direct myoplasmic effect of the electrical field without associated changes in membrane potential. Smooth muscle that has been depolarized by placing it in a potassium-rich medium can still show a contractile response to acetylcholine. The mechanism of this effect was studied by Durbin & Jenkinson (26, 27) who found that when carbachol was added to the fluid bathing depolarized tenia coli of guinea pigs, the tension of the muscle increased and the flux of potassium, chloride, and bromide was increased in both directions. These effects could be counteracted by atropine. Thus cholinergic agents can increase the permeability of the cell membrane even when ionic movements secondary to depolarization have been prevented. Both the effect on ion movements and the development of tension required the presence of calcium ions in the medium. At appropriate low concentrations of calcium, carbachol produced a large effect on permeability without a contractile response, suggesting that the movement of calcium into the cell may be the crucial factor in evoking contraction.

The opposite dissociation, that is, persistence of electrical activity with abolition of the tension response, was demonstrated by Axelsson working with tenia coli of the guinea pig in a medium deficient in sodium (28) or in glucose (29). Axelsson et al. (30) believe that the inhibitory action of epinephrine on smooth muscle is caused by an increase in phosphorylase activity leading to an increase in the energy required for stabilization of the cell membrane and not by the direct depolarizing action of the drug.

The relation between motor and electric activity of the duodenum was studied in unanesthetized dogs by Bass and co-workers (31). They call the slow waves the basic electric rhythm and found that it was always present and that its rate, about 18 per minute, did not vary significantly. The slow waves appeared simultaneously at different radial sites around the circumference of the gut, and they were almost always propagated caudally at a rate that showed little variation, 19 to 20 cm per second. Superimposed on the slow waves were spike potentials. These occurred in bursts that started at a constant point on the downslope of the slow waves. Spike potentials were not present on each slow wave, but they were always recorded when contraction was detected by pressure changes, and the number and amplitude of the spikes were directly related to the strength of the contractions. In contrast to the slow waves, the spike potentials either were not conducted or passed over a distance of only a few centimeters.

When these same workers applied their exploring electrodes to the gastroduodenal junction, an entirely different pattern of activity was found [Bass *et al.* (32)]. Between the pyloric sphincter and the duodenal bulb there is a thin segment about one centimeter long which the authors choose to call the "pylorus". The slow waves of the gastric antrum (4.4 cycles/min) and those of the duodenal bulb (18 cycles/min) were either greatly attenuated or absent in the thin segment and the same was true of the spike potentials when these were present. Thus the thin segment acted as an electric insulator between the stomach and duodenum.

MOTOR ACTIVITY

Esophagus.—New methods can quickly revolutionize a field of study. Nowhere in gastrointestinal physiology is this more evident than in the study of the esophagus. In the few years during which accurate manometric methods have been applied to the study of the esophagus, a whole new discipline has arisen; a reasonably clear picture of normal esophageal activity has been provided and many applications to clinical problems have been made. This record of accomplishment is not likely to be duplicated quickly for other levels of the digestive tract; the esophagus is a particularly favorable organ for such studies because it is readily accessible, its major function is a motor one, and the patterns of activity are relatively simple and reproducible.

Nagler & Spiro (33) made repeated measurements of esophageal pressures at monthly intervals for a year in a group of normal young subjects. Certain indices such as the maximum pressure in the upper and lower esophageal sphincters and the maximal pressure developed during peristalsis were found to vary between subjects but to be quite reproducible in any one subject. Nonperistaltic activity, simultaneous contractions at all levels, occurred rather often in certain subjects; this apparently is not always a sign of disease. Small doses of methacholine produced a small rise in pressure in some normal subjects indicating that this response is not confined to patients with achalasia.

The phenomenon of secondary peristalsis was studied in dogs by Siegel & Hendrix (34). Distention of the esophagus produced a peristaltic wave that started at the upper esophageal sphincter. Transection and reanastomosis of the esophagus did not alter the secondary peristaltic response, which indicates that it is mediated by the same central reflexes as those for primary peristalsis and not by a local chain of reflexes as suggested by Meltzer.

Carveth and co-workers(35) studied the effect of various kinds of denervation on the activity of the lower esophageal sphincter in dogs. Cervical vagotomy produced a relaxation of resting tone and abolished the inhibitory and contractile responses to deglutition. Vagotomy at the level of the hilus of the lung had a much smaller effect, and removal of the esophageal branches of the vagus over the lower esophagus, transection and reanastomosis, stripping away the muscle of the lower esophagus, or phrenicotomy had no effect at all. This study gives much useful information, but it does not give a final answer to the question of how the vagal fibers controlling relaxation and contraction of the lower sphincter reach their target; presumably they travel both within and outside the wall of the esophagus.

Lest we forget that physiological studies can be done without strain gauges and oscilloscopes, consider the studies of Clark & Vane (35a) who perfused the lower esophageal segment of the anesthetized cat under a constant head of pressure and recorded the lateral pressure in the system by a simple water manometer as an index of activity of the lower esophageal sphincter. Stimulation of either the central or the peripheral end of the vagus caused dilatation of the sphincter. Distention of the esophagus led to immediate relaxation of the sphincter even when the esophagus was transected and only the vagal fibers bridged the gap. Moderate distention of the stomach caused the sphincter to contract. Acetylcholine given intravenously reproduced the inhibitory effects of vagal stimulation. Perfusion of the sphincter itself or of the stomach with weak acid solutions caused an increase in sphincter tone, an effect not abolished by vagotomy. Clark & Vane believe that vagal cholinergic effects are purely inhibitory to the sphincter.

Gahagan (36) found that removal of the entire muscular coat of the lower esophagus in dogs did not lead to the development of esophagitis but that removal of the oblique portions of the inner muscular coat of the stomach which loop around the gastroesophageal junction did result in severe inflammation and erosions of the esophageal mucosa. Before one concludes that the effective barrier to gastroesophageal reflux resides on the gastric side of the junction, it would be necessary to show that the operation on the stomach did not remove the lowermost circular fibers of the esophagus.

Tuttle et al. (37) described two mechanisms for producing the symptom of heartburn in patients. One mechanism involved exposure of the esophageal mucosa to acid, either by perfusing it into the lumen or by spontaneous reflux from the stomach. Under these circumstances the symptom of heart-burn was rarely associated with any change in motor activity of the esophagus. The second mechanism was associated with belching, either spontaneous or induced by putting air into the stomach. Immediately preceding the eructa-tion, pressures in the gastric fundus and at all levels of the esophagus rose simultaneously and equally while the subject experienced heartburn.

Atkinson (38) has reviewed the subject of mechanisms protecting against gastroesophageal reflux, and Ingelfinger (39) has made a general review of recent literature on the esophagus.

Stomach.—Lind and co-workers (39a) made vagally innervated pouches of the fundus of the stomach, that is, the portion orad to the entrance of the esophagus, in dogs. A distinctive pattern of motility occurred in this portion of the stomach. Slow phasic changes in pressure lasting one to two minutes oc-curred during 80 per cent of the time in which the pouch was active. Waves lasting about 30 seconds and reaching pressures in excess of 50 cm of water occurred infrequently, but they were encountered only in this portion of the stomach. Inhibition of motor activity and reduction of pressure were recorded from the fundic pouch after swallowing, thus documenting the concept of receptive relaxation of the stomach. When simultaneous records were made from the fundic pouch and the lower portion of the lower esophageal sphincter, good correlation was usually observed in the motor behavior of these two regions.

Aylett (40) found that the rate of emptying of water from the stomach of human subjects was speeded by insulin and slowed by glucagon. Glucose, given orally or intravenously, produced less slowing of emptying than did glucagon although the effects of all these procedures on blood glucose levels were comparable. In studies on rats Lish (41) showed that dioctyl sodium sulfosuccinate introduced into the duodenum inhibited gastric emptying and gastric secretion.

A method for recording gastric motility in man by detecting externally the movements of a small swallowed magnet has been described by Wenger *et al.* (42). Bella & Rognoni (43) used an isolated preparation of the stomach with nerves preserved to study the action of drugs. Hunt (44) has summarized his important work on the osmotic control of gastric emptying.

Small intestine.—A favorite puzzle for gastrointestinal physiologists has long been the mechanism that operates to make the contents of the small intestine move in a predominantly aboral direction. Most of those who have theorized on this problem have invoked the well-known aboral gradients of rate of muscular contraction and of oxygen consumption of the small intes-tine. An important contribution to this problem has been made by Dorman & Steggerda (45) who studied the oxygen consumption of intact segments, circular muscle only (without ganglion cells), submucosa plus mucosa, seg-ments without serosa or longitudinal muscle (myenteric plexus absent), and segments without mucosa or submucosa (submucosal plexus absent) taken from various levels of the small intestine of the cat. The steepest gradient was found in the intact segments. There was no gradient at all in the preparations consisting solely of circular muscle or in those with the mucosa and sub-mucosa stripped off. The authors offer a reasonable explanation of these findings; they assume that there are two components to the gradient: (a) a gradient within the mucosal and submucosal layers, presumably neural, and (b) a gradient of the muscular layers that is controlled by the neural cells and is absent when the muscle cells are removed from the neural elements. Hasselbrack & Thomas (46) measured the rate of contraction of various levels of the small intestine of the dog in the intact animal and in excised segments. In the intact dog the rate in the duodenum was 18 to 19 per minute, in the terminal ileum 13 to 14 per minute. In the excised segments a similar gradient was found but all of the rates were about 30 per cent lower than in the intact animal. Local cooling of a short segment of the upper duodenum caused a significant decrease in frequency of rhythmic contractions throughout the intestine below the cooled area but not above. The conclusion was drawn that influences transmitted from the duodenum increase the frequency of contrac-tions throughout the small intestine, probably by stimulating the muscle to contract at a frequency above its inherent rhythm. In my opinion the enigma about the gradients and polarity of the small intestine will probably be solved by studies of the electric activity of the gut. The slow electric rhythm occurs at the same rate as the muscular rhythm, it can be readily measured in both the intact animal and in excised segments, and, most importantly, its propa-gation can easily be studied.

Colon.—After treating rabbits with reserpine, Gillespie & Mackenna (47) found that stimulation of the sympathetic nerves caused contraction of the colon rather than the usual inhibition. The inhibitory effect of sympathetic stimulation could be restored by soaking the preparation in catecholamines. The authors conclude from their analysis of the phenomenon that the reversal produced by reserpine is caused by activation of parasympathetic cholinergic fibers and not by cholinergic fibers in the sympathetics.

Chaudhary & Truelove (48) have reviewed methods for recording colonic motility.

Biliary tract.—The ability of vagal stimulation to cause contraction and sympathetic stimulation relaxation of the gall bladder has been confirmed (49). Caroli and co-workers (50) have found an inhibitor of cholecystokinin in the urine; they assume that it plays a physiological role in regulating contrac-tion of the gall bladder. It has once again been suggested (51) that the com-mon bile duct contains smooth muscle and can manifest peristalsis but no convincing evidence for this has been presented.

SALIVARY SECRETION

Many of the classical observations on the physiology of secretion were made on the salivary glands. The factors that made the salivary glands at-tractive objects for physiological study in the early days are just as compel-ling today; the physiology of salivary secretion is a thriving industry and these little factories are still serving as models for some of our most advanced notions on the mechanisms of the secretory process in general. The monograph by Burgen & Emmelin (52) is welcome because it provides a concise and critical summary of the entire field of salivary secretion.

Schneyer & Schneyer (53) approached the problem of the role of the ducts in salivary secretion by studying two kinds of preparations that have an almost total deficiency of acinar tissue, namely, the normal glands of rats in the early postnatal period and the glands of adult rats whose ducts had been ligated several weeks before the study. Flow rates and sodium and potassium concentrations were nearly normal in both kinds of preparations, showing that the ducts can perform these functions in the virtual absence of acinar elements. Henriques (54) addressed the same problem with the techniques of stop-flow analysis, injection of dilute solutions of mercuric bichloride into the ducts, and analysis of the initial portion of juice after a period of rest in the submaxillary gland of the dog. He concluded that the ducts resorb sodium and secrete potassium at all flow rates. Also occupied with the relative function of ducts and acini, Brusilow & Diaz (55) gave acetazolamide to dogs during the collection of juice from the parotid gland. The drug prevented the rise in bicarbonate concentration of the juice that usually occurs with increased rates of flow but it was not possible to decide whether this was an action on acini, ducts, or both.

When rats were made deficient in potassium by dietary restriction, Schneyer & Schneyer (56) found that the concentration of this element in the salivary gland tissue fell and the rate of flow of saliva was greatly reduced, but the sodium and potassium concentrations of the juice were normal. In subjects residing at altitudes above 15,000 feet, Williams (57) found that the concentration of sodium in saliva was increased and potassium decreased, an effect that he felt might be attributed to a decrease in aldosterone production.

The salivary glands rival the thyroid in their avidity for iodine. Negri & Pochin (58) reported that although potassium perchlorate reduced the concentration of radioiodine in human saliva it did not lower the radioiodine content of the salivary glands.

Langley and co-workers (59) found that the concentration of calcium in parotid saliva of the dog was two to three times that of the plasma but that the phosphate level in the juice was less than one-fifth that of plasma. These same workers (60) showed that the concentration of magnesium was lower in saliva than in plasma but that the two concentrations could be made equal by elevating the plasma level. Stop-flow studies indicated that all of these ions are transported primarily by the ducts but at different sites along the ducts.

Van Harreveld and co-workers (61) believe that the decline in electrical conductivity of the submaxillary gland of the rabbit which occurs during continuing secretion is caused by a loss of fluid and electrolytes from the extracellular spaces. Langley & Brown (62) showed that the secretory pressure of the salivary glands of the dog is directly related to the rate of salivary flow. At high flow rates the maximum values observed were 165 mm Hg for the submaxillary and 72 mm Hg for the partoid gland. Administration of isoproterenol to rats caused an increase in the weight of the submandibular glands (63).

Emmelin (64, 65, 66) has continued his elegant studies on the mechanism of supersensitivity of the salivary glands after denervation. His recent studies continue to support his hypothesis that supersensitivity results from a reduction in the number of stimuli acting on the gland cells and that this can be brought about in a variety of ways other than denervation. For example, the retrograde injection of botulin toxin into the duct of the gland causes supersensitivity comparable to that produced by parasympathetic denervation. Botulin toxin is believed to act by interfering with the release of acetylcholine. Supersensitivity could also be produced by section of afferent nerves of the glands, presumably by reducing extent of reflex stimulation. This finding also provided an explanation for the phenomenon of "antilytic" secretion, a spontaneous flow of saliva from the intact gland in an animal with unilateral section of the parasympathetic fibers to the submaxillary gland. As with the "paralytic" secretion from the denervated gland, the "antilytic" secretion occurs only when the animal is under morphine anesthesia. Morphine releases epinephrine from the adrenal medulla which then acts on the glands which are supersensitive, the "paralytic" one by reason of efferent denervation, the "antilytic" one by reason of partial afferent denervation.

Somers (67 to 70) reports that sheep secrete about 2.5 liters of saliva a day containing about 0.3 grams of nitrogen, mainly in the form of urea. The concentration of nitrogen in saliva increases linearly with rate of flow and also with dietary nitrogen intake. The recovery of intravenously injected urea in the saliva is much greater in sheep that are in negative nitrogen balance than in those in positive balance. Since urea can be utilized in the rumen for protein synthesis, the relatively greater amount of urea delivered to the rumen in the saliva during nitrogen deficiency can serve a useful purpose.

GASTRIC SECRETION

This topic continues to generate more papers than any other aspect of gastrointestinal physiology. While it is apparent that much further work is justified because most of the fundamental problems in the field remain unsolved, one suspects that much of the activity in this area stems from the inertia of tradition; people study gastric secretion because that is what their preceptors studied and that is what they know how to do.

Mechanism of acid formation.—The carbonic anhydrase inhibitor, acetazolamide, continues to be the favorite tool of those who want to know how the parietal cell forms acid. New light on the action of this agent comes from the studies of Byers and co-workers (71) who found that it failed entirely to produce the expected inhibition of gastric secretion of acid when it was given to an animal with metabolic acidosis. This adds strong support to the view that carbonic anhydrase does not play an essential role in acid secretion. Rehm and co-workers (72) showed that the potential difference across the gastric mucosa fell during inhibition of gastric secretion by acetazolamide and they interpreted this as evidence in favor of their view that hydrogen and chloride ions are secreted by separate active processes in separate cells. Powell and co-workers (73) also found comfort in the results they obtained with acetazolamide. They confirmed the inhibitory effect of the drug on secretion of acid induced by histamine in dogs and they added the new finding that the output, as well as the concentration, of sodium goes up. This they take as strong support for their theory that the primary secretion of the gastric glands is sodium chloride and that the sodium is then exchanged across the mucosa for hydrogen ions. This is the latest in a long series of papers from Hirschowitz's laboratory espousing this theory. To me the theory is untenable for the following reasons. The well-known reciprocal relation between hydrogen- and sodium-ion concentration in gastric juice can be fully accounted for by two established mechanisms: (a) the two-component hypothesis of Hollander, and (b) the exchange of hydrogen ion in the lumen for sodium ion in the plasma as originally postulated by Teorell (74) and recently confirmed by others (75). In the many papers that Hirschowitz has written on his theory he fails even to mention the exchange of hydrogen ions in the lumen for sodium ions in the plasma, an established mechanism which would fully account for his findings. Finally, the almost total barrier that the gastric mucosa bathed with acid offers to movement of sodium ions from lumen to blood (76) would preclude the operation of Hirschowitz's proposed mechanism.

Regulation of acid secretion.—The theory that all modalities which stimulate the stomach to secrete acid act by causing local release of histamine in the mucosa has been tested by Irvine and co-workers (77). Their findings failed to support the theory; the concentration of free histamine in plasma of gastric venous blood did not rise when secretion of acid was provoked by insulin hypoglycemia. As the authors point out, their findings do not preclude the possibility that locally released histamine may pass into the gastric venous blood in amounts too small to be detected by the methods used.

It is usually taught that release of gastrin is the sole mechanism in the gastric phase of acid secretion. I (78, 79) have suggested that there is also an important nervous component to the gastric phase. Distention of the vagally innervated fundic gland area in dogs with the pyloric gland area resected produced a flow of acid juice with very high pepsin content. Distention of Heidenhain pouches resulted in traces of acid secretion, but when distention was combined with injection of histamine or of gastrin greatly augmented responses occurred. I interpret this evidence to indicate that distention acts to produce local cholinergic reflexes and vago-vagal cholinergic reflexes which act as direct stimuli for acid and pepsin secretion and also greatly augment the responsiveness of the glands to gastrin. In both the cephalic phase and the gastric phase there are two mechanisms operating, namely, (a) cholinergic release of gastrin and (b) direct cholinergic activation of the fundic glands.

Working with vagally innervated pouches of the fundic gland area of the abomasum of sheep, Ash (80, 81) found that distention of the fundic gland area of the main portion of the abomasum caused the pouch to secrete, an effect comparable to that described by me in dogs.

The concepts of maximal acid output and of parietal cell mass are now important items in our thinking about gastric secretion, and the review of these topics by Marks (82) is timely.

Gastrin.—The long awaited full description of Gregory & Tracy's (83) improved method for preparing gastrin has now appeared. Previous methods of preparation were unreliable, often yielding inactive material. I have used Gregory & Tracy's method, slightly modified, for more than a year, and all of more than a hundred batches have been uniformly potent. One of the interesting properties of this material is that it is highly effective when given by subcutaneous injection, thus dispelling the notion that gastrointestinal hormones are active only when given intravenously. The material is virtually devoid of both free and bound histamine. When carried through all the stages of purification described by Gregory & Tracy, it is slightly more potent than histamine on a weight basis in stimulating acid secretion, and, since this material still is highly inhomogeneous, it is likely that pure gastrin will be found to be many times more potent than histamine. The old questions about whether gastrin is histamine, or whether gastrin is a bound form of histamine, or whether gastrin is a general releaser of histamine (84) can now all be answered with a resounding no. Atropine is a strong antagonist of the action of gastrin in unanesthetized dog and man (83) but not in the anesthetized cat (85). The meaning of this discrepancy is not apparent. Gastrin and cholinergic drugs act together to give a potentiated response (greater than the additive effects of the two agents given separately) (86) and, as already discussed above (78, 79), there is reason to believe that both cholinergic effects and gastrin operate during both the cephalic and gastric phases of secretion.

Methods for the preparation of gastrin from bovine and ovine sources have been described (87, 88). Lythgoe and co-workers (89) found that reserpine did not deplete the pyloric gland mucosa of gastrin in the dog; this experiment eliminated the unlikely possibility that reserpine stimulates gastric secretion by releasing gastrin. Studies on "antibodies" to gastrin can not really be interpreted until the pure hormone is available as an antigen (90).

No greater fillip can come to an area of physiological investigation than the discovery that it has important clinical meaning. This has been provided to the field of research on gastrin by the discovery by Gregory and co-workers (91) that the tumors of the islet cells of the pancreas in patients with the Zollinger-Ellison syndrome are extremely rich in a gastrinlike substance. Little time was lost in confirming this in additional patients (92, 93, 94). This, of course, raises the question of whether gastrin or a gastrinlike substance is present in the normal pancreas and, if so, whether there is a pancreatic phase of gastric secretion. To date, attempts to extract gastrinlike materials from normal pancreases have been unsuccessful, but a negative answer of this kind is inconclusive.

Inhibition of acid secretion.—It is now fully established that when the pyloric gland area is bathed with acid, agencies which are otherwise capable of stimulating gastric secretion through release of gastrin are rendered in-effective. The great battle rages on over whether this effect is produced by (*a*) inhibition of the release of gastrin or (*b*) release by acid of an inhibitory hormone that counteracts the action of gastrin on the fundic glands. Voting yes on proposition (*a*) are Shapira & State (95) whose meticulous studies not only confirmed the observation that acid had to be in the same portion of the pyloric gland area as the stimulant for release of gastrin if inhibition was to occur, but also explained why the results of some previous workers had ap-peared to support proposition (*b*). They showed that when alcohol was used to irrigate a pouch of the pyloric gland area the secretion of acid was not sus-tained even when the alcohol was not acidified. Thus those who used alcohol as the stimulant for gastrin release would see apparent inhibition that had nothing to do with acidification. On the other side of the issue stand Thomp-son and co-workers (96) who found that cross-transfusion of portal vein blood from a dog having acid irrigated in a pouch of the pyloric gland area into a dog with a Heidenhain pouch that was secreting in response to a meal caused marked inhibition of this secretion. Appropriate control experiments with perfusion of the pyloric pouch of the donor dog with saline showed no inhibi-tion. At present the two sets of results (95, 96) are irreconcilable. If an inhibi-tory hormone exists, it should not require cross-transfusion experiments to demonstrate it, and we shall now await evidence that it can be shown in a single animal. DuVal and co-workers (97) also performed some experiments that they interpreted as supporting proposition (*b*), but the data given are too meager to evaluate.

Oberhelman and co-workers (98) performed some ingenious surgical manipulations to determine why the secretion of a Heidenhain pouch in re-sponse to a meal is increased by vagotomy. Selective vagal denervation of only the pyloric gland area caused the secretion to fall below control levels; subsequent thoracic vagotomy produced the expected rise above control levels. Selective vagal denervation of the fundic gland area produced an increase in secretion. The authors justifiably conclude that it is the fundic vagal denerva-tion which causes the increase in secretion from the Heidenhain pouch. They believe that this could be caused by either a delay in gastric emptying or a de-crease in acid secretion by the main stomach, leading to lessened inhibition of gastrin release. It seems unlikely that selective fundic denervation would delay gastric emptying or, if it did, that delayed emptying would be a signifi-cant additional stimulus for gastrin release. Any effect of delayed emptying to produce increased gastrin would be quickly overcome by a rise in gastric acidity to inhibit further gastrin release. Chapman and co-workers (99) showed that if the pyloric gland area was defunctionalized by isolating it as a pouch with an acid-secreting cuff of fundic mucosa, vagotomy then produced no increase in secretion from the Heidenhain pouch. From these and previous studies it seems clear that complete vagotomy augments the production of gastrin in response to a meal. It is equally clear that the amount of acid secreted by the main stomach in response to a meal is reduced by vagotomy. The explanation for this apparent contradiction is, I believe, that vagotomy reduces the responsiveness of the fundic glands to gastrin to such an extent that less acid is secreted despite the increased amount of gastrin. The magnitude of this decrease in responsiveness produced by vagotomy is well shown in the data of Gelb and co-workers (100) who found that the maximal acid response to histamine was reduced by 70 per cent in patients who had had vagotomy and pylorplasty for the treatment of duodenal ulcer. This decrease is unlikely to be the result of a reduction in the number of parietal cells for it can be detected within a day after vagotomy, which indicates that maximal acid output cannot always be taken as an index of parietal cell mass.

Andersson & Uvnäs (101) studied the inhibition of acid secretion from a Pavlov pouch responding to a meal. The inhibition that can be produced by introduction of acid into the duodenum still occurs when only the first four centimeters, the duodenal bulb, is exposed to the acid. Since the contents of the bulb may at times have a much lower pH than is found lower in the duodenum, such a mechanism could operate under normal conditions.

Enterogastrone prepared from the intestines of hypophysectomized dogs was shown by Kaulbersz and co-workers (102) to inhibit gastric secretion as effectively as that from normal dogs. Previous studies had shown that the urine of hypophysectomized dogs did not contain urogastrone, so it is concluded that urogastrone is probably not excreted enterogastrone.

Intravenous infusion of 30 grams of glucose over a 30-minute period was found by Dotevall & Muren (103) to inhibit the secretory response of a Pavlov pouch to a meal. Smaller amounts of glucose that produced blood glucose levels more nearly like those expected after a meal did not inhibit.

Electrolytes.—The behavior of potassium in gastric juice continues to occupy researchers (104 to 107). Although the concentration of potassium bears no fixed relation to the concentration of acid, thus differing from the inverse linear relation between sodium and acid, two patterns emerge (106, 107. (a) With the onset of secretion of acid there is a short-lived rise in potassium concentration, the so-called potassium transient, like that seen with onset of activity in many other glands and tissues. (b) Apart from this transient and despite minor fluctuations, there is a strong positive correlation between output of potassium and output of acid. While the latter observation does not prove that potassium is a constituent of parietal juice, it does show that the processes of potassium secretion and acid secretion are quantitatively linked.

Davenport & Alzamora (108) made careful measurements of the water and electrolyte content of frog gastric mucosa. They had difficulty in finding a suitable measure of extracellular volume; radioiodinated serum albumin space gave the most reasonable values, 230 ml per kg wet weight. Using this value for extracellular space, the following intracellular concentrations were obtained by calculation: sodium 35, potassium 103, and chloride 38 meq per kg water. Mucosas stripped of surface epithelial cells had increased sodium and chloride and reduced potassium as compared with intact mucosas. The authors speculate that the oxyntic cells may be the only cells that contain significant amounts of sodium.

Drugs and hormones.—A procedure for studying the gastric secretory response to histamine in unanesthetized, unoperated rats has been described by Valberg & Witts (109). They found that 25 mg per kg of histamine phosphate produced maximal secretory responses. Tsukamoto (110) observed acid secretion in response to submucosal injection of histamine in the exteriorized stomach of the rat by coating the mucosa with a mixture of Carbowax and Congo red. Secretion of acid was detected by the appearance of black dots at the sites of the gastric foveolae, observed through a magnifying lens. Submucosal injection of atropine or acetazolamide inhibited the response to histamine. Compound 48/80, a histamine releaser, did not stimulate secretion of acid when injected submucosally. The triazole analogue of histamine was shown by Lin and co-workers (111) to have about 70 per cent of the potency of histamine in stimulating gastric secretion and also in its effects on blood pressure and smooth muscle. These same workers (112) have summarized their extensive studies on a large number of analogues of histamine. Substitution of methyl groups for one or both of the hydrogens on the side-chain nitrogen of histamine gives compounds that are two to three times more potent than histamine in stimulating acid secretion but considerably less potent than histamine in lowering blood pressure or contracting smooth muscle. These compounds are not acted on by diamine oxidase and, probably for this reason, are effective when given orally. Lozzio and co-workers (113) gave aminoguanidine to rats with the pylorus ligated and found only a small increase in gastric secretion but marked ulceration of the glandular mucosa.

No satisfactory explanation is available for the antagonism of the action of histamine by atropine in some experimental situations but not in others. In rats, Aarsen & Van Noordwijk (114) found that anticholinergic drugs blocked vagally induced gastric contractions but did not inhibit histamine-stimulated gastric secretion. Skyring and co-workers (115) found that sodium pentobarbital inhibited secretion stimulated by histamine in dogs with Heidenhain pouches. Resnick and co-workers (116) gave an antagonist of serotonin to human subjects and noted that it produced strong stimulation of acid secretion. Prior administration of the serotonin precursor, 5-hydroxytryptophan, prevented the stimulatory effect. The authors suggest that endogenous serotonin may normally play a role in regulating gastric secretion.

Why some investigators find that long-term administration of adrenal corticosteroids causes an increase in gastric secretion while others do not remains unexplained. The two latest additions to this literature (117, 118) are on the majority side, finding that these agents do increase the daily output of acid from Heidenhain pouches. The effect of administration of cortisone on the parietal cell population of the gastric mucosa of dogs was studied by Reid *et al.* (119). An increase in the concentration and in the total number of parietal cells was found to occur but the results were erratic. Until a method is found for studying the number of parietal cells and the secretion of acid in the same stomach before and after treatment with corticosteroids, judgment should be deferred on whether these agents cause increased acid secretion by increasing the number of parietal cells. Smith and co-workers (120) confirmed the finding that most patients with Addison's disease or hypopituitarism secrete little or no acid in response to histamine. Treatment with cortisone failed to restore the acid secretion to normal levels.

Nasset (121) has extended his observations on the effect of thyroid hormone on gastric secretion. From studies in dogs, rats, and frogs he concluded that the inhibition of gastric secretion by thyroid hormone is caused by a reduction of the ability of the gastric mucosa to mobilize secretory energy in response to a stimulus. In frog gastric mucosa the acid-to-oxygen ratio was unaffected during inhibition of secretion by thyroid hormone.

The inhibitory effect of glucagon on gastric secretion in man was confirmed by Aylett (122). A study of the effect of hypercalcemia on gastric secretion in one dog had too many variables to allow interpretation (123).

Pepsin.—Some semblance of order has been brought to the chaotic field of gastric proteinases by the hypotheses of Taylor (124). He suggests that there are two pepsins and that each of these pepsins has two pH optima, one near pH 2 and the second near pH 3.5. The first pepsin is secreted by the chief cells of the fundic glands, the second by the mucoid neck cells of the fundic glands and by the pyloric gland cells. The first pepsin has one phosphate group per molecule, the second has none. Taylor believes that the second pepsin is the same enzyme which has been variously named "cathepsin", "gastricsin", "pyloric pepsin", and "parapepsin II" by others. Until simple reproducible methods are available for the separate measurement of these two enzymes, progress will be slow.

Roy and co-workers (125) gave alloxan to rats and found that the gastric mucosal content of pepsinogen rose sharply during the permanent hyperglycemic phase but that the effect was not sustained. In an uncontrolled non-quantitative study Fattah and co-workers (126) observed the histological appearance of the pepsinogen granules of the gastric mucosa after a variety of manipulations.

Muirden (127) observed elevation of plasma pepsinogen activity in patients treated with phenylbutazone. Since this drug is capable of producing injury of the gastric mucosa and since other agents, such as x-ray, that injure the mucosa also cause elevation of plasma pepsinogen, disintegration of peptic cells may be one mechanism for delivering pepsinogen into the blood.

Peptic ulcer.—With the exception of the work on gastrin in the Zollinger-Ellison syndrome mentioned above, research in this field is following old established patterns. A sampling of clinical and experimental work in this area is provided by the publication of the proceedings of a recent symposium (128). Dragstedt (129) has given his answer to the question of why the stomach does not digest itself. He believes that pure gastric juice can digest any tissue and that ulceration is normally prevented by mechanisms holding secretion in check. Kuroyanagi & Necheles (130) have produced ulcers in rats subjected to the Mann-Williamson operation.

The mechanism for the increase in gastric secretion that follows the Mann-Williamson operation is not fully understood. If, instead of the entire duodenum, just that portion that receives the biliary and pancreatic ducts is drained into the distal ileum, hypersecretion still ensues according to the work of Menguy & Mings (131). This shows that hypersecretion is not prevented even when the duodenum still receives the gastric acid, thus dismissing the possibility that absence of duodenal inhibition by acid is the cause of the hypersecretion. In another study Menguy (132) showed that hypersecretion occurs when only the biliary duct is diverted to the distal ileum, but in this instance it was delayed in onset and did not return to control levels when the bile was returned to the duodenum. Absence of pancreatic juice from the duodenum can also produce hypersecretion of gastric juice as shown by the work of Greenlee and co-workers (133). They found that the separation of the pancreas from the duodenum resulted in an increase in the amount of acid secreted by Heidenhain pouches and that prior resection of the pyloric gland area of the stomach did not prevent this effect. Several groups of workers are now engaged in exploring the possibility that the effects of pancreatic or biliary diversion on gastric secretion are caused by a change in liver function that permits secretagogues in the portal blood which are normally inactivated by the liver to pass through the liver and act on the stomach. Should this hypothesis prove correct, the hypersecretion attending the Mann-Williamson operation could then be considered analogous to that which occurs after portal-systemic shunting (134).

There is no dearth of ways to produce ulcer in animals. One currently in vogue is simply to immobilize rats whereupon they develop multiple erosions of the glandular portion of the stomach within a day. Brodie and co-workers (135) report that in rats with chronic gastric fistula restraint produced an increase in concentration of acid with a decrease in volume so that the output of acid was unchanged. Imipramine, a so-called psychic energizer, was found to prevent restraint-induced ulcers in rats, probably by inhibiting gastric secretion of acid (136).

Singh and co-workers (137) produced ulcers in guinea pigs by giving a single large dose of histamine together with an antihistaminic. The ulcerative process was maximal in 4 to 24 hours and by 16 days complete healing had occurred. Häkkinen and co-workers (138, 139) found that the uptake of radioactive sulfate by the duodenal mucosa was greatly increased following injection of histamine in guinea pigs, implying that an alteration in metabolism of sulfated mucopolysaccharides was involved in histamine-induced ulceration. Zadi and co-workers (140) produced ulcers in guinea pigs by feeding phenylbutazone. After 30 days of such treatment the gastric mucosa appeared to be totally depleted of mucin stainable by the periodic acid Schiff reaction. The catchwords "mucosal resistance" and "mucous barrier" have been bandied for years in theories of ulcer formation. Advances in knowledge of the chemistry and metabolism of mucopolysaccharides should now permit a more telling attack on this aspect of the ulcer problem.

Polymyxin B produces hemorrhages in the gastric glandular mucosa of rats. Moreno and Brodie (141) report that epinephrine or antihistaminics are effective in preventing this lesion. The old observation that intra-arterial injection of particulate material which lodges in the capillaries can produce gastric ulcers has been brought up to date; this time it was done with polyethylene microspheres (142).

Miscellaneous topics.—Ridges & Singleton (143) calculated that in goats 80 per cent of the soluble carbohydrate is fermented in the rumen and is then absorbed as volatile fatty acids. Murray (144) has written a brief account of the fascinating phenomenon of sprouting of nerves, a process in which the intact fibers of incompletely severed nerves send out side branches that reinnervate the cut fibers. This process has been demonstrated to occur in the vagus nerve, and it undoubtedly accounts for the remarkable recovery of function that is seen when these nerves are incompletely divided. Pregnant rats secrete less acid and have a higher content of histaminase in the gastric mucosa than nonpregnant controls, according to Lozzio and co-workers (145). Walder (146) has written an interesting historical account of knowledge about the nature of the gastric fluid.

Pancreatic Secretion

Top billing in this section unquestionably goes to Jorpes & Mutt (147) who after many years of labor have isolated what they consider to be essentially pure secretin. The potency of the material was 20,000 clinical units per milligram. The dose now used for the standard clinical secretin test, 70 clinical units, would be represented by 4 μg of this purified material. The amino acid analysis revealed five moles of leucine, three moles of arginine, two moles each of glutamic acid and glycine, and one mole each of aspartic acid, alanine, and valine. With the powerful tools now available for isolation and determination of the structure of polypeptides, it should not be many years before all of the gastrointestinal hormones have been structurally identified. Jorpes & Mutt (148) have also described their further efforts in the purification of pancreozymin.

The old question of whether the liver inactivates secretin has become popular again. Recent investigations have given conflicting results. The latest report, by Skillman and co-workers (149), indicates that the response to secretin injected into the portal vein is 20 per cent lower than when it is injected into a systemic vein. Before this small difference is accepted as representing the true state of affairs, tests should be performed with pure secretin. Crude secretin consists mainly of inert denatured protein. The liver is a powerful trap for denatured protein; in fact, the rate of disappearance of denatured protein from the blood has been used as a measurement of hepatic blood flow (150). It seems reasonable to postulate that secretin adsorbed to inert protein could be removed by the liver.

Christodoulopoulos and co-workers (151) gave secretin by continuous intravenous injection to unanesthetized dogs and noted that, although the flow rate remained constant for as long as 12 hours, the bicarbonate concentration gradually fell. Magee (152) used the method of transduodenal cannulation of the duct to study pancreatic secretion in unanesthetized sheep. Introduction of abomasal content, fatty acid solutions, or dilute hydrochloric acid into the duodenum produced secretory responses. The bicarbonate concentration of the juice was low, never exceeding 35 meq per liter.

Corticosteroids appear to produce no more consistent effects on pancreatic secretion than have been found for gastric secretion. Two studies of the effect of chronic administration of cortisone on pancreatic secretion in dogs have been made. In one (153) a distinct increase in flow in response to a meal or to secretin was found; in the other (154) the effects were erratic, but there was a predominant downward trend.

In human subjects with the pancreatic duct cannulated, Hong and co-workers (155) showed that hexamethonium, a ganglionic blocking drug, prevented the secretory response to the feeding of milk or a solution of methionine. Whether such an effect is caused by blocking reflexes that produce the secretion, or by removing tonic vagal activity and thus reducing the responsiveness of the pancreas, or by interfering with a nervous mechanism concerned in the release of secretin is not known. My earlier view (156) that hormonal mechanisms dominate the regulation of pancreatic secretion requires complete reevaluation.

Serotonin is being examined for possible effects on all of the digestive organs and now it has been found by Drapanas and co-workers (157) to inhibit pancreatic secretion. Two groups (158, 159) have reported that placing hypertonic glucose solution into the duodenum inhibits pancreatic secretion in dogs.

Baker and co-workers (160) have continued their studies on the involution of the pancreas of the rat following hypophysectomy. The weight of the pancreas falls to about one half the control value, but the concentration of proteolytic enzymes does not decline. No single hormone is fully effective in restoring the pancreas to normal size and enzyme content, but a combination of somatotropin, corticosterone, and thyroxine makes the gland almost completely normal.

Little is known about the fate of pancreatic enzymes once they have entered the intestine. Pelot and I (161) measured the amount of trypsin, chymotrypsin, and lipase in the contents of various levels of the small intestine of the rat. Prolonged fasting led to only moderate lowering of enzymatic activity, but diversion of pancreatic juice to the exterior was followed by a profound fall within a few hours and at the end of 16 hours almost no enzymatic activity remained. The most surprising finding was that the lower half of the small intestine contained more enzymatic activity than the upper half. We postulate that this is a result of the relative rate of transport of material in these two portions of the gut; contents move more slowly through the lower half and thus tend to accumulate there. The enzymes undergo inactivation at different rates, so the pattern of enzymes changes as the gut is descended. We found that the order of stability from most to least was trypsin, chymotrypsin, and lipase. Wohlman and co-workers (162), using another method of study, arrived at a different conclusion. They found that crystalline chymotrypsin added to human intestinal juice was more stable than crystalline trypsin.

The pancreas is known to have good ability to regenerate, but this process has usually been studied only by histological methods. White & Magee (163) ligated the pancreatic duct of dogs for varying periods and then determined the time required for recovery of secretory function after removal of the ligature. Occlusion for five days produced marked depression of secretion but full recovery occurred within three weeks after flow was reestablished.

Pancreatitis.—The hemorrhage and necrosis that are so characteristic of pancreatitis are presumed to result from the action of the proteolytic pancreatic enzymes on the gland substance. Plausible as this hypothesis is, no one has yet demonstrated that the pancreatic proteases are transformed from their normally inactive form to the active state during the course of clinical or experimental pancreatitis. Also no mechanism has been proposed to explain how such activation could occur. Greenbaum & Hirshkowitz (164) have made the important observation that endogenous cathepsin of pancreatic tissue is capable of activating trypsinogen at pH 3.6, but it remains to be determined whether a pH low enough to permit this reaction to occur would ever be present in the living pancreas. Negulescu and co-workers (165) have confirmed earlier work from my laboratory showing that the concentration of trypsin inhibitor in pancreatic juice of dogs decreases when pancreatitis is produced by injecting ethionine. Anderson (166, 167, 168) incubated trypsin with blood and found that the resulting mixture produced much more damage when injected into tissues than did trypsin alone; he believes that such a mechanism might operate in pancreatitis. Helms & Meredith (169) divided the pancreas of dogs into two portions and then produced pancreatitis in one portion by forcibly injecting bile into the duct. No pancreatitis was observed in the uninjected portion. From this they conclude that systemic factors do not operate to cause pancreatitis, but this deduction would be valid only for the particular form of experimental pancreatitis that they studied.

SECRETION OF BILE

Wheeler (170) has summarized recent work on the electrolyte composition of bile, a subject to which he has contributed importantly. Schanker & Hogben (171) have opened a new chapter in biliary physiology by their study of the secretion of water-soluble lipid-insoluble nonelectrolytes that are not metabolized in the body and do not appear in the bile in significantly higher concentration than in the plasma. Inulin, sucrose, and mannitol were chosen as models of this class of substances with widely varying molecular weights. The bile-to-plasma concentration ratios were related to molecular weight: inulin, 0.1; sucrose, 0.2; and mannitol, 1.2. Because these substances were found to invade substantial hepatic spaces, 24 to 72 per cent of the wet tissue weight depending on the size of the molecule, it was concluded that permeability to large, lipid-insoluble molecules was a special feature of the hepatic parenchymal cell membrane. From kinetic analysis of steady-state distribution of sucrose between plasma, liver, and bile it was concluded that the boundary between plasma and cell interior and the boundary between cell interior and bile are equally permeable.

Three steps are involved in the secretion of bilirubin into bile: (a) uptake of bilirubin from plasma by the liver cell, (b) conjugation of bilirubin, primarily with glucuronic acid, and (c) secretion of conjugated bilirubin into bile. Using Gunn rats, a strain of animals with a genetic defect which renders them incapable of conjugating bilirubin with glucuronic acid, Arias and co-workers (172) showed that when conjugated bilirubin was injected intravenously, these animals secreted it into the bile at the same maximum rate as normal rats which received either unconjugated or conjugated bilirubin. This suggests that step (c) in the above scheme is the rate-limiting process under normal conditions.

Dumont and co-workers (173) gave thorium dioxide to block the reticuloendothelial system of dogs with common bile and cystic ducts ligated and found that this prevented the expected rise in bilirubin level in thoracic duct lymph. They conclude that this supports the view that bilirubin is formed from hemoglobin in the reticuloendothelial system. While this conclusion is consistent with the results obtained, it would have been more convincing if they had shown that thorium dioxide did not interfere with the ability of the liver to handle intravenously injected bilirubin.

Barber-Riley and co-workers (174) find that the rate of disappearance of sulfobromophthalein from plasma of human subjects can be described by two exponential rates; they take the first of these to represent the transfer from plasma to liver, the second the transfer from liver to bile. The first rate is three times the second one. Kim & Hong (175) concluded that the secretion of various phenol-red derivatives by the liver and by the kidney was accomplished by a similar transport system.

In two hypercholesterolemic patients, Linstedt & Ahrens (176) found that the size of the pool of bile acids was normal but that turnover rate was only one fourth of normal with a corresponding decrease in rate of degradation of cholesterol. In dogs, Gans & McEntee (177) showed that feeding thyroid hormone resulted in a decrease in size of bile acid pool without a change in biliary cholesterol secretion. Conversion of cholesterol to bile acids is undoubtedly a major pathway of cholesterol metabolism, but we have much to learn about the factors regulating this process.

By studying the metabolism of labeled chenodeoxycholic acid in human subjects, Hellström & Sjövall (178) concluded that lithocholic acid is formed by intestinal bacteria. Blomstrand (179) applied the method of gas-liquid chromatography to the analysis of individual bile acids in human bile and found values similar to those reported by others using different methods. Nakayama & Johnston (180) gave a detailed analysis of the lipids of human bile as measured by chromatography on columns of silicic acid.

Absorption

The major business transacted by the alimentary tract is digestion and absorption in the small intestine. This area of investigation is now beginning to assume its rightful dominant place as the major interest of gastrointestinal physiologists.

Water and electrolytes.—An excellent summary of present knowledge in this field appears in the proceedings of a recent symposium (181 to 185). Clarkson and co-workers (186) concluded that the electric potential difference across the small intestine was the result of active transport of sodium ion followed passively by an equivalent amount of chloride ion.

Two extensive studies (187, 188) of ileal discharges in patients with ileostomy provide good information on the nature of the material delivered to the colon. The average weight of discharge was 500 grams containing 92 per cent water, 60 meq sodium, and 4 meq potassium.

During niacin deficiency in dogs, Nelson and co-workers (189) found that the flux of water, sodium, and potassium from lumen to blood decreased, but the flux in the other direction did not change. This resulted in net movement of these substances from blood to lumen and this was associated with diarrhea.

Two groups (190, 191) using different methods have shown that in dogs iron absorption from the intestine reaches a peak and then quickly falls despite the continued presence of iron in the luminal contents. Duthie and co-workers (191) showed that this cessation of absorption was caused by a change in the state of the iron in the intestinal contents; iron in intestinal contents from a dog that had stopped absorbing was not absorbed when placed in the intestine of another dog, and fresh iron was absorbed at the same rate as the initial dose when a new portion was placed in the intestine of a dog that had stopped absorbing the first dose. This important observation calls for re-formulation of the "mucosal block" concept.

Cramer & Dueck (192) found that the kinetics of absorption of calcium from Thiry-Vella loops in dogs conformed to the requirements of an active transport system. Concentrations above 13 mM produced maximal rates of absorption. Schachter and co-workers (193, 194) continue to further our understanding of calcium absorption. They found that the small intestine of the rat responds facultatively to a diet low in calcium by increasing the active transport of the cation. They also showed that vitamin D influenced both steps in the active transport of calcium, mucosal uptake, and efflux from mucosa to serosa. Transport of phosphate across rat intestinal mucosa against a concentration gradient was found by Harrison & Harrison (195) to depend on simultaneous active transport of calcium. According to Ross (196) magnesium does not move against a concentration gradient in everted sacs of rat intestine.

Carbohydrate.—A concise review of what is known about glucose absorption and what remains to be learned has been written by Smyth (197). The middle section of rat small intestine was shown by Barry and co-workers (198) to transfer both glucose and water at higher rates than segments above or below. Glucose and water transfer did not, however, run parallel; the ileum had little capacity to transfer glucose but considerable ability to move water. Water transfer can be divided into two mechanisms, one of which is glucose dependent. Using appropriate tracers, Lee & Lifson (199) showed that neither hydrogen nor oxygen of water was incorporated into stably bound positions of glucose during transport across the intestinal wall. Csaky (200) showed that the dependence of active transport upon the presence of sodium ions was not limited to glucose but was equally true of amino acids and uracil. He believes that in each instance sodium is required for the performance of the osmotic work involved in active transport. Bogner (201, 202) has shown that the active transport mechanism for sugars is not present at birth in chicks but develops to full capacity within two days.

Crane (203, 204) continues his brilliant record of making outstanding contributions to the field of carbohydrate absorption. The relative distribution of the products of hydrolysis of sucrose, maltose, and glucose-1-phosphate between the intestinal epithelium and the medium bathing it indicated that all three compounds are hydrolyzed within the epithelial cell. The enzymes were localized to an intracellular site superficial to the barrier sensitive to phlorizin and to the active transport process for sugars. The epithelial brush-border membrane was isolated as a morphologically distinct entity from homogenates of intestinal mucosa and was found to contain virtually all of the invertase and maltase activity of the unfractionated homogenate. Dahlqvist & Borgström (205) performed studies in human subjects which fully supported the view that hydrolysis of disaccharides occurs intracellularly. The intestinal contents had neglible glycosidase activity in relation to the rate of absorption of the sugars, and the sugars in the contents remained almost entirely in the unhydrolyzed form. Lactose was most rapidly absorbed from the upper intestine, maltose from the midportion, and sucrose from the distal segment. Dahlqvist (206) made extracts of human intestinal mucosa and studied the specificity of the disaccharidases. He believes that there are at least six different enzymes; some enzymes split more than one sugar and some sugars are split by more than one enzyme. The subject is of considerable clinical importance because several cases of inherited inability to utilize one or another disaccharide have recently been described.

Protein.—Holt & Miller (207) state that the brush border of the intestinal mucosal cell is the locus of the aminopeptidase activity. The implications are the same as those for carbohydrate discussed above. Apparently dipeptides, and perhaps larger peptides, are hydrolyzed intracellularly after transport across the luminal membrane of the brush border. The idea that the intestinal enzymes are intracellular and act on their substrates after these have entered the cell is quite old. Recent evidence has firmly established the validity of this concept, and it can now be stated with some assurance that the terminal stages of hydrolysis of carbohydrates and proteins occurs within the brush border of the intestinal epithelial cells. Digestion and absorption are intimately linked. The huge surface presented by the microvilli serves not only absorptive but also digestive functions.

Spencer and co-workers (208) found the following structural requirements for absorption of amino acids against a concentration gradient. An amino group must be present, and it must be in the alpha position to the carboxyl group, and a moiety replacing an amino hydrogen must not be sterically bulky.

Christensen (209) took a panoramic look at amino acid transport and suggested that the transport mechanism for amino acids in the intestine probably does not differ fundamentally from that used by other cells.

Fat.—In what form is fat presented to the intestinal mucosa for absorption? The usual answer to this question is, "an emulsion", but Hofmann & Borgström (210) have given a radically different answer that should revolutionize our thinking about fat absorption. They centrifuged at very high speed the intestinal content of human subjects who had eaten fat. About half of the fat was found in the particulate phase that rose to the top, but the other half was found in the transparent aqueous phase. They determined that this "soluble" fat was present in the form of mixed micelles, small molecular aggregates composed of bile acids acting as detergents, monoglycerides that expand the micelles and increase their capacity for solubilizing such substances as fatty acids and cholesterol, and the fatty acids and cholesterol so solubilized. Hofmann & Borgström believe that it is this micellar phase that is presented to the mucosal surface for absorption. As absorption occurs the bile acids are released, becoming available for the formation of new mixed micelles; this fits with the finding that bile salts are preferentially absorbed from the distal portion of the small intestine (211).

Mattson & Volpenheim (212) determined the distribution of labeled palmitic acid in the 1 and 2 positions of the glycerol molecule of lymph lipids after feeding the fatty acid in various forms. When it was fed as a free fatty acid together with unlabeled fatty acid or unlabeled triglyceride, it was randomly distributed on the glycerol of lymph lipids. However, when it was fed as a triglyceride with the labeled acid in either the 1 or the 2 position, it was found to be predominantly in the same position in the lymph lipid as it was in the fed lipid. This constitutes essentially incontrovertible evidence that significant quantities of glyceride, presumably mainly monoglyceride, are absorbed and reincorporated into triglyceride. Evidence that intestinal mucosal cells have a special capacity to synthesize triglyceride from monoglyceride has recently been presented (213).

Fernandes and co-workers (214) found that children with steatorrhea caused by celiac disease excreted in their feces a higher percentage of dietary long-chain fatty acids than of short-chain ones; unsaturated fatty acids were relatively well absorbed. Similar but less pronounced differences are known to occur in normal subjects. Differences in solubility of the various fatty acids and their monoglycerides in the micellar system described by Hofmann & Borgström could account for this selectivity in absorbability.

A clear demonstration of the validity of "Hogben's law" (215) that the rate of absorption of water soluble substances which do not have a special transport mechanism will depend upon the degree of solubility of the un-ionized moiety in lipid has been provided by Schedl's study (216) of absorption of steroids from the small intestine of the rat. The more polar the compound, and thus the lower its lipid solubility, the lower was its absorption rate.

General Remarks

Many papers have not been cited; whole areas have been omitted from consideration including the ultrastructure of the alimentary tract, cell turn-over in the mucosa, effects of bacteria on alimentary function, the distribution of serotonin, secretion and metabolism of mucus, absorption of vitamins including B_{12}, the circulation in the digestive organs, and entry of plasma proteins into the alimentary tract. A supplementary list of references has been deposited with the American Documentation Institute.[2]

Two recently published books deserve special mention. Davenport's (217) text will surely become the primer for all who want a general introduction to the study of gastrointestinal function. It is concise, up-to-date, comprehensive, lucid, and, above all, highly readable. Gregory's (218) monograph gives the investigator and the graduate student with a special interest in the processes that regulate the secretory activity of the gastrointestinal tract an ordered view of this area of study.

[2] The supplementary references have been deposited as Document No. 7339 with ADI Auxiliary Publications Project, Photoduplication Service, Library of Congress, Washington 25, D.C., and can be purchased by sending check or money order to Chief, Photoduplication Service, Library of Congress ($6.25 for photoprints, $2.50 for 35 mm microfilm).

LITERATURE CITED

1. Anand, B. K., *Physiol. Rev.*, **41**, 677–708 (2961)
2. Morgane, P. J., *Am. J. Physiol.*, **201**, 420–28 (1961)
3. Morgane, P. J., *Am. J. Physiol.*, **201**, 838–44 (1961)
4. Grossman, S. P., *Science*, **132**, 301–2 (1960)
5. Epstein, A. N., *Am. J. Physiol.*, **199**, 969–74 (2960)
6. Quadde, F., *Am. J. Med. Sci.*, **243**, 427–46 (1962)
7. Anand, B. K., Subberwal, U., Manchanda, S. K., and Singh, B. *Indian J. Med. Research*, **49**, 717–24 (1961)
8. Anand, B. K., Talwar, G. P., Dua, S., and Mhatre, R. M. *Indian J. Med. Research*, **49**, 725–32 (1961)
9. Debons, A. F., Silver, L. Cronkite, E. P., Johnson, H. A., Brecher, G., Tenzer, D., and Schwartz, I. L., *Am. J. Physiol.*, **202**, 743–50 (1962)
10. Sharma, K. N., Anand, B. K., Dua, S., and Singh, B., *Am. J. Physiol.*, **201**, 593–98 (1961)
11. Andersson, B., and Larsson, B., *Acta Physiol. Scand.*, **52**, 75–89 (1961)
12. Anand, B. K., Malhotra, C. L., Dua, S., and Singh, B., *Indian J. Med. Research*, **49**, 152–7 (1961)
13. Carlisle, H. J., and Reynolds, R. W., *Am. J. Physiol.*, **201**, 956–57 (1961)
14. Anand, B. K., Dua, S., and Chhina, G. S., *Indian J. Med. Research*, **49**, 491–97 (9161)
15. Robinson, B. W., and Mishkin, M., *Science*, **136**, 260–62 (1962)
16. Rozin, P., and Mayer, J., *Am. J. Physiol.*, **201**, 968–74 (1961)
17. Hollifield, G., and Parson, W., *J. Clin. Invest.*, **41**, 250–53 (1962)
18. Sanahuja, J. C., and Harper, A. E., *Am. J. Physiol.*, **202**, 165–70 (1962)
19. Durnin, J. V. G. A., *J. Physiol. (London)*, **156**, 294–306 (1961)
20. Fitzsimons, J. T., *J. Physiol. (London)*, **159**, 297–309 (1961)
21. Cizek, L. J., *Am. J. Physiol.*, **201**, 577–66 (1961)
22. Barr, L., *Am. J. Physiol.*, **200**, 1251–55 (1961)
23. Bortoff, A., *Am. J. Physiol.*, **201**, 203–8 (1961)
24. Bortoff, A., *Am. J. Physiol.*, **201**, 209–12 (1961)
25. Sperelakis, N., *Am. J. Physiol.*, **202**, 731–42 (1962)
26. Durbin, R. P., and Jenkinson, D. H., *J. Physiol.*, *(London)*, **157**, 74–89 (1961)
27. Durbin, R. P., and Jenkinson, D. H., *J. Physiol.*, *(London)* **157**, 90–96 (1961)
28. Axelsson, J., *J. Physiol. (London)*, **158**, 381–98 (1961)
29. Axelsson, J., and Bülbring, E., *J. Physiol. (London)*, **156**, 344–56 (1961)
30. Axelsson, J., Bueding, E., and Bülbring, E., *J. Physiol. (London)*, **156**, 357–74 (1961)
31. Bass, P., Code, C. F., and Lambert, E. H., *Am. J. Physiol.*, **201**, 287–91 (1961)
32. Bass, P., Code, C. F., and Lambert, E. H. *Am. J. Physiol.*, **201**, 587–92 (1961)
33. Nagler, R., and Spiro, H. M., *Gastroenterology*, **41**, 371–79 (1961)
34. Siegel, C. I., and Hendrix, T. R., *Bull. Johns Hopkins Hosp.*, **108**, 297–307 (1961)
35. Carveth, S. W., Schlegel, J. F., Code, C. F., and Ellis, F. H., Jr., *Surg., Gynecol. Obstet.*, **114**, 31–42 (1962)
35a. Clark, C. G., and Vane, J. R., *Gut*, **2**, 252 (1951)
36. Gahagan, T., *Surg., Gynecol. Obstet.*, **114**, 293–303 (1962)
37. Tuttle, S. G., Rufin, F., and Bettarello, A., *Ann. Internal Med.*, **55**, 292–300 (1961)
38. Atkinson, M., *Gut*, **3**, 1–15 (1962)
39. Ingelfinger, F. J., *Gastroenterology*, **41**, 264–76 (1961)
39a. Lind, J. F., Duthie, H. L., Schlegel, J. F., and Code, C. F., *Am. J. Physiol.*, **201**, 197–202 (1961)
40. Aylett, P., *Clin. Sci.*, **22**, 171–78 (1962)
41. Lish, P. M., *Gastroenterology*, **41**, 580–84 (1961)
42. Wenger, M. A., Engel, B. T., Clemens, T. L., and Cullen, T. D., *Gastroenterology*, **41**, 479–85 (1961)
43. Bella, D. D., and Rognoni, F., *J. Pharmacol. Exptl. Therap.*, **134**, 184–89 (1961)
44. Hunt, J. N., *Gastroenterology*, **41**, 49–51 (1961)
45. Dorman, H. L., and Steggerda, F. R., *Am. J. Physiol.*, **201**, 292–94 (1961)
46. Hasselbrack, R., and Thomas, J. E., *Am. J. Physiol.*, **201**, 955–60 (1961)
47. Gillespie, J. S., and Mackenna, B. R., *J. Physiol. (London)*, **156**, 17–34 (1961)
48. Chaudhary, N. A., and Truelove, S. C., *Am. J. Med.*, **31**, 86 (1961)

49. Pallin, B., and Skoglund, S., *Acta Physiol. Scand.*, **51**, 187–92 (1961)

50. Caroli, J., Plessier, J., and Plessier, B., *Am. J. Digest. Diseases*, **6**, 646 (1961)

51. Daniels, B. T., McGlone, F. B., Job, H., and Sawyer, R. B. *J. Am. Med. Assoc.*, **178**, 394–97 (1961)

52. Burgen, A. S. V., and Emmelin, N. G., *Physiology of the Salivary Glands* (Williams & Wilkins Co., Baltimore, Md., 1961)

53. Schneyer, C. A., and Schneyer, L. H., *Am. J. Physiol.*, **201**, 939–42 (1961)

54. Henriques, B. L., *Am. J. Physiol.*, **201**, 935–38 (1961)

55. Brusilow, S. W., and Diaz. C. L., *Am. J. Physiol.*, **202**, 158–60 (1962)

56. Schneyer, C. A., and Schneyer, L. H., *Proc. Soc. Exptl. Biol. Med.*, **108**, 584–86 (1961)

57. Williams, E. S., *Clin. Sci.*, **21**, 37–42 (1961)

58. Negri, M., and Pochin, E. E., *Clin. Sci.*, **21**, 289–94 (1961)

59. Langley, L. L., Grimes, O. R., Jr., and Cockrell, D. F., Jr., *Am. J. Physiol.*, **201**, 599–602 (1961)

60. Langley, L. L., Grimes, O. R., Jr., and Cockrell, D. F., Jr., *Am. J. Physiol.*, **202**, 707–10 (1962)

61. Van Harreveld, A., Potter, R. L., and Sloss, L. J., *Am. J. Physiol.*, **201**, 1002–6 (1961)

62. Langley, L. L., and Brown, R. S., *Am. J. Physiol.*, **201**, 285–86 (1961)

63. Wells, H., *Am. J. Physiol.*, **202**, 425–28 (1962)

64. Emmelin, N., *J. Physiol. (London)*, **156**, 121–27 (1961)

65. Emmelin, N., *J. Physiol. (London)*, **157**, 402–9 (1961)

66. Emmelin, N., *J. Physiol. (London)*, **157**, 410–13 (1961)

67. Somers, M., *Australian J. Exptl. Biol. Med. Sci.*, **39**, 111–22 (1961)

68. Somers, M., *Australian J. Exptl. Biol. Med. Sci.*, **39**, 123–32 (1961)

69. Somers, M., *Australian J. Exptl. Biol. Med. Sci.*, **39**, 133–44 (1961)

70. Somers, M., *Australian J. Exptl. Biol. Med. Sci.*, **39**, 145–56 (1961)

71. Byers, F. M., Jr., Jordan, P. H., Jr., and Maren, T. H., *Am. J. Physiol.*, **202**, 429–36 (1962)

72. Rehm, W. S., Canosa, C. A., and Schlesinger, H. S., *Am. J. Physiol.*, **200**, 1074–82 (1961)

73. Powell, D. W., Robbins, R. C., Boyett J. D., and Hirschowitz, B. I., *Am. J. Physiol.*, **202**, 293–301 (1962)

74. Teorell, T., *J. Physiol. (London)*, **97**, 308–15 (1940)

75. Bornstein, A. M., Dennis, W. H., and Rehm, W. S., *Am. J. Physiol.*, **197**, 332–36 (1959)

76. Reitemeier, R. J., Code, C. F., and Orvis, A. L., *J. Appl. Psychol.*, **10**, 261–66 (1957)

77. Irvine, W. T., Ritchie, H. D., and Adam, H. M., *Gastroenterology*, **41**, 258–63 (1961)

78. Grossman, M. I., *Gastroenterology*, **41**, 385–90 (1961)

79. Grossman, M. I., *Gastroenterology*, **42**, 718–21 (1962)

80. Ash, R. W., *J. Physiol. (London)*, **156**, 93–111 (1961)

81. Ash. R. W., *J. Physiol. (London)*, **157**, 185–207 (1961)

82. Marks, I. N., *Gastroenterology*, **41**, 599–603 (1961)

83. Gregory, R. A., and Tracy, H. J., *J. Physiol. (London)*, **156**, 523–43 (1961)

84. Brahmadutt, A. P. D., and Lake, H. J., *J. Physiol. (London)*, **159**, 71P–72P (1961)

85. Blair, E. L., Harper, A. A., Lake, H. J., and Reed, J. D., *J. Physiol. (London)*, **159**, 72P–73P (1961)

86. Grossman, M. I., *J. Physiol. (London)*, **157**, 14P–15P (1961)

87. Anderson, W. R., Fletcher, T. L., McAlexander, R. A., Pitts, C. L., Cohen, R. L., and Harkins, H. N., *J. Dairy Sci.*, **44**, 2218–26 (1961)

88. Anderson, W. R., Fletcher, T. L., Pitts, C. L., and Harkins, H. N., *Nature*, **193**, 1286–87 (1962)

89. Lythgoe, J. P., Dickinson, J. C., and Waddell, W. R., *Proc. Soc. Exptl. Biol. Med.*, **108**, 760–62 (1961)

90. Waddell, W. R., Lythgoe, J. P., and Monaco, A. P., *Science*, **134**, 2099–100 (1961)

91. Gregory, R. A., Tracy, H. J., French, J. M., and Sircus, W., *Lancet*, **I**, 1045–48 (1960)

92. Grossman, M. I., Tracy, H. J., and Gregory, R. A., *Gastroenterology*, **41**, 87–91 (1961)

93. Freisen, S. R., Tracy, H. J., and Gregory, R. A., *Ann. Surg.*, **155**, 167–74 (1962)

94. Summerskill, W. H. J., Code, C. F., Hallenbeck, G. A., and Priestley, J. T., *Proc. Staff Meetings Mayo Clinic*, **36**, 611–17 (1961)

95. Shapira, D., and State, D., *Gastroenterology*, **41**, 16–23 (1961)

96. Thompson, J. C., Lerner, H. J., and Tramontana, J. A., *Am. J. Physiol.*, 202, 716–20 (1962)

97. DuVal, M. K., Fagella, R. M., and Price, W. E., *Surgery*, 49, 569–72 (1961)

98. Oberhelman, H. A., Jr., Johnson, A. N., and Dragstedt, L. R. II, *Am. J. Physiol.*, 201, 171–74 (1961)

99. Chapman, N. D., Nyhus, L. M., DeVito, R. V., Condon, R. E., and Harkins, H. N., *Surgery*, 51, 378–81 (1962)

100. Gelb, M., Baronofsky, I. D., and Janowitz, H. D., *Gut*, 2, 240–45 (1961)

101. Andersson, S., and Uvnäs, B., *Gastroenterology*, 41, 486–90 (1961)

102. Kaulberzs, J., Patterson, T. L., and Sandweiss, D. J., *Gastroenterology*, 42, 169–70 (1962)

103. Dotevall, G., and Muren, A., *Acta Physiol. Scand.*, 52, 234–41 (1961)

104. DeMuro, P., Rowinski, P., Galaresu, I., and Fraghi, A., *Acta Med. Scand.*, 170, 403–10 (1961)

105. Piper, D. W., and Stiel, M. C., *Gut*, 2, 230–32 (1961)

106. Werther, J. L., and Hollander, F., *Am. J. Physiol.*, 202, 721–24 (1962)

107. Blair, E. L., and Yassin, A. K., *J. Physiol. (London)*, 159, 82P–83P (1961)

108. Davenport, H. W., and Alzamora, F., *Am. J. Physiol.*, 202, 711–15 (1962)

109. Valberg, L. S., and Witts, L. J., *Gut*, 2, 32–36 (1961)

110. Tsukamoto, M., *Gastroenterology*, 41, 572–79 (1961)

111. Lin, T. M., Alphin, R. S., Henderson, F. G., and Chen. K. K. *J. Pharmacol. Exptl. Therap.*, 134, 88–94 (1961)

112. Lin, T. M., Alphin, R. S., Henderson, F. G., Benslay, D. N., and Chen, K. K., *Ann. N. Y. Acad. Sci.*, 99, 30–44 (1962)

113. Lozzio, B. B., Biempica, L., Royer, M., and Gorodisch, S., *Am. J. Digest. Diseases*, 6, 534–45 (1961)

114. Aarsen, P. N., and Van Noordwijk, J., *Brit. J. Pharmacol.*, 17, 41–50 (1961)

115. Skyring, A. P., Milton, G. W., and Maxwell, G. A., *Am. J. Physiol.*, 201, 574–76 (1961)

116. Resnick, R. H., Adelardi, C. F., and Gray, S. J., *Gastroenterology*, 42, 22–25 (1962)

117. Chaikof, L., Janke, W. H., Pesaros, P. C., Ponka, J. L., and Brush, B. E., *Arch. Surg.*, 83, 32–41 (1961)

118. Nicoloff, D. M., Stone, N. H., Peter, E. T., Doberneck, R., and Wangensteen, O. H., *J. Am. Med. Assoc.*, 178, 1005–7 (1961)

119. Reid, R. W., Hackett, R. M., and Welbourn, R. B., *Gut*, 2, 119–22 (1961)

120. Smith, A. W. M., Delamore, I. W., and Williams, A. W., *Gut*, 2, 163 (1961)

121. Nasset, E. S., and Goldsmith, D. P. G., *Am. J. Physiol.*, 201, 567–70 (1961)

122. Aylett, P., *Clin. Sci.*, 22, 179–84 (1962)

123. Neely, J. C., and Goldman, L., *Ann. Surg.*, 155, 406–11 (1962)

124. Taylor, W. H., *Gastroenterology*, 40, 823–26 (1961)

125. Roy, A. K., Balkrishna, and Zaidi, S. H., *Indian J. Med. Research*, 49, 461–65 (1961)

126. Fattah, F., Griffin, W. O., Nicoloff, D. M., Castaneda, A., and Wangensteen, O. H., *Surgery*, 49, 593–98 (1961)

127. Muirden, K. D., *Gut*, 2, 40–43 (1961)

128. Sun, D. C. H., *Ann. N. Y. Acad. Sci.*, 99, 1–229 (1962)

129. Dragstedt, L. R., *J. Am. Med. Assoc.*, 177, 758–62 (1961)

130. Kuroyanagi, Y., and Necheles, H., *Proc. Soc. Exptl. Biol. Med.*, 108, 771–72 (1961)

131. Menguy, R., and Mings, H., *Surgery*, 50, 662–67 (1961)

132. Menguy, R., *Gastroenterology*, 41, 568–71 (1962)

133. Greenlee, H. B., Johnson, A. N., Jr., Nelsen, T. S., and Dragstedt, L. R., *Arch. Surg.*, 83, 872–77 (1961)

134. Irvine, W. T., *Gastroenterology*, 42, 337–39 (1962)

135. Brodie, D. A., Marshall, R. W., and Moreno, O. M., *Am. J. Physiol.*, 202, 812–14 (1962)

136. Bonfils, S., Dubrasquet, M., and Lambling, A., *J. Appl. Physiol.*, 17, 299–300 (1962)

137. Singh, G. B., Zaida, S. H., and Paul, S. P., *Indian J. Med., Research*, 49, 768–74 (1961)

138. Ball, P., Hakkinen, I., and Hartiala, K., *Acta Physiol. Scand.*, 52, 185–87 (1961)

139. Hakkinen, I. P. T., *Acta Physiol. Scand.*, *Suppl.* 177, 51 (1961)

140. Zaidi, S. H., Singh, G. B., and Bajpa, R. P., *Indian J. Med. Research*, 49, 16–22 (1961)

141. Moreno, O. M., and Brodie, D. A., *J. Pharmacol. Exptl. Therap.*, **135**, 259–64 (1962)

142. Seirafi, R., and Reid, L. C., *Surgery*, **51**, 233–40 (1962)

143. Ridges, A. P., and Singleton, A. G., *J. Physiol. (London)*, **161**, 1–9 (1962)

144. Murray, J. G., *Gastroenterology*, **42**, 197–200 (1962)

145. Lozzio, B. B., Gagliardi, O. P., and Biempica, L., *Gastroenterology*, **41**, 126–28 (1961)

146. Walder, A. I., *Surgery*, **51**, 546–53 (1962)

147. Jorpes, E., and Mutt, V., *Acta Chem. Scand.*, **15**, 1790–91 (1961)

148. Jorpes, J. E., and Mutt, V., *Ann. Internal Med.*, **55**, 395–405 (1961)

149. Skillman, J. J., Silen, W., and Harper, H. A., *Am. J. Physiol.*, **202**, 347–48 (1962)

150. Shaldon, S., Chiandussi, L., Guevara, L., Caesar, J., and Sherlock, S., *J. Clin. Invest.*, **40**, 1346–54 (1961)

151. Christodoulopoulos, J. B., Jacobs, W. H., and Klotz, A. P., *Am. J. Physiol.*, **201**, 1020–24 (1961)

152. Magee, D. F., *J. Physiol. (London)*, **158**, 132–43 (1961)

153. Nelp, W. B., Banwell, J. G., and Hendrix, T. R., *Bull. Johns Hopkins Hosp.*, **109**, 292–301 (1961)

154. Sircus, W., *Gut*, **2**, 338–45 (1961)

155. Hong, S. S., Chin, D. S., and Hur, K. B., *J. Appl. Physiol.*, **16**, 810–14 (1961)

156. Grossman, M. I., *Physiol. Rev.*, **30**, 33–90 (1950)

157. Drapanas, T., Pollack, E. L., and Shim, W. K. T., *Arch. Surg.*, **83**, 462–66 (1961)

158. Lawrence, W., Khentigan, A., Huddock, J., and Vanamee, P., *Surgery*, **49**, 666–75 (1961)

159. Drapanas, T., and Shim, W. K. T., *Ann. Surg.*, **154**, 935–38 (1931)

160. Baker, B. L., Clapp, H. W., Annable, C. R., and Dewey, M. M., *Proc. Soc. Exptl. Biol. Med.*, **108**, 238–42 (1961)

161. Pelot, D., and Grossman, M. I., *Am. J. Physiol.*, **202**, 285–88 (1962)

162. Wohlman, A., Kabacoff, B. L., and Avakian, S., *Proc. Soc. Exptl. Biol. Med.*, **109**, 26–28 (1962)

163. White, T. T., and Magee, D. F., *Surg. Gynecol. Obstet.*, **114**, 463–66 (1962)

164. Greenbaum, L. M., and Hirshkowitz, A., *Proc. Soc. Exptl. Biol. Med.*, **107**, 74–76 (1961)

165. Negulescu, P., Harper, H. A., Crane, J. T., and Goldman, L., *Am. J. Surg.*, **102**, 196 (1961)

166. Anderson, M. C., *Arch. Surg.*, **83**, 467–74 (1961)

167. Anderson, M. C., and Bergan, J. J., *Ann. Surg.*, **154**, 58–67 (1961)

168. Anderson, M. C., Wright, P. W., and Bergan, J. J., *J. Am. Med. Assoc.*, **178**, 560–63 (1961)

169. Helms, C. H., and Meredith, J. H., *Ann. Surg.*, **27**, 665–70 (1961)

170. Wheeler, H. O., *Arch. Internal Med.*, **108**, 156–61 (1961)

171. Schanker, L. S., and Hogben, C. A. M. *Am. J. Physiol.*, **200**, 1087–90 (1961)

172. Arias, I. M., Johnson, L., and Wolfson, S., *Am. J. Physiol.*, 1091–94 (1961)

173. Dumont, A. E., Stertzer, S. H., and Mulholland, J. H., *Am. J. Physiol.*, **202**, 704–6 (1962)

174. Barber-Riley, G., Goetlee, A. E., Richards, T. G., and Thomson, J. Y., *Clin. Sci.*, **20**, 149–60 (1961)

175. Kim, J. H., and Hong, S. K., *Am. J. Physiol.*, **202**, 174–78 (1962)

176. Lindstedt, S., and Ahrens, E. H., Jr., *Proc. Soc. Exptl. Biol. Med.*, **108**, 286–88 (1961)

177. Gans, J. H., and McEntee, K., *Am. J. Physiol.*, **201**, 577–81 (1961)

178. Hellström, K., and Sjövall, J., *Acta Physiol. Scand.*, **51**, 218–23 (1961)

179. Blomstrand, R., *Proc. Soc. Exptl. Biol. Med.*, **107**, 126–28 (1961)

180. Nakayama, F., and Johnston, C. G., *J. Lab. Clin. Med.*, **59**, 364–70 (1962)

181. Hogben, C. A. M., *Am. J. Digest. Diseases*, **7**, 1–3 (1962)

182. Grim, E., *Am. J. Digest. Diseases*, **7**, 17–27 (1962)

183. Scholer, J. F., *Am. J. Digest. Diseases*, **7**, 43–49 (1962)

184. Code, C. F., *Am. J. Digest. Diseases*, **7**, 50–56 (1962)

185. Groisser, V. W., and Farrar, J. T., *Am. J. Digest. Diseases*, **7**, 57–68 (1962)

186. Clarkson, T. W., Cross, A. C., and Toole, S. R., *Am. J. Physiol.*, **200**, 1233–35 (1961)

187. Nuguid, T. P., Bacon, H. E., and Boutwell, J. E., Jr., *Surg. Gynecol. Obstet.*, **113**, 733–42 (1961)

188. Kramer, P., Kearney, M. M., and Ingelfinger, F. J., *Gastroenterology*, **42**, 535–46 (1962)

189. Nelson, R. A., Code, C. F., and Brown, A. L., Jr., *Gastroenterology*, **42**, 26–35 (1962)

190. Stewart, W. B., and Gambino, S. R., *Am. J. Physiol.*, **201**, 67–70 (1961)
191. Duthie, H. L., Code, C. F., and Owen, C. A., Jr., *Gastroenterology*, **42**, 599–61 (1962)
192. Cramer, C. F., and Dueck, J., *Am. J. Physiol.*, **202**, 161–64 (1962)
193. Schachter, D., Kimberg, D. V., and Schenker, H., *Am. J. Physiol.*, **200**, 1263–71 (1961)
194. Kimberg, D. V., Schachter, D., and Schenker, H., *Am. J. Physiol.*, **200**, 1256–62 (1961)
195. Harrison, H. E., and Harrison, H. C., *Am. J. Physiol.*, **201**, 1007–12 (1961)
196. Ross, D. B., *J. Physiol. (London)*, **160**, 417–28 (1962)
197. Smyth, D. H., *Gastroenterology*, **42**, 76–79 (1962)
198. Barry, B. A., Matthews, J., and Smyth, D. H., *J. Physiol. (London)*, **157**, 279–88 (1961)
199. Lee, J. S., and Lifson, N., *Biochim. Biophys. Acta*, **54**, 284–87 (1961)
200. Csaky, T. Z., *Am. J. Physiol.*, **201**, 999–1001 (1961)
201. Bogner, P. H., *Proc. Soc. Exptl. Biol. Med.*, **107**, 263–65 (1961)
202. Bogner, P. H., and Haines, I. A., *Proc. Soc. Exptl. Biol. Med.*, **107**, 265–67 (1961)
203. Miller, D., and Crane, R. K., *Biochim. Biophys. Acta*, **52**, 281–93 (1961)
204. Miller, D., and Crane, R. K., *Biochim.*

205. Dahlqvist, A., and Borgström, B., *Biochem. J.*, **81**, 411–18 (1961)
206. Dahlqvist, A., *J. Clin. Invest.*, **41**, 463–70 (1962)
207. Holt, J. H., and Miller, D., *J. Lab. Clin. Med.*, **58**, 827 (1961)
208. Spencer, R. P., Bow, T. M., and Markulis, M. A., *Am. J. Physiol.*, **202**, 171–73 (1962)
209. Christensen, H. N., *Federation Proc.*, **21**, 37–42 (1962)
210. Hofmann, A. F., and Borgström, B., *Federation Proc.*, **21**, 43–50 (1962)
211. Weiner, I. M., and Lack, L., *Am. J. Physiol.*, **202**, 155–57 (1962)
212. Mattson, F. H., and Volpenheim, R. A., *J. Biol. Chem.*, **237**, 52–55 (1962)
213. Senior, J. R., and Isselbacher, K. J., *Program of 54th Annual Meeting*, *Am. Soc. Clin. Invest.*, 64–65 (1962)
214. Fernandes, J., Van De Kamer, J. H., and Weijers, H. A., *J. Clin. Invest.*, **41**, 488–94 (1962)
215. Hogben, C. A. M., *Ann. Rev. Physiol.*, **22**, 381–406 (1960)
216. Schedl, H. P., and Clifton, J. A., *Gastroenterology*, **41**, 491–99 (1961)
217. Davenport, H. W., *Physiology of the Digestive Tract* (Year Book Medical Publishers Inc., Chicago, 1961)
218. Gregory, R. A., *Secretory Mechanisms of the Gastro-Intestinal Tract* (Edward Arnold Ltd., London, 1962)

Biophys. Acta, **52**, 293–98 (1961)

BLOOD: LEUKOCYTES

By John W. Athens

Department of Medicine, University of Utah College of Medicine, Salt Lake City, Utah

Previous discussions of leukocytes in the *Annual Review of Physiology* have comprised only a portion of more extensive considerations of all the formed elements of blood (1, 2, 3). Each author's interests and his appraisal of the relative significance of developments in leukocyte physiology as compared to erythrocyte and thrombocyte physiology have influenced the nature of these reviews. Because the literature dealing with each of the formed elements of the blood has become massive and because there has been a rapid expansion of interest in leukocyte physiology in recent years, the editors have seen fit to indulge the present author in his desire to confine this review to leukocytes alone, a subject last treated in detail in 1953 by Dougherty & Dougherty (3). The period covered is from July 1953 to July 1962, but a few papers from before 1953 are mentioned, when needed to make a particular point. In an attempt to keep the bibliography to a reasonable length, reference has been made where possible to summary-type articles.

Several of the methodologic advances which have contributed to our improved understanding will be discussed first. Each leukocyte type normally found in the blood will then be considered in more detail with particular emphasis on what is known of its life history.

METHODS

Leukocyte separation.—In general, the available methods for separating leukocytes from blood make use of the difference in specific gravity between leukocytes and the other formed elements, the ability of several agents (fibrinogen, dextran, phyto-agglutinin, etc.) to agglomerate erythrocytes and thus accelerate their sedimentation, the hemolysis of erythrocytes, or the tendency of granulocytes to stick to various surfaces or to ingest particulate matter. The comparative evaluations of Skoog & Beck (4) and Seabright (5) should be helpful to anyone interested in isolating leukocytes from blood as will the critical discussion by Jago (6). The extensive review by Walford cites the pertinent literature to 1960 (7) and includes useful comments derived from his vast experience with these techniques. A new red cell agglomerating agent, hexadimethrine bromide (Polybrene) has been introduced by Lalezari (8) since Walford's review. This agent has been more effective than dextran in pathologic bloods and in dog studies and we therefore now use it almost exclusively.

Throughout the literature on leukocyte separation, two points are given considerable attention and to some extent remain controversial: the necessity for using nonwettable surfaces and the anticoagulant of choice. Wasastjerna

(9) believes siliconized glassware is useful in minimizing erythrocyte contamination in sedimentation separations but is not crucial to white cell preservation, while Lapin & co-workers (10) believe nonwettable surfaces are essential in the isolation of the hydrophilic leukocytes and platelets. Actually the use of nonwettable surfaces seems less critical than was initially supposed as evidenced by the isolation of viable granulocytes from glass surfaces to which they had adhered (11). There has been a general impression that the yield of leukocytes achieved with most separation schemes is reduced if nonsiliconized surfaces are used. However, this is not consistent with the findings of Wildy & Ridley (11) who found granulocytes adhere better to siliconized or wax-coated glass than to uncoated surfaces.

The methods for rendering blood incoagulable prior to leukocyte separation include defibrination; passage through resins; and the use of heparin, citrate, oxalate, ethylenediamine tetraacetic acid, and a mixture of citric acid, sodium citrate, and dextrose anticoagulant. Defibrination markedly reduces the leukocyte yield, while the leukotoxic effect of citrate and excessive heparin and the production of morphologic alterations by oxalate are well known. Since most of these agents have been used successfully in a variety of studies, the choice of anticoagulant does not appear to be critical to most experiments. However, it seems likely that the choice of anticoagulant may be of importance if the leukocytes obtained are to be used in immunologic studies; Killmann (12) and Brittingham (13) should be consulted in this regard.

The realization that the different morphologic leukocyte types must be studied individually has led a number of investigators to devise methods for separating the various cell types from one another. These methods include: repeated centrifugation under carefully controlled conditions, thus permitting the lighter lymphocytes to remain in the supernate while the heavier granulocytes are collected at the bottom (14), the centrifugation of leukocyte suspensions in various devices which facilitate collection of lymphocyte-rich and granulocyte-rich fractions (15, 16), and the collection of lymphocytes by passing blood through a column of glass wool to which the granulocytes adhere (17). In addition, fairly pure leukocyte suspensions have been obtained from sites other than blood. For example, polymorphonuclear neutrophils have been aspirated from the peritoneal cavity (18, 19) and skin blisters (20) after the induction of a cellular reaction; lymphocytes have been collected from the thoracic duct of several animal species; and macrophages have been obtained from lung washings (21). However, in at least one instance there is evidence that such cells differ in their properties from identical morphologic cell types obtained from blood (22). This fact must be kept in mind when comparing studies carried out on leukocytes obtained from different sites.

From all of this it should be evident that the selection of a method for leukocyte isolation must be based on the requirements of the proposed study.

Factors to consider are leukocyte yield; purity of the final suspension, both as to presence of erythrocytes and platelets and as to the uniformity of the leukocyte population obtained; viability of the cells obtained; influence of the separation method on the cell properties to be studied; and the simplicity, rapidity, and cost of the procedure.

Autoradiography.—A technique which has cut across many biologic disciplines and has seemed especially promising in leukocyte studies is the autoradiographic examination of cells labeled with radioactive isotopes emitting weak beta particles, particularly tritium (H^3), but also with other isotopes such as S^{35}, C^{14}, and P^{32}. The particular advantage in the combined use of isotopic labels and autoradiography is the highly differentiated information obtained; that is to say, the degree of labeling of single cells can be ascertained rather than a mean value from a large population of cells. Several examples of information obtained with this technique, but impossible to achieve otherwise, may be cited. Kurth *et al.* (23) used tritiated diisopropylfluorophosphate and autoradiography to validate the impression derived from less definitive studies that, among the white cells, only neutrophilic granulocytes are labeled with diisopropylfluorophosphate. Also, it can be seen from this study that the improved resolving power of autoradiography is obtained at the expense of sensitivity. Thus, these workers found that in the same autoradiographs in which neutrophilic granulocytes were heavily labeled, erythrocytes contained no label. Since diisopropylfluorophosphate is known to bind to erythrocytes, the reason no radioactivity was found in them is that the autoradiographic technique was not sensitive enough to detect the small amount present.

A second example of information obtained with this technique is the combined use of tritiated thymidine and autoradiography by Bond & co-workers (24) to demonstrate that a small number of lymphocytes and monocytes in the circulating blood, when incubated with tritiated thymidine, are capable of synthesizing DNA, a rather startling demonstration that not all circulating leukocytes are end-stage cells incapable of dividing. Tritiated thymidine gives superb autoradiographs and would appear to provide an ideal means of investigating the dynamics of leukocyte proliferation since it is incorporated into the DNA of cells preparing to divide and is lost only by cell death or by dilution in subsequent divisions. Indeed, much useful information has been obtained and will be cited in later sections, but it is apparent that the extremely tedious process of grain counting and the many pitfalls of the technique, cited by Lajtha (25), have somewhat tempered the initial enthusiasm.

Cell labeling.—Much effort has been expended in an attempt to label the various leukocyte types in the hope of then being able to measure their life span, or some portion thereof. As will be apparent later, the success achieved with the different cell types has varied greatly. The types of label used can be classified into "uniform-age" (or "cohort") labels and "all-age" labels with the same connotation as that applied to erythrocyte studies (26). The uniform-age labels might be expected to approximate the life span from cell formation to egress from the blood; the all-age labels should give information about the blood phase.

The uniform-age labels that have achieved popular use have been DNA precursors containing radioactive isotopes, $Na_2HP^{32}O_4$ and H^3Th being the most extensively used, but C^{14}-labeled compounds have been used as well. Unfortunately the uniform-age labels are probably reutilized to some extent after cell breakdown (27); and since the life span of the granulocyte appears to be quite short as compared to the erythrocyte, this reincorporation of label makes interpretation of the later portions of curves obtained from such studies difficult if not impossible. In addition, $Na_2HP^{32}O_4$ may be available to label newly formed cells for several days after injection (15), further complicating interpretation. From our present vantage point it would appear that only the first portion of the curves from such studies provides us with valid and interpretable information. The uniform-age labels have so far been used with some success for studies of all leukocyte types except the basophil.

Diisopropylfluorophosphate (28), $Na_2Cr^{51}O_4$ (29), and atabrine (30) have been used as all-age labels but only the first appears to have been used with any success. The $Na_2Cr^{51}O_4$ method has not been studied intensively and atabrine is not firmly enough bound to be a satisfactory label (31). An attempt has been made to use morphologically distinguishable cells as all-age labeled leukocytes. Thus, alkaline phosphatase positive rat granulocytes have been transfused into mice (which have alkaline phosphatase negative granulocytes) (31), and Pelger-Huet cells from a human subject have been given to a normal recipient (32), and the disappearance of the transfused cells from the blood was followed. The obvious incompatibility of the interspecies transfusion is apparent. The other study will be referred to in the next section. To date only the polymorphonuclear neutrophil has been labeled with an all-age label.

THE NEUTROPHILIC GRANULOCYTE

Proliferation in the bone marrow.—Japa (33) and, more recently, Killmann & co-workers (34) have examined mitotic cell division in the bone marrow of human subjects. The latter workers found 8.86 mitoses per 1000 nucleated cells, 28 per cent of which were in the granulocytic series, i.e., 2.5 mitoses per 1000 granulocytes. In the granulocytic series of cells, only myeloblasts, promyelocytes, and myelocytes were seen in mitosis. In the studies of Patt & Maloney (35) in the dog and of Cronkite *et al.* (36) in man, these same morphologic cell types were labeled by tritiated thymidine, the specific precursor of DNA which is taken up only during the period of DNA synthesis that precedes cell division. For these reasons, and because metamyelocytes and polymorphonuclear cells have not been seen to divide or to be labeled by tritiated thymidine (except when descended from labeled precursor cells), it is believed that the production of granulocytes results from the proliferation of the first three cell types only. Since cells intermediate in appearance between myeloblasts and promyelocytes and between promyelocytes and myelocytes are often seen, it has seemed likely that cells progress from one morphologic type to the next with perhaps several cell divisions at each stage (37). However, proof of this is lacking.

Osgood (38) has described several cell proliferation schemes that will provide an arithmetic flow of cells from a steady-state system. He divides cells capable of division into two types, the "alpha cell" and the "n cell" (39). The alpha cell can perpetuate itself by a division which produces two daughter cells, at least one of which does not differentiate and remains an alpha cell (alpha, 2 alpha or alpha, n division). An n cell differentiates and ultimately dies. The n cell can divide to produce more n cells (n, $2n$ division), but has lost its ability to perpetuate the cell line. Of the several proliferation schemes suggested by Osgood, the one which apparently best fits the data of Japa, Killmann et al., Patt & Maloney, and Cronkite et al., described above, has been presented diagramatically by several authors (40, 41, 42), and may be described as follows: the earliest cell in the series, the myeloblast, divides to yield two daughter cells each of which again divides (n, $2n$ division), thus yielding four cells, perhaps recognizable as promyelocytes. Two more cell divisions would result in sixteen cells, perhaps recognized as myelocytes, and a final division would yield thirty-two cells which then mature without further cell division. This scheme fits nicely with the observation of Killmann et al. (34) that the relative numbers of granulocytes in the marrow are 1:4: 16:36 (myeloblasts:promyelocytes:myelocytes:nondividing granulocytes). Unfortunately, serious objections can be raised to this apparently simple scheme. A major objection is derived from the studies of Brooke & Osgood (43) in which blood from chronic myelocytic leukemia patients continued to grow in culture for extended time periods. This could not happen if myeloblasts, promyelocytes, and myelocytes are only capable of (n, $2n$) divisions, as hypothesized in such a scheme. Therefore, Osgood has suggested that perhaps the myelocyte is an alpha cell (44). Other assumptions inherent in the above scheme, such as no cell death during proliferation and uniform mitotic and intermitotic times for each cell type, may also be questioned as Stohlman (45) has pointed out. Indeed, the observations of Killmann et al. (34) that the specific mitotic index is greatest for myeloblasts and least for myelocytes suggests that the intermitotic time for each cell type is different. However, without belaboring the difficulties, it should be apparent that although considerable information on neutrophil proliferation has been accumulating, the production of neutrophilic granulocytes by the bone marrow is, as yet, incompletely understood.

The means by which proliferation is regulated are also unknown. Osgood (38, 46) favors self-regulation by means of hypothetical inhibitor(s) formed in the maturing cells of each cell line. Craddock (37, 47) has recently presented some evidence to support this thesis. On the other hand, Gordon et al.

(48, 49) and Shen & Hoshino (50) have presented evidence for the existence of a leukocytosis-inducing factor(s). Regardless of the control system, another area of interest is the means by which cell production can be increased when necessary. Of the possible mechanisms, namely, the differentiation of more stem cells into myeloblasts, a diminution of premature cell death, or a decrease in intermitotic time, evidence has been brought forth in favor of the last process only (51).

Maturation and storage in the bone marrow.—Ottesen (15) and Perry *et al.* (52) using $Na_2HP^{32}O_4$ and Bond *et al.* (41) using H^3Th to label myeloblasts, promyelocytes, and myelocytes in the bone marrow of human subjects have found a four- to six-day lag period before labeled polymorphonuclear neutrophils appeared in the blood. These observations clearly establish the existence of a mass of nondividing, and therefore initially unlabeled, cells interposed between the proliferating cells in the marrow and the cells circulating in the blood. In the study by Cronkite *et al.* (36), serial bone marrow samples obtained after tritiated thymidine injection and examined by means of high-resolution autoradiography have demonstrated fixation of the label in myeloblasts, promyelocytes, and myelocytes immediately after the injection, with maximal levels achieved by one hour. Metamyelocytes, band cells, and polymorphonuclear neutrophils were not labeled initially. However, labeled metamyelocytes began to appear by three hours, labeled band cells were seen at twelve hours, and labeled polymorphonuclear neutrophils were evident in the marrow at twenty-four to thirty-six hours after label was injected. Labeled polymorphonuclear neutrophils appeared in the blood after about four days (41).

From these studies in man and similar studies by Patt & Maloney (35) in dogs and by Bryant & Kelly (53) in mice, it seems clear that neutrophils move in a sequential manner from the myelocyte stage through the metamyelocyte, band, and polymorphonuclear stages in the marrow to the blood. Under normal, steady-state conditions the minimum transit time from the last myelocyte division to the blood is about four days in man, three days in the dog, and two days in the mouse, and, not unexpectedly, there is some variation in the values obtained. The mean transit time is perhaps one day longer than these minimum figures.

The nature and purpose of this maturation process and sequential movement are unknown, but Craddock (37) has suggested that perhaps the mature polymorphonuclear granulocyte is better equipped to ingest and destroy bacteria than its more immature predecessors. More information on this subject is needed, but the studies by Boggs (54) and Perillie & Finch (55), in which only metamyelocytes and polymorphonuclear granulocytes appeared in inflammatory exudates induced in leukemic subjects, seem compatible with this concept.

One may regard this mass of metamyelocytes, bands, and polymorphonuclear neutrophils in the bone marrow as a reserve of nonproliferating, maturing, and mature cells available for an emergency, a marrow granulocyte reserve. Craddock *et al.* (56) have shown that irradiated dogs incapable of myeloproliferation develop a marked leukocytosis after blood leukocytes are removed by leukopheresis. When leukopheresis was repeated on several successive days, cells continued to be released into the blood until the marrow granulocyte reserve was exhausted. From these studies and the demonstration that leukopheresis accelerates the appearance in the blood of cells whose DNA was labeled with P^{32} (57), it is concluded that the majority of leukocytes which replace those removed came from this marrow granulocyte reserve. Similar results obtained by Perry *et al.* (58), using killed typhoid bacilli to produce a leukocytosis, and results in patients with acute infections (59) suggest that such a reserve is the main source of neutrophils in pathologic states as well.

In the irradiation plus leukopheresis studies just mentioned, Craddock & co-workers (56) removed up to 18.4×10^{10} leukocytes from a single dog, seven times the number circulating in the blood. They point out that many more cells were probably lost via other routes, such as the gastrointestinal tract, and this figure is thus an underestimate of the dog's marrow granulocyte reserve. Other workers have also estimated the size of such a reserve by various indirect means, but the only direct measurements of marrow leukocyte mass are those of Donohue & co-workers (60) using the Fe^{59} dilution technique developed by Suit (61). The marrow granulocyte reserve calculated for a 70 kg man from their data is 61.6×10^{10} cells, a value 30 times the circulating granulocyte mass, but only 15 times the total intravascular mass of granulocytes (see section below). From the two facts just cited, the reserve of 61.6×10^{10} cells and the five-day lag between DNA labeling of human granulocytes in marrow and their appearance in blood, one can estimate the daily turnover of cells through the blood at 12×10^{10} cells per day for a 70 kg man. This value can be compared with the direct measurement of the blood granulocyte turnover rate described in the next section.

Intravascular phase.—Mauer *et al.* (28) have labeled neutrophilic granulocytes with radioactive diisopropylfluorophosphate by means of a method analogous to the Cr^{51} technique of labeling erythrocytes. These workers have used this technique and the isotope dilution principle to measure the total blood granulocyte pool in human subjects and have found that the circulating granulocyte pool, as determined from the blood volume and blood granulocyte count, comprises only about one half of the intravascular neutrophils. The remaining cells are marginated along the walls of small blood vessels where they are in a state of rapid and continuous exchange with circulating cells, and from which site they can be mobilized by exercise or epinephrine injection (62, 63). With this method Athens & co-workers (64) have demonstrated that an elevated blood granulocyte count may occur as a result of intravascular shifts of cells without an increase in the size of the total blood granulocyte pool, a "pseudoleukocytosis," to use a term popular in discussions of this subject at the turn of the century (65). It is also of interest that they have identified a pseudoleukopenia that is a shift of circulating cells to marginal sites with no change in size of the total blood granulocyte pool. The anatomic site of the marginated cells is not known but is presumably diffuse (66, 67) and more related to vessel size and blood flow than to a specific organ.

In addition to the measurements of neutrophil pool size and distribution, it is possible to follow neutrophil disappearance from the blood with this same method (28). From these studies it is evident that labeled neutrophils leave the blood in a random or exponential manner rather than according to their age as is the case for the erythrocyte. The time required for half of the labeled cells to leave the blood $(T_{\frac{1}{2}})$ was only 6.6 ± 1.16 hours. From these findings it is apparent that the average neutrophil spends 9.5 hours in the blood and the total blood granulocyte pool turns over 2.5 times a day!

This rather unorthodox concept is supported by several independent investigations. Patt & Maloney (35) noted that a uniform population of tritiated thymidine-labeled dog neutrophils disappeared from the blood in an exponential manner with a $T_{\frac{1}{2}}$ of less than eight hours, a finding in fairly good agreement with recent diisopropylfluorophosphate studies in dogs (68, 69). Also Bond & co-workers (41) from their tritiated thymidine studies estimated the turnover time of neutrophils in human blood to be less than 24 hours. Finally, Rosse & Gurney (32) transfused Pelger-Huet cells, labeled only by their characteristic morphology, into a normal recipient and normal cells into a Pelger-Huet recipient. They found one half to two thirds of the transfused cells had disappeared within six to eight hours, and a plot of their data roughly fits an exponential line.

From the size of the total blood granulocyte pool, the $T_{\frac{1}{2}}$, and the equation for exponential disappearance, Athens et al. (62) calculated the turnover of granulocytes in the blood of 45 normal subjects to be 180×10^7 cells/kg/day or 12.6×10^{10} cells/day in a 70 kg man. In the steady state this value is the number of cells produced and destroyed each day and, though it at first appears astronomical, it is amazingly close to the figure calculated (from erythrocyte mass and survival) for erythrocyte production (270×10^7 red blood cells/kg/day or 18.9×10^{10} cells per day in a 70 kg man).

A point of controversy in regard to granulocyte turnover is whether cells return to the intravascular compartment once they have left it. Conclusive evidence to rule out some return from tissues is not available, but a number of observations are against a return of any magnitude. Craddock et al. (70) have been unable to show re-entry of labeled cells once they have entered peritoneal exudates or migrated into areas of infection, and Patt & co-workers (71) noted that during the recovery phase from immune-serum induced leukopenia of severe degree most of the leukocytes were band forms. Cronkite et al. (42) state that Algire, in the course of his microscopic studies in vivo, has frequently seen neutrophils leave the circulation but has never seen one re-enter, and Mauer et al. (28) followed the diisopropylfluorophosphate-labeled granulocyte disappearance curve for four days and noted it to be a single exponential reaching background levels with no late irregularities or any suggestion of re-entry of cells. However, the latter authors point out (62, 72) that a small amount of return from tissues or dilution of blood cells in a large tissue neutrophil pool would not be detectable and the most one can do is to set limits on the amount of return which would be undetected in the above studies.

A final piece of evidence against significant return from tissues is the study by Little *et al.* (73) in which tritiated thymidine was given to rats by continuous infusion. In these animals all of the granulocytes were labeled by the third or fourth day. If there were a large tissue pool of mature neutrophils from which cells returned to the circulation, 100 per cent labeling would be achieved, if ever, only after a much longer interval.

Fate in tissues and destruction.—The above described flow of cells, through the processes of proliferation, maturation, and storage in the bone marrow, release into the blood with rapid disappearance therefrom, and the lack of evidence for significant return from tissues seems to indicate a unidirectional movement of cells to ultimate destruction in the tissues. The extrusion and disintegration of neutrophils at sites of infection are obvious but the fate of these cells in the normal organism is unclear. Ambrus & Ambrus (74) have presented evidence for a migration of neutrophils into the alveoli and loss thereby, but there are undoubtedly other routes of destruction as well. That damaged cells may be trapped in the lungs and eventually reach the spleen and liver is clear from the studies of Leahy *et al.* (75) and Weisberger & coworkers (76) in which the label from P^{32}-tagged cells was found in these sites. Brecher *et al.* (77) using atabrine-labeled cells found them trapped in the lungs and later in the spleen and liver also. However, the significance of these routes in normal leukocyte disposal remains to be demonstrated.

Biochemistry and phagocytosis.—The metabolic patterns and enzymatic and biochemical constitution of leukocytes have been studied by many workers and cannot be reviewed in detail here. Valentine (78) has cited much of the descriptive data accumulated in studies of normal leukocytes and has contrasted this information with the findings in cells from patients with leukemia and other disease. Though the significance of these many variations from normal remains unexplained, quantitative differences in cell enzyme activity have sometimes been useful clinically and may provide clues to an eventual understanding of pathological states. For example, leukocyte alkaline phosphatase activity (79 to 83) is usually low in polymorphonuclear neutrophils from patients with chronic myelocytic leukemia but is increased in morphologically identical cells from patients with polycythemia rubra vera and myeloid metaplasia. Furthermore, in chronic myelocytic leukemia the alkaline phosphatase activity ordinarily remains low even during remissions induced by therapy, but in an exceptional case it will return to normal. These observations have led Valentine to suggest that chronic myelocytic leukemia may be an overgrowth of a new population of cells (alkaline phosphatase negative) and only in an unusual instance is a sufficiently good remission induced to permit the normal alkaline phosphatase positive cell lineage to reassert itself. This interesting concept deserves further investigation.

Of great interest is the recent demonstration by Sbarra & Karnovsky (84) that active glycolysis is essential for phagocytosis. This finding and the studies by Cohn & Hirsch (85, 86, 87) in which granule lysis and specific alterations in the activity and distribution of enzymes were shown to follow phagocytosis are beginning to bring the manifold and varied observations on leukocyte metabolism into a meaningful pattern in terms of leukocyte function.

THE BASOPHIL

The physiology and functions of this, the least numerous of the blood leukocytes, remain largely unknown. The development of a technique for the direct enumeration of basophils in the blood by Moore & James (88) made possible a number of studies relating changes in basophil counts to various physiological and clinical states (89). Basophils appear to have the same diurnal rhythm as eosinophils, being present in the blood in greatest numbers during the night and in smallest numbers in the morning (90, 91). In women the number of basophils may also fluctuate during the menstrual cycle and may decrease during pregnancy (89). Cortisone and ACTH produced a parallel reduction in the number of both basophils and eosinophils in normal subjects, but the eosinopenia was more pronounced than the basopenia (92). However, not all workers have been able to confirm this (89). Hypothyroid patients have a mild basophilia while a decrease in the basophil count is seen in thyrotoxicosis (93). The highest basophil counts are seen in the myeloproliferative disorders, especially chronic myelocytic leukemia (94). Beyond these descriptive studies little information is available. There is essentially no information on basophil kinetics or proliferation (except that they are formed in the bone marrow), and there is recurring disagreement as to whether the blood basophil and tissue mast cell are the same cell in different sites or are cells with similar properties but of different origin (92, 95, 96). The presence of heparin in both cell types (97, 98, 99), the demonstration by Valentine *et al.* (100) and Graham & co-workers (101) that the basophil is the main repository of blood histamine, and the demonstration of histamine in mast cells by Riley (102), Benditt (103), and Lagunoff *et al.* (104) serve to emphasize the similarities of these two cells but scarcely solve the question of their relationship to one another. Riley (102) has considered this topic at some length and presents evidence from comparative anatomical studies which suggests that in higher vertebrates they are separate in origin and habitat. The studies of Hartman & co-workers (105) show that basophils can convert histidine to histamine and may be more than passive storehouses for this material. That tissue mast cells and blood basophils stain metachromatically, contain heparin and histamine, and release these substances when the cell undergoes degranulation upon appropriate stimulation seems clear. The interesting studies of Shelley & Juhlin (106, 107), Riley (102), Humphrey & Mota (108), and Archer (109) appear to link this degranulation with certain antigen antibody interactions both *in vitro* and *in vivo*.

THE EOSINOPHIL

The distinct appearance and staining characteristics of the eosinophil, the fact that methods for its enumeration have been available for many years, and the variation in eosinophil counts with adrenocortical activity undoubtedly account for the tremendous interest in this cell, even though it is one of the least numerous leukocytes in the blood. Bryant & Kelly (53) have shown in the mouse that tritiated thymidine-labeled eosinophils move through the marrow and into the blood more rapidly than neutrophils but with the same general pattern. As a result of this study and the sequence of events observed in the marrow, blood, and tissues after the induction of an eosinophilic response (110), it is generally agreed that eosinophils are produced only in the bone marrow, travel via the blood to the tissues where they perform their function(s), and are destroyed or extruded. Correct or not, most studies of eosinophils have been interpreted with this scheme in mind. The variations in eosinophil counts seen clinically and the applications thereof have been cited by Speirs (111) and will not be repeated here. However, at least two of these variations should offer a clue to the physiology and function of this cell and deserve further comment.

The eosinopenia which develops within a few hours after the administration of ACTH or glucocorticoids has been examined for some indication as to how these hormones effect this change. Gordon, in his review (112), points out that there is little change apparent in the bone marrow eosinophil pattern at the time of blood eosinopenia and therefore inhibition of marrow eosinophil production or release seems unlikely. Attempts to attribute the eosinopenia to a redistribution of eosinophils with sequestration in organs such as the spleen have not been convincing either (112). Since degenerative changes are seen in blood and peritoneal eosinophils of stressed rats and after a single injection of cortisone, and since these changes are well correlated with the blood eosinopenia (112), it seems most likely that the eosinopenia results from increased destruction of eosinophils. However, until suitable methods for measuring circulating eosinophil mass, eosinophil disappearance rate, and blood eosinophil turnover are developed, acceptance of this interpretation must remain tentative.

The association of eosinophilia with clinical allergy and parasitic infestation, and extensive studies of experimentally induced eosinophilia, have led many workers to postulate that the eosinophil is intimately involved in the immune responses of the body. The demonstration by Speirs (111, 113) and by Litt (114, 115, 116) that the magnitude of the eosinophilic response in the blood and at tissue injection sites increases with serial injections of antigen and is highly specific appears to document this belief amply. However, the induction of an eosinophilic response by a single injection of heparin (111), asbestos particles (111), histamine (117), or Ascaris extract (118) into animals not previously exposed to these agents, though at times not reproduced (111, 114), must also be explained since an immune response would not seem to be operative here. Litt (115) has proposed that the eosinophilic response to repeated injections of antigen involves antigen-antibody reaction whereas the eosinophilic response to asbestos, heparin, and histamine or to a single injection of antigen may be a nonspecific reaction resulting from tissue destruction. "In both instances, unidentified, perhaps identical, eosinophilotactic substance(s) may be released from the tissues." He has prepared tissue extracts containing an eosinophilotactic material that appears to be a large molecule (nondialyzable), stable to mild heating and precipitable by trichloroacetic acid. Histamine does not appear to be the mediating substance since it is dialyzable and since antihistaminics did not block the reaction. In view of the degranulation of basophils and tissue mast cells by both antigen-antibody reaction and other less specific stimuli and in view of the demonstration that eosinophils are attracted to sites of antigen-antibody reaction and, albeit inconstantly, to sites of histamine and heparin injection (substances known to be present in basophils and mast cells), it is tempting to hypothesize that these two cell types are closely associated with one another at sites of tissue injury. Certainly identification of the stimulus which induces eosinophilia should provide a major clue to the functions of the eosinophil and may also provide further information about basophil and tissue mast cells.

THE LYMPHOCYTE

Proliferation.—The demonstration by Bryant & Kelly (53) that the DNA precursor C^{14}-adenine is rapidly incorporated into large and medium lymphocytes in the thymus and lymph nodes of mice, and less rapidly and less extensively incorporated into small lymphocytes, is consistent with the hypothesis that the sequence of events in the formation of lymphocytes is from reticular cell to large lymphocyte to medium lymphocyte to small lymphocyte as postulated by Sainte-Marie & LeBlond (119). The appearance of tritiated thymidine-labeled cells in the thoracic duct lymph of the guinea pig was followed by Yoffey et al. (120) and is also compatible with this hypothesis. Sainte-Marie & LeBlond made extensive studies of the mitotic indices and relative numbers of these several cell types in the thymus of rats and compared the results obtained with what would be expected from an assortment of possible patterns of lymphocyte proliferation. They found an excellent correlation between predicted and experimental results when a scheme which they entitled the "Stem Cell Renewal Theory" was used. This scheme may be described, using Osgood's (39) terminology again, as follows: only the reticular cell is capable of (alpha, n) divisions and it divides infrequently (mitotic index .015) as compared to the later cell forms (large lymphocyte, medium lymphocyte, and small lymphocyte) which are capable only of (n, $2n$) divisions and have mitotic indices of .069, .133, and .026, respectively. The initial reticular cell (alpha, n) division is followed by four (n, $2n$) divisions at the large lymphocyte stage, two (n, $2n$) divisions at the medium lymphocyte stage, and two (n, $2n$) divisions at the small lymphocyte stage. Although the experimental results and those predicted by this scheme are in good accord, the scheme is only as valid as the assumptions inherent in it, as Sainte-Marie & LeBlond carefully pointed out. Certainly the scheme and observed facts agree closely enough to suggest that attempts at evaluating the assumptions be pursued with vigor.

Of further interest in relation to the proliferation of lymphocytes are the recent studies which suggest that the thymus is essential to the production of lymphocytes. Thus Good et al. (121) showed that primitive fishes which have no lymphoid tissue lack the ability to produce antibodies whereas the development of antibody-forming ability and the appearance of lymphoid tissue appear together in the phylogenetic scale. When the earliest appearing lymphoid tissue, the thymus in mammals and the organ of Fabricius in chickens, is removed in neonatal life a lymphopenia and a morphologically defective lymphoid system result, and such animals do not develop normal immunologic competence (121 to 124). These findings and the more rapid and extensive uptake of C^{14}-adenine into mouse (53) and P^{32} into rat (125) thymus as compared with lymph nodes suggest that the thymus is involved in the centrifugal distribution of immunologically competent cells. It should not be construed from these remarks that lymphocyte production takes place only in the thymus. However, the measurements of relative DNA turnover in several lymphoid organs by Andreasen & Ottesen (125) and the histologic studies of mitotic index by Kindred (126) indicate that the thymus is probably most active in this regard, especially in young animals.

Intravascular phase.—Yoffey & Courtice (127) and Gowans (128) have reviewed the many studies of lymphatic duct output which show that enough cells enter the circulation by this route to replace all the blood lymphocytes between four and twenty-four times per day. It has been difficult to reconcile the rapid turnover of lymphocytes implied by these studies with the very long life span of 100 to 200 days suggested by DNA-labeling studies of Ottesen (15), Hamilton (129), and Little et al. (73). However, the recent demonstration by Gowans (130) that lymphocytes recirculate from the blood to the lymph and back to blood again convincingly explains this apparent paradox. In a series of ingenious experiments he showed: that the prolonged drainage of lymph from a thoracic duct fistula results in a decreased output of lymphocytes from the fistula and in a severe blood lymphopenia; that both abnormalities could be alleviated by transfusing genetically similar lymphocytes into the animal; that the transfusion of P^{32}-labeled lymphocytes into a lymphocyte-depleted animal resulted in their rapid appearance in the thoracic duct lymph; and finally, that the number of new lymphocytes formed each day as determined from studies with tritiated thymidine amounted to only a small fraction of the normal output from the thoracic duct.

Thus it seems clear that lymphocytes survive a much longer time in the body than granulocytes (53, 73) and that lymphocytes repeatedly circulate from the blood through the lymph and back to the blood again.

Fate and function.—The above described recirculation of lymphocytes gives no information as to their ultimate fate, but it does markedly reduce the number of cells that are produced and must be disposed of each day. Whether lymphocytes are extruded into the intestine or degenerate in the skin or the intestinal wall or in lymph nodes as Andreasen (131) believes, whether they leave the blood to become stem cells in the bone marrow as suggested by Yoffey & Courtice (127), or whether they undergo some other transformation before discharging whatever function they may have is still a subject of controversy. The definitive experiments remain to be done. However, from the fascinating studies of Gowans (132) it seems that the small lymphocyte from the thoracic duct lymph in the rat can mediate the immunologic rejection of skin homografts, and in the process perhaps becomes a new, but as yet unidentified, cell type. The demonstration by MacKinney *et al.* (133) that the small lymphocyte in human blood is capable of dividing in cultures and may undergo morphologic transformations is in agreement with Gowan's results in intact rats.

The Monocyte

Studies on the monocyte have been infrequent and difficult to interpret. Trowell (134) observed what he interpreted as a transformation of lymphocytes to monocytes in lymph node cultures in the rat. Others have observed similar changes in the appearance of small lymphocytes under both *in vitro* and *in vivo* conditions (132, 133). Furthermore, the uptake *in vitro* of tritiated thymidine by human blood leukocytes that have the morphologic appearance of monocytes (24) and by similar cells in thoracic duct lymph (120) shortly after this tritiated thymidine injection suggests that the monocyte is an immature cell capable of cell division that is released into the blood, presumably from lymph nodes. However, Schooley & Berman (135) placed *in vivo*-labeled thoracic duct lymph cells (only large mononuclear cells would be labeled under the conditions used) in millipore chambers and implanted these intraperitoneally in mice and rats. The dilution of grain counts which occurred with time led them to conclude that large mononuclear cells were transformed into medium lymphocytes and these in turn into small lymphocytes, just the reverse of the transformations described by others. At least part of this discrepancy is undoubtedly a result of the difficulty in differentiating large and medium lymphocytes from monocytes in smears and especially in autoradiographs. In any case the origin of monocytes is still in question.

Fliedner & co-workers (136) followed the appearance of tritiated thymidine in the blood monocytes of man and found a small number of labeled "monocytoid" cells in the blood as early as one to two hours after the thymidine injection. They point out that there is a very short "maturation time", if any, for monocytes; and from the rate of appearance of labeled cells in the blood they calculated that the blood monocyte pool turned over at least once every six days in their normal subject. In another subject with infection the turnover time was less than 2.2 days. It seems likely that these cells are the same as the short-lived population of lymphocytes referred to by Ottesen (15).

The ultimate fate and function of the monocyte are, like its origin, really unknown.

LITERATURE CITED

1. Cartwright, G. E., and Wintrobe, M. M., *Ann. Rev. Physiol.*, **11**, 335 (1949)
2. Jacobs, M. H., *Ann. Rev. Physiol.*, **20**, 405 (1958)
3. Dougherty, T. F., and Dougherty, J. H., *Ann. Rev. Physiol.*, **15**, 195 (1953)
4. Skoog, W. A., and Beck, W. S., *Blood*, **11**, 346 (1956)
5. Seabright, M., *J. Med. Lab. Technol.*, **14**, 85 (1957)
6. Jago, M., *Brit. J. Haematol.*, **2**, 439 (1956)
7. Walford, R. L., *Leukocyte Antigens and Antibodies* (Grune & Stratton, New York, 182 pp., 1960)
8. Lalezari, P., *Blood*, **19**, 109 (1962)
9. Wasastjerna, C., *Scand. J. Clin. Lab. Invest.*, **8**, 14 (1956)
10. Lapin, J. H., Horonick, A., and Lapin, R. H., *Blood*, **13**, 1001 (1958)
11. Wildy, P., and Ridley, M., *Nature*, **182**, 1801 (1958)
12. Killmann, S. A., *Acta Pathol. Microbiol. Scand.*, **45**, 17 (1959)
13. Brittingham, T. E., *Proc. Soc. Exptl. Biol. Med.*, **99**, 252 (1958)
14. Athens, J. W., Mauer, A. M., Ashenbrucker, H., Cartwright, G. E., and Wintrobe, M. M., *Blood*, **14**, 303 (1959)
15. Ottesen, J., *Acta Physiol. Scand.*, **32**, 75 (1954)
16. Ventzke, L. E., Perry, S., and Crepaldi, G., *J. Lab. Clin. Med.*, **53**, 319 (1959)
17. Johnson, T. M., and Garvin, J. E., *Proc. Soc. Exptl. Biol. Med.*, **102**, 333 (1959)
18. Hirsch, J. G., *J. Exptl. Med.*, **103**, 589 (1956)
19. Fruhman, G. J., *Blood*, **16**, 1753 (1960)
20. Boggs, D. R., Athens, J. W., Haab, O. P., Raab, S. O., Cartwright, G. E., and Wintrobe, M. M. (Unpublished data)
21. Myrvik, Q. N., Leake, E. S., and Fariss, B., *J. Immunol.*, **86**, 133 (1961)
22. Kaiser, H. K., and Wood, W. B., Jr., *J. Exptl. Med.*, **115**, 27 (1962)
23. Kurth, D., Athens, J. W., Cronkite, E. P., Cartwright, G. E., and Wintrobe, M. M., *Proc. Soc. Exptl. Biol. Med.*, **107**, 422 (1961)
24. Bond, V. P., Fliedner, T. M., Cronkite, E. P., Rubini, J. R., Brecher, G., and Schork, P. K., *Acta Haematol.*, **21**, 1 (1959)
25. Lajtha, L. G., *The Kinetics of Cellular Proliferation*, 173 (Grune & Stratton, New York, 456 pp., 1959)
26. Eadie, G. S., *Ann. N. Y. Acad. Sci.*, **77**, 737 (1959)
27. Hamilton, L. D., *The Kinetics of Cellular Proliferation*, 151 (Grune & Stratton, New York, 456 pp., 1959)
28. Mauer, A. M., Athens, J. W., Ashenbrucker, H., Cartwright, G. E., and Wintrobe, M. M., *J. Clin. Invest.*, **39**, 1481 (1960)
29. McCall, M. S., Sutherland, D. A., Eisentraut, A. M., and Long, H., *J. Lab. Clin. Med.*, **45**, 717 (1955)
30. White, L. P., *Blood*, **9**, 73 (1954)
31. Brecher, G., and Peden, J. C., Jr., *The Kinetics of Cellular Proliferation*, 227 (Grune & Stratton, New York, 456 pp., 1959)
32. Rosse, W. F., and Gurney, C. W., *Blood*, **14**, 170 (1959)
33. Japa, J., *Brit. J. Exptl. Pathol.*, **23**, 272 (1942)
34. Killmann, S. A., Cronkite, E. P., Fliedner, T. M., and Bond, V. P., *Blood*, **19**, 743 (1962)
35. Patt, H. M., and Maloney, M. A., *The Kinetics of Cellular Proliferation*, 201 (Grune & Stratton, New York, 456 pp., 1959)
36. Cronkite, E. P., Bond, V. P., Fliedner, T. M., and Killmann, S. A., *Hemopoiesis, Ciba Found. Symp.*, 70 (Little, Brown, Boston, 490 pp., 1960)
37. Craddock, C. G., Jr., *Am. J. Med.*, **28**, 711 (1960)
38. Osgood, E. E., *Brookhaven Symp. Biol.*, **10**, 31 (1958)
39. Osgood, E. E., *The Kinetics of Cellular Proliferations*, 282 (Grune & Stratton, New York, 456 pp., 1959)
40. Craddock, C. G., Jr., Perry, S., and Lawrence, J. S., *The Kinetics of Cellular Proliferation*, 242 (Grune & Stratton, New York, 456 pp., 1959)
41. Bond, V. P., Fliedner, T. M., Cronkite, E. P., Rubini, J. R., and Robertson, J. S., *The Kinetics of Cellular Proliferation*, 188 (Grune & Stratton, New York, 456 pp., 1959)
42. Cronkite, E. P., Fliedner, T. M., Bond, V. P., and Robertson, J. S., *The Kinetics of Cellular Proliferation*, 1 (Grune & Stratton, New York, 456 pp., 1959)
43. Brooke, J. H., and Osgood, E. E., *Blood*, **14**, 803 (1959)
44. Osgood, E. E. (Personal communication)

45. Stohlman, F., Jr., *The Kinetics of Cellular Proliferation*, 318 (Grune & Stratton, New York, 456 pp., 1959)
46. Osgood, E. E., *J. Natl. Cancer Inst.*, **18,** 155 (1957)
47. Craddock, C. G., Jr., *Hemopoiesis, Ciba Found. Symp.*, 237 (Little, Brown, Boston, 490 pp., 1960)
48. Gordon, A. S., Nevi, R. O., Siegel, C. D., Dornfest, B. S., Handler, E. S., Labue, J., and Eisler, M., *Acta Haematol.*, **23,** 323 (1960)
49. Gordon, A. S., *Hemopoiesis, Ciba Found. Symp.*, 325 (Little, Brown, Boston, 490 pp., 1960)
50. Shen, S. C., and Hoshino, T., *Blood*, **17,** 434 (1961)
51. Widner, W. R., Storer, J. B., and Lushbaugh, C. C., *Cancer Res.*, **11,** 877 (1951)
52. Perry, S., Craddock, C. G., Jr., and Lawrence, J. S., *J. Lab. Clin. Med.*, **51,** 501 (1958)
53. Bryant, B. J., and Kelly, L. S., *Proc. Soc. Exptl. Biol. Med.*, **99,** 681 (1958)
54. Boggs, D. R., *Blood*, **15,** 466 (1960)
55. Perillie, P. E., and Finch, S. C., *J. Clin. Invest.*, **39,** 1353 (1960)
56. Craddock, C. G., Jr., Adams, W. S., Perry, S., Skoog, W. A., and Lawrence, J. S., *J. Lab. Clin. Med.*, **45,** 881 (1955)
57. Craddock, C. G., Jr., Perry, S., and Lawrence, J. S., *J. Clin. Invest.*, **35,** 285 (1956)
58. Perry, S., Weinstein, I. M., Craddock, C. G., Jr., and Lawrence, J. S., *Blood*, **12,** 549 (1957)
59. Perry, S., Craddock, C. G., Jr., and Lawrence, J. S., *J. Lab. Clin. Med.*, **51,** 501 (1958)
60. Donohue, D. M., Reiff, R. H., Hanson, M. L., Betson, Y., and Finch, C. A., *J. Clin. Invest.*, **37,** 1571 (1958)
61. Suit, H. D., *J. Clin. Pathol.*, **10,** 267 (1957)
62. Athens, J. W., Raab, S. O., Haab, O. P., Mauer, A. M., Ashenbrucker, H., Cartwright, G. E., and Wintrobe, M. M., *J. Clin. Invest.*, **40,** 159 (1961)
63. Bierman, H. R., Kelly, K. H., Cordes, F. L., Byron, R. L., Polhemus, J. A., and Rappaport, S., *Blood*, **7,** 683 (1952)
64. Athens, J. W., Haab, O. P., Raab, S. O., Mauer, A. M., Ashenbrucker, H., Cartwright, G. E., and Wintrobe, M. M., *J. Clin. Invest.*, **40,** 989 (1961)
65. Goldschieder, A., and Jacob, P., *Z. Klin. Med.*, **25,** 373 (1894)
66. Villalobos, T. J., Adelson, E., Riley, P. A., Jr., and Crosby, W. H., *J. Clin. Invest.*, **37,** 1 (1958)
67. Vejlens, G., *Acta Pathol. Microbiol. Scand.*, Suppl. 33 (1938)
68. Alexanian, R., Donohue, D. M., and Finch, C. A. (Personal communication)
69. Raab, S. O., Haab, O. P., Boggs, D. R., Cartwright, G. E., and Wintrobe, M. M. (Unpublished data)
70. Craddock, C. G., Jr., Perry, S., Ventzke, L. E., and Lawrence, J. S., *Blood*, **15,** 840 (1960)
71. Patt, H. M., Maloney, M. A., and Jackson, E. M., *Am. J. Physiol.*, **188,** 585 (1957)
72. Mauer, A. M., Athens, J. W., Warner, H. R., Ashenbrucker, H., Cartwright, G. E., and Wintrobe, M. M., *The Kinetics of Cellular Proliferation*, 231 (Grune & Stratton, New York, 456 pp., 1959)
73. Little, J. R., Brecher, G., Bradley, T. R., and Rose, S., *Blood*, **19,** 236 (1962)
74. Ambrus, C. M., and Ambrus, J. L., *Ann. N. Y. Acad. Sci.*, **77,** 445 (1959)
75. Leahy, W. V. C., McNickle, T. E., and Smith, P. K., *Am. J. Physiol.*, **179,** 570 (1954)
76. Weisberger, A. S., Heinle, R. W., Storaasli, J. P., and Hannah, R., *J. Clin. Invest.*, **29,** 336 (1950)
77. Brecher, G., Cronkite, E. P., Bond, V. P., and Dutcher, T. F., *Acta Haematol.*, **20,** 179 (1958)
78. Valentine, W. N., *Am. J. Med.*, **28,** 699 (1960)
79. Wiltshaw, E., and Moloney, W. C., *Blood*, **10,** 1120 (1955)
80. Kaplow, L. S., *Blood*, **10,** 1023 (1955)
81. Kenny, J. J., and Moloney, W. C., *Blood*, **12,** 295 (1957)
82. Hayhoe, F. G. J., and Quaglino, D., *Brit. J. Haematol.*, **4,** 375 (1958)
83. Tanaka, K. R., Valentine, W. N., and Fredricks, R. E., *New Engl. J. Med.*, **262,** 912 (1960)
84. Sbarra, A. M., and Karnovsky, M. L., *J. Biol. Chem.*, **234,** 1355 (1959)
85. Cohn, Z. A., and Hirsch, J. G., *J. Exptl. Med.*, **112,** 983 (1960)
86. Hirsch, J. G., and Cohn, Z. A., *J. Exptl. Med.*, **112,** 1005 (1960)
87. Cohn, Z. A., and Hirsch, J. G., *J. Exptl. Med.*, **112,** 1015 (1960)
88. Moore, J. E. III., and James, G. W. III, *Proc. Soc. Exptl. Biol. Med.*, **82,** 601 (1953)

89. Thonnard-Neumann, E., *Acta Haematol.*, **25,** 261 (1961)
90. Osada, Y., *Bull. Inst. Public Health Japan*, **5,** 5 (1956)
91. Boseila, A. A., *Acta Med. Scand.*, **163,** 525 (1959)
92. Code, C. F., Mitchell, R. G., and Kennedy, J. C., *Proc. Staff Meetings Mayo Clinic*, **29,** 200 (1954)
93. Inagaki, S., *Acta Endocrinol.*, **26,** 477 (1957)
94. Fredricks, R. E., and Moloney, W. C., *Blood*, **14,** 571 (1959)
95. Michels, N. A., *Handbook of Hematology*, **I,** 326 (Hoeber, New York, 698 pp., 1938)
96. Riley, J. F., *Blood*, **9,** 1123 (1954)
97. Amann, R., and Martin, H., *Acta Haematol.*, **25,** 209 (1961)
98. Riley, J. F., *Lancet*, **I,** 841 (1954)
99. Martin, V. H., and Roka, L., *Acta Haematol.*, **10,** 26 (1953)
100. Valentine, W. N., Lawrence, J. S., Pearch, M. L., and Beck, W. S., *Blood*, **10,** 154 (1955)
101. Graham, H. T., Lowry, O. H., Wheelwright, F., Lenz, M. A., and Parrish, H. H., *Blood*, **10,** 467 (1955)
102. Riley, J. F., *The Mast Cells*, 73 (Livingstone, Edinburgh & London, 182 pp., 1959)
103. Benditt, E. P., *Ann. N.Y. Acad. Sci.*, **73,** 204 (1958)
104. Lagunoff, D., Phillips, M., and Benditt, E. P., *J. Histochem. Cytochem.*, **9,** 534 (1961)
105. Hartman, W. J., Clark, W. G., and Cyr, S. D., *Proc. Soc. Exptl. Biol. Med.*, **107,** 123 (1961)
106. Juhlin, L., and Shelley, W. B., *J. Am. Med. Assoc.*, **177,** 371 (1961)
107. Shelley, W. B., and Juhlin, L., *Blood*, **19,** 208 (1962)
108. Humphrey, J. H., and Mota, I., *Immunology*, **2,** 31 (1959)
109. Archer, G. T., *Australian J. Exptl. Biol. Med. Sci.*, **38,** 147 (1960)
110. Vaughn, J., *Blood*, **8,** 1 (1953)
111. Speirs, R. S., *Ann. N.Y. Acad. Sci.*, **59,** 706 (1955)
112. Gordon, A. S., *Ann. N.Y. Acad. Sci.*, **59,** 907 (1955)
113. Speirs, R. S., *Ann. N.Y. Acad. Sci.*, **73,** 283 (1958)
114. Litt, M., *Blood*, **16,** 1318 (1960)
115. Litt, M., *Blood*, **16,** 1330 (1960)
116. Litt, M., *J. Immunol.*, **87,** 522 (1961)
117. Archer, R. K., *Nature*, **187,** 155 (1960)
118. Vaughn, J., *J. Pathol. Bacteriol.*, **64,** 91 (1952)
119. Sainte-Marie, G., and LeBlond, C. P., *Proc. Soc. Exptl. Biol. Med.*, **97,** 263 (1958)
120. Yoffey, J. M., Everett, N. B., and and Reinhardt, W. O., *Nature*, **182,** 1608 (1958)
121. Good, R. A., Martinez, C., Archer, R. K., and Papermaster, B. W., *J. Clin. Invest.*, **41,** 1361 (1962)
122. Waksman, B. H., Arnason, B. G., and Jankovic, B. D., *Federation Proc.*, **21,** 274 (1962)
123. Arnason, B. G., and Jankovic, B. D., *Federation Proc.*, **21,** 274 (1962)
124. Mueller, A. P., Wolfe, H. R., and Meyer, R. K., *J. Immunol.*, **85,** 172 (1960)
125. Andreasen, E., and Ottesen, J., *Acta Physiol. Scand.*, **10,** 258 (1945)
126. Kindred, J. E., *Am. J. Anat.*, **71,** 207 (1942)
127. Yoffey, J. M., and Courtice, R. C., *Lymphatics, Lymph and Lymphoid Tissue*, 323 (Harvard Univ. Press, Cambridge, Mass., 510 pp., 1956)
128. Gowans, J. L., *Brit. Med. Bull.*, **15,** 50 (1959)
129. Hamilton, L. D., *The Leukemias, Etiology, Pathophysiology and Treatment*, 381 (Academic, New York, 711 pp., 1957)
130. Gowans, J. L., *J. Physiol. (London)*, **146,** 54 (1960)
131. Andreasen, E., *The Kinetics of Cellular Proliferation*, 19 (Grune & Stratton, New York, 456 pp., 1959)
132. Gowans, J. L., Gesner, B. M., and McGregor, D. D., *Biological Activity of the Leukocyte, Ciba Found. Study Group No. 10.*, 32 (Little, Brown, Boston, 120 pp., 1961)
133. MacKinney, A. A., Jr., Stohlman, F., Jr., and Brecher, G., *Blood*, **19,** 349 (1962)
134. Trowell, O. A., *Exptl. Cell Res.*, **9,** 258 (1955)
135. Schooley, J. C., and Berman, I., *Blood*, **16,** 1133 (1960)
136. Fliedner, T. M., Cronkite, E. P., and Bond, V. P., *Proc. Congr. European Soc. Hematol., 8th*, **I,** Article 62 (Karger, Basel, Switzerland, 1962)

THE SYSTEMIC CIRCULATION[1]

By Robert S. Alexander

Department of Physiology, Albany Medical College of Union University,
Albany, New York

The excitement of science springs from the periodic breakthroughs in the frontiers of knowledge and the attendant rush to reconstruct previous information so as to make it compatible with the new advances. The literature of the systemic circulation of the past year reveals little sign of excitement. It is concerned with the mundane task of reworking existing knowledge with endless variations in an attempt to define the weak spots in our present frontier. It would be a great mistake to confuse this pedestrian type of activity with dormancy of the field; it is from such a "re-search" that one may anticipate the direction if not the nature of the next significant advances. To map certain features of this frontier is the function of this review.

Inasmuch as a comprehensive treatise on the circulation (1) is in press as these lines are being written, we would seem to be absolved from the necessity of covering the field. Only those topics have been selected which happen to appeal to our own particular bias. In addition to many individual papers which have been omitted, intentionally or unintentionally, two major fields will be passed by. One is the area of the pulmonary circulation, which will not be included herein, although a wealth of interesting but often controversial studies has appeared whose appraisal will require a more critical attention to details of methodology than is suitable to a review of this type. Secondly, the always prolific field of hypertension research will be ignored. A rough count would suggest that about half of the present authors continue to find impressive evidence that the renin-angiotensin system is a significant mechanism in hypertension, while about an equal number have presented very substantial evidence that the renin-angiotensin system has nothing to do with chronic hypertension. With that cryptic summary, we will refer the reader to a specific review of this topic (2).

Neural Regulation of the Peripheral Circulation

Rushmer and his associates have continued to develop, and brilliantly document, their thesis that vascular patterns of reactivity in the unanesthetized dog must be initiated by hypothalamic mechanisms, relatively independent of peripheral feedback (3). This group has also offered further demonstration that injected drugs cannot mimic the precise pattern of responses observed in the conscious animal, while appropriate hypothalamic stimulation can (4). While it would be a mistake to underestimate the importance of this work, it would be a similar error to overinterpret such data. Precise

[1] The survey of literature pertaining to this review was concluded in March 1962.

patterns of functional changes in blood flow must reflect the integration of a vast spectrum of time-intensity curves of activation of each of the elements contributing to the net flow pattern. Surely it is unreasonable to expect that an investigator's thumb pressing the plunger of a drug-filled syringe would be capable of reproducing such a pattern. The different mode of application of the stimulus provides ample grounds for differences in pattern of response, and offers no basis for accepting or rejecting the material in the syringe from being associated with the mechanism contributing to the responses observed in the normal activities of the animal. Adrenalectomy alters the cardiovascular effects of hypothalamic stimulation (5), and there is direct evidence of release of catecholamines into adrenal venous blood during such sympathetic activations as anoxia and blood loss (6).

In spite of this current interest in diencephalic structures, recent studies (7, 8, 9) have reaffirmed the classical view that the primary site for integrating the outflow of sympathetic constrictor tone to the vascular system is located within the bulbar reticular centers of the brainstem. This view in no way conflicts with evidence that diencephalic structures constitute important subsidiary centers for correlating and relaying information from cortical (9), cerebellar (10), and other brain centers. Correlating with this functional relationship are reports that the carotid sinus reflex, a major governor of the bulbar centers, can counteract vasomotor activation evoked by diencephalic stimulation (3). Similarly, while our neo-Pavlovian Russian colleagues have stressed the importance of cerebral mechanisms in regulating vascular reactivity (11, 12, 13), they report that simulation or depression of appropriate cortical areas does not interfere with the function of the carotid sinus reflex (14).

Two qualifications must be recognized in this supremacy of the bulbar integrating centers. First is the possible extent to which higher nerve centers may regulate the vascular bed by the direct release of vasoactive humoral substances. Stimulation of the reticular system continues to evoke pressor responses after transection of the spinal cord, suggesting the operation of a vasopressin-like mechanism (15). The second qualification is that there are increasing indications of neural pathways designed for mediating specific vascular responses which are not an integral part of the bulbar-controlled sympathetic constrictor system for homeostatic regulation of arterial pressure. Most cutaneous areas of the head, neck, and upper chest accomplish temperature regulation through active dilator pathways as opposed to release from sympathetic tone, as demonstrated by dilation in excess of that produced by nerve block (16, 17). The cholinergic dilator system described by Uvnäs (18) continues to be reaffirmed (19), even though its presumed role as some sort of shunt mechanism remains controversial (20). Observations of the passage of microspheres through the vascular bed before and after stimulation of this system offer meager support for the idea that shunts of any significant size are opened (21). Nevertheless, these dilators do not seem to have a nutritional function, since their stimulation failed to improve a depression in muscle contractility resulting from partial ischemia of the muscle (22). The fact remains that the hypothalamic areas which evoke this muscle dilator response are closely associated with areas which evoke cardiac responses of the exercise type (6). The Uvnäs system would be excluded from temperature regulation of deep tissues, since clearance studies demonstrate that the increased blood flow in muscle with a rising temperature is a nutritional flow (23).

Further evidence of active dilator systems is observed in the buffer reflex compensation for a rise in arterial pressure (24, 25, 26). Significant dilator action persists after sympathectomy (24) and atropinization (25). By an ingenious but tenuously indirect analysis based upon comparative drug inhibitions, Sakuma & Beck (26) have calculated that 86 per cent of the dilation brought about by buffer reflexes is caused by a nonadrenergic system which they believe to be histaminergic. Use of cathecholamines to evoke a buffer reflex response, however, must not overlook the possibility of coincidental block of the sympathetic ganglia (25).

Returning to the sympathetic constrictor system, evidence continues to support much older work that this system, in conjunction with its buffer afferent supply, is primarily concerned with maintenance of an adequate arterial pressure head rather than with regulation of blood flow. Artificial stimulation of the buffer receptors may cause wide swings in arterial pressure without changes in cardiac output or splanchnic blood flow (27). In this connection, it is of interest that operations designed to produce hypertension by chronic cerebral ischemia are claimed to be lethal if an ischemia is actually produced; hypertension in the surviving animals results from damage to the carotid sinus nerve in the absence of any effectual restriction in blood flow (28). In acute cerebral ischemia, however, a powerful constrictor response is elicited which is four or five times as powerful as the carotid sinus reflex (29). Since the magnitude of this response shows a hyperbolic relationship to blood flow, and a less well-defined relationship with pressure, it is interpreted as a metabolic or chemical effect. This reflex is an excellent example of a negative feedback loop, in that changes in cerebral blood perfusion will produce inverse changes in systemic pressure to re-establish normal rates of cerebral blood flow. In a challenging paper, Sagawa, Taylor & Guyton (30) have "opened" this loop by isolating the cerebral circulation and supplying it from an external pump, while the behavior of the efferent arm of the loop has been studied by measuring the arterial pressure responses in the trunk of the animal. Use of sinusoidal alterations in the mean pressure supplying the head resulted in undulations in pressure in the trunk with a measurable phase lag and a very impressive gain in amplitude of trunk pressure undulations as compared with cerebral pressure undulations. This method of analysis, previously applied in principle to the carotid sinus by Warner (31), would seem to be a valuable tool for studying circulatory regulation if one knows how to ask such a preparation the correct questions and knows how to properly relate its answers. In the present cerebral ischemia study, an appreciable phase lag plus a significant gain factor renders the system quite susceptible to oscillation at lower pressures, thus supporting the contention that the vasomotor waves seen frequently in the hypotensive animal are attributable to oscillatory behavior of this feedback loop.

Reports are continuing to appear which attempt to compare the differential effect of neural regulation in different areas. Chemical and pressor reflexes appear to be most effective in muscle beds, less effective in the intestine, and least effective on the renal circulation (32, 33). With a lowered carbon dioxide, the carotid sinus effect on muscle becomes further exaggerated over that on the kidney (34). In contrast, the renal circulation is more reactive to humoral agents. Studies of stimulation of the cerebrum suggest that potential mechanisms exist for fairly discrete regulation of blood flow to specific areas (9), yet a review of splanchnic blood flow stresses that in most instances splanchnic blood flow appears to vary in the same manner as does total cardiac output (35). Reflex responses to thermal stimuli exhibit symmetrical spread even though the exact time-course for the responses varies in different areas (36), and are more prompt and more intense in those areas that are directly heated (37). The latter observation not only adds to the evidence of a peripheral component in the temperature regulation of the heated areas, but also demonstrated some dilation in unheated areas before there was any increase in general body temperature.

Differential effects of the chemoreceptor reflexes have been confirmed in a clearer demonstration that anoxia stimulates the sympathetic outflow to the blood vessels, but does not stimulate either the chronotropic or ionotropic sympathetic supply to the heart (38). Even more remarkable is an actual inhibition of the cardiac sympathetics with chemoreceptor stimulation. A rigorous control of arterial pressure will be required to make certain that the latter is not a secondary manifestation of pressoreceptor activity. In the other direction, pure oxygen breathing elicits a modest fall in pressure in cats under chloralose anesthesia, and a somewhat smaller fall in pressure in barbitalized cats (39). Part of this differences is caused by a lower arterial oxygen saturation under chloralose, but analysis of the effect reveals that both the different magnitudes of response to oxygen breathing and the different basal saturations are a reflection of changes in the sensitivity of the chemoreceptor reflex under the different anesthetics. A special case of differential effects of vascular reflexes is that observed between the mother and the fetus. Maternal vascular responses are in general mirrored by the fetus although the fetal cerebral blood flow follows the maternal responses better than does the fetal heart rate, presumably because compensatory mechanisms within the fetus will tend to buffer changes in the fetal heart rate (40).

The probe for additional pressor reflexes continues. Evidence is presented of a pressor reflex originated by distention of the main pulmonary artery, which was unmasked by perfusing the systemic circulation artificially to eliminate the participation of the arterial pressoreceptors (41). There appears to be an ample supply of receptor organs in this general area (42), although it is disconcerting that pressoreceptors are most numerous in the right pulmonary artery, from which the systemic pressor reflex could not be elicited, and almost absent from the main pulmonary artery where the systemic pressor reflex was evoked. By contrast, rapid intravenous infusions were found to elicit a depressor reflex after sinoaortic reflexes had been excluded in cats (43). As one surveys the long-fought battle to elucidate the pressoreceptor mechanisms associated with the heart and great vessels, one can nourish the suspicion that we may be dealing with a fairly complex coding of information from multiple sensors, and the bulbar computer may be integrating a lot more information than many of the polemics on this subject would give it credit for doing. The problem of pressoreceptors from the abdominal viscera has either been clarified or confounded (depending upon one's bias) by a report that there are two afferent receptor systems (44). One responds to distention of the blood vessels by generating brief action potentials which elicit a depressor reflex. Another elicits a pressor reflex when there is distention of the lumen of the viscus, and is associated with slow potential changes which to this reviewer are more suggestive of muscle potentials than afferent nerve potentials. In the dog, attempts to demonstrate vascular reflexes from such abdominal receptors by obstructing the anterior mesenteric artery have not been very rewarding (45).

Constrictor Agents

In analyzing the mode of action of constrictor agents, part of the complex response to injections of 5-hydroxytryptamine (serotonin) is attributable to chemoreceptor stimulation (46), while a pressor response to intravenous insulin seems to be mediated centrally (47). A number of studies have been carried out on the pressor effect of hypertonic solutions, particularly by the Russians who believe that intra-arterial injections of hypertonic solutions may be of some value in treatment of oligemic hypotension (48). Hemodynamically insignificant volumes of 20 per cent saline or 40 per cent glucose evoke a marked pressor response associated with constriction of both the arteriolar bed and the lymphatic system (49), an effect which can be reproduced after ischemic block of the central nervous system (50). The fact that this response survives deep general anesthesia but is blocked by the use of local anesthetics (51) suggests some type of receptor system in the blood vessels. This system is conspicuously present in the pulmonary circuit (52); as a consequence, intravenous injections of hypertonic solutions produce a central obstruction to the circulation which negates the systemic pressure rise.

The availability of synthetic angiotensin preparations has stimulated a number of studies of the action of this compound as reviewed by Page & Bumpus (53). It is clearly a vastly more powerful constrictor compound than is norepinephrine (53, 54, 55) although quantitative comparisons should not be taken very seriously because of the much slower response to angiotensin (54, 56) and the fact that the material exhibits a phenomenon resembling tachyphylaxis (57), apparently depending upon the background of humoral agents in the system (53). A further difficulty in quantitating humoral or drug effects is an increasing awareness of the variability of sensitivities both between species and between different vascular beds of the same species. In compounds so similar as epinephrine and norepinephrine, isolated renal arteries of the rabbit are more sensitive to norepinephrine than to epinephrine while the mesenteric arteries are more sensitive to epinephrine (58).

DILATOR AGENTS

Considerable support has been offered for the contention of Lundholm (59) that the dilator effect of epinephrine is a secondary consequence of its stimulation of tissue metabolism. Significant increases in both lactic and pyruvic acids appear in the venous effluent from muscles to which epinephrine was administered (60), although there does not appear to be a good quantitative correlation between lactic acid levels and the dilator effect (61). In agreement with the theory, dibenzyline does not block either the dilator action or the release of lactic acid. It is probable that the metabolite theory is correct but that the specific metabolite having the greatest potency is something other than lactic acid. The studies of Berne (62) on the coronary bed should encourage examination of the role of nucleotides in this connection (63, 64). The dilation observed in extreme cold appears to be a direct smooth muscle block rather than release of metabolites (65).

Among the specific dilator humoral materials, bradykinin appears to be a compound of great functional potentiality. In man, it is a very powerful dilator on a mole-per-mole comparison with acetylcholine and histamine (66). On the basis of details of patterns obtained during digital plethysmography, Burch (67) points out that bradykinin is the only compound in his experience which can reproduce the details of the pattern observed in reactive hyperemia. While such evidence can certainly not be accepted at face value as proof of a normal regulator function for bradykinin, recent concern with the action of bradykinin in inflammation should not lead us to forget that it was initially associated with normal vascular regulation of salivary blood flow.

One particular phase of the problem of vasodilation that is being pursued vigorously is the regulation of blood flow to exercising muscle. Recent work seems to agree with the postulate that there is a fairly complete dichotomization between the mobilization of the general circulation in exercise, and the regulation of flow to the active muscles. The former appears to be largely controlled by the diencephalon, and blocking the motor activity in the muscles does not significantly alter the pattern of changes in the general circulation (3). By contrast, the local circulatory changes within the active muscle appear to be regulated autonomously by metabolites (68), and blocking the innervation of the muscle has only minor influences on the changes in its own blood supply (69). Indeed, a very interesting study by Hirvonen & Sonnenschein (22) demonstrates that the more active a muscle becomes, the more autonomous does its regulation of its own blood supply become. The dilator action of epinephrine, discussed above, disappears as the muscle is stimulated to active contraction. This is obviously compatible with the concept that the epinephrine effect is a secondary effect of metabolic stimulation which becomes masked by the increased metabolic activity of the contracting muscle. If both carotid arteries are clamped under conditions where the perfusion pressure to the muscle is held constant, the carotid sinus reflex is capable of counteracting to a degree the autonomous dilator effect in active muscle. Nevertheless, if the higher systemic pressure evoked by carotid clamping is also allowed to perfuse the muscle, the reduction in muscle flow evoked by the carotid sinus reflex is outweighed, as shown by an increase in blood flow. Under the conditions of these experiments (22), in which maximal stimuli to the motor nerve were employed, changes in blood flow to the exercising muscle were in general correlated with changes in the active force developed by the muscle, indicating that these contractions were limited by blood flow. Such experimental results should not be considered a model of normal exercise, but rather a demonstration of the necessity for central mobilization of the circulation to act synergistically with the autonomous dilators within the peripheral bed in order to achieve adequate regulation of muscle blood flow in exercise.

In agreement with the above concept, studies in man reveal that when the essentially normal pattern of treadmill exercise is studied, circulatory adjustments are adequate to supply the increased metabolic needs of the muscle without any increased extraction ratio of oxygen (70). In contrast, the more abnormal situation of forcing exercise in the supine posture compromises the circulatory adjustment to some degree so that increased oxygen extraction is required to satisfy the metabolic requirements (71). Similarly, in the resting muscle, the metabolic compensation for short periods ($2\frac{1}{2}$ minutes) of arterial occlusion are satisfied to a considerable degree by increased oxygen extraction, but longer periods of occlusion elicit the autonomous dilator system within the muscle so that metabolic needs are compensated by flow increases and average oxygen extraction actually decreases (72).

AUTOREGULATION

In philosophical opposition to the cocept of central regulation of the peripheral vascular bed, an intensive effort is being expended to clarify its intrinsic autoregulation in organs operating at their basal state. Some degree of autoregulation appears to be demonstrable in all tissues, with the possible exception of malignant tumors which lack muscular blood vessels (73). It is probable that we are dealing with a variety of phenomena under this category. The excellent regulation of the coronary bed is probably a special case of an exercising muscle, as discussed above. The cerebral circulation is geared to carbon dioxide levels, which maintains autoregulation within a range of ± 30 per cent (74). The kidney represents a particular challenge, since its copious blood supply casts doubt on the role of metabolic regulators.

Some persist in their argument that renal autoregulation is a consequence of tissue pressure created by changes in vascular distention, whereby an increased pressure entering the organ will automatically build up tissue pressure to throttle flow (75). Others have confirmed the presence of renal autoregulation under conditions where they doubt a dominant role of tissue pressure (76). Autoregulation has been confirmed in the intestine, an organ lacking the encapsulated structure to develop tissue pressures very effectively (77). Further positive findings of autoregulation in skeletal muscle have been presented (78 to 81). The great variety of organs which exhibit autoregulation seriously weakens the case for explaining renal autoregulation in terms of a mechanism which depends upon its relatively unique encapsulated structure.

In Mississippi, autoregulation is still rarely seen, either in the kidney (82) or in the cerebral bed (83); autoregulation occurs in the leg only as a consequence of anoxia (84). These claims challenge a critical appraisal of the case for autoregulation, which brings out some disturbing facts. Most authors confess that autoregulation is not reliably reproducible. "Such factors as the animal's general condition, operative trauma, hemorrhage, and depth of anesthesia were important to the successful demonstration of renal autoregulation" in a study in which five out of twenty dog kidneys refused to autoregulate (76). "Some preparations" ceased to show autoregulation after a period of time (79). Such reservations are warnings that published records are likely to be "best" records, and the bias of the authors is likely to slant their evaluation of their data. "Complete" autoregulation—a compensatory change in resistance following a change in perfusion pressure which returns flow to exactly the control level—has been reported so rarely that we may question whether it really exists in the absence of other coincidental variables. We therefore would reject the term "isoemic autoregulation" (80) as being inaccurate, not to mention its redundancy and lack of euphony. The fact that flow does show some small changes is extremely important, for complete autoregulation would exclude many of the proposed feedback stimuli for its operation. The argument, however, extends far beyond the issue of completeness. It seems to be agreed that severe trauma can completely obliterate autoregulation (76, 82). It has further been argued that moderate damage, possibly interfering with lymphatic drainage, is actually the cause of autoregulation (82). It is most discomforting to find ourselves faced with a phenomenon which is caused by moderate surgical damage and obliterated by severe surgical damage, since the invitations to personal recriminations of technical competence are distressingly apparent.

Where, then, does the problem stand? Extending the approach to autoregulation which was defended by Waugh (85), it is mandatory that investigators accept the multiple influences which can contribute to this phenomenon. It is unequivocal fact that under some circumstances increased blood flow can increase tissue pressure and thereby tend to reduce inflow, and in a similar factual category is the property of all organs to exhibit the phenomenon of reactive hyperemia, either through the action of metabolites or as a result of specific local regulators (67, 86). Equally factual is the property of all muscle tissue, including vascular smooth muscle (87), to develop a greater force of contraction with an increase in stretch. It has been argued that this latter myogenic mechanism may be effectively negated in blood vessels because the Laplacian principle dictates that an increase in vessel diameter will reduce the mechanical effectiveness of tangential tension developed by the muscle. This reasoning has overlooked the finite thickness of the muscular media. When a blood vessel constricts, the inner muscle layer becomes lax and eventually wrinkles, which passes the burden of maintaining wall tension to the outer muscle layers (88). When such a vessel is stretched, there will be a progressive mobilization of the mechanical effectiveness of the inner muscular layers. The myogenic theory, therefore, has a very substantial basis, and all data seem to be compatible with the claim that the degree of autoregulation is dependent upon the pre-existence of a relatively normal degree of myogenic tone in the vascular bed (81).

The urgent need is to abandon polemics in this area, and seek to design experiments which can accurately assess the contribution of these various autoregulatory factors in the regulation of the peripheral circulation. Until this has been accomplished, we will be plagued by some very fundamental controversies in our concepts of circulatory regulation. "Vascular reactivity", for example, is usually defined as the magnitude of the resistance change which a vascular bed exhibits when confronted with a standard vasoactive agent. A devout believer in autoregulation might turn this concept completely around, and defend the thesis that the most reactive beds would be those showing the least change in response to an external stimulus. It has been shown that after removal of all neural control, dogs can increase their cardiac output so as to very nearly maintain a normal flow to peripheral tissues in spite of the opening of a very large arteriovenous fistula (89). The authors of this study, being disbelievers in autoregulation, give credit to the heart for this compensation; an alternative interpretation would be to credit peripheral autoregulation for this maintenance of blood flow. We must not forget that after removal of the buffer regulators, the otherwise intact animal exhibits a linear pressure-flow relationship (90). Such a relationship is surely not compatible with anything approaching complete autoregulation in such important vascular segments as the renal, intestinal, and skeletal muscle beds. Future research must attempt to analyze how local autoregulatory mechanisms act synergistically with other blood flow regulators to achieve the net regulation of flow in the intact animal (80).

In addition to dynamic autoregulatory adjustments of blood flow discussed above, the ability of local vascular beds to adjust chronically to altered functional demands must be appreciated. For example, it has been possible to demonstrate cold adaptation in the vasculature of a single digit (91), which would effectively refute the suggestion that local vascular adaptation to cold might be a statistical artifact (92). Similarly, physical training for endurance can significantly alter local patterns of blood flow adaptation, even though physical training for strength does not induce such changes (93).

VEINS AND BLOOD VOLUME

The role of the venous system continues to be ignored by a majority of investigators of cardiovascular physiology. Authors attempting to explain the maintenance of cardiac output in the face of the increased peripheral resistance produced by carotid occlusion, for example, dismiss the contribution of the venous system with the comment that "the increase in venous pressure can be explained in any one of various obvious ways" (94). An "obvious way" is the well-documented increase in venomotor tone under these circumstances, which reduces the capacity of the venous bed, shifts more blood back to the heart, and thereby assists in the maintenance of cardiac output.

As we have reviewed elsewhere (1), there is a considerable literature establishing that in general the venous system acts synergistically with the arterial system in maintaining circulatory homeostasis. Circulatory demands evoking pressor responses are associated with venous constriction to shift blood pooled in the veins back towards the heart, while depressor reactions are associated with the relaxation of venous beds so as to increase their storage of the blood volume. The past year has witnessed the usual crop of rediscoveries of these phenomena (95, 96, 97), including the fact that veins normally exhibit an appreciable degree of venomotor tone which may be lowered by anesthesia (98), ganglionic blockade (95), or sleep (99). Confirmation of earlier observations that venous tone is high in patients with heart failure (95) should prompt more investigation of this unexplained phenomenon which is of potential clinical importance. Older hypotheses that cardiac glycosides might derive some of their therapeutic action from a diminution of this venous tone appear to lack any substantial support (100).

It has been claimed that venous distensibility tends to increase during pregnancy, especially in those patients who show a tendency to develop venous varicosities (101). Unfortunately the technique used in this study was a plethysmographic method which appears particularly susceptible to quantitative distortion because it includes a tissue fluid component in the venous volume measurement; the increase in interstitial fluid volume in late pregnancy could therefore be an adequate explanation of the data without recourse to changes in venous distensibility.

Most of the above observations were obtained from a variety of modifications of the plethysmographic method which assumes that volume changes in the arm following venous occlusion are quantitatively equal to venous distention. While these methods have a degree of qualitative validity, their quantitative accuracy cannot be accepted, not only because of the tissue fluid problem alluded to above, but also because end points are subjective approximations of equilibria which are never achieved (1). An interesting variation in this approach is one that concerns itself with the volume required to "fill" empty veins (102), the region of the curve which most investigators have studiously avoided. Veins are drained by gravity and then a measurement is made of the rate of arterial inflow and the time required for filling of the arm veins by an ingenious double-plethysmograph method. The authors estimate that their experimental arrangement will indicate the veins as being "filled" at a mean distending pressure of about 15 mm Hg. Since the gravitational shift in arm position should not alter the rate of arterial inflow (78), this method might give some very useful information, provided it is clearly recognized that this is not measuring the same parameter as in most venous distensibility determinations. Exactly how venous distensibility is related to total venous capacity is a much more complex problem than is generally recognized (103).

There is particular interest in those situations where arterial and venous effects are not working in the same direction. It has been reported that isoproterenol, a potent dilator of the arterioles, is a venous constrictor, both as measured plethysmographically (96) and as inferred from a disproportionate reduction in venous transit time of injected dyes (104). Since central venous pressure falls (and since our own experience with this agent has failed to demonstrate any very impressive venoconstrictor effects), it seems clear that a direct cardiac action is chiefly responsible for the ability of isoproterenol to increase cardiac output, but protection against venous pooling in the face of increased arterial inflow would certainly assist in maintaining this output. Conversely, angiotensin appears to have no detectable influence on the venous system in spite of its powerful action as an arterial constrictor (56, 105). In confirmation of earlier studies, 5-hydroxytryptamine (serotonin) continues to be a more effective venous constrictor than an arterial constrictor, and histamine is a definite venous constrictor in spite of its arterial dilator action (105). Cold is also a more effective venous constrictor than an arterial constrictor, and this could account for the significant trapping of blood in pools which do not equilibrate with indicators during hypothermia (106). Also, the sympathetic cholinergic dilators are apparently more effective on the arterial side of the capillaries than on the venous side, since tissue tends to gain weight when this dilator system is activated (20).

The full significance of these effects becomes apparent when one recognizes the delicate balance between blood volume, arterial resistance, postcapillary venous resistance, and venous capacity. In their well-known studies on the vascular bed, Pappenheimer & Soto-Rivera (107) presented a brilliant clarification of circulatory dynamics by demonstrating the nature of the steady state in an isogravimetric limb. Under these conditions, capillary hydrostatic pressure must be in equilibrium with plasma protein osmotic pressure, and venous pressure must proceed downhill from this point of equilibrium. In such a system, venous tone serves only to alter the volume of blood pooled between the capillaries and the heart. As every investigator knows who has tried to run an isogravimetric experiment or standardize a plethysmographic volume method, the isogravimetric state is a highly idealized steady state which fails to describe the dynamic adjustments occurring from moment to moment. Neural or humoral agents constricting the arterial circulation more than the venous circulation will lower capillary pressure and conserve or augment blood volume. In contrast, agents such as methacholine, histamine, or 5-hydroxytryptamine produce a relative dilation of the arterial system as compared with the venous system, and capillary pressure rises with a consequent shift of the blood volume into tissue spaces (105). Acid has been reported to have a similar effect in promoting capillary transudation by a relative increase in venular pressure, and it is of interest that the buffering action of THAM [tris(hydroxymethyl)aminomethane] will act to reduce capillary fluid loss caused by the acidemia of shock (108).

Insofar as these mechanisms alter the blood volume, profound influences on the circulation will be felt. Blood volume and sympathetic tone appear to be the prime determinants of blood pressure and vascular reactivity (109). Blood volume is a very important and surprisingly linear determinant of the mean circulatory filling pressure, which was reduced from a normal value of 7 mm Hg to 0 mm by a hemorrhage of 15 per cent of the blood volume, or raised to 30 mm by a transfusion to achieve a blood volume 150 per cent of normal (110). Since this elevation of mean circulatory filling pressure is of the same order as that which can be produced by maximal sympathetic stimulation, it is apparent that blood volume and the tone of the capacity elements are key features in circulatory dynamics.

Unfortunately, in spite of their widespread use, indicators to measure this important parameter of blood volume do not appear to be reliable in the hands of critical workers (111). An explanation for this is suggested in a report by Swann and associates who have carefully tracked indicators through the intestine (112). They find a very satisfactory disappearance curve for labeled red blood cells, but a distressingly unsatisfactory disappearance curve for labeled plasma. Their data suggest that the plasma is equilibrating with three different compartments, the first of which appears to be identical with that of the cells, and an additional two compartments which the authors feel are extravascular. A possible avenue of communication with extravascular compartments is seen in the surprisingly large channels which have been demonstrated in the living animal between the veins and the lymph nodes (113). This area of circulatory physiology is urgently in need of some imaginative new techniques that can break through some of the bottlenecks which currently frustrate our understanding.

CIRCULATORY SHOCK

The ultimate challenge to students of the peripheral circulation has been the problem of circulatory shock. The outstanding development in this field was the publication of an extraordinarily competent review of the subject, reporting a symposium sponsored by the National Academy of Sciences-National Research Council (114). This review excels both in its wide spectrum of expert opinions and in its excellent bibliography. The vastness of the shock literature has made it difficult for investigators to avoid repeating studies; let it be hoped that no future shock experiments are designed without a careful analysis of the material in this volume.

One of the great quests has been the search for some vasodilator or vasotoxin which could account for a failure of the peripheral circulation, producing either an intravascular pooling of blood or an extravascular escape of plasma. This review of shock clearly indicates the necessity for recognizing three distinct types of experimental shock: traumatic or tourniquet shock, endotoxin shock, and hemorrhagic shock. In the case of traumatic shock, the answer appears quite clear in general though not in specifics. There is a definite release of substances in the traumatized area which result in extravasation of plasma and loss of the circulating blood volume (115). Histamine may play some role in this during the initial phases, but substances of the bradykinin type are the real culprits. On the other hand, it should be stressed that this is essentially a local problem that does not involve the general systemic circulation; adequate fluid replacement to correct for fluid loss into the traumatized areas is capable of completely ameliorating the shock state resulting from trauma (116). In endotoxin shock, on the other hand, there is clear evidence of materials released into the general circulation which play the crucial role in this shock process. Just how they act, and whether their action is similar in different species, is far from clear. For example, endotoxin administration to the dog precipitates an acute vascular collapse which is not characteristic of other species (117). The ferritin VDM (vasodilator material) system has been excluded from endotoxin shock even by its proponents (118), and there are many reasons for implicating histamine (119). The hemodynamic picture of profound arterial dilation and venous constriction in endotoxin shock is certainly compatible with histamine action (120). The marked release of catecholamines in endotoxin shock (121) may aggravate rather than counteract this action of histamine (122, 123). The picture seems to be one of a complex humoral interaction in the control of the arterial and venous elements of the peripheral vascular bed which is critically thrown out of balance by endotoxin. No one element can be identified as the specific vasotoxin; indeed, under some circumstances it appears that exogenous histamine can be beneficial (124).

The picture in hemorrhagic shock is quite different. In a comprehensive examination of the assumption that some form of vasomotor collapse occurs in hemorrhagic shock, Green (125) finds scanty evidence of such a failure. A wide variety of dilator substances have been identified in shock blood and are still being reported (126, 127, 128); yet Page (129) finds no sound basis for linking any humoral dilator agents in a causal relation with shock. Most importantly, Selkurt & Rothe (130) review the work of others and add some experiments of their own which would seem to offer rigorous proof that circulating vasodilators are not the lethal agent in the circulatory shock which follows severe hemorrhage. It would seem high time to call off the search for something which has never been shown to exist, and which has been proven not to be there.

There remains substantial evidence of some form of peripheral blood pooling, however, which, in the absence of significant failure of the arterial vasomotor system, points the finger of suspicion towards the venous segment of the circulation. A number of reviewers leaned towards this conclusion. Since we have personally espoused this interpretation in the past and offered some documentation for it, it will appear out of character for us to be critical of this point of view; yet, as indicated below, we are reluctant to believe that venous failure is THE answer.

Any discussion of shock which is going to be truly comprehensive must include some proponent of the old idea that the heart is the element that fails. In this symposium, it was Guyton & Crowell who rose to the defense of the peripheral circulation and argued that the blame should be shifted towards the heart (131). Their discussion of fundamental relationships between cardiac output, tissue oxygen demands, and myocardial function presents a provocative analysis, but it will probably not help to convince their critics. The more pointed challenge is their demonstration (132) that if the heart of the shocked animal is forced to maintain cardiac output by an artificial servomechanism which returns blood to the heart at whatever rate is necessary to maintain a normal cardiac output, gross evidence of myocardial failure appears. This experiment is easy to criticize. As must be common knowledge to every experienced shock investigator, it is not difficult to precipitate acute heart failure by techniques that were intended to produce shock. With a technique as artificial as that employed by these authors, one may dismiss their experiments as quite irrelevant, and deny myocardial failure by citing the extensive literature which exonerates the heart from any primary responsibility for shock.

After sober reflection, we have come to feel that this is not a proper answer to the cardiac problem in shock, and would like to take the liberty to suggest that the cardiac factor in shock has been misinterpreted. The usual picture of heart failure and its manifestations of venous distention, dilated heart, pulmonary congestion, enlarged liver, and peripheral edema are all evidences of a system capable of mobilizing a large venous return, usually with the aid of a chronic elevation of blood volume. To a degree, this copious venous reservoir for filling the heart will help to compensate for the myocardial failure. In shock, we are at the opposite hemodynamic pole of a primary inability to mobilize a substantial venous return. Faced with this deficiency in the reservoir from which it may fill, a heart must be capable of an exceedingly efficient operation to maintain its output, and prevent deterioration of the circulation. We have all been impressed by the fact that central venous pressures are not high in shock, but have paid little attention to the fact, well-documented in the older literature, that venous pressures are not as low as they should be. In reference to the tendency for portal pressure to rise in shock, for example, Simeone (133) stressed that too little attention has been paid to the fact that caval pressure is not low enough to drain out this splanchnic pool. If, instead of effectively pumping out the meager venous return, the heart shows some minimum myocardial failure, small rises in central venous pressure which would be of no consequence in the normal animal will serve to aggravate the tendency for peripheral pooling in the shock animal. As a consequence, effective venous return and cardiac output will progressively deteriorate. The resulting tissue oligemia and anoxia will aggravate the peripheral problem, particularly in such metabolically important sites as the liver (134). The data seem to indicate clearly that the various dilator agents in the blood of an animal in shock which lead to peripheral pooling are of no consequence when cross-transfused to an animal with a normal heart, and hence these agents or the phenomenon of peripheral pooling cannot be specifically blamed for irreversibility. When, however, this pooling phenomenon is combined with a heart that has suffered mild damage so that it cannot maintain output without an ample venous return, a viciously lethal synergy may result. Shock is not a problem restricted to the heart or to the peripheral vascular bed; it is a combined failure of the circulatory system.

PROPERTIES OF BLOOD VESSELS AND BLOOD FLOW

According to the bias of this reviewer, the development in relation to the circulation which has the greatest potentialities for generating real excitement has turned up in the remote area of muscle protein fractionation. From the earliest literature, one can trace a thread of the suggestion that blood vessels possess two modes of contraction. A commonplace example is the local spasm in blood vessels which may be induced by trauma, which has markedly different properties from the more typical form of functional vasoconstriction. More equivocal examples can be cited in a variety of occlusive vascular diseases and even in hypertension itself, where there appears to be an active narrowing of the vascular lumen which has defied clear explanation in terms of the conventional neural and humoral mechanisms for regulating vascular tone.

There is, therefore, unique significance in the demonstration by Laszt & Hamoir that it is possible to extract two different contractile proteins from the carotid arteries (135). One of these appears to possess the same general chemical and physical properties as the conventional actomyosin system of skeletal muscle. By carrying out the extraction at an ionic strength much weaker than that required to solubilize this actomyosin, one can obtain another distrinct protein fraction which also appears to be a complex between an F actin and a myosin, which the authors call "tonoactomyosin". It appears to be quite similar to a comparable protein extractable from the uterus (136). Functionally, tonoactomyosin has the property of exhibiting marked changes in viscosity with changes in ionic strength, or with changes in the ATP concentration. Because of its solubility at low ionic strengths, Laszt & Hamoir do not believe that it could maintain its integrity as a discrete contractile filament within the cells, but is rather dispersed through the ground substance of the muscle cells where it can have a profound influence on the physical characteristics of the cell through its syneresis properties.

Underlying the isolation of tonoactomyosin, earlier studies had demonstrated that the tension measured in isolated carotid rings varied significantly with the ionic composition of the medium without any apparent activity of the usual energy systems (137). At the same ionic strength, different cations were effective as a function of their ionic radius. A more extensive investigation into these physical changes was carried out by an analysis of the tension developed by carotid rings subjected to oscillatory stretches (138). Application of epinephrine, which presumably activates the conventional actomyosin system, produced a significant contraction but did not alter the modulus of elasticity of the vessel. Addition of 60–70 mM of K^+, on the other hand, produced marked changes in both the modulus of elasticity and the viscosity of the vessel wall. The latter is assumed to represent an action upon tonoactomyosin, and required about twelve minutes for full development. It is perfectly clear that these slow changes in the vessel attributed to the tonoactomyosin are the same phenomena which this reviewer has been describing as the ratchet-like behavior of a "passive" component, which acts synergistically with the active component in veins (103).

One might hope to rush to the literature and immediately find many of our problems of vascular reactivity solved. Unfortunately, it is not that simple. The concentrations of K^+ which Laszt employed in his studies of the properties of tonoactomyosin were far beyond the physiological range. With moderate elevations within the physiological range, K^+ and Mg^{++} are usually dilators, but K^+ produces constriction at higher concentrations, as recently confirmed in the coronary bed (139). In the hamster cheek pouch, high potassium levels are very effective vasoconstrictors, but their action seems to involve indirect adrenergic stimulation (140). In dealing with cations, it is important to recognize that we are dealing with very complex ionic equilibria, involving both membrane and intracellular phenomena locally and a wide spectrum of systemic effects. Isolated blood vessels show efflux of K^+ when stimulated to contraction by epinephrine (141), and the vascular bed of the leg shows efflux of K^+ when stimulated by catecholamines and pitressin (142), observations compatible with known properties of membrane mechanisms. On the other hand, contractions of the vascular bed induced by 5-hydroxytryptamine or angiotensin do not exhibit any K^+ efflux, and no consistent change in K^+ was observed with dilation produced by acetylcholine or histamine (142). It is possible that some of these shifts of K^+ may be consequences of changes in H^+ secondary to general metabolic effects. This appears to be a particularly plausible answer to the report that vascular changes in hypothermia are correlated with potassium shifts (143). In one of the experiments quoted above (142), Na^+ was the only ion which appeared to correlate with vascular responses; yet gross alterations in total Na^+ do not alter vascular reactivity (110). The fact that removal of Ca^{++} from the medium did not prevent efflux of K^+, although it did cause relaxation of the vessels (141), should encourage greater attention to the role of Ca^{++}.

In further reference to vasculature structure, an interesting analysis has been presented of the dimensional relations of blood vessels in the wing of the living bat which challenges the usually quoted figures based upon post mortem studies. Wiedeman (144) finds a fairly even gradation of diameter reductions and increase in total cross-sectional area in progressing from arteries to capillaries, rather than the disproportionate transitions from arteries to arterioles to capillaries which is advertised in most textbooks. While the bat's wing might not be a reliable prototype, it would certainly be desirable to pursue further studies which preserve the pressure distention to which the larger vessels are exposed *in vivo*, and at the same time avoid the fixation shrinkage of smaller vessels in histological preparations.

Studies of the physical properties of blood vessels are being continued (145), gradually overcoming the handicap that rigorous control of physical parameters is not easily achieved. Recognition that longitudinal thrusts created by cardiac contraction complicate the stress-strain diagrams of blood vessel studies *in vivo* (146), for example, will avoid misinterpreting data on this account. There is appearing a conspicuous scattering of investigators, however, who assume that the physics of blood vessels is virgin territory. To pick one example, we find a report of authors who have employed the relatively crude technique of angiography to make the profound "discovery" that the aorta does not obey Hooke's law (147). These authors speak with great humility of the work of nineteenth century physicists, but apparently regard any physiological studies made prior to 1960 as obsolete. A monograph (148) has appeared which presents an excellent review of many aspects of this subject; it should be required reading for anyone who would attempt to advance knowledge in this basic area.

At a much more sophisticated level, two significant papers have appeared to revise and extend our concepts of arterial pulses. The first, by Spencer & Greiss (149), extends the analysis of the correlation between aortic pressure and electromagnetically recorded flows in the ascending aorta to the rather startling claim that aortic pressure actually exceeds ventricular pressure during the last half of systole. The energy responsible for this pressure gradient, which is in violation of the flow gradient, is derived from the deceleration of the ejected blood. This is an interesting turnabout from older arguments that acceleration forces were responsible for a disproportionate pressure gradient in the other direction. Completely independently, however, additional evidence of flow dynamics has been presented (150) which emphasizes the deceleration of the blood column which occurs during late systole. The technical problems in this area are enormous, and one must be very hesitant to accept data which contradict the recordings made by critical masters of manometry, especially in the presence of a possible distortion resulting from the restraint of the aorta imposed by the meter probe. Arguments over the precise value of pressure gradients, however, should not miss the important point that inertial forces in the blood column may be very important factors in pulse dynamics. Tracing the pulse out towards the periphery, a second significant contribution is that of Meisner & Remington (151) who have published an ambitious attempt to map and identify the contour characteristics of pulses in the brachiocephalic system including both its carotid and brachial divisions. Unlike the aortic-femoral system, which is dominated by a clearly identifiable standing-wave system, the brachiocephalic systems show subtle and less reproducible pulse transformations, somewhat obscured by appreciable damping of the pulse. The most significant finding was an oscillation in the brachial-radial division which showed no correlation with the incisura or the aortic standing-wave system, and which seemed to retain its basic frequency in spite of the experimental occlusion of all major branches. This led to the tentative conclusion that the wave was related to the elastic frequency characteristics of the major vessels themselves rather than to any discrete geometry of wave reflection. This view is well worth taking seriously. Because of the historical development of ideas in this area, many of us have searched too vigorously for discrete reflection points which might generate a positive or negative wave to summate with the transmitted pulse. Such reflections do exist, as illustrated in this paper by a pressure peak which correlates with a reflection from the region of the subscapular artery. Nevertheless, blood vessels are not built like rigid-walled flutes with finger holes at set intervals; their elastic walls give them excellent potentialities for being resonators in their own right.

After years of attempting to calculate cardiac output from measurements of aortic pulse and aortic elasticity, a novel but logical reversal has been introduced, that of estimating aortic elasticity from cardiac output and pressure data (152). This study offers confirmation in man for the view that adrenergic constriction increases the elastic contribution of the muscular component of the aorta and hence produces an increase in aortic distensibility.

Studies of blood flow itself have offered a theoretical extension of the rheological phenomena involved in blood viscosity (153) dealing with the consequences of the imperfections in laminar flow. An even further departure from laminar flow is also still being defended in reference to "sludged" blood. The evidence for this phenomenon is still largely an attempt to generalize on the basis of observations made in terminal malaria (154), reinforced by microscopic observations of frog vessels in which mechanisms are inferred rather than proven (155). It is unfortunate that the ratio of speculation to fact has been too great to encourage other investigators to assess the possible significance of this phenomenon.

This is not to decry the need for speculation in circulation research. The field is starving for lack of imaginative attacks, new methodologies, and unorthodox approaches, and is confronted with a log jam of transistorized versions of old ideas. But let new thoughts frame themselves into lucidly designed experiments which can convincingly show us the error of our ways and release a flood of new advances.

LITERATURE CITED

1. Hamilton, W., Ed., *Handbook of Physiology*, Sec. II, **II** (Am. Physiol. Soc., Washington, in press)
2. Skelton, F. R., Ed., *Circulation Res*, **9**, 715 (1961)
3. Wilson, M. F., Clarke, N. P., Smith, O. A., and Rushmer, R. F., *Circulation Res.*, **9**, 491 (1961)
4. Rushmer, R. F., Franklin, D. L., Van Citters, R. L., and Smith, O. A., *Circulation Res.*, **9**, 675 (1961)
5. Rosen, A., *Acta Physiol. Scand.*, **52**, 291 (1961)
6. Fowler, N. O., Shabetai, R., and Holmes, J. C., *Circulation Res.*, **9**, 427 (1961)
7. Chai, C. Y., and Wang, S. C., *Am. J. Physiol.*, **202**, 25 (1962)
8. Lindgren, P., *Circulation Res.*, **9**, 250 (1961)
9. Löfving, B., *Acta Physiol. Scand.*, **53**, Suppl. 184 (1961)
10. Sawyer, C. H., Hilliard, J., and Ban, T., *Am. J. Physiol.*, **200**, 405 (1961)
11. Kononiachenko, V. A., *Pavlov J. Higher Nervous Activity (Engl. Transl.)*, **9**, 563 (1959)
12. Rogov, A. A., Gorlanova, T. T., and Kovaleva, N. T., *Sechenov Physiol. J. USSR (Engl. Transl.)*, **46**, 328 (1960)
13. Golubykh, L. I., and Savchuk, V. I., *Pavlov J. Higher Nervous Activity (Engl. Transl.)*, **10**, 31 (1960)
14. Belenkov N. I., and Smetankin, G. N., *Sechenov Physiol. J. USSR (Engl. Transl.)*, **46**, 1218 (1960)
15. Sharpless, S. K., and Rothballer, A. B., *Am. J. Physiol.*, **200**, 909 (1961)
16. Blair, D. A., Glover, W. E., and Roddie, I. C., *J. Appl. Physiol.*, **16**, 119 (1961)
17. Fox, R. H., Goldsmith, R., and Kidd, D. J., *J. Physiol. (London)*, **161**, 298 (1962)
18. Uvnäs, B., *Federation Proc.*, **40**, Suppl. 4, 69 (1960)
19. Rosell, S., and Rosen, A., *Acta Physiol. Scand.*, **52**, 53 (1961)
20. Folkow B., Mellander, S., and Öberg, B., *Acta Physiol. Scand.*, **53**, 7 (1961)
21. Piiper, J., and Rosell, S., *Acta Physiol. Scand.*, **53**, 214 (1961)
22. Hirvonen, L., and Sonnenschein, R. R., *Circulation Res.*, **10**, 94 (1962)
23. Hyman, C., and Paldino, R. L., *Circulation Res.*, **10**, 89 (1962)
24. Beck, L., *Am. J. Physiol.*, **201**, 123 (1961)
25. Jones, J. J., *Circulation Res.*, **10**, 156 (1962)
26. Sakuma, A., and Beck, L., *Am. J. Physiol.*, **201**, 129 (1961)
27. LaCroix, E., *Arch. Intern. Physiol. Biochim.*, **69**, 112 (1961)
28. Lowe, R. D., *Circulation Res.*, **10**, 73 (1962)
29. Sagawa, K., Ross, J. M., and Guyton, A. C., *Am. J. Physiol.*, **200**, 1164 (1961)
30. Sagawa K., Taylor, A. E., and Guyton, A. C., *Am. J. Physiol.*, **201**, 1164 (1961)
31. Warner, H. R., *Circulation Res.*, **6**, 35 (1958)
32. Löfving, B., *Med. Exptl.*, **4**, 307 (1961)
33. McGiff, J. C., and Aviado, D. M., *Circulation Res.*, **9**, 1327 (1961)
34. Folkow, B., Johansson, B., and Löfving, B., *Med. Exptl.*, **4**, 321 (1961)
35. LaCroix, E., *Acta Gastro-Enterol. Belg.*, **23**, 534 (1960)
36. Senay, L. C., Jr., Christensen, M., and Hertzman, A. B., *J. Appl. Physiol.*, **16**, 655 (1961)
37. Rawson, R. O., and Randall, W. C., *J. Appl. Physiol.*, **16**, 1006 (1961)
38. Downing, S. E., Remensnyder, J. P., and Mitchell, J. H., *Circulation Res.*, **10**, 676 (1962)
39. Bevan, J. A., and Verity, M. A., *J. Appl. Physiol.*, **16**, 858 (1961)
40. Geber, W. F., *Am. J. Physiol.*, **202**, 653 (1962)
41. Lewin, R. J., Cross, C. E., Rieben, P. A., and Salisbury, P. F., *Circulation Res.*, **9**, 585 (1961)
42. Coleridge, J. C. G., Kidd, C., and Sharp, J. A., *J. Physiol. (London)*, **156**, 591 (1961)
43. Okada, H., Okamoto, K., and Nisida, I., *Japan. J. Physiol.*, **11**, 520 (1961)
44. Anikina, N. A., *Bull. Biol. Med. Exptl. URSS*, **50**, 28 (1960)
45. LaCroix, E., *Arch. Intern. Physiol. Biochim.*, **70**, 120 (1962)
46. Braun, K., and Stern, S., *Am. J. Physiol.*, **161**, 369 (1961)
47. Pereda, S. A., Eckstein, J. W., and Abboud, F. M., *Am. J. Physiol.*, **202**, 249 (1962)
48. Akopian, S. A., *The Plasma Substitute and Antishock Preparation "A—RM-IPK" and the Physiological Mechanism of Its Therapeutic Effect* [Erevan (Armenian SSR) State U.

Press, 241 pp., 1958, Reviewed in I. C. R. S. Med. Rept., No. 5, 24, 1959]

49. Kotova, G. N., *Sechenov Physiol. J. USSR (Engl. Transl.)*, **46**, 695 (1960)

50. Knoradi, G., and Gal' Perin, Y. U. M., *Sechenov Physiol. J. USSR (Engl. Transl.)*, **46**, 33 (1960)

51. Kuchuk, A. P., *Sechenov Physiol. J. USSR (Engl. Transl.)*, **46**, 338 (1960)

52. Eliakim, M., Stern, S., and Nathan, H., *Circulation Res.*, **9**, 327 (1961)

53. Page, I. H., and Bumpus, F. M., *Physiol. Rev.*, **41**, 331 (1961)

54. Barer, G. R., *J. Physiol. (London)*, **156**, 49 (1961)

55. Finnerty, F. A., Massaro, G. D., Chupkovich, V., and Tuckman, J., *Circulation Res.*, **9**, 256 (1961)

56. Folkow, B., Johansson, B., and Mellander, S., *Acta Physiol. Scand.*, **53**, 99 (1961)

57. Langford, H. G., and Allison, F., Jr., *Am. J. Physiol.*, **200**, 130 (1961)

58. Bevan, J. A., *Circulation Res.*, **9**, 700 (1961)

59. Lundholm, L., *Acta Physiol. Scand.*, **39**, Suppl. 133 (1956)

60. deLaLande, I. S., Parks, V. J., Sandison, A. G., Skinner, S. L., and Whelan, R. F., *J. Physiol. (London)*, **157**, 177 (1961)

61. Allwood, M. J., and Cobbold, A. F., *J. Physiol. (London)*, **157**, 328 (1961)

62. Berne, R. M., *Federation Proc.*, **20**, 101 (1961)

63. Gordon, D. B., *Am. J. Physiol.*, **201**, 1127 (1961)

64. Gordon D. B., and Hesse, D. H., *Am. J. Physiol.*, **201**, 1123 (1961)

65. Keatinge, W. R., *J. Physiol. (London)*, **159**, 101 (1961)

66. Fox, R. H., Goldsmith, R., Kidd, D. J., and Lewis, G. P., *J. Physiol. (London)*, **157**, 589 (1961)

67. Burch, G. E., and DePasquale, N. P., *Circulation Res.*, **10**, 105 (1962)

68. Carlson, L., and Pernow, B., *Acta Physiol. Scand.*, **52**, 328 (1961)

69. Sonnenschein, R. R., *Am. J. Physiol.*, **200**, 685 (1961)

70. Reeves, J. T., Grover, R. F., Blount, S. G., and Filley, G. F., *J. Appl. Physiol.*, **16**, 283 (1961)

71. Reeves, John T., Grover, R. F., Filley, G. F., and Blount, S. G., *J. Appl. Physiol.*, **16**, 279 (1961)

72. Abramson, D. I., Tuck, S., Jr., Bell,

Y., Mitchell, R. E., and Zayas, A. M., *J. Appl. Physiol.*, **16**, 851 (1961)

73. Natadze, T. G., *Vopr. Onkol.*, **5**, 654 (1959)*

74. Wasserman, A. J., and Patterson, J. L., *J. Clin. Invest.*, **40**, 1297 (1961)

75. Hinshaw, L. B., and Worthen, D. M., *Circulation Res.*, **9**, 1156 (1961)

76. Schmid, H. E., and Spencer, M. P., *J. Appl. Physiol.*, **17**, 201 (1962)

77. Texter, E. C., Jr., Merrill, S., Schwartz, M., Van Derstappen, G., and Haddy, F. J., *Am. J. Physiol.*, **202**, 253 (1962)

78. Abramson, D. I., Tuck, S., Jr., Zayas, A. M., and Mitchell, R. E., *J. Appl. Physiol.*, **17**, 191 (1962)

79. Stainsby, W. N., and Renkin, E. M., *Am. J. Physiol.*, **201**, 117 (1961)

80. Stainsby, W. N., *Am. J. Physiol.*, **202**, 273 (1962)

81. Folkow, B., and Öberg, B., *Acta Physiol. Scand.*, **53**, 105 (1961)

82. Langston, J. B., Guyton, A. C., Hull, C. C., and Armstrong, G. G., *Am. J. Physiol.*, **201**, 495 (1961)

83. Sagawa, K., and Guyton, A. C., *Am. J. Physiol.*, **200**, 711 (1961)

84. Ross, J. M., Fairchild, H. M., Weldy, J., and Guyton, A. C., *Am. J. Physiol.*, **202**, 21 (1962)

85. Waugh, W. H., and Shanks, R. G., *Circulation Res.*, **8**, 871 (1960)

86. Schayer, R. W., *Am. J. Physiol.*, **202**, 66 (1962)

87. Sparks, H. V., and Bohr, D. F., *Am. J. Physiol.*, **202**, 835 (1962)

88. Van Citters, R. L., Wagner, B. M., and Rushmer, R. F., *Circulation Res.*, **10**, 668 (1962)

89. Guyton, A. C., and Sagawa K., *Am. J. Physiol.*, **200**, 1157 (1961)

90. Levy, M. N., Brind, S. H., Brandlin, F. R., and Phillips, F. A., *Circulation Res.*, **2**, 372 (1954)

91. Adams, T., and Smith, R. E., *J. Appl. Physiol.*, **17**, 317 (1962)

92. Hildes, J. A., Irving, L., and Hart, J. S., *J. Appl. Physiol.*, **16**, 617 (1961)

93. Vanderhoof, E. R., Imig, C. J., and Hines, H. M., *J. Appl. Physiol.*, **16**, 873 (1961)

94. Polosa, C., and Rossi, G., *Am. J. Physiol.*, **200**, 1185 (1961)

95. Sharpey-Schafer, E. P., *Brit. Med. J.*, **II**, 1589 (1961)

96. Watson, W. E., *Brit. Heart J.*, **24**, 26 (1962)

97. Freund, H., Schlepper, M., and Witzleb, E., *Klin. Wochschr.*, **39**, 1233 (1961)

98. Eckstein, J. W., Hamilton, W. K., and McCammond, J. M., *Anesthesiology*, **22**, 525 (1961)

99. Watson, W. E., *J. Physiol. (London)*, **161**, 392 (1962)

100. Lendle, L., and Mercker, H., *Ergeb. Physiol.*, **51**, 199 (1961)

101. McCausland, A. M., Hyman, C., Winsor, T., and Trotter, A. D., Jr., *Am. J. Obstet. Gynecol.*, **81**, 472 (1961)

102. Mackay, I. F. S., and Walker, R. L., *J. Appl. Physiol.*, **17**, 147 (1962)

103. Remington, J. W., Ed., *Tissue Elasticity*, 111 (Am. Physiol. Soc., Washington, 1957)

104. Gorten, R., Gunnells, J. C., Weissler, A. M., and Stead, E. A., *Circulation Res.*, **9**, 979 (1961)

105. Haddy, F. J., Molnar, J. I., and Campbell, R. W., *Am. J. Physiol.*, **201**, 631 (1961)

106. Kahler, R. L., Goldblatt, A., and Braunwald, E., *Am. J. Physiol.*, **202**, 523 (1962)

107. Pappenheimer, J. R., and Soto-Rivera, A., *Am. J. Physiol.*, **152**, 471 (1948)

108. Hinshaw, L. B., Vick, J. A., Nelson, D. L., Wittmers, L. E., and Swenson, O. P., *Am. J. Physiol.*, **200**, 751 (1961)

109. Takagi, H., Dustan, H. P., and Page, I., *Circulation Res.*, **9**, 1233 (1961)

110. Richardson, T. Q., Stallings, J. O., and Guyton, A. C., *Am. J. Physiol.*, **201**, 471 (1961)

111. Baker, C. H., and Remington, J., *Am. J. Physiol.*, **201**, 910 (1961)

112. Swann, H. G., Stegall, H. F., and Collings, W. D., *Am. J. Physiol.*, **201**, 943 (1961)

113. Pressman, J. J., and Simon, M. B., *Surg., Gynecol. Obstet.*, **113**, 537 (1961)

114. Seeley, S. F., and Weisiger, J. R., Eds., *Federation Proc.*, **20**, Suppl. 9 (1961)

115. Miles, A. A., *Federation Proc.*, **20**, Suppl. 9, 141 (1961)

116. Stoner, H. B., *Federation Proc.*, **20**, Suppl. 9, 38 (1961)

117. Kuida, N., Gilbert, R. P., Hinshaw, L. B., Brunson, J. G., and Visscher, M. B., *Am. J. Physiol.*, **200**, 1197 (1961)

118. Janoff, A., Zweifach, B. W., Nagler, A. L., and Ovary, Z., *Circulation Res.*, **9**, 407 (1961)

119. Hinshaw, L. B., Jordan, M. M., and Vick, J. A., *J. Clin. Invest.*, **40**, 1631 (1961)

120. Hinshaw, L. B., Vick, J. A., Jordan, M. M., and Wittmers, L. E., *Am. J. Physiol.*, **202**, 103 (1962)

121. Nykiel, F., and Glaviano, V. V., *J. Appl. Physiol.*, **16**, 348 (1961)

122. Fine, J., *Federation Proc.*, **20**, Suppl. 9, 166 (1961)

123. Stetson, C. A., *Federation Proc.*, **20**, Suppl. 9, 206 (1961)

124. Fox, C. L., and Lasker, G. W., *Am. J. Physiol.*, **202**, 111 (1962)

125. Green, H. D., *Federation Proc.*, **20**, Suppl. 9, 61 (1961)

126. Baez, S., Hershey, S. G., and Rovenstine, E. A., *Am. J. Physiol.*, **200**, 1245 (1961)

127. Hershey, S. G., Baez, S., and Rovenstine, E. A., *Am. J. Physiol.*, **200**, 1239 (1961)

128. Rothe, C. F., and Selkurt, E. E., *Am. J. Physiol.*, **200**, 1177 (1961)

129. Page, I. H., *Federation Proc.*, **20**, Suppl. 9, 75 (1961)

130. Selkurt, E. E., and Rothe, C. F., *Federation Proc.*, **20**, Suppl. 9, 30 (1961)

131. Guyton A. C., and Crowell, J. W., *Federation Proc.*, **20**, Suppl. 9, 51 (1961)

132. Crowell, J. W., and Guyton, A. C., *Am. J. Physiol.*, **201**, 893 (1961)

133. Simeone, F. A., *Federation Proc.*, **20**, Suppl. 9, 3 (1961)

134. Frank, E. D., Frank, H. A., Jacob, S. W., and Fine, J., *Am. J. Physiol.*, **202**, 7 (1962)

135. Laszt, L., and Hamoir, G., *Biochem. Biophys. Acta*, **50**, 430 (1961)

136. Huys, J., *Arch. Intern. Physiol.*, **69**, 677 (1961)

137. Laszt, L., *Nature*, **187**, 329 (1960)

138. Harding, V., and Laszt, L., *Nature*, **187**, 330 (1960)

139. Scott, J. B., Frohlich, E. D., Hardin, R. A., and Haddy, F. J., *Am. J. Physiol.*, **201**, 1095 (1961)

140. Sudak, F. N., and Fulton, G. P., *Circulation Res.*, **10**, 587 (1962)

141. Briggs, A. H., and Melving, S., *Am. J. Physiol.*, **201**, 365 (1961)

142. Jamieson, J. D., and Friedman, S. M., *Circulation Res.*, **9**, 996 (1961)

143. Yonce, L. R., Dykers, J. R., Jr., and McGee, J. W., *Am. J. Physiol.*, **202**, 277 (1962)

144. Wiedeman, M. P., *Circulation Res.*, **10**, 686 (1962)

145. Barnett, G. O., Mallos, A. J., and

Shapiro, A., *J. Appl. Physiol.*, **16**, 545 (1961)

146. Van Citters, R. L., and Rushmer, R. F., *Am. J. Physiol.*, **200**, 732 (1961)

147. Evans, R. L., Bernstein, E. F., Johnson, E., and Reller, C., *Am. J. Physiol.*, **202**, 619 (1962)

148. McDonald, D. A., *Blood Flow in Arteries* (Williams & Wilkins, Baltimore, 1960)

149. Spencer, M. P., and Greiss, F. C., *Circulation Res.*, **10**, 274 (1962)

150. Rudewald, B., *Acta Physiol. Scand.*, **54**, Suppl, 187 (1962)

151. Meisner, J. E., and Remington, J. W., *Am. J. Physiol.*, **202**, 527 (1962)

152. Cope, F. W., *Bull. Math. Biophys.*, **23**, 337 (1961)

153. Klip, W., *Circulation Res.*, **9**, 1380 (1961)

154. Knisely, M. H., *Acta Anat.*, **44**, Suppl. 41 (1961)

155. Knisely, M. H., Warner, L., and Harding, F., *Angiology*, **11**, 535 (1960)

* English translation will be announced in *Technical Translations,* issued by the Office of Technical Services, U. S. Department of Commerce, and will be made available by the Photoduplication Service, Library of Congress, and by the SLA Translation Center at the John Crerar Library, Chicago, Illinois.

HEART[1]

By William V. Whitehorn

Department of Physiology, University of Illinois College of Medicine, Chicago, Illinois

Cardiac Muscle

Structural characteristics.—The significant advances in description and understanding of the structure and function of skeletal muscle cells have stimulated interest in similar analyses of cardiac muscle. Stenger & Spiro (1) have reviewed their own work and that of others in the field. There seems to be no histologic evidence that the basic contractile organization differs in the two tissues. Unfortunately, such similarity does not suggest explanations for the obvious differences in the maximum tension production of which the two tissues are capable, or for the significantly greater resting tension found in cardiac muscle at the length associated with maximum tension development. The basic similarities of structure should not obscure the consideration of recognized differences. Fawcett (2) considers the nature of the sarcoplasmic reticulum in heart and skeletal muscles and points to the somewhat less well-developed character of this system in the former. Such difference is certainly quantitative rather than qualitative, however, since the complexity of the system varies directly with the heart rate characteristic of the species and does not justify implications of differences in function. In sheep ventricle, demonstration of a transverse tubular system at the level of the Z lines with communication between tubule lumen and extracellular space supplies additional evidence for the suggested role of the system in excitation and metabolism (3). The relationship between endoplasmic reticulum and relaxing factors established for skeletal muscle has not yet been demonstrated in cardiac tissue.

The properties of the cardiac contractile proteins have been reviewed (4). Again one is impressed by the similarities between cardiac and skeletal materials although the molecular weight of cardiac myosin may be lower than that of the skeletal protein.

Contractility.—The basic processes of contraction in cardiac muscle have been discussed theoretically by Podolsky (5, 6), essentially on the basis of the formulations of Hill and the implications of the structural models. Analysis of contractile modifications in cardiac muscle in these terms is still in its infancy. Sonnenblick (7) has considered such inotropic mechanisms as length changes, frequency of contraction, and action of catecholamines and of calcium ions in terms of the force-velocity relationships of isolated cat papillary muscles. Changes in length influence maximum developed force (P_0) but do not influence maximum velocity of shortening (V_{max}). Changes in chemical

[1] This review includes material available to the author between June 1, 1961, and June 1, 1962.

235

environment induced by catecholamines or calcium ions and changes in the frequency of stimulation influence V_{max} with variable effects on P_0. It is suggested that contractility may thus be more accurately defined in terms of changes in V_{max} and that the ability of cardiac muscle to modulate its contractile force by changing maximum rates of shortening constitutes an important functional characteristic not shared by skeletal muscle.

The phenomenon of postextrasystolic potentiation and related events has been further investigated. Meijler and his colleagues (8, 9) studied isotonic contractions in intact isolated rat hearts. Increase in amplitude of contractions following the compensatory pause was found to counterbalance the decreased amplitude of the premature beat so that for constant net rate the average height of contraction was constant. Effects of an interpolated extra beat were similar to those of increased rate of stimulation. The effects noted were considered to be compatible with a "restitution" of contractility beginning at some time after contraction and increasing at a rate dependent on the frequency of stimulation.

These suggestions are quite similar to those of Kruta & Braveny (10) who have continued their earlier work and conclude that the restitution process proceeds in two phases which may differ quantitatively or actually be dissociated from each other. Blinks & Koch-Weser (11) also suggest that interval-strength relationships can be quantitatively assessed by considering that activation of muscle produces two opposing effects on contractility. Each beat produces a relatively small positive inotropic effect which decays slowly and exponentially and a negative inotropic effect which is large at first and decays rapidly and then exponentially. Both states are capable of cumulation, and the resultant interaction determines the strength of subsequent contractions.

As with Meijler's and Kruta's "restitution", the magnitude of the positive and negative influences and the characteristics of their decay curves are not necessarily independent of the rate of stimulation. The processes responsible for the strength-interval effects have not been defined. The length-tension relationship is not involved. Blinks & Koch-Weser suggest that the force-velocity relationships rather than active state duration are primarily modified, while Kruta & Braveny speculate on undefined changes in cellular energy production and utilization. The point of view that frequency-dependent changes in strength of contraction are based on modification of the intracellular ionic concentration, particularly of sodium and potassium, may require re-evaluation. Tuttle & Farah (12) reinvestigated the effects of glycosides on these phenomena and found that conditions which depressed contractility also abolished the frequency-force relationships. In contradiction of the earlier suggestions of Hajdu and Szent Györgyi, they report that the action of the glycosides depends on whether or not they increase or decrease the contractile response and thus that their mode of action involves the frequency-dependent mechanism.

The possible importance of calcium in these events is suggested by

Winegrad (13) and Winegrad & Shanes (14). In guinea pig atria, kinetic studies with Ca^{45} revealed a large increase in Ca entry with contraction. Modification of contractile strength by changes in frequency of stimulation or by modification of the concentration of Ca in the solution resulted in changes in Ca^{45} influx which were proportional to the strength of the beat. The data are certainly consistent with the hypothesis that Ca movement into the cell somehow couples excitation with contraction and, in addition, that this linkage may be involved in the determination of the amount of tension developed. Some points of doubt are, however, present. Total content of cellular Ca was not changed by contraction but no evidence of the implied efflux of Ca was obtained. Moreover, since it is known that changes in Ca concentration are capable of modifying the active state of cardiac muscle, the reported constancy of this parameter during frequency-induced inotropy would seem to cast doubt on the significance of a Ca-dominated mechanism. The rate of development and magnitude of the contracture induced in toad ventricle by sucrose hypertonicity does, however, as is the case with contractures induced in other tissues, depend on the presence and concentration of Ca (15). Although the basic mode of action of Ca is still unclear, the relationships between Ca binding and the physiological relaxing factor of muscle (16), and the association of the latter with the endoplasmic reticulum and its role in excitation-coupling, provide grounds for fertile speculation and research. In the meantime, the effect of the ion on the reactions of artificial contractile protein solutions continues to draw attention (17).

Cardiac Adaptation

It would seem axiomatic that the mechanisms of adaptation of the functioning heart to changes in demand be based on the appropriate properties of the cardiac muscle. Attention continues to be directed to the relative significance of responses based on the length-tension relationship in contrast to those not so related. Braunwald and his colleagues (18) have continued to evaluate the operation of Starling's law under a variety of conditions in the human heart. When autonomic activity was reduced by drug administration in slightly anemic subjects, elevation of left ventricular end-diastolic pressure by transfusion of 1500 ml of the subject's own blood was associated with a corresponding elevation of left ventricular performance as measured from determinations of stroke work, power, and tension-time indices. Such relationship was not apparent in the presence of intact neural mechanisms. In view of the recognized assumptions in the extrapolation from pressure to volume, estimations of left ventricular volume were made from biplane angiocardiograms on a series of cardiac patients (19). Beat-to-beat analyses of end-diastolic and end-systolic volumes and of the corresponding stroke volumes were made. Again with reservations based on the technical aspects of the study, stroke volumes were found to vary directly with the preceding diastolic volumes. In one subject with pulsus alternans, the direct relationship between diastolic and stroke volumes was similarly valid. The function of the atrium in providing an effective level of ventricular filling pressure at a minimal atrial pressure has been emphasized (20). Maintenance of this relationship assumes additional significance in the presence of cardiac disease. The data indicate that both atria and ventricles follow the Starling relationship in man and support the generalization that relationships between atrial pressures and ventricular stroke work are determined by performance characteristics of both cardiac chambers (21). Attempts to separate the "Starling" and "non-Starling" components of a cardiac adaptation were also made by Guyton & Sagawa (22). In dogs with reflexes suppressed by anesthesia, opening of an arteriovenous fistula equal to the cardiac output resulted in an instantaneous increase in output of about 75 per cent. In the presence of reflexes, compensation was 82 per cent. It is concluded that the nonreflex compensation is of primary importance and can be explained by increased venous return and cardiac adaptation in accordance with the Starling principle.

Of importance to the interpretation of studies involving relationships between ventricular pressure and volume are the observations of Hefner *et al.* (23). In open-chest experiments on dogs, plots of ventricular pressure-circumference were linear and subject to a relatively small degree of scatter. The slow infusion of epinephrine increased ventricular distensibility and the scatter of the data. The magnitude of the change in distensibility was great enough to produce significant changes in ventricular function at a given filling pressure. These data are in some contrast to earlier indications that autonomic stimulation is without effect on ventricular distensibility (24).

It is generally believed that the regulation of balance of outputs of the right and left ventricles provides a prime example of the functional importance of the Starling law. Franklin, Van Citters & Rushmer (25) have now questioned this doctrine. Relationships between the outputs of the two ventricles were studied with implanted ultrasonic flow meters in unanesthetized dogs. Normal respiration produced slight variations in output of the two chambers which were almost in phase. Hydrothorax or atalectasis greatly exaggerated these changes, and outputs were now clearly out of phase. Change in posture resulted in cardioacceleration and large in-phase changes of both left and right outputs. Similar in-phase changes were produced by the sudden onset of treadmill exercise. It is accordingly concluded that the data do not support the concept that changes in venous return are dominant mechanisms inducing changes in cardiac output.

The cardiac response to increase in output resistance has been carefully studied by Imperial, Levy & Zieske (26). In a modified heart-lung preparation of the dog, they were able to induce rapid diastolic increases in outflow resistance by means of a solenoid valve. There were no changes in diastolic volume or pressure. Increased outflow resistance produced an immediate increase in peak aortic pressure and a reduction in stroke volume which were proportional to the magnitude of the resistance. Stroke work was little affected at low levels of resistance but fell at higher levels. The effect seems to be an independent determinant of cardiac muscle response and to be related to the influences of afterload, an area not yet thoroughly studied in cardiac muscle. The same basic considerations are probably involved in the findings of Pieper (27) who compared the pressure changes in a model pump system with those occurring in the circulation of the dog. When the volume of the arterial system was rhythmically modified by a sinusoidal pump, the aortic pressure pulse of the dog, in contrast to that of the model, was a linear function of the presystolic aortic pressure. Measurement of stroke volume showed that the heart compensated quantitatively for the induced changes in arterial content. The author's suggestion that this adjustment is actually an expression of the Starling relationship, the work of the heart remaining constant during the sinusoidal variations, does not seem to be borne out by the data. Salisbury, Cross & Rieben (28) measured intramyocardial pressure by imbedding a segment of fluid-filled artery in the myocardial wall. Their suggestion that all factors known to regulate the strength of ventricular contraction act by a common mechanism which involves elevation of intramyocardial pressure and release of some potentiating agent would seem to be entirely speculative at the present time. A comprehensive consideration of the regulation of cardiac performance has been provided by Sarnoff & Mitchell (29).

It is recognized that the rate of ventricular tension production, as well as the total tension produced, is an important parameter of cardiac adaptation. In normal man the mean left ventricular systolic ejection rate increased with exercise, whether or not there were changes in stroke volume (30). Failing left ventricles showed no increase in rate. Insofar as mean ejection rates can be taken to be a measure of the velocity of fiber shortening, these data are consistent with the force-velocity relationships of isolated muscles. Similar comparisons of left ventricular ejection times, stroke volumes, and heart rates were made on a large number of normal subjects and patients with cardiovascular disease by Weissler, Peeler & Roehll (31). Mean rate of ventricular ejection showed a curvilinear relationship to stroke volume which was not significantly different in the normal or cardiac groups. Ejection times were prolonged in the presence of aortic stenosis. The finding of normal rates of ejection in patients with congestive heart failure is in contrast to the prolongation of ejection time observed experimentally on the descending limb of ventricular function curves and suggests that the state in heart failure is not analogous to this portion of the Starling curve. More detailed analysis of rate changes in tension production during a cardiac cycle is possible by recording of the electronically differentiated ventricular pressure pulse (32).

The significance of rates of ventricular contraction is further suggested by observations of Spencer & Greiss (33). On the basis of theoretical considerations, these workers proposed that factors of blood mass and vascular compliance should be important in flow of a pulsatile nature in large channels with low resistance and that ventricular ejection dynamics should be primarily inertial rather than frictional. In confirmation of this hypothesis, they found that ventricular pressure exceeds aortic pressure for only about 45 per cent of the ejection period. During the remainder of ejection the gradient is against the direction of flow and produces deceleration of flow to zero. It is concluded that the major phenomenon relating pressure and flow in the ascending aorta is that governing mass acceleration, a generalization which would seem to have important implications for understanding of ventricular dynamics.

Interesting relationships between heart size, heart rate, end-diastolic volumes, end-systolic volumes, stroke volume, and cardiac output have been determined by Holt and his colleagues in anesthetized mammals with a 54-fold range in body weight and a heart weight variation from 104 to 3600 grams (34). There was no simple relationship between body weight or heart weight and end-diastolic volume, a finding in keeping with the variations of the heart-body weight ratio in different species. End-diastolic volume and stroke work are, however, linearly related and stroke volume constitutes a constant fraction of end-diastolic volume throughout the range of animals studied. The value of 43 per cent for the stroke volume fraction of end-diastolic volume compares remarkably well with the estimate of 37 per cent made by Folse & Braunwald (35) in man using a precordial detection technique for the determination of isotope dilution rather than the electrical conductivity method of the Louisville group. The constancy of the relationships studied provides weighty evidence for the similarities of cardiac dynamics in normal hearts of all sizes.

Myocardial failure.—The basic deficiency in cardiac failure continues to be sought in several areas. Olson, Ellenbogen & Iyengar (36) state the case for modification of the physicochemical properties of cardiac myosin extracted from the hearts of dogs subjected to tricuspid insufficiency and pulmonic stenosis. The significant finding is a marked increase in the molecular weight of the myosin from experimental hearts, without change in amino acid composition or enzymatic activity. Previous work both supporting and rejecting changes in contractile protein is discussed and reservations regarding etiologic significance and extrapolation to the human syndrome are expressed. Since the basic observation is a matter of physicochemical technique, confirmation from other laboratories should be awaited. Although changes in ATPase activity of contractile proteins has not been a consistent finding in studies on experimental heart failure, such changes have been found by Alpert & Gordon (37). In a small series of comparisons between patients dying of congestive failure following chronic essential hypertension and those suffering traumatic death, myofibrillar ATPase activity at optimum substrate concentration was 35 per cent lower in tissue from failing hearts. With increasing concentrations of magnesium ion the failure group also showed significantly less increase in activity than did the normals. If extrapolations from relationships of enzymic activity and tension production in glycerol-extracted models can be made to the intact heart, these findings would support the view that changes in contractile protein properties with resultant loss of work capacity are important features in the development of human cardiac failure. As the authors point out, however, factors related to age and the presence of muscle hypertrophy must be clarified before firm conclusions are possible.

The question of significant metabolic alterations in failing myocardium has been reopened. Furchgott & Lee (38) have reviewed the relationships between levels of high-energy phosphates and the force of myocardial contraction under a variety of conditions. Consistent correlations do not occur, since changes in contractile force independent of changes in phosphate are readily observed. Similarly, experimental failure may develop with or without changes in energy stores. Decrease in contractile force without change in high-energy phosphate levels is considered to be evidence of inefficient utilization of energy and is the generally considered finding in the types of cardiac failure usually studied. With this background, Schwartz & Lee (39) undertook a more careful study of mitochondrial function in experimental failure induced by more or less severe constriction of the aorta in guinea pigs. Animals with chronic experimental failure showed evidence of a congestive syndrome and exhibited reduced ventricular contractility as determined by peak isometric pressure values. With a more sensitive technique than was possible in earlier work, it was clearly demonstrated that mitochondria from failing hearts showed depression of the phosphorylation associated with the oxidation of a number of substrates. Homogenates of such hearts likewise showed depression of oxygen and glucose consumption and of lactic acid formation.

It is of interest that administration of cardiac glycosides improved ventricular contractility without alteration of the metabolic defect. Mitochondria in acute failure showed uncoupling of oxidative phosphorylation which increased in severity with increased degrees of aortic constriction. In a complementary study Feinstein (40) assayed the left ventricles of guinea pigs for ATP and related compounds. Congestive failure was associated with significant reductions in phosphocreatine, ATP, and total creatine. The loss of high-energy phosphates paralleled the severity of the failure and correlated well with the disturbances of mitochondrial metabolism described by Schwartz & Lee. Ouabain again produced inotropic effects without increase in phosphate levels. These studies certainly indicate the possible significance of disturbances of energy production as significant factors in the development of this type of experimental failure. The similarity of the metabolic findings to those produced by hypoxia, however, would lead one to wonder whether this factor plays a more prominent role in the production of this particular type of experimental failure than is the case with other procedures.

The complexity of the clinical syndrome of congestive failure is emphasized by the observation that improvement in contractility induced by a sympathomimetic amine did not improve the clinical condition of patients (41).

Cardiac hypertrophy.—Perhaps related to the problems of cardiac failure is the question of the physiological consequences of hypertrophy. Although it is still generally neglected, there have been some contributions to this field. Meerson (42) has provided a summary in English of the work and views of himself and others on compensatory hyperfunction of the heart and cardiac insufficiency. His concept of stages of compensation and eventual exhaustion is hardly new but his findings of metabolic changes in failing hearts associated with a fall in concentration of DNA and a depression of myocardial protein synthesis should stimulate additional attempts to define the problem in basic terms. In dogs subjected to aortic stenosis, electron micrography revealed elongation and apparent fusion of mitochondria into rodlike structures 8 or 10 sarcomeres long (43). The ratio of mitochrondrial volume to that of the myofibrils was reduced under these conditions (44) and the changes may reflect deviations in function of the organelle. The ATPase activity of the ventricular but not of the skeletal muscle of exercised albino rats has been reported to be increased (45), as has the amount of creatine phosphate (46). Total ventricular protein and lactic dehydrogenase may also be increased (47). Alexander, Goldfarb & Drury (48) studied the maximal isometric pressure development of rabbit heart lung preparations after the development of hypertrophy following aortic stenosis. Their findings of increased performance which did not necessarily correlate with the degree of hypertrophy perhaps places their animals in the compensation stage of Meerson's scheme.

   Miscellaneous adaptations.—Cardiac output was found to correlate well with the venous gradient in exercise in normal dogs, but increments in venous gradient are reduced in mild experimental failure and neither output nor gradient changes with exercise in the presence of severe failure (49). There was a close correlation between rise in inferior caval pressure and heart rate during exercise suggesting a Bainbridge-like reflex. Jones (50) has pointed out that inconsistencies in demonstration of this reflex are related to the level of the initial heart rate before infusion of fluid. He suggests that the heart rate is adjusted to a level optimal for production of an increase in cardiac output and that venous pressure is thereby restored to normal levels. Maintenance of cardiac output during the increased peripheral resistance of carotid occlusion is dependent on autonomic reflex action on the myocardium (51), but the contribution of sympathetic stimulation to the increased output of severe anemia is questioned since administration of dichloroisoproterenol produced no significant effects (52). Chien & Billig (53) distinguished between neural and non-neural factors in the cardiac output changes following hemorrhage. Neural factors became increasingly important as reduction in blood volume increased. Acute bleeding resulted in increased cardiac rate and myocardial force as measured with a strain-gauge arch until arterial pressure fell below 90 mm Hg. Below this level myocardial depression appeared, perhaps related to inadequate coronary perfusion (54).

   The central or afferent components of the vagal slowing reflex in the rat are blocked at degrees of hypothermia which still permit efferent conduction in the nerve (55). Quantitations of cardiac and peripheral circulatory responses to acute heat stress have been reported (56). Influences of posture on cardiac output are reflected in the response to exercise, increments being lower in the sitting position than in the supine (57). The importance of differences between open- and closed-chest preparations is again emphasized by studies of effects of pulmonary insufflation on right ventricular volume (58). Insufflation produced increased ventricular volume with the chest open but reduction of volume with the chest closed. Thoracotomy was much more significant than intermittent positive pressure in reducing the cardiac output in the dog (59). The decrease in heart rate and cardiac output and the rise in mean arterial pressure and peripheral resistance produced by oxygen breathing in man have again been reconfirmed (60, 61). Reduction in cardiac output is not invariably accompanied by a drop in arterial pressure during the Valsalva maneuver (62). Steiner & Mueller (63) noted that effects of forward acceleration on heart rate depended on the position of the carotid baroceptors relative to the trunk of the subject. Cardiac output changes were minimal (64).

A description of the hemodynamics of normal cattle is timely in view of the recent interest in high-altitude-induced pulmonary hypertension and subsequent right heart failure in this species (65, 66). As in other mammals, bradycardia is a prominent feature of the circulatory adjustment to diving in man (67), an effect shared, incidentally, by the American alligator (68). Techniques of intracardiac phonocardiography have been combined with measurements of other parameters to define further the mechanisms and hemodynamic correlates of the heart sounds (69 to 72). The heart sounds of the monkey are described (73). Harrison and his colleagues (74, 75, 76) have studied the sequence of human precordial movements in relation to pressure curves and rates of pressure change in dog ventricles and have suggested an analysis of ventricular dynamics based on these observations. Studies on four subjects in India credited with ability to arrest the heart voluntarily showed that three used variations of the Valsalva maneuver without cardiac asystole and the fourth produced cardiac slowing by mechanisms not clearly defined (77). The dynamics of the heart in shock have been discussed (78).

Neural regulation.—The details of the central nervous mechanisms concerned with cardiovascular control have been investigated by a number of workers. Chai & Wang (79, 80) isolated the lower brainstem of the cat by decerebration in order to study the effects of centers located in this region uninfluenced by connections with more rostral areas. Stereotaxic exploration and stimulation of dorsal medullary areas gave characteristic pressor and cardioacceleratory responses. Simultaneous increases in pulse pressure indicated concurrent augmentation of cardiac contraction. In confirmation of earlier observations of others, cardioacceleration was more frequently observed on right-sided stimulation and cardiac augmentation on left. Comparable effects on cardiac rate were obtained before and after decerebration or additional ablations of the midbrain and upper pons. The results support the concept of important medullary integrative mechanisms for cardiovascular function and are contrary to the suggestion that such centers are afferent relays to higher controlling areas. Rosen (81) found similar coupling of cardiac augmentation and vasoconstriction from circumscribed dorsal medullary stimulation in the cat. Ventrolateral stimulation revealed a pattern of cardiac stimulation coupled with vasodilation in muscle, a combination interestingly similar to that occurring with exercise. The release of adrenomedullary catecholamines may contribute partially to the cardiac responses to stimulation of this "vasodilator outflow" but not to the vascular effects (82). Hypothalamic areas have been shown to be also involved in the responses described (83). The role of more rostral areas has been additionally clarified by the work of Löfving (84) on the limbic cortex of the cat. Regions of the anterior cingulate gyrus and the subcallosal area were found to contain relatively well-delineated sympathoexcitatory and sympathoinhibitory neurons. Excitatory effects sometimes were fairly selective in terms of differential modifications of muscle, renal, or intestinal flow. Inhibitory responses tended to be more constant but were significantly modified by the existing level of activity of lower centers so that differential local responses were possible. In the light of the studies of Wang, Chai, and Rosen it is of interest that the cingulate depressor area exerts its effects via the depressor areas of the lower brainstem. Stella & Stevan (85) noted that stimulation of cerebellar cortex might also induce changes in the heart rate of the dog.

These attempts to delineate central mechanisms serve as background for the observations of Mack, Davenport & Dykman (86) that cardiovascular conditioning as exhibited by heart rate and arterial pressure changes in dogs is more reliable than motor conditioning and for the peripherally oriented confirmation of O'Brien (87) that left stellate stimulation augmented heart rate and stroke volume in the dog-heart-lung preparation. Ulmer & Randall (88) found augmentation of atrial as well as ventricular contraction with stellate stimulation. The augmentation was sufficient to modify ventricular filling and so make an additional contribution to resulting changes in ventricular output. On the other hand, Chidsey et al. (89) found that large doses of a rauwolfia alkaloid reduced the pulse rate but did not interfere with the increase in cardiac output resulting from acute hypoxemia or exercise. If the dosage was in fact sufficient to modify autonomic cardiac catecholamine effects, the contribution of the latter to the exercise response is questioned.

The effects of vagal stimulation and of acetylcholine on the ventricle were studied by Eliakim and his colleagues (90) in dogs with heart block. Occasional bradycardia and decreased force of ventricular contraction were noted. The possibility of some functional parasympathetic fibers to the ventricle certainly exists but the question of modification of ventricular function secondary to changes in atrial hemodynamics would seem important in this respect. Singh (91) found that vagal stimulation inhibited the frog heart even in the presence of high concentrations of acetylcholine and suggests the release of a more potent ester. Warner & Cox (92) analyzed the relationship between heart rate and the frequency of stimulation of cardiac afferents with a mathematical model system capable of computer solution. The resulting predictive equations represent one aspect necessary to an adequate quantitative description of over-all circulatory control. Hauss & Kemper (93) hypothesize that carotid baroceptors may be stimulated by rise in endosinus pressure or by differential distortion of the layers of the vessel wall. The baroceptor reflexes in the cat seem to be so balanced as to maintain cardiac output constant despite changes in peripheral resistance [Groom and colleagues (94)].

ELECTRICAL ACTIVITY

Although the basic structure and function of the contractile apparatus of cardiac muscle seems to be highly similar to that in skeletal tissues, this similarity certainly does not extend in the same degree to the properties of the cardiac membranes. Hutter & Noble (95) have continued their study of these properties in the Purkinje tissue of the sheep and dog heart. In such resting cardiac fibers, chloride ions carried not more than 0.3 of the total membrane current as compared to approximately 0.7 in skeletal muscles. The permeability of the cardiac membranes to iodide, nitrate, bromide, and chloride ions is essentially similar to that of erythrocytes but again differs from that of skeletal muscle. From the functional point of view, the low chloride conductance of the cardiac membrane makes the muscle more sensitive to changes in cation permeability whether occurring during pacemaker activity, the conducted action potential or as a consequence of autonomic nerve activity. The relatively high chloride content of cardiac tissue, as determined by Lamb (96), results in an equivalent potential of about 47 millivolts.

The particular generator properties of cardiac pacemaker tissue have been investigated by Trautwein & Kassebaum (97). Diminution of external sodium concentration resulted in hyperpolarization and cessation of rhythmic activity in sheep Purkinje fibers and rabbit atria suggestive of the existence of a significant resting sodium current in these tissues. A constant cathodal current enhanced the tendency for rhythmicity, and reduction in extracellular calcium reduced the required current strength. It is believed that these effects are related to an increase in the steady state sodium conductance. The postulated mechanism for spontaneous activity is considered to be this high resting sodium current acting in conjunction with a diastolic decrease in potassium conductance to produce the pacemaker potential. Although the current-voltage relationships of nonbeating papillary muscles were similar to those of pacemaker tissue, the former did not develop rhythmic activity when stimulated by constant current or subjected to reduction in external sodium. Failure of increase in potassium conductance as a precondition for diastolic depolarization apparently does not obtain in nonpacemaker myocardial fibers. The structure of the pacemaker tissue in man (98) and steer (99) has been discussed.

The resemblance of the intracellularly recorded cardiac action potential to the endplate potential of skeletal muscle has led Wright & Ogata (100) to consider whether or not it too is a composite of two separate depolarizations. Recordings from atrial frog tissue characteristically reveal a notch between the spike and the slow plateau phase which may serve to differentiate the two processes. Reduction of oxygen tension and microinjection of acetylcholine produce specific reduction of the plateau phase without effect on the initial spike. The Q_{10} of the spike phase is markedly different from that of the normal prolonged response and suggests the presence of two distinct ion carrier systems operating at different rates and times. The initial rapid spike system may in fact be the trigger for the slower response. It is of interest that the mechanical activity of the muscle is associated with the plateau response and is inhibited simultaneously with that response by the action of acetylcholine. It is suggested that the cardiac membranes may be made up of two structures, one operating more or less similarly to that in nerve, the other more directly related to contraction. The concept of dual processes in the electrical responses of frog heart muscle and in the changes in ion conductance associated with them is also suggested by the observations of Ware (101). Reduction in external calcium concentration reduced the resting potential, increased the degree of overshoot, and enhanced the maximum rate of depolarization. Under such conditions the "spike" portion of the action potential was abolished. High calcium concentrations augmented both spike and plateau. Theoretical explanation of these phenomena in terms of sodium and potassium conductance would be facilitated if, in fact, two components are involved. In the presence of calcium deficiency, magnesium can substitute for calcium insofar as modification of membrane events is concerned (102). The associated depression of contractility is not, however, corrected.

The electrophysiological properties of human right atrial and ventricular muscle removed during open heart surgery have been studied by Trautwein et al. (103). Transmembrane resting and action potentials, effects of modification of sodium concentration, effects of anoxia and increasing rate of stimulation, and the actions of acetylcholine and epinephrine were all similar to those described for other mammalian hearts. Ventricular conduction velocities were greater than those described for the dog and may have been related to hypertrophy of the fibers. The fundamental membrane processes of human heart, like its contractile and structural features, would accordingly seem to be entirely similar to those of other mammals.

Investigations of stimulation and conduction in the heart have been conducted in a number of areas. Weidmann (104) and Hecht (105) have summarized some aspects of this area. Ushiyama & Brooks (106) have determined the thresholds for excitation of trabecular muscle of dogs by rectangular pulses and the minimal current gradient (Lambda) required for stimulation. Under a variety of conditions including catelectronic currents, modifications of calcium concentration, and the administration of drugs expected to modify cardiac excitability, they found that these parameters varied inconsistently with respect to each other. The observations point to the importance of considering the characteristics of the stimulus when attempting to define cardiac excitability and to the lack of real understanding of the basic processes involved. Hoshiko & Sperelakis (107) produced impaired impulse propagation and prepotentials in frog ventricle strips bathed with magnesium-Ringer's solution and subjected to conditioning pulses. Under these conditions prepotentials were more common when strips were stimulated from one end than from the other. After further treatment, propagation failed in the direction of negative current flow. Reversal of conditioning pulse polarity reversed the direction of conduction. It is proposed that junctional transmission at the region of the intercalated disks may be responsible for the effects noted. The functional significance of these structures is further suggested by the finding of a relative impedance at 10,000 cps compared to that at 10 cps of 75 per cent and 48 per cent in Ringer's and sucrose solutions, respectively, for strips of cardiac muscle. These results suggest the presence of structures of high resistance and capacity absent in skeletal muscle in which impedance was independent of frequency in similar solutions (108).

The localization of cholinesterase and the high concentration of muco-polysaccharide reported by Joó & Csillik (109) in mammalian intercalated disks lend further support to the concept of the importance of these structures in relation to ion-transfer mechanisms.

The morphology of the human atrioventricular node has been carefully described (110). Of particular significance is the finding of "bypass tracts" of fibers many of which appear to be composed of Purkinje tissue. One group of these re-enters the inferior margin of the node, the other terminates at the base of the tricuspid valve. The structural configuration suggests the possibility of a dual conduction system with slow conduction through the node itself and rapid conduction by way of the bypass. On the other hand, electrocardiograms taken during the lives of the individuals studied revealed no evidence of such functional activity. The morphologic data should lead to a careful re-evaluation of the functional significance of the nodal area. Summaries of the development of the conducting system (111) and its physiology (112) are available. A histologic approach has also been made to the identification of the tissue involved in retrograde atrioventricular block (113). Exploration with microelectrodes and subsequent identification of the stimulated cells indicate the sensitive point to lie just above the bifurcation of the His bundle.

Continued attention has been paid to the problems of arrhythmia. West & Lande (114) evaluated the significance of re-entry excitation in the initiation and maintenance of arrhythmia in isolated atrial tissue. The minimal mass in which such disturbances of rhythm could be produced was compared with theoretical calculations of such critical mass from determinations of conduction times and refractory periods of the isolated segments. The findings support the concept of re-entry as the dominant factor. Similar conclusions were reached by Covino & D'Amato (115) on the basis of studies of the ventricular fibrillation of hypothermia. At muscle temperatures of about 15°C, isolated papillary muscles and intact hearts showed marked slowing of conduction times not counterbalanced by proportionate increase in refractory period. Small hearts did not show irreversible fibrillation and the arrhythmia was abolished when large hearts were cut into smaller pieces. It is suggested that depression of cellular metabolism by cold results in failure of adequate energy generation with resulting depression of conduction velocity and development of circus rhythms. The contribution of adrenal catecholamines to the initiation of ventricular fibrillation in the dog is questioned by Bass & Glaviano (116). Heart rate, arterial pressure, adrenal blood flow, and adrenal plasma concentrations of epinephrine and norepinephrine were compared before and after ligation of the anterior coronary artery in dogs. Animals which developed fibrillation showed more severe reductions in heart rate and arterial pressure, but output of adrenal catecholamines per minute was not different in the two groups and was unrelated to the early or late occurrence of fibrillation. The importance of technical details with regard to placement of electrodes and timing of stimuli in determination of ventricular fibrillation thresholds is emphasized by van Tyn & MacLean (117). Interpretation of the antifibrillatory action of a number of agents in terms of modification of basic electrical properties of the myocardium has been attempted by Szekeres & Vaughan Williams (118). In isolated atria, measurements of mechanical activity, conduction velocity, effective refractory period, and transmembrane potentials were made before and after exposure to quinidine, procaine, papaverine, dibenamine, and procaine amide. All produced lengthening of the effective refractory period, decreased conduction velocity and decreased rate of rise of the action potential. Resting potential did not change nor was there significant change in duration of the total action potential. Effects on contraction did not parallel effects on effective refractory period or rate of rise of the action potential. The data suggest that the common denominator for antifibrillatory action may be concerned with mechanisms of depolarization rather than those of repolarization. In the case of quinidine such action could not be attributed to changes in intracellular concentration of either sodium or potassium (119). Birnbaum, Weiner & Farah (120) have confirmed the predisposing effect of anoxia or asphyxia and the importance of concomitant vagal activity in the initiation of atrial fibrillation.

The field of electrocardiography has been omitted from this review.

CORONARY CIRCULATION AND MYOCARDIAL OXYGEN METABOLISM

Smith (121) has reviewed some aspects of the anatomy of the human coronary bed and has called particular attention to the controversy concerning the presence and significance of intercoronary anastomoses. The question of the nature of the stimuli necessary to bring them into use is raised and the possible participation of hypoxia and such hormonal factors as hypophyseal somatotropin is considered. Of comparative interest in this connection are the observations of Truex and his colleagues (122) on the coronary vasculature of the whale heart in which large communications between right and left coronary arteries, between branches of the left coronary system, and between arterial and venous channels are characteristic. Of collateral interest in these studies was the finding that coronary atherosclerosis was found only in the sperm whale and was apparently related to factors of diet, stress, and environment which have a familiar human ring. The functional significance of such collateral circulation to the myocardium has been sought by Levy, Imperial & Zieske (123). The clearance of Rb^{86} was used as an index of coronary blood flow in open-chest experiments on dogs, and the weight of the ischemic zone defined by rubidium clearances following ligation of the left circumflex artery was determined. The resulting values were about half of those expected on the basis of injection of dye into the distal end of the occluded artery indicating significant dual supply in the marginal regions. Estimates of collateral flow from the isotope measurements were consistently greater than those simultaneously determined by retrograde flow techniques and suggest an appreciable circulation through vessels communicating with the capillary beds of the ischemic area and not contributing to the retrograde estimate.

Hormonal factors influencing extracoronary anastamoses are suggested by Zweens (124) who noted that the diameter of connections between the internal mammary and coronary circulations of the rat is increased by the actions of estrogen and progesterone. Caution with respect to interpretation of data is urged by the observations that post mortem estimation of the relative dominance of right or left arterialization from arteriography showed no correlation with estimates based on flows at constant perfusion pressures (125). Observations with deuterium uptake as an indication of coronary flow indicate a uniform distribution of blood flow per unit weight in different regions of the right and left ventricles under normal conditions (126). Mena et al. (127) noted that disappearance rates of intravenously injected slugs of radioactive material were slower when followed by precordial detection than were those monitored from a peripheral artery. The ratio between the two slopes may serve as an index of coronary blood flow. Hirche & Lochner (128) estimated coronary flow by indicator-dilution technique following intracoronary injection of test material on the dog with closed chest. Salazar (129) describes an electrolytic method for selective production of coronary occlusion in the closed-chest experiments which would seem to have useful significance.

Determinants of coronary flow and myocardial oxygen consumption were studied in the dog by Feinberg, Katz & Boyd (130) in a preparation with controlled circulation and open-chest. Relationships between coronary flow, myocardial oxygen extraction, and myocardial oxygen consumption were determined under conditions of increased input, resistance, and modifications of pH and pCO_2; and statistical analysis of such relationships was attempted. Oxygen extraction remained remarkably constant in spite of such manipulations until deterioration of the preparation intervened. Coronary flow, initially minimum for a given degree of cardiac effort, tends to increase with time, the oxygen extraction falling. In support of earlier conclusions of this group and others, myocardial oxygen consumption remained closely related to an index of cardiac effort given by the product of heart rate and aortic mean pressure. Their data support the concept that coronary oxygen consumption determines coronary flow but provide no evidence that flow may in itself determine oxygen consumption. The inotropic effects of calcium ions raised coronary flow and oxygen consumption per beat if ventricular volume was not controlled but did not affect the ratio of myocardial oxygen consumption to heart rate and left ventricular pressure in the isovolumic preparation (131). Whalen (132) has attempted to clarify the relation between work and oxygen consumption in isolated myocardial strips. Work and qO_2 were not correlated as they were in the classical findings in skeletal muscle. The results are not incompatible with the observations relating tension rather than work with oxygen consumption in the intact heart but deserve careful consideration and confirmation because of their theoretical importance. Observations by Messer *et al.* (133) in man confirm the constancy of oxygen extraction during the normal response to exercise in spite of wide individual variations in relationship between extraction and flow at rest. In individuals with coronary disease, about half showed reduced oxygen extractions at rest and most demonstrated increased extractions during exercise. Patients with low cardiac outputs had high extractions at rest but the pattern of response to exercise was determined by the presence or absence of significant cornonary abnormality.

Since flow varies with consumption and the latter with heart rate and aortic pressure, Elliot (134) suggests the use of a regression equation relating these parameters rather than actual determination of flow. Since the equation applies only under the specific conditions of its derivation, it is obviously limited in its application. Another sometime index of coronary flow, the coefficient of oxygen utilization or oxygen extraction ratio, has been considered by Scott (135). The relationship between the coefficient and coronary flow depended on the level of arterial oxygen saturation. At levels above 20 volumes per cent an increase in the coefficient was associated with reduced flow whereas the opposite obtained at low levels of saturation. At any level of arterial oxygen the index does not appear reliable unless oxygen consumption is also known. A more direct and perhaps eventually more accurate approach to myocardial energetics has been initiated by studies of ventricular heat production and loss. Neill and his colleagues (136) calculated the total net heat production of the ventricle and estimated the fraction removed by coronary perfusion from the coronary flow and venoarterial temperature gradient. The fraction so determined is of course proportional to the coronary flow rate and is sufficiently reproducible to provide an estimate of total heat from that portion of ventricle drained. With sufficient accuracy (not yet obtained) such data provide the basis for exhaustive analysis of myocardial energetics. In a very similar way, Adolph, Pinardi & Rushmer (137) demonstrated changes in coronary heat loss with drug-induced modification of cardiac activity and call attention to the significance of noncoronary avenues of loss.

Huckabee (138) continued his interest in relationships between pyruvate and lactate as indicators of the relative degrees of aerobic and anaerobic processes in tissues. Cardiac "excess lactate" became positive in animals breathing mixtures low in oxygen and in those in whom mild exercise was induced. These data suggest that oxygen delivery was not adequate to meet tissue requirements even during mild stresses, but their functional significance seems to be still in question. Coffman & Gregg (139) examined the question of cardiac oxygen debts in dogs and found that ischemia stimulated coronary flow and myocardial oxygen consumption and that small oxygen debts were incurred and repaid. Following anoxic arrest in the perfused heart of the dog, concentrations of creatine phosphate and ATP decreased. Partial resuscitation restored creatine phosphate levels but ATP fell further and deaminated derivatives of the nucleotide appeared (140). Hypoxia had apparently "wrecked the machinery" for breakdown and resynthesis of ATP.

The effects of numerous drugs and other agents on the coronary bed will not be reviewed. It is perhaps of significance that the response of these vessels to $CaCl_2$, KCl, MgCl, and $MgSO_4$ is similar to that of the vasculature of the dog foreleg (141).

The question of the occurrence of significant intercoronary reflexes has been approached by two groups using newer techniques. West, Kobayashi & Anderson (142) catheterized the left anterior descending and left circumflex coronary arteries and produced selective embolization by the injection of lycopodium spores. Coronary blood flow showed a marked initial decrease followed by a maintained increase, accompanied by an increase in coronary sinus venous oxygen saturation. These findings were supported by selective coronary angiograms which showed marked diminution in the circulation of the embolized vessel and continued reflux into the uncatheterized branches of the coronary system. Neither autonomic blocking agents, surgical denervation of the heart, nor adrenalectomy produced significant changes in the responses noted. It is the interpretation of the authors that the changes noted are the direct effect of mechanical blockage of coronary blood flow by the lycopodium spores and that no evidence of reflex coronary spasm is obtained. On the other hand, Guzman, Swenson & Jones (143), using essentially similar techniques, interpreted the angiographically demonstrable decrease in the size of the coronary vascular bed, together with the considerable delay in the disappearance time of the injected radio-opaque material to be indicative of generalized left coronary vasoconstriction following embolization of a single branch of the artery. In keeping with this interpretation was the observation that to a great extent the prior injection of atropine prevented the described changes. These differences in interpretation obviously indicate the necessity for further study and perhaps serve to emphasize the difficulties of physiologic interpretation made on the basis of angiographic visualizations.

Cross (144), using more conventional techniques of coronary flow in the dog, reported that overdistention of the right ventricle produced a marked reduction in the resistance in both coronary beds. It is suggested that a humorally transmitted agent, produced as a result of tension modification in the ventricular wall, may be involved in the modifications of coronary flow.

Other metabolic aspects.—Green & Goldberger (145) have reviewed the significant features of metabolic pathways in cardiac muscle with emphasis on the importance of the mitochondria. An analogous summary for the case of the intact heart has been provided (146). Particular attention has been paid to cardiac lipid metabolism. Rothlin & Bing (147) found that the extraction of oleic acid by dog or human heart was greater than that of other free fatty acids of the blood. This acid was also released at a greater rate from fat depots of the dog, and cardiac lipoprotein lipase activity may be involved in exchange between plasma and myocardial triglycerides. Williamson & Krebs showed that acetoacetate contributed 70 to 80 per cent of the respiration in the perfused heart of the rat and suppressed glucose oxidation (148). This observation is compatible with the findings of Newsholme and colleagues (149) that oxidation of ketone bodies and fatty acids inhibits the phosphofructokinase reaction in rat heart and may be associated with the accumulation of cardiac glycogen characteristic of diabetes, starvation, and the action of hypophyseal growth hormone. Myocardial extraction of carbohydrate and, accordingly, the respiratory quotient increased during ether anesthesia in dogs (150). Determination of the amino acid sequence of cytochrome C of horse heart by Margoliash *et al.* (151) will allow for comparison with similar enzymes of other mammalian tissues as regards physicochemical and functional similarities. Hanson (152) was unable to find increase in myocardial lactate content in hibernating animals. Moreland (153) noted an increase in myocardial mitochondria in hibernating ground squirrels which was not accompanied by significant change in size and may be related to increased storage of phosphorylating enzymes during this period of modified metabolism. Adaptation to chronic hypoxia may also involve metabolic changes in cardiac mitochondria (154).

HORMONES AND DRUGS

Catecholamines.—Siegel, Gilmore & Sarnoff (155) have provided a detailed analysis of myocardial catecholamine extraction, release, and effect. With the use of a vagotomized dog preparation, provided with a right heart bypass, they were able to determine arterial and coronary venous concentrations of catecholamines and to compare these with simultaneous changes in cardiac dynamics. It is of methodologic significance that values obtained by the ethylenediamine method were inconsistent with those given by the trihydroxindol technique and that only the latter correlated with changes in cardiac dynamics.

Stimulation of cardiac sympathetic efferent nerves was accompanied by a release of catecholamines in coronary blood which was proportional to the intensity of the stimulation. As with substrates of other types, the magnitude of the myocardial catecholamine extraction in the unstimulated state appeared to be a function of the quantity of catecholamines delivered per minute to the myocardium. The pattern of extraction was also modified by the quantity of catecholamines already present. The extracted materials may contribute to the repletion of the store of amines depleted by continued stimulation of sympathetic nerves. The abolition of the cardiac effects of sympathetic stimulation by dichloroisoproterenol is not accompanied by changes in myocardial extraction or release. Data indicated that the direct effect of cardiac sympathetic nerve stimulation is coronary vasoconstriction, the vasodilatation usually observed being traceable to overriding metabolic factors. Glaviano & Coleman (156) compared the myocardial catecholamine content in normal rabbits with that following exposure to three hours at a mean arterial pressure of 50 mm of mercury. Myocardial norepinephrine values declined from 1.05 to 0.16 micrograms per gram. It is suggested that this marked drop may be associated with the recognized myocardial depression in hemorrhagic shock. In the dog, prolonged stimulation of the stellate ganglion produces subendocardial hemorrhages similar to those found with hypotension, elevated intracranial pressure, and the infusion of large quantities of catecholamines (157). The concept that the hemodynamic actions of epinephrine and norepinephrine may be associated with relative myocardial insufficiency is supported by the findings of Barger, Herd & Liebowitz (158). Chronic catheterization of the coronary artery of the dog with intracoronary injection of the catecholamines produced electrocardiographic changes similar to those attributed to subendocardial ischemia in man. No structural changes were noticed even after several months of infusion. Beznak (159) found that subcutaneous injections of isoproterenol resulted in severe histologic changes in the myocardium accompanied by a reduction of functional capacity.

The influence of catecholamines on cardiac phosphorylase activity and formation of adenosine 3',5'-phosphate has been studied by several groups. In general there seems little question but that the functional changes induced by the amines are accompanied by modifications of enzymic activity [LaCroix & Leusen (160); Hess et al. (161); Murad et al. (162)]. The link between such modifications and the functional mechanisms remains speculative. Klarwein et al. (163) found a transient rise in phosphorylase activity succeeded by a fall following cardiac arrhythmias in the dog. Hypoxia was apparently a factor.

Because of the widespread use of autonomic blocking agents as tools for the study of cardiac regulation, it is perhaps timely to note the reminder of Nickerson & Chan (164) and Moran & Perkins (165) that the classical blocking agents of the dibenamine and dibenzyline type do not block the chronotropic and inotropic responses of the heart to epinephrine nor interfere with physiologic response of the heart to adrenergic stimulation.

The reserpine-induced reduction of lipoprotein lipase activity in rat heart slices noted by Dury (166) suggests relationships in an area of catecholamine action not yet clearly defined. Administration of bretylium produces an increase in myocardial contractility accompanied by a release of catecholamines. Sympathetic stimulation after administration of the drug results in no change in contractility nor in the release of amines. The effect comes from blockage of the nerve release mechanism (167).

The question of the interaction between catecholamines and the thyroid hormone in the production of myocardial effects has received some further consideration. Goodkind, Fram & Roberts (168) compared the concentration of myocardial norepinephrine with the level of thyroid activity in the guinea pig. Although there was elevation of amine concentration with excessive degrees of hyperthyroidism, this was not the case with lower levels nor was there good correlation with the level of PBI. Hypothyroidism was associated with reduction in myocardial norepinephrine concentration. Under conditions of changes in temperature or the addition of epinephrine, rates of atrial contraction varied with levels of thyroid activity (169). Pretreatment with reserpine lowered the rates, but values in thyroid-treated animals were still significantly greater than those in controls. The level of thyroid hormone activity was of obviously greater significance than the presence or absence of reserpine. Gans & Mercer (170) report that catecholamines did not induce a high incidence of arrhythmias in hyperthyroid dogs and that although reserpine administration significantly reduced heart rate in such animals, arterial pressure and oxygen consumption were inconsistently modified. These studies cast additional doubt on the firmly entrenched but poorly documented concept that the physiological actions of the thyroid hormone are solely mediated by autonomic catecholamines. Milani (171) noted a stimulatory effect of small doses of thyroxine and triiodothyronine on oxygen consumption of rat atrium *in vitro* which became depressant with higher concentrations.

The effects of dopamine, a biological precursor of epinephrine, have been studied. Conversion of injected material to epinephrine-norepinephrine apparently does not occur in the dog heart since levels of these substances do not change following dopa infusion (172). In the dog heart-lung preparation, Holmes & Fowler (173) noted increase in heart rate at low levels of dopamine and elevation of contractile force, cardiac output, and arterial pressure with higher dosages. Generally similar findings are reported for man by Horwitz, Fox & Goldberg (174), although these workers point out differences in the action of dopamine as compared with epinephrine-norepinephrine.

The complex series of cardiac and circulatory events, during and following the infusion of epinephrine in man, has been carefully studied and analyzed by Allwood and his colleagues (175). Rubinstein (176) found that hypothermia modified the pressor response to vasoactive amines, a finding also reported by Cotton & Cooper (177) who further noted that cardiac glycosides blocked the positive inotropy under these conditions. Catecholamine-containing granules are characteristic of specific cells of the hearts of cyclostome fishes, although the cardiac tissue of these animals is not responsive to these agents (178).

Other agents.—A number of polypeptides have been reported to exert cardiac efforts. In normal human subjects, angiotensin II is ten times as potent as norepinephrine which it resembles in its effect on diastolic arterial pressure, cardiac output, heart rate, and total peripheral resistance (179). In anesthetized dogs, there is a cardioinhibitory action secondary to baroceptor reflexes and a cardioaccelerator effect which seems to be related to efferent cardiac nervous action since the literature indicates that the isolated denervated heart is not accelerated by this agent (180). Peptide preparations of corticotropin and of alpha-intermedin induce a rate increase in the heart-lung preparation of the dog without effect on impulse propagation or the force of the contraction [Krayer *et al.* (181)].

Arrhythmia following insulin hypoglycemia would seem easily understandable (182) but Pareda, Eckstein & Abboud (183) noted a pressor response unrelated to glucose levels and presumably dependent on central nervous system stimulation. Wittels & Hackel (184) found myocardial glucose utilization to be increased following tolbutamide administration. Extraction and utilization of carbohydrate substrates, oxygen, sodium, and potassium were not modified. Khachadurian, Karam & Badeer (185) obtained similar results.

The potentially important question of the role of physiological steroids in cardiac regulation remains clouded. Tanz (186) reported an inotropic action of aldosterone on cat papillary muscle and whole isolated heart which was shared and not antagonized by spirolactone. Rat cardiac muscle does not show such effects, and the inconsistencies and dosage-dependent relationships which characterize the literature in this area demand careful re-evaluation. The presence and possible significance of other substances found in the blood plasma under normal and abnormal conditions and capable of influencing cardiac contractility have been reviewed and discussed by Hajdu & Leonard (187). Particular attention has been paid by these authors to the description, assay, and possible clinical correlations of a described cardioglobulin system (188, 189).

Cardiac glycosides.—The mechanism of the inotropic action of the digitalis drugs remains obscure, but evidence that effects on sodium and potassium transport are not necessarily involved continues to accumulate. Tuttle, Witt & Farah (190) determined the intracellular concentrations of these ions in isolated atria or in the rabbit heart *in situ*. There were no characteristic ionic changes associated with positive inotropism, and potassium concentration only decreased after negative effects had become evident. Attention has now shifted to relationships to calcium and its role in excitation and contraction. Holland & Sekul (191) feel that ouabain acts on calcium-dependent steps early in the excitation-contraction coupling mechanism. In quiescent atria, changes in temperature did not materially affect Ca^{45} entry or resting tension, but Q_{10} values for the influence of ouabain on calcium uptake tension were 6.6

and 4.2 respectively. It would seem, therefore, that the glycoside must influence a mechanism different from that involved in the resting exchange (192).

Schaer (193) has found that the binding of cardiac glycosides to skeletal muscle myosin is on an equimolar basis and that the strength of binding varies between glycosides. Whatever the fundamental process involved, effects of ouabain on contractility and automaticity are not influenced by reserpine pretreatment in the dog and therefore are presumably not dependent on catecholamine release (194). The decrease in cardiac output produced by glycosides in normal dogs is not the result of changes in blood volume (195). The elevated rate of aldosterone excretion in experimental or spontaneous heart failure in dogs was reduced by digitalis if the glycoside improved the hemodynamic situation, but not in the absence of such improvement (196). The evidence clearly favors an indirect influence on steroid regulation. Hypothermia reduced the incidence of arrhythmia produced by toxic doses of ouabain but did not alter the over-all mortality (197).

METHODS, TECHNIQUES, ETC.

The use of cultures of cardiac cells and of embryonic hearts provides opportunity for an additional approach to basic problems. Cunningham, Lunell & Rylander (198) and Paff & Boucek (199) describe methods and techniques for studying electrical and mechanical properties of such preparations. The 72-hr chick embryo heart contains cells which resemble those of the adult conducting system and are relatively resistant to alterations in potassium and calcium ions. Impairment of contractility and S-T segment changes occur with loss of glucose from the medium or with metabolic inhibitors [Boucek & Paff (200)]. Cooling of whole hearts in culture reduces rate with little change in the magnitude of electrical potential (201). Klein (202) correlates changes in specific ATPase activity with changes in sodium content of embryonic ventricle and the possible development of ion-transfer systems. The differentiation of myocardial myofibrils and the onset of contraction is discussed by Rumery, Blandau & Hagey (203). General aspects of myogenesis are discussed by Konigsberg (204).

The year has been characterized by the widespread study and application of the indicator-dilution technique and its variations. Attention is directed particularly to a symposium on the use of indicator-dilution techniques in the study of circulation published in *Circulation Research*, Volume 10 for March 1962 (205). The complete and authoritative coverage provided here should constitute required reading for those contemplating use of the method. In addition to the contents of the symposium, articles have appeared on the factors modifying the contours of the indicator dilution curve (206), comparisons of areas of simultaneously sampled central and peripheral curves (207), consideration of the nature of curves obtained from physical models and physiological systems (208), details of the transport of K^{42}, Na^{24}, and I^{131} by the pulmonary circulation, and the calculation of cardiac output and volume from such dilution curves [Yudilevich (209)]. A single injection cardiac output measurement using Kr^{85} has been described (210) as have other aspects of the cardiac output measurement technique (211 to 214). The detection and measurement of valvular regurgitation have been reported (215, 216).

The cardiac output of rats may be measured by a thermal dilution technique with a transistor bridge (217). Bernstein & Evans (218) have developed a pulse contour formula for stroke volume. New techniques for the continuous recording of cardiovascular functions in unrestrained dogs have been described by Olmsted (219), and Hawthorne & Harvey (220) report the telemetering of ventricular circumference in such animals. Information on reliable miniaturized cardiotachometers for multiple applications is available (221). Beginnings have been made in the application of computer analysis to the electrocardiograph (222, 223). Agress and his colleagues (224) have made further studies on the low-frequency vibrations of the precordium and their relationship to physiologic and cardiodynamic events. The important problem of the determination of the volume of cardiac chambers may be made less formidable by the application of the scanner-computer technique described by Baker, Khalaf & Chapman (225). Detailed analysis of cardiovascular motion is facilitated by a method of high speed cinematography utilizing a dual lens system for simultaneous recording of motion picture and oscillographic frames. The electrocardiogram, pressure pulses, and other hemodynamic parameters can thus be recorded simultaneously with the movements (March & Stephanos (226)]. A test circulation for artificial heart valves (227) and a pressure generator for the testing of catheters and manometers (228) have been developed. Roston (229) provides a mathematical model for a two-chambered cardiovascular system, and Rothe & Selkurt (230) a system model for teaching. The characteristics of a stable heart-lung preparation of the rat are reported (231).

LITERATURE CITED

1. Stenger, R. J., and Spiro, D., *Am. J. Med.*, **30**, 653–65 (1961)
2. Fawcett, D. W., *Circulation*, **24**, 336–48 (1961)
3. Simpson, F. O., and Oertelis, S. J., *J. Cellular Biol.*, **12**, 91–99 (1962)
4. Olson, R. E., *Am. J. Med.*, **30**, 692–707 (1961)
5. Podolsky, R. J., *Am. J. Med.*, **30**, 708–19 (1961)
6. Podolsky, R. J., *Circulation*, **34**, 399–409 (1961)
7. Sonnenblick, E. H., *Am. J. Physiol.*, **202**, 931–39 (1962)
8. Meijler, F. L., van der Bogaard, F., van der Tweel, L. H. and Durrer, D., *Am. J. Physiol.*, **202**, 631–35 (1962)
9. Meijler, F. L., *Am. J. Physiol.* **202**, 636–40 (1962)
10. Kruta, V., and Braveny, P., *Arch. Intern. Physiol.*, **69**, 645–67 (1961)
11. Blinks, J. R., and Koch-Weser, J., *J. Pharmacol. Exptl. Therap.*, **134**, 373–89 (1961)
12. Tuttle, R. S., and Farah, A., *J. Pharmacol. Exptl. Therap.*, **135**, 142–50 (1962)
13. Winegrad, S., *Circulation*, **24**, 523–29 (1961)
14. Winegrad, S., and Shanes, A. M., *J. Gen. Physiol.*, **45**, 371–94 (1962)
15. Nayler, W. G., *Am. J. Physiol.*, **201**, 682–86 (1961)
16. Ebashi, F., and Ebashi, S., *Nature*, **194**, 378–79 (1962)
17. Weber, A., and Winicur, S., *J. Biol. Chem.*, **236**, 3198–202 (1961)
18. Braunwald, E., Frahm, C. J., and

Ross, J., Jr., *J. Clin. Invest.*, **40**, 1882–90 (1961)

19. Gleason, W. L., and Braunwald, E., *Circulation*, **25**, 841–48 (1962)

20. Braunwald, E. and Frahm, C. J., *Circulation*, **24**, 633–42 (1961)

21. Mitchell, J. H., Gilmore, J. P., and Sarnoff, S. J., *Am. J. Cardiol.*, **9**, 237–47 (1962)

22. Guyton, A. C., and Sagawa, K., *Am. J. Physiol.*, **200**, 1157–63 (1961)

23. Hefner, L. L., Coghlan, H. C., Jones, W. B., and Reeves, T. J., *Am. J. Physiol.*, **201**, 97–101 (1961)

24. Milnor, W. R., *Ann. Rev. Physiol.*, **24**, 169–98 (1962)

25. Franklin, D. L., Van Citters, R. L., and Rushmer, R. F., *Circulation Res.*, **10**, 17–26 (1962)

26. Imperial, E. S., Levy, M. N., and Zieske, H., Jr., *Circulation Res.* **9**, 1148–55 (1961)

27. Pieper, H. P., *Circulation Res.*, **10**, 285–94 (1962)

28. Salisbury, P. F., Cross, C. E., and Rieben, P. A., *Circulation Res.*, **10**, 608–23 (1962)

29. Sarnoff, S. J., and Mitchell, J. H., *Am. J. Med.*, **20**, 747–71 (1961)

30. Levine, H. J., Neill, W. A., Wagman, R. J., Krasnow, N., and Gorlin, R., *J. Clin. Invest.*, **41**, 1050–58 (1962)

31. Weissler, A. M., Peeler, R. G., and Roehll, W. H., Jr., *Am. Heart J.*, **62**, 367–78 (1961)

32. Gleason, W. L., and Braunwald, E., *J. Clin. Invest.*, **41**, 80–91 (1962)

33. Spencer, M. P., and Greiss, F. C., *Circulation Res.*, **10**, 274–79 (1962)

34. Holt, J. P., Rhode, E. A., Peoples, S. A., and Kines, H., *Circulation Res.*, **10**, 798–806 (1962)

35. Folse, R., and Braunwald, E., *Circulation*, **25**, 674–85 (1962)

36. Olson, R. E., Ellenbogen, E., and Iyengar, R., *Circulation*, **24**, 471–82 (1961)

37. Alpert, N. R., and Gordon, M. S., *Am. J. Physiol.*, **202**, 940–46 (1962)

38. Furchgott, R. F., and Lee, K. S., *Circulation*, **24**, 416–28 (1961)

39. Schwartz, A., and Lee, K. S., *Circulation Res.*, **10**, 321–32 (1962)

40. Feinstein, M. B., *Circulation Res.*, **10**, 333–46 (1962)

41. Frye, R. L., Kahler, R. L., and Braunwald, E., *Am. Heart J.*, **62**, 301–3 (1961)

42. Meerson, F. Z., *Circulation Res.*, **10**, 250–58 (1962)

43. Wollenberger, A., and Schulze, W., *J. Biophys. Biochem. Cytol.*, **10**, 285–88 (1961)

44. Wollenberger, A., and Schulze, W., *Naturwissenschaften*, **49**, 161–62 (1962)

45. Hearn, G. R., and Gollnick, P. D., *Intern. Z. Angew. Physiol.*, **19**, 23–26 (1961)

46. Gangloff, E. C., Hemmings, I. L., and Krause, R. F., *Am. J. Physiol.*, **201**, 363–64 (1961)

47. Gollnick, P. D., and Hearn, G. R., *Am. J. Physiol.*, **201**, 694–96 (1961)

48. Alexander, N., Goldfarb, T., and Drury, D. R., *Circulation Res.*, **10**, 11–16 (1962)

49. Barger, A. C., Metcalfe, J., Richards, V., and Günther, B., *Am. J. Physiol.*, **201**, 480–83 (1961)

50. Jones, J. J., *J. Physiol. (London)*, **160**, 298–305 (1962)

51. Polosa, C., and Rossi, G., *Am. J. Physiol.*, **200**, 1185–90 (1961)

52. Gowdey, C. W., *Circulation Res.*, **10**, 354–58 (1962)

53. Chien, S., and Billig, S., *Am. J. Physiol.*, **201**, 475–79 (1961)

54. Greenfield, L., Ebert, P. A., and Austen, W. G., *Proc. Soc. Exptl. Biol. Med.*, **107**, 858–61 (1961)

55. Krieger, E. M., *Acta Physiol. Latinoam.*, **11**, 127–34 (1961)

56. Koroxenidis, G. T., Shepherd, J. T., and Marshall, R. J., *J. Appl. Physiol.*, **16**, 869–72 (1961)

57. McGregor, M., Adam, W., and Sekelj, P., *Circulation Res.*, **9**, 1089–92 (1961)

58. Maulsby, R. L., and Hoff, H. E., *Am. J. Physiol.*, **202**, 505–9 (1962)

59. Finlayson, J. K., Luria, M. N., and Yu, P. N., *Circulation Res.*, **9**, 862–68 (1961)

60. Daly, W. J., and Bondurant, S., *J. Clin. Invest.*, **41**, 126–32 (1962)

61. Eggers, G. W. N., Jr., Paley, H. W., Leonard, J. J., and Warren, J. V., *J. Appl. Physiol.*, **17**, 75–79 (1962)

62. Booth, R. W., Ryan, J. M., Mellett, H. C., Swiss, E., and Neth, E., *J. Lab. Clin. Med.*, **59**, 275–85 (1962)

63. Steiner, S. H., and Mueller, G. C. E., *J. Appl. Physiol.*, **16**, 1078–80 (1961)

64. Lindberg, E. F., Marshall, N. W., Sutterer, W. F., McGuire, T. F., and Wood, E. H., *Aerospace Med.*, **33**, 81–91 (1962)

65. Reeves, J. T., Grover, R. F., Will, D. H., and Alexander, A. F., *Circulation Res.*, **10**, 166–71 (1962)

66. Will, D. H., Alexander, A. F., Reeves, J. T., and Grover, R. F., *Circulation Res.*, **10**, 172–77 (1962)
67. Scholander, P. F., Hammel, H. T., LeMessurier, H., Hemmingsen, E., and Garey, W., *J. Appl. Physiol.*, **17**, 184–90 (1962)
68. Anderson, H. T., *Acta Physiol. Scand.*, **53**, 23–45 (1961)
69. di Bartoli, G., Nunez-Day, D., Muiesan, G., MacCanon, D. M., and Luisada, A. A., *Am. J. Physiol.*, **201**, 888–92 (1961)
70. Muiesan, G., MacCanon, D. M., Nunez-Day, D. and di Bartoli, G., *Am. J. Physiol.*, **201**, 1090–94 (1961)
71. Crevasse, L., Wheat, M. W., Wilson, J. R., Leeds, R. F., and Taylor, W. J., *Circulation*, **25**, 635–42 (1962)
72. Sloan, A. W., and Jarvis, J. F., *Am. J. Physiol.*, **202**, 649–52 (1962)
73. Hamlin, R. L., Robinson, F. R., Smith, C. R., and Marsland, W. P., *J. Appl. Physiol.*, **17**, 199–200 (1962)
74. Coghlan, C., Prieto, G., and Harrison, T. R., *Am. Heart. J.*, **62**, 65–82 (1961)
75. Prieto, G., Coghlan, C., and Harrison, T. R., *Am. Heart J.*, **62**, 528–41 (1961)
76. Harrison, T. R., Coghlan, C., and Prieto, G., *Am. Heart J.*, **62**, 804–20 (1961)
77. Wenger, M. A., Bagchi, B. K., and Amand, B. K., *Circulation*, **24**, 1319–25 (1961)
78. Guyton, A. C., and Crowell, J. W., *Federation Proc.*, **20**, Part III Suppl. 9, 51–60 (1961)
79. Chai, C. Y., and Wang, S. C., *Am. J. Physiol.*, **202**, 25–30 (1962)
80. Wang, S. C., and Chai, C. Y., *Am. J. Physiol.*, **202**, 31–34 (1962)
81. Rosen, A., *Acta Physiol. Scand.*, **53**, 255–69 (1961)
82. Rosen, A., *Acta Physiol. Scand.*, **53**, 270–75 (1961)
83. Rosen, A., *Acta Physiol. Scand.*, **52**, 291–308 (1961)
84. Löfving, B., *Acta Physiol. Scand.*, **53**, Suppl., 184 (1961)
85. Stella, G., and Stevan, G., *Arch. Intern. Pharmacodyn.*, **136**, 1–11 (1962)
86. Mack, R. L., Davenport, O. L., and Dykman, R. A., *Am. J. Physiol.*, **201**, 437–39 (1961)
87. O'Brien, L. J., *Am. J. Physiol.*, **201**, 855–57 (1961)
88. Ulmer, R. H., and Randall, W. C., *Am. J. Physiol.*, **201**, 134–38 (1961)
89. Chidsey, C. A., Frye, R. L., Kahler, R. L., and Braunwald, E., *Circulation Res.*, **9**, 989–95 (1961)
90. Eliakim, M., Bellet, S., Tawil, E., and Muller, O., *Circulation Res.*, **9**, 1372–79 (1961)
91. Singh, I., *Arch. Intern. Pharmacodyn.*, **132**, 317–21 (1961)
92. Warner, H. R., and Cox, A., *J. Appl. Physiol.*, **17**, 349–55 (1962)
93. Hauss, W. H., and Kemper, F., *Arch. Intern. Pharmacodyn.*, **132**, 372–77 (1961)
94. Groom, A. C., Lofvking, B. M. A., Rowlands, S., and Thomas, H. W., *Acta Physiol. Scand.*, **54**, 116–27 (1962)
95. Hutter, O. F., and Noble, D., *J. Physiol. (London)*, **157**, 335–50 (1961)
96. Lamb, J. F., *J. Physiol. (London)*, **157**, 415–25 (1961)
97. Trautwein, W., and Kassebaum, D. G., *J. Gen. Physiol.*, **45**, 317–30 (1961)
98. James, T. N., *Anat. Record*, **141**, 109–39 (1961)
99. Rhodin, J. A. G., del Missier, P., and Reid, L. C., *Circulation*, **24**, 349–67 (1961)
100. Wright, E. B., and Ogata, M., *Am. J. Physiol.*, **201**, 1101–8 (1961)
101. Ware, F., *Am. J. Physiol.*, **201**, 1113–19 (1961)
102. Surawicz, B., Lepeschkin, E., and Herrlich, H. C., *Circulation Res.*, **9**, 811–17 (1961)
103. Trautwein, W., Kassebaum, D. G., Nelson, R. M., and Hecht, H. H., *Circulation Res.*, **10**, 306–12 (1962)
104. Weidmann, S., *Circulation*, **24**, 499–505 (1961)
105. Hecht, H. H., *Am. J. Med.*, **30**, 720–46 (1961)
106. Ushiyama, J., and Brooks, C. McC., *Am. J. Physiol.*, **202**, 245–48 (1962)
107. Hoshiko, T., and Sperelakis, N., *Am. J. Physiol.*, **201**, 873–80 (1961)
108. Sperelakis, N., and Hoshiko, T., *Circulation Res.*, **9**, 1280–83 (1961)
109. Joó, F., and Csillik, B., *Nature*, **193**, 1192–93 (1962)
110. James, T. N., *Am. Heart J.*, **62**, 756–71 (1961)
111. DeHaan, R. L., *Circulation*, **24**, 458–70 (1961)
112. Hoffman, B. F., *Circulation*, **24**, 506–17 (1961)
113. Sano, T., Tsuchihashi, H., and Shima-

moto, T., *Circulation Res.*, 9, 1299–304 (1961)

114. West, T. C., and Lande, J. F., *Am. J. Physiol.*, 202, 232–36 (1962)

115. Covino, B. G., and D'Amato, H. E., *Circulation Res.*, 10, 148–55 (1962)

116. Bass, N. M., and Glaviano, V. V., *Am. J. Physiol.*, 201, 109–11 (1961)

117. van Tyn, R. A., and MacLean, L. D., *Am. J. Physiol.*, 201, 457–61 (1961)

118. Szekeres, L., and Vaughan Williams, E. M., *J. Physiol. (London)*, 160, 470–82 (1962)

119. Goodford, P. J., and Vaughan Williams, E. M., *J. Physiol. (London)*, 160, 483–93 (1962)

120. Birnbaum, L., Weiner, A., and Farah, A., *Am. Heart J.*, 63, 676–87 (1962)

121. Smith, G. T., *Am. J. Cardiol.*, 9, 327–41 (1962)

122. Truex, R. C., Nolan, F. G., Truex, R. C., Jr., Schneider, H. P., and Perlmutter, H. I., *Anat. Record*, 141, 325–53 (1961)

123. Levy, M. N., Imperial, E. S., and Zieske, H., Jr., *Circulation Res.*, 9, 1035–43 (1961)

124. Zweens, J., *Cardiologia*, 40, 17–23 (1962)

125. Vasko, J. S., Gutelius, J., and Sabiston, D. C., Jr., *Am. J. Cardiol.*, 8, 379–84 (1961)

126. MacLean, L. D., Hedenstrom, P. H., and Rayner, R. R., *Circulation Res.*, 10, 45–50 (1962)

127. Mena, I., Kattus, A., Greenfield, M. A., and Bennett, L. R., *Circulation Res.*, 9, 911–17 (1961)

128. Hirche, H., and Lochner, W., *Arch. Ges. Physiol.*, 274, 624–32 (1962)

129. Salazar, A. E., *Circulation Res.*, 9, 1351–56 (1961)

130. Feinberg, H., Katz, L. N., and Boyd, E., *Am. J. Physiol.*, 202, 45–52 (1962)

131. Feinberg, H., Boyd, E., and Katz, L. N., *Am. J. Physiol.*, 202, 643–48 (1962)

132. Whalen, W. J., *J. Physiol. (London)*, 157, 1–17 (1961)

133. Messer, J. V., Wagman, R. J., Levine, H. J., Neill, W. A., Krasnow, N., and Gorlin, R., *J. Clin. Invest.*, 41, 725–42 (1962)

134. Elliot, E. C., *Circulation Res.*, 9, 1357–63 (1961)

135. Scott, J. C., *Circulation Res.*, 9, 906–10 (1961)

136. Neill, W. A., Levine, H. J., Wagman, R. J., Messer, J. V., Krasnow, N., and Gorlin, R., *J. Appl. Physiol.*, 16, 883–90 (1961)

137. Adolph, R. J., Pinardi, G., and Rushmer, R. F., *Am. J. Physiol.*, 202, 41–44 (1962)

138. Huckabee, W. E., *Am. J. Physiol.*, 200, 1169–76 (1961)

139. Coffman, J. D., and Gregg, D. E., *Am. J. Physiol.*, 201, 881–87 (1961)

140. Benson, E. S., Evans, G. T., Hallaway, B. E., Phibbs, C., and Freier, E. F., *Am. J. Physiol.*, 201, 687–93 (1961)

141. Scott, J. B., Frohlich, E. D., Hardin, R. A., and Haddy, F. J., *Am. J. Physiol.*, 201, 1095–100 (1961)

142. West, J. W., Kobayashi, T., and Anderson, F. S., *Circulation Res.*, 10, 722–38 (1962)

143. Guzman, S. V., Swenson, E., and Jones, M., *Circulation Res.*, 10, 739–52 (1962)

144. Cross, C. E., *Am. J. Physiol.*, 202, 12–16 (1962)

145. Green, D. E., and Goldberger, R. F., *Am. J. Med.*, 30, 666–77 (1961)

146. Bing, R. J., *Am. J. Med.*, 30, 679–81 (1961)

147. Rothlin, M. E., and Bing, R. J., *J. Clin. Invest.*, 40, 1380–86 (1961)

148. Williamson, J. R., and Krebs, H. A., *Biochem. J.*, 80, 540–47 (1961)

149. Newsholme, E. A., Randle, P. J., and Manchester, K. L., *Nature*, 193, 270–71 (1962)

150. Galla, S. J., Henneman, D. H., Schweizer, H. J., and Vandam, L. D., *Am. J. Physiol.*, 202, 241–44 (1942)

151. Margoliash, E., Smith, E. L., Kreil, G., and Tuppy, H., *Nature*, 192, 1121–27 (1961)

152. Hanson, A., and Johansson, B. W., *Acta Physiol. Scand.*, 53, 137–41 (1961)

153. Moreland, J. E., *Anat. Record*, 142, 155–67 (1962)

154. Strickland, E. H., Ackerman, E., and Anthony, A., *Aerospace Med.*, 32, 746–50 (1961)

155. Siegel, J. H., Gilmore, J. P., and Sarnoff, S. J., *Circulation Res.*, 9, 1336–50 (1961)

156. Glaviano, V. V., and Coleman, B., *Proc. Soc. Exptl. Biol. Med.*, 107, 761–63 (1961)

157. Kaye, M. P., McDonald, R. H., and Randall, W. C., *Circulation Res.*, 9, 1164–70 (1961)

158. Barger, A. C., Herd, J. A., and Liebowitz, M. R., *Proc. Soc. Exptl. Biol. Med.*, 107, 474–77 (1961)

159. Beznak, M., *Can. J. Biochem. Physiol.*, **40**, 25–36 (1962)
160. Lacroix, E., and Leusen, I., *Arch. Intern. Pharmacodyn.*, **133**, 89–100 (1961)
161. Hess, M. E., Shanefield, J., and Haugaard, W., *J. Pharmacol. Exptl. Therap.*, **135**, 181–96 (1962)
162. Murad, F., Chi, Y. M., Rall, T. W., and Sutherland, E. W., *J. Biol. Chem.*, **237**, 1233–38 (1962)
163. Klarwein, M., Kako, K., Chrysohou, A., and Bing, R. J., *Circulation Res.*, **9**, 819–25 (1961)
164. Nickerson, M., and Chan, G. C. M., *J. Pharmacol. Exptl. Therap.*, **133**, 186–91 (1961)
165. Moran, N. C., and Perkins, M. E., *J. Pharmacol. Exptl. Therap.*, **133**, 192–201 (1961)
166. Dury, A., *Proc. Soc. Exptl. Biol. Med.*, **107**, 299–302 (1961)
167. Gilmore, J. P., and Siegel, J. H., *Circulation Res.*, **10**, 347–53 (1962)
168. Goodkind, M. J., Fram, D. H., and Roberts, M., *Am. J. Physiol.*, **201**, 1049–52 (1962)
169. Thier, M. D., Gravenstein, J. S., and Hoffman, R. G., *J. Pharmacol. Exptl. Therap.*, **136**, 133–41 (1962)
170. Gans, J. H., and Mercer, P. F., *Arch. Intern. Pharmacodyn.*, **137**, 179–87 (1962)
171. Milani, M., *Arch. Intern. Pharmacodyn.*, **132**, 392–412 (1961)
172. Wegmann, A., Kako, K., and Chrysohou, A., *Am. J. Physiol.*, **201**, 673–76 (1961)
173. Holmes, J. C., and Fowler, N. O., *Circulation Res.*, **10**, 68–72 (1962)
174. Horwitz, D., Fox, S. M., and Goldberg, L. I., *Circulation Res.*, **10**, 237–43 (1962)
175. Allwood, M. J., Keck, E. W., Marshall R. J., and Shepherd, J. T., *J. Appl. Physiol.*, **17**, 71–74 (1962)
176. Rubinstein, E. H., *Acta Physiol. Latinoam.*, **11**, 30–37 (1961)
177. Cotten, M. de V., and Cooper, T., *J. Pharmacol. Exptl. Therap.*, **136**, 97–106 (1962)
178. Bloom, G., Ostlund, E., von Euler, U. S., Lishajko, F., Ritzen, M., and Adams-Ray, J., *Acta Physiol. Scand.*, **53**, Suppl., 185 (1961)
179. Finnerty, F. A., Jr., *Circulation*, **25**, 255–58 (1962)
180. Nishith, S. D., Davis, L. D., and Youmans, W. B., *Am. J. Physiol.*, **202**, 237–40 (1962)
181. Krayer, O., Astwood, E. B., Waud, D. R., and Alper, M. H., *Proc. Natl. Acad. Sci. US*, **47**, 1227–36 (1961)
182. Leak, D., and Starr, P., *Am. Heart J.*, **63**, 688–91 (1962)
183. Pereda, S. A., Eckstein, J. W., and Abboud, F. M., *Am. J. Physiol.*, **202**, 249–52 (1962)
184. Wittels, B., and Hackel, D. B., *Proc. Soc. Exptl. Biol. Med.*, **107**, 375–77 (1961)
185. Khachadurian, A. K., Karam, J. D., and Badeer, H. S., *Arch. Intern. Pharmacodyn.*, **132**, 42–48 (1961)
186. Tanz, R. D., *J. Pharmacol. Exptl. Therap.*, **135**, 71–78 (1962)
187. Hajdu, S., and Leonard, E., *Circulation*, **24**, 530–36 (1961)
188. Hajdu, S., and Leonard, E., *Circulation Res.*, **9**, 881–90 (1961)
189. Leonard, E., and Hajdu, S., *Circulation Res.*, **9**, 891–96 (1961)
190. Tuttle, R. S., Witt, P. N., and Farah, A., *J. Pharmacol. Exptl. Therap.*, **133**, 281–87 (1961)
191. Holland, W. C., and Sekul, A., *J. Pharmacol. Exptl. Therap.*, **133**, 288–94 (1961)
192. Briggs, A. H., and Holland, W. C., *Am. J. Physiol.*, **202**, 641–42 (1962)
193. Schaer, H., *Cardiologia*, **40**, 48–60 (1962)
194. Yelnovsky, J., and Ervin, R., *Am. Heart J.*, **62**, 687–89 (1961)
195. Cotten, M. de V., and Williams, B. J., *Am. J. Physiol.* **201**, 112–16 (1961)
196. Carpenter, C. C. J., Davis, J. O., Wallace, C. R., and Hamilton, W. F., *Circulation Res.*, **10**, 178–87 (1962)
197. Angelakos, E. T., and Hurwitz, H. I., *Circulation Res.*, **9**, 1144–47 (1961)
198. Cunningham, A. W. B., Lunell, N. O., and Rylander, B. J., *Acta Physiol. Scand.*, **52**, 101–7 (1961)
199. Paff, G. H., and Boucek, R. J., *Anat. Record*, **142**, 73–79 (1962)
200. Boucek, R. J., and Paff, G. H., *Am. J. Physiol.*, **201**, 668–72 (1961)
201. Cunningham, A. W. B., Lunell, N. O., and Rylander, B. J., *J. Cellular Comp. Physiol.*, **58**, 169–73 (1961)
202. Klein, R. L., *Am. J. Physiol.*, **201**, 858–62 (1961)
203. Rumery, R. E., Blandau, R. J., and Hagey, P. W., *Anat. Record*, **141**, 253–61 (1961)
204. Konigsberg, I. R., *Circulation*, **24**, 447–57 (1961)
205. Symposium, *Circulation Res.*, **10**, 377–581 (1962)
206. Marshall, R. J., *Circulation Res.*, **10**, 123–30 (1962)

207. Bassingthwaighte, J. B., Edwards, A. W. T., and Wood, E. H., *J. Appl. Physiol.*, **17**, 91–98 (1962)

208. Sheppard, C. W., Jones, M. P., and Murphree, E. L., *Circulation Res.*, **9**, 936–44 (1961)

209. Yudilevich, D., *Circulation Res.*, **9**, 925–35 (1961)

210. Cornell, W. P., Braunwald, E., and Brockenbrough, E. C., *Circulation Res.*, **9**, 984–88 (1961)

211. McGregor, M., Sekelj, P., and Adam, W., *Circulation Res.*, **9**, 1083–88 (1961)

212. Miller, D. E., Gleason, W. L., and McIntosh, H. D., *J. Lab. Clin. Med.*, **59**, 345–59 (1962)

213. Thorburn, G. D., *J. Appl. Physiol.*, **16**, 891–95 (1961)

214. Hansen, J. T., and Pace, N., *J. Appl. Physiol.*, **17**, 163–66 (1962)

215. Newcombe, C. P., Sinclair, J. D., Donald, D. E., and Wood, E. H., *Circulation Res.*, **9**, 1196–207 (1961)

216. Levison, W. H., Jackson, W. D., Sherman, H., and McGuire, L. B., *Circulation Res.*, **9**, 1109–25 (1961)

217. Richardson, A. W., Cooper, T., and Pinakatt, T., *Science*, **135**, 317 (1962)

218. Bernstein, E. F., and Evans, R. L., *Am. J. Physiol.*, **202**, 622–30 (1962)

219. Olmsted, F., *J. Appl. Physiol.*, **17**, 152–56 (1962)

220. Hawthorne, E. W., and Harvey, E., *J. Appl. Physiol.*, **16**, 1124–25 (1961)

221. Kahn, A. R., *J. Appl. Physiol.*, **16**, 902–5 (1961)

222. Rikli, A. E., Tolles, W. E., Steinberg, C. A., Carbery, W. J., Freiman, A. H., Abraham, S., and Caceres, C. A., *Circulation*, **24**, 643–49 (1961)

223. Caceres, C. A., Steinberg, C. A., Abraham, S., Carbery, W. J., McBride, J. M., Tolles, W. E., and Rikli, A. E., *Circulation*, **25**, 356–62 (1962)

224. Agress, C. M., Fields, L. G., Wagner, S., Wilburne, M., Shickman, M. D., and Muller, R. M., *Am. J. Cardiol.*, **8**, 22–31 (1961)

225. Baker, O., Khalaf, J., and Chapman, C. B., *Am. Heart J.*, **62**, 797–803 (1961)

226. March, H. W., and Stephanos, S. P., *Am. Heart J.*, **62**, 652–58 (1961)

227. Seidel, W., and Kolff, W. J., *J. Appl. Physiol.*, **16**, 906–8 (1961)

228. Vierhout, R. R., and Vendrik, A. J. H., *J. Lab. Clin. Med.*, **58**, 330–33 (1961)

229. Roston, S., *Ann. N. Y. Acad. Sci.*, **96**, 962–74 (1962)

230. Rothe, C. F., and Selkurt, E. E., *J. Appl. Physiol.*, **17**, 156–58 (1962)

231. Tedingham, J. M., *Circulation Res.*, **9**, 1255–67 (1961)

REPRODUCTION[1,2]

By Claude A. Villee and Dorothy B. Villee

Harvard Medical School, Boston, Massachusetts

A major event in the field of reproductive physiology in 1961–1962 was the appearance of the long awaited third edition of *Sex and Internal Secretions*, edited by Young (1). This two-volume work is an excellent broad survey of present knowledge and current problems in reproductive physiology. The two-volume monograph on the ovary, edited by Zuckerman (2), and *The Mammalian Egg*, edited by Austin (3), provide excellent general discussions of maturation, fertilization, and cleavage. The chemical properties, biosynthesis, and methods of assay of sex hormones, together with average values for their amounts in normal and in certain disease states, primarily human, are summarized in the monograph edited by Gray & Bacharach (4). Several symposia dealing with reproductive physiology were published. These include *Progress in Comparative Endocrinology* (5), the VIIth International Conference of the Society of Geographic Pathology (6), which contains a general review of both the anatomical and functional aspects of eclampsia, and a symposium on the effects of progestational agents (7), which includes ten papers on the clinical aspects of the effects of progestins on vaginal epithelium and vaginal smears. The 1961 Laurentian Hormone Conference (8) contains several papers dealing with the metabolism and mechanism of action of sex steroids.

Hypothalamic and Hypophyseal Control of the Reproductive Tract

The role of the hypothalamus in the production and release of gonadotropins was reviewed by Hansel (9). There seems little doubt that the hypothalamus influences gonadotropin release and lactation, though the exact site of the regulating center(s) is incompletely known and may vary with the species. In the hypophysectomized male rat, stereotaxic implantation of neonatal pituitary glands on the floor of the hypothalamus near the supraopticohypophyseal tract resulted in enlarged testes and spermatogenesis, indicating FSH production (10). Implants elsewhere in the brain were viable but had no effect on the testis. Implantation into various hypothalamic regions produced no evidence of TSH or ACTH activity.

McCann (11) injected extracts of the stalk-median eminence region of rat brain into immature rats pretreated with gonadotropin. Depletion of ovarian

---

[1] The survey of literature pertaining to this review was completed in June 1962.

[2] The abbreviations used in this article include: ACTH (adrenocorticotropic hormone); ADH (antidiuretic hormone); DPN, DPNH (oxidized and reduced forms of diphosphopyridine nucleotide); FSH (follicle-stimulating hormone); ICSH (interstitial cell-stimulating hormone); LH (luteinizing hormone); LTH (luteotropic hormone); TPN, TPNH (oxidized and reduced forms of triphosphopyridine nucleotide).

ascorbic acid occurred, demonstrating that an LH-releasing factor was present in the extract. From experiments with precisely placed electrolytic lesions, Desclin *et al.* (12, 13) concluded that there are two regions of the hypothalamus which control the release of LH. The anterior region is responsible for the cyclic discharge of LH whereas the posterior one governs a continuous release of LH. The activity of the latter is decreased by estrogens. This gonadotropin-inhibiting action of estrogens is demonstrated clearly by Davidson & Sawyer (14) who implanted minute amounts of estradiol benzoate into the posterior median eminence-basal tuberal region of the hypothalamus, an area which regulates gonadotropin release in the rabbit. Rabbits so treated did not ovulate in response to copulation and eventually underwent ovarian atrophy. When estradiol benzoate was implanted into the pituitary, the mammillary body, or other parts of the brain, no such results were obtained. Van Rees *et al.* (15) produced prolonged estrus in rats by placing basal lesions in the anterior hypothalamus. The uterus had the weight of normal rats in estrus but the size of the pituitary gland increased markedly over normal. The pituitary glands of these rats had a very high content of ICSH but the serum had a low level (16). This suggests that the hypothalamic lesion blocks the release of ICSH but not its storage in the pituitary.

The role of the hypothalamus in initiating milk secretion in the rabbit was found by Haun & Sawyer (17) to be localized in the region of the arcuate nucleus and the base of the ventral medial nucleus. Lesions in these regions initiated or enhanced milk secretion, indicating a release of prolactin. This same region had been shown to be essential for the release of the pituitary ovulating hormone; this observation supports the concept that the hypothalamohypophyseal mechanism which stimulates release of gonadotropins simultaneously inhibits the release of prolactin. The authors feel that during lactogenesis in the rabbit the pituitary may liberate prolactin as a consequence of suppression of the release of gonadotropin. Lactation in the cat is suppressed and the mammary glands undergo involution if lesions are made in the rostral mesencephalon or caudal hypothalamus (18). This apparently interrupts the pathway for prolactin secretion. Control lesions in other parts of the brain had no effect. In the rat, lactation can be severely impaired by electrolytic lesions in the median eminence of the hypothalamic tuber cinereum, apparently because such lesions block release of ACTH (19). Milk secretion in the rat requires ACTH for milk synthesis and oxytocin for milk ejection. When rats with lesions in the median eminence were given oxytocin to permit milk ejection, the severity of the impairment in lactation was correlated with the degree of atrophy of the adrenal glands. This impairment was improved by the administration of cortisol but not by LTH. Adrenalectomized mice require 100 μg cortisol daily for normal lactation (20).

Normal or hypophysectomized rats with bilateral lesions of the ventral medial nucleus of the mammillary body were injected with ADH, oxytocin, 5-hydroxytryptamine, or epinephrine through a cannula in the third ventricle (21). The lesioned controls remained sexually retarded but the oxytocin-treated animals had sexual development. Hypophysectomized animals did not respond to any treatment. Thus, it is inferred that oxytocin, which is elaborated by the hypothalamus, directly activates the hypophysis to cause the production and release of gonadotropins, but has no direct effect on the gonads.

GONADOTROPINS

Using the weights of testes and prostates of immature, hypophysectomized rats, Taymore (22) estimated the relative amounts of FSH and ICSH in urines from women in the follicular phase and in midcycle. These studies indicate a qualitative difference in urinary gonadotropin secretion in the two phases of the cycle. The urinary gonadotropins of normal men and women have similar FSH:LH ratios but those of eunuchs have an FSH:LH ratio twice as great as normal males or females (23).

Mixtures of FSH and LH (optimal ratio 80:20) can affect uterine weight in immature mice (24), but such effects probably are secondary to effects on the gonads. Miyake (25) demonstrated that gonadectomy induces gonadotropic hypersecretion in parabiotic rats, and that estradiol is more active than androgens in inhibiting gonadotropin production in either male or female pituitaries. The biosynthesis of progesterone *in vitro* in the corpus luteum of the cow is stimulated by adding gonadotropins of pituitary or urinary origin (26). In contrast, ACTH or albumin had no effect.

The purification and properties of gonadotropins from urine and pituitary glands were compared by Butt, Crooke & Cunningham (27). Purification by column chromatography gave two fractions, one of which had mainly FSH activity and the other primarily ICSH activity. Antibodies developed against similar fractions, when tested *in vivo*, were found to inhibit both the urinary human menopausal gonadotropin and the pituitary gonadotropin but to be ineffective against HCG. Pituitary gonadotropin from the urine of post-menopausal women was purified 35-fold with no change in the ratio of FSH to LH activity (28). Pure PMS gonadotropin was shown to be 30 per cent protein, with a high percentage of cystine, proline, serine, and threonine; 50 per cent consisted of carbohydrate (29).

Soffer *et al.* have found a substance in urine of normal children (30) and adults (31) which prevents the effect of HCG on mouse uterine weight but does not inhibit the mouse uterine response to estrone.

Follicle-stimulating hormone.—Further purification of sheep FSH (32) and human FSH has been reported. Extensive immunologic studies (33) have been performed on an FSH fraction from human pituitary glands. Antiserum to HCG is relatively ineffective against this fraction, while antiserum to the FSH fraction is effective against human pituitary gonadotropin and meno-pausal urine gonadotropin but is ineffective against HCG.

Single injections of human pituitary FSH with or without subsequent HCG increased urinary excretion of estrogens in amenorrheic women, according to Johannisson, Gemzell & Diczfalusy (34). When HCG was administered 48 hours after the FSH there was an additional increase in the urinary estrogen output, attributable to corpus luteum activity, and a concomitant increased excretion of pregnanediol. Effects of the FSH on the cells and vaginal smears were evident within one to three days after treatment. Administration of bovine FSH to women during the proliferative or secretory phase of the cycle led to a significant increase in urinary estrogens in six of ten patients. The others showed a significant decrease in estrogen output when the FSH was stopped (35).

Just as FSH appears to influence estrogen appearance, so the estrogens exert an effect on the release and possibly the production of FSH. Beyler & Potts (36) found that the FSH content of male rat pituitaries is decreased when estradiol is administered *in vivo*. Injection of testosterone (or progesterone) at the same time prevents the estradiol effect, suggesting that the interplay of gonadal hormone action is at the pituitary level. Pituitaries grafted under the kidney capsule rapidly lose their FSH (37) but the decrease is counteracted by the injection of testosterone (or progesterone). Estradiol counteracts the effect of testosterone. This suggests that the production of FSH in the pituitary is regulated by hypothalamic influences but the release of the hormone is regulated by direct action of the steroid sex hormones on the pituitary. In agreement with this concept is Rothchild's (38) evidence that progesterone inhibits only the release not the formation of FSH and LH. Injections of FSH and HCG decrease the level of rat ovarian proteinases which are active at acid pH but increase levels of proteinases active at alkaline pH (39); FSH alone was effective but HCG alone was ineffective.

Luteinizing hormone.—Assays by the ovarian ascorbic acid depletion method revealed that the pituitaries of three infants and one child had small but definite amounts of LH. The average value for 28 adults was 2.86 mg per g wet wt; the amount was highest in postmenopausal women (40). The ovarian ascorbic acid depletion method for LH has been critically assessed by Schmidt-Elmendorff & Lorraine (41), who conclude that the method is sensitive and specific but has a rather low level of precision. Some progress has been made in determining the chemical composition of LH. Luteinizing hormone activity in material prepared from sheep pituitaries was found to be associated with a glycoprotein (42) which behaves as a single substance on chromatographic and electrophoretic analysis. Its amino acid composition resembles that of TSH and they have similar molecular weights, but their activities can be separated on starch gel electrophoresis.

The secretion of LH is induced by the injection of vasopressin or epinephrine but not by other drugs tested or by stressful procedures (43). Although no LH activity is detectable by the ovarian ascorbic acid method in 0.5 ml serum of normal female rats, it becomes detectable in the same amount of serum from rats two weeks after castration, and high titers of plasma LH are observed in female animals that have been castrated for more than 12 months. No LH is detectable in castrate rats treated with progesterone. Using the ovarian ascorbic acid depletion assay, McCann & Taleisnik (44) found detectable amounts of LH in the plasma of ovariectomized rats. The LH activity of ovariectomized rat plasma was decreased within a day by a single subcutaneous injection of estradiol. This furthers the conclusion that estradiol acts by way of a negative feedback on the LH-controlling areas.

A single injection of testosterone propionate to prepubertal female rats caused permanent sterility and persistent estrus. Electrical stimulation of the median eminence of the hypothalamus of such rats failed to cause ovulation but produced ovulation in the normal animal. The rats given testosterone propionate apparently had insufficient LH in the pituitary to respond to the electrical stimulation (45). The pituitary of the androgen sterilized rat had only one third the normal LH content. Progesterone priming of the sterile rat caused a 75 per cent increase in its LH content, and subsequent hypothalamic stimulation caused ovulation. Ovulation was accompanied by a decrease in the pituitary LH content to about half of its pre-stimulation level. Progesterone injected into rats caused some decrease in plasma LH as measured by ovarian ascorbic acid depletion (46). Pretreatment with estrogen sensitized the rats and progesterone administration caused a much greater decrease in plasma LH activity.

Armstrong & Greep (47) observed that the addition of purified LH *in vivo* stimulates the uptake of glucose by slices of luteinized rat ovaries but not of other tissues. Neither FSH nor prolactin had this effect. Carbons one and six of glucose are metabolized to CO_2 and lipid at the same rate in both control and LH-stimulated ovaries. The stimulation of glucose uptake by LH closely parallels the rate at which ascorbic acid depletion of the ovary occurs.

Interstitial cell-stimulating hormone.—To study the role of the testis in release of pituitary gonadotropins, groups of normal, cryptorchid, and castrate adult rats were joined parabiotically to immature male or female rats for a period of seven days (48). There was no appreciable release of gonadotropin during the short period of parabiosis in normal rats. The spermatogenic epithelium appears to liberate a hormone which inhibits the release of FSH whereas the interstitial cells liberate a hormone which inhibits the release of ICSH. Release of the gonadotropin which causes luteinization of the granulosa cells is not activated by cryptorchidism or castration. The authors conclude that this gonadotropin is different from the one responsible for stimulation of growth and functional activity of the Leydig cells and believe that the term LH should be confined to the former and ICSH to the latter. In contrast, LH preparations of nonprimate (sheep and horse) as well as of primate origin (human pituitary and placenta) were found to stimulate the interstitial cells of Leydig in hypophysectomized male rhesus monkeys (49). Thus, there is no species specificity for LH as there is for growth hormone. Woods & Simpson (50) studied the effects of purified sheep FSH and ICSH on the maintenance and repair of the reproductive system of hypophysectomized male rats.

Treatment with estradiol benzoate increases the ICSH content of the pituitary of female, but not male, castrates (51). Higher doses decrease the

ICSH content of the pituitary of both male and female castrates. Estrogen appears to depress the production of ICSH and inhibit its release in the male. A few studies have been done on the effects of ICSH on the metabolism of the testis. Gunn, Gould & Anderson (52) found that the capacity of the rat testis to take up administered Zn^{65} is markedly depressed below control levels in rats 11 days following hypophysectomy, even though microscopically there was only slight decrease in the number of germinal epithelial and interstitial elements. When ICSH (5 μg per day) was administered from the fifth to the tenth postoperative days, it prevented this effect on Zn^{65} uptake; FSH was less effective and the preparation may have been contaminated with ICSH. Growth hormone and prolactin were ineffective. Hall & Eik-Nes (53) were unable to demonstrate an effect of ICSH *in vitro* upon the permeability of rabbit testicular cells to D-xylose-1-C^{14} and to α-aminoisobutyric acid-1-C^{14} under the same conditions which had previously revealed an effect of the hormone on the incorporation of acetate-1-C^{14} into testosterone. Thus, it would appear that the hormone effect is not primarily on transport across the cell membrane.

Prolactin.—On the twelfth day of pregnancy, rats were subjected to removal of either the anterior pituitary lobe or the entire pituitary, and given prolactin and ACTH from parturition to the tenth day of lactation (54). Those animals with anterior lobectomies showed 53 per cent of normal lactational performance, whereas complete removal of the pituitary reduced the performance to 43 per cent of normal. The milk ejection reflex was completely restored in the anterior lobectomized animals by the time of parturition but the hypophysectomized rats required an additional two days of treatment. The experiments confirm observations that prolactin and ACTH are important factors in the maintenance of milk secretion in the rat. Anterior pituitaries from adult female rats were cultured for six or seven days by the watchglass technique (55). The medium was then assayed by the pigeon-crop method and found to show prolactin activity of 0.1 I.U. per day per pituitary. The addition of 0.5 μg of estradiol increased prolactin production *in vitro* an average of 45 per cent above the control; hence, estradiol can act directly on the pituitary, and prolactin does not need neurohypophyseal stimulation. Neither oxytocin nor vasopressin influenced the rate of prolactin production of rat anterior pituitary tissues *in vitro*. The explants synthesize each day ten times the amount of prolactin present at the beginning of the culture (56).

Previous attempts to purify and characterize sheep prolactin have shown a mixture of three electrophoretic components of about equal crop-sac stimulating activity. Reisfeld *et al.* (57) fractionated sheep pituitary glands by diethylaminoethyl cellulose columns and found a major component of prolactin with markedly greater biological activity than that of the accompanying substances. This component, which appears to be homogeneous by electrophoresis and ultracentrifugation, exhibits a significant growth-hormonelike activity in causing in female rats an increase in body weight which has reached a plateau, and a rise in plasma nonesterified fatty acids.

Damm and co-workers (58) showed that intradermal injection of lacto-genic hormone over one side of the crop-sac of the pigeon produced an ipsi-lateral stimulation of P^{32} uptake by the crop-sac. They suggested the use of this effect as an index of lactogenic hormone.

CONTROL OF OVULATION

The sixth in a series of articles reviewing the endocrine induction of hu-man ovulation concerns itself primarily with the gonadotropins (59). It is clear that the human ovary is responsive to sheep pituitary gonadotropin and ovulation can be induced in a relatively large number of cases (60). Ovulation in the monkey was induced by treating with human urinary gonadotropins (61). Multiple ovulation was induced by the use of human postmenopausal gonadotropin. Luteinization of the ovary could then be produced by administering HCG. Gemzell (62) reports that purified hu-man pituitary FSH administered to women who had been treated for several months with HCG but had not ovulated caused ovulation when given at the level of 5 to 10 mg per day for 8 to 10 days. This treatment causes an enlarge-ment of the ovaries and an increased secretion rate of estrogens. Multiple ovulations ensued and fraternal twins resulted in two women treated. In the ewe, the average number of offspring born can be substantially increased (twin births increased) by treatment with PMS (63). During the ovulatory period in the ewe there is a marked drop in both FSH and LH in the pituitary gland (64). Extracts of bovine or rat median eminence, infused intrapitui-tarily, produced immediate ovulation in most of the rats treated (65); this suggests that the extract contains some substance involved in the release of the ovulating hormone from the rat pituitary. Purshottam, Mason & Pincus (66) describe an assay for ovulation-inhibiting substances. Mice that are superovulated by PMS followed by HCG are used; the substances to be tested are injected along with the HCG, and the ova in the oviduct 20 hours after the injection are counted. Progesterone completely inhibits ovulation as do several tranquilizers such as chlorpromazine.

HORMONAL EFFECTS ON UTERUS AND VAGINA

A review by Gross (67) of biochemical changes in the reproductive cycle summarizes the changes in the levels of the enzymes in various reproductive tract tissues. Gross proposes that anaerobic mechanisms play an important role in the maintenance of sperm viability and in the fertilization process itself.

The carbonic anhydrase activity of uteri is maximal at early estrus and minimal at diestrus in the mouse. The rat uterus shows the reverse. Estradiol, but not progesterone, restores the level to normal in ovariectomized rats (68). Progesterone inhibits the estrogenic effect in ovariectomized or immature mice. The uteri of mice have a high level of carbonic anhydrase (69). This level is increased during estrus or by administered estrogen; the latter effect is counteracted by progesterone. Histamine dihydrochloride administered intravaginally, like estrone, increased the rate of tetrazolium reduction and caused epithelial growth and cornification. However, massive doses were required, and the ineffectiveness of histamine releasers and of antihistaminics indicates that histamine release is not involved in the response of the vagina to estrogens (70).

Peptidase activity in uterine fluid and in homogenates of uterine tissue varies with the estrous cycle, reaching a peak at proestrus and estrus (71). The highest values in rat uterine homogenates and rabbit endometrial homogenates were found during pseudopregnancy, with the peak at implantation.

Cortisone, but not corticotropin, increases the glycogen content of both endometrial and myometrial cells of the rabbit. The percentage increase is twice as large in rabbits treated with estradiol, which suggests some interaction of cortisone and estradiol (72). The uterine glycogen content is doubled by administering estrogen but is unaffected by insulin (73); the reverse holds true for muscle, heart, and liver. The location of β-glucuronidase in vaginal cells changes during the cycle; in diestrus the greatest activity is in the superficial layer of the epithelium and in succeeding stages it is most intense in the germinal layer (74).

Evidence is mounting that the uterus has some hormonal influence on the ovary. Hysterectomy on the fifth day of the luteal phase in the guinea pig inhibited the estrous cycle for eight months, during which corpora lutea persisted (75). Hysterectomy on the tenth day of the luteal phase caused the corpora lutea to enlarge as in pregnancy and to persist for a period equal to that of gestation. Perry & Rowlands (76) found that the normal periodicity of the estrous cycle of rats is not permanently altered by hysterectomy. Hysterectomy performed during or shortly after estrus caused a variable prolongation of the diestrous interval. Subtotal hysterectomy in gilts led to a decreased concentration of progesterone in the corpus luteum for a prolonged period (77). Evidence that the endometrium may produce a luteolytic substance which causes involution of the corpora lutea was obtained by Butcher et al. (78).

Testosterone administered to spayed ewes induced behavioral estrus, apparently by some direct effect on the central nervous system and not as a precursor of estradiol, for the vaginal smears showed no estradiol effect (79). The amount of free progestin in mouse plasma varies from 0.5 units per ml in diestrus to 4 units per ml during estrus (80). Houssay & Blumenkrantz (81) observed a cyclic variation in the amount and quality of the mucoprotein in the serum and aqueous humor of the rat during the cycle, with the lowest content at estrus. Zarrow & Yochim (82) developed a method to measure in vitro the dilatability and tensile strength of the uterine cervix of the rat during estrous cycle and gestation. These increased through gestation and were maximal at parturition, decreasing to nonpregnant levels 48 hours post partum. Lutwak-Mann (83) presented values for the glucose, bicarbonate, lactate, fructose, and citric acid content of uterine and cervical fluids in the rabbit.

TESTIS AND SPERMATOGENESIS

The oxygen consumption of rat testicular tissue is related to the levels of the pituitary gonadotropins (84). This appears to depend primarily on the response of the Leydig cells to gonadotropins. Mongrel dogs infused with acetate-1-C^{14} were cannulated in the spermatic vein, HCG was injected, and the testes fractionated and analyzed. The specific activity of testosterone was doubled by HCG injection in animals where the output of steroids was already high and was not increased. Thus the effect of the HCG must be on some step in the biosynthesis of testosterone which precedes the rate-limiting step (85). Placing rat testes in warm water (44°) for 20 minutes led to a temporary suppression of spermatogenesis with histologic evidence of damage to the seminiferous epithelium (86). Guinea pig testicular cells grown *in vitro* showed spermatocytogenesis and possible spermiogenesis (87). The coiled internal spermatic artery of the ram serves as an efficient heat exchange system which keeps the temperature deep in the testis remarkably close to that inside the scrotal skin [Waites & Moule (88)]. Further useful contributions have been made to the following topics: composition of prostatic fluid (89, 90); effects of temperature and centrifugation on sperm viability (91, 92); chemical characteristics of semen and sperm (93, 94, 97, 98); sperm motility (95, 96, 99); male hypogonadism (100).

ANTIFERTILITY AND ANABOLIC AGENTS

The several methods of interfering with the reproductive process in man have been reviewed by Nelson (101) and by Parkes (102, 103) and the role of studies with inhibitors in our understanding of the mechanism of fertilization were summarized by Metz (104). The clinical problems of the use of progestins as oral contraceptives have been discussed (105, 106). Clinical trials have shown that 17α-ethinyl-$\Delta^5(10)$-estrenolone (107); 17α-ethinyl-19-nortestosterone (108); 17α-methyl-19-nortestosterone, 17α-ethinyl-17β-hydroxy-4-estrene (109); and 17α-allyl-17β-hydroxy-4-estrene (110) are effective oral contraceptives. The binding of aldosterone to plasma proteins is similar in pregnant and nonpregnant women but is increased in the plasma of women treated with 17α-ethinyl-$\Delta^5(10)$-estrenolone (111).

Elton & Nutting (112) observed that 17α-ethinyl-4-estrene-3,17-diol diacetate is more potent than progesterone in producing proliferation of uterine epithelium in rabbits and is estrogenic according to the mouse uterine growth assay and the rat vaginal smear assay but is an estrogen antagonist when administered with estrone. Enol etherification reduces the antifertility effects of 6α-methyl-17α-acetoxyprogesterone but strongly enhances the antifertility effects of 17α-ethinyl-19-nortestosterone acetate in rats (113). Also, 17α-acetoxyprogesterone cyclopentyl enol ether has strong progestational effects and maintains pregnancy in spayed rabbits but fails to interfere with estrus, mating, or ovulation. It does not impair gonadotropic pituitary function and has no masculinizing action on the external genitalia of the fetuses. Thus progestational compounds may have little or no effect in inhibiting ovulation (114). The cyclopentyl ethers of 17α-ethinylestradiol and 17α-methylestradiol appear to be the most potent oral estrogenic agents yet described (115). A comparison of the physiologic properties of certain heterocyclic steroids led to the conclusion that the degree of unsaturation alters the magnitude but not the kind of hormonal activity of the parent compound (116).

It was found that 17-methyl-androstan-17ol-3-one has protein anabolic actions in man which are not as potent as those of testosterone but it is less highly virilizing (117). The androgenic effects of progestational compounds were tested by measuring the degree of masculinization of female fetuses in rats. Neither progesterone nor 6-dehydroretroprogesterone produced malformations, while a variety of other testosterone derivatives all produced masculinization of the female fetuses (118). Clinical studies of oxymetholone showed that it has anabolic effects, causing nitrogen retention without sodium or fluid retention, and is not androgenic (119). The anabolic, androgenic, and antigonadotropic properties of synthetic 19-nortestosterone analogues were assessed in parabiotic rats; all but 17α-propyl-19-nortestosterone produced significant increases in seminal vesicle weights. Testosterone and 17α-ethyl-19-nortestosterone were the most effective anabolic agents. Increasing or decreasing the length of the two-carbon side chain at the 17α position decreased both the anabolic:androgenic ratio and the ability of the compound to inhibit the hypersecretion of pituitary gonadotropins. The antigonadotropic activity was decreased by the addition of a double bond but was increased by the introduction of a third bond and was maximal with the ethinyl configuration. No compound was as active as testosterone itself in inhibiting ovarian growth (120). Mirestrol is strongly estrogenic and inhibits pituitary function (121).

OVARY AND FEMALE REPRODUCTIVE TRACT

The human ovum undergoes several metabolic alterations which are detectable by histochemical means during its life history (122). A study of the development of the ovary showed that its surface epithelium is not a germinal epithelium. Germ cells migrate to the medial slope of the mesonephric ridge by the eighth week of intrauterine life: proliferation occurs until the twentieth week and then diminishes and stops at birth. Histochemical maturation of the ova begins at about the fifteenth week (123). Irradiating ovaries of adult female rats caused no immediate irregularity in vaginal cycles but the cycles disappeared at progressively earlier times with the heavier doses (124). There is no change in the activity of several dehydrogenases in the human ovary during the menstrual cycle (125). Minced human ovary converted progesterone to 16α-hydroxyprogesterone; Stein-Levinthal ovaries may have greater 16α-hydroxylase activity than normal ovaries (126). Estrone inhibited the growth *in vitro* of theca cells but stimulated the growth of corpus luteum fragments from rats in diestrus. Progesterone inhibited the growth of theca cells from follicles in estrus. Gonadotropins as well as steroid hormones may inhibit or stimulate directly the growth of certain ovarian cells (127). Thyroidectomy in rabbits brought about enlarged polycystic ovaries containing giant follicles (128).

A dose response relationship was demonstrated between ovarian weight and injected estrogen in hypophysectomized immature rats (129). The increased weight was largely caused by the proliferation of granulosa cells which resulted in many solid follicles. Histochemical studies of the localization of phosphorylase and certain oxidative enzymes in the human ovary showed some relevance to the sites of hormone production (130). The concentration of estrogens, especially estriol, in the ovary increased greatly in pregnancy. The amounts found were 1.4 μg per g in normal ovaries, 2.6 in Stein-Levinthal ovaries, and 9.8 μg per g in ovaries during pregnancy (131). The corpora lutea of several mammalian species were found to be rich in a variety of glycosidases. In contrast, the activity of these enzymes in the follicular fluid was usually negligible (132). The secretion in control dogs of 0.71 μg progesterone per ovary per minute was increased three- to fourfold by repeated intramuscular doses of HCG. Little or no progesterone was found in the blood from ovaries lacking corpus luteum tissues (133). The concentration of progesterone and 20β-hydroxy-4-pregnene-3-one in the ovary of the cow was found to be 29 μg per g on day 8 and 47 μg per g on day 16. Two-hour incubation led to an increase of 46 and 53 μg progesterone, respectively, on days 8 and 16. There was no progesterone nor 20β-hydroxy-4-pregnene-3-one in placental fluids and only a trace of progesterone in one of the six placentas. Bowerman & Melampy (134) conclude that the bovine placenta does not make progesterone.

By means of an indwelling catheter, oviduct fluid was collected from monkeys over a total of four cycles. The amount varied from 0.2 ml per day at the time of menstruation to a sharp peak of 3 ml during the ovulatory phase (135). Fertilized sheep ova transplanted to oviducts of rabbits were sent by air from England to South Africa. When transferred to ewes they developed normally to birth (136). Finn & Keen (137) injected histamine in doses of 10 to 500 μg in each uterine horn but were unable to cause the formation of deciduomata as reported by Schelesnyak (138).

The circulatory space of the uterus, estimated by measuring the amount of hemoglobin in a weighed amount of uterine tissue, is about twice as great in the uterus and myometrium of progesterone-dominated animals as in tissues under estrogen domination (139). Kao (140) found larger amounts of unextractable K and Na in the estrogen-dominated uterus than in progesterone-dominated tissues. The effect of oxytocin on uterine contraction was unchanged in the presence of widely varying amounts of potassium but was reduced when the amount of calcium present was reduced. Oxytocin may have some direct effect on the contractile elements of the muscle cell in addition to its effect on the membrane of the fiber (141). Uterine motility of the rat is inhibited by a substance extracted from the placenta which, when injected intraperitoneally, causes ovarian hyperemia (142). The motility of the guinea pig uterus is increased by the addition of guinea pig sperm. The effect lasted two to three hours and may play some role in sperm transport (143). Experiments of Rowlands (144) suggest that the uterus may have a direct effect on the maintenance and regression of the corpus luteum in the guinea pig.

IMPLANTATION

The implantation site in the rabbit has been studied by electron micros-copy (145). The marked rise in rat uterine β-glucuronidase on the fourth day of pregnancy may result from estrogen stimulation and play a role in the implantation of the ovum (146). Fetuses transferred as five-day-old ova to the uterine horns of rats weighed significantly more on day 18 than ova transferred at the age of four days (147). The embryonic survival of transplanted rabbit ova was correlated with the number of implantation sites but the diameter of the implantation swellings was not related to the number of implantations per recipient (148). Implantation in the rat was delayed three to eighteen days by making an autograft of the pituitary onto the kidney on the second day of pregnancy (149). Ovariectomy of the rabbit on day 6 prevents implantation on day 7. Unimplanted blastocysts continue to have mitotic activity and can be transplanted to culture media where they will grow for another day. The weight, glucose, and bicarbonate content of the unimplanted blastocysts are normal (150). Rabbit blastocysts normally show a decreased concentration of bicarbonate and an increased concentration of glucose and lactate at the time of implantation, but glucose and lactate do not increase in unimplanted blastocysts (151).

THE PLACENTA

The ultrastructure of the human full-term placenta has been studied by Rhodin & Terzakis (152) and the early trophoblast was reviewed by Levine (153). The mechanism for the active transport of inorganic phosphate across the placenta appears to be localized in the chorionic cells, probably at their boundary towards the intervillus space (154). No appreciable transplacental passage of I^{131} insulin could be demonstrated either in rats (155) or in women (156). By administering progesterone-4-C^{14} to women just before the interruption of pregnancy, Castren et al. (157) demonstrated a rapid transfer of ether-soluble radioactivity to the fetus. Within ten minutes, radioactivity in the fetal blood equaled that in the maternal blood. The umbilical vessels and Wharton's jelly play a significant role in the water exchange of the amniotic fluid (158).

Pig fetuses were kept alive for seven hours with the aid of an artificial placenta (159). The fetal cells of the mouse placenta were shown to be immunologically competent (160); this makes the success of the placenta as a homograft even more remarkable.

Human term placenta contains 40 μg estrone, 100 μg estradiol, and

180 µg estriol per kg placenta (161). The amount of choline acetylase in the human placenta increases during pregnancy, reaching a peak at the thirty-fourth week after which it decreases (162). Phosphorylcholine and phosphorylethanolamine are quantitatively important phospholipids of the goat placenta (163). Re-examination of the mechanism of fructose formation in the goat placenta makes it more likely that this occurs by way of phosphoric acid esters than by way of sorbitol (164). The human placenta perfused *in vitro* converted C^{14} estradiol to C^{14} estriol only if HCG was added to the perfusing fluid. Other products of estradiol tentatively identified were 2-methoxyestrone and epiestriol (165). Both free and conjugated Porter-Silber chromogens were produced by human placentas perfused *in vitro*, especially in the latter hours of perfusion (166). Analyses of human pregnancy urine showed that estrone, estriol, 16-epiestriol, and estradiol-17β but not 2-methoxyestrone increased after 20 weeks of pregnancy (167). The giant trophoblast cells of the fetal placenta have marked 3β-hydroxysteroid dehydrogenase activity and an active TPNH-generating system, which suggests that they play a role in the formation of steroid hormones (168).

Pregnancy

Another case of successful pregnancy following hypophysectomy during gestation was reported (169). Progesterone levels in rabbit ovarian vein blood rise gradually and reach a peak of 2.36 µg per ml at midpregnancy, declining to 0.41 µg per ml two days prior to parturition (170). Pregnancy is maintained in rabbits castrated on the fourteenth day by the administration of 6α-methyl,17α-acetoxyprogesterone (171). Pregnancy could be maintained in castrate rats by a fairly wide range of estradiol:progesterone ratios with or without relaxin (172), or by 16α,17α-dihydroxyprogesterone acetophenone but not by 17-hydroxyprogesterone or 17α-ethinyl-19-nortestosterone (173).

There is little acid phosphatase activity demonstrable histochemically in the virgin or pregnant uterus, but there is a great deal of activity post partum around the placental detachment site in epithelial cells and in macrophages in all of the uterine layers. Similar changes occur in the uteri of ovariectomized rats during hormonal withdrawal following the administration of estradiol and progesterone (174). During pregnancy there is a progressive increase in the amount of collagen and noncollagenic protein in the myometrium of both rat and human uteri. Within 7 days postpartum in the rat and 22 days postpartum in women, the levels of collagen and noncollagenic protein have decreased to within basal levels (175).

The demonstration of isohemagglutinins in secretions of the human uterine cervix may explain the deficiency of certain types of offspring in ABO incompatible matings (176). The ovarian contribution to the excretion of estrogens and pregnanediol during pregnancy is very small, for oöphorectomy does not change the excretory rates of these substances (177).

Maternal-Fetal Relationships

Human fetal liver, lung, kidneys, adrenals, and skeletal muscle all can carry out the conjugation of estrogens *in vitro* even at relatively early stages in gestation (178). Apparently, such conjugation also takes place *in vivo* in the fetus and newborn (179). The increased concentration of circulating thyroid hormone during pregnancy in the primate results from a decrease in the fractional rate of thyroxine turnover (180). The effects of diabetes on metabolism in pregnancy are approximately additive in maternal tissues, and the metabolic defects in the fetus are primarily the result of an oversupply of glucose to the fetus *in utero* (181). Substantial concentrations of fructose were found in the fetal blood of animals having epitheliochorial or syndesmochorial placentas (182).

Lactation

The milk yield of lactating goats is decreased by hypophysectomy and increased by ox or sheep anterior pituitary extracts, or by prolactin. Prolactin and growth hormone appear to be the major components of the lactogenic complex in the goat (183). Goat udders perfused with acetate or glucose alone gave very low milk yields, but perfusion with acetate plus glucose gave good milk yield (184). Developmental changes in the mammary gland during pregnancy and lactation are accompanied by an increased stimulation of the ATP radioactive pyrophosphate exchange in the presence of leucine and glutamate (185). Griffith & Turner (186) studied the involution of the mammary gland following lactation by estimating its DNA content. Estradiol benzoate administered from the day of weaning augmented the involution of the mammary gland.

Metabolism of Sex Hormones

Rubin & Strecker (187) found two 3β-hydroxysteroid dehydrogenases in rat liver, one in the particulate and one in the soluble fraction. Males have a more active particulate enzyme than females but the activity of the enzyme in female liver can be increased by injecting testosterone. Hofmann (188) reported that though neither the testis nor the adrenal cortex of the rat can convert progesterone to cortisol, a mixture of homogenates of the two tissues can bring about this conversion. Leybold & Staudinger (189) present evidence that DPNH as well as TPNH can serve as hydrogen donor for ring A reduction of steroid hormones by rat liver microsomes but the reduction by DPNH requires inorganic phosphate.

Progesterone.—As much as two thirds of the dose of C^{14}-progesterone injected into the cat was excreted in the bile; the urinary excretion of C^{14}-labeled metabolites never exceeded 1 per cent of the amount injected (190). The 20α-hydroxysteroid dehydrogenase of rat ovary was partially purified and shown to have a specific requirement for TPN; its inability to serve as a TPNH-DPN transhydrogenating system may be explained by its lack of dual nucleotide specificity (191). With cholesterol-26-C^{14} or 20α-hydroxycho-lesterol-22-C^{14} as substrate, Tamaoki & Pincus (192) demonstrated the presence of a desmolase in the ovarian tissue of the cow. Homogenates of corpora lutea converted cholesterol to progesterone, and the conversion of $Δ^5$-pregnenolone to progesterone was observed in both luteal and follicular tissue. Several types of gonadotropins were added to the incubations but none increased the rate of reaction *in vitro*.

Testosterone.—The conversion of testosterone-4-C^{14} to 3α,18-dihydroxy-5β-androstan-17-one in man was shown by Fukushima & Bradlow (193). Lipsett (194) presented evidence that adrenal androgen biosynthesis is decreased in some patients with gonadal dysgenesis. The testes of rabbits or guinea pigs can incorporate labeled acetate into 3α-hydroxy-16-androstene *in vitro* (195). Evidence that testosterone and dehydroepiandrosterone are the major products of pregnenolone incubated with slices of human fetal testis was presented by Acevedo *et al.* (196). The major androgenic substances present in spermatic venous blood of the bull are testosterone and androstenedione (197). 4,14-Androstadiene-3,17-dione was produced from progesterone by cystic bovine ovary (198), but not by the normal ovary.

Estrogens.—Human testis, ovary, and adrenal can carry out a trans-methylation reaction from methionine to 2-hydroxyestradiol (199). Human fetal liver converted estradiol-17β to estriol, 16-epiestriol, and estrone, and produced estriol glucosiduronic acid. The poor yields of metabolites and the low recovery of the substrate indicate that fetal liver is very active in metabolizing estrogens (200).

The very low level of $Δ^5$-3β-hydroxysteroids in the follicular fluid of the mare suggests that the conversion of pregnenolone to progesterone proceeds rapidly and the pathway to 17-hydroxypregnenolone and dehydroepiandros-terone is of minor importance (201). The luteal tissue of the mare contains progesterone, 20α-hydroxy-4-pregnene-3-one, and a small amount of 17-hydroxyprogesterone. Follicular fluid contains progesterone, 17-hydroxy-progesterone, androgens, and estrogens (202). It was inferred that the cells of the theca interna convert progestins to estrogens and that the luteinized granulosa cells, with diminished 17-hydroxylation ability, cannot cleave the side chain but do have the 20-reductase. Qualitative differences exist in the patterns of steroids present in the follicular fluids of cow and mare (203).

Inducing abortion by injecting 50 per cent dextrose into the amniotic sac leads to an increased excretion of estradiol and decreased excretion of estrone and estriol [Timonen, Hirvonen & Wichmann (204)]; this led to the suggestion that placental metabolism is altered during the asphyxia which precedes fetal death. The luteinized ovary of the rat produces progesterone and 20α-hydroxy-4-pregnene-3-one but no estrogens (205). Prolactin added *in vitro* did not alter the pattern of products from acetate. An increased level of thyroid hormone in man decreased the fraction of estradiol-C^{14} converted to estriol and increased the fraction converted to 2-methoxyestrone, but produced no change in the fraction of estrone produced (206). Injection of neutral steroids in man led to an increased excretion of estrogens but these accounted for less than 0.1 per cent of administered steroid (207). Estrone and estradiol-17β are interconverted by enzymes present in human and rat blood cells but the reduction of estrone by bovine erythrocytes produces estradiol-17α (208). Estrone-16-C^{14} is oxidized by peroxidase (209). A preparation of S-adenosylmethionine-o-diphenyl-o-methyl transferase from rat liver will methylate 2-hydroxyestradiol-17β to 2-methoxyestradiol-17β (210). Minced ox adrenal can carry out the 11β-hydroxylation and the 16α-hydroxylation of estrone (211). Evidence that estrogens might be metabolized by the disruption of ring A was presented by Werbin, Imada & Chaikoff (212). A preparation of rat liver microsomes can metabolize estradiol-17β to 17β-hydroxyestra-p-quinol-(10β) by a free radical mechanism (213). In five cases of human pregnancy with anacephalic monsters, the only endocrine abnormality noticed was low estrogen excretion, which suggests that the fetal adrenal (which was hypoplastic in all cases) may be involved in the elaboration of estrogens during pregnancy (214). The sulfates of estradiol and estrone were identified in extracts of lungs, liver, and kidneys of human fetuses treated with estradiol-17β. An additional compound, probably a conjugated form of 2-methoxyestradiol-17β, was detected in the liver of such fetuses (215). Conjugates, largely glucosiduronates, of estriol were formed by human intestinal tract when estriol was introduced into the duodenal loop (216). The metabolism of estradiol-17β in infants differs from that of adults (217); during the second year the child attains the adult type of metabolism. Experiments on estrogen metabolism in the human fetus by Diczfalusy et al. (218) indicate that the placental-amniotic barrier is permeable to maternal estrogens only to a very limited extent and that the human fetus can carry out estrogen conversions and conjugations as early as 17 weeks of gestation.

Human ovaries from gonadotropin-stimulated patients, when incubated in vitro, converted progesterone to androstenedione and testosterone (219), androstenedione to estrone and estradiol in good yield (220); and cholesterol-4-C^{14} to estrone-C^{14} (221). 2-Hydroxyestradiol-17β administered to postmenopausal women was converted to 2-hydroxyestrone, 2-hydroxyestriol, 2-methoxyestrone, 2-methoxyestradiol, and 2-methoxyestriol (222). The incubation of testosterone, androstenedione, or 19-hydroxyandrostenedione with human placenta microsomes in the presence of TPNH led to the production of formaldehyde and the corresponding estrogen (223). This provides evidence that the angular C-19 methyl group is removed as formaldehyde. The human newborn excretes estriol and not estrone or estradiol. Andrén & Borglin (224) had reported that infants with congenital dislocation of the hip excrete estrone and estradiol-17β in significant amounts. Further study (225) showed that the excretion of estriol varied widely in the first few days, with no significant sex difference. The excretion of estriol in 18 newborns with congenital dislocation of the hip was within the normal range. Important observations on metabolism of polycystic ovaries are cited at the end of this review.

Mechanism of Action of Sex Hormones

Progesterone.—The traumatized uterine horns of ovariectomized rats showed a graded increase in weight and DNA content compared to controls when injected with progesterone (226). Neither estradiol nor thyroxine alone had any effect on the progesterone stimulation of placentomata growth but the two together produced a highly significant increase (227). The concentration of α-amino nitrogen in the plasma was significantly decreased by the intramuscular administration of progesterone (228). The catabolic effect of administered progesterone was enhanced by increasing dietary protein intake and repressed by its restriction (229).

Progesterone inhibition of myometrial contraction *in vitro* is more pronounced in late pregnant than in post partum myometria; calcium-deficient solutions have an effect similar to that of progesterone in both states (230). The presence of progesterone increases the number of spikes in a train of impulses, and blocks propagation of the impulse in the muscle. The increase in endometrial carbonic anhydrase which follows the administration of progesterone is inhibited by androgens or by estrogens (231, 232).

Estrogens.—Stilbestrol increases the level of gamma globulin in the serum of the guinea pig some 170 per cent over controls (233). Administration of synthetic estrogens to virilized women leads to a significant and sustained decrease in urinary 17-ketosteroid excretion (234). Diethylstilbestrol injected daily into hypophysectomized and intact immature rats increased ovarian weight in both groups for a period of eight days (235). The administration of estradiol-17β to immature chicks increased the rate of oviduct growth and its content of fat, protein, RNA, and DNA (236).

Rats injected with estradiol show a distribution of labeled urea and sucrose between uterus and serum which indicates a greater initial rate of uptake of these two substances from the serum by the uterus, but within five minutes after the injection of estradiol the control rate and that of the estrogen-treated animal are the same (237). Estrogen increases initial flux of substances across the barrier but does not influence the steady-state relations between blood and tissue. Estradiol markedly stimulates the uptake of α-aminoisobutyric acid into the rabbit uterus but has no effect on muscle, liver, or pubic symphysis (238). The increased uptake of α-aminoisobutyric acid by the uterus of the ovariectomized rat following estradiol injection is first evident at 3 to 4 hours, reaches a peak at 12, and declines nearly to the control at 20 hours after administration (239). Prolonged estrogen stimulation of the rat uterus causes both hypertrophy and hyperplasia. Progesterone given simultaneously with the estradiol suppresses the growth effect but given prior to estradiol has a synergistic effect (240). Estradiol injected into rats leads to a marked increase in the concentration of ATP and of guanosine and uridine phosphates. The addition of progesterone does not change the level of adenosine nucleotides but does increase further the guanosine and uridine nucleotides (241). The injection of estradiol into castrate rats increases DNA phosphorus content of the uterus 18 hours after the injection and causes a two- to threefold increase in the total nitrogen of the mitochondrial, micro-somal, and soluble fractions of the uterus 24 hours after injection. The total succinic dehydrogenase activity per cell reached a peak at 24 hours; most of this increase appeared in the mitochondrial fraction (242). The uterine phenol-activated DPNH oxidase has been partially purified but was not separated from the uterine peroxidase (243). The authors suggest the en-zymes may be the same. Paul (244) showed that the oxidase is not in uterine cells but is located in the white blood cells and the increase on estrogen stimulation comes from the invasion of the uterus by leukocytes containing the enzyme.

Estradiol alone or in combination with progesterone produces changes in the histochemical localization of β-glucuronidase and alkaline phosphatase in the uterus and vagina of castrate rats (245). The pattern of enzyme changes following estrogen stimulation could be related to the formation of muco-polysaccharides in the vaginal epithelium from glycogen (246). Estrogen treatment of the castrate rabbit leads to a marked increase in DPN and uridine nucleotides and smaller increases in ATP concentration (247). Mer-25, an analogue of the synthetic estrogen Tace (chlorotrianisene), pre-vents the estrogen-induced pituitary hypertrophy and inhibits the utero-tropic effect and vaginal cornification in the rat (248). Estradiol stimulated the rate of oxygen consumption, the conversion of acetate-2-C^{14} to $C^{14}O_2$, and the incorporation of acetate-2-C^{14} into protein, lipid, and nucleic acids in slices of human term placenta (249). The effects are consistent with the hypotheses that estrogen increases oxidative metabolism by stimulating the pyridine nucleotide transhydrogenase and that the synthesis of cell con-stituents is limited by the rate of ATP production. The estradiol dehydrogen-ase(s) of human placenta was purified 2500-fold (250). The dehydrogenase and transhydrogenase activities of the enzyme had a constant ratio during the course of the purification, and attempts to separate these activities by electrophoresis or by chromatography were unsuccessful.

Androgens.—Hypophysectomized castrate rats given testosterone re-sponded with increased wet weight, protein, and RNA in both ventral pros-tate and seminal vesicle. The effect of testosterone was enhanced by the ad-ministration of growth hormone (251). Cells of the prostate of the rat show a slight ability to concentrate testosterone from the blood and to oxidize it. The radioactivity was found to be highest in the microsomal frac-tion where the DPN 17β-hydroxysteroid dehydrogenase is located (252). Castration decreases the DNA and RNA content of seminal vesicles of the mouse; the changes are reversed by testosterone (253). The succinic dehy-drogenase of rat seminal vesicle is decreased by castration and stimulated by testosterone (254). Fluoxymesterone has androgenic and anabolic effects on the hypophysectomized male rat when given orally (255). 17α-Methyl-19-nortestosterone had no effect on the production or secretion of 17-ketosteroids by the testis (256).

Using minces of pooled ventral prostate glands from rats, Farnsworth &

Brown (257) showed that the site of action of testosterone is not on the metabolism of citric acid but on the synthesis of citric acid, fatty acids, and proteins. They suggest that testosterone facilitates the activation of acyl residues by ATP. Wilson (258) found that testosterone enhances protein synthesis in slices of seminal vesicle and prostate from normal and castrate rats and prevents the inhibition of microsomal ribonucleoprotein synthesis by puromycin. Testosterone stimulates protein synthesis not by inducing an effect on amino acid transport or synthesis but by stimulating the conversion of RNA-amino acid complexes to microsomal ribonucleoproteins with peptide bonding (259). Castration leads to a gradual decrease of amino acid-activating enzymes in seminal vesicles, and the administration of testosterone or other androgens restores this enzyme activity. The effects of the androgens were similar for several different amino acid-activating enzymes tested (260).

The decanoate ester of nandrolone (17β-hydroxy-4-estrene-3-one) was relatively more anabolic and less androgenic than the corresponding ester of testosterone (261). The respiratory rate of *Euglena* was increased by the presence of testosterone in the incubation medium if a nitrogen source was available. This suggests that an early effect of this steroid is on the permeability of the cells to nitrogen-containing compounds with a resulting effect on protein metabolism and oxygen consumption (262).

EFFECTS OF SEX HORMONES ON OTHER TISSUES

The growth of the mammary gland requires thyroxine in addition to estrogens and progesterone. The addition of pituitary growth hormone or mammotropin increased alveolar development. Optimal production of milk in genetically hormone-deficient dwarf mice required a combination of estradiol, progesterone, cortisol, mammotropin, growth hormone, and thyroxine (263). Mammary tissues from the mouse were subjected in organ culture to various hormone treatments. Insulin and cortisol given together led to the maintenance of all of the tissue, but cortisol alone was ineffective and insulin alone had only a slight effect. The secretory state of late prelactating mammary tissue could be maintained by adding mammotropin and somatotropin to the insulin and cortisol (264). Pregnenolone, 17-hydroxyprogesterone, androstenedione, or testosterone could to some extent replace progesterone in acting with estradiol to cause growth of mammary tissues (265). Testosterone in oil applied locally to the skin of the mammary gland of rats caused lobule-alveolar development (266). This is evidence for a direct local action of testosterone on growth in mammary glands. Experiments with mitochondria from guinea pig mammary glands suggest that phosphorylation is uncoupled from oxidation of succinate or α-ketoglutarate in all functional states except during lactation. The mammary gland may produce some unspecific uncoupling factor since the mitochondrial fraction from the guinea pig mammary gland uncoupled oxidative phosphorylation in rat liver mitochondria (267). The oral administration of 7,12-dimethylbenzanthracene increases the activity of a soluble enzyme in the rat mammary gland and in perirenal fat that catalyzes the oxidation of reduced pyridine nucleotides by vitamin K, but does not affect the activity of glutathione reductase (268).

Estradiol lowered and progesterone increased the seizure thresholds for rats given electroshock treatments. Similar effects are produced in normal and hypophysectomized rats; therefore, the effect is not mediated through some pituitary tropic hormone (269). Sexual responsiveness in the male rat was shown to be related to the androgen level (270). Estriol produces morphologic changes in the pituitary gland and adrenal cortex of gonadectomized rats which are similar to but weaker than those of estradiol (271). Both natural and synthetic estrogens inhibit erythropoesis in young male rats (272). The administration of estradiol *in vivo* decreased the rate of incorporation of glycine into the organic matrix of surviving bone fragments of rats incubated *in vitro*, but increased the rate of incorporation of glycine in comparable experiments in mice (273). Estradiol benzoate, but not iodoestradiol or iodoestrone, inhibits coronary atherosclerosis in cholesterol-fed cockerels (274). Estradiol inhibits goitrogenesis in rats receiving propylthiouracil but progesterone enhances goiter formation (275). Estradiol stimulates the rate of thyroxine secretion in ovariectomized rats. The effect is not directly on the thyroid gland for it did not occur when exogenous thyroxine was used to suppress pituitary function (276). Adrenal slices of female rats produce more corticoids when incubated *in vitro* than do comparable male adrenals. Ovariectomized females have a rate of adrenal corticoid synthesis which is depressed to the male level. The addition of estradiol to the incubation medium increased corticoid synthesis in the male or ovariectomized female but not in the intact female (277).

The amount of mucopolysaccharides in rat skin was slightly increased by the topical application of testosterone and slightly decreased by the application of estradiol [Allalouf & Ber (278)]. The aryl esterase of the blood plasma of pigs is controlled by a set of alleles and by the concentration of androgens. Androgens decrease the biosynthesis of the active protein, and castration increases it (279). The number of polynucleated cells in a strain of hamster ascites tumors is increased by transplantation into male rather than female hamsters (280). Castration causes a decrease in the weight of the kidney, prostate, and seminal vesicle of the rat and proportional decreases in the amount of soluble RNA in the cell. The administration of testosterone reversed these effects and increased the total concentration of RNA to values above normal (281).

OXYTOCIN

Through use of cross-circulation experiments, evidence was obtained for the release of oxytocin in the ewe in response to vaginal distention and in the ram in response to massage of the seminal vesicles and ampullae (282). The infusion of oxytocin into pregnant ewes led to an increased tonus but did not induce rhythmic contraction of the gravid uterus, even at doses many times those that elicit rhythmic uterine contraction in the human. These experiments suggest that oxytocin is effective only in the presence of oxytocinase, since sheep blood contains no oxytocinase (283). The oxytocinase level of the plasma of pregnant women increases with pregnancy and is maximal at about the thirty-sixth week, decreasing after delivery (284). Measurements of oxytocin activity in the blood from women during pregnancy and labor do not support the postulate that oxytocin is involved in the onset of parturition (285). The stimulatory action of oxytocin on rat uteri was unchanged in the presence of a tenfold increase in the potassium concentration but was decreased by a reduction in calcium concentration. Since oxytocin can exert an effect in calcium-free solution, it is suggested that it has a direct action on contractile elements of the muscle cells in addition to its postulated effect on the excitable membrane of the muscle fiber (286).

Oxytocin, vasopressin, and insulin, hormones containing disulfide groups, greatly stimulate the respiration-dependent uptake of water by mitochondria isolated from rat liver or kidney. The disulfide hormones are 50 to 100 times more active than simple disulfides such as glutathione; this suggests that the amino acid sequence and the peptide chain conformation has some specific enhancing effect on the swelling action of the disulfide group. Lehninger & Neubert (287) suggest that the swelling action of the disulfide hormones may be a useful experimental model for the action of these hormones on their normal target sites, which appear to be membranes of one type or another.

Methods

Ovulation can be detected by the increased sugar content of cervical secretion which reaches a peak at ovulation (288). A histochemical method for measuring the depletion of ascorbic acid in the rat ovary following the injection of LH is described by Goldstein & Sturgis (289). A sensitive, accurate, and rapid pregnancy test has been devised by Wide, Roos & Gemzell (290) based on the immunologic determination by a hemagglutination reaction using rabbit anti-HCG sera and formalinized sheep red cells sensitized with HCG. Pituitary and urinary LH have the same immunologic properties as HCG and the same test is used for both. There was no cross reaction with FSH or growth hormone activities. The test has been used (291) to measure the variation in LH in the urine during the menstrual cycle. Luteinizing hormone reaches a peak at the time of ovulation. An alternative method using gel agar Ouchterlony plates has been described by Keele *et al.* (292).

A method is described for the isolation of an estrogen mirestrol from the plant *Pueraria mirifica* from Thailand (293). Mirestriol is one-quarter as active as estradiol in the rat vaginal cornification test. The purification of urinary conjugated estrogens by filtration on sephadex gel is described (294). Thewalt & Zimmermann (295) describe a routine method for determining urinary estrogens. Methods for the hydrolysis of conjugated estrogens from pregnancy urine were investigated by Bugge *et al.* (296). A general discussion of the isotope dilution method for estimating secretory rates from urinary metabolites is described by Gurpide *et al.* (297). The application of the method to a situation in which a hormone made by the placenta is excreted both into maternal and fetal pools and is metabolized differently in the two compartments is discussed. Assays for the estimation of estrogens and progesterone by their effects on carbonic anhydrase activity and endometrium are described by Bialy & Pincus (298) and Kurogochi & Pincus (299). A method for separating and characterizing 24 steroid estrogens by their movement on thin-layer chromatography in different solvent systems is described by Lisboa & Diczfalusy (300). An ultramicrobioassay for androgens, based on their effect in elongating the anal fin of the guppy, is described by Cohen (301). Methods were reported for determining the level of testosterone in plasma (302) and for the simultaneous determination of pregnanediol and pregnanetriol in urine (303).

THE POLYCYSTIC OVARY

Human polycystic ovaries produce more androgen and less estrogen than do normal ovaries (304 to 308), contain dehydroepiandrosterone and 17-hydroxyprenenolone (399), and when incubated with acetate-1-C^{14} produce testosterone-C^{14} (310) and dehydroepiandrosterone-C^{14} (311). Such ovaries are deficient in the aromatization reactions (beyond 19-hydroxy or 19-aldo-testosterone), in 17-hydroxylation, and in 3β-ol-dehydrogenase, leading to decreased synthesis of estradiol and to accumulation of testosterone and dehydroepiandrosterone (312). The defect in biosynthesis of estrogens by polycystic kidneys is postulated to involve diaxial transelimination of the 19β-carbon and the 1α-hydrogen (313). The effect of wedge resection on polycystic ovaries varies widely (314).

LITERATURE CITED

1. Young, W. C., Ed., *Sex and Internal Secretions*, 3rd ed., 2 vols. (Williams & Wilkins, Baltimore, Md., 1961)
2. Zuckerman, Sir Solly, Ed., *The Ovary*, 2 vols. (Academic, New York, 1962)
3. Austin, C. R., *The Mammalian Egg* (Blackwell, Oxford, 1961)
4. Gray, C. H., and Bacharach, A. L., *Hormones in Blood* (Academic, London & New York, 1961)
5. Kiyoshi, T., *Progress in Comparative Endocrinology* (Academic, New York, 1962)
6. *Proc. Intern. Conf. Intern. Soc. Geograph. Pathol., 7th, London, June 28–30, 1960, Pathol. Microbiol.*, **24**, 428 (1961)
7. *Symp. Effects of Progestational Agents*, *Acta Cytol.*, **6**, 278 (1962)
8. Pincus, G., Ed., *Recent Progress in Hormone Research*, **22** (Academic, New York, 1962)
9. Hansel, W., *Intern. J. Fertility*, **6**, 241 (1961)
10. Knigge, K. M., *Am. J. Physiol.*, **202**, 387 (1962)
11. McCann, S. M., *Am. J. Physiol.*, **202**, 395 (1962)
12. Desclin, L., Flament, J., and Gepts, W., *Compt. Rend. Acad. Sci.*, **252**, 4192 (1961)
13. Desclin, L., Flament-Durand, J., and Gepts, W., *Endocrinology*, **70**, 429 (1962)
14. Davidson, J. M., and Sawyer, C. H., *Acta Endocrinol.*, **37**, 385 (1961)
15. Van Rees, G. P., Van der Werff ten Bosch, J. J., and Wolthuis, O. L., *Acta Endocrinol.*, **40**, 95 (1962)
16. Van der Werff ten Bosch, J. J., Van Rees, G. P., and Wolthuis, O.L., *Acta Endocrinol.*, **40**, 103 (1962)
17. Haun, C. K., and Sawyer, C. H., *Acta Endocrinol.*, **38**, 99 (1961)
18. Beyer, C., Mena, F., Pacheco, P., and Alcaraz, M., *Am. J. Physiol.*, **202**, 465 (1962)
19. Gale, C. C., Taleisnik, S., Friedman,

H. M., and McCann, S. M., *J. Endocrinol.*, **23**, 303 (1961)

20. Anderson, R. R., and Turner, C. W., *Proc. Soc. Exptl. Biol. Med.*, **110**, 98 (1962)

21. Corbin, A., and Schottelius, B. A., *Am. J. Physiol.*, **201**, 1176 (1961)

22. Taymore, M. L., *J. Clin. Endocrinol. Metab.*, **21**, 976 (1961)

23. Rosemberg, E., and Engel, I., *J. Clin. Endocrinol. Metab.*, **22**, 377 (1962)

24. Brown, P. S., and Billewicz, W. Z., *J. Endocrinol.*, **24**, 65 (1962)

25. Miyake, T., *Endocrinology*, **69**, 534 (1961)

26. Mason, N. R., Marsh, J. M., and Savard, K., *J. Biol. Chem.*, **236**, PC 34 (1961)

27. Butt, W. R., Crooke, A. C., and Cunningham, F. J., *Biochem. J.*, **81**, 596 (1961)

28. Albert A., Derner, I., Stellmacher, V., Leiferman, J., and Barnum, J., *J. Clin. Endocrinol. Metab.*, **21**, 1260 (1961)

29. Harbon-Chabbat, S., Legault-Démare, J., Jolles, P., and Clauser, H., *Bull. Soc. Chim. Biol.*, **43**, 1339 (1961)

30. Soffer, L. J., Futterweit, W., and Salvaneschi, J., *J. Clin. Endocrinol. Metab.*, **21**, 1267 (1961)

31. Soffer, L. J., Salvaneschi, J., and Futterweit, W., *J. Clin. Endocrinol. Metab.*, **22**, 532 (1962)

32. Jutisz, M., Hermier, C., Colonge, A., and Courrier, R., *Compt. Rend. Acad. Sci.*, **252**, 3922 (1961)

33. Butt, W. R., Crooke, A. C., and Cunningham, F. J., *Proc. Roy. Soc. Med.*, **54**, 647 (1961)

34. Johannisson, E., Gemzell, C., and Diczfalusy, E., *J. Clin. Endocrinol. Metab.*, **21**, 1068 (1961)

35. Maner, F. D., Saffan, B. D., and Preedy, J. R. K., *J. Clin. Endocrinol. Metab.*, **22**, 525 (1962)

36. Beyler, A. L., and Potts, G. O., *Endocrinology*, **70**, 611 (1962)

37. Van Rees, G. P., and Wolthuis, O. L., *Acta Endocrinol.*, **39**, 103 (1962)

38. Rothchild, I., *Endocrinology*, **70**, 303 (1962)

39. Reichert, L. E., Jr., *Endocrinology*, **70**, 697 (1962)

40. Ryan, R. J., *J. Clin. Endocrinol. Metab.*, **22**, 300 (1962)

41. Schmidt-Elmendorff, H., and Lorraine, J. A., *J. Endocrinol.*, **23**, 413 (1962)

42. Ward, D. N., Walborg, E. F., Jr., and Adams-Mayne, M., *Biochim. Biophys. Acta*, **50**, 224 (1961)

43. Giuliani, G., Martini, L., Pecile, A., and Fochi, M., *Acta Endocrinol.*, **38**, 1 (1961)

44. McCann, S. M., and Taleisnik, S., *Endocrinology*, **69**, 909 (1961)

45. Gorski, R. A., and Barraclough, C. A., *Acta Endocrinol.*, **39**, 13 (1962)

46. McCann, S. M., *Am. J. Physiol.*, **202**, 601 (1962)

47. Armstrong, D. T., and Greep, R. O., *Endocrinology*, **70**, 701 (1962)

48. Taira, A. M., and Tarkhan, A. A., *Acta Endocrinol.*, **40**, 175 (1962)

49. Knobil, E., and Josimovich, J. B., *Endocrinology*, **69**, 139 (1961)

50. Woods, M. C., and Simpson, M. E., *Endocrinology*, **69**, 91 (1961)

51. Gans, E., and Van Rees, G. P., *Acta Endocrinol.*, **39**, 245 (1962)

52. Gunn, S. A., Gould, T. C., and Anderson, W. A. D., *J. Endocrinol.*, **23**, 37, (1961)

53. Hall, P. F., and Eik-Nes, K. B., *Proc. Soc. Exptl. Biol. Med.*, **110**, 148 (1962)

54. Cowie, A. T., and Tindal, J. S., *J. Endocrinol.*, **22**, 403 (1961)

55. Nicoll, C. S., and Meites, J., *Endocrinology*, **70**, 272 (1962)

56. Nicoll, C. S., and Meites, J., *Endocrinology*, **70**, 927 (1962)

57. Reisfeld, R. A., Tong, G. L., Riches, E. L., and Brink, N. G., *J. Am. Chem. Soc.*, **83**, 3717 (1961)

58. Damm, H. C., Pipes, G. W., von Berswordt-Wallrabe, R., and Turner, C. W., *Proc. Soc. Exptl. Biol. Med.*, **107**, 144 (1961)

59. Kotz, H. L., and Herrman, W., *Fertility Sterility*, **12**, 96 (1961)

60. Jones, G. S., Aziz, Z., and Urbina, G., *Fertility Sterility*, **12**, 217 (1961)

61. Simpson, M. E., and van Wagenen, G., *Fertility Sterility*, **13**, 140 (1962)

62. Gemzell, C. A., *Fertility Sterility*, **13** 153 (1962)

63. Palsson, H., *J. Reprod. Fertility*, **3**, 55 (1962)

64. Robertson, H. A., and Hutchinson, J. S. M., *J. Endocrinol.*, **24**, 143 (1962)

65. Nikitovitch-Winer, M. B., *Endocrinology*, **70**, 350 (1962)

66. Purshottam, N., Mason, M., and Pincus, G., *Fertility Sterility*, **12**, 346 (1961)

67. Gross, M., *Fertility Sterility* **12**, 245 (1961)

68. Ogawa, Y., and Pincus, G., *Endocrinology*, **70**, 359 (1962)

69. Madjerek, Z., and van der Vies, J., *Acta Endocrinol.*, **38**, 315 (1961)

70. Martin, L., J. *Endocrinol.*, **23**, 329 (1962)

71. Albers, H. J., Bedford, J. M., and Chang, M. C., *Am. J. Physiol.*, **201** 554 (1961)

72. Vaes, G., *Acta Endocrinol.*, **39**, 513 (1962)

73. Swigart, R. H., Wagner, C. E., Herberrer, G. H., and Atkinson, W. B., *Endocrinology*, **70**, 600 (1962)

74. Hayashi, M., and Fishman, W. H., *Acta Endocrinol.*, **39**, 154 (1962)

75. Rowlands, I. W., *J. Reprod. Fertility*, **2**, 341 (1961)

76. Perry, J. S., and Rowlands, I. W., *J. Reprod. Fertility*, **2**, 332 (1961)

77. Anderson, L. L., Butcher, R. L., and Melampy, R. M., *Endocrinology*, **69**, 571 (1961)

78. Butcher, R. L., Chu, K. Y., and Melampy, R. M., *Endocrinology*, **70**, 442 (1962)

79. Lindsay, D. R., and Robinson, T. J., *Nature*, **192**, 761 (1961)

80. Guttenberg, I., *Endocrinology*, **68**, 1009 (1961)

81. Houssay, A. B., and Blumenkrantz, N., *Nature*, **194**, 482 (1962)

82. Zarrow, M. X., and Yochim, J., *Endocrinology*, **69**, 292 (1961)

83. Lutwak-Mann, C., *Biochim, Biophys. Acta*, **58**, 637 (1962)

84. Steinberger, E., and Wagner, C., *Endocrinology*, **69**, 305 (1961)

85. Mason, N., and Samuels, L., *Endocrinology*, **68**, 899 (1961)

86. Turpeinen, P., Turpeinen, O., and Talanti, S., *Endocrinology*, **70**, 731 (1962)

87. Jordan, R. T., Katsh, S., and de Stackelburg, N., *Nature*, **192**, 1053 (1961)

88. Waites, G. M. H., and Moule, G. E., *J. Reprod. Fertility*, **2**, 213 (1961)

89. Harding, B. W., and Samuels, L. T., *Biochem. Biophys. Acta*, **54**, 42 (1961).

90. MacKenzie, A. R., Hall, T., and Whitman, W. F., Jr., *Nature*, **193**, 72 (1962)

91. Fox, R. R., *Proc. Soc. Exptl. Biol. Med.*, **108**, 663 (1961)

92. Napier, R. A., *J. Reprod. Fertility*, **2**, 246 (1961)

93. White, I. G., and Wales, R. G., *J. Reprod. Fertility*, **2**, 225 (1961)

94. Hartree, E. F., and Mann, T., *Biochem. J.*, **80**, 464 (1961)

95. Tampion, D., and Gibbons, R. A., *Nature*, **194**, 695 (1962)

96. Tampion, D., and Gibbons, R. A., *Nature*, **194**, 381 (1962)

97. Goldberg, E., and Norman, C., *J. Cellular Comp. Physiol.*, **58**, 175 (1961)

98. Lake, P. E., Lorenz, F. W., and Reiman, W. D., *Nature*, **194**, 545 (1962)

99. Bishop, D. W., *Physiol. Rev.*, **42**, 1 (1962)

100. Johnsen, S. G., *Acta Endocrinol.*, **40**, Suppl. 66 (1962)

101. Nelson, W. O., *Fertility Sterility*, **12**, 109 (1961)

102. Parkes, A. S., *Nature*, **191**, 1256 (1961)

103. Parkes, A. S., *J. Reprod. Fertility*, **3**, 159 (1962)

104. Metz, C. B., *Intern. Rev. Cytol.*, **2**, 219 (1961)

105. Rock, J., *Fertility Sterility*, **37**, 689 (1961)

106. Greenblatt, R. B., *Med. Clin. N. Am.* **45**, 973 (1961)

107. Mears, E., *Brit. Med. J.*, No. 5261 1179 (1961)

108. Tyler, E. T., Olson, H. J., Wolf, L., Finkelstein, S., Thayer, J., Kaplan, N., Levin, M., and Weintraub, J., *Obstet. Gynecol.*, **18**, 363 (1961)

109. Ferin, J., *Acta Endocrinol.*, **39**, 47 (1962)

110. Aydar, C. K., and Greenblatt, R. B., *Acta Endocrinol.*, **38**, 419 (1961)

111. Meyer C. J., Sayne, D. S., Tait, J. F., and Pincus, G., *J. Clin. Invest.*, **40**, 1663 (1961)

112. Elton, R. L., and Nutting, E. F., *Proc. Soc. Exptl. Biol. Med.*, **107**, 991 (1961)

113. Falconi, G., and Ercoli, A., *Proc. Soc. Exptl. Biol. Med.*, **108**, 3 (1961)

114. Falconi, G., Gardi, R., Bruin, G., and Ercoli, A., *Endocrinology*, **69**, 638 (1961)

115. Ercoli, A., and Gardi, R., *Chem. Ind.* (July 8, 1961)

116. Beyler, A. L., Potts, G. O., and Arnold, A., *Endocrinology*, **68**, 987 (1961),

117. Harris, L. H., *J. Comp. Exptl. Med.*, **21**, 1099 (1961)

118. Schöler, H. F. L., and de Wachter, A. M., *Acta Endocrinol.*, **38**, 128 (1961)

119. Myerson, R., *Am. J. Med. Sci.*, **241**, 732 (1961)

120. Perrine, J. W., *Acta Endocrinol.*, **37**, 376 (1961)

121. Jones, H. E. H., Waynforth, H. B., and Pope, G. S., *J. Endocrinol.*, **22**, 124 (1961)

122. McKay, D., Pinkerton, J. H. M., Hertig, A., and Danziger, S., *Obstet. Gynecol.*, **18**, 13 (1961)
123. Pinkerton, J. H. M., McKay, D. G., Adams, E. C., and Hertig, A. T., *Obstet. Gynecol.*, **18**, 152 (1961)
124. Slate, W. G., and Bradbury, J. T., *Endocrinology*, **70**, 1 (1962)
125. Ikonen, M., Niemi, M., Pesonen, S. and Tirvonen, S. T., *Acta Endocrinol.*, **38**, 293 (1961)
126. Warren, J. C., and Salhanick, H. A., *J. Clin. Endocrinol. Metab.*, **21**, 1376 (1961)
127. Kullander, S., *Acta Endocrinol.*, **38**, 598 (1961)
128. Thorsøe, H., *Acta Endocrinol.*, **37**, 199 (1961)
129. Smith. B. D., and Bradbury, J. T., *Proc. Soc. Exptl. Biol. Med.*, **107**, 946 (1961)
130. Foraker, A. G., and Crespo, J. Z., *Fertility Sterility*, **12**, 425 (1961)
131. Kecskés, L., Mutschler, F., Thán, E., and Farkas, I., *Acta Endocrinol.*, **39**, 483 (1962)
132. Levvy, G. A., McAllan, A., and Hay, A. J., *J. Endocrinol.*, **23**, 19 (1961)
133. Romanoff, E. B., Deshpande, N., and Pincus, G., *Endocrinology*, **70**, 532 (1962)
134. Bowerman, A. M., and Melampy, R. M., *Proc. Soc. Exptl. Biol. Med.*, **109**, 45 (1962)
135. Mastroianni, L., Shah, U., and Abdul-Karim, R., *Fertility Sterility*, **12**, 417 (1961)
136. Hunter, G. C., Bishop, G. P., Adams, C. E., and Rowson, L. E., *J. Reprod. Fertility*, **3**, 33 (1962)
137. Finn, C. A., and Keen, P. M., *Nature*, **194**, 602 (1962)
138. Schelesnyak, M. C., *Am. J. Physiol.*, **170**, 522 (1952)
139. Kao, C. Y., and Gams, R. S., *Am. J. Physiol.*, **201**, 714 (1961)
140. Kao, C. Y., *Am. J. Physiol.*, **201**, 717 (1961)
141. Berger, E., and Marshall, J. M., *Am. J. Physiol.*, **201**, 931 (1961)
142. Stamm, O., Monnier, J., and Loor, U., *Bull. Soc. Chim. Biol.*, **43**, 1347 (1961)
143. Freund, M., and Lefkovitz, A. M., *Fertility Sterility*, **12**, 459 (1961)
144. Rowlands, I. W., *J. Endocrinol.*, **24**, 105 (1962)
145. Larsen, J. F., *Am. J. Anat.*, **109**, 319 (1961)
146. Prahlad, K. V., *Acta Endocrinol.*, **39**, 407 (1962)
147. Noyes, R. W., Doyle, L. L., and Bentley, D. L., *J. Reprod. Fertility*, **2**, 238 (1961)
148. Hafez, E. S. E., *Proc. Soc. Exptl. Biol. Med.*, **107**, 680 (1961)
149. Cochrane, R. L., Prasad, M. R. N., and Meyer, R. K., *Endocrinology*, **70**, 228 (1962)
150. Lutwak-Mann, C., Hay, M. F., and Adams, C. E., *J. Endocrinol.*, **24**, 185 (1962)
151. Lutwak-Mann, C., *Nature*, **193**, 653 (1962)
152. Rhodin, J. A. G., and Terzakis, J., *J. Ultrastruct. Res.*, **6**, 88 (1962)
153. Levine, B., *Obstet. Gynecol.*, **17**, 769 (1961)
154. Fuchs, A. R., and Fuchs, S., *Acta Physiol. Scand.*, **52**, 65 (1961)
155. Goodner, C. J., and Freinkel, N., *Diabetes*, **10**, 383 (1961)
156. Buse, M. G., Roberts, W. J., and Buse, J., *J. Clin. Invest.*, **41**, 29 (1962)
157. Castren, O., Hirvonen, L., Närväen, S., and Soiva, K., *Acta Endocrinol.*, **39**, 506 (1962)
158. Plentl, A. A., *Proc. Soc. Exptl. Biol. Med.*, **107**, 622 (1961)
159. Lawn, L., and McCance, R. A., *Proc. Roy. Soc. (London)*, *B*, **155**, 500 (1962)
160. Dancis, J., Samuels, B. D., and Douglas, G. W., *Science*, **136**, 382 (1962)
161. Schmidt-Elmendorff, H. W., *Acta Endocrinol.*, **38**, 527 (1961)
162. Bull, G., Hebb, C., and Ratkovic, D., *Nature*, **190**, 1202 (1961)
163. Neil, M. W., *Biochem. J.*, **80**, 187 (1961)
164. Neil, M. W., Walker, D. G., and Warren, F. L., *Biochem. J.*, **80**, 181 (1961)
165. Troen, P., *J. Clin. Endocrinol. Metab.*, **21**, 895 (1961)
166. Troen, P., *J. Clin. Endocrinol. Metab.*, **21**, 1511 (1961)
167. Hobkirk, R., and Nilsen, M., *J. Clin. Endocrinol. Metab.*, **22**, 134, 142 (1962)
168. Deane, H. W., Rubin, B. L., Driks, E. C., Lobel, B. L., and Leipsner, G., *Endocrinology*, **70**, 407 (1962)
169. Kaplan, N. M., *J. Clin. Endocrinol. Metab.*, **21**, 1139 (1961)
170. Mikhail, G., Noall, M. W., and Allen, W. M., *Endocrinology*, **69**, 504 (1961)
171. Wu, D. H., *Fertility Sterility*, **12**, 236 (1961)
172. Yochim, J., and Zarrow, M. X., *Fertility Sterility*, **12**, 263 (1961)
173. Lerner, L. J., Brennan, D. M.,

Yiacas, E., DePhillipo, M., and Borman, A., *Endocrinology*, **70**, 283 (1962)

174. Lobel, B. Z., and Deane, H. W., *Endocrinology*, **70**, 567 (1962)

175. Montfort, I., and Pérez-Tamayo, R., *Lab. Invest.*, **10**, 1240 (1961)

176. Solish, G. I., Gershowitz, H., and Behrman, S. J., *Proc. Soc. Exptl. Biol. Med.*, **108**, 645 (1961)

177. Diczfalusy, E., and Borell, U., *J. Clin. Endocrinol. Metab.*, **21**, 1119 (1961)

178. Diczfalusy, E., Cassmer, O., Alonso, C., de Miguel, M., and Westin, B., *Acta Endocrinol.*, **37**, 516 (1961)

179. Troen, P., Nilsson, B., Wiqvist, N., and Diczfalusy, E., *Acta Endocrinol.*, **38**, 361 (1961)

180. Dowling, J. T., Hutchinson, D. L., Hindle, W. R., and Kleeman, C. R., *J. Clin. Endocrinol. Metab.*, **21**, 779 (1961)

181. Hagerman, D. D., *Endocrinology*, **70**, 88 (1962)

182. Huggett, A. St. G., and Nixon, D. A., *Nature*, **190**, 1209 (1961)

183. Cowie, A. T., and Tindal, J. S., *J. Endocrinol.*, **23**, 79 (1961)

184. Hardwick, D. C., Linzell, J. L., and Price, S. M., *Biochem. J.*, **80**, 37 (1961)

185. Bucovaz, E. T., and Davis, J. W., *J. Biol. Chem.*, **236**, 2015 (1961)

186. Griffith, D. R., and Turner, C. W., *Proc. Soc. Exptl. Biol. Med.*, **107**, 668 (1961)

187. Rubin, B., and Strecker, H., *Endocrinology*, **69**, 257 (1961)

188. Hofmann, F. G., *Biochim. Biophys. Acta*, **58**, 343 (1962)

189. Leybold, K., and Staudinger, H., *Arch. Biochem. Biophys.*, **96**, 626 (1962)

190. Taylor, W., and Scratcherd, T., *Biochem. J.*, **81**, 398 (1961)

191. Wiest, W. G., and Wilcox, R. B., *J. Biol. Chem.*, **236**, 2425 (1961)

192. Tamaoki, B., and Pincus, G., *Endocrinology*, **69**, 527 (1961)

193. Fukushima, D. K., and Bradlow, H. L., *J. Biol. Chem.*, **237**, PC 975 (1962)

194. Lipsett, M. B., *J. Clin. Endocrinol. Metab.*, **22**, 119 (1962)

195. Gower, D. B., and Haslewood, G. A. D., *J. Endocrinol.*, **23**, 253 (1961)

196. Acevedo, H. F., Axelrod, L. R., Ishikawa, E., and Takaki, F., *J. Clin. Endocrinol. Metab.*, **21**, 1611 (1961)

197. Savard, K., Mason, N., Ingram, J. T., and Gassner, F. X., *Endocrinology*, **69**, 324 (1961)

198. Gawienowski, A. M., Lee, S. L., and Marrian, G. B., *Endocrinology*, **69**, 388 (1961)

199. Axelrod, L. R., and Goldzieher, J. W., *Endocrinology*, **70**, 943 (1962)

200. Engel, L. L., Baggett, B., and Halla, M., *Endocrinology*, **70**, 907 (1962)

201. Short, R. V., *J. Endocrinol.*, **23**, 277 (1961)

202. Short, R. V., *J. Endocrinol.*, **24**, 59 (1962)

203. Short, R. V., *J. Endocrinol.*, **23**, 401 (1962)

204. Timonen, S., Hirvonen, E., and Wichmann, K., *J. Endocrinol.*, **24**, 7 (1962)

205. Huang, W. Y., and Pearlman, W. H., *J. Biol. Chem.*, **237**, 1060 (1962)

206. Fishman, J., Hellman, L., Zuniff, B., and Gallagher, T. F., *J. Clin. Endocrinol. Metab.*, **22**, 384 (1962)

207. Breuer, H., *Acta Endocrinol.*, **40**, 111 (1962)

208. Brown, B. T., Golder, W. S., and Wright, S. E., *Australian J. Exptl. Biol. Med. Sci.*, **39**, 345 (1961)

209. Jellinck, P. H., and Irwin, L., *Can. J. Biochem. Physiol.*, **40**, 459 (1962)

210. Breuer, H., Vogel, W., and Knuppen, R., *Z. Physiol. Chem.*, **327**, 217 (1962)

211. Knuppen, R., and Breuer, H., *Biochim. Biophys. Acta*, **58**, 147 (1962)

212. Werbin, H., Imada, M. R., and Chaikoff, I. L., *Biochim. Biophys. Acta*, **58**, 136 (1962)

213. Hecher, E., and Zayed, S. M., *Biochim. Biophys. Acta*, **50**, 607 (1961)

214. Frandsen, V. A., and Stakemann, G., *Acta Endocrinol.*, **38**, 383 (1961)

215. Diczfalusy, E., Cassmer, O., Alonso, C., and de Miguel, M., *Acta Endocrinol.*, **38**, 31 (1961)

216. Diczfalusy, E., Franksson, C., and Martinsen, B., *Acta Endocrinol.*, **38**, 59 (1961)

217. Barr, M., Diczfalusy, E., and Tillinger, K. G., *Acta Endocrinol.*, **37**, 241 (1961)

218. Diczfalusy, E., Cassmer, O., Alonso, C., and de Miguel, M., *Acta Endocrinol.*, **37**, 353 (1961)

219. Smith, O. W., and Ryan, K. J., *Endocrinology*, **69**, 970 (1961)

220. Smith, O. W., and Ryan, K. J., *Endocrinology*, **69**, 869 (1961)

221. Ryan, K. J., and Smith, O. W., *J. Biol. Chem.*, **236**, 2204 (1961)

222. Axelrod, L. R., Rao, P. N., and Gold-

zieher, J. W., *Arch Biochem. Biophys.*, **94**, 265 (1961)

223. Breuer, H., and Grill, P., *Z. Physiol. Chem.*, **324**, 254 (1961)

224. Andrén, N., and Borglin, N. E., *Acta Endocrinol.*, **37**, 427 (1961)

225. Borglin, N. E., *Acta Endocrinol.*, **37**, 511 (1961)

226. von Berswordt-Wallrabe, R., and Turner, C. W., *Proc. Soc. Exptl. Biol. Med.*, **107**, 469 (1961)

227. von Berswordt-Wallrabe, R., and Turner, C. W., *Proc. Soc. Exptl. Biol. Med.*, **107**, 471 (1961)

228. Landau, R. L., and Lugibihl, K., *J. Clin. Endocrinol. Metab.*, **21**, 1355 (1961)

229. Landau, R. L., and Lugibihl, K., *J. Clin. Endocrinol. Metab.*, **21**, 1345 (1961)

230. Kuriyama, H., *J. Physiol. (London)*, **159**, 26 (1961)

231. Yamashita, K., and Kurouji, K., *Nature*, **190**, 1013 (1961)

232. Yamashita, K., and Kurouji, K., *Proc. Soc. Exptl. Biol. Med.*, **107**, 444 (1961)

233. Charles, L. M., and Nicol, T., *Nature*, **192**, 565 (1961)

234. Mellinger, R. C., and Smith, R. W., *J. Clin. Endocrinol. Metab.*, **21**, 931 (1961)

235. Smith, B. D., *Endocrinology*, **69**, 238 (1961)

236. Brown, W. O., and Badman, H. G., *Endocrinology*, **69**, 275 (1961)

237. Kalman, S. M., Lombrozo, M. E., and Lavis, V., *Science*, **134**, 1372 (1961)

238. Noall, M. W., and Allen, W. M., *J. Biol. Chem.*, **236**, 2987 (1961)

239. Kalman, S. M., and Daniels, J. R., *Biochem. Pharmacol.*, **8**, 250 (1961)

240. Brody, S., and Wiqvist, N., *Endocrinology*, **68**, 971 (1961)

241. Volfin, P., Clauser, H., Gautheron, D., and Eboué, D., *Bull. Soc. Chim. Biol.*, **43**, 107 (1961)

242. Wakid, N. W., and Needham, D. M., *J. Biophys. Biochem. Cytol.*, **10**, 136 (1961)

243. Beard, J., and Hollander, V. P., *Arch. Biochem. Biophys.*, **96**, 592 (1962)

244. Paul, K. G., *Excerpta Med.*, **51**, 182 (1962)

245. Hayashi, M., and Fishman, W. H., *Acta Endocrinol.*, **38**, 107 (1961)

246. Takeuchi, T., Hayashi, M., and Fishman, W. H., *Acta Endocrinol.*, **39**, 395 (1962)

247. Bengtsson, L. P., *Acta Endocrinol.*, **40**, 82 (1962)

248. Cutler, A., Ober, W., Epstein, J., and Kupperman, H., *Endocrinology*, **69**, 473 (1961)

249. Joel, P. B., Hagerman, D. D., and Villee, C. A., *J. Biol. Chem.*, **236**, 3151 (1961)

250. Jarabak, J., Adams, J. A., Williams-Ashman, H. G., and Talalay, P., *J. Biol. Chem.*, **237**, 345 (1962)

251. Lostroh, A. J., *Endocrinology*, **70**, 747 (1962)

252. Harding, B. W., and Samuels, L. T., *Endocrinology*, **70**, 109 (1962)

253. Kassenaar, A., Kouwenhoven, A., and Querido, A., *Acta Endocrinol.*, **39**, 223 (1962)

254. Telkkä, A., Kivikoski, A., and Hopsu, V. K., *Acta Endocrinol.*, **39**, 129 (1962)

255. Kräbenbühl, C., *Acta Endocrinol.*, **37**, 394 (1961)

256. Huis in't Veld, L. G., Louwerens, B., and van der Spek, P. A. F., *Acta Endocrinol.*, **37**, 217 (1961)

257. Farnsworth, W. E., and Brown, J. R., *Endocrinology*, **68**, 978 (1961)

258. Wilson, J. D., *J. Clin. Invest.*, **40**, 1088 (1961)

259. Wilson, J. D., *J. Clin. Invest.*, **41**, 153 (1962)

260. Kochakian, C. D., Tanaka, R., and Hill, J., *Am. J. Physiol.*, **201**, 1068 (1961)

261. Overbeek, G. A., and de Visser, J., *Acta Endocrinol.*, **38**, 285 (1961)

262. Buetow, D. E., and Levedahl, B. H., *Arch. Biochem. Biophys.*, **94**, 358 (1961)

263. Pissott, L. E., and Nandi, S., *Acta Endocrinol.*, **37**, 161 (1961)

264. Rivera, E., and Bern, H., *Endocrinology*, **69**, 340 (1961)

265. Damm, H. C., Miller, W. R., and Turner, C. W., *Proc. Soc. Exptl. Biol. Med.*, **107**, 989 (1961)

266. Ahrén, K., and Hamburger, L., *Acta Endocrinol.*, **40**, 265 (1962)

267. Nelson, W. L., Butsu, R. A., and Ciaccio, E. I., *Arch. Biochem. Biophys.*, **96**, 500 (1962)

268. Williams-Ashman, H. G., and Huggins, C., *Med. Exptl.*, **4**, 223 (1961)

269. Wooley, D. E., and Timiras, P. J., *Endocrinology*, **70**, 196 (1962)

270. Whalen, R. E., Beach, F. A., and Kuehn, R., *Endocrinology*, **69**, 373 (1961)

271. Borglin, N. E., and Bjersing, L., *Acta Endocrinol.*, **38**, 50 (1961)

272. Dukes, P., and Goldwasser, E., *Endocrinology*, **69**, 21 (1961)

273. Vaes, G., and Nichols, G., Jr., *Endocrinology*, **70**, 890 (1962)

274. Peck, W. A., Woods, W. D., Raines, M., Dutton, A. M., and Orbison, J. L., *Proc. Soc. Exptl. Biol. Med.*, **108**, 786 (1961)

275. Eskin, B. A., Draftman, M. B., and Pettit, M. D., *Endocrinology*, **69**, 195 (1961)

276. Grosvenor, C. E., *Endocrinology*, **70**, 673 (1962)

277. Kitay, J. I., *Nature*, **192**, 358 (1961)

278. Allalouf, D. A., and Ber, A., *Endocrinology*, **69**, 210 (1961)

279. Augustinsson, K.-B., and Olsson, B., *Nature*, **192**, 969 (1961)

280. Stevens, D. F., *Exptl. Cell Res.*, **25**, 59 (1961)

281. Kochakian, C. D., and Harrison, D. G., *Endocrinology*, **70**, 99 (1962)

282. Debachere, M., Peeters, G., and Tuyttens, N., *J. Endocrinol.*, **22**, 321 (1961)

283. Reynolds, S. R. M., and Mackie, J. D., *Proc. Soc. Exptl. Biol. Med.*, **108**, 649 (1961)

284. Melander, S., E., *Nature*, **191**, 176 (1961)

285. Hawker, R. W., Walmsley, C. F., Roberts, V. S., Blackshaw, J. K., and Downes, J. C., *J. Clin. Endocrinol. Metab.*, **21**, 985 (1961)

286. Berger, E., and Marshall, J. M., *Am. J. Physiol.*, **201**, 931 (1961)

287. Lehninger, A. L., and Neubert, D., *Proc. Natl. Acad. Sci. US*, **47**, 1929 (1961)

288. Ghosh, B. P., and Bose, S. N., *Med. Exptl.*, **4**, 78 (1961)

289. Goldstein, D. P., and Sturgis, S. H., *Am. J. Physiol.*, **201**, 1053 (1961)

290. Wide, L., Roos, P., and Gemzell, C., *Acta Endocrinol.*, **37**, 445 (1961)

291. Wide, L., and Gemzell, C., *Acta Endocrinol.*, **39**, 536 (1962)

292. Keele, D. K., Rimple, J., Bean, J., and Webster, J., *J. Clin. Endocrinol. Metab.*, **22**, 287 (1961)

293. Jones, H. E. H., and Pope, G. S., *J. Endocrinol.*, **22**, 303 (1961)

294. Beling, C. G., *Nature*, **192**, 326 (1961)

295. Thewalt, K., and Zimmermann, W., *Acta Endocrinol.*, **38**, 121 (1961)

296. Bugge, S., Nilsen, M., Metcalfe-Gibson, A., and Hobkirk, R., *Can. J. Biochem. Physiol.*, **39**, 1501 (1961)

297. Gurpide, E., Mann, J., Van de Wiele, R. L., and Lieberman, S., *Acta Endocrinol.*, **39**, 213 (1962)

298. Bialy, G., and Pincus, G., *Endocrinology*, **70**, 781 (1962)

299. Kurogochi, Y., and Pincus, G., *Endocrinology*, **70**, 940 (1962)

300. Lisboa, B. P., and Diczfalusy, E., *Acta Endocrinol.*, **40**, 60 (1962)

301. Cohen, R. R., *Nature*, **194**, 601 (1962)

302. Oertel, G. W., *Acta Endocrinol.*, **37**, 237 (1961)

303. Martin, M. M., Reddy, W. J., and Thorn, G. W., *J. Clin. Endocrinol. Metab.*, **21**, 923 (1961)

304. Axelrod, L. R., and Goldzieher, J. W., *Arch. Biochem. Biophys.*, **95**, 547 (1961)

305. Warren, J. C., and Salhanick, H. A., *J. Clin. Endocrinol. Metab.*, **21**, 1218 (1961)

306. Lanthier, A., and Sandor, T., *Acta Endocrinol.*, **39**, 145 (1962)

307. Short, R. V., and London, D. R., *Brit. Med. J.*, 1724 (June 17, 1961)

308. Mahesh, V. B., and Greenblatt, R. B., *Nature*, **191**, 888 (1961)

309. Mahesh, V. B., and Greenblatt, R. B., *J. Clin. Endocrinol. Metab.*, **22**, 441 (1962)

310. Leon, N., Neves e Castro, M., and Dorfman, R. I., *Acta Endocrinol.*, **39**, 411 (1962)

311. Noaḷl, M. W., Alexander, F., and Allen, W. M., *Biochim. Biophys. Acta*, **59**, 520 (1962)

312. Axelrod, L. R., and Goldzieher, J. W., *J. Clin. Endocrinol. Metab.*, **22**, 431 (1962)

313. Axelrod, L. R., and Goldzieher, J. W., *J. Clin. Endocrinol. Metab.*, **22**, 537 (1962)

314. Goldzieher, J. W., and Green, J. A., *J. Clin. Endocrinol. Metab.*, **22**, 325 (1962)

ENDOCRINE CONTROL OF METABOLISM[1,2]

By P. J. Randle

The Department of Biochemistry, University of Cambridge, Cambridge, England

The aim of this review is to give a brief but detailed account of steps in metabolism which are under hormonal control and of the mechanism of this control so far as it is understood. Major emphasis has been placed on carbohydrate metabolism in muscle and adipose tissue and its relation to fatty acid metabolism because it seems to the author (who admits to be biased) that progress in this area has been substantial and that some account of the scope of hormonal control in this field may now be given. An attempt has been made in other areas to give a full bibliography of papers published between June 1961 and May 1962.

Although generalizations may be dangerous, it would nevertheless appear that hormonal control of transport processes in cell membranes and of enzyme-catalyzed reactions on major routes of metabolism in cells is indirect, i.e., brought about by activators and inhibitors (referred to collectively as regulators) whose intracellular concentration is changed by the hormone rather than by a direct reaction between hormones and enzymes or transport systems. Such regulators may have a specific role (i.e., their function may be solely that of activating or inhibiting particular enzymes) or they may be metabolites or coenzymes with an additional activating or inhibiting influence on enzymes for which they may not even be substrates or products. Thus the role of cyclic 3′,5′-AMP appears specifically to be that of a regulator, for example, of enzymes which in various tissues activate phosphorylase; whereas glucose-6-phosphate (hexokinase and uridine diphosphate glucose glycogen transglucosylase), 5′-AMP (muscle phosphorylase-b, phosphofructokinase), and inorganic phosphate (hexokinase and phosphofructokinase) are common metabolites with the additional role of activating or inhibiting the enzymes listed.

CARBOHYDRATE AND FAT METABOLISM

Reviews.—The action of insulin has received general reviews in Banting Lectures by Levine (1) and Chain (2), in a monograph by Krahl (3), in a general review by the Teppermans (4), in the proceedings of a Symposium (5), and in a British Medical Bulletin (6). The regulation of glucose uptake by muscle has been surveyed in detail by Randle & Morgan (7) and accounts of particular aspects are summarized in references (8 to 12). Glucose transport

---

[1] The survey of literature pertaining to this review was concluded in May 1962.

[2] Among the abbreviations used in this review are: AMP (adenosine monophosphate); NAD$^+$ (nicotinamide-adenine dinucleotide); NADH (nicotinamide-adenine dinucleotide, reduced form); NADP$^+$ (nicotinamide-adenine dinucleotide phosphate); NADPH (nicotinamide-adenine dinucleotide phosphate, reduced form); UDPG (uridine diphosphate glucose); UTP (uridine triphosphate).

has been reviewed by Wilbrandt & Rosenberg (13) and in the proceedings of a symposium (14), and Hechter has summarized his views on cell permeability and hormone action in a controversial and stimulating paper (15). The role of cyclic 3′,5′-AMP in hormone action has been reviewed by Sutherland and colleagues (16); various aspects of the hormonal regulation of carbohydrate metabolism in liver have been considered by Ashmore & Weber (17), by Miller (18), and by Renold & Cahill (19); and Ashmore *et al.* (20) have reviewed hormone effects on alternate pathways of glucose utilization in isolated tissues. Kennedy (21) and Lynen (22) have surveyed the biochemistry of lipid synthesis and breakdown; general reviews on the metabolism of adipose tissue and of factors influencing fatty acid oxidation and synthesis, including endocrine control, have been provided by Wertheimer & Shafrir (23), Fritz (24), Vaughan (25), Cahill *et al.* (26), and Winegrad *et al.* (27), while Scow & Chernick (28) have dealt with studies on hormonal control of fat metabolism in the rat.

MUSCLE

Carbohydrate metabolism: glucose transport.—Glucose uptake by muscle may be regarded as commencing with passage of sugar from capillary to cell surface, but available evidence suggests that this process is so rapid relative to the rate at which glucose is metabolized by muscle cells that it is only of quantitative importance in muscles with a sparse capillary network or at low plasma glucose concentrations (7). This step is not known to be influenced by hormones but it could conceivably be of importance to accelerating effects of exercise or anoxia on glucose uptake in muscles with a poor capillary circulation (7). Glucose uptake by the cell begins with transfer of the sugar across the cell membrane. This is currently believed to involve interaction of the sugar with stereospecific sites at the cell membrane (i.e., a transport process—referred to as membrane transport of glucose) because (*a*) the transfer rate is rapid at low concentrations but approaches a plateau at higher concentrations, i.e., shows saturation kinetics—shown for eviscerated cats and perfused hindlimbs (29), perfused rat heart (30), and frog sartorius (31); (*b*) competition for transfer has been demonstrated for a number of hexoses and pentoses in the rat diaphragm (32) and heart (33, 34) *in vitro;* (*c*) different sugars are transferred at markedly different rates (32, 35); (*d*) transfer of sugars is markedly inhibited by phloridzin (32, 33); and (*e*) uphill transport can be induced by counterflow—a phenomenon which provides the strongest evidence that a transport process is involved according to the definition adopted above (33, see also 13).

Membrane transport of glucose in muscle is a freely reversible process (see 7, 31, 33) and it is generally held that the direction of net movement of sugar is in the direction of the concentration gradient [though Eichton & Hechter have recently reported that the nonmetabolized sugar D-xylose may apparently be accumulated against a concentration gradient in insulin-stimulated diaphragm muscle *in vivo* (36)]. Since the hexokinase reaction which leads to the conversion of intracellular glucose to glucose-6-phosphate is both irreversible and under many conditions more rapid than membrane transport, net movement of glucose is into the cell. The mechanism of glucose transport and, in particular, the chemical nature of the sites in the membrane which react with glucose are not known but evidence has been obtained that a peptide may be involved (32, 37).

Stein (38) has presented evidence that a somewhat similar system in the red blood cell may involve the formation of dimers between pairs of glucose molecules. Progress in the biochemistry of glucose transport in muscle has been somewhat hampered by the lack of suitable methods of isolating muscle cell membranes but two procedures have recently been described for the preparation of skeletal muscle cell membranes and some enzymic activities assayed (39, 40, 41). Membrane transport of glucose in muscle is accelerated by insulin (1, 29, 31, 42 to 46), by anoxia (44, 46), by inhibitors of respiration or respiratory chain phosphorylation such as cyanide, 2,4-dinitrophenol, and salicylate (35, 44, 46 to 49) and in muscles of hypophysectomized rats by growth hormone added *in vitro* (50) and by acute administration of growth hormone *in vivo*. Muscular contraction can also accelerate glucose transport (51, 52), and the suggestion has been made that working muscles may release a humoral factor which can accelerate glucose transport in other muscles (53). This latter conclusion has, however, been questioned (54).

Membrane transport of glucose in muscle is restrained by the respiration of ketone bodies and fatty acids (55) and pyruvate (56). Membrane transport of glucose is impaired in rat heart and diaphragm by hypophysectomy (9, 57) and alloxan diabetes (58, 59), changes which have been attributed to a lower concentration of circulating insulin (cf. 60). The sensitivity of the membrane transport system to stimulation by physiological concentrations of insulin is enhanced by hypophysectomy and diminished in alloxan diabetes in the rat heart (57, 58); this sensitivity is enhanced in rat diaphragm muscle by hypophysectomy or adrenalectomy, by treatment of normal or hypophysectomized rats with growth hormone, and by treatment of normal or adrenalectomized rats with cortisol (61).

Guidotti & Foa (62) and Guidotti, Kanameishi & Foa (63) have made interesting observations concerning the development of an insulin-responsive membrane transport system for glucose in the heart of the chick embryo. They find that the uptake of glucose per gram of heart and the permeability to sorbitol (which is confined to extracellular water in the adult heart) diminish as the embryo develops, particularly between days 5 and 10. They find also that accelerating effects on glucose uptake of insulin and of 2,4-dinitrophenol appear only after day 7 of development whereas anoxia stimulated glucose uptake at all stages. They conclude that phosphorylation of glucose limits uptake of the sugar before day 7 [it is known that phosphorylation of glucose is accelerated by anoxia in rat heart (46)] and that transport limits uptake of glucose and is capable of stimulation by insulin (and presumably by anoxia and 2,4-dinitrophenol) after day 7. These findings may be correlated with the findings of Grillo (64) that in the chick embryo β cells are histologically demonstrable on days 11–12, that granulation can be detected on day 12 and is general by day 16, and that insulin can be detected in acid ethanol extracts of the pancreas by bioassay with rat diaphragm by day 12.

The kinetics of glucose transport in the rat heart (30, 65) and frog sartorius (31) have been described. In the heart of the rat, the Michaelis-Menten type of relationship for transport rate as a function of concentration gradient appears to hold and the effects of insulin, anoxia, diabetes, and hypophysectomy on the K_m and V_{max} have been analysed by Park and Morgan and their colleagues (30, 57, 58). Anoxia lowers the K_m of transport whereas the V_{max} is unchanged, a finding which suggests that anoxia may remove a competitive inhibitor of transport. Insulin increased both the K_m and V_{max} of transport and in this connexion Fisher & Zachariah find that insulin lowers the affinity (i.e. increases the K_m) of the putative membrane carrier for L-arabinose and D-xylose in the rat heart (34). These findings might suggest that insulin both alters the structure and increases the number of transport sites in the membrane. Alloxan diabetes lowered the V_{max} and possibly the K_m whereas hypophysectomy reduced the V_{max} without altering the K_m (findings which may be compatible with the view that effects of alloxan diabetes and hypophysectomy on glucose transport are traceable to insulin deficiency).

The mechanism by which these various factors influence the membrane transport system for glucose and thereby alter the rate of glucose transport in muscle is not known in biochemical terms. Randle & Smith have suggested that, since anoxia and cell poisons which inhibit the generation of high-energy phosphate compounds such as ATP accelerate membrane transport of glucose, the membrane transport system is inhibited by reaction with a high-energy phosphate compound such as ATP (12, 44). This view is compatible with the suggestion, derived from kinetic analysis (see above), that anoxia leads to the removal of a competitive inhibitor of transport. Other possibilities to be considered are that increases in the intracellular concentrations of 5'-AMP or of inorganic phosphate induced by anoxia (55) may activate the membrane transport system [cf. (66) and see also regulation of hexokinase and phosphofructokinase]. The possibility that cyclic 3',5'-AMP may activate membrane transport of glucose in muscle and other tissues has also to be borne in mind in this connexion since there is evidence that corticotropin, which stimulates cyclic 3'5'-AMP production in the adrenal cortex, accelerates sugar transport in this tissue (15, 16). Randle & Smith have also suggested that the carrier for glucose may exist in phosphorylated and nonphosphorylated forms, that it may transport sugars most effectively in the nonphosphorylated form, and that insulin may accelerate glucose transport by increasing the proportion of nonphosphorylated carrier. This idea has been taken up also by the Teppermans (4) and Levine (1). Fisher & Zachariah (34) suggest that insulin may activate the carrier by combining with it. Evidence has been presented that activation of the transport system or functioning of the activated transport system involves sulphydryl groups. Battaglia & Randle (32) observed that the sulphydryl poison N-ethylmaleimide inhibits insulin-stimulated transport of D-xylose in rat diaphragm muscle; and Cadenas, Kaji & Park find that, whereas the basal transport of glucose in rat heart is unaffected by N-ethylmaleimide, insulin stimulation of glucose transport is completely prevented by prior treatment of the heart with the poison (67). Kaji & Park (see 7) find also that anoxia fails to accelerate sugar transport in hearts briefly exposed to the poison. Since N-ethylmaleimide did not impair sugar transport in hearts treated with insulin prior to exposure to the poison, it would appear that its effect may be on the activation of the transport system rather than on transport *per se*, a conclusion which has been questioned on the basis of experiments in rat diaphragm by Carlin & Hechter (68).

Carbohydrate metabolism: phosphorylation of glucose.—The phosphorylation of glucose by hexokinase is held to be an intracellular reaction (i.e., to follow membrane transport), and in keeping with this idea preparations of skeletal muscle cell membranes possess little or no hexokinase activity (40, 41). The hexokinase reaction, which leads to the formation of glucose-6-phosphate is essentially irreversible (glucose-6-phosphatase, which forms glucose from glucose-6-phosphate in liver, is not found in muscle). Muscle hexokinase is inhibited noncompetitively by its product, glucose-6-phosphate, the K_i for heart muscle hexokinase being of the order of 0.1 mM (69). The intracellular concentration of glucose-6-phosphate in the heart and diaphragm muscle of the rat *in vitro* under aerobic conditions is of the order of 0.5 to 0.7 mM (70) so that the enzyme is likely to be markedly inhibited unless much of the glucose-6-phosphate is combined with other intracellular structures or unless other metabolites can modify this inhibition (see below). The phosphorylation of glucose in rat heart is accelerated by anoxia (46) and salicylate (55) but not by insulin given *in vitro* (11, 30, 58), and it is inhibited in alloxan diabetes (58) by starvation (46, 71) and *in vitro* by the respiration of ketone bodies, *n*-octanoate, pyruvate (72) and by palmitate and other long-chain fatty acids carried by bovine serum albumin (71, 73). The inhibitory effects of diabetes can be suppressed by hypophysectomy of the rat and by treatment with insulin *in vivo* but not by insulin *in vitro* (11, 74). Treatment of the rat with growth hormone and cortisol restores marked inhibition of glucose phosphorylation in perfused hearts from hypophysectomized alloxan diabetic rats but leads to only a mild degree of inhibition in hearts from normal rats. Phosphorylation of glucose in the rat heart is not impaired by the addition of growth hormone or cortisol *in vitro* (74) .The effects of insulin, growth hormone, and cortisol on glucose phosphorylation are thus indirect effects and the suggestion has been made by Newsholme, Randle & Manchester (72) that they are brought about by alterations in the rate of respiration of fatty acids and ketone bodies. The phosphorylation of glucose in rat diaphragm muscle is also impaired in alloxan diabetes and by starvation (reversed by adrenalectomy), but not influenced by insulin *in vitro* (9, 52, 59, 75).

The mechanism of regulation of glucose phosphorylation by these factors is not fully known. Since glucose-6-phosphate is known to inhibit muscle hexokinase, it has been natural to enquire whether alterations in the intra-cellular concentration of glucose-6-phosphate may regulate the activity of hexokinase. Factors which accelerate hexokinase (e.g. anoxia, salicylate) do lower the intracellular concentration of glucose-6-phosphate and those which inhibit hexokinase raise its concentration (70, 72, 76), but these changes occur over a range of concentrations of glucose-6-phosphate which are some 3 to 13 times greater than the K_i for heart muscle hexokinase. The possibility exists therefore that other metabolites such as inorganic phosphate or 5′-AMP may modify the inhibitory action of glucose-6-phosphate, and there is some evidence that inorganic phosphate may do this [(77), cf. phosphofructo-kinase—see below]. Further evidence on this point is, however, required.

Carbohydrate metabolism: glycogen cycle.—Understanding of the synthesis and breakdown of glycogen has been greatly clarified by the recognition that there are independent pathways for synthesis and breakdown of the poly-saccharide. Synthesis of glycogen from glucose-6-phosphate involves, in sequence, conversion to glucose-1-phosphate (by phosphoglucomutase), the formation of uridine diphosphate glucose (UDPG) by reaction with UTP (catalyzed by UDPG pyrophosphorylase), and the transfer of the glucose residue to glycogen to form a 1:4 α-linked glucose residue in glycogen by UDPG glycogen transglucosylase (referred to henceforth as glucosylase). The discovery of this pathway of synthesis stems from the original work of Leloir & Cardini (78) in liver, and an essentially similar system in muscle has been identified by Larner & Villar-Palasi and their colleagues (79). The last two enzymic steps in glycogen synthesis are essentially irreversible (the pyrophosphorylase reaction on account of the low pyrophosphate concentra-tion in cells), thus emphasising the purely synthetic role of this pathway. The rate-limiting step in glycogen synthesis is the transglucosylase reaction (80, see also 81 to 84). The enzyme is activated by glucose-6-phosphate (83, 85) in the range of concentrations found in muscle cells (70). The activity of the transglucosylase is enhanced in extracts of diaphragm muscle previously in-cubated in the presence of insulin (80, 83, 84) whereas the activities of other enzymes involved in the synthesis of glycogen from glucose-6-phosphate and its breakdown to glucose-6-phosphate are unchanged (83).

The action of insulin does not appear to be caused by alterations in the intracellular concentration of glucose-6-phosphate (83). Evidence has been presented that the enzyme may exist in two forms, one dependent for activity upon glucose-6-phosphate (*D* or dependent) and the other independent (or *I*) of glucose-6-phosphate. Friedman & Larner (84) believe that the action of insulin leads to an increase in the proportion of the *I* form and that the con-version of *I* to *D* may involve transfer of phosphate from ATP to the enzyme in the presence of Mg^{++} (it is interesting that this is the reverse of the situa-tion with phosphorylase where conversion from the 5′-AMP-independent form to the 5′-AMP-dependent form involves loss of phosphate and vice versa). It is presumably this action of insulin which accounts for the fact that a substantial proportion of glucose residues taken up under the influence of the hormone are converted to glycogen (80, 86). In the perfused rat heart insulin effects a much smaller increase in glycogen synthesis than in diaphragm muscle thus suggesting possible variations in the properties of the glucosylase in different tissues (87, 88). The concentration of glycogen in the heart is markedly increased in diabetes and starvation and in starved hypophysectomized rats treated with growth hormone. Since ketone bodies (72, 88) and fatty acids (89) accelerate glycogen synthesis in the perfused heart of the rat *in vitro*, it has been suggested (72) that the effects of diabetes, starvation, and growth hormone on cardiac glycogen are brought about by enhanced respiration of fatty acids and ketone bodies. Newsholme, Randle & Manchester have proposed that this change is caused primarily by inhibition of the phosphofructokinase reaction which leads to the accumulation of glucose-6-phosphate in the cell and thereby to activation of UDPG glycogen transglucosylase.

The breakdown of glycogen in muscle proceeds by way of reaction between glycogen and inorganic phosphate under the influence of phosphorylase to yield glucose-1-phosphate (converted to glucose-6-phosphate by phosphoglucomutase) and modified glycogen. The equilibrium position of the reaction is governed by the ratio of glucose-1-phosphate to inorganic phosphate; this is so low in muscle that the enzyme catalyzes breakdown and not synthesis of the polysaccharide (81). In muscle, phosphorylase exists in two forms, one dependent upon 5'-AMP for its activity (phosphorylase b), the other (phosphorylase a) independent of 5'-AMP. Conversion of b to a involves an activating enzyme, and two molecules of b are combined, with the transfer of phosphate from ATP to the enzyme. This reaction is accelerated by Ca^{++} and by cyclic 3'5'-AMP. Conversion of a to b involves release of phosphate and rupture of a and is catalyzed by an inactivating enzyme. The K activation of phosphorylase b by 5'-AMP is 0.05 mM which is well below the intracellular concentration of 5'-AMP in the perfused heart of the rat under aerobic conditions which is 0.1 to 0.4 mM (55, 87). This must mean either that much of the intracellular 5'-AMP is unavailable to the enzyme or that activation of phosphorylase b by 5'-AMP is modified by other metabolites (since glycogen breakdown is slow in aerobic muscle). In this connexion Madsen (90) finds that UDPG can inhibit rabbit muscle phosphorylase.

Glycogen breakdown in muscle is accelerated by epinephrine, anoxia, and muscle contraction. Epinephrine accelerates glycogen breakdown by increasing the formation of cyclic 3'5'-AMP which activates conversion of phosphorylase b to a (91 to 94). Anoxia and glucagon increase the proportion of phosphorylase a in heart muscle (95) but the mechanism is not known. Anoxia may also activate phosphorylase b by increasing tissue concentrations of 5'-AMP (55, 87, 95).

Carbohydrate metabolism: pentose phosphate cycle.—Glucose-6-phosphate may be directly oxidized by glucose-6-phosphate and 6-phosphogluconate dehydrogenases to yield the pentose derivative ribulose-5-phosphate, carbon dioxide, and NADPH (reduced coenzyme II or TPNH). Ribulose-5-phosphate may be converted to a number of other pentose phosphates (by mutase, isomerase, and epimerase enzymes) or reconverted to fructose and glucose-6-phosphates (by transketolase and transaldolase enzymes). The pathway whose function appears to be that of generating NADPH (for lipogenesis especially) and pentose phosphates is very poorly developed in skeletal muscle (20, 96) though it appears to be present (97, 98). Though the role of this pathway has yet to be fully evaluated in cardiac muscle, it seems unlikely to be a quantitatively important pathway for the disposal of glucose-6-phosphate in muscle tissues. The relative roles of the glycolytic and pentose phosphate pathways in the utilization of glucose in a number of different foetal and adult tissues has been evaluated by Villee & Loring (99).

Carbohydrate metabolism: phosphorylation of fructose-6-phosphate.—The third route for the disposal of glucose-6-phosphate in muscle is by the glycolytic pathway. The conversion of glucose-6-phosphate to fructose-6-phosphate by phosphoglucoisomerase is a reversible reaction and is not known to be influenced by hormones. The ratio of glucose-6-phosphate to fructose-6-phosphate in heart and diaphragm muscle is higher than that achieved by isolated phosphoglucoisomerase (70); the reason for this is not known. The phosphorylation of fructose-6-phosphate to fructose-1,6-diphosphate, by the transfer of phosphate from ATP, catalyzed by phosphofructokinase is an essentially irreversible reaction. Since the concentrations of glucose- and fructose-6-phosphates are higher than that of fructose-1,6-diphosphate in muscle and since fructose-1,6-diphosphate does not inhibit phosphofructokinase (100), this reaction is believed to be rate limiting for glycolysis (7, 70). Since the phosphofructokinase reaction is essentially irreversible, an additional enzyme, fructose-1,6-diphosphatase, is required for the formation of fructose-6-phosphate from the diphosphate and hence for the reversal of glycolysis. The activity of this enzyme in extracts of heart and diaphragm muscle is so low that it is questionable whether the enzyme is present and therefore whether glycolysis can be reversed to a significant extent in these muscles (101).

The rate of the phosphofructokinase reaction has been assayed indirectly in the perfused heart and in the diaphragm muscles of the rat by measurement of the intracellular concentrations of glucose-6-phosphate, fructose-6-phosphate, and fructose-1,6-diphosphate. Since the fructose-1,6-diphosphatase activity of these muscles is extremely low, a rise in the concentration of the diphosphate in association with a fall in that of the monophosphates has been interpreted as reflecting an increase in the activity of phosphofructokinase and vice versa. With this technique, evidence has been obtained that anoxia and inhibitors of respiratory chain phosphorylation, such as salicylate and 2,4-dinitrophenol, accelerate the phosphorylation of fructose-6-phosphate in the perfused heart and in the isolated diaphragm of the rat (70, 72) whereas the respiration of ketone bodies, octanoate, pyruvate, and albumin-bound palmitate leads to inhibition of the phosphofructokinase reaction in rat heart (71, 72). The phosphorylation of fructose-6-phosphate in rat heart is also impaired by starvation and in alloxan diabetes though not in hearts from starved or diabetic hypophysectomized rats (55, 70, 76). The inhibitory effects of starvation and diabetes on the rate of phosphorylation of fructose-6-phosphate have been attributed to enhanced respiration of fatty acids and ketone bodies (72).

The mechanism of phosphofructokinase control may be attributed to the influence on the activity of the enzyme of the common metabolites ATP, ADP, 5′-AMP, fructose-1,6-diphosphate and of cyclic 3′5′-AMP. The activity of skeletal muscle phosphofructokinase has been found by Lardy & Parks (102) and Passonneau & Lowry (100, 103) to be inhibited by excess of ATP (one of its substrates); further Passonneau & Lowry find that the enzyme is activated by 5′-AMP, inorganic phosphate, fructose-1,6-diphosphate (its product), cyclic 3′5′-AMP and to a lessser extent by ADP. In extracts of guinea pig heart, Mansour, Clague & Bearnink (104) find that phosphofructokinase activity is inhibited by excess of ATP and activated by 5′-AMP, inorganic phosphate, and cyclic 3′5′-AMP. In the liver fluke *Fasciola hepatica*, Mansour (105) finds that phosphofructokinase activity is enhanced by cyclic 3′5′-AMP and that this may be responsible for the activating effect of 5-hydroxytryptamine (serotonin) in this organism (by stimulating production of the nucleotide). In view of these findings it seems likely that acceleration of the phosphofructokinase reaction by anoxia is caused by the fall in ATP concentration and by rises in the 5′-AMP and inorganic phosphate concentrations which this agent induces in heart and muscle by inhibition of respiration (55). The effects of salicylate and 2,4-dinitrophenol may come from a similar mechanism. The process of activation may also be, to a certain extent, autocatalytic since the product fructose-1,6-diphosphate can also activate the enzyme. The inhibitory effects of respiration of fatty acids and ketone bodies (and hence perhaps of diabetes and starvation) could result from contrary changes in concentrations of these metabolites but evidence on this point is lacking.

The major effect of alterations in the activity of phosphofructokinase is likely to be that of changing the rate of glycolysis. Inhibition of phosphofructokinase may also, by increasing the intracellular concentration of glucose-6-phosphate, impair glucose phosphorylation and accelerate glycogen synthesis (see above).

Carbohydrate metabolism: formation of glycerol phosphate.—The breakdown of fructose-1,6-diphosphate by aldolase leads to the formation of glyceraldehyde-3-phosphate and dihydroxyacetone phosphate (triose phosphates). The action of glycerol phosphate dehydrogenase can lead to the reduction of dihydroxyacetone phosphate with NADH (reduced coenzyme I or DPNH) to glycerol-1-phosphate. This pathway, which leads to the production of glycerol-1-phosphate required for esterification of fatty acids to triglycerides and phosphatides, may be of considerable importance in the regulation of carbohydrate metabolism by regulating the intracellular concentration and thereby the respiration of free fatty acids and hence of the activities of hexokinase and phosphofructokinase (see above). (Its importance in this connexion in adipose tissue appears to be firmly established.) In muscle, glycerol can be formed, presumably by the breakdown of triglyceride (106). The heart of the rat, unlike its adipose tissue, appears to be able to incorporate glycerol into triglycerides and phospholipids (107).

Carbohydrate metabolism: metabolism of pyruvate.—The intervening reactions of glycolysis between triose phosphates and pyruvate have yet to be proved significant in the regulation of metabolism in muscle but there are important endocrine influences on pyruvate metabolism. In muscle pyruvate may either be reduced by NADH to lactate with lactate dehydrogenase or oxidized by pyruvate dehydrogenase (and with the participation of coenzyme A, lipoate, and thiamine pyrophosphate) to acetyl coenzyme A. The oxidation of pyruvate by rat diaphragm and ventricle muscle slices has long been known to be impaired in alloxan diabetes (108, 109). Moreover, the blood pyruvate concentration may be increased in alloxan diabetes (110), in certain cases of human diabetes (111), in patients treated with corticosteroids (112), and in dogs treated with growth hormone (113). Furthermore pyruvate tolerance is impaired in patients treated with corticosteroids (112) and in dogs treated with growth hormone (113). The factors responsible for these disturbances in pyruvate metabolism have yet to be defined but Weil, Altszuler & Kessler (113) have suggested that enhanced respiration of fatty acids may impair pyruvate oxidation by competition for coenzyme A.

The effects of alloxan diabetes, starvation, fatty acids, and ketone bodies on pyruvate uptake, oxidation, and conversion to lactate and on pyruvate and lactate production from glucose have been studied in the perfused heart and in the diaphragm of the rat *in vitro* (71). In diabetes and starvation, pyruvate uptake and oxidation were impaired and similar changes could be induced in tissues from normal rats by addition *in vitro* of ketone bodies, octanoate, butyrate, and albumin-bound palmitate. Moreover, in spite of the fact that glucose uptake by the heart was diminished by diabetes and starvation and in hearts from normal rats by the *in vitro* addition of fatty acids and ketone bodies, the combined output of pyruvate and lactate was not diminished (71, see also 88, 114, 115) from which it was inferred that these factors had also impaired the oxidation of pyruvate formed from glucose. The ratio of pyruvate to lactate formed from glucose was increased by diabetes and starvation but reduced by fatty acids (71). Garland *et al.* have concluded from these studies that enhanced respiration of fatty acids (and perhaps of ketone bodies) may be responsible for the impaired uptake of pyruvate and for the impaired oxidation of pyruvate derived from glucose in muscles of diabetic and starved rats. They have suggested that the altered ratio of pyruvate to lactate in heart muscle in diabetes and starvation may be traceable to other changes which lead to an alteration in the ratio of cytoplasmic NAD^+ to NADH. These findings suggest that alterations in blood pyruvate and in pyruvate tolerance in diabetes and in patients or animals treated with corticosteroids or growth hormone may be caused at least in part by enhanced respiration of fatty acids and ketone bodies by muscle. The earlier observations of Hall (116) showing that in rat heart acetoacetate suppresses the oxidation of [^{14}C] glucose to $^{14}CO_2$ and increases output of lactate; of Williamson (117, 118) showing that in rat heart glucose oxidation is suppressed by lactate, acetate, and starvation, and that lactate oxidation is impaired by starvation; of Williamson & Krebs showing that acetoacetate impairs glucose oxidation in rat heart (88); and of von Holt, Schmidt & Feldmann (119) who find that starvation of the rat impairs $^{14}CO_2$ production from [^{14}C] glucose are consonant with these conclusions and suggestions.

Carbohydrate metabolism: dicarboxylic acid shuttle, citrate cycle, and respiration.—There are a number of observations which suggest that the dicarboxylic acid shuttle (the sequence of reactions pyruvate to malate, by the malic enzyme, malate to oxalacetate by malic dehydrogenase and oxalacetate to phosphoenol pyruvate by oxaloacetate decarboxylase) by which phosphoenol pyruvate can be formed from pyruvate may be lacking in muscle. This may be another factor (in addition to low fructose-1,6-diphosphatase, see above) in the poor reversibility of glycolysis in muscle. A discussion of the citrate cycle and respiratory chain in muscle is beyond the scope of this review but some recent studies on respiration of muscle are worthy of comment. Fisher & Williamson (120, 121) have studied the oxygen uptake of the perfused heart of the rat with a rotating platinum electrode and find the Q_{O_2} to be 39 and the $Q_{10}O_2$ to be 2.3. Oxygen uptake was not influenced by glucose±insulin or by β-hydroxybutyrate, but acetoacetate±insulin lowered uptake slightly whereas 2,4-dinitrophenol markedly enhanced oxygen uptake. The preferential use of different substrates for respiration has already been considered in the section on pyruvate metabolism and has been studied in particular by Williamson, Williamson & Krebs, and Shipp, Opie & Challoner (88, 89, 114, 116 to 119) though mention should be made of earlier pioneer work by Drury & Wick (122). In general, fatty acids and ketone bodies, pyruvate, and lactate are oxidized in preference to glucose; the studies of Newsholme *et al.* and of Garland *et al.* (55, 71, 72) appear to show that this results from inhibition of membrane transport of glucose, phosphorylation of glucose, and phosphorylation of fructose-6-phosphate by respiration of these alternative substrates. Moreover, fatty acids and ketone bodies are in general oxidized in preference to pyruvate or lactate (71). The extent to which respiration of fatty acids and ketone bodies impairs the catabolism of glucose at different steps in the perfused heart of the rat appears to be in the sequence (from least to greatest degree of impairment): membrane transport, hexokinase, phosphofructokinase, and pyruvate dehydrogenase (because respiration of these substrates leads to accumulations of pyruvate and lactate-, fructose-, and glucose-6-phosphates and glucose although over-all glucose uptake is inhibited). The author suggests that the physiological importance of this sequence may be to permit the continued entry of glucose residues into glycogen and to permit sufficient glycolysis to take place to allow for the synthesis from intermediates of glycolysis of such important cell constituents as phospholipids, amino acids, purines, and pyrimidines. The author suggests that the important role of glycolysis as a synthetic pathway may perhaps have been overlooked.

Gourley (123) finds that in frog leg muscles insulin may stimulate oxygen uptake, perhaps by increasing lactate oxidation. Effects of insulin on oxygen uptake and K^+ uptake were distinguished with cardiac glycosides such as digoxin and ouabain which blocked only the K^+ uptake.

Fatty acid metabolism in muscle.—The biochemistry and physiology of fatty acid oxidation have recently been reviewed extensively by Fritz (24). The oxidation of [^{14}C] palmitate to $^{14}CO_2$ in the perfused heart (89) and in the extensor muscles (124) of the rat has been demonstrated. In extensor muscles Eaton & Steinberg find that the rate of oxidation is a function of medium concentration of fatty acid and is uninfluenced by glucose or epinephrine (cf. 89). This is in keeping with findings of Armstrong *et al.* (125) in studies with [^{14}C] palmitate in the intact dog that the turnover rate of plasma free fatty acids is proportional to their concentration. These studies suggest perhaps that hormones such as growth hormone regulate uptake of fatty acids by muscle by changing the rate of release from adipose tissue rather than by directly influencing uptake of fatty acids by muscle. Spitzer *et al.* (126) find that 2,4-dinitrophenol exaggerates the arteriovenous difference in fatty acids in dog leg muscles and suggest that the poison may accelerate fatty acid uptake.

Adipose Tissue

Pathways of carbohydrate metabolism.—These have been fully reviewed by Vaughan (25) and Winegrad *et al.* (27). Pathways of glycolysis, glycogen synthesis and breakdown, and pyruvate oxidation appear to be similar to those of muscle though detailed knowledge of a number of the enzymatic steps is lacking. It remains to be shown whether a membrane transport system for glucose is present in adipose tissue and whether regulatory mechanisms similar to those in muscle exist at the levels of membrane transport, hexokinase, and phosphofructokinase. As in muscle, glucose-6-phosphatase and fructose-1,6-diphosphatase may be lacking (127, 128). The pathway of glycogen synthesis is similar but the activating role of glucose-6-phosphate has not been tested though there is evidence that insulin may, as in muscle, activate glycogen synthesis specifically. Glycogen breakdown is by way of phosphorylase; and glycogenolysis is accelerated and phosphorylase activated by epinephrine, norepinephrine, glucagon, 5-hydroxytryptamine (serotonin), and corticotropin. Adipose tissue forms cyclic 3'5'-AMP and this may be responsible for activation of phosphorylase by catecholamines and 5-hydroxytryptamine. There is evidence from experiments with reserpinized animals that corticotropin may act by releasing catecholamines, especially norepinephrine (129). The pentose phosphate cycle is extremely active in adipose tissue and a significant proportion of glucose metabolized may pass through the cycle according to Winegrad & Renold (130). The oxidation of glucose through the pentose phosphate cycle is in general enhanced when fatty acid synthesis is increased, and diminished when fatty acid synthesis is impaired and lipolysis increased.

Current evidence increasingly favours the view that activation of the pentose phosphate cycle is secondary to increased lipogenesis (which generates the $NADP^+$ required from NADPH), rather than the converse. Earlier evidence on this point has been summarized by Fritz (24). More recently, in experiments with mammary gland slices, MacLean (131, 132) has added strong evidence for this view. She finds that the electron acceptor phenazine methosulphate can activate the pentose phosphate cycle, that HCO_3^- (needed for fatty acid synthesis) also stimulates glucose oxidation through this cycle, and that iodoacetate which inhibits lipogenesis, but not the dehydrogenases, of the cycle impairs glucose oxidation through the cycle.

The formation of L-glycerol-1-phosphate from glucose by glycolysis is of particular importance in adipose tissue because of its essential role in esterification of fatty acid to triglyceride. Glycerol, released by the hydrolysis of triglyceride, cannot be phosphorylated in adipose tissue [Steinberg, Vaughan & Margolis (133)] and re-esterification of fatty acid is thus dependent upon glycerol phosphate formation from glucose. The formation of the latter in homogenates of adipose tissue has been described by Margolis & Vaughan (134). Further evidence for the role of glycerol phosphate in re-esterification of fatty acids has accrued from studies with inhibitors of glycolysis (135, 136).

Glucose may also be oxidized following glycolysis, by the citrate cycle and also via the uronic acid pathway which has been suggested for adipose tissue by Winegrad et al. (27). Some studies of the cytochromes of adipose tissue have been reported by Joel & Ball (137).

Uptake of glucose by adipose tissue, as in muscle, is stimulated in vitro by insulin and by 2,4-dinitrophenol, and inhibited by starvation and diabetes (26, 27, 138, 139, 140). In contrast to muscle, anoxia depresses glucose uptake in adipose tissue (26). When glucose uptake is accelerated by insulin, glycogen synthesis, oxidation of glucose (by pentose phosphate cycle more than by glycolysis and citrate cycle), glyceride glycerol formation (and hence that of glycerol phosphate), lactate output, and lipogenesis are enhanced (130, 141, 142). With the exception of glycogen synthesis the changes in metabolism induced by insulin are explicable in terms of a single action of the hormone at membrane transport or hexokinase reactions since the action of insulin may be mimicked by raising the glucose concentration of the medium (except insofar as glycogen synthesis is concerned) (141). The action of insulin in adipose tissue could thus be similar to its action in muscle where the hormone activates membrane transport of glucose and UDPG glycogen transglucosylase, but such a view has yet to be substantiated. In starvation and diabetes, depressed uptake of glucose is associated in particular with impaired lipogenesis, oxidation of glucose, and synthesis of glycogen; but glyceride glycerol production is also depressed (26). As in the case of muscle the effects of diabetes may be attributable to insulin deficiency and, in keeping with this, insulin *in vitro* or *in vivo* corrects the metabolic defects within two to three hours (27). The oxygen consumption of adipose tissue is little influenced by insulin.

The uptake of glucose by adipose tissue is also enhanced by epinephrine, norepinephrine, corticotropin, glucagon (143), and growth hormone (27). These agents also accelerate triglyceride breakdown and fatty acid release (see following section). The action of epinephrine leads to a relatively greater oxidation of glucose by pathways other than the pentose phosphate cycle and to a marked conversion of glucose to glyceride glycerol whereas the synthesis of fatty acids from glucose is depressed (144). The effects of corticotropin, glucagon, and growth hormone are in these respects similar to those of epinephrine, and the actions of corticotropin may in fact be caused by catecholamine release in the tissue. Growth hormone, according to Winegrad *et al.*, has the additional effect of stimulating the oxidation of glucose through the uronic acid pathway (27). Cahill and his colleagues believe that these particular effects of these hormones on glucose metabolism are secondary to enhanced lipolysis with a consequent rise in the intracellular concentration of fatty acids in the tissue. The increased formation of glyceride glycerol is attributed to enhanced re-esterification of fatty acid, and the suggestion is made that enhanced utilization of glucose by pathways other than the pentose phosphate cycle may be traceable to uncoupling of respiratory chain phosphorylation by fatty acids (139, 144). Perhaps, in keeping with this suggestion, growth hormone, and under certain conditions epinephrine, may accelerate oxygen uptake (145, 146, 147). Evidence for simultaneous enhanced breakdown of triglycerides and re-esterification of fatty acid has been provided by Vaughan & Steinberg (148). The pituitary-dependent fat-mobilizing factor extracted from human urine also has effects on glucose metabolism in adipose tissue resembling those of epinephrine (149).

Glucose uptake by adipose tissue may also be depressed following hypophysectomy, possibly as a result of deficiency of either insulin or growth hormone (150). Glucose uptake is also depressed *in vitro* in adipose tissue from rats treated with cortisone (151), and recently Munck & Koritz (152, 153) have demonstrated inhibition of glucose uptake by adipose tissue with cortisol both *in vivo* and, significantly, by addition of the steroid *in vitro* at concentrations approximating those found under physiological conditions. This latter finding has received some confirmation (154, 155). Munck & Koritz believe that the inhibitory effect of cortisol on glucose uptake by adipose tissue *in vivo* precedes changes in the rate of uptake by muscle or in the rate of gluconeogenesis and they believe this effect may be of major importance to the acute hyperglycaemic effect of cortisol.

The metabolism of adipose tissue from hereditary obese hyperglycaemic mice has been compared with that of normal mice; glucose oxidation and response to epinephrine or insulin were depressed (156, 157).

Fatty acid and triglyceride synthesis.—Lynen (22) has reviewed the biochemistry of fatty acid synthesis and Kennedy (21) that of triglyceride synthesis. The major route of fatty acid synthesis from acetyl CoA appears to be different from that of oxidation of fatty acids and to be located in the supernatant fraction of the cell. It involves essentially the reaction of acetyl CoA with CO_2 to yield malonyl CoA (synthesized by acetyl carboxylase requiring biotin). The subsequent steps have been attributed to a single enzyme, fatty acid synthetase which condenses acetyl CoA, or in subsequent steps the CoA derivatives of higher fatty acids, with malonyl CoA. The condensation product is reduced by NADPH with loss of CO_2 to yield a higher fatty acid acyl CoA. Repetition of the process ultimately yields naturally occurring fatty acids such as palmitate. The system has been demonstrated in extracts both of liver and adipose tissue (158, 159), and purification of a fatty acid synthetase from liver has recently been described (160). The formation of triglyceride involves stepwise addition of fatty acid (reacting as the acyl CoA derivative) to L-glycerol-1-phosphate to yield diglyceride phosphate followed by removal of phosphate and addition of a third molecule of fatty acid. In adipose tissue, glycerol phosphate is formed necessarily from glucose but in liver, glycerol derived from triglyceride by hydrolysis may be rephosphorylated.

The rate-limiting step in fatty acid synthesis (which may be expected to be the step by which hormonal control is exercised) is believed by Numa, Matsuhashi & Lynen (161) to be the acetyl carboxylase reaction. In supernatant fractions of rat liver, the specific activity of acetyl carboxylase was approximately equal to that of the over-all system for fatty acid synthesis. In the system prepared from livers of fasted rats, both lipogenesis and the activity of acetyl carboxylase were depressed (161), and the rate of incorporation of acetyl CoA into fatty acid was depressed relative to that of malonyl CoA (162). There is evidence that the condensation of acetyl CoA and malonyl CoA may also be impaired by starvation (163). The mechanism by which fatty acid synthesis is regulated is not clear but since fatty acid synthesis is impaired under conditions where lipolysis is more rapid than esterification of fatty acid and vice versa it seems possible that the tissue level of fatty acid may regulate fatty acid synthesis (see above). If this should be the case, then glycerol phosphate formation from glucose would be a significant step in the promotion of lipogenesis. Masoro, Porter & Korchak (164) have presented evidence that the microsome fraction of rat liver may contain a regulator of fatty acid synthesis, and Martin & Vagelos (165) have observed activation of acetyl carboxylase by citrate.

In adipose tissue, lipogenesis from glucose is accelerated by insulin and prolactin *in vitro* and impaired by epinephrine and growth hormone and by diabetes and starvation. It seems probable that these latter effects may be secondary to enhanced lipolysis or failure of re-esterification and, as Vaughan has emphasized (25), it would appear that the formation of sufficient glycerol phosphate from glucose for esterification of existing free fatty acid is a necessary prerequisite for lipogenesis from glucose.

Triglyceride breakdown and release of fatty acid.—The acquisition of knowledge concerning the breakdown of triglyceride and release of fatty acids from adipose tissue has been greatly facilitated by the development by Gordon & Cherkes (166) and White & Engel (167) of *in vitro* techniques in which the release of fatty acid to serum albumin (the physiological carrier) may be measured. Fatty acid release is believed to involve hydrolysis of triglyceride by lipases and transfer to albumin. Since glycerol is poorly metabolized, its release has been used to measure the rate of lipolysis in adipose tissue *in vitro* (as opposed to net release of fatty acid) (148). Epinephrine, norepinephrine, and corticotropin [which may act by releasing catecholamines in adipose tissue (129)] stimulate fatty acid release by adipose tissue *in vitro*, and their action is associated with activation of lipases in the tissue (166 to 169).

The adrenal-stimulating activity of corticotropin has been dissociated from its action in stimulating fatty acid release by periodate oxidation (170). Fatty acid release is also enhanced *in vitro* by glucagon, by growth hormone [which does not, however, activate lipases (169)], by a pituitary-dependent factor from the urine of starved people (171), and by peptides isolated from hog anterior pituitary which appear to be different from known pituitary hormones (172, 173). With the exception of corticotropin, each of these hormones has been shown to stimulate fatty acid release *in vivo*. Growth hormone appears to be more potent in stimulating fatty acid release *in vivo* than *in vitro*.

The release of fatty acids *in vitro* both in the presence and absence of insulin is inhibited by glucose (135, 136) but particularly by glucose and insulin. These effects are presumed to accrue from re-esterification of fatty acids by glycerol phosphate formed from glucose though Jungas & Ball (174) have recently suggested that insulin may have an additional antilipolytic action. By using glycerol output as a measure of the rate of lipolysis, evidence has been obtained *in vitro* that epinephrine, glucagon, and corticotropin accelerate both lipolysis and esterification, the former more than the latter (148). The stimulating effect of epinephrine on fatty acid release is unlikely to be traceable to cyclic 3′5′-AMP thereby formed; for 5-hydroxytryptamine (serotonin), which stimulates cyclic 3′5′-AMP production, does not promote fatty acid release (25), and indeed 3′5′-AMP and other nucleotides inhibit fatty acid release *in vitro* (175). The release of fatty acids *in vivo* and in perfused adipose tissue is accelerated by starvation (176, 177) and diabetes(178). The ability of starvation to elevate plasma levels of nonesterified fatty acids is not dependent on pituitary, thyroid, or adrenal secretions though the magnitude of the response is thus dependent (177). The results of recent studies on fatty acid release in the dog with growth hormone have been described by Winkler *et al.* (179) and with epinephrine and norepinephrine by Spitzer *et al.* (180) who find that the effect of norepinephrine is influenced by insulin and glucose to a much smaller extent than that of epinephrine. Armstrong *et al.* (181) find that there is a rebound rise in nonesterified fatty acids in dogs with insulin infusion which is blocked by dibenzyline or guanethidine. Smith *et al.* (182) find that the lipid content of the testicular fat body is diminished by cortisol, epinephrine, and growth hormone and increased by insulin. Goodman & Knobil (183) find that the pituitary, adrenal, and thyroid glands are unnecessary for the nonesterified fatty acid elevating effect of growth hormone but that the effect is diminished by adrenalectomy but not by destruction of the medullae. This is in accord with the generally accepted view of synergism between growth hormone and corticosteroids in fatty acid release. In view of the recent findings of Munck (153), it may be that this action of corticosteroids is a result of their ability to depress uptake of glucose by adipose tissue. Although the fatty acid released by adipose tissue is presumably derived from triglyceride, the fatty acids released are different in composition from the fatty acids of tissue glyceride (25) and the residual glyceride is altered in composition both *in vivo* and *in vitro* (184).

LIVER

Pathways of carbohydrate metabolism.—Although the liver cell is known to be freely permeable to glucose and other sugars (185), it has yet to be established whether a membrane transport system is present. It seems unlikely, however, that permeability is an important point of control for uptake or release of glucose by the liver cell. Thus the production of glucose is generally enhanced when uptake is impaired, and the concentration of glucose in the liver cell is therefore likely to be high. The metabolism of glucose by liver differs radically from that of muscle and adipose tissue by virtue of the presence of highly active glucose-6-phosphatase and of fructose-1,6-diphosphatase. As a consequence, glycolysis is readily reversible and glucose may be produced either from glycogen or from 3-carbon precursors of fructose-1,6-diphosphate. The over-all direction of flow thus depends in particular upon the relative activities of hexokinase and glucose-6-phosphatase and of phosphofructokinase and of fructose-1,6-diphosphatase.

The synthesis and breakdown of glycogen are by pathways similar to those of muscle though it is not clear as to whether specific stimulation of glycogen synthesis by insulin can take place in liver. Breakdown of glycogen by phosphorylase is accelerated by glucagon and epinephrine through activation of the enzyme by cyclic 3'5'-AMP. Liver phosphorylase differs from that of muscle in that the inactive form of the enzyme is not responsive to 5'-AMP and in that activation involves transfer of phosphate from ATP without dimerization. It has been claimed (186) that cortisol treatment of the rat may lead to activation of liver phosphorylase. The pentose phosphate cycle is active in liver, and pathways of glycolysis and glycerol phosphate formation are similar to those of muscle and adipose tissue apart from differences noted above. Liver, unlike adipose tissue, is capable of reforming glycerol phosphate from glycerol because of the presence of glycerol kinase. The dicarboxylic acid shuttle is active in liver, and it has been calculated that some 90 per cent of pyruvate converted to phosphoenol pyruvate traverses this pathway.

The phosphorylation of glucose by hexokinase in liver appears to be regulated almost wholly by insulin (20). Thus the phosphorylation of glucose (and mannose) is impaired in diabetes (and starvation) and may be restored by treatment with insulin but not by hypophysectomy or adrenalectomy; and, moreover, treatment of adrenalectomized or diabetic adrenalectomized rats with cortisol has little influence on glucose phosphorylation. The situation is thus radically different from that in muscle (see above). Since the phosphorylation of galactose or fructose is unimpaired in the diabetic, Ashmore *et al.* conclude that defective phosphorylation of glucose must be caused by an alteration in the activity of hexokinase (20). Glucose-6-phosphate is unlikely to be the regulator of hexokinase in this connexion since its concentration falls in diabetes and starvation (187) (though it is possible that this may contribute to impaired glycogen synthesis in these conditions by regulation of UDPG glycogen transglucosylase). The activities of glucose-6-phosphatase (17, 188) and of fructose-1,6-diphosphatase (189) are increased under conditions where gluconeogenesis is enhanced, i.e., by diabetes, starvation, and treatment with cortisol. The increased activity of glucose-6-phosphatase in diabetes (unlike that of diminished hexokinase activity) is reversed by hypophysectomy (17).

The mechanism of glucose-6-phosphatase control is not known, but the control of fructose-1,6-diphosphatase may involve two forms of the enzyme. Thus, activity of the enzyme from the liver of normal rats is doubled by treatment with proteolytic enzymes, and the latter have a smaller effect when the enzyme has been activated *in vivo*, e.g., by cortisol (189, 190). Information is lacking about the possible importance of phosphofructokinase in regulating glycolysis in liver though the latter process appears to be depressed in diabetes. Since evidence has been presented that, in muscle and in adipose tissue, availability of free fatty acids may modify carbohydrate metabolism, it seems reasonable to suggest that some of the abnormalities of carbohydrate metabolism in the liver in diabetes and starvation may also be linked to excessive oxidation of fatty acid. Renold & Cahill (19), in discussing ketosis, make the suggestion that reversal of glycolysis in liver may lead to enhanced oxidation of fatty acids (to provide NADH needed for reversal of glycolysis). Since the primary event in impairment of glucose uptake in muscle, and of glucose oxidation through the pentose phosphate cycle in adipose tissue appears to be increased availability of fatty acid, it seems at least a possibility that the oxidation of fatty acid might contribute to the reversal of glycolysis in the diabetic liver rather than *vice versa*. In this connexion, Sweeney, Mahler & Ashmore (191) find that, in animals in which insulin deficiency has been induced acutely by injection of insulin antiserum, changes in lipogenesis and acetoacetate production precede alterations in carbohydrate metabolism.

The dicarboxylic acid shuttle in liver may be of importance in regulating the synthesis and breakdown of amino acids from and to pyruvate. Fitch & Chaikoff (192) find that in alloxan diabetic rats the activity of the malic enzyme is depressed and they suggest that this is in keeping with the view that the flow of products of deamination of amino acids to pyruvate is through the oxalacetate decarboxylase reaction and that the malic enzyme is of major importance in amino acid synthesis. They advance the general view that changes such as this in the pattern of enzyme activity in diabetes may represent atrophy or hypertrophy of enzyme activities induced by the flow of substrates. In keeping with this they find in diabetes increased activities of transaminases and of fumarase and glucose-6-phosphatase and depressed activities of dehydrogenases of the pentose phosphate cycle [first shown by Glock & McLean (193)] and of glycerol phosphate dehydrogenase. Landau *et al.* (194) find evidence that cortisone treatment of the rat may activate the dicarboxylic acid shuttle since the conversion of carbon dioxide and pyruvate to glucose and glycogen was increased. The increased incorporation of [^{14}C] from a number of radioactive amino acids into glucose was enhanced in liver slices of diabetic rats but found to be normal in those of diabetic adrenalectomized rats by Wagle & Ashmore (195).

The biochemistry of fatty acid synthesis in liver and the possible mechanism of its endocrine control have been mentioned in considering fatty acid synthesis in adipose tissue. Wertheimer & Shafrir (23) believe that liver is quantitatively less important in fatty acid synthesis and suggest that its major role may be to provide serum lipids. Leal & Greenbaum (196) find that treatment of the rat with growth hormone depresses acetate incorporation into phospholipid and conclude that this is caused in part by a depressed rate of conversion of acetyl CoA to palmityl CoA, a finding that is in keeping with earlier observations by Greenbaum that growth hormone treatment depresses hepatic lipogenesis.

The oxidation of glucose by liver is markedly depressed in diabetes, though, for reasons which are not understood, the oxidation of glucose through the pentose phosphate cycle is somewhat less markedly reduced than oxidation of the sugar by glycolysis and the citrate cycle. This is attributable in part to depressed phosphorylation of glucose, partly to a depressed rate of glycolysis, and also to impaired oxidation of pyruvate (20, 193). The latter could conceivably be traceable to the enhanced oxidation of fatty acids in diabetes in view of observations in muscle (see p. 301). Beyer *et al.* (197) have been unable to obtain evidence for impaired efficiency of respiratory chain phosphorylation or for alterations in adenosine triphosphatase activity or the rate of phosphate exchange in mitochondria prepared from livers of depancreatized cats, even though more mitochondria were obtained.

Glucose uptake and output by liver.—Whether or not the liver puts out or takes up glucose is presumably dependent upon the relative rates of phosphorylation of glucose and hydrolysis of glucose-6-phosphate. Soskin *et al.* (198) calculate that, in the dog *in vivo*, rates of output and uptake of glucose are equal at a blood glucose concentration of 150 mg per 100 ml. Both uptake and output of glucose by liver *in vitro* have been demonstrated with modern perfusion techniques by Haft & Miller (see 19) and by Huston *et al.* (199). The dispute as to whether or not insulin has a direct effect on hepatic uptake or output of glucose continues unabated. The author does not wish to become drawn into this controversy by covering the entire field of investigations which have followed the provocative review of Levine & Fritz in 1956 (200). The literature has been very extensively reviewed by Huston *et al.* (198) in a recent paper. The author suggests that there may be general agreement that insulin infusion prevents the enhanced hepatic glucose output which is otherwise the response to hypoglycaemia. The results of recent experiments *in vitro* with perfused liver of the rat (18) and the dog (198) appeared to show that insulin can cause uptake of glucose by livers from normal animals, can enable glycogen synthesis to take place at lower glucose concentrations in the perfusate and suppress glucose output in livers of diabetic rats, and can increase oxidation of glucose. Shoemaker *et al.* (201) have failed to find any effect of insulin given by infusion or single injection into portal, femoral, or caval veins in adrenalectomized, depancreatized, or depancreatized adrenalectomized dogs on hepatic glucose output or free glucose or glycogen concentration in the liver measured by sampling of arterial, portal, and hepatic venous blood and of the liver. Leonards *et al.* (202), on the other hand, using both isotope and cannula techniques, found that with insulin the net uptake of glucose by the liver occurred at lower than normal plasma glucose concentrations. Mortimore (203) could obtain no evidence in rats that insulin inhibited release of glucose by the perfused liver, though loss of potassium was inhibited. Using the isotope method, Dunn *et al.* (204) obtained evidence that insulin may diminish hepatic glucose output in dogs fed a high carbohydrate diet.

Other direct hormonal influences on liver metabolism.—Miller (19) finds in rats that urea output is depressed by glucose or fructose in normal but not diabetic perfused livers and that the catabolism of liver and plasma proteins is enhanced in diabetes. The output of amino acids by the liver was unchanged in diabetes and diminished in normal livers by addition of insulin to the perfusate. Glucagon, in addition to its expected effect on glucose output, impaired oxidation of glucose and increased the output of urea in a remarkable way, suggesting stimulation of catabolism of proteins and amino acids. Cortisol did not stimulate urea output. In livers from adrenalectomized rats the effect of glucagon was markedly reduced, but the response to glucagon was restored when the liver was perfused with cortisol. The effect of a given dose of glucagon on urea output was markedly reduced by insulin though the effect of glucagon on hepatic output of glucose was not diminished.

PROTEIN METABOLISM

Pathways of protein biosynthesis.—The biosynthesis of protein is held to involve in sequence: membrane transport of amino acids; activation of amino acids (reaction with ATP to yield amino acyl adenylate and pyrophosphate with a number of activating enzymes); transfer to a soluble, low molecular weight ribonucleic acid (s-RNA); assembly into protein in the form of ribonucleoprotein in the ribosomes (requiring guanosine triphosphate, GTP); and release of protein from ribonucleoprotein. All reactions up to incorporation into ribonucleoprotein occur in the soluble fraction of the cell. There is evidence in bacterial systems (205, 206) that ribosomes require activation by another ribonucleic acid (messenger RNA) formed under the influence of deoxyribonucleic acid and passing thence to the ribosome. It is not known whether a similar messenger functions in mammalian tissues. In general, rate-limiting steps in protein biosynthesis in mammalian tissues are not known, but there is evidence for hormonal influences on membrane transport of amino acids and on the incorporating ability of ribosomes. Hendler (207), following the suggestion of Kipnis, Reiss & Helmreich (208) that the amino acids of the cell pool cannot be in equilibrium with those entering cell protein, has suggested that protein is synthesized at an interface between a lipoprotein membrane and a ribonucleoprotein film and that the process of synthesis differs for amino acids entering from inside or outside of the cell.

Insulin and protein biosynthesis.—The action of insulin on protein synthesis has been very thoroughly reviewed by Krahl (3) and Manchester & Young (209). In muscle (rat diaphragm or rat heart), insulin has a direct accelerating effect *in vitro* on incorporation of [14C]-labelled amino acids into muscle proteins. This action of insulin is independent of accelerating effects of the hormone on glucose uptake (61, 209 to 212) and takes place at concentrations of the hormone encountered in blood plasma (213). Evidence that insulin may accelerate transport of amino acids into muscle cells has accrued from increased intracellular accumulation of glycine (214) and α-aminoiso-butyric acid (an amino acid not appreciably metabolized) (214, 215). There is evidence that insulin may enhance the incorporation of amino acids within the cell into protein (i.e., a process not involving transport through the limit-ing membrane of the cell), and Manchester (216) has obtained evidence that the effect of insulin on amino acid transport may be secondary to an effect of the hormone on amino acid incorporation into protein within the cell. The effects of insulin on the transport of a number of amino acids into the rat diaphragm have been described by Akedo & Christensen (217).

Wool (218) has studied the effect of insulin on the distribution of radio-activity in the proteins of cell fractions of diaphragm incubated with [14C] phenylalanine. Radioactivity was found in all fractions and increased therein by insulin though at early periods of incubation the microsome (containing ribosomes) and mitochondrial fractions were somewhat more heavily labelled. In an interesting paper on the effect of insulin on labelling of nucleotides of rat diaphragm incubated with [32P]orthophosphate, Volfin, Eboué & Clauser (219) have obtained evidence that insulin action may accelerate reactions involving pyrophosphate cleavage of ATP; activation of amino acids for pro-tein biosynthesis is one such reaction. In adipose tissue, stimulation by insulin of amino acid entry into protein is dependent upon the presence of an oxidiz-able substrate such as glucose in the incubation medium (220 to 223), and the same is true for mammary gland and heart slices (223). The effects of insulin on amino acid metabolism in the alligator have been described by Hernandez & Coulson (224).

Evidence for hormonal influences on the ability of rat liver ribosomes to incorporate [14C] leucine into protein in a cell-free system has been provided by Korner. The ability of the microsomal fraction (containing ribosomes) to incorporate radioactive leucine into protein was depressed when the fraction was prepared from the livers of rats with alloxan diabetes, and treatment of normal, hypophysectomized, or alloxan diabetic rats with insulin increased the ability of the microsomes to incorporate amino acids. Treatment with the hormone also enhanced (to a much lesser extent) the ability of the soluble fraction to prepare amino acids for incorporation. The hormone was, however, ineffective *in vitro* (225, 226). Doell (227) has made similar observations concerning effects of insulin administration to the intact rat. Penhos & Krahl (228) find that the incorporation of [14C] leucine into protein in liver slices *in vitro* is decreased following partial pancreatectomy and that insulin and glucose *in vitro* may stimulate incorporation under these conditions. Marsh (229), on the other hand, found that synthesis of albumin by the perfused liver was depressed by fasting and by diabetes but that insulin did not appreciably alter albumin synthesis.

Growth hormone and protein biosynthesis.—In isolated rat diaphragm muscle, prior hypophysectomy of the rat and treatment with growth hormone depress and increase, respectively, incorporation of radioactive amino acids into protein. Hypophysectomy may possibly impair and growth hormone enhance this response to low concentrations of insulin (61). In diaphragm muscle from hypophysectomized rats, growth hormone *in vitro* can stimulate amino acid incorporation into protein and enhance α-aminoisobutyric acid transport. These effects are presumably manifestations of the so-called insulin-like action of growth hormone and are not necessarily related to its physiological role (7, 209, 230). Korner finds that the incorporating ability of liver microsomes is impaired following hypophysectomy of the rat and increased by treatment with growth hormone (231). Similar observations have been made in respect of ribosomes purified from the microsome fraction (232), and incorporation into serum albumin has been demonstrated (233). The effects of growth hormone in the liver, like those of insulin, thus appear to be exerted principally upon the ribosomes.

Moon, Jentoft & Li (234) find that human growth hormone (HGH) can increase the rate of nuclear multiplication in human liver cells in tissue culture and that the effect was abolished by an antiserum to HGH and not manifested by bovine growth hormone. In hypophysectomized rats, treatment with growth hormone enhanced incorporation of [35S] into costal cartilage (235); and in the parakeet, this hormone increased the concentration of plasma albumin (236). The total amount and amount per mole of labelled glycine incorporated into hippuric acid in dogs fed benzoate was increased by GH (237). Talwar *et al.* (238) find that treatment of the rat with growth hormone increases 32P incorporation into a number of RNA fractions in the liver. Treatment with growth hormone has also revealed correlations between ability to induce growth and alterations in activities of guanase, xanthine oxidase, and 5′-nucleotidase (239).

Adrenal corticosteroids.—Adrenalectomy of the rat increases, and treatment with cortisol depresses, incorporation of amino acids into protein and the stimulating effects thereon of insulin in rat diaphragm *in vitro* (61). On the other hand, the incorporating ability of liver microsomes is depressed following adrenalectomy and enhanced by treatment with cortisol (240). These findings are in keeping with the generally accepted view that the action of corticosteroids leads to the breakdown of protein in peripheral tissues and the transfer of amino acids to the liver where protein synthesis may be enhanced. In adrenalectomized mice, treatment with cortisol depressed incorporation of [^{14}C] leucine into protein in muscle but enhanced it in liver (241). In rat adductor muscles glycine incorporation was depressed by treatment of the rat with cortisol and evidence for effects of the hormone obtained *in vitro* (242). Weinshelbaum & Wool (243) find that adrenalectomy increases, and cortisol treatment diminishes, incorporation of [^{14}C] phenylalanine into all fractions of rat heart slices. Smith *et al.* (244) could find no effect of treatment with cortisone on the amino acid-activating enzymes of rat liver, an observation consistent with the view that the major effect of treatment with the hormone is on the ribosome. In keeping with this view, Feigelson *et al.* (245) find that treatment of rats with cortisone stimulates markedly the incorporation of [^{14}C] glycine and [^{32}P] into the RNA of all subcellular constituents of normal and regenerating livers. MacLean (246) has observed a diminution in the activities of enzymes involved in urea synthesis and especially of arginine synthetase in rat liver following adrenalectomy whereas changes in hepatic transaminases following adrenalectomy or cortisol treatment have been noted by Harding *et al.* (247).

Mechanism of control of protein biosynthesis.—The results of studies summarized above suggest that the major control of protein biosynthesis is at the level of the ribosome with the possibility of subsidiary but less important regulatory mechanisms at the level of membrane transport and amino acid activation. The possibility that a regulator, possibly similar in some respects to that of messenger RNA in bacterial systems, may transmit endocrine control of protein biosynthesis is one which is clearly feasible. In this connexion Sokoloff *et al.* (248, 249) find that thyroxin can enhance amino acid incorporation into protein in homogenates of the rat's liver and that this effect of thyroxin is exerted at the stage of incorporation of amino acid into microsomal protein. They have obtained evidence that mitochondria are necessary for this effect and an oxidizable substrate and that the effects of mitochondria cannot be reproduced by adding ATP and an ATP-generating system. Clearly the mechanism of control of protein biosynthesis is little understood at the present time, but it seems possible that, as in the case of carbohydrate and fat metabolism, the steps of protein biosynthesis may be controlled by regulators generated within the cell.

GENERAL ASPECTS OF ENDOCRINE CONTROL

Insulin.—Chromatographic methods for the identification of insulin in pancreatic extracts have been described (250, 251) and evidence obtained for the incorporation of [^{14}C] from labelled glucose into insulin in incubation of islet tissue from *Opsanus tau in vitro* (252). The injection of a number of metabolic intermediates such as pyruvate, β-hydroxybutyrate, and citrate into rabbits led to a fall of blood glucose concentration which may have been caused by insulin secretion (253). Simon and his colleagues have obtained evidence that D-mannoheptulose exerts a specific inhibitory effect on glucose stimulation of insulin secretion (254). Lacy & Williamson (255, 256) have identified, with quantitative histochemical methods, lactate, malate, and glucose-6-phosphate dehydrogenases in the β cells of rabbit islets and assayed the insulin content of single β cells, whereas Hellman & Larsson have identified a number of transaminases in teleost islets (257). The nonutilizable sugar, 3-methyl-glucose, in addition to glucose, has been found to be capable of protecting islets against the diabetogenic effect of alloxan (258). Insulin secretion in the perfused pancreas of the rat has been studied by Grodsky *et al.* (259) who find that glucose stimulates insulin secretion whereas a number of other sugars and growth hormone were inactive. Coore & Randle (260) have studied insulin secretion by pieces of rabbit pancreas *in vitro;* glucose and tolbutamide stimulated insulin secretion and pyruvate, and other substrates enhanced glucose action, but other sugars were inactive.

The state of insulin in blood has been further studied by Antoniades and his colleagues (261 to 264) who believe that insulin in blood is in free and bound (β-γ globulin) forms and that the latter is available to adipose tissue but not to muscle. Samaan *et al.* (265) have described, on the basis of bioassay *in vitro*, two forms of circulating insulin which are neutralized (typical) and not neutralized (atypical) by antiserum to insulin; Mahon *et al.* (266) failed to find insulin in cerebrospinal fluid either by bioassay or following injection of [^{131}I] insulin. A manometric bioassay for insulin in serum using the epididymal fat pad of the rat has been described by Ball & Merrill (267). Tomizawa (268) has described an enzyme in beef liver which couples the reductive cleavage of interchain disulphide linkages in insulin with oxidation of low molecular weight sulphydryl compounds, and Katzen & Stetten (269) have shown that such a system with glutathione and glutathione reductase may oxidize NADPH.

Evidence that insulin may be attached to cells by disulphide interchange, following the original observations of Rasmussen (270, 271) and his colleagues for similar attachment of neurohypophyseal hormones to the toad bladder, has been provided (67, 272) though this conclusion has been questioned (68).

In the rat lens, insulin has been found to stimulate glucose uptake and accelerate monosaccharide transport (273), in confirmation of earlier findings of Ross, and to accelerate oxidation of C_1 of glucose and diminish oxidation of C_6 of glucose (274). In adipose tissue the resting potential was elevated by insulin (275), in keeping with earlier findings in skeletal muscle by Zierler. Lynn & Brown (276) have obtained evidence that insulin may cause a redistribution of various enzyme activities amongst cell fractions in adipose tissue. Scarpelli (277) claims that insulin can accelerate phagocytosis by macrophages. Colwell & Lein (278) find, interestingly, that insulin given by the portal vein may lower plasma nonesterified fatty acids (NEFA) without lowering blood glucose whereas insulin given into a systemic vein may lower blood glucose without changing the plasma NEFA. The utilization of glucose in sheep has been measured with an isotope method and found to be lowered by starvation (279).

Growth hormone and corticosteroids.—Young (280) has reviewed hormonal control of growth in a Brailsford Robertson Memorial Lecture. Huggins & Ottaway (281) have described the purification and properties of an hypoglycaemic peptide separated from preparations of bovine growth hormone. The metabolic properties of the peptide are such that it is doubtful whether it is responsible for the so-called insulin-like action of growth hormone. Bornstein & Hyde have described the isolation of a peptide from sheep pituitary glands with an insulin-like effect on glucose uptake by rat diaphragm (282). Fenton & Duguid (283) have studied effects of environmental temperature and strain of mice on maintenance of cardiac glycogen and effects of growth hormone thereon. Stein *et al.* (284) find that the retention of potassium by rats produced by growth hormone in short-term experiments is not critically influenced by the protein content of the diet or vice versa.

Hockaday (285) finds that the blood pyruvate concentration in cats is lowered by adrenalectomy and raised by treatment with cortisol hemisuccinate and attributes this to changes in protein and amino acid metabolism. From studies of glucose tolerance and serum inorganic phosphate concentrations in man, Danowski *et al.* (286) obtained evidence suggesting that in short term experiments a single dose of cortisone increased gluconeogenesis without diminishing peripheral glucose uptake or insulin action. With chronic treatment there was evidence for increased gluconeogenesis, impaired utilization of glucose by glycolysis, and impaired insulin action. Glasser & Izzo (287) have concluded that the protein catabolic effect of glucagon in the intact rat is not dependent upon the adrenal cortex though its action is diminished (cf. 18). Goetsch & Donald (288) find that oxygen uptake by liver homogenates is increased by prior acute injection of corticosteroids into the rat but depressed following chronic treatment. Lee & Baltz (289) have obtained evidence for a permissive role of adrenocortical steroids in the induction of tryptophan pyrrolase in rat liver. Segal & Menon (290) find that treatment of the rat with prednisolone can increase activities in liver mitochondria of enzymes cleaving β-hydroxy β-methyl glutaryl CoA and converting acetoacetyl CoA to acetoacetate.

Kokka & Bennett (291) have studied the effect of hypophysectomy on insulin action on extrahepatic galactose transfer. The threshold dose was lowered and the response to a given dose of insulin increased by removal of the pituitary. These findings are in substantial agreement with earlier studies using [^{14}C] glucose in the dog (292) and with *in vitro* studies using rat heart and diaphragm (61). The mechanism of control of insulin sensitivity in muscle, in particular by pituitary and adrenocortical secretions, is still far from clear, though it is recognized that impairment of glucose phosphorylation and of the sensitivity of the membrane transport system to stimulation by insulin are involved. The crux of the problem is the failure of growth hormone and corticosteroids to impair glucose metabolism by muscle *in vitro*. This has led to a search for pituitary- and adrenal-dependent factors in serum with a direct inhibitory action on glucose uptake by muscle. A number of such factors have been described (3, 6) but their physiological significance is not known. The impaired phosphorylation of glucose by muscle induced by growth hormone and cortisol *in vivo* appears to be explicable on the basis of increased respiration of fatty acids. The author has proposed a cycle of regulation between muscle and adipose tissue which, it is suggested, may be called the glucose fatty acid cycle (293). The component features of this cycle are (*a*) the ability of insulin and glucose to impair fatty acid release by adipose tissue and thereby to lower serum nonesterified fatty acids (NEFA), (*b*) the ability of growth hormone and cortisol to stimulate fatty acid release by adipose tissue and thereby to elevate serum NEFA and (*c*) the ability of fatty acids and ketone bodies to impair glucose utilization in muscle.

Thyroxin.—Macho (294) finds that thyroxin and 2,4-dinitrophenol may increase glucose utilization and may elevate serum pyruvate and impair pyruvate assimilation in rabbits (295). Barker and his colleagues (296, 297) have made further studies *in vitro* on the effects in rats of thyroxin on the metabolism of glucose and amino acids in kidney slices and of the specificity of the effect of thyroxin on O_2 uptake during prolonged incubation. Rall *et al.* (298) have noted similarities between effects of thyroxin and of iodine on rat liver mitochondria. Evidence has been obtained by Tonone (299) that effects of thyroxin on oxygen uptake by liver homogenates *in vitro* may depend upon ATP concentration and pO_2. Effects of thyroxin derivatives on glycolysis and oxygen uptake by ascites tumour cells have been reported by Cerajo-Santalo (300). Barker has obtained effects of tetraiodothyropropionic acid on yeast metabolism (301).

Cyclic 3',5'-AMP.—Sutherland and his colleagues have reported on the distribution, preparation, and properties of adenyl cyclase (the enzyme forming cyclic 3',5'-AMP from ATP) and find the enzyme in all animal tissues and animals of four phyla studied except perhaps in the dog erythrocyte (302, 303). With dog myocardial and liver adenyl cyclase, stimulation was observed with a number of catecholamines, the relative order of potencies in descending order in the heart system being L-isopropylarterenol, L-epinephrine, L-norepinephrine, and D-epinephrine. The effect was reduced by dichloro-isopropylarterenol, ergotamine, and acetylcholine (91). The activities of adenyl cyclase from the brain, and a number of other tissues (including erythrocytes) were increased by epinephrine (304). The purification and properties of cyclic 3',5'-nucleotide phosphodiesterase (the enzyme which inactivates cyclic 3'5'-AMP) have been described (305). The enzyme is inhibited by methyl xanthines and has been used to identify cyclic 3',5'-AMP in human urine.

Action of tropic hormones.—Following the original demonstration by Haynes & Sutherland that corticotropin causes release of cyclic 3'5'-AMP and thereby activates phosphorylase and accelerates glycogen breakdown, and the suggestion that steroidogenesis might thereby be enhanced through provision of NADPH, a number of papers in support of this mechanism of control of steroidogenesis have appeared (306, 307). The addition of cyclic 3',5'-AMP to slices of human adrenal cortex has been found to be as effective as corticotropin in stimulating corticosteroid production *in vitro* (308). Mason, Marsh & Savard (309) and Savard *et al.* (310) find that gonadotropin preparations and also NADP and glucose-6-phosphate and glucose-6-phosphate dehydrogenase can stimulate progesterone synthesis by bovine luteal slices *in vitro*. Marsh finds that luteinizing hormone preparations (but not corticotropin, glucagon serum albumin, or luteinizing hormone inactivated with peroxide) may activate phosphorylase and progesterone synthesis in luteal slices (311). Williams, Johnson & Field (312), on the other hand, find that crude anterior pituitary extracts, chorionic gonadotropin, and growth hormone preparations increase phosphorylase activity in bovine corpus luteum slices but that luteinizing hormone is inactive. The reason for this discrepancy is not clear. These findings suggest that cyclic 3',5'-AMP formation may regulate both corticosteroid and progesterone biosynthesis. The influences of corticotropin and growth hormone on adrenal nucleic acids in the dog have been described by Bransome & Reddy (313).

In thyroid slices *in vitro*, thyrotropin stimulates the preferential oxidation of glucose through the pentose phosphate cycle. Glucose uptake is also stimulated but this is unlikely to be responsible for enhanced oxidation through the pentose phosphate cycle since insulin, which also stimulates glucose uptake, does not have this effect (314). In further studies Field and his colleagues obtained evidence that thyrotropin increases the concentration of $NADP^+$ in the thyroid by promoting the conversion of NAD^+ to $NADP^+$ (315, 316). Mulvey *et al.* (317) have confirmed that thyrotropin stimulates oxidation of glucose through the pentose phosphate cycle and find that this is inhibited by propylthiouracil. Glucose oxidation in the thyroid is also accelerated by epinephrine (318) and acetylcholine (319). There is evidence that thyrotropin may stimulate production of cyclic 3'5'-AMP by the thyroid (304).

The oxidation of glucose through the pentose phosphate pathway in rat pituitary is increased by epinephrine, norepinephrine, and 5-hydroxytryptamine (320). Wool *et al.* (321) find that the rate of incorporation of [14C] from [14C] phenylalanine into corticotropin (but not into total protein) in rat pituitary *in vitro* is enhanced following adrenalectomy.

LITERATURE CITED

1. Levine, R., *Diabetes*, **10**, 421–31 (1961)
2. Chain, E. B., *Ciba Found. Symp.*, 95–114 (Little, Brown, Boston, 1962)
3. Krahl, M. E., *The Action of Insulin on Cells* (Academic Press, New York, 202 pp., 1961)
4. Tepperman, J., and Tepperman, M. M., *Pharmacol. Rev.*, **12**, 301–54 (1960)
5. *The Mechanism of Action of Insulin* (Young, F. G., Broom, W. A., and Wolff, W. F., Eds., Blackwell, Oxford, 320 pp., 1960)
6. "Insulin," *Brit. Med. Bull.*, **16**, 175–259 (1960)
7. Randle, P. J., and Morgan, H. E., *Vitamins and Hormones* (1962)
8. de Bodo, R. C., Altszuler, N., Dunn, A., Steele, R., Armstrong, D. T., and Bishop, J. S., *Ann. N. Y. Acad. Sci.*, **82**, 431–51 (1959)
9. Kipnis, D. M., *Ann. N. Y. Acad. Sci.*, **82**, 354–65 (1959)
10. Larner, J., Villar-Palasi, C., and Richman, D. J., *Ann. N. Y. Acad. Sci.*, **82**, 345–53 (1959)
11. Park, C. R., Morgan, H. E., Henderson, M. J., Regen, D. M., Cadenas, E., and Post, R. L., *Recent Progr. Hormone Research*, **17**, 493–529 (1960)
12. Smith, G. H., Randle, P. J., and Battaglia, F. C., *Mem. Soc. Endocrinol.*, **11**, 124–33 (1961)
13. Wilbrandt, W., and Rosenberg, T., *Pharmacol. Rev.*, **13**, 109–83 (1961)
14. *Membrane Transport and Metabolism* (Kleinzeller, A., and Kotyk, A., Eds., Publ. House Czechoslov. Acad. Sci., Prague, 608 pp., 1961)
15. Hechter, O., and Lester, G., *Recent Progr. Hormone Research*, **16**, 139–79 (1960)
16. Haynes, R. C., Jr., Sutherland, E. W., and Rall, T. W., *Recent Progr. Hormone Research*, **16**, 121–33 (1961)
17. Ashmore, J., and Weber, G., *Vitamins and Hormones*, **17**, 92–132 (1959)
18. Miller, L. L., *Recent Progr. Hormone Research*, **17**, 539–64 (1961)
19. Renold, A. E., and Cahill, G. F., Jr., in *The Metabolic Basis of Inherited Disease*, 65–120 (Stanbury, J. B., Wyngaarden, J. B., and Fredrickson, D. S., Eds., McGraw Hill Book Co., Inc., New York, 1477 pp., 1960)
20. Ashmore, J., Cahill, G. F., Jr., and Hastings, A. B., *Recent Progr. Hormone Research*, **16**, 547–73 (1960)
21. Kennedy, E. P., *Federation Proc.*, **20**, 934–40 (1961)
22. Lynen, F., *Federation Proc.*, **20**, 941–51 (1961)
23. Wertheimer, E., and Shafrir, E., *Recent Progr. Hormone Research*, **16**, 467–90 (1960)
24. Fritz, I. B., *Physiol. Rev.*, **41**, 52–129 (1961)
25. Vaughan, M., *J. Lipid Research*, **2**, 293–316 (1961)
26. Cahill, G. F., Jr., Leboeuf, B., and Renold, A. E., *Am. J. Clin. Nutrition*, **8**, 733–39 (1960)
27. Winegard, A. I., Shaw, W. N., Lukens, F. D. W., and Stadie, W. C., *Am. J. Clin. Nutrition*, **8**, 651–65 (1960)
28. Scow, R. O., and Chernick, S. S., *Recent Progr. Hormone Research*, **16**, 497–541 (1960)
29. Lundsgaard, E., *Upsala Läkareören. Förh.*, **45**, 143 (1939)
30. Morgan, H. E., Henderson, M. J., Regen, D. M., and Park, C. R., *J. Biol. Chem.*, **236**, 253–61 (1961)
31. Narahara, H. T., Ozand, P., and Cori, C. F., *J. Biol. Chem.*, **235**, 3370–78 (1960)
32. Battaglia, F. C., and Randle, P. J., *Biochem. J. (London)*, **75**, 408–16 (1960)
33. Park, C. R., Reinwein, D., Henderson, M. J., Cadenas, E., and Morgan, H. E., *Am. J. Med.*, **26**, 674–84 (1959)
34. Fisher, R. B., and Zachariah, P., *J. Physiol. (London)*, **158**, 73–85 (1961)
35. Carlin, H., and Hechter, O., *J. Gen. Physiol.*, **45**, 309–16 (1961)
36. Eichton, J., and Hechter, O., *J. Gen. Physiol.*, **45**, 15–22 (1961)
37. Walaas, O., Borreback, B., Kristiansen, T., and Walaas, E., *Biochem. Biophys. Acta*, **40**, 562–67 (1960)
38. Stein, W. D., *Nature*, **191**, 1277–80 (1961)
39. McCollester, D. L., *Biochim. Biophys. Acta*, **57**, 427–37 (1962)
40. McCollester, D. L., and Randle, P. J., *Biochem. J.*, **78**, 27P (1961)
41. Kono, T., and Colowick, S. P., *Arch. Biochem. Biophys.*, **93**, 520–33 (1961)
42. Park, C. R., Post, R. L., Kalman, C. F., Wright, J. H., Jr., Johnson, L. H., and Morgan, H. E., *Ciba*

Foundation Colloq. Endocrinol., 9, 240–60 (1956)

43. Fisher, R. B., and Lindsay, D. B., J. Physiol. (London), 131, 526–41 (1956)

44. Randle, P. J., and Smith, G. H., Biochem. J. (London), 70, 490–508 (1958)

45. Kipnis, D. M., and Cori, C. F., J. Biol. Chem., 224, 681–93 (1957)

46. Morgan, H. E., Randle, P. J., and Regen, D. M., Biochem. J. (London), 73, 573–79 (1959)

47. Forbath, N., and Clarke, D. W., Can. J. Biochem. Physiol., 38, 13–17 (1960)

48. Seltzer, H. S., J. Clin. Invest., 41, 289–300 (1962)

49. Kono, T., and Colowick, S. P., Arch. Biochem. Biophys., 93, 514–19 (1961)

50. Henderson, M. J., Morgan, H. E., and Park, C. R., J. Biol. Chem., 236, 2157–61 (1961)

51. Helmreich, E., and Cori, C. F., J. Biol. Chem., 224, 663–79 (1957)

52. Kipnis, D. M., Helmreich, E., and Cori, C. F., J. Biol. Chem., 234, 165–70 (1959)

53. Goldstein, M. S., Am. J. Physiol., 200, 67–70 (1961)

54. Dulin, W. E., and Clark, J. J., Diabetes, 10, 289–97 (1961)

55. Newsholme, E. A., and Randle, P. J. (Unpublished data)

56. Zachariah, P., J. Physiol. (London), 158, 59–72 (1961)

57. Henderson, M. J., Morgan, H. E., and Park, C. R., J. Biol. Chem., 236, 273–77 (1961)

58. Morgan, H. E., Cadenas, E., Regen, D. M., and Park, C. R., J. Biol. Chem., 236, 262–68 (1961)

59. Kipnis, D. M., and Cori, C. F., J. Biol. Chem., 235, 3070–75 (1960)

60. Randle, P. J., Ciba Foundation Colloq. Endocrinol., 11, 115–32 (1957)

61. Manchester, K. L., Randle, P. J., and Young, F. G., J. Endocrinol., 18, 395–408 (1959)

62. Guidotti, G., and Foa, P. P., Am. J. Physiol., 201, 869–72 (1961)

63. Guidotti, G., Kanameishi, D., and Foa, P. P., Am. J. Physiol., 201, 863–68 (1961)

64. Grillo, T. A. I., J. Endocrinol., 22, 285–92 (1961)

65. Post, R. L., Morgan, H. E., and Park, C. R., J. Biol. Chem., 236, 269–72 (1961)

66. Randle, P. J., in Membrane Transport and Metabolism, 431–38 (Klein-

zeller, A., and Kotyk, A., Eds., Publ. House Czechoslov. Acad. Sci., Prague, 608 pp., 1961)

67. Cadenas, E., Kaji, H., Park, C. R., and Rasmussen, H., J. Biol. Chem., 236, Pc 63–64 (1961)

68. Carlin, H., and Hechter, O., J. Biol. Chem., 237, Pc 1371–72 (1962)

69. Sols, A., and Crane, R. K., Federation Proc., 13, 301 (1954)

70. Newsholme, E. A., and Randle, P. J., Biochem. J. (London), 80, 655–62 (1961)

71. Garland, P. B., Newsholme, E. A., and Randle, P. J., Nature, 195, 381–83 (1962)

72. Newsholme, E. A., Randle, P. J., and Manchester, K. L., Nature, 193, 270–71 (1962)

73. Bowman, R. H., Biochem. J. (London), 84, 14P (1962)

74. Morgan, H. E., Regen, D. M., Henderson, M. J., Sawyer, T. R., and Park, C. R., J. Biol. Chem., 236, 2162–68 (1961)

75. Kipnis, D. M., and Cori, C. F., J. Biol. Chem., 234, 171–77 (1959)

76. Regen, D. M., Davies, W. W., and Morgan, H. E., Federation Proc., 20, 83 (1961)

77. Tiederman, H., and Born, J., Z. Naturforsch., 14b, 477–78 (1959)

78. Leloir, L. F., and Cardini, C. E., J. Am. Chem. Soc., 79, 6340–41 (1957)

79. Villar-Palasi, C., and Larner, J., Biochim. Biophys. Acta, 30, 449 (1958)

80. Larner, J., Villar-Palasi, C., and Richman, J. W., Ann. N. Y. Acad. Sci., 82, 345–53 (1959)

81. Larner, J., Villar-Palasi, C., and Richman, D. J., Arch. Biochem. Biophys., 86, 56–60 (1960)

82. Villar-Palasi, C., and Larner, J., Arch. Biochem. Biophys., 86, 61–66 (1960)

83. Villar-Palasi, C., and Larner, J., Arch. Biochem. Biophys., 94, 436–42 (1961)

84. Friedman, D. L., and Larner, J., Federation Proc., 21, 206 (1962)

85. Leloir, L. F., Olavarria, J. M., Goldemberg, S. H., and Carminatti, H., Arch. Biochem. Biophys., 81, 508–20 (1959)

86. Beloff-Chain, A., Catanzarro, R., Chain, E. B., Masi, I., Pochiari, F., and Rossi, C., Proc. Roy. Soc. (London), B, 143, 481–503

87. Morgan, H. E., and Randle, P. J. (Unpublished data)

88. Williamson, J. R., and Krebs, H. A.,

Biochem. J. (London), **80**, 540–47 (1961)

89. Shipp, J. C., Opie, L. H., and Challoner, D., *Nature*, **189**, 1018–19 (1961)

90. Madsen, N. B., *Biochem. Biophys. Research Commun.*, **6**, 310–12 (1961)

91. Murad, F., Chi, Y. M., Rall, T. W., and Sutherland, E., *J. Biol. Chem.*, **237**, 1233–38 (1962)

92. Rall, T. W., and Sutherland, E. W., *J. Biol. Chem.*, **232**, 1077–91 (1958)

93. Sutherland, E. W., and Rall, T. W., *J. Biol. Chem.*, **232**, 1065–76 (1958)

94. Krebs, E. G., Graves, D. J., and Fisher, E. H., *J. Biol. Chem.*, **234**, 2867–73 (1959)

95. Cornblath, M., Morgan, H. E., and Randle, P. J., *J. Biol. Chem.* (In press)

96. Bloom, B., Stetten, M. R., and Stetten, D., Jr., *J. Biol. Chem.*, **204**, 681–94 (1953)

97. Glock, G. E., and McLean, P., *Biochem. J. (London)*, **56**, 171–75 (1954)

98. Beloff-Chain, A., Catanzaro, R., Chain, E. B., Longinotti, L., Masi, I., and Pocchiari, F., *Biochim. Biophys. Acta*, **56**, 153–55 (1962)

99. Villee, C. A., and Loring, J. M., *Biochem. J. (London)*, **81**, 488–94 (1961)

100. Passonneau, J. V., and Lowry, O. H., *Biochem. Biophys. Research Commun.*, **7**, 10–15 (1962)

101. Newsholme, E. A., and Randle, P. J., *Biochem. J. (London)*, **83**, 387–92 (1962)

102. Lardy, H. A., and Parks, R. E., Jr., in *Enzymes: Units of Biological Structure and Function*, 584–87 (Gaebler, O. H., Ed., Academic Press, New York, 624 pp., 1956)

103. Passonneau, J. V., and Lowry, O. H., *Federation Proc.*, **21**, 187 (1962)

104. Mansour, T. E., Clague, M. E., and Bearnink, K. D., *Federation Proc.*, **21**, 238 (1962)

105. Mansour, T. E., *J. Pharmacol. Exptl. Therap.*, **135**, 94–101 (1962)

106. Garland, P. B., and Randle, P. J. (Unpublished data)

107. Marinetti, G. V., Griffith, M., and Smith, T., *Biochim. Biophys. Acta*, **57**, 543–54 (1962)

108. Villee, C. A., and Hastings, A. B., *J. Biol. Chem.*, **181**, 131–39 (1949)

109. Pearson, O. H., Hsieh, C. K., Du Toit, C. H., and Hastings, A. B., *Am. J. Physiol.*, **158**, 261–68 (1949)

110. El Hawary, M. F. S., and Thompson, R. H. S., *Biochem. J.*, **58**, 518–20 (1954)

111. Smith, M. J. H., and Taylor, K. W., *Brit. Med. J.*, **11**, 1035–38 (1956)

112. Hernes, A. R., Wajchenberg, B. L., Fajans, S. S., and Conn, J. W., *Metabolism, Clin. Exptl.*, **6**, 339–45 (1957)

113. Weil, R., Altszuler, N., and Kessler, J., *Am. J. Physiol.*, **201**, 251–54 (1961)

114. Krebs, H. A., *Biochem. J. (London)*, **80**, 225–33 (1961)

115. Ottaway, J. H., and Sarkar, A. K., *Nature*, **181**, 1791–92 (1958)

116. Hall, L. M., *Biochem. Biophys. Research Commun.*, **6**, 177–79 (1961)

117. Williamson, J. R., *Biochem. J. (London)*, **83**, 373–83 (1962)

118. Williamson, J. R., *Biochem. J. (London)*, **81**, 16P (1961)

119. von Holt, C., Schmidt, H., and Feldmann, H., *Biochem. Z.*, **334**, 545–59 (1961)

120. Fisher, J. B., and Williamson, J. R., *J. Physiol. (London)*, **158**, 86–101 (1961)

121. Fisher, R. B., and Williamson, J. R., *J. Physiol. (London)*, **158**, 102–12 (1961)

122. Drury, D. R., and Wick, A. N., *Ciba Foundation Colloq. Endocrinol.*, **6**, 224–30 (ca. 1941)

123. Gourley, D. H., *Am. J. Physiol.*, **200**, 1320–26 (1961)

124. Eaton, P., and Steinberg, D., *J. Lipid Research*, **2**, 376–82 (1961)

125. Armstrong, D. T., Steele, R., Altszuler, N., Dunn, A., Bishop, J. S., and de Bodo, R. C., *Am. J. Physiol.*, **201**, 9–15 (1961)

126. Spitzer, J. J., McElroy, W. T., Jr., and Issekutz, B., Jr., *Proc. Soc. Exptl. Biol. Med.*, **108**, 89–91 (1961)

127. Vaughan, M., *J. Biol. Chem.*, **235**, 3049–53 (1960)

128. Weber, G., Banerjee, G., and Ashmore, J., *Biochem. Biophys. Research Commun.*, **3**, 182–86 (1960)

129. Paoletti, R., and Smith, R. L., *Biochem. Biophys. Research Commun.*, **5**, 424–29 (1961)

130. Winegrad, A. I., and Renold, A. E., *J. Biol. Chem.*, **233**, 273–76 (1958)

131. MacLean, P., *Biochem. Biophys. Acta*, **57**, 620–22 (1962)

132. MacLean, P., *Biochem. Biophys. Acta*, **37**, 296–309 (1960)

133. Steinberg, D., Vaughan, M., and Margolis, S., *J. Biol. Chem.*, **236**, 1631–37 (1961)

134. Margolis, S., and Vaughan, M., *J. Biol. Chem.*, **237**, 44–48 (1962)
135. Buckle, R. M., Rubinstein, D., McGarry, E. E., and Beck, J. C., *Endocrinology*, **69**, 1009–15 (1961)
136. Buckle, R. M., and Beck, J. C., *Metabolism, Clin. Exptl.*, **11**, 235–44 (1962)
137. Joel, C. D., and Ball, E. G., *Biochemistry*, **1**, 281–87 (1962)
138. Krahl, M. E., *Ann. N. Y. Acad. Sci.*, **54**, 649–70 (1952)
139. Leboeuf, B., and Cahill, G. F., Jr., *J. Biol. Chem.*, **236**, 41–46 (1961)
140. Urrutia, G., and Cahill, G. F., Jr., *Proc. Soc. Exptl. Biol. Med.*, **109**, 573–75 (1962)
141. Jeanrenaud, B., and Renold, A. E., *J. Biol. Chem.*, **234**, 3082–87 (1959)
142. Jungas, R. L., and Ball, E. G., *J. Biol. Chem.*, **235**, 1894–99 (1960)
143. Vaughan, M., *J. Biol. Chem.*, **236**, 2196–99 (1961)
144. Cahill, G. F., Jr., Leboeuf, B., and Flinn, R. B., *J. Biol. Chem.*, **235**, 1246–50 (1960)
145. Hagen, J. H., and Ball, E. G., *Endocrinology*, **69**, 752–60 (1961)
146. Joel, C. D., and Shackney, S. E., *Federation Proc.*, **21**, 184 (1962)
147. Jungas, R. L., *Biochem. Biophys. Acta*, **54**, 304–14 (1961)
148. Vaughan, M., and Steinberg, D., *Federation Proc.*, **21**, 284 (1962)
149. Cahill, G. F., Jr., Pawan, G. L. S., and Chalmers, T. M., *Endocrinology*, **69**, 648–51 (1961)
150. Mezey, A. P., Foley, H. T., and Altszuler, N., *Proc. Soc. Exptl. Biol. Med.*, **107**, 689–91 (1961)
151. Williamson, J. R., *Federation Proc.*, **21**, 203 (1962)
152. Munck, A., and Koritz, S. B., *Biochem. Biophys. Acta*, **57**, 310–17 (1962)
153. Munck, A., *Biochem. Biophys. Acta*, **57**, 318–26 (1962)
154. Fain, J. N., *Federation Proc.*, **21**, 187 (1962)
155. Leboeuf, B., Renold, A. E., and Cahill, G. F., Jr., *J. Biol. Chem.*, **237**, 988–91 (1962)
156. Leboeuf, B., Lochaya, S., Leboeuf, N., Wood, F. C., Jr., Mayer, J., and Cahill, G. F., Jr., *Am. J. Physiol.*, **201**, 19–22 (1961)
157. Lochaya, S., Leboeuf, N., Mayer, J., and Leboeuf, B., *Am. J. Physiol.*, **201**, 23–26 (1961)
158. Ganguly, J., *Biochim. Biophys. Acta*, **40**, 110–18 (1960)
159. Martin, D. B., Horning, M. G., and Vagelos, P. R., *J. Biol. Chem.*, **236**, 663–68 (1961)
160. Bressler, R., and Wakil, S. J., *J. Biol. Chem.*, **236**, 1643–51 (1961)
161. Numa, S., Matsuhashi, M., and Lynen, F., *Biochem. Z.*, **334**, 203–17 (1961)
162. Korchak, H. M., and Masoro, E. J., *Biochim. Biophys. Acta*, **58**, 354–56 (1962)
163. Hubbard, D. D., McCaman, R. E., Smith, M. R., and Gibson, D. M., *Biochem. Biophys. Research Commun.*, **5**, 339–43 (1961)
164. Masoro, E. J., Porter, E., and Korchak, H., *Am. J. Physiol.*, **202**, 129–32 (1962)
165. Martin, D. B., and Vagelos, P. R., *Biochem. Biophys. Research Commun.*, **7**, 101–6 (1962)
166. Gordon, R. S., Jr., and Cherkes, A., *Proc. Soc. Exptl. Biol. Med.*, **97**, 150–51 (1958)
167. White, J. E., and Engel, F. L., *Proc. Soc. Exptl. Biol. Med.*, **99**, 375–78 (1958)
168. Rizack, M. A., *J. Biol. Chem.*, **236**, 657–62 (1961)
169. Hollenberg, C. H., Raben, M. S., and Astwood, E. B., *Endocrinology*, **68**, 589–98 (1961)
170. Boright, H. A., Engel, F. L., Lebovitz, H. E., Kostyo, J. L., and White, J. E., Jr., *Biochem. J.* (*London*), **83**, 95–101 (1962)
171. Chalmers, T. M., Pawan, G. L. S., and Kekwick, A., *Am. J. Clin. Nutrition*, **8**, 728–32 (1960)
172. Rudman, D., Seidman, F., Brown, S. J., and Hirsch, R. L., *Endocrinology*, **70**, 233–42 (1962)
173. Friesen, H., Barrett, R. J., and Astwood, E. B., *Endocrinology*, **70**, 579–88 (1962)
174. Jungas, R. O. L., and Ball, E. G., *Federation Proc.*, **21**, 202 (1962)
175. Dole, V. P., *J. Biol. Chem.*, **236**, 3125–30 (1961)
176. Scow, R. O., and Chernick, S. S., *Federation Proc.*, **21**, 201 (1962)
177. Goodman, H. M., and Knobil, E., *Am. J. Physiol.*, **201**, 1–3 (1961)
178. Spitzer, J. J., and Hohenleiter, F. J., *J. Lipid Research*, **2**, 396–99 (1961)
179. Winkler, B., Steele, R., Altszuler, N., Dunn, A., and de Bodo, R. C., *Federation Proc.*, **21**, 198 (1962)
180. Spitzer, J. J., and McElroy, W. T., Jr., *Am. J. Physiol.*, **201**, 815–18 (1961)
181. Armstrong, D. T., Steele, R., Altszuler, N., Dunn, A., Bishop, J., and

de Bodo, R. C., *Am. J. Physiol.*, **201**, 535–39 (1961)

182. Smith, T. C., Hill, L., Oleson, J., Benitz, K. F., Perrine, J., and Ringler, I., *Am. J. Physiol.*, **200**, 1277–84 (1961)

183. Goodman, H. M., and Knobil, E., *Endocrinology*, **69**, 187–89 (1961)

184. Hollenberg, C. H., and Douglas, D. E., *Nature*, **193**, 1074–75 (1962)

185. Cahill, G. F., Jr., Ashmore, J., Earle, A. S., and Zottu, S., *Am. J. Physiol.*, **192**, 491–96 (1958)

186. Eisenstein, A. B., *Federation Proc.*, **21**, 191 (1962)

187. Steiner, D. F., and Williams, R. H., *J. Biol. Chem.*, **234**, 1342–46 (1959)

188. Harper, A. E., and Young, F. G., *Biochem. J.* (*London*), **71**, 696–705 (1959)

189. Mokrasch, L. C., Davidson, W. D., and McGilvery, R. W., *J. Biol. Chem.*, **222**, 179–84 (1956)

190. Mokrasch, L. C., and McGilvery, R. W., *J. Biol. Chem.*, **221**, 909–17 (1956)

191. Sweeney, M. J., Jr., Mahler, R., and Ashmore, J., *Federation Proc.*, **21**, 202 (1962)

192. Fitch, W. M., and Chaikoff, I. L., *Biochim. Biophys. Acta*, **57**, 583–95 (1962)

193. Glock, G. E., and McLean, P., *Biochem. J.* (*London*), **61**, 390–97 (1955)

194. Landau, B. R., Mahler, R., Ashmore, J., Elwyn, D., Hastings, A. B., and Zottu, S., *Endocrinology*, **70**, 47–53 (1962)

195. Wagle, S. R., and Ashmore, J., *J. Biol. Chem.*, **236**, 2868–71 (1961)

196. Leal, R. S., and Greenbaum, A. L., *Biochem. J.* (*London*), **80**, 27–33 (1961)

197. Beyer, R. E., Shamoian, C. A., and Abend, M. N., *Metabolism, Clin. Exptl.*, **11**, 394–403 (1962)

198. Soskin, S., Essex, H. E., Herrick, J. P., and Mann, F. C., *Am. J. Physiol.*, **124**, 558–67 (1958)

199. Huston, C. J. W., Adams, L. C., Field, R. A., and McDermott, W. V., Jr., *Lancet*, **I**, 357–59 (1962)

200. Levine, R., and Fritz, I. B., *Diabetes*, **5**, 209–19 (1956)

201. Shoemaker, W. C., Carruthers, P. J., Powers, I. C., and Yanof, H. M., *Am. J. Physiol.*, **201**, 804–10 (1961)

202. Leonards, J. R., Laundau, B. R., Craig, J. W., Martin, F. I. R., Miller, M., and Barry, F. M., *Am. J. Physiol.*, **201**, 47–54 (1961)

203. Mortimore, G. E., *Am. J. Physiol.*, **200**, 1315–19 (1961)

204. Dunn, A., Steele, R., Altszuler, N., Bishop, J. S., and de Bodo, R. C., *Federation Proc.*, **21**, 205 (1962)

205. Jacob, F., and Monod, J., *J. Mol. Biol.*, **3**, 318–56 (1961)

206. Brenner, S., Jacob, F., and Meselson, M., *Nature*, **190**, 576–81 (1961)

207. Hendler, R. W., *Nature*, **193**, 821–23 (1962)

208. Kipnis, D. M., Reiss, E., and Helmreich, E., *Biochim. Biophys. Acta*, **51**, 519–24 (1961)

209. Manchester, K. L., and Young, F. G., *Vitamins and Hormones*, **19**, 95–132 (1961)

210. Manchester, K. L., and Young, F. G., *Biochem. J.* (*London*), **70**, 353–58 (1958)

211. Wool, I. G., and Krahl, M. E., *Am. J. Physiol.*, **196**, 961–64 (1959)

212. Battaglia, F. C., Manchester, K. L., and Randle, P. J., *Biochim. Biophys. Acta*, **43**, 50–54 (1960)

213. Manchester, K. L., Randle, P. J., and Young, F. G., *J. Endocrinol.*, **19**, 259–62 (1959)

214. Manchester, K. L., and Young, F. G., *Biochem. J.* (*London*), **75**, 487–95 (1960)

215. Kipnis, D. M., and Noall, M. W., *Biochim. Biophys. Acta*, **28**, 226–27 (1958)

216. Manchester, K. L., *Biochem. J.* (*London*), **81**, 135–47 (1961)

217. Akedo, H., and Christensen, H. N., *J. Biol. Chem.*, **237**, 118–22 (1962)

218. Wool, I. G., *Biochim. Biophys. Acta*, **52**, 574–76 (1961)

219. Volfin, P., Eboué, D., and Clauser, H., *Nature*, **192**, 166–68 (1961)

220. Krahl, M. E., *Biochim. Biophys. Acta*, **35**, 556 (1959)

221. Herrera, M. G., and Renold, A. E., *Biochim. Biophys. Acta*, **44**, 165–67 (1960)

222. Carruthers, B. M., and Winegrad, A. I., *Am. J. Physiol.*, **202**, 605–10 (1962)

223. Wool, I. G., and Manchester, K. L., *Nature*, **193**, 345–46 (1962)

224. Hernandez, T., and Coulson, R. A., *Biochem. J.* (*London*), **79**, 596–605 (1961)

225. Korner, A., *J. Endocrinol.*, **20**, 256–65 (1960)

226. Korner, A., *Biochem. J.* (*London*), **74**, 471–78 (1960)

227. Doell, R. G., *Biochim. Biophys. Acta*, **39**, 237–41 (1960)

228. Penhos, J. C., and Krahl, M. E., *Am. J. Physiol.*, **202**, 349–52 (1962)

229. Marsh, J. B., *Am. J. Physiol.*, **201**, 55–57 (1961)

230. Kostyo, J. L., and Schmidt, J. E., *Endocrinology*, **70**, 381–85 (1962)

231. Korner, A., *Biochem. J. (London)*, **73**, 61–71 (1959)

232. Korner, A., *Biochem. J. (London)*, **81**, 292–97 (1961)

233. Korner, A., *Biochem. J. (London)*, **83**, 69–74 (1962)

234. Moon, H. D., Jentoft, V. L., and Li, C. H., *Endocrinology*, **70**, 31–38 (1962)

235. Denko, C. W., and Bergenstall, D. M., *Endocrinology*, **69**, 769–77 (1961)

236. Rudolph, H. J., and Pehrson, N. C., *Endocrinology*, **69**, 661–64 (1961)

237. Gaebler, O. H., Choitz, H. C., and Kurrie, D., *Am. J. Physiol.*, **201**, 255–58 (1961)

238. Talwar, G. P., Panda, N. C., Sarin, G. S., and Tolani, A. J., *Biochem. J. (London)*, **82**, 172–75 (1962)

239. Panda, N. C., Goel, B. K., Mansoor, M., and Talwar, G. P., *Biochem. J. (London)*, **82**, 176–79 (1962)

240. Korner, A., *J. Endocrinol.*, **21**, 177–89 (1960)

241. Kaplan, S. A., and Shimizu, C. S. N., *Federation Proc.*, **21**, 185 (1962)

242. Loecker, W. de, and Reddy, J., *Federation Proc.*, **21**, 187 (1962)

243. Weinshelbaum, E. I., and Wool, I. G., *Nature*, **191**, 1401–2 (1961)

244. Smith, A. L., Koeppe, O. J., and Franz, J. M., *Endocrinology*, **69**, 872–74 (1961)

245. Feigelson, M., Gross, P. R., and Feigelson, P., *Biochim. Biophys. Acta*, **55**, 495–504 (1962)

246. MacLean, P., *Nature*, **191**, 1302–3 (1961)

247. Harding, H. R., Rosen, F., and Nichol, C. A., *Am. J. Physiol.*, **201**, 271–75 (1961)

248. Sokoloff, L., Kauffman, S., and Gelboin, H. V., *Biochim. Biophys. Acta*, **52**, 410–12 (1961)

249. Sokoloff, L., Campbell, P. L., and Francis, C. M., *Federation Proc.*, **21**, 217 (1962)

250. Taylor, K. W., and Smith, G. H., *Biochem. J. (London)*, **82**, 2P (1962)

251. Taylor, K. W., Humbel, R. E., Steinke, J., and Renold, A. E., *Biochim. Biophys. Acta*, **54**, 391–94 (1961)

252. Humbel, R. E., Renold, A. E., Herrera, M. G., and Taylor, K. W., *Endocrinology*, **69**, 874–77 (1961)

253. Brahmachari, H. D., and Raghupathy Sarma, G., *Nature*, **191**, 491–92 (1961)

254. Simon, E., Scow, R. O., and Chernick, S. S., *Am. J. Physiol.*, **201**, 1073–97 (1961)

255. Lacy, P. E., *Diabetes*, **11**, 96–100 (1962)

256. Lacy, P. E., and Williamson, J. R., *Diabetes*, **11**, 101–4 (1962)

257. Hellman, B., and Larsson, S., *Experientia*, **18**, 180–81 (1962)

258. Carter, W. J., and Younathan, E. S., *Proc. Soc. Exptl. Biol. Med.*, **109**, 611–12 (1962)

259. Grodsky, G. M., Bennett, L., Batts, A., McWilliams, N., and Vcella, C., *Federation Proc.*, **21**, 202 (1962)

260. Coore, H. G., and Randle, P. J., *Biochem. J. (London)* (In press)

261. Antoniades, H. N., Gundersen, K., and Pyle, H. M., *Endocrinology*, **69**, 163–69 (1961)

262. Antoniades, H. N., Beigelman, P. M., Tranqueda, R. B., and Gundersen, K., *Endocrinology*, **69**, 46–54 (1961)

263. Antoniades, H. N., and Gundersen, K., *Endocrinology*, **70**, 95–98 (1962)

264. Antoniades, H. N., *Federation Proc.*, **21**, 203 (1962)

265. Samaan, N., Dempster, W. J., Fraser, T. R., and Stillman, D., *Biochem. J. (London)*, **82**, 29P (1962)

266. Mahon, W. A., Steinke, J., McKhannaud, G. M., and Mitchell, M. L., *Metabolism, Clin. Exptl.*, **11**, 416–20 (1962)

267. Ball, E. G., and Merrill, M. A., *Endocrinology*, **69**, 596–607 (1961)

268. Tomizawa, H., *J. Biol. Chem.*, **237**, 428–31 (1962)

269. Katzen, H. M., and Stetten, D. J., Jr., *Federation Proc.*, **21**, 201 (1962)

270. Rasmussen, H., Schwartz, I. L., Schoessler, M. A., and Hochstes, G., *Proc. Natl. Acad. Sci. US*, **46**, 1278–87 (1960)

271. Rasmussen, H., *Recent Progr. Hormone Research*, **17**, 488–90 (1961)

272. Fong, C. T. O., Silver, L., Popenoe, E. A., and Debons, A. F., *Biochim. Biophys. Acta*, **56**, 190–92 (1962)

273. Levari, R., Kornblueth, W., and Wertheimer, E., *J. Endocrinol.*, **22**, 361–69 (1961)

274. Levari, R., Wertheimer, E., Berman, E. R., and Kornblueth, W., *Nature*, **192**, 1075–76 (1961)

275. Beigelman, P. M., and Hollander, P. B., *Federation Proc.*, **21**, 205 (1962)

276. Lynn, W. S., and Brown, R. H., *Federation Proc.*, **21**, 202 (1962)
277. Scarpelli, D. G., and McMahon, S. M., *Federation Proc.*, **21**, 203 (1962)
278. Colwell, J. A., and Lein, A., *Federation Proc.*, **21**, 205 (1962)
279. Annison, E. F., and White, R. R., *Biochem. J.* (*London*), **80**, 162–69 (1961)
280. Young, F. G., *Australian J. Exptl. Biol. Med. Sci.*, **39**, S2–14 (1961)
281. Huggins, A. K., and Ottaway, J. H., *J. Endocrinol.*, **23**, 193–209 (1961)
282. Bornstein, J., and Hyde, D., *Nature*, **187**, 125–26 (1960)
283. Fenton, P. F., and Duguid, J. R., *Can. J. Biochem. Physiol.*, **40**, 337–41 (1962)
284. Stein, J. D., Bennett, L. L., and Nelson, M. M., *Endocrinology*, **70**, 223–27 (1962)
285. Hockaday, T. D. R., *Experientia*, **18**, 87–88 (1962)
286. Danowski, T. S., Balash, W. R., and Moses, C., *Diabetes*, **11**, 31–34 (1962)
287. Glasser, S. R., and Izzo, J. L., *Endocrinology*, **70**, 54–61 (1962)
288. Goetsch, D. D., and McDonald, L. E., *Am. J. Physiol.*, **202**, 343–46 (1962)
289. Lee, N. D., and Baltz, B. E., *Endocrinology*, **70**, 84–87 (1962)
290. Segal, H. L., and Menon, G. K. K., *J. Biol. Chem.*, **236**, 2872–77 (1961)
291. Kokka, N., and Bennett, L. L., *Am. J. Physiol.*, **200**, 1311–14 (1961)
292. Wall, J. S., Steele, R., de Bodo, R. C., and Altszuler, N., *Am. J. Physiol.*, **189**, 51–56 (1957)
293. Randle, P. J., In *Disorders of Carbohydrate Metabolism*. (ca. 1962)
294. Macho, L., *Nature*, **191**, 604 (1961)
295. Macho, L., *Experientia*, **18**, 73–74 (1962)
296. Hanson, R. W., Lindsay, R. H., and Barker, S. B., *Endocrinology*, **69**, 883–95 (1961)
297. Pittman, C. S., Lindsay, R. H., and Barker, S. B., *Endocrinology*, **69**, 761–68 (1961)
298. Rall, J. E., Roche, J., Michel, R., Michel, O., and Varrone, S., *Biochem. Biophys. Research Commun.*, 111–15 (1962)
299. Tonone, T., *Endocrinology*, **70**, 68–70 (1962)
300. Cerajo-Santalo, R., Di Nella, R., Park, C. R., and Park, J. H., *Endocrinology*, **69**, 422–29 (1961)
301. Barker, S. B., Ng, W. G., and Marx, W., *Endocrinology*, **70**, 333–39 (1962)
302. Sutherland, E. W., Rall, T. W., and Menon, T., *J. Biol. Chem.*, **237**, 1220–27 (1962)
303. Rall, T. W., and Sutherland, E. W., *J. Biol. Chem.*, **237**, 1228–32 (1962)
304. Klainer, L. M., Chi, Y. M., Friedberg, S. L., Rall, T. W., and Sutherland, E. W., *J. Biol. Chem.*, **237**, 1239–43 (1962)
305. Butcher, R. L., and Sutherland, E. W., *J. Biol. Chem.*, **237**, 1244–50 (1962)
306. Peron, F. G., *J. Biol. Chem.*, **236**, 1764–68 (1961)
307. Troop, R. C., and Possanza, G. J., *Federation Proc.*, **21**, 189 (1962)
308. Studzinski, G. P., and Grant, J. K., *Nature*, **193**, 1075–76 (1962)
309. Mason, N. R., Marsh, J. M., and Savard, K., *J. Biol. Chem.*, **236**, Pc 34–35 (1961)
310. Savard, K., Graubert, A. S., and Howell, D. S., *Federation Proc.*, **21**, 209 (1962)
311. Marsh, J. M., *Federation Proc.*, **21** 209 (1962)
312. Williams, H. E., Johnson, P. L., and Field, J. B., *Biochem. Biophys. Research Commun.*, **6**, 129–33 (1961)
313. Bransome, E. D., Jr., and Reddy, W. J., *Endocrinology*, **69**, 997 (1961)
314. Field, J. B., Paston, I., Johnson, B., and Herring, B., *J. Biol. Chem.*, **235**, 1863–66 (1960)
315. Field, J. B., Paston, I., Herring, B., and Johnson, P., *Biochim. Piophys. Acta*, **50**, 513–20 (1961)
316. Paston, I., Herring, B., and Field, J. B., *J. Biol. Chem.*, **236**, Pc 25 (1961)
317. Mulvey, P. F., Jr., Kelleher, J. B., and Slingerland, D. W., *Endocrinology*, **70**, 481–85 (1962)
318. Paston, I., Herring, B., Johnson, P., and Field, J. B., *J. Biol. Chem.*, **237**, 287–90 (1962)
319. Paston, I., Herring, B., and Field, J. B., *J. Biol. Chem.*, **236**, 340–42 (1961)
320. Barondes, S. H., Johnson, P., and Field, J. B., *Endocrinology*, **69**, 809–18 (1961)
321. Wool, I. G., Scharff, R., and Mages, N., *Am. J. Physiol.*, **201**, 547–50 (1961)

PARATHYROID GLAND[1,2]

By Paul L. Munson, Philip F. Hirsch, and Armen H. Tashjian, Jr.[3]

Biological Research Laboratories, Harvard School of Dental Medicine, and Department of Pharmacology, Harvard Medical School, Boston, Massachusetts

Since the excellent review by Bartter in the 1954 *Annual Review of Physiology* (1) there have been a number of advances in the understanding of the physiology of the parathyroid gland. The classic hormone of the gland, which has as its major function the maintenance of the normal level of blood calcium, has been isolated in the form of an apparently homogeneous polypeptide, molecular weight approximately 9000; and a relatively simple method for its preparation in a high state of purity has been developed. Both bone and kidney have been shown conclusively to be sites of direct action of the hormone. Contrary to the hypotheses of Albright and associates, the effect of the hormone on blood calcium has been shown not to be dependent on renal or extrarenal effects on blood phosphate. The modes and mechanisms of action of the hormone on bone and kidney, currently being investigated in a number of laboratories, are still obscure. The gut and the mammary gland are among other suggested sites of action of the hormone, direct or indirect. The interrelationships of parathyroid hormone and vitamin D are controversial. Proposed methods for the bioassay of parathyroid hormone in blood and urine are still inadequate; the recent successful production of a specific antibody to bovine parathyroid hormone in the rabbit may lead to a feasible assay method. A second parathyroid hormone, thought to lower the blood calcium, has been proposed. A suitable name for the classic parathyroid hormone, not yet coined, is needed to take the place of the etymologically unsatisfactory although widely accepted "parathormone".

Recent general reviews of parathyroid physiology, all somewhat dated by rapid developments in a very active field, include those by Fraser & King (2), Geschwind (3), Greep & Kenny (4), Irving (5), Kenny (6), McLean & Budy (7), Munson (8, 9), Nordin (10), and Rasmussen (11). Critical reviews of the literature are also to be found in the published symposium on Parathyroid Research Trends held in Houston, Texas, February 1960, and edited by Greep & Talmage (12).

CHEMISTRY

Crude preparations containing as little as 1 or 2 per cent of hormone by weight have been used in much of the research on parathyroid hormone. The

[1] The survey of the literature was concluded in June 1962. Because of limitations of space it was necessary to omit the citation of many relevant papers.

[2] The preparation of this Chapter was supported in part by a grant (A-1787) from the National Institute of Arthritis and Metabolic Disease, Public Health Service. The authors wish to express their appreciation to Mrs. Joan C. Carlow and Mrs. Ruth M. Powers for secretarial help.

[3] Fellow of the National Foundation.

development of a relatively simple method for the preparation of highly purified parathyroid hormone by Rasmussen & Craig (13) should make better material generally available, thereby providing a sounder basis for future work. The efficient early stages of the new procedure, beginning with the extraction of dehydrated, defatted parathyroid tissue of cattle with phenol, were devised by Aurbach (14). Gel filtration on Sephadex for the final purification (13) was substituted for the relatively elaborate countercurrent distribution procedures used earlier by Aurbach (14) and Rasmussen & Craig (15). The biological activity of the final product in the Munson assay method (16) was reported to be 2200 to 3000 units per mg, essentially the same as that of the countercurrent distribution products reported earlier (14, 15). The practicability of the entire procedure has been substantiated by its ready reproducibility in three independent laboratories [(13, 17); Aurbach, personal communication].

Early attempts to improve on the original procedures of Hanson (18) and of Collip (19) for preparation of the hormone, reviewed elsewhere (4, 20), were hampered by the limitations of the bioassay methods available at the time and by lack of the more recently developed powerful tools for peptide fractionation.

The present era began with the work of Davies & Gordon (21), who utilized acetic acid as well as the classic dilute hydrochloric acid as a reagent for initial extraction of the hormone from parathyroid tissue. A fractionation step introduced early in the procedure, ultrafiltration through cellophane, one sort of "molecular sieving", foreshadowed the current gel filtration. However, the yield and specific activity of the product reported by Davies and Gordon were low. Rasmussen & Westall (22) developed and improved on the processes introduced by Davies & Gordon (21), while Friedman, Munson, and associates (8, 23, 24) concentrated and purified parathyroid extracts with dilute hydrochloric acid (both hot and cold) with the aid of selective precipitation with ammonium sulfate and chromatography on carboxymethyl-cellulose.

The most highly developed and currently most useful procedure for the preparation of purified parathyroid hormone (13), however, stems from Aurbach's introduction of phenol for extraction of the hormone (25), a reagent suggested by the work of Tweedy (26) years earlier, which also supplied guidelines for subsequent fractionation steps. After precipitation of inactive material in the initial phenol extract with acetic acid-acetone, the active fraction was precipitated by addition of ether. The resulting crude hormone was then fractionated by differential solubility in acetic acid, sodium chloride, and trichloracetic acid solutions. Final purification was achieved by repeated countercurrent distribution. This procedure was amply confirmed, with slight modifications, by Rasmussen & Craig (15), who also undertook a study of the purity and the amino acid composition of the final product. Reservations about the implied homogeneity of the final products of Aurbach (14) and of Rasmussen & Craig (15) have been expressed (8, 27). Possibly they may be hypercritical both on semantic grounds and in relation to the concept of "microheterogeneity" of proteins and polypeptides (28). However, evidence of heterogeneity on electrophoretic analysis of these products reported by Barrett *et al.* (29) cannot be ignored, although artifact formation during the analytical procedure was not ruled out.

Extensive studies of the amino acid composition and molecular weight of the parathyroid polypeptide isolated from phenol extracts have been published by Rasmussen & Craig (13, 15, 30, 31, 32). Partly because of methodological limitations, various estimates of the molecular weight have been advanced, ranging from 8447 to 9438. In round numbers the figure of 9000 would appear to be a reasonable approximation. All the more common amino acids, with the exception of cystine, 17 in number, were represented. The sulfur content of the polypeptide was accounted for by methionine. The absence of cystine and the isolation of a single N-terminal amino acid, alanine, supported the conclusion that the hormone is a single-chain polypeptide.

Rasmussen and co-workers (22, 31 to 35) have also studied the characteristics of purified active fractions prepared from acetic acid and hydrochloric acid extracts. The initial steps (22) in the preparation from a hot acetic acid extract involved differential precipitation with acetone and ultrafiltration in 2.2 M acetic acid, following Davies & Gordon (21). The lyophilized ultrafiltrate was then subjected to repeated zonal electrophoresis on polyvinyl chloride (33). The biological activity of the most active product obtained was 220 units per mg, representing an improvement of approximately sevenfold over the ultrafiltrate. Electrophoresis and ultracentrifugation did not reveal any heterogeneity in this product. However, in a later study (31) the product was found by countercurrent distribution to contain at least three inactive components in addition to the highly active (1200 to 1600 units per mg) hormone fraction. It was also found feasible to apply the procedure of countercurrent distribution directly to the acetic acid ultrafiltrate, omitting zone electrophoresis. Amino acid analyses of two products obtained by the revised procedure were in fair agreement and led to an estimate of 6943 for the molecular weight, substantially less than that for the polypeptide isolated from phenol extract. Subsequently, the molecular weights of active polypeptides obtained from hydrochloric acid extracts were estimated still lower (36).

The preliminary fractionation of the hydrochloric acid extracts (22, 36), including acetone precipitation and ultrafiltration, was similar to that used for acetic acid extracts and followed closely the scheme introduced by Davies & Gordon (21). The lyophilized ultrafiltrate was then subjected to countercurrent distribution. Amino acid analyses of three separate products (36) differed considerably. Assuming homogeneity for all three products, Rasmussen estimated the minimum molecular weights to be, respectively, 3788, 5239, and 5635. The biological activity was estimated at 750 to 1250 units per mg. Munson (8) reported a product of equal or higher biological activity obtained from hydrochloric acid extracts by carboxymethylcellulose chromatography but considered it to be heterogeneous and susceptible to further purification.

The three types of polypeptide preparation studied by Rasmussen and co-workers, corresponding to the three different reagents used for the initial extraction of the gland powder, were designated parathormone A (hydrochloric acid), B (acetic acid), and C (phenol) (31). Amino acid analysis and estimation of molecular weights were, for the most part, consistent with the hypothesis that polypeptides A and B were partial degradation products of C, which was tentatively considered to be the native hormone. With respect to the amino acid analyses, the values for threonine, indicating two residues per mole in B, and only one in C, were the only data inconsistent with the hypothesis. The A and B peptides were still highly active biologically but considerably less so than C. Peptide A has about one ninth the activity of C per mole so that, although the lower molecular weight peptides must include an "active segment" of the hormone molecule, the portion of the C structure eliminated during preparation must also be of great biological importance. Evidence for the chemical homogeneity of the three polypeptide types is stronger for C than it is for A or B.

Parathyroid extracts (34), like ACTH preparations (37), can be reversibly inactivated with hydrogen peroxide. The biological activity may be restored or even increased above the preinactivation value by treatment with cysteine (34, 35). The nature of the effect of cysteine, which also enhances the activity of preparations that have not been deliberately inactivated (6, 16, 35, 38), is unsettled, as is that of hydrogen peroxide. The effect of cysteine is not easy to differentiate from that of other agents, oil, heparin, and gelatin, for example, that stabilize or enhance the serum calcium raising activity of crude as well as purified preparations in parathyroidectomized rats (16, 35, 38, 39, 40). Rasmussen (30) has suggested that mild oxidation converts the methionine in the hormone to methionine sulfoxide with an associated loss in biological activity that is recovered by reduction of the sulfoxide back to methionine by cysteine. Substantiation of this hypothesis by analysis of the peroxide-inactivated preparations for methionine sulfoxide has been hampered by methodological difficulties that apparently have now been resolved (32, 41, 42). Other aspects of the stability *in vitro* of polypeptide B were studied in detail by Rasmussen (35), and Reichert and L'Heureux (43) have reported their observations that incubation of U.S.P. parathyroid extract with rat plasma protects the hormone from loss of activity by dialysis and by treatment with peroxide.

Certain similarities in the biological effects of parathyroid hormone and vitamin D have led for many years to the speculation that parathyroid hormone might be a steroid derivative. This idea was more plausible before the recent work on purification of active parathyroid polypeptides, which has been generally accepted as establishing the peptide nature of the hormone. Raoul, Marnay and associates, following earlier studies of antirachitic and hypercalcemic substances derived chemically from cholesterol or extracted from higher plants [reviewed by Fieser & Fieser (44)], turned to an examination of parathyroid tissue as a possible source of related products (45). Two types of nitrogen-free lipid-soluble fractions were obtained. One was reported to be hypercalcemic and the other hypocalcemic, as tested in intact rabbits and in intact and parathyroidectomized rats and dogs (46 to 49). The lowest dose found to be active in the rat was 0.8 mg. Attempts to confirm the preparation of lipid extracts of parathyroid tissue that raise the serum calcium have been unsuccessful in two independent laboratories (6, 39), so at this time the validity of the observations of Raoul, Marnay et al. is in question.

That the blood calcium-raising and phosphaturic effects of parathyroid extracts might be caused by two separate hormones, as suggested earlier (21, 50 to 53), now appears to be unlikely, since highly purified preparations have been found to possess both activities (8, 54, 55). However, the possibility that there is more than one parathyroid hormone is still not excluded, since crude extracts have effects for which tests with purified preparations, if made, have not yet been reported.

Other current reviews of the chemistry of parathyroid hormone are by Rasmussen & Craig (32) and Tashjian & Munson (27).

BIOLOGICAL ASSAY

For standardization, the *U. S. Pharmacopeia* (56) still specifies the classic dog method originally developed by Collip & Clark (57). The reliability of this assay method, which functions without a reference standard, is attested by the extensive and generally satisfactory use of the U.S.P. extract supplied by Eli Lilly and Co. as an assay standard by laboratories interested in purification of parathyroid extracts.

For following the purification of extracts, the method of Munson et al. (16, 50, 58) has been used most extensively (8, 13, 14, 15). In this method young male rats, after receiving a calcium-free diet for four days, are parathyroidectomized by hot wire cautery. Immediately thereafter they are injected subcutaneously with a parathyroid extract or standard. Within six hours after parathyroidectomy the serum calcium of untreated rats has fallen to about 6 mg per cent. The degree of maintenance of serum calcium above this level bears a linear relationship to the log of the dose of extract. The index of precision (λ) of 26 assays conducted in 1959 was 0.23, with a standard deviation of 0.05 (16). This assay method has been a serviceable one in spite of some unexplained peculiarities. For example, the level of serum calcium in control rats 6 hr after parathyroidectomy differs depending on the method of parathyroidectomy and is slightly higher following injection of 15 per cent gelatin or 0.12 M cysteine than it is in rats that are uninjected or injected with neutral or acidified physiological salt solution (16). Furthermore, the effect of almost all types of crude and purified parathyroid extracts is enhanced by addition of gelatin, cysteine, or oil (16, 35, 40).

The methods of Davies et al. (59) and Tepperman et al. (60) have also been used in recent purification studies. In the first method, which is reported to be considerably less precise than that of Munson *et al.*, rats on a stock diet are parathyroidectomized 3 to 21 days before the assay. Blood for calcium analysis is drawn 21 hr after injection of extract. A 6-hr time interval was found to be preferable to 21 hr for assessment of the potency of purified preparations, which have a relatively short duration of action (61). In the method of Tepperman *et al.* (60), the fall in serum phosphate 3 hr after injection of extract is measured. This method has sometimes been termed inexactly a measurement of phosphaturic activity. Clark *et al.* (62) have developed an assay method based on the withdrawal of ^{45}Ca from the skeleton of the intact rat given ^{45}Ca 6 weeks prior to the assay. In the assay method of Kenny & Munson for phosphaturic activity (53), the excretion of phosphate in the urine during the first 6 hr after injection of hormone and parathyroidectomy is measured. Other biological assay methods for parathyroid hormone have been described by Dulce *et al.* (63), Iwanowska *et al.* (64), Mouzas & Weiss (65), Polin *et al.* (66), and Thieblot *et al.* (67).

The small amounts of parathyroid hormone required to maintain the serum calcium of the parathyroidectomized rat (Hirsch and Munson, unpublished) and dog (68), when given by continuous intravenous infusion, indicate that the concentration of hormone in blood and urine must be low. A more delicate assay method than is yet available, coupled with a simple efficient method for concentrating the hormone from blood and urine, will greatly facilitate adequate quantitative assay of these fluids. Two major possibilities for a more delicate assay method are now apparent. One, under investigation by Raisz (69) and by Goldhaber (personal communication), is based on the observation of Gaillard (70) that addition of as little as 0.1 unit of hormone *in vitro* stimulates resorption of bone in tissue culture. The other is a projected immunochemical assay method utilizing the specific antibody to bovine parathyroid hormone produced in the rabbit (17, 32, 70a).

In the meantime several attempts have been made to detect and quantitate roughly the concentrations of parathyroid hormone in blood and urine with the aid of more conventional assay methods.

Davies (71) treated 48-hr human urine specimens (adjusted to pH 3.5) with benzoic acid to adsorb parathyroid hormone. The residue, insoluble in ethanol (after dissolving the benzoic acid), was assayed by the method of Davies *et al.* (51), which involves measurement of the phosphate excreted by intact mice during a $3\frac{1}{2}$-hr period following injection of urine extracts in comparison with standards. A twin crossover design was used. Recovery of Lilly parathyroid extract added to urine ranged from 76 to 85 per cent. The precision of the assay method was only fair (λ approximately 0.4), but this was compensated for in part by the use of large numbers of mice (48 per dose level), each of which required only 0.2 to 1 unit of parathyroid hormone. The values for 24-hr urine collections obtained from 5 normal subjects averaged 60 units (range 47 to 72); from 4 cases of confirmed hyperparathyroidism, 121 (range 103 to 146). In 5 cases of hypoparathyroidism there was too little activity to detect it, less than 30 units.

The benzoic acid adsorption method of Davies (71) was also used by Fujita *et al.* (72) for the assay of parathyroid hormone in human urine. A modification of the method of Rubin & Dorfman (73) was used for the biological assay. Six or more hours after parathyroidectomy, young male rats were waterloaded by stomach tube, $Na_2H^{32}PO_4$ was injected intraperitoneally, and urine extract or standard was injected subcutaneously. Urine voided during the next 6 hr was collected and analyzed for ^{32}P. Increasing effects were observed after injection of 5 to 40 units of commercial parathyroid extract. In confirmation of Davies (71), recovery of parathyroid extract added to urine ranged from 51 to 87 per cent. Somewhat lower values for parathyroid hormone excretion than those found by Davies were observed. In 3 normal subjects, 10 to 30 units per 24 hr was found; in 2 other normal subjects as well as 2 cases of postoperative hypoparathyroidism, no hormone was detected. An elevated value was found in one case of hyperparathyroidism, but also in 6 out of 7 untreated cases of hyperthyroidism, 3 cases of hypertension, and one case of nephrolithiasis. In 17 patients with miscellaneous disorders, the hormone was undetectable in 7 and ranged from 6 to 30 units in the others. These results of Fujita *et al.* (72) suggest that the specificity of the assay method may be open to question.

The experiments of Buckner & Nellor (74), using a procedure patterned after the assay method of Davies *et al.* (59) as modified by Rasmussen & Westall (22), indicated that 8 to 29 days after placing young male rats on a diet free of calcium and vitamin D, but not earlier, parathyroid hormone-like activity was elicited in the assay rat by the injection of as little as 0.25 to 1.0 ml of plasma. By reference to the results of similar tests with U.S.P. parathyroid extract, the authors estimated the hormone concentration in the calcium-depleted rats' serum as 20 to 64 units per ml. Data from only 26 assay rats were reported, an inadequate number for meaningful quantitative conclusions.

Using a similar assay method, except that serum calcium was determined in blood drawn 6 hr after intraperitoneal injection of plasma or plasma fractions, Reichert & L'Heureux (75) also failed to detect parathyroid hormone in the blood of rats on a normal diet. After injection of U.S.P. parathyroid extract or addition of this extract to rat plasma, small effects on serum calcium were observed in test rats given the α-globulin fraction (Cohn Fraction IV), results indicative of partial recovery of parathyroid hormone in this fraction. Tests of fractions from normal human plasma resulted in a significant effect in the assay animals only for Cohn Fraction II+III, and here the mean increase in serum calcium was only 1.0 mg per cent. The authors estimated 40 units of hormone per 100 ml of human plasma, obviously on rather shaky grounds.

Fujita *et al.* (76), using their phosphaturic assay method (72), tested plasma from normal, hypertensive (Goldblatt clamp), and oxalate-injected rabbits. The plasma was treated with phenol, acetic acid-acetone, and ether, somewhat like the procedure of Aurbach (14) for preliminary fractionation of parathyroid extracts. The equivalent of 5 ml of plasma was injected into each test rat. Commerical parathyroid extract added to rabbit plasma, then subjected to the phenol extraction procedure, was recovered to the extent of 68 to 87 per cent. The hormone in plasma from normal and oxalate-treated rabbits was barely detectable, but a marked and highly significant increase in ^{32}P excretion occurred in the rats injected with plasma from the hypertensive rabbits. The authors speculated on possible relationships between hypertension and parathyroid function, but lack of specificity of the assay method is a plausible alternative explanation of the results.

Effects of Parathyroid Hormone

The critical function of the parathyroid hormone is to maintain the normal level of plasma calcium. Contrary to the hypothesis of Albright and co-workers (77), still widely accepted at the time of Bartter's review (1), it does so mainly by an effect on bone that is direct and not secondary to changes in the plasma level of inorganic phosphate. The basis for the current concept of the mode of action of parathyroid hormone was reviewed recently by Munson (8). The most compelling evidence has been the demonstration by Barnicot (78), Chang (79), and Gaillard (70) of direct effects of the gland and the hormone on bone, the activity of the hormone in nephrectomized animals (80 to 83), documentation of the sequence of changes in serum calcium and phosphate following parathyroidectomy and administration of hormone (50), and the observations of normal serum phosphate values in a majority of patients with hypo- (84) and hyperparathyroidism (85). It has been suggested, although not established with certainty, that parathyroid hormone also conserves calcium by stimulating absorption from the gut and reabsorption by the renal tubule (see below), but these effects are undoubtedly less important in the homeostasis of plasma calcium than the effect on bone. Aside from the disposal of excess phosphate, a process that may contribute indirectly to the stabilization of the plasma calcium level (11), the physiological significance of the phosphaturic effect of parathyroid hormone is not clear.

Bone.—Several, but not all (86) recent investigations support the idea, expounded by McLean & Urist (87), that it is a relatively stable fraction of bone mineral rather than the small exchangeable "labile" fraction (88) that is the primary target of parathyroid hormone. Using nephrectomized rats and employing the technique of peritoneal lavage, Talmage & Elliott (89) showed that if ^{45}Ca was administered less than 24 hr before parathyroidectomy, the concentration of radioactivity in the lavage fluid was unaffected by the loss of the parathyroid glands, although the concentration of stable calcium declined in parallel with plasma calcium. On the other hand, if the ^{45}Ca was injected 2 to 3 weeks before parathyroidectomy, then radioactive and stable calcium in the lavage decreased together after parathyroidectomy. It was concluded that ^{45}Ca had not reached areas of bone affected by the parathyroid gland within 24 hr after injection. The work of Woods & Armstrong (90) and Clark & Geoffroy (91), in which rats were given parathyroid extract 60 to 72 days after the administration of ^{45}Ca, was in agreement with the conclusion of Talmage & Elliott that the hormone acts on stable bone.

The mechanism by which the bone calcium is made available to extracellular fluid by parathyroid hormone is unknown. Nor is it certain whether the major effect of the hormone is on bone mineral, bone matrix, or both. That parathyroid hormone may have a direct effect on bone matrix, including mucoprotein and seromucoid [using the classification of Winzler (92)], glycoprotein, and mucopolysaccharide, has been suggested in several laboratories. As emphasized by Kenny (6), the terminology in this area of bone physiology is confused and care is needed to appreciate the site and specificity of any changes seen.

Engel (93) interpreted the increased mucoprotein level in the blood of the rat following administration of large doses of U.S.P. parathyroid extract as an indication of an action of the hormone on bone matrix. However, Shetlar et al. (94) showed that an increased blood "seromucoid" hexose level could be produced by injecting formaldehyde-inactivated parathyroid extract, indicating that the effect observed by Engel was nonspecific. On the other hand, Shetlar et al. (95) also reported an increase in rat serum glycoprotein following injection of parathyroid extract, an effect which, unlike that on seromucoid, was not seen when a formaldehyde-inactivated extract was administered. Pepsin treatment of the extract abolished both effects. Evidence is lacking that changes in the serum level of glycoproteins or mucoproteins is a measure of the release of these substances from bone matrix. In this connection, the calculations by Hausmann (96) showed that the observed blood mucoprotein levels (93, 94) were far too high to have been derived from bone.

The observation by Bernstein & Handler (97) that administration of parathyroid extract enhanced the incorporation of $^{35}SO_4$ into and its release from cartilage in rachitic rats was taken as an indication of an effect of parathyroid hormone on matrix mucopolysaccharide metabolism. Bronner (98) has found that administration of parathyroid extract to rats pretreated with $^{35}SO_4$ and ^{45}Ca increased the level of $^{35}SO_4$ in plasma, the ratio of $^{35}SO_4$ in humerus ends to $^{35}SO_4$ in humerus shafts, the urinary excretion of $^{35}SO_4$, and the specific activity of urinary ^{45}Ca. These findings were interpreted to indicate a stimulation by parathyroid extract of simultaneous release of both the organic and inorganic constituents of bone. Johnston et al. (99) reported, likewise, that the mobilization of calcium from bone stimulated both in intact and parathyroidectomized rats by parathyroid extract was closely associated in time with a decrease in bone hexosamine content. In a later study (100) it was found that incorporation of proline-^{14}C into bone matrix of rats was depressed following administration of parathyroid extract. These observations need further elaboration before they can be fitted into a clear exposition of the mechanism of action of parathyroid hormone on bone.

Although a direct or even an indirect effect of the hormone on acellular bone matrix may exist, more convincing data have accumulated to suggest that the mobilization of bone mineral is, to a large, although possibly not exclusive extent (101), the result of active bone cellular metabolism. The mechanism of this resorptive process remains speculative. One prominent hypothesis widely discussed, and yet to be disproved, emphasizes the role of local pH and organic acid production and its modification by parathyroid hormone.

Following the early observation by Sjöström (102) in 1937 that an increase in parathyroid function was accompanied by a corresponding change in blood citric acid, numerous investigators have recorded the interrelationships between parathyroid hormone and the metabolism of calcium and citric acid (103 to 110). A definite positive correlation exists between endogenous parathyroid gland activity and blood citric acid concentration (103, 111 to 114). Net citrate turnover tends to be low in hypoparathyroid man (115). Furthermore, parathyroid extract (usually in massive dosage) has been shown to increase bone citrate concentration or release in the dog (104, 106, 116). Likewise, certain (117 to 120), but not all (121) studies *in vitro* of bone taken from animals pretreated with large doses of parathyroid extract have demonstrated increased citrate content or production, often, however, with as much as 100 times more basal lactate synthesis, which the hormone does not appear to increase (120). Resorbing bone in tissue culture favors net citrate, rather than lactate, synthesis (122); and pigeon bone during the resorptive phase of the egg-laying cycle contains approximately eight times its resting citrate content (123). Bone contains the enzymatic mechanisms for both synthesis (124) and catabolism (125, 126) of citrate; however, a large portion of that present in bone may reflect surface adsorption (127, 128), although peptide-bound citrate has been isolated from human dentine (129).

Interest in these interrelationships persists because of the obscurity of the mechanism by which parathyroid hormone mobilizes calcium from bone. A bold attempt to organize existing knowledge into a unified theory of bone resorption, the so-called "acid-theory", was made by Neuman *et al.* in 1956 (104), and it has been further explained by Neuman, Firschein *et al.* (106, 110, 130). The postulate, in brief, suggests that parathyroid hormone stimulates the production of organic acids (citrate, lactate, and possibly others) by bone cells. The acids so formed produce a local pH gradient conducive to dissolution of hydroxyapatite which, combined with the solubilizing effect of the citrate ion exchanging with bone phosphate and complexing with calcium, would lead to a liberation of calcium into the general circulation. No attempt was made to explain the effect, direct or indirect, of the hormone on the organic matrix of bone. Compatible with this concept are the observation that the pH in the immediate proximity of osteoclasts is relatively acidic (131) and the attraction of resorbing bone for radioyttrium (132), a process which may be the result of a local pH below 7.0 (133). Also favoring a pH gradient as the mechanism of calcium mobilization are experiments *in vitro* in which the ability of viable bone chips to maintain a higher concentration of calcium in the incubation medium than dead bone fragments could produce at pH 7.4 (134, 135) was lost by reducing the pH of the medium to 6.5. Against the hypothesis is the lack of correlation between the amount of acid (principally lactate) produced and the amount of calcium mobilized (121, 136). The experiments of Harrison *et al.* (137) also argue against the importance of circulating citrate *per se* in calcium mobilization. By treating rats with cortisol they were able to prevent the rise in serum citrate that occurs when vitamin D-deficient rats are given vitamin D, yet there was no interference with the rise in serum calcium. In view of the increased rate of citrate disappearance from the blood following adrenocortical steroid administration (115), however, it is conceivable that in the experiments of Harrison *et al.* increased catabolism masked a local skeletal increase in citrate synthesis.

One must conclude that, although little understood at present, some association must exist between intermediary carbohydrate metabolism and skeletal calcium mobilization. That inhibition of glycolysis eliminates calcium mobilization from bone fragments supports this concept.

Although the importance of glycolysis in the respiration of bone *in vitro* has been emphasized (101, 110, 136, 138, 139, 140), the Krebs cycle also plays an important role in the over-all metabolism of bone (110, 141). Goldhaber (142) has found that the enhancement of the resorption of bone induced in tissue culture by parathyroid extract is dependent on the presence of oxygen in the gas phase.

Gaillard was the first to demonstrate an effect of parathyroid hormone on bone in tissue culture. His first experiments (143) involved cultivating parathyroid gland tissue from human newborns next to fragments of bone taken from nearly full-term mouse embryos. Marked resorption of the bone occurred associated with the appearance of large multinuclear osteoclasts in the immediate vicinity of the parathyroid tissue. Later (144), similar observations were made when minute amounts (as little as 0.1 unit per ml) of U.S.P. parathyroid extract were substituted for the parathyroid organ cultures, and most recently (70) highly purified parathyroid hormone preparations supplied by Rasmussen were found to be effective. Gaillard has interpreted his results to mean that parathyroid hormone creates a condition favoring the formation, survival, and specific function of osteoclasts. In addition to the effect on resorption and on osteoclasts, Gaillard found that parathyroid hormone caused disappearance of osteoblasts and cessation of bone matrix deposition (70), a result, with respect to bone formation, similar to that of Bronner (145) studying $^{35}SO_4$ incorporation into bone. In addition Gaillard reported that glycine incorporation into bone matrix was inhibited by parathyroid hormone, in agreement with Vaes & Nichols (146), who demonstrated a decreased incorporation *in vitro* of glycine into bone fragments of rats that had been pretreated 12 hr previously with parathyroid extract. The tissue culture technique appears to provide a sensitive, readily controlled system to study the metabolic events associated with parathyroid activity.

Although commercial parathyroid extract has been reported to affect several enzymes (108, 147 to 150) and a coenzyme (151), all known to be present in bone, these changes have yet to be shown to be either specific or related to the effect of the hormone on bone resorption.

Urinary inorganic phosphate.—The controversial question of the major site of the phosphaturic action of parathyroid hormone has been partially resolved. Studies with the relatively crude U.S.P. parathyroid extract convinced most investigators that the phosphaturia came from an effect on the renal tubule, even though a concomitant increase in glomerular filtration rate could not be ruled out. Data in man, for example, obtained by Hiatt & Thompson (152), Nemeth (153), and Gershberg *et al.* (154), using U.S.P. extract, indicated uniformly that the increase in the excretion of phosphate was caused largely by decreased tubular reabsorption. The same conclusion was also reached by Foulkes & Perry (155) from their experiments with the intravenous infusion of U.S.P. extract in the dog. The decrease in urinary excretion of phosphate by rats after parathyroidectomy and the increase in phosphate excretion after injection with parathyroid extract found by Beutner & Munson (156) were considered too large to be explained by alterations in renal hemodynamics. The effect of parathyroidectomy on serum phosphate, glomerular filtration rate, and tubular reabsorption of phosphate in the rat was measured by Ito *et al.* (157); only the tubular reabsorption of phosphate was changed markedly from control values.

Results of experiments with purified hormone preparations indicate, furthermore, that the hormone acts directly on the kidney to alter tubular function without affecting glomerular filtration rate. Samiy *et al.* (158) injected parathyroidectomized dogs intravenously with 200 to 400 units of partially purified parathyroid hormone and observed that the increased excretion of phosphate, ascribed to decreased phosphate reabsorption, occurred without any increase in filtered load. Pullman *et al.* (54) not only provided evidence for the tubular action of the hormone but also for the direct action of the hormone on the kidney by infusing 10 to 30 units of highly purified parathyroid hormone per hour into one renal artery of the intact dog. Unilateral or preferential phosphaturia from the kidney on the infused side was found in the majority of the experiments. Similar preferential or unilateral phosphaturic responses from the infused kidney of parathyroidectomized dogs receiving 1 to 10 units of hormone per hour have been observed in the recent unpublished studies of Hirsch and Munson. Since no consistent changes in glomerular filtration rate were noted in either of these series of experiments, they lend strong support to the conclusion that parathyroid hormone acts directly on the renal tubule. Contaminants in crude parathyroid preparations must have been responsible for the previously observed increases in glomerular filtration rate (159, 160), although "parathormone B", presumably highly purified, was reported to raise glomerular filtration rate significantly (161).

Whether the major effect of the hormone is to decrease tubular reabsorption or to stimulate tubular secretion is still a matter of controversy; the published data do not yet permit a clear decision between the two alternatives. Bartter (162) and Giebisch (163) recently reviewed the evidence concerning the site of action of parathyroid hormone within the renal tubule.

Levinsky & Davidson (164) utilized the renal portal system of the chicken for unilateral infusions of parathyroid extract and phosphate. In some periods the excretion of phosphate exceeded the filtered load, indicating tubular secretion. The preferential phosphaturic response from the kidney unilaterally infused with parathyroid extract demonstrated a direct effect on the renal tubule. However, it was not certain whether the effect of the extract came from increased secretion or from inhibition of reabsorption.

The occurrence of tubular secretion of phosphate is also well substantiated in lower marine vertebrates (165). Although several recent investigations have given some indication of phosphate secretion in mammals, the process has not been demonstrated conclusively. Carrasquer & Brodsky (166) observed phosphate excretion transiently exceeding that of creatinine in dogs following a direct renal arterial injection of equimolar quantities of creatinine and sodium phosphate and interpreted the results to be an indication of secretion, although the possibility was conceded that the intra-arterial injections may have reduced tubular reabsorption on the injected side. Nicholson & Shepherd (167) studied the effect of selective damage to various parts of the renal tubule of dogs on the excretion of phosphate. When the first third of the proximal tubule was damaged by the renal arterial injection of a solution of potassium dichromate, there was a marked increase in the excretion of phosphate relative to the control kidney, supporting the generally accepted concept that phosphate is actively reabsorbed in the proximal tubule. Damage to the latter two-thirds of the proximal tubule by renal arterial administration of sodium tartrate solution produced no significant change in the excretion of phosphate. However, when the distal tubule was damaged by a retrograde ureteral injection of a mercuric chloride solution, the excretion of phosphate was greatly reduced, a result that suggested active secretion of phosphate in the distal tubule. Nicholson (168) administered 20 units of U.S.P. parathyroid extract per kg to dogs in which these three types of renal tubular lesions had been produced. While increased excretion of phosphate occurred from the kidneys with proximal tubular damage, the phosphaturic action of the hormone was markedly depressed or absent following lesions in the distal tubule. Nicholson concluded that the site of action of the hormone is the distal segment and that the mode of action is the stimulation of active secretion of phosphate.

That tubular secretion, if it occurs at all, is of minor importance was indicated by the results of Bronner & Thompson (169), who investigated the transtubular flux of radioactive phosphate in dogs. They concluded, on the basis of the similarity of the excretion patterns of creatinine and ^{32}P injected into one renal artery, that only a small amount of phosphate in the urine is derived from the transtubular influx. Taugner et al. (170), who studied the distribution of inorganic phosphate in the tubules of the cat from 2.5 to 15 min following the intravenous administration of labeled phosphate, concluded that only a small amount of excreted phosphate could have arisen by tubular secretion. Similar conclusions were drawn from the results of stop-flow experiments in which ^{32}P was injected before the release of the ureteral clamp (171, 172).

Evidence from other experiments does not support the hypothesis that phosphate is secreted by the renal tubules of the dog. Stop-flow experiments localized avid reabsorption of phosphate in the proximal tubule with no indication of tubular secretion (173). Handler (174) also found no evidence for secretion in the dog when, by employing a multiplicity of techniques, he was unable to produce an excretion of phosphate in excess of the filtered load.

Using the stop-flow technique, Samiy et al. [(158, 171) and unpublished results] studied the renal effect of parathyroid hormone in parathyroidectomized dogs and concluded that the increase in phosphate excretion observed was mainly the result of inhibition of proximal tubular reabsorption of phosphate. This conclusion was based on the fact that under the conditions of the experiments there was practically no excretion of phosphate observed either in the free-flow or stop-flow periods prior to the administration of hormone, while after hormone administration there was a large rise in phosphate excretion, and that the excretion patterns for phosphate during the stop-flow periods, similar to those obtained by Pitts et al. (173) in intact dogs, showed no evidence for secretion under conditions in which secretion should have been easily detectable.

The usefulness of stop-flow techniques and selective renal tubular damage as a means of revealing the normal tubular site of action of parathyroid hormone is limited, in part, by the unphysiological nature of experiments using these methods. In addition, evidence from stop-flow data that parathyroid hormone inhibits proximal tubular reabsorption of phosphate may be questioned because of difficulties in the assignment of functions to the proximal tubule (175, 176). Conclusions drawn from experiments with selective renal damage by nephrotoxic agents are likewise insecure, because they were based on the assumptions that functional changes in the tubule occurred only in regions of histologically identified lesions and that back-diffusion of creatinine and phosphate in the damaged kidneys was approximately equal (167).

Although the site of action of parathyroid hormone in the mammalian kidney has not been established with certainty, it is conservative to conclude that the hormone inhibits the well-established process of renal tubular reabsorption rather than that it stimulates a yet unproved tubular secretory process. Future investigations of the effect of parathyroid hormone on urinary phosphate must also take into account the convincing demonstration by Walser (177, 178) of the complex state of plasma inorganic phosphate.

Urinary calcium.—Talmage and associates (179, 180, 181), in experiments on rats, were the first to indicate that parathyroid hormone might act on the kidney in such a way as to conserve calcium. In the first few hours after parathyroidectomy, at the same time that the plasma calcium and filtered load were falling, they observed a marked increase in the rate of urinary calcium excretion. The results following administration of parathyroid extract were confirmatory, since the excretion of calcium fell at the same time that the plasma calcium was rising. Similar results were reported for the mouse by Buchanan *et al.* (182), and for the dog by Kleeman *et al.* (183), and Widrow & Levinsky (184).

Kleeman *et al.* (183) also conducted extensive studies in normal, hypo-, and hyperparathyroid human subjects. Over a wide range of filtered loads of calcium, either spontaneous or induced by administration of calcium salts orally or by intravenous infusion, the injection of parathyroid extract or elevated endogenous supply of the hormone consistently increased the tubular reabsorption of calcium above that seen at the same filtered load in controls. In the study by Gordan *et al.* (185), also in man, it was observed, in agreement with Kleeman *et al.*, that in normal human subjects with plasma calcium levels elevated to the hyperparathyroid range by infusion of calcium glucono-galacto-gluconate, the percentage of filtered calcium reabsorbed by the tubule was considerably less than in hyperparathyroid patients. However, Gordan *et al.* attributed the lower reabsorption in the normal subjects to an elevated excretion of calcium complexed with the gluconate ion, as suggested by the experiments of Chen & Neuman (186) and Howard *et al.* (187), rather than to the lower level of parathyroid hormone as proposed by Kleeman *et al.* (183).

Other investigators also do not agree that parathyroid hormone increases the renal reabsorption of calcium. In studies in man, Canary & Kyle (188) found no consistent relationship between parathyroid status and calcium excretion, and Horwith *et al.* (161) reported a small but significant increase in calcium excretion without change in plasma calcium during brief periods of intravenous infusion of purified parathyroid hormone. In the dog, the data collected by Jahan & Pitts (189) on the effect of parathyroid extract were reinterpreted by Kenny (6) in comparison with the effect of hypercalcemia induced by calcium infusion [Poulos (190)] and seemed to indicate that the hormone decreased rather than increased calcium reabsorption.

Recent years have seen some progress toward a better understanding of the renal handling of calcium, a process that is apparently complicated by an interrelation with sodium ion. Results from stop-flow studies (191) indicate that calcium is actively reabsorbed in a far distal tubular area. There did not appear to be any active reabsorption of calcium by the proximal tubule, but passive reabsorption by this segment could not be excluded. Micropuncture studies on rats and hamsters by Lassiter *et al.* (192) have indicated an area of active reabsorption not only in the distal tubule but also in the late proximal tubule and in the ascending limb of the loop of Henle. Walser (193) recently reported the most interesting observation that calcium ion clearance is approximately equal to sodium clearance under a variety of conditions studied in the dog. The significance of parathyroid hormone for this relationship has not yet been evaluated. However, the effect of parathyroid extract on calcium excretion reported by Widrow & Levinsky (184) was observed under conditions in which the level of plasma sodium was carefully controlled.

It is necessary to conclude that although the majority of investigations favor an effect of parathyroid hormone on the kidney to increase the reabsorption of calcium, additional work will be required to settle the question conclusively.

Gastrointestinal absorption and secretion.—*In vitro* (194, 195) as well as *in vivo* (196, 197, 198) methods for measuring the absorption of calcium from the gut have been used to determine whether or not parathyroid hormone affects the process. The first report favoring such an effect was by Talmage & Elliott (199), who observed that in parathyroidectomized rats the absorption of ^{45}Ca and ^{85}Sr *in vivo* was only 50 per cent that of intact controls, but this was not confirmed by later work in the same laboratory (196). Rasmussen (195), utilizing everted duodenal sacs *in vitro*, demonstrated that active transport of ^{45}Ca from mucosa to serosa was less efficient in sacs from parathyroidectomized rats than from intact controls. No consistent effect was observed from the addition of parathyroid hormone *in vitro*. Toverud (200) has reported a decrease in calculated "true calcium absorption" following parathyroidectomy of vitamin D-deficient rats and its restoration to normal by large doses of commercial parathyroid extract. In Toverud's experiments, use of the net balance data alone would have been misleading. The validity of his conclusions rests on the corrections for digestive juice calcium and other assumptions underlying the calculation of "true calcium absorption".

The experiments of Cramer *et al.* (196) are difficult to assess, since no effect of parathyroidectomy was found on the absorption of carrier-free ^{45}Ca, while administration of U.S.P. parathyroid extract to intact rats resulted in a fourfold increase in net positive calcium balance. Dowdle *et al.* (201), extending previous observations from their laboratory (194) on the importance of vitamin D for the maintenance of an active calcium transport mechanism in the upper small intestine of the rat, reported that calcium transport was reduced in everted gut sacs from thyroparathyroidectomized rats on a stock diet. The operation had no effect on the already subnormal calcium transport of sacs from D-deficient rats. However, in a later report from the same laboratory (202), there was also no effect of thyroparathyroidectomy when purified diets containing vitamin D and either low or high in calcium were fed.

In several other investigations no effect of parathyroid status on intestinal absorption was observed. In the careful experiments of Wasserman &

Comar (198), parathyroidectomy in rats with a normal vitamin D intake did not alter the movement of ^{45}Ca or ^{85}Sr across the intestine either *in vivo* or *in vitro*, and the transport of ^{32}P was also unaltered *in vivo*. Gran (203) reported that calcium absorption in rats was independent of the level of plasma calcium and that parathyroidectomy in vitamin D-deficient rats did not affect absorption, conclusions similar to those of Dowdle *et al.* (201). In man, no effect on the intestinal absorption of ^{45}Ca was observed by Mazzuoli *et al.* (204) whether the plasma ionic calcium level was increased by intravenous calcium or decreased by giving ethylenediaminetetraacetate; both procedures undoubtedly affect parathyroid hormone secretion (205). Clarkson *et al.* (206), studying a patient with severe general intestinal malabsorption that improved functionally and histologically during parathyroid extract administration, attributed the abnormality to hypoparathyroidism. However, definite parathyroid deficiency was not demonstrated, and the complex clinical and pathological features of the case might better be attributed to primary gastrointestinal disease.

From these rather discordant observations it is necessary to conclude that the effect of parathyroid hormone on intestinal calcium absorption, if any, is of small magnitude, and its demonstration depends on special experimental conditions. The vitamin D status of the subject would appear to be particularly important. Certainly the effect on over-all calcium economy cannot be highly significant.

Effects of parathyroid hormone on the digestive tract other than the absorption of calcium have also been postulated. The nature of the interrelationship between peptic ulcer disease and primary hyperparathyroidism is uncertain (207). The consistent production of the pathologic lesion of peptic ulcer has not been accomplished in experiments in which U.S.P. parathyroid extract was administered to a variety of experimental animals. Blanshard *et al.* (208) reported that chronic hypo- or hyperparathyroidism as well as chronic hypervitaminosis D produced gastric ulcers in rats. However, there were no changes in gastric acid, pepsin, or electrolyte composition. Letwinter & Spiro (209) have claimed that gastric chief cell hyperplasia in rabbits and rats followed hypercalcemia produced either by vitamin D or parathyroid extract. After the intramuscular injection of 1000 units of parathyroid extract in normal human subjects (210), an increase in gastric secretory volume and total pepsin was noted. In the same study (210), hypoparathyroidism was associated with decreased gastric secretion that could be restored to normal by infusion of calcium without parathyroid hormone. As Ostrow *et al.* in their excellent review (207) have concluded, any direct effect of parathyroid hormone on gastric secretory processes has yet to be differentiated from changes secondary to blood calcium concentration. An effect of crude parathyroid extract on intestinal motility (211) has also been reported.

Lactation.—The effect of the parathyroid gland on lactation has been reviewed recently by Cowie (212). The decline in milk production following thyroparathyroidectomy of rats early in lactation (4th day) was duplicated by parathyroidectomy alone and was largely corrected by replacement therapy with parathyroid extract (213 to 216). The greater importance of the parathyroid than of the thyroid gland in lactation was also supported by Bruce & Sloviter (217) who could detect no deleterious effect of long-term thyroidectomy on lactation in mice with intact parathyroid glands. Toverud (200) parathyroidectomized rats later in lactation (12th to 14th day) and, like Cowie and Folley (214), observed a decrease but not cessation of milk secretion. Thyroparathyroidectomy prevented lactation in goats (218) but not in cows (219); it did not interfere with the artificial stimulation of mammary gland growth in ovariectomized rats by estrogen and progesterone (220).

Toverud & Munson (8, 50, 200, 221) discovered that parathyroidectomy of lactating rats was followed by increases both in the concentration of total solids in the milk and in the calcium concentration of the solids—in the face of the expected profound decrease in serum calcium. Both changes were reversed toward normal by administration of parathyroid extract. Parathyroidectomy was performed on the 12th to 14th day of lactation and the milk samples were collected 24 hr later. The related observation, reported in the first publication (50), that a low-calcium diet, presumed to stimulate parathyroid hormone secretion, reduced the milk calcium concentration, did not prove to be a consistent finding according to more recent studies by Toverud (200) in which, however, the effects of parathyroidectomy were thoroughly confirmed in a different strain of rats. A range of serum calcium levels was produced in intact and parathyroidectomized lactating rats by feeding diets lacking vitamin D and varying in calcium and phosphate composition. In these rats, the total milk solids concentration varied inversely with the serum calcium level whether the parathyroid glands were present or absent. It was concluded, therefore, that the total solids concentration of milk is related to parathyroid function only indirectly and nonspecifically through the effect of the gland on blood calcium. On the other hand, the calcium concentration of milk solids appeared to be affected specifically by the gland, since it was increased following parathyroidectomy, but in intact rats it was unaffected by wide variations in serum calcium produced by dietary manipulations. Thus, parathyroid hormone may conserve blood calcium not only by its action on bone (and possibly on gut and kidney) but also by reducing the rate of transport of calcium from blood to milk.

Studies of calcium and strontium metabolism in intact lactating goats by Twardock & Comar (222) included limited data indicating a decrease in milk calcium concentration during periods of hypocalcemia following hypercalcemia induced by infusions of calcium salts. In some cases the change in milk composition was associated with general toxicity and decreased milk production. Since hypocalcemia might be considered an indication of hypoparathyroidism, these observations in goats did not confirm Toverud's findings in rats. However, Twardock & Comar did not distinguish between total solids concentration and the calcium concentration of the solids and did not determine the effect of parathyroidectomy. In cows no effect of parathyroidectomy or of administration of parathyroid extract on the milk calcium was detected by Todd *et al.* (223). The observations were made two to three weeks after parathyroidectomy at a time when the serum calcium had returned to the normal preoperative level.

Distribution of electrolytes.—Further study will be required to define the extent and significance of the suggested effect of parathyroid hormone on the distribution of electrolytes such as inorganic phosphate (224 to 228), calcium (229), and magnesium (230, 231) between intra- and extracellular compartments. Observations on the degree to which the hormone affects the state, bound or free, of an electrolyte within a body compartment, such as plasma and tissue cells, are also of interest. Although there are three reports (232, 233, 234) that the percentage of blood calcium not bound to plasma proteins is higher in primary hyperparathyroid patients than in normal subjects, most studies indicate that plasma protein binding of calcium is not affected by parathyroid hormone (235 to 241), a conclusion most impressively supported by the investigation of Walser (178). Manunta *et al.* reported that the distribution of bound calcium between specific plasma proteins was affected by parathyroidectomy (242). The exchangeability of bone inorganic phosphate *in vitro* is apparently enhanced in hyperparathyroidism (243). The reports that parathyroid hormone causes a release of mitochondrial bound calcium (244) and affects the intracellular distribution of phosphate (245) represent basic investigations that, when amplified, may illuminate transport systems or ion-macromolecular interactions either or both of which could be fundamental to hormone action.

Lens.—An effect of parathyroid hormone on lens is suggested by the prevalence of cataracts in hypoparathyroidism (246), the observation that lens calcium is increased in parathyroidectomized animals at a time when extracellular fluid calcium is low (247, 248), and the decrease in lens calcium content following incubation with crude parathyroid extract *in vitro* (249). In addition, Firschein's (250) preliminary observations *in vitro* suggest lower than normal glucose uptake and lactate production by lens taken from parathyroidectomized rats and restoration to normal levels by addition to the medium of U.S.P. parathyroid extract from which phenol, an inhibitor of the *in vitro* system, had been removed by extraction with ether.

Magnesium metabolism.—The careful fractionation by Walser (178) of plasma magnesium of hyperparathyroid patients into its various fractions revealed variable total and ionic magnesium concentration, being higher than normal in some and low in others. The complexed and protein-bound magnesium were usually normal. Other laboratories, mostly reporting only total magnesium, have found normal (230, 251) or elevated (252) levels. Following removal of hyperactive parathyroid tissue (eight cases), a consistent fall in total blood magnesium was reported (230, 251), a finding not duplicated in Walser's report (178) on two patients. In hypoparathyroidism the plasma magnesium is usually within the normal range, but the level in erythrocytes may be elevated (230). Blood magnesium was increased by administration of parathyroid extract to parathyroidectomized dogs (253). The effect of U.S.P. parathyroid extract on the tissue electrolyte composition of rats was studied by Cheek & Teng (231). In addition to a decrease in bone calcium and magnesium concentrations, muscle chloride and sodium were lowered, while muscle magnesium and potassium were raised. A remarkable enhancement of the effect of parathyroid extract in increasing the calcium concentration of the kidney occurred following administration of magnesium in the drinking water.

"Calciphylaxis".—"Calciphylaxis" is a term introduced by Selye (254) for the experimentally induced process underlying a multitudinous variety of local and systemic calcinoses. The condition appears to be an unusual sensitivity state that is incited by agents with primary effects on mineral metabolism (notably vitamin D, dihydrotachysterol, and parathyroid extract). If one of a host of unrelated challenging compounds is administered at a critical time after the inducing agent has been given, calcium salts will be deposited at certain sites, which differ depending on the agent used. Calcification of the parathyroid gland, produced in rats by Selye & Dieudonne (255), is a particularly relevant example of calciphylaxis. Young female Holtzman rats were sensitized by oral dihydrotachysterol (1 mg, orally). Chromous (3.5 mg) or chromic (10 mg) chloride as the "challenger" was given intravenously 24 hr later and the animals were killed after 5 days. At autopsy, intense calcification of the parathyroid stroma was the major finding. Neither agent alone produced an alteration in appearance of the parathyroid gland. As Selye concedes, the extraordinary specificity of the calciphylactic lesion, despite the nonspecificity of the sensitizing agent, remains a major enigma. The relation of the phenomenon to normal physiology or natural disease processes has yet to be determined, although there is no doubt that it will be vigorously explored.

The studies undertaken by Lehr (256) on experimental cardiovascular disease demonstrate a similar calcifying process that is initiated by renal injury or nephrectomy and is dependent on parathyroid hormone for its fullest manifestations. An additional interrelationship was postulated between the parathyroid gland and the adrenal cortex.

Miscellaneous renal effects.—Interest in possible effects of parathyroid hormone on the reabsorption of water by the kidney, urinary pH, and the excretion of ions other than phosphate and calcium has recently been revived. Epstein *et al.* (257), in studies on dogs, and Fourman *et al.* (258), studying hyperparathyroid patients, reported that excess parathyroid hormone tended to impair renal concentrating ability. However, it was not determined whether the effect came from hormone or from the hypercalcemia produced by the hormone (259, 260). Nordin (261) found not only an increase in water excretion but also an increase in pH, an increase in the excretion of bicarbonate, sodium, potassium, and chloride, as well as a moderate phosphaturia in man after intravenous U.S.P. parathyroid extract. In addition, increased urinary citrate excretion has been shown following intravenous administration of highly purified parathyroid hormone (161). Whether this effect is mediated through the proposed inhibition of renal citrate degradation by parathyroid extract (262), an effect on tubular transport, or an extrarenal effect is not known.

REGULATION OF SECRETION OF PARATHYROID HORMONE AND OTHER TOPICS

Talmage & Toft (263) reviewed the literature on the regulation of secretion of parathyroid hormone and discussed some of the difficulties that have hampered investigation of the problem. The principal difficulties have been lack of suitable methods for assaying the hormone in blood, urine, and small amounts of parathyroid tissue, absence of easily recognized histological changes in the parathyroid gland that are correlated with the level of hormone secretion, and the interrelation between calcium and inorganic phosphate in plasma which complicates efforts to study the effect of one independently of the other.

At present there is no conclusive experimental or clinical evidence indicating that parathyroid secretion is under either nervous or trophic hormone control (263). However, occasional reports suggest the importance of neural factors (264, 265, 266), and unpublished experiments in rats by Wells, Lloyd, and Munson again raise the question of the relation between the pituitary and parathyroid glands, since it was found that the rise in serum calcium 4 hr after nephrectomy (113) was dependent on the presence of the pituitary gland as well as the parathyroid gland.

Most, although not all (1, 11), of the recent evidence is consistent with the generally accepted view that the concentration of calcium ion in the blood circulating through the parathyroid gland is the major factor controlling the rate of hormone secretion, a high concentration inhibiting or blocking secretion and a low concentration permitting increased secretion. The best-controlled dietary experiments of Stoerk & Carnes (267), in which varying levels of serum calcium and inorganic phosphate were induced in rats by giving diets differing widely in the ratio of calcium to phosphorus and in the absolute amounts of the two elements, demonstrated a highly consistent inverse linear relationship between the level of serum calcium and the size (volume) of the parathyroid gland. On the other hand, there was no regular or significant correlation between the level of serum inorganic phosphate and size of the gland. Other studies in which the dietary levels of calcium and phosphate were manipulated in order to alter the plasma levels acutely (268, 269, 270) or chronically (271) also favor calcium rather than phosphate as the more important ion influencing rate of hormone secretion, as indicated, usually, by the size of the parathyroid gland.

Additional indirect evidence for control of parathyroid activity by the plasma calcium level was supplied by the experiments of Talmage & Toft

(263) in rats, using calcium-free or phosphate-free peritoneal lavage to induce changes in plasma levels of the ions, and bone osteoclast count as an index of hormone secretion (272). The experiments of Patt & Luckhardt (273), in which the effluent from parathyroid glands perfused with decalcified blood produced a rise in serum calcium in recipient dogs, are usually cited as offering definitive evidence for the control of parathyroid hormone secretion by the level of blood calcium. However, the phosphate content of the decalcified blood used for perfusion was not reported and probably it was high because of the technique of decalcification used. In more recent experiments of this type by Copp & Davidson (205), an increase in systemic blood calcium similar in character to that following intravenous parathyroid extract was demonstrated when the thyroparathyroid apparatus was perfused with blood to which disodium ethylenediaminetetraacetate (EDTA) had been added. On the other hand, when the glands were perfused with hypercalcemic (12 mg per cent) blood, a small decrease in the systemic blood calcium level was observed. Utmost attention to experimental detail was required in these experiments, for in each instance it was necessary to balance exactly the calcium or EDTA added to the blood perfusing the parathyroid gland by an opposing infusion into the systemic circulation. In interpreting the results it was assumed that variable changes in plasma inorganic phosphate were insignificant and that the perfused parathyroid gland was indifferent to calcium complexed with EDTA. Raisz (274) has reported that the amount of cytoplasm per cell of embryonic chick parathyroid gland grown in organ culture varied inversely with the concentration of calcium in the medium and that the highest mitotic index was observed in glands cultured in a medium low in calcium.

With the postulation and presentation of data (275) suggesting the existence of a second parathyroid hormone, "calcitonin" (see below), that depresses plasma calcium and is secreted when the level of calcium ion in the circulation rises above normal, an elegant revision of McLean's (276) feedback theory is possible. An interplay between two parathyroid hormones, each responsive to a different stimulus and with opposing effects, would readily explain the maintenance of the plasma calcium at a constant level.

Estimates of normal rate of secretion.—The normal rate of parathyroid hormone secretion has not yet been determined by direct assay of the hormone in blood, but estimates have been made indirectly. According to Copp's data (68), U.S.P. (bovine) parathyroid extract administered by continuous intravenous infusion at the rate of 0.1 unit per kg per hr will maintain the blood calcium at the normal concentration of the intact dog. From experiments with parathyroidectomized rats given U.S.P. extract subcutaneously, Premachandra & Blumenthal (277) estimated the average requirement in the rat to be 20 units per kg per hr. Although the data on which this estimate was based were highly variable, the conclusion is in reasonable agreement with inferences from the results with U.S.P. extract in the Munson bioassay method (16) and with the unpublished experiments of Hirsch & Munson in which purified parathyroid extract was given to parathyroidectomized rats by continuous intravenous infusion. There are insufficient data in man for a reliable estimate of the hormone requirement. However, it may be noted that in hypoparathyroid patients, 2 units per kg per hr of highly purified bovine parathyroid hormone by intravenous infusion were sufficient to produce marked phosphaturia (161).

Binding and degradation of hormone.—The important problems of the binding of parathyroid hormone to plasma proteins and the effect of such interactions on the activity and stability of the hormone have been explored only in a preliminary manner (35, 43, 75).

The rapidity with which the plasma calcium and the urinary inorganic phosphate fall after parathyroidectomy (50, 156) indicates that the life of parathyroid hormone in the circulation and the major target tissues must be short. Specific measurement of the rate of disappearance from the circulation of physiological amounts of parathyroid hormone must await the development of adequate quantitative methods for the assay of small concentrations of hormone. That the liver may be a site of degradation of parathyroid hormone was concluded by Davis & Talmage (278) from their experiments in which rat parathyroid glands autotransplanted into the spleen displayed a lower functional capacity than glands *in situ* or glands transplanted into the testis. The functional capacity of the glands was estimated by the degree to which the calcium concentration of peritoneal lavage fluid was maintained above that in the parathyroidectomized rat. However, an opposite conclusion was reached by Aivazyan (279), whose experiments with hepatectomy, splenectomy, and parathyroidectomy in dogs indicated that the spleen and the liver participate in an activation of parathyroid hormone.

Relation to vitamin D.—On the basis of experiments in which the serum calcium of young vitamin D-deficient rats did not rise after injection of 200 units of parathyroid extract, Harrison *et al.* (280) suggested that vitamin D is necessary for the action of parathyroid hormone. The results of Harrison *et al.* have been confirmed by Marnay & Raoul (281, 282). Other investigators however, have observed definite increases in serum calcium after administration of parathyroid extract to vitamin D-deficient animals: Schartum & Nichols (283) in mice, Toverud (200) in adult female rats, and Hertelendy & Taylor (284) in hens. The relatively uncommon occurrence of marked hypocalcemia in clinical rickets (285), as compared with the early and consistent appearance of hyperaminoaciduria in vitamin D-deficient infants (286) suggests that in man very little if any vitamin D is necessary for the effect of parathyroid hormone on serum calcium.

The active transport of calcium *in vitro* in the isolated gut sac was reduced by parathyroidectomy in rats on a stock diet but not in rats on a vitamin D-deficient diet, according to Dowdle *et al.* (201). However, in a later report from the same laboratory (202), no significant effect of parathyroidectomy was observed when purified low- or high-calcium diets containing vitamin D were fed, so that vitamin D alone may not explain the apparent dependence of the parathyroidectomy effect on the use of the stock diet. The effect of parathyroid hormone *in vitro* on the release of calcium from kidney mitochondria of normal rats (244, 287) was not observed in preparations from vitamin D-deficient rats.

In future investigations which will be needed to clarify the degree of dependence of parathyroid hormone action on vitamin D, care will be needed to discriminate between vitamin D deficiency *per se*, and secondary effects of long-term D deficiency such as inadequate stores of mobilizable calcium. The question has been discussed extensively by Rasmussen & Reifenstein (288) from the point of view that vitamin D is essential for parathyroid hormone activity.

Microscopic structure and histochemistry.—A number of recent investigations have contributed to knowledge of the fine structure and histochemistry of the parathyroid gland, but the interrelationships between structure and function still remain to be elucidated.

The absence of oxyphil cells in the parathyroid glands of rodents (guinea pig, rat, and mouse), as indicated by light microscopy, has been confirmed, in the case of the rat, by the electron-microscopic studies of Lever (289). However, within the single-cell type there was heterogeneity: "light" and "dark" cells could be discriminated. In a later study (290) Lever attempted to correlate cytological with functional changes in rat parathyroid glands. Within seven weeks after unilateral parathyroidectomy, a simple twofold compensatory hypertrophy was observed. A high-phosphate diet or bilateral nephrectomy led to a marked increase in the number and size of "dark cells", which contained a high concentration of cytoplasm with increased RNA, an increased number of Palade granules (291), and a greatly expanded endoplasmic reticulum. However, no changes in Golgi complexes or lipid bodies were noted. Injection of intact rats with a single large dose (500 units) of bovine parathyroid extract produced no change in the size or other characteristics of the cells. Smaller doses of parathyroid extract given to rats repeatedly over a longer period of time were reported by Hanssler (292) to cause a decrease in the size of the parathyroid cell nuclei. Vitamins D_2 and D_3 had a similar effect. Weymouth (293) also observed an increase in cytoplasmic RNA after nephrectomy in rats but no depletion of argyrophilic granules. These granules, which may represent hormone, were increased, however, following hormone administration. Davis & Enders (294) made somewhat similar observations in rat glands after stimulation by nephrectomy and speculated that the intracytoplasmic droplets, increased in the activated gland, originate in the Golgi apparatus and represent an intracellular form of hormone secretion. Roth (295), in an excellent general review of parathyroid structure, refers to unpublished work by Munger and Roth further describing the electron-dense bodies located near the Golgi apparatus. They consider these bodies to represent secretory granules.

Trier's (296) careful electron-microscopic study of the primate (macaque) gland revealed the fine structural detail of both the oxyphil and chief cell types. Increased numbers of mitochondria and peculiar lamellar whorls appeared characteristic of the oxyphil cell. Vesiculation and fenestration of the capillary endothelium produced pores of sufficient size to pass high molecular weight proteins. In view of the low molecular weight of the isolated hormone polypeptides, the significance of this vascular structure remains to be explained. Histochemical studies of primate glands have revealed, as suspected from the electron-microscopic appearance, greater oxidative enzyme activity in the oxyphil than in the chief cell. Succinic, lactic, malic, glutamic, isocitric, β-hydroxybutyric, and glucose-6-phosphate dehydrogenases as well as cytochrome oxidase and DPNH and TPNH diaphorases (297, 298, 299) were found to be more active in the oxyphil cell, a type previously thought to be waning metabolically (300), than in the chief cell. No consistent enzyme pattern distinguishing normal, hyperplastic, and adenomatous human parathyroid glands was found by Balogh & Cohen (299); the predominant cell type in functioning hyperplastic or adenomatous tissue, as it has long been known, is the chief cell, which retains its weakly staining oxidative enzyme pattern. Nachlas *et al.* (301) and Pearse & Tremblay (302) have demonstrated leucine aminopeptidase in chief cells, but protein synthetic function has yet to be studied in the parathyroid gland.

Immunology and transplantation.—The immunologic properties of the parathyroid gland are currently of interest to research workers in a wide variety of scientific disciplines. Most investigations to date have been concerned with parathyroid cellular antigens and the host response to auto- or homotransplantation (303, 304), but the recent production of a specific antibody to bovine parathyroid hormone in the rabbit [Tashjian *et al.* (17); Lawrence & Rasmussen, unpublished experiments cited in (32); and G. D. Aurbach, personal communication] opens new avenues for exploration of the concentration and state of parathyroid hormone in biological fluids.

Homotransplantation of fetal (305), young (306), and adult tissue (307, 308) has been performed in numerous species using a variety of techniques including direct implantation (307, 308, 309), intravenous infusion of tissue suspensions (310), tissue culture prior to implantation with gradual adaptation to recipient's serum (311, 312, 313), implantation in Millipore chambers (304), and total transplantation with vascular anastomosis (314). Despite clinical evidence of some functional activity based usually on improved symptomatology or serum calcium values, no histological proof of persistently viable tissue has been demonstrated in man. That such homotransplants are actually functioning is possible; however, the effects of nonspecific tissue transplantation (307) and adaptation to or spontaneous improvement of the hypoparathyroid state are equally probable (315, 316). Likewise, the clinically "successful" implantation of heterologous goat parathyroid tissue in a patient with hypoparathyroidism of eight years' duration was associated with histologic evidence of graft destruction and abnormal provocative tests of parathyroid gland function (317). Although the imaginative histologic and functional study of Russell & Gittes (309) demonstrated a relative deficit of effective transplantation antigens in rat parathyroid tissue as compared with skin, further work by these investigators in the mouse (318) has demonstrated definite male histocompatibility antigens in parathyroid tissue entirely comparable to those of skin. The efficacy of parathyroid transplantation will remain in doubt until improved methods of assessing parathyroid gland function become available.

In clinical endocrinology the impression (315) persists that patients develop immune resistance to repeated administration of commercial bovine parathyroid extract, although documentation is sparse. The continued responsiveness to this preparation demonstrated in a 7-year-old child during chronic administration over a period of 18 months is evidence to the contrary (306).

Comparative physiology.—Although the parathyroid physiology of man, dog, and rat has received most attention, some information is available about other species. The chapter on parathyroid glands in the *Textbook of Comparative Endocrinology* by Gorbman & Bern (165) is particularly helpful on the comparative anatomy.

Recent studies in *Rana pipiens* by Cortelyou *et al.* (319, 320) indicate that 2 hr after parathyroidectomy both plasma and urinary inorganic phosphate had increased. The urinary calcium was also increased at 2 hr, but the expected fall in plasma calcium was not detected until 48 hr. Plasma calcium continued to decline until it reached 50 per cent of the normal level at one to two weeks after parathyroidectomy. There was then a gradual rise, so that at 29 weeks the plasma calcium had returned to the rather low level of the normal frog.

In the chicken, as a representative of *Aves*, the total calcium concentration in plasma is regulated by estrogens as well as parathyroid hormone. The interrelating effects of the two hormones, which are additive, not mutually potentiating (237), have been studied by Polin & Sturkie (321), Urist *et al.* (237), and Siegmund *et al.* (322). Urist *et al.* (237) concluded that parathyroid hormone maintains the normal level of ionic (ultrafilterable) calcium in the plasma, while estrogen, endogenous in the egg-laying hen or administered to the rooster (323), increases total plasma calcium without increasing ionic calcium by the formation of a calcium-phosphoprotein complex. The effects of parathyroidectomy and administration of parathyroid extract on plasma ionic calcium in the chicken are essentially the same as in mammals (63, 66, 321). The phosphaturic effect of parathyroid hormone in the chicken (164) was discussed in an earlier section.

Thyroparathyroidectomy of cows (324) and goats (218) results in a prompt fall in serum calcium, and in calves (219) and kids (218) may eventuate in death. However, mature cows on a natural diet with a high calcium-to-phosphate ratio can maintain pregnancy, deliver, and lactate after parathyroidectomy (324). In goats, on the contrary, there is no udder development as well as no lactation after this operation (218). The possibility that accessory parathyroid tissue might explain some of these differences is a difficult question to investigate; even in the rat the ingenious study of this problem by Kenny (325) revealed unexpected complexities.

Relatively little is known about the species-specificity of parathyroid hormone. Parathyroid hormone preparations found to be active in a variety of species have been almost exclusively of bovine origin. Raoul *et al.* (45) reported that extracts of porcine and equine parathyroid tissue raised the serum calcium of rabbits, and extracts of human parathyroid tissue have been found to be active in rats (Kenny, unpublished) and in dogs (183). On the negative side, Lotz *et al.* (326) failed to observe any rise in serum calcium in sheep injected with bovine parathyroid extract, although effects on phosphate metabolism were recorded, and Irving & Solms (327) reported that bovine extract had no effect on the serum calcium of the amphibian *Xenopus laevis*. The differing amounts of bovine parathyroid extract, administered by continuous intravenous infusion, that are required to produce an effect in rat, dog, and man, noted in a previous section, may possibly be related to species differences in parathyroid hormone.

"*Calcitonin*".—Recently, Copp *et al.* (275) have emphasized the importance for calcium homeostasis of two parathyroid hormones, one to lower plasma calcium as well as one to raise it (discussed briefly above under regulation of secretion). The proposed second hormone, named "calcitonin", is thought to be secreted in response to the stimulus of hypercalcemia. The observation of Sanderson *et al.* (316), that after production of hypercalcemia by infusion of calcium gluconate the plasma calcium returned to the pre-infusion value much more rapidly in dogs with intact parathyroid glands than it did in parathyroidectomized dogs, could be explained readily by the action of calcitonin in the intact dogs and the absence of calcitonin in the parathyroidectomized dogs.

Additional indirect evidence for the presence of a plasma calcium-lowering factor in the parathyroid gland was advanced by Copp *et al.* (275). In one series of dogs, it was shown that the systemic plasma calcium fell more rapidly after perfusion of the thyroparathyroid apparatus with hypercalcemic blood than it did after thyroparathyroidectomy. (Hypercalcemic perfusion of the thyroid gland alone had no effect.) In another series of dogs, the parathyroid gland was perfused with blood made low in ionic calcium by addition of ethylenediaminetetraacetate with a resulting rise in systemic plasma calcium. In one group of these dogs the parathyroid gland was then perfused with hypercalcemic blood, and a fall in systemic blood calcium occurred within 15 min as before. The other group of dogs was parathyroidectomized and there was no immediate fall in plasma calcium; instead the plasma calcium continued to rise for at least 2 hr.

More direct evidence for calcitonin has also been obtained. It was first observed (328) that within 20 minutes after a rapid intravenous injection of 300 to 1000 units of U.S.P. parathyroid extract into dogs there was a small but significant fall in the plasma calcium. The expected rise in serum calcium was not seen until 60 min after the injection. Intravenous injection of 50 ml of plasma from the perfusate of dog parathyroid gland with hypercalcemic (12 mg per cent) blood also resulted in a small (average, 0.37 ± 0.05 mg per cent) and transient decrease in plasma calcium, which returned to normal in about 60 min (275). Finally, two types of extracts of bovine parathyroid tissue were prepared. Type C extracts produced a mean fall of 0.51 mg per cent in the serum calcium of dogs 20 min after intravenous injection of a dose equivalent to 5 to 10 g of parathyroid tissue. Type P extracts, on the other hand, produced no effect 20 min after injection, but at 60 min there was a significant rise in plasma calcium. Thus Type C extracts appeared to contain only calcitonin, Type P extracts only the classic plasma calcium-raising hormone, while U.S.P. extract contained both hormones.

The smallness of the effect of calcitonin on plasma calcium, requiring for its detection a degree of precision in calcium analysis uncommon or as yet unattained in many laboratories, will hamper independent confirmation and extension of the work of Copp *et al.* (275). The effect has been demonstrated thus far only in dogs. Tashjian & Munson (27) were unable to detect calcitonin activity in U.S.P. parathyroid extract injected into rats, and Copp's results (personal communication) were negative in rats and guinea pigs and equivocal in rabbits.

Earlier, Marnay & Prelot (47, 48) also had reported the preparation of hypocalcemic parathyroid extracts. Both a nitrogen-containing extract made according to the method of Collip (19) and a lipid-soluble preparation were observed to lower the serum calcium of rabbits and dogs 3 to 3.5 hr after subcutaneous administration. Copp *et al.* (275) have not yet published the methods of preparation of the parathyroid extracts used in their experiments. However, in contradistinction to the lipid extract of Marnay & Prelot, calcitonin was stated not to be extractable with ether, and, at least when administered by the intravenous route, its duration of action was much shorter.

The relation of calcitonin to "parotin", a protein from bovine parotid glands reported to lower the serum calcium of rabbits [cf. review by Ito (329), has not yet been explored.

LITERATURE CITED

1. Bartter, F. C., *Ann. Rev. Physiol.*, **16**, 429–44 (1954)
2. Fraser, R., and King, E. J., in *Biochemical Disorders in Human Disease*, 352–400 (Thompson, R. H. S., and King, E. J., Eds., Academic, New York, 843 pp., 1957)
3. Geschwind, I. I., in *Mineral Metabolism*, **1**, 434–52 (Comar, C. L., and Bronner, F., Eds., Academic, New York, 879 pp., 1961)
4. Greep, R. O., and Kenny, A. D., in *The Hormones*, **III**, 153–74 (Pincus G., and Thimann, K. V., Eds., Academic, New York, 1012 pp., 1955)
5. Irving, J. T., *Calcium Metabolism* (Methuen, London, 177 pp., 1957)
6. Kenny, A. D., *World Rev. Nutr. Dietet.*, **2**, 161–83 (1960)
7. McLean, F. C., and Budy, A. M., *Vitamins and Hormones*, **19**, 165–87 (1961)
8. Munson, P. L., *Federation Proc.*, **19**, 593–601 (1960)
9. Munson, P. L., *Ann. Rev. Pharmacol.*, **1**, 315–50 (1961)
10. Nordin, B. E. C., *Advances Clin. Chem.*, **4**, 275–320 (1961)
11. Rasmussen, H., *Am. J. Med.*, **30**, 112–38 (1961)
12. Greep R. O., and Talmage, R. V., Eds., *The Parathyroids* (Thomas, Springfield, Ill., 473 pp., 1961)
13. Rasmussen, H., and Craig, L. C., *Biochim. Biophys. Acta*, **56**, 332–38 (1962)
14. Aurbach, G. D., *J. Biol. Chem.*, **234**, 3179–81 (1959)
15. Rasmussen, H., and Craig, L. C., *J. Biol. Chem.*, **236**, 759–64 (1961)
16. Munson, P. L., in *The Parathyroids*, 94–118 (Thomas, Springfield, Ill., 473 pp., 1961)
17. Tashjian, A. H., Jr., Levine, L., and Munson, P. L., *Biochem. Biophys. Res. Commun.*, **8**, 259–65 (1962)
18. Hanson, A. M., *Military Surg.*, **52**, 280–84 (1923)
19. Collip, J. B., *J. Biol. Chem.*, **63**, 395–438 (1925)
20. Greep, R. O., in *The Hormones*, **I**, 255–99 (Academic, New York, 886 pp., 1948)
21. Davies, B. M. A., and Gordon, A. H., *Biochem. J.*, **61**, 646–51 (1955)
22. Rasmussen, H., and Westall, R. G., *Biochem. J.*, **67**, 658–63 (1957)
23. Friedman, S., and Munson, P. L., *Bio-chim. Biophys. Acta*, **28**, 204–5 (1958)
24. Friedman, S., and Munson, P. L., *Biochim. Biophys. Acta*, **35**, 509–15 (1959)
25. Aurbach, G. D., *Arch. Biochem. Biophys.*, **80**, 466–68 (1959)
26. Tweedy, W. R., *J. Biol. Chem.*, **88**, 649–57 (1930)
27. Tashjian, A. H., Jr., and Munson, P. L., *J. Chronic Diseases* (In press)
28. Colvin, J. R., Smith, D. B., and Cook, W. H., *Chem. Rev.*, **54**, 687–711 (1954)
29. Barrett, R. J., Friesen, H., and Astwood, E. B., *J. Biol. Chem.*, **237**, 432–39 (1962)
30. Rasmussen, H., in *The Parathyroids*, 60–68 (Thomas, Springfield, Ill., 473 pp., 1961)
31. Rasmussen, H., and Craig, L. C., *J. Biol. Chem.*, **236**, 1083–86 (1961)
32. Rasmussen, H., and Craig, L. C., *Recent Progr. Hormone Res.*, **18**, 269–95 (1962)
33. Rasmussen, H., *J. Biol. Chem.*, **229**, 781–87 (1957)
34. Rasmussen, H., *Science*, **128**, 1347–48 (1958)
35. Rasmussen, H., *J. Biol. Chem.*, **234**, 547–50 (1959)
36. Rasmussen, H., *J. Biol. Chem.*, **235**, 3442–48 (1960)
37. Dedman, M. L., Farmer, T. H., and Morris, C. J. O. R., *Biochem. J.*, **66**, 166–77 (1957)
38. Rasmussen, H., *Endocrinology*, **64**, 367–72 (1959)
39. Rasmussen, H., and Westall, R., *Nature*, **180**, 1429 (1957)
40. Aurbach, G. D., *Endocrinology*, **64**, 296–98 (1959)
41. Lo, T., Dixon, J. S., and Li, C. H., *Biochim. Biophys. Acta*, **53**, 584–86 (1961)
42. Neumann, N. P., Moore, S., and Stein, W. H., *Biochemistry*, **1**, 68–75 (1962)
43. Reichert, L. E., Jr., and L'Heureux, M. V., *Acta Endocrinol.*, **37**, 148–52 (1961)
44. Fieser, L. F., and Fieser, M., *Steroids*, 163–68 (Reinhold, New York, 945 pp., 1959)
45. Raoul, Y., Marnay, C., and Prelot, M., *Compt. Rend.*, **240**, 1151–53 (1955)
46. Marnay, C., Prelot, M., and Raoul, Y., *Compt. Rend.*, **243**, 681–83 (1956)

47. Marnay, C., *Compt. Rend. Soc. Biol.*, 151, 2058–61 (1957)
48. Marnay, C., and Prelot, M., *Arch. Sci. Physiol.*, 11, 77–86 (1957)
49. Raoul, Y., and Marnay, C., *J. Physiol. (Paris)*, 50, 471–75 (1958)
50. Munson, P. L., *Ann. N. Y. Acad. Sci.*, 60, 776–95 (1955)
51. Davies, B. M. A., Gordon, A. H., and Mussett, M. V., *J. Physiol. (London)*, 130, 79–95 (1955)
52. L'Heureux, M. V., and Melius, P., *Biochim. Biophys. Acta*, 20, 447–48 (1956)
53. Kenny, A. D., and Munson, P. L., *Endocrinology*, 64, 513–21 (1959)
54. Pullman, T. N., Lavender, A. R., Aho, I., and Rasmussen, H., *Endocrinology*, 67, 570–82 (1960)
55. Lavender, A. R., Pullman, T. N., Rasmussen, H., and Aho, I., in *The Parathyroids*, 406–14 (Thomas, Springfield, Ill., 473 pp., 1961)
56. *US Pharmacopeia*, 16th revision, 491 (1960)
57. Collip, J. B., and Clark, E. P., *J. Biol. Chem.*, 64, 485–507 (1925)
58. Munson, P. L., Kenny, A. D., and Iseri, O. A., *Federation Proc.*, 12, 249 (1953)
59. Davies, B. M. A., Gordon, A. H., and Mussett, A. V., *J. Physiol. (London)*, 125, 383–95 (1954)
60. Tepperman, H. M., L'Heureux, M. V., and Wilhelmi, A. E., *J. Biol. Chem.*, 168, 151–65 (1947)
61. Rasmussen, H., and Westall, R. G., *Nature*, 178, 1173–74 (1956)
62. Clark, I., Bowers, W., and Geoffroy, R., *Endocrinology*, 66, 527–32 (1960)
63. Dulce, H. J., Bauditz, W., and Siegmund, P., *Deut. Med. Wochschr.*, 86, 210–11 (1961)
64. Iwanowska, J., Deptula, S., and Smyk, W., *Acta Physiol. Polon.*, 7, 185–96 (1956)
65. Mouzas, G. L., and Weiss, J. B., *Brit. Med. J.*, I, 181–82 (1961)
66. Polin, D., Sturkie, P. D., and Hunsaker, W., *Endocrinology*, 60, 1–5 (1957)
67. Thieblot, L., Simonnet, H., and Bataille, L., *Ann. Endocrinol.*, 15, 539–44 (1954)
68. Copp, D. H., in *Bone as a Tissue*, 289–99 (Rodahl, K., Nicholson, J. T., and Brown, E. M., Jr., Eds., McGraw-Hill, New York, 358 pp., 1960)
69. Raisz, L. G., *Clin. Res.*, 10, 233 (1962)
70. Gaillard, P. J., in *The Parathyroids*, 20–45 (Thomas, Springfield, Ill. 473 pp., 1961)
70a. Gordan, G. S., Eisenberg, E., Loken, H. F., Gardner, B., and Hayashida, T., *Recent Progr. Hormone Res.*, 18, 297–336 (1962)
71. Davies, B. M. A., *J. Endocrinol.*, 16, 369–77 (1958)
72. Fujita, T., Morii, H., Ibayashi, H., Takahashi, Y., and Okinaka, S., *Acta Endocrinol.*, 38, 321–29 (1961)
73. Rubin, B. L., and Dorfman, R. I., *Proc. Soc. Exptl. Biol. Med.*, 83, 223–25 (1953)
74. Buckner, B., and Nellor, J. E., *Endocrinology*, 67, 82–89 (1960)
75. Reichert, L. E., Jr., and L'Heureux, M. V., *Endocrinology*, 68, 1036–44 (1961)
76. Fujita, T., Morii, H., and Okinaka, S., *Endocrinology*, 70, 711–14 (1962)
77. Albright, F., and Reifenstein, E. C., Jr., *Parathyroid Glands and Metabolic Bone Disease* (Williams & Wilkins, Baltimore, Md., 393 pp., 1948)
78. Barnicot, N. A., *J. Anat.*, 82, 233–48 (1948)
79. Chang, H., *Anat. Record*, 111, 23–47 (1951)
80. Stewart, G. S., and Bowen, H. F., *Endocrinology*, 48, 568–75 (1951)
81. Talmage, R. V., Kraintz, F. W., Frost, R. C., and Kraintz, L., *Endocrinology*, 52, 318–23 (1953)
82. Talmage, R. V., and Elliott, J. R., *Endocrinology*, 59, 27–33 (1956)
83. Grollman, A., *Endocrinology*, 55, 166–72 (1954)
84. Krane, S. M., *J. Clin. Endocrinol. Metab.*, 17, 386–89 (1957)
85. Keating, F. R., Jr., *J. Am. Med. Assoc.*, 178, 547–55 (1961)
86. Bronner, F., in *The Parathyroids*, 123–38 (Thomas, Springfield, Ill., 473 pp., 1961)
87. McLean, F. C., and Urist, M. R., *Bone* (Univ. of Chicago Press, Chicago, 182 pp., 1955)
88. Neuman, W. F., and Neuman, M. W., *The Chemical Dynamics of Bone Mineral* (Univ. of Chicago Press, Chicago, 209 pp., 1958)
89. Talmage, R. V., and Elliott, J. R., *Endocrinology*, 62, 717–22 (1958)
90. Woods, K. R., and Armstrong, W. D., *Proc. Soc. Exptl. Biol. Med.*, 91, 255–58 (1956)
91. Clark, I., and Geoffroy, R., *J. Biol. Chem.*, 233, 203–05 (1958)

92. Winzler, R. J., in *Ciba Found. Symp. Chem. Biol. Mucopolysaccharides,* 245–67 (1958)

93. Engel, M. B., *Arch. Pathol.,* **53,** 339–51 (1952)

94. Shetlar, M. R., Howard, R. P., Joel, W., Courtright, C. L., and Reifenstein, E. C., Jr., *Endocrinology,* **59,** 532–39 (1956)

95. Shetlar, M. R., Bradford, R. H., Joel, W., and Howard, R. P., in *The Parathyroids,* 144–55 (Thomas, Springfield, Ill., 473 pp., 1961)

96. Hausmann, E., *Endocrinology,* **68,** 722–23 (1961)

97. Bernstein, D. S., and Handler, P., *Proc. Soc. Exptl. Biol. Med.,* **99,** 339–40 (1958)

98. Bronner, F., *Am. J. Physiol.,* **198,** 605–8 (1960)

99. Johnston, C. C., Jr., Deiss, W. P., Jr., and Holmes, L. B., *Endocrinology,* **68,** 484–91 (1961)

100. Johnston, C. C., Jr., Miner, E. B., and Deiss, W. P., Jr., *J. Clin. Invest.,* **41,** 1369 (1962)

101. Schartum, S., and Nichols, G., Jr., *J. Clin. Invest.,* **40,** 2083–91 (1961)

102. Sjöström, P., *Acta Chir. Scand.,* **79,** Suppl. 49, 1–226 (1937)

103. Harrison, H. E., *Am. J. Med.,* **20,** 1–3 (1956)

104. Neuman, W. F., Firschein, H. E., Chen, P. S., Jr., Mulryan, B. J., and Di Stefano, V., *J. Am. Chem. Soc.,* **78,** 3863–64 (1956)

105. Dixon, T. F., and Perkins, H. R., in *The Biochemistry and Physiology of Bone,* 309–23 (Bourne, G. H., Ed., Academic, New York, 875 pp., 1956)

106. Firschein, H. E., Neuman, W. F., Martin, G. R., and Mulryan, B. J., *Recent Progr. Hormone Res.,* **15,** 427–54 (1959)

107. Lichtwitz, A., Hioco, D., Parlier, R., and de Seze, S., *Presse Med.,* **69,** 5–8, 51–54 (1961)

108. Walker, D. G., *Bull. Johns Hopkins Hosp.,* **108,** 80–99 (1961)

109. Freeman, S., in *Bone as a Tissue,* 314–29 (Rodahl, K., Nicholson, J. T., and Brown, E. M., Jr., Eds., McGraw-Hill, New York, 358 pp., 1960)

110. Firschein, H. E., *Trans. N. Y. Acad. Sci.,* **24,** 262–64 (1962)

111. Fantl, P., and Rome, N., *Proc. Roy. Australasian Coll. Physicians,* **2,** 52–55 (1947)

112. L'Heureux, M. V., and Roth, G. J., *Proc. Soc. Exptl. Biol. Med.,* **84,** 7–9 (1953)

113. Elliott, J. R., and Freeman, S., *Endocrinology,* **59,** 181–89 (1956)

114. Komarkova, A., Pacovsky, V., Vostal, J., Blahá, O., and Vitkova, E., *Z. Ges. Inn. Med.,* **16,** 778–81 (1959)

115. Tashjian, A. H., Jr., and Whedon, G. D., *J. Clin. Endocrinol. Metab.* (In press)

116. Dickens, F., *Biochem. J.,* **35,** 1011–23 (1941)

117. Lussier, J. P., *Rev. Can. Biol.,* **16,** 434–44 (1957)

118. Lekan, E. C., Laskin, D. M., and Engel, M. B., *Am. J. Physiol.,* **199,** 856–58 (1960)

119. Ranney, R. E., *Endocrinology,* **67,** 166–69 (1960)

120. Vaes, G., and Nichols, G., Jr., *J. Biol. Chem.,* **236,** 3323–29 (1961)

121. Raisz, L. G., Au, W. Y. W., and Tepperman, J., *Endocrinology,* **68,** 783–94 (1961)

122. Kenny, A. D., Draskoczy, P. R., and Goldhaber, P., *Am. J. Physiol.,* **197,** 502–4 (1959)

123. Lehman, D., Engel, M. B., and Laskin, D. M., *Science,* **130,** 222–23 (1959)

124. Dixon, T. F., and Perkins, H. R., *Biochem. J.,* **52,** 260–65 (1952)

125. Van Reen, R., *J. Biol. Chem.,* **234,** 1951–54 (1959)

126. Krane, S. M., Shine, K. I., and Pyle, M. B., in *The Parathyroids,* 298–309 (Thomas, Springfield, Ill., 473 pp., 1961)

127. Armstrong, W. D., and Singer, L., in *Ciba Found. Symp., Bone Struct. Metab.,* 103–16 (1956)

128. Taylor, T. G., *Biochim. Biophys. Acta,* **39,** 148–49 (1960)

129. Leaver, A. G., Eastoe, J. E., and Hartles, R. L., *Arch. Oral Biol.,* **2,** 120–26 (1960)

130. Neuman, W. F., and Dowse, C. M., in *The Parathyroids,* 310–26 (Thomas, Springfield, Ill., 473 pp., 1961)

131. Cretin, A., *Presse Med.,* **59,** 1240–42 (1951)

132. Jowsey, J., Sissons, H. B., and Vaughan, J., *J. Nucl. Energy,* **2,** 168–76 (1956)

133. Neuman, W. F., Mulryan, B. J., and Martin, G. R., *Clin. Orthopedics,* **17,** 124–34 (1960)

134. Bassett, C. A. L., and Nordin, B. E. C., *Acta Orthopaed. Scand.,* **28,** 241–54 (1959)

135. Schartum, S., and Nichols, G., Jr., *J. Clin. Invest.,* **41,** 1163–68 (1962)

136. Vaes, G. M., and Nichols, G., Jr., *Endocrinology*, **70**, 546–55 (1962)

137. Harrison, H. C., Harrison, H. E., and Park, E. A., *Proc. Soc. Exptl. Biol. Med.*, **96**, 768–73 (1957)

138. Cohn, D. V., and Forscher, B. K., *Biochim. Biophys. Acta*, **52**, 596–99 (1961)

139. Borle, A. B., Nichols, N., and Nichols, G., Jr., *J. Biol. Chem.*, **235**, 1206–10 (1960)

140. Borle, A. B., Nichols, N., and Nichols, G., Jr., *J. Biol. Chem.*, **235**, 1211–14 (1960)

141. Vaes, G., and Nichols, G., Jr., *Nature*, **193**, 379–80 (1962)

142. Goldhaber, P., *New Engl. J. Med.*, **266**, 870–77, 924–31 (1962)

143. Gaillard, P. J., *Exptl. Cell Res., Suppl.*, **3**, 154–69 (1955)

144. Gaillard, P. J., *Develop. Biol.*, **1**, 152–81 (1959)

145. Bronner, F., *Trans. N. Y. Acad. Sci.*, **24**, 265–72 (1962)

146. Vaes, G. M., and Nichols, G., Jr., *Endocrinology*, **70**, 890–901 (1962)

147. Laskin, D. M., and Engel, M. B., *Arch. Pathol.*, **62**, 296–302 (1956)

148. Tessari, L., *Endocrinology*, **66**, 890–92 (1960)

149. Hekkelman, J. W., *Biochim. Biophys. Acta*, **47**, 426–27 (1961)

150. Van Reen, R., and Michalakis, E. J., *Federation Proc.*, **21**, 79 (1962)

151. Reichert, L. E., Jr., and L'Heureux, M. V., *J. Endocrinol.*, **20**, 123–28 (1960)

152. Hiatt, H. H., and Thompson, D. D., *J. Clin. Invest.*, **36**, 557–65 (1957)

153. Nemeth, S., *Bratislav. Lekarske Listy*, **40**, 656–68 (1960)

154. Gershberg, H., Shields, D. R., and Kove, S. S., *J. Clin. Endocrinol. Metab.*, **19**, 681–91 (1959)

155. Foulks, J. G., and Perry, F. A., *Am. J. Physiol.*, **196**, 567–71 (1959)

156. Beutner, E., and Munson, P. L., *Endocrinology*, **66**, 610–16 (1960)

157. Ito, Y., Tsurufuji, S., and Shikita, M., *Endocrinol. Japon.*, **8**, 68–70 (1961)

158. Samiy, A. H., Hirsch, P. F., Ramsay, A. G., Giordano, C., and Merrill, J. P., *Endocrinology*, **67**, 266–70 (1960)

159. Handler, P., and Cohn, D. V., *Am. J. Physiol.*, **169**, 188–93 (1952)

160. Stewart, G. S., and Bowen, H. F., *Endocrinology*, **51**, 80–86 (1952)

161. Horwith, M., Rich, C., Thompson, D. D., and Rasmussen, H., in *The Parathyroids*, 415–20 (Thomas, Springfield, Ill., 473 pp., 1961)

162. Bartter, F. C., in *The Parathyroids*, 388–403 (Thomas, Springfield, Ill., 473 pp., 1961)

163. Giebisch, G., *Ann. Rev. Physiol.*, **24**, 357–420 (1962)

164. Levinsky, N. G., and Davidson, D. G., *Am. J. Physiol.*, **191**, 530–36 (1957)

165. Gorbman, A., and Bern, H. A., *Textbook of Comparative Endocrinology*, 173–92 (Wiley, New York, 468 pp., 1962)

166. Carrasquer, G., and Brodsky, W. A., *Am. J. Physiol.*, **199**, 1239–44 (1960)

167. Nicholson, T. F., and Shepherd, G. W., *Can. J. Biochem. Physiol.*, **37**, 103–11 (1959)

168. Nicholson, T. F., *Can. J. Biochem. Physiol.*, **37**, 113–17 (1959)

169. Bronner, F., and Thompson, D. D., *J. Physiol. (London)*, **157**, 232–50 (1961)

170. Taugner, R., Egidy, H. v., and Iravani, J., *Arch. Exptl. Pathol. Pharmakol.*, **238**, 419–26 (1960)

171. Samiy, A. H., Hirsch, P. F., and Ramsay, A. G., *J. Clin. Invest.*, **40**, 1078 (1961)

172. Rees, S. B., Franklin, S. S., August, J. T., Small, H., Kendall, A. R., Merrill, J. P., and Gibson, J. G., *Federation Proc.*, **18**, 126 (1959)

173. Pitts, R. F., Gurd, R. S., Kessler, R. H., and Hierholzer, K., *Am. J. Physiol.*, **194**, 125–34 (1958)

174. Handler, J. S., *Am. J. Physiol.*, **202**, 787–90 (1962)

175. Leaf, A., *Ann. Rev. Physiol.*, **22**, 111–68 (1960)

176. Berliner, R. W., *Circulation*, **21**, 892–901 (1960)

177. Walser, M., *J. Clin. Invest.*, **40**, 723–30 (1961)

178. Walser, M., *J. Clin. Invest.*, **41**, 1454–71 (1962)

179. Talmage, R. V., and Kraintz, F. W., *Proc. Soc. Exptl. Biol. Med.*, **87**, 263–67 (1954)

180. Talmage, R. V., Kraintz, F. W., and Buchanan, G. D., *Proc. Soc. Exptl. Biol. Med.*, **88**, 600–4 (1955)

181. Talmage, R. V., *Ann. N. Y. Acad. Sci.*, **64**, 326–35 (1956)

182. Buchanan, G. D., Kraintz, F. W., and Talmage, R. V., *Proc. Soc. Exptl. Biol. Med.*, **101**, 306–9 (1959)

183. Kleeman, C. R., Bernstein, D., Rockney, R., Dowling, J. T., and Maxwell, M. H., *Yale J. Biol. Med.*, **34**, 1–30 (1961)

184. Widrow, S. H., and Levinsky, N. G., *Federation Proc.*, **21**, 435 (1962)

185. Gordan, G. S., Loken, H. F., Blum, A., and Teal, J. S., *Metab. Clin. Exptl.*, **11**, 94–102 (1962)

186. Chen, P. S., Jr., and Newman, W. F., *Am. J. Physiol.*, **180**, 632–36 (1955)

187. Howard, P. J., Wilde, W. S., and Malvin, R. L., *Am. J. Physiol.*, **197**, 337–41 (1959)

188. Canary, J. J., and Kyle, L. H., *J. Clin. Invest.*, **38**, 994 (1959)

189. Jahan, I., and Pitts, R. F., *Am. J. Physiol.*, **155**, 42–49 (1948)

190. Poulos, P. P., *J. Lab. Clin. Med.*, **49**, 253–57 (1957)

191. Wesson, L. G., Jr., and Lauler, D. P., *Proc. Soc. Exptl. Biol. Med.*, **101**, 235–36 (1959)

192. Lassiter, W. E., Gottschalk, C. W., and Mylle, M., *Federation Proc.*, **21**, 435 (1962)

193. Walser, M., *Am. J. Physiol.*, **201**, 769–73 (1961)

194. Schachter, D., and Rosen, S. M., *Am. J. Physiol.*, **196**, 357–62 (1959)

195. Rasmussen, H., *Endocrinology*, **65**, 517–18 (1959)

196. Cramer, C. F., Suiker, A. P., and Copp, D. H., in *The Parathyroids*, 158–66 (Thomas, Springfield, Ill., 473 pp., 1961)

197. Wasserman, R. H., Kallfelz, F. A., and Comar, C. L., *Science*, **133**, 883–84 (1961)

198. Wasserman, R. H., and Comar, C. L., *Endocrinology*, **69**, 1074–79 (1961)

199. Talmage, R. V., and Elliott, J. R., *Federation Proc.*, **17**, 160 (1958)

200. Toverud, S. U., in *The Transfer of Calcium and Strontium Across Biological Membranes* (Wasserman, R. H., Ed., Academic, New York, in press)

201. Dowdle, E. B., Schachter, D., and Schenker, H., *Am. J. Physiol.*, **198**, 269–74 (1960)

202. Kimberg, D. V., Schachter, D., and Schenker, H., *Am. J. Physiol.*, **200**, 1256–62 (1961)

203. Gran, F. C., *Acta Physiol. Scand.*, **49**, 211–15 (1960)

204. Mazzuoli, G., Samachson, J., and Laszlo, D., *J. Lab. Clin. Med.*, **52**, 522–32 (1958)

205. Copp, D. H., and Davidson, A. G. F., *Proc. Soc. Exptl. Biol. Med.*, **107**, 342–44 (1961)

206. Clarkson, B., Kowlessar, O. D., Horwith, M., and Sleisenger, M. H., *Metab. Clin. Exptl.*, **9**, 1093–106 (1960)

207. Ostrow, J. D., Blanshard, G., and Gray, S. J., *Am. J. Med.*, **29**, 769–79 (1960)

208. Blanshard, G., Arabekety, J. T., and Gray, S. J., *Am. J. Physiol.*, **196**, 844–46 (1959)

209. Letwinter, P., and Spiro, H. M., *Metab. Clin. Exptl.*, **9**, 847–52 (1960)

210. Donegan, W. I., and Spiro, H. M., *Gastroenterology*, **38**, 750–59 (1960)

211. Scaletta, S., and Consolo, F., *Boll. Soc. Ital. Biol. Sper.*, **36**, 529–31 (1960)

212. Cowie, A. T., in *Milk: the Mammary Gland and Its Secretion*, **1**, 188–91 (Kon, S. K., and Cowie, A. T., Eds., Academic, New York, 515 pp., 1961)

213. Folley, S. J., Scott Watson, H. M., and Amoroso, E. C., *J. Endocrinol.*, **3**, 178–91 (1942)

214. Cowie, A. T., and Folley, S. J., *Nature*, **156**, 719–20 (1945)

215. Von Berswordt-Wallrabe, R., and Turner, C. W., *J. Dairy Sci.*, **42**, 1986–94 (1959)

216. Von Berswordt-Wallrabe, R., and Turner, C. W., *Proc. Soc. Exptl. Biol. Med.*, **104**, 113–16 (1960)

217. Bruce, H. M., and Sloviter, H. A., *J. Endocrinol.*, **15**, 72–82 (1957)

218. Smith, V. R., Stott, G. H., and Walker, C. W., *J. Animal Sci.*, **16**, 312–17 (1957)

219. Stott, G. H., and Smith, V. R., *J. Dairy Sci.*, **40**, 897–904 (1957)

220. Von Berswordt-Wallrabe, R., Turner, C. W., and Powell, M. E., *Proc. Soc. Exptl. Biol. Med.*, **103**, 536–37 (1960)

221. Toverud, S. U., and Munson, P. L., *Ann. N.Y. Acad. Sci.*, **64**, 336 (1956)

222. Twardock, A. R., and Comar, C. L., *Am. J. Physiol.*, **201**, 645–50 (1961)

223. Todd, A. S., Fosgate, O. T., Cragle, R. G., and Kamal, T. H., *Am. J. Physiol.*, **202**, 987–90 (1962)

224. Tweedy, W. R., and Campbell, W. W., *J. Biol. Chem.*, **154**, 339–47 (1944)

225. Howard, J. E., Hopkins, T. R., and Connor, T. B., *J. Clin. Endocrinol. Metab.*, **13**, 1–19 (1953)

226. Foulks, J. G., and Perry, F. A., *Am. J. Physiol.*, **196**, 561–66 (1959)

227. Neuman, W. F., and Overslaugh, C., *US At. Energy Comm.*, *UR-589*, 1–13 (1960)

228. Canary, J. J., Carreon, G. G., Bloomer, H. A., Kyle, L. H., and Meloni, C. R., *J. Clin. Endocrinol. Metab.*, 22, 229–39 (1962)

229. Reaven, G., Schneider, A., and Reaven, E., *Proc. Soc. Exptl. Biol. Med*, 102, 70–7 (1959)

230. Wallach, S., Cahill, L. N., Rogan, F. H., and Jones, H. L., *J. Lab. Clin. Med.*, 59, 195–210 (1962)

231. Cheek, D. B., and Teng, H. C., *Clin. Sci.*, 19, 195–208 (1960)

232. Fanconi, A., and Rose, G. A., *Quart. J. Med.*, 27, 463–94 (1958)

233. Lloyd, H. M., and Rose, G. A., *Lancet*, II, 1258–61 (1958)

234. Lloyd, H. M., Rose, G. A., and Smeenk, D., *Clin. Sci.*, 22, 353 (1962)

235. Terepka, A. R., Toribara, T. Y., and Dewey, P. A., *J. Clin. Invest.*, 37, 87–98 (1959)

236. Loken, H. F., Havel, R. J., Gordan, G. S., and Whittington, S. L., *J. Biol. Chem.*, 235, 3654–58 (1960)

237. Urist, M. R., Deutsch, N. M., Pomerantz, G., and McLean, F. C., *Am. J. Physiol.*, 199, 851–55 (1960)

238. Breen, M., and Freeman, S., *Am. J. Physiol.*, 200, 341–44 (1961)

239. Hopkins, T. R., Connor, T. B., and Howard, J. E., *Bull. Johns Hopkins Hosp.*, 93, 249–68 (1953)

240. Thomas, W. C., Jr., Wiswell, J. G., Connor, T. B., and Howard, J. E., *Am. J. Med.*, 24, 229–39 (1958)

241. Fowler, D. I., Fone, D. J., and Cooke, W. T., *Lancet*, II, 284–87 (1961)

242. Manunta, G., Saroff, J., and Turner, C. W., *Proc. Soc. Exptl. Biol. Med.*, 94, 790–91 (1957)

243. Smeenk, D., *J. Clin. Invest.*, 40, 433–44 (1961)

244. DeLuca, H., Engstrom, G. W., and Rasmussen, H., *Proc. Natl. Acad. Sci. US*, 48, 1604–8 (1962)

245. De Verdier, C. H., *Acta Physiol. Scand.*, 39, 1–11 (1957)

246. Hanno, H. A., and Weiss, D. I., *Arch. Ophthalmol.*, 65, 238–42 (1961)

247. Lo Cascio, G., *Ann. Ottalmol. Clin. Ocul.*, 65, 801–11 (1937)

248. Rinaldi, S., *Ann. Ottalmol. Clin. Ocul.*, 65, 667–83 (1937)

249. Clark, J. H., *Am. J. Physiol.*, 126, 136–41 (1939)

250. Firschein, H. E., *Biochim. Biophys. Acta*, 58, 626–28 (1962)

251. Hanna, S., *J. Clin. Pathol.*, 14, 410–14 (1961)

252. Prasad, A. S., Flink, E. B., and McCollister, R., *J. Lab. Clin. Med.*, 58, 531–41 (1961)

253. Durlach, J., Stoliaroff, M., Dauduchon, J., Leluc, R., and Thuong, C.-T., *Ann. Endocrinol. (Paris)*, 21, 235–43 (1960)

254. Selye, H., *Calciphylaxis* (Univ. of Chicago Press, Chicago, 234 pp., 1962)

255. Selye, H., and Dieudonne, J. M., *Experientia*, 17, 496–97 (1961)

256. Lehr, D., *Ann. N. Y. Acad. Sci.*, 72, 901–69 (1959)

257. Epstein, F. H., Beck, D., Carone, F. A., Levitin, H., and Manitius, A., *J. Clin. Invest.*, 38, 1214–21 (1959)

258. Fourman, P., McConkey, B., and Smith, J. W. G., *Lancet*, I, 619–22 (1960)

259. Manitius, A., Levitin, H., Beck, D., and Epstein, F. H., *J. Clin. Invest.*, 39, 693–97 (1960)

260. Gill, J. R., Jr., and Bartter, F. C., *J. Clin. Invest.*, 40, 716–22 (1961)

261. Nordin, B. E. C., *Clin. Sci.*, 19, 311–19 (1960)

262. Komarkova, A., Vostal, J., and Pacovsky, V., *Nature*, 185, 173–74 (1960)

263. Talmage, R. V., and Toft, R. J., in *The Parathyroids*, 224–40 (Thomas, Springfield, Ill., 473 pp., 1961)

264. Raybuck, H. E., *Anat. Record*, 112, 117–24 (1952)

265. Foldes, I., Kosa, C., Orosz, A., and Dobronyi, J., *Acta Physiol. Acad. Sci. Hung.*, 10, 229–38 (1956)

266. Deineka, G. K., *Probl. Endokrinol. Gormonoterap.*, 5, 8–17 (1959)

267. Stoerk, H. C., and Carnes, W. H., *J. Nutr.*, 29, 43–50 (1945)

268. Hanssler, H., *Z. Ges. Exptl. Med.*, 123, 91–100 (1954)

269. Harrison, M., and Fraser, R., *J. Endocrinol.*, 21, 207–11 (1960)

270. Bloom, W., Nalbandov, A. V., and Bloom, M. A., *Clin. Orthopedics*, 17, 206–9 (1960)

271. Engfeldt, B., Hjertquist, S. O., and Strandh, J. R. E., *Acta Endocrinol.*, 15, 119–28 (1954)

272. Toft, R. J., and Talmage, R. V., *Proc. Soc. Exptl. Biol. Med.*, 103, 611–13 (1960)

273. Patt, H. M., and Luckhardt, A. B., *Endocrinology*, 31, 384–92 (1942)

274. Raisz, L. G., *Federation Proc.*, 21, 207 (1962)

275. Copp, D. H., Cameron, E. C., Cheney,

B. A., Davidson, A. G. F., and Henze, K. G., *Endocrinology*, **70**, 638–49 (1962)

276. McLean, F. C., *Science*, **127**, 451–56 (1958)

277. Premachandra, B. N., and Blumenthal, H. T., *Proc. Soc. Exptl. Biol. Med.*, **107**, 842–45 (1961)

278. Davis, R., and Talmage, R. V., *Endocrinology*, **66**, 312–14 (1960)

279. Aivazyan, L. A., *Uch. Zap., Azerb. Gos. Univ., Ser. Biol. Nauk*, No. **3**, 57–62 (1959)

280. Harrison, H. C., Harrison, H. E., and Park, E. A., *Am. J. Physiol.*, **192**, 432–36 (1958)

281. Marnay, C., and Raoul, Y., *Compt. Rend. Soc. Biol.*, **153**, 1949–51 (1959)

282. Marnay, C., *J. Physiol. (Paris)*, **53**, 423–24 (1961)

283. Schartum, S., and Nichols, G., Jr., *Acta Physiol. Scand.* (In press)

284. Hertelendy, F., and Taylor, T. G., *Biochim. Biophys. Acta*, **44**, 200–2 (1960)

285. Chisolm, J. J., Jr., and Harrison, H. E., *J. Pediat.*, **60**, 206–19 (1962)

286. Jonxis, J. H. P., *J. Pediat.*, **59**, 607–15 (1961)

287. DeLuca, H. F., and Engstrom, G. W., *Proc. Natl. Acad. Sci. US.*, **47**, 1744–50 (1961)

288. Rasmussen, H., and Reifenstein, E. C., Jr., in *Textbook of Endocrinology*, 3d ed., 785–91 (Williams, R. H., Ed., Saunders, Philadelphia, 1204 pp., 1962)

289. Lever, J. D., *J. Anat.*, **91**, 73–81 (1957)

290. Lever, J. D., *J. Endocrinol.*, **17**, 210–17 (1958)

291. Palade, G. E., *J. Biophys. Biochem. Cytol.*, **1**, 59–68 (1955)

292. Hanssler, H., *Z. Ges. Exptl. Med.*, **121**, 209–27 (1953)

293. Weymouth, R. J., *Anat. Record.*, **127**, 509–26 (1957)

294. Davis, R., and Enders, A. C., in *The Parathyroids*, 76–92 (Thomas, Springfield, Ill., 473 pp., 1961)

295. Roth, S. I., *Arch Pathol.*, **73**, 495–510 (1962)

296. Trier, J. S., *J. Biophys. Biochem. Cytol*, **4**, 13–22 (1958)

297. Tremblay, G., and Pearse, A. G. E., *Brit. J. Exptl. Pathol.*, **40**, 66–70 (1959)

298. Tremblay, G., and Cartier, G. E., *Endocrinology*, **69**, 658–61 (1961)

299. Balogh, K., Jr., and Cohen, R. B., *Lab. Invest.*, **10**, 354–60 (1961)

300. Castleman, B., and Mallory, T. B., *Am. J. Pathol.*, **11**, 1–72 (1935)

301. Nachlas, M. M., Crawford, D. T., and Seligman, A. M., *J. Histochem. Cytochem.*, **5**, 264–78 (1957)

302. Pearse, A. G. E., and Tremblay, G., *Nature*, **181**, 1532–33 (1958)

303. Brooks, J. R., *Ann. Rev. Med.*, **12**, 271–80 (1961)

304. Brooks, J. R., and Hill, G. J. II, *Am. J. Surg.*, **99**, 588–99 (1960)

305. Kempe, C. H., and Jawetz, M. J. M., *Transplantation Bull.*, **5**, 155 (1958)

306. Akers, D. R., Binkley, E. L., and Miller, A. P., *Pediatrics*, **21**, 974–79 (1958)

307. Schatten, W. E., Bloom W. L., and Hamm, W. G., *Surg., Gynecol. Obstet.*, **112**, 196–202 (1961)

308. Jordan, G. L., Cunningham, D. S., Deere, H., Tullos, H., and Gyorkey, F., *J. Am. Med. Assoc.*, **178**, 488–90 (1961)

309. Russell, P. S., and Gittes, R. F., *J. Exptl. Med.*, **109**, 571–88 (1959)

310. Reid, M. R., and Ransohoff, J., *Am. J. Med. Sci.*, **206**, 731–35 (1943)

311. Escamilla, R. F., Kempe, C. H., Crane, J., Goodman, L., and Gordan, G. S., *Ann. Internal Med.*, **46**, 649–61 (1957)

312. Stone, H. B., Owings, J. C., and Gey, G. O., *Surg., Gynecol. Obstet.*, **60**, 390–93 (1935)

313. Gaillard, P. J., in *Ciba Found. Symp. Preservation Transplantation Normal Tissues*, 100–9 (1954)

314. Conway, H., Nickel, W. F., and Smith, J. W., *Plastic Reconstruct. Surg.*, **23**, 469–79 (1959)

315. Wilson, R. E., Zollinger, R. M., Jr., Mahan, J. H., and Brooks, J. R., *Surg. Forum*, **10**, 94–99 (1959)

316. Sanderson, P. H., Marshall, F. II, and Wilson, R. E., *J. Clin. Invest.*, **39**, 662–70 (1960)

317. Dunphy, J. E., and Jacob, S. W., *New Engl. J. Med.*, **264**, 371–74 (1961)

318. Gittes, R. F., and Russell, P. S., *J. Natl. Cancer Inst.*, **26**, 283–303 (1961)

319. Cortelyou, J. R., Hibner-Owerko, A., and Mulroy, J., *Endocrinology*, **66**, 441–50 (1960)

320. Cortelyou, J. R., *Endocrinology*, **70**, 618–21 (1962)

321. Polin, D., and Sturkie, P. D., *Endocrinology*, **63**, 177–82 (1958)

322. Siegmund, P., Korber, F., and Dulce, H. J., *Arch. Exptl. Pathol. Pharmakol.*, **240**, 327–35 (1961)

323. Urist, M. R., Schjeide, O. A., and McLean, F. C., *Endocrinology*, **63**, 570–85 (1958)

324. Stott, G. H., and Smith, V. R., *J. Dairy Sci.*, **40**, 897–904 (1957)

325. Kenny, A. D., *Endocrinology*, **70**, 715–22 (1962)

326. Lotz, W. E., Talmage, R. V., and Comar, C. L., *Proc. Soc. Exptl. Biol. Med.*, **85**, 292–95 (1954)

327. Irving, J. T., and Solms, C. M., *S. African J. Med. Sci.*, **20**, 32 (1955)

328. Copp, D. H., and Cameron, E. C., *Science*, **134**, 2038 (1961)

329. Ito, Y., *Ann. N. Y. Acad. Sci.*, **85**, 228–310 (1960)

THYROID[1,2,3]

By Sidney H. Ingbar[4] and Valerie Anne Galton

Department of Medicine, Harvard Medical School, Boston, Massachusetts, and Department of Physiology, Dartmouth Medical School, Hanover, New Hampshire

Previous reviews of this field have traditionally been introduced by explanations of the difficulty in reconciling available data with available space. This review will not deviate from that pattern, for, if anything, publications concerning the physiology of the thyroid gland and its hormones have increased during the past three years, while the space here allotted has declined. For this reason, and in view of the editors' request for a selective, expository review, the authors have chosen to discuss only three major areas of thyroid physiology, others being omitted entirely. Even so, a completely comprehensive consideration of these areas has not been possible. For the resulting intentional omissions, and for those which were unintended, the authors' apologies are therefore rendered.

Biosynthesis of Thyroid Hormones

Traditionally, stages in the biosynthesis of thyroid hormones are categorized in the following sequence: (*a*) concentration of inorganic iodide, (*b*) oxidation of iodide and binding of the oxidized form to tryosyl radicles in thyroglobulin to form intra-protein iodotyrosines, (*c*) coupling of iodotyrosines to form iodothyronines, (*d*) proteolysis of thyroglobulin and release into the blood of constituent iodothyronines, and (*e*) dehalogenation of free iodotyrosines liberated by hydrolysis of thyroglobulin. The extent to which this categorization represents an oversimplification of complex processes is increasingly apparent. Nevertheless, it is presented here to provide a frame of reference for the more detailed discussion of the several stages of hormonal biosynthesis which follows.

Thyroidal iodide transport mechanism.—Three major aspects of the mech-

---

[1] The survey of literature pertaining to this review was concluded in May 1962.

[2] Among the abbreviations used in this chapter are: DIT (diiodotyrosine); DPN (diphosphopyridine nucleotide); DPNH (diphosphopyridine nucleotide, reduced form); HMP (hexose monophosphate); MIT (monoiodotyrosine); T_3 (3,5,3'-triiodo-L-thyronine); T_4 (L-thyroxine); TA_3 (3,5,3'-triiodothyroacetic acid); TA_4 (3,5,3',5'-tetraiodothyroacetic acid); TSH (anterior hypophyseal thyroid-stimulating hormone); TPN (triphosphopyridine nucleotide); TPNH (triphosphopyridine nucletide, reduced form).

[3] From the Thorndike Memorial Laboratory, Second and Fourth (Harvard) Harvard Medical Services, Boston City Hospital and the Department of Medicine, Harvard Medical School, Boston, Mass., and the Department of Physiology, Dartmouth Medical School, Hanover, New Hampshire.

[4] Investigator, Howard Hughes Medical Institute.

anism whereby the thyroid gland is able to retain high concentrations of inorganic iodide (often termed the iodide-trapping or iodide-concentrating mechanism) have continued to excite extensive investigation: the nature of the mechanism itself, the manner in which it is influenced by physiological and pharmacological agents, and its metabolic dependencies.

Two hypotheses concerning the nature of the iodide-concentrating mechanism have received consideration. One, advocated by Lewitus and his co-workers (1), favors the passive adsorption, the other the active transport, of iodide. Consistent with the former hypothesis are the observations which indicate that several anions, including perchlorate and fluoroborate, whose ionic volume, configuration, and charge are similar to those of iodide, are either concentrated by the thyroid, inhibit the concentrating of iodide, or both [Anbar, Guttman & Lewitus (2, 3)]. Concentration of such anions would presumably not require specific energy expenditure or an active carrier compound, but might represent chelation by a specifically adapted protein. The active transport concept, on the other hand, would suggest that actively concentrated anions are complexed by a specific carrier substance located within or adjacent to the cell membrane, are transported from regions of lesser to regions of higher concentration, and are there deposited. From this locus they would be more or less free to diffuse along concentration gradients, ultimately to return to the plasma. Halmi (4), in a comprehensive review, has summarized evidence in favor of the active transport concept. First, the physicochemical properties which characterize the several anions concentrated by the thyroid may condition their affinity for a carrier substance as much as for a hypothetical binding protein. Second, iodide-concentrating requires the expenditure of metabolic energy. Third, iodide and the various monovalent anions which inhibit iodide-concentrating are not equipotent in depressing concentration gradients for each other (3). Finally, and perhaps most important, are the data which indicate that thiocyanate competitively inhibits iodide-concentrating without itself undergoing active concentration [Wollman (5)]. The latter data strongly favor the active transport hypothesis and, in addition, clearly differentiate the mode of action of thiocyanate in depressing iodide-concentrating from that of anions such as perchlorate and fluoroborate, for which active concentration can be achieved and can be increased by administration of TSH [Lewitus et al. (6)].

Great interest has evolved in the kinetics of iodide transport by the thyroid, largely as a result of the development both of mathematical models describing iodide transport and of methods for subjecting experimental data to analysis in these model systems. A comprehensive consideration of the mathematical and physiological assumptions upon which these models are based, as well as their mode of utilization, has been presented by Wollman (7) and by Halmi (4). Briefly, these models permit the estimation of a unidirectional rate of clearance of plasma iodide by a unit mass of thyroid tissue (C_{mT}) and an exit rate constant (K_{TB}), describing the proportional rate of loss of iodide from the thyroid into the plasma. The modes of action of such agents as thiouracils, thiocyanate, perchlorate, and TSH upon the iodide transport mechanism have been studied by such techniques (4, 7). Other, hitherto unexplained, phenomena have also been elucidated by analyses of this type. Thus, as Halmi and co-workers have shown, TSH, when administered to hypophysectomized or to T_3-treated rats, decreases thyroid/plasma (T/S) concentration ratios for iodide before its characteristic stimulatory effect on this function is manifest (8). Evidently, TSH increases K_{TB} earlier, though less intensely, than it stimulates C_{mT} (8, 9). An intriguing observation which appears to merit analysis by kinetic techniques is the finding that T/S ratios of thiouracilized rats are lowered more markedly by T_3 than by hypophysectomy. T/S ratios as low as those found in normal rats given T_3 could not be produced by T_3 in hypophysectomized rats, even when these animals were given cortisone and growth hormone in addition. It was suggested that, besides inhibiting secretion of TSH, T_3 interferes with iodide transport by another mechanism involving the pituitary in a mediating or permissive capacity [Halmi *et al.* (10)]. The possibility that this effect depends upon the elaboration of some thyroid inhibitor in the pituitary is raised by the older observations which indicated that extract of the pituitary of thyroid-fed rats reduces the thyroid weight, cell height, and basal metabolism rate of guinea pigs to which it is administered.

Evidence continues to accumulate attesting to the importance of thyroidal intermediary metabolism in conditioning the activity of the iodide transport mechanism. Low concentrations of cardiac glycosides and their aglycones, as well as quinidine, reduce thyroid slice/medium iodide concentration ratios *in vitro* [Wolff (11)]. Ouabain inhibits the transport of K^{42} and I^{131} to approximately the same extent, and its inhibition of iodide transport can be overcome by increasing the concentration of potassium in the suspending medium. The latter manipulation has no effect, however, on the inhibitory action of perchlorate or dinitrophenol (11). These findings might suggest that the potassium transport mechanism, or perhaps the sodium-pumping mechanism with which it is associated, are specifically linked to iodide transport. An alternative explanation would suggest that inhibition of thyroidal transport associated with loss of intracellular potassium results from secondary disturbances in intracellular metabolism, since iodide transport is known to be highly dependent upon energy (especially phosphate bond energy) derived from this source (4). In this regard, it is of interest that thiocyanate, in concentrations inhibitory to iodide transport, also inhibits oxidative phosphorylations in thyroid slices [Kanaya (12)].

Conventional concepts have indicated that iodide brought into the thyroid gland by the iodide transport mechanism is probably the sole source of substrate for organic iodinations. The quantitative importance of iodide delivered into the thyroid gland by this mechanism is beyond doubt. In both animals and man, agents which inhibit this function produce goitrous myxedema which can be relieved by dietary iodide supplementation. Furthermore, Stanbury & Chapman (13) have described a patient in whom there was an apparently idiopathic loss of the iodide transport function, not only in the thyroid, but also in the salivary and gastric glands, sites which share with the placenta and mammary glands many, but not all, features of the thyroidal iodide transport mechanism (14, 15). Clinically, this patient manifested goitrous myxedema.

Despite this evidence for the importance of thyroidal iodide transport and of the thyroidal iodide pool which it maintains, recently reported data suggest that there exists within the thyroid a second iodide pool of considerably greater content [Halmi & Pitt-Rivers (16)]. In rats in which organic binding of thyroidal iodide is allowed to proceed, T/S ratios for inorganic I^{131} rise progressively following administration of radioiodine, ultimately to exceed greatly both the T/S ratios found during early time periods and the moderately increased ratios found in animals in whom inorganic binding has been blocked prior to the administration of I^{131}. Studies by Nagataki in the authors' laboratory have led to similar conclusions; in double-isotope experiments, T/S ratios for inorganic I^{131}, chronically administered, far exceeded those for acutely administered inorganic I^{132}. In view of the preponderant concentration of organic iodine within the thyroid, even slight artifactual deiodination of organic compounds could produce sufficient iodide to account for that in the hypothetical second pool. However, in those studies which suggested the presence of such a pool, care was taken to select methods in which artifactual deiodination was likely to be minimized, and results obtained by different techniques agreed closely. If a second iodide pool does indeed exist, it is apparently not readily in communication with the pool of transported iodide, since the radioiodine in the second pool is not discharged by thiocyanate, perchlorate (16), or large doses of stable iodide.

While the deiodination of free iodotyrosines by the thyroidal dehalogenase unquestionably liberates inorganic iodide within the thyroid, the metabolic fate of this material is unknown. When proteolytic reactions are acutely accelerated by TSH, iodide of organic origin is lost into the thyroidal venous effluent [Nagataki et al. (17), Rosenberg et al. (18)]. The provisional demonstration of a second iodide pool suggests that at least a portion of the iodide derived from deiodination is retained in the thyroid for a time. It is not certain, however, whether such iodide can be utilized for new hormone formation, and, if so, whether this reaction is inhibited by antithyroid agents. Thus, the anatomical locus, storage capacity, and metabolic fate of iodide within the second pool are unknown. Nevertheless, it is apparent that the potential for a substantial internal recirculation of iodide which, under ordinary circumstances of experimentation with radioiodine, would be largely unlabeled, will necessitate both a reconsideration of the rates of turnover of individual iodinated compounds within the thyroid gland and a re-examination of the effects of physiologically active agents upon specific aspects of hormonal synthesis.

Thyroidal oxidative mechanisms and organic iodinations.—Thyroidal iodinations have been mainly studied in homogenate systems or fractions thereof. In view of the attendant dilution or loss of substrates, enzymes, co-factors, and inhibitors, and the disruption of their normal cytostructural orientation, findings in such systems are often variable and difficult to interpret. Nevertheless, two factors mitigate against the use of more normally organized preparations. First, in cellular preparations penetration of materials under study may be limited. Second, where rates of incorporation of radioiodine into organic moieties are to be used as indices of iodinating activity, erroneous conclusions may result from the influence of experimental manipulations on the iodide transport, rather than the organic-binding, mechanism. Destruction of the cell membrane eliminates the diffusion barrier for metabolites as well as the active transport of iodide into apposition with intracellular constituents. The numerous studies of iodine metabolism in broken cell systems recently performed have employed systems varying in their content of subcellular constituents, organic and inorganic co-factors, and content of iodine. It is not surprising, therefore, that certain inconsistencies in both data and interpretation have resulted.

Nevertheless, the observations make possible certain general conclusions concerning the nature of the thyroidal iodinating mechanism. Whole or partially clarified homogenates of thyroid tissue (18 to 24), mitochondrial-microsomal resuspensions (18, 19, 22, 24, 25, 26), and soluble extracts thereof (27, 28), if appropriately supplemented, are capable of carrying out the iodination of intrinsic proteins (18, 19, 22, 23, 24), exogenous nonthyroidal proteins (24, 29), or free tyrosine (20, 21, 22, 24), using inorganic I^{131} as substrate. These reactions are inhibited by azide, fluoride, and cyanide (21, 23); by reducing substances, such as ascorbic acid and compounds containing free SH groups (22, 23, 24); by a number of antithyroid agents, including thiouracils, methimazole, p-aminobenzoate, aminotriazole, and thiocyanate; and by catalase (21, 22, 23). Organic iodinations require the presence of molecular oxygen unless hydrogen peroxide is supplied to the system (20). Reaction products vary with the nature of the original preparation, the presence of added substrates susceptible to iodination, and the concentration of iodide in the system. In the absence of added tyrosine, intrinsic proteins are iodinated to yield peptide-bound MIT, occasional small amounts of DIT, but no iodothyronines (18, 19, 22 to 25). Iodinated lipids and a chromatographically separable inorganic oxidation product of iodine are formed in some systems (22, 23, 24). The latter compound does not appear to be an intermediate in organic iodinations in more physiological systems (30). When systems are supplemented with free tyrosine, free MIT appears; free DIT is also formed, in amounts which vary with the quantity of iodine organified (20, 21, 22, 24, 28).

The iodinated lipids formed by the homogenate system are thought to originate from iodination of lipids in particle membranes (22, 23, 24) and have been shown to be comprised in part of phosphatidylserine, sphingomyeline, and nonphosphatides [Suzuki *et al.* (24)]. Proteins iodinated in particulate systems are particle-bound (22, 23, 25), but can be solubilized by vigorous treatment (22). In sheep thyroid preparations, the solubilized iodo-proteins contain a major component with an electrophoretic mobility similar to that of serum albumin, an S_{20w} of approximately 2.5, and no immunologic cross-reactivity with homologous thyroglobulin [DeGroot & Carvalho (22)]. The particulate iodoprotein formed in cell-free systems has some features in common with particulate iodoproteins studied in human and animal thyroid glands following administration of I^{131} *in vivo* (31, 32), although the latter contain appreciable proportions of DIT and iodinated thyronines. In both instances, however, the evidence would suggest that the iodinated protein associated with subcellular particles is not a precursor of thyroglobulin (31, 33). The physiological significance of these products remains in doubt; but it may be supposed that under most conditions they, like the iodinated lipids, represent products of random reactions between oxidized iodine and adjacent iodine-accepting substrates. From the apparent randomicity of the iodina-tions which occur in cell-free systems, however, it should not be inferred that the oxidative reactions which have been studied bear no relationship to those processes which mediate the iodination of thyroglobulin in the intact gland, since thyroglobulin can be iodinated by particulate systems, if added in sufficient concentration [Kondo (25)].

The organic iodinations which occur within subcellular systems appear to be mediated by one, and possibly two, enzyme systems. Alexander (21) has conclusively demonstrated in thyroid tissue of several species an enzymic system capable of carrying out iodinations of protein or of free tyrosine in the presence of a hydrogen peroxide generating system, such as glucose-glucose oxidase. Systems capable of iodinating tyrosine have been demonstrated in a number of nonthyroidal tissues, but only in the thyroid has it been shown that the iodinating system is specific for this halide (21). Manometric ob-servations have indicated that the thyroidal system is truly peroxidatic in nature (21), and it has also been possible to dissociate the apoenzyme from the active prosthetic group, which is apparently ferriprotoporphyrin IX [Alexander (34)].

It has been further postulated that organification of oxidized iodine gen-erated via the peroxidase mechanism requires the mediation of an additional enzyme, tyrosine iodinase (20, 27). Evidence for the role of this enzyme, as distinct from that of the peroxidase, appears to the present authors to be considerably less conclusive, although several differences were noted between the ability of the thyroidal iodinating system and a model tissue-free iodinat-ing system to carry out iodinations of individual aromatic substrates [Serif & Kirkwood (20)].

In the supernatant fraction of thyroid homogenates are inhibitors of organic iodinations which are dialyzable and, at least in part, heat labile. It has variously been suggested that the inhibitor(s) may be stable inorganic iodide (22), catalase (22), glutathione or a closely related SH compound (23), or ascorbic acid (23, 24), with which glutathione is in oxidation-reduction equilibrium. The possibility that physiological regulation of the rate of organic iodinations in the intact thyroid can be carried out through variations in the concentration of endogenous inhibitory factors appears to merit direct evaluation.

Several studies have been directed toward elucidating the source of the oxidative potential requisite for organic iodinations. In view of the apparent importance of a peroxidatic system, attempts have been made to ascertain the metabolic source of hydrogen peroxide within thyroid tissue. On the basis of enhancement of organic iodinations attendant upon the addition of various substrates and co-factors both to whole homogenates (23) and to particulate suspensions (29), it has been suggested that a principal source of hydrogen peroxide may be the auto-oxidation of reduced flavoproteins, the reduction of which is, in turn, dependent upon electron transfers from reduced pyridine nucleotides. Direct comparisons in particulate systems have indicated that the TPN and TPNH may be more potent stimulators of iodinations than are DPN and DPNH (22, 29). However, it is not as yet certain whether this difference in potency is an artifact of the cell-free system, since the effects on organic iodinations of other oxidation-reduction mediators are greatly conditioned by the precise composition of the system in which they are employed [Tong & Chaikoff (26)].

Diiodination, coupling, and proteolytic mechanisms.—Little or no DIT is formed by thyroid homogenates, even when the formation of MIT is greatly increased by addition of stimulatory co-factors or of stable iodide (19, 23). In the intact animal, a variety of agents which inhibit organic iodinations, including large doses of stable iodide itself [Galton & Pitt-Rivers (35)], acutely inhibit the synthesis of DIT, relative to MIT (36). These data supplement earlier findings which indicate that, in the thyroid, the formation of DIT does not follow passively from the same processes which lead to the synthesis of MIT (37). It is uncertain, however, whether the synthesis of DIT requires a separate enzymic mechanism, whether it depends upon the prevailing oxidative potential at the iodination site, or whether other factors are operative.

No data have been reported which would disturb the prevailing concept that the synthesis of iodotyrosines and their coupling to yield iodothyronines occurs within the matrix of the thyroglobulin molecule. On the other hand, there has been no significant clarification of the nature of the molecular rearrangements which must occur during the coupling reaction or of the change in the physiocochemical properties of thyroglobulin which these may produce. Evidence accumulates, however, that the coupling reaction is specifically, and perhaps enzymically, regulated. Thus, in man, one variety of goitrous hypothyroidism is associated with an apparently spontaneous coupling defect [Stanbury *et al.* (38)]. In rats, hypophysectomy disproportionately reduces the synthesis of T_4 and T_3, relative to MIT and DIT [Taurog *et al.* (39)]. Similar inhibition of coupling is induced by antithyroid agents which block organic binding (37, 40, 41), and the former reaction is probably more sensitively affected than the latter.

Efforts continue to characterize the enzymes involved in the hydrolysis of thyroglobulin. Two proteases [Haddad & Rall (42)] and at least two peptidases (43) have been separated from each other. While their precise interrelation is uncertain, it would appear that the proteases function to prime thyroglobulin by cleaving it into subunits susceptible to the action of the peptidase [Litonjua (44)]. Physiological correlations, however, remain poor. Thus, in the rat thyroid stimulated by endogenous or exogenous TSH, the total quantity, but not the concentration, of the peptidase, cysteinyltyrosinase, is increased. Under similar conditions, proteolytic activity is increased when the substrate employed is hemoglobin, but not when it is thyroglobulin [Laughlin *et al.* (45)].

Dehalogenation of iodotyrosines.—The thyroidal iodotyrosine dehalogenase is usually thought to conserve thyroidal iodine by effecting the deiodination of iodotyrosines prior to their release from the gland. On the basis of recent observations, the efficacy of these enzymes may be questioned. First, studies of the peripheral metabolism of iodotyrosines indicate that the peripheral dehalogenases are capable of rapidly deiodinating large quantities of iodotyrosines, the iodide from which is available for reaccumulation by the thyroid. Thus, the extent to which the glandular enzymes contribute to the ultimate conservation of iodine would be directly proportional to that quantity of the iodide which they liberate which can be directly re-utilized within the thyroid. Following administration of TSH, large quantities of iodide drawn from organic sources are released from the thyroid (17, 18). This suggests that under these conditions, at least, iodide derived from deiodination is inefficiently utilized. Although goitrous hypothyroidism occurs in patients lacking the glandular iodotyrosine dehalogenase, in such patients the peripheral enzyme is also absent and iodotyrosines are lost into the urine, forestalling reaccumulation of the iodine which they contain (46).

Further doubt concerning the efficacy of the glandular dehalogenases arises from the application of the ceric-arsenite reaction to chromatograms of extensively concentrated extracts of normal serum. Catalytically active materials amounting to roughly half of the apparent total iodine appear in the iodotyrosine zones of paper or column chromatograms (47). Similar results have been obtained by several (48, 49), though not all (50), groups of workers. Several objections to the interpretation that these findings indicate the presence of iodotyrosines may be cited: (*a*) when separative techniques are applied to the serum of patients given I[131], few or no labeled iodotyrosines are found; (*b*) both chloride and thiouracil derivatives may react catalytically in the ceric-arsenite system and, by virtue of their migration, may be confused with iodotyrosines (48, 50); (*c*) in normal individuals, at the proposed plasma concentrations, rapid peripheral deiodination of iodotyrosines would result in the urinary excretion of quantities of iodine in excess of those normally found; (*d*) since, during most protein precipitation procedures, iodotyrosines are poorly protein-bound, a greater discrepancy between serum protein-bound and total iodine than that normally found would be expected. Furthermore, since iodotyrosines are not measured in the "butanol-extractable iodine", a greater discrepancy than that usually found would be expected between this measurement and the serum total iodine. To these objections, the following rebuttal has been offered: (a) the stable iodotyrosines in the circulation may be drawn from a glandular pool which turns over more slowly than that which yields labeled iodothyronines (47); (b) catalytically active materials have been noted in the iodotyrosine zone in extracts of serum to which no thiouracils had been added (47); (c) although an earlier report indicated that I^{127} (as judged by activation analysis) could not account for the catalytically active material [Dimitriadou et al. (48)], a more recent report (in abstract form) from the same laboratory indicates that it can (51).

In contrast to their action upon the iodotyrosines, thyroid preparations fail to deiodinate iodothyronines, and it has been presumed that an enzyme for this purpose is lacking in the gland. It has been shown, however, that thyroglobulin, by binding T_4 and T_3, can interfere with the dehalogenation of these hormones by a peripheral T_4 deiodinase [Lissitzky (52)]. A similar inhibition within the thyroid, wherein the concentration of thyroglobulin is exceedingly high, rather than an absence of the enzyme, may explain the absence of iodothyronine dehalogenase activity in thyroid preparations.

Heterogeneity of thyroid function.—In most studies of thyroid physiology, for purposes of convenience and because evidence to the contrary was lacking, it has been assumed that each functional subunit of the thyroid gland behaves synchronously with others—that a single functional pool exists for each of the hormonal precursors and products. Recent evidence suggests that this is not the case and that there may be considerable heterogeneity of function within a single gland. Triantaphyllidis & Cukier (53) have presented evidence indicating that follicles may differ in their oxidation-reduction potential, rate of incorporation of I^{131}, and rates of turnover of I^{131}-labeled iodotyrosines and iodothyronines. Furthermore, in some patients with endemic iodine-deficient goiter, the specific activity of the plasma organic iodine may, for a time, exceed that in the thyroid [Ermans et al. (54)]. This suggests the presence of a second iodide pool with a rapid rate of turnover. Studies of thyroglobulin from a single gland have revealed that this protein, which appears electrophoretically and ultracentrifically homogeneous following preparation by standard salting-out techniques, can be separated into a number of similar, but not precisely identical, molecular species which vary in both their chromatographic behavior on DEAE cellulose and the extent of their labeling with I^{131} (55, 56). Finally, Mayberry & Astwood (57) have reported that, in rats given I^{131} followed 24 hours later by continued doses of propylthiouracil, the proportion of total organic I^{131} contributed by labeled T_4 and T_3 declines rapidly while the proportion of labeled MIT and DIT remains constant or increases. Such was not the case in control animals or in those treated with perchlorate; here, the proportion of the several iodinated amino acids remained relatively constant as total glandular iodine declined. It was suggested that the iodothyronines might be released from thyroglobulin faster than iodotyrosines, an indication that secretion of thyroid hormone may not require the complete hydrolysis of thyroglobulin. This, too, would indicate that the glandular organic iodine pool cannot be treated as a homogeneous entity.

These evidences of thyroidal inhomogeneity, if confirmed and extended, will necessitate a re-evaluation of previous data concerning both the kinetics of hormonal synthesis and release, and the action of those physiologic and pharmacologic agents which alter thyroid function. The recently described technique [van Middlesworth (58)] which makes possible the uniform labeling of all intra- and extrathyroidal iodine pools would appear to be the best method by which such re-evaluation could be effected.

SELECTED ASPECTS OF THYROID INTERMEDIARY METABOLISM

During recent years, a large literature has accumulated concerning the intermediary metabolism of thyroid tissue. Considerable attention has been focused upon lipid, especially phospholipid, metabolism (59, 60, 61). In contrast, relatively little attention has been directed toward the metabolism of nucleic acids and synthesis of protein. The present discussion will be concerned, however, with recent findings related to thyroidal intermediary carbohydrate metabolism, its response to various agents, and its possible relation to hormonal biogenesis.

A variety of evidence indicates that the major pathways of glucose dissimilation found in other tissues also exist in the thyroid. Enzymes mediating the first two reactions of the direct oxidative pathway or hexose monophosphate (HMP) shunt have been demonstrated by direct assay [Glock & McLean (62)]. In addition, studies with labeled substrates have revealed both a more rapid generation of $C^{14}O_2$ from C-1- than from C-6-labeled glucose (63, 64), and the capacity to carry out the oxidative decarboxylation of C-1-labeled gluconate and gluconolactone (64). These findings indicate that the HMP shunt does indeed function in thyroid tissue. That the carbon atoms of uniformly labeled glucose are assimilated into thyroid lipids [Freinkel (65)] provides evidence for the operation of the Embden-Meyerhof pathway. Furthermore, observations by Barakat in the authors' laboratory reveal the generation of substantial proportions of labeled lactic acid from both C-1- and C-6-labeled glucose. Finally, fluoroacetate and malonate greatly inhibit the evolution of labeled CO_2 from C-6-labeled glucose [Dumont (66)]. The latter finding, together with the demonstrated generation of $C^{14}O_2$ from labeled acetate and pyruvate [Field et al. (63)], would also indicate the operation of the tricarboxylic acid cycle, all seven enzymes of which have been found in thyroid tissue by direct assay [Dumont (67)].

The relative disposition of glucose along alternate pathways of metabolism, however, remains unclear. The marked preponderance in the generation of $1\text{-}C^{14}O_2$ over $6\text{-}C^{14}O_2$ does not necessarily indicate that the HMP shunt is the major pathway of oxidative metabolism (68), especially in view of evidence that Krebs cycle activity in the thyroid may be slight. Thyroid concentrations of stable citric acid are high (69), while, in the rat, histochemical analyses reveal that isocitric dehydrogenase is absent or minimal in the unstimulated gland [Lindsay & Jenks (70)]. The activity of Krebs cycle enzymes in the thyroid is far lower than in the liver of the same species (67). Thus, in the thyroid, lower yields of $6\text{-}C^{14}O_2$ may reflect a slower functioning of the Krebs cycle or a greater dilution of labeled intermediates within the substrate pool, or both. This interpretation would be consonant with the progressive decline of $1\text{-}C^{14}O_2/6\text{-}C^{14}O_2$ ratios during prolonged incubation experiments (66). Furthermore, only a small proportion of assimilated glucose (uniformly labeled) is evolved as labeled CO_2 (65). An even smaller proportion is incorporated into thyroidal lipids (65). As the thyroid is rich in glycoproteins and free hexosamines (71, 72), the possibility that a large proportion of assimilated glucose is diverted into nontriosephosphate pathways is considerable, though unexplored. The demonstration of nucleotide conjugates of hexoses and hexosamines is also consistent with a high level of activity of those pathways leading to glycoprotein and mucopolysaccharide synthesis [Gregoire *et al.* (73)].

Correlating with this evidence for the existence of the common pathways of glucose metabolism are recent analyses which have defined the presence or concentration within thyroid tissue of associated electron carriers, including pyridine, and flavin nucleotides, TPNH and DPNH diaphorases, and cytochrome oxidase (62, 70, 74, 75, 76). To a limited extent, adenosine nucleotides have been measured and adenosine triphosphatase demonstrated (73).

These metabolic studies have provided a background upon which the effects of physiologically active agents have been projected. Greatest interest has been aroused by the demonstration that TSH enhances both the assimilation and oxidative decarboxylation of glucose (65). Exogenous and endogenous TSH also increases the activity of a variety of histochemically demonstrable enzymes related to glucose metabolism and hydrogen transfer (70). *In vitro*, effects of TSH on glucose metabolism can be elicited with physiological concentrations of the hormone and are evident within five minutes after its addition [Field *et al.* (77)]. In short-term experiments *in vitro*, the increase in $C^{14}O_2$ generation induced by TSH is greater with C-1- than with C-6-labeled glucose (23, 77, 78). This has led to the suggestion that TSH stimulates mainly or entirely the HMP shunt. This effect does not result from a stimulation of glucose-6-phosphate dehydrogenase or 6-phosphogluconate dehydrogenase activity (77), nor does it follow from an increased ability to oxidize TPNH (63). Rather, it has been proposed that TSH increases the intrathyroidal concentration of TPN, apparently at the expense of DPN, suggesting that it may stimulate a DPN phosphokinase (75).

For reasons cited above, it appears hazardous on the basis of measurements of $C^{14}O_2$ generation alone to conclude that TSH selectively stimulates the HMP shunt. Indeed, recent observations by Barakat in the author's laboratory indicate that TSH stimulates the generation of labeled lactic acid from C-1-labeled glucose as much as it does the generation of $C^{14}O_2$. That the effects of TSH may be more widespread than merely those which would follow an increase in TPN is suggested by the finding that the generation of $C^{14}O_2$ from labeled acetate and pyruvate is also increased by the hormone (63).

While it is evident that the entire effects of TSH upon intermediary metabolism of the thyroid remain to be elucidated, those effects already described would serve well to stimulate or facilitate reactions involved in hormonal biosynthesis, including the energy-dependent iodide transport mechanism, the oxidative mechanism for organic iodinations, and the TPNH-dependent iodotyrosine dehalogenase.

Finally, it is apparent that the processes involved in hormonal biosynthesis may themselves influence thyroidal intermediary metabolism. Thus, supplementation of incubation media with inorganic iodide in concentrations which result in an increase in organic iodinations induces augmented glucose metabolism by thyroid slices (79). Enhancement of the oxidation of C-1-labeled glucose has also been observed following addition of stable iodotyrosines (66), possibly because their deiodination is coupled to the oxidation of TPNH or possibly because they liberate stimulatory concentrations of iodide. One might then visualize that a stimulation of proteolysis by TSH, with consequent liberation of iodotyrosines and hence iodide, would accelerate glucose oxidation and thereby make possible increases in the rate of hormone formation. A self-stimulating mechanism might thereby be set in motion. However, a self-damping mechanism has also been proposed (23). Triphosphopyridine nucleotide is usually stimulatory to organic iodinations in thyroid homogenates, but, under certain circumstances, may produce inhibition, presumably by enhancing the conversion of oxidized to reduced glutathione, an inhibitor of iodinations (23). The balanced interaction of such self-stimulatory and self-damping mechanisms may provide an effective means for subtle control of the rate of hormone biogenesis and release.

PERIPHERAL METABOLISM OF THE THYROID HORMONES

Metabolism of thyroid hormones in vivo.—It is generally accepted that the peripheral metabolism of the thyroid hormones *in vivo* is in part conditioned by their interactions with the proteins of the extracellular fluids, which serve to regulate the rate of delivery of the hormones to peripheral tissues. At the cellular level, the thyroid hormones undergo at least three types of metabolic transformation: deiodination, conjugation of the phenolic group, oxidative deamination and decarboxylation of the side chain, and possibly 0-methylation [Roche *et al.* (80)]. Because of the almost exclusive use of I^{131} for labeling the hormones, the complete elucidation of the metabolic pathways and of the products formed has not been possible; once deiodination has occurred, the molecule can no longer be traced. Although a few experiments have been conducted with C^{14}-labeled T_4 (81), interpretation of the results is difficult since the low specific activity of the administered hormone has necessitated the administration of pharmacological doses.

Deiodination, as indicated by the liberation of inorganic iodide, appears quantitatively to be the most important metabolic pathway, but the organic products of the deiodination reactions have not been thoroughly characterized. Although specific instances of the conversion of T_4 to T_3 or its derivatives have been described (82), it is not certain whether this reaction is general to most tissues and species. A particularly interesting example, however, is the formation of T_3 from T_4 by thyrotrophic pituitary tumors of the mouse [Werner et al. (83)]. Conversion of T_3 to $3:3'-T_2$ has been observed in several species (82, 84, 85). In addition, in dogs, T_4 is converted to $3:3'5'-T_3$ (86). This reaction appears to proceed principally in the liver, but some activity is found in hepatectomized animals. Preferential deiodination of the inner ring indicates a high degree of biochemical specificity, since the carbon-iodine bond in this ring is known to be more stable than that in the phenolic ring. Thus, data obtained *in vivo* provide considerable evidence that partial deiodination of iodothyronines can occur, although this is difficult to demonstrate *in vitro*.

In the rat, T_4 and T_3 can be conjugated with glucuronic acid in the liver, and the resulting glucuronides are secreted into the bile (87, 88). The liver is not essential for this process since glucuronide formation also occurs in hepatectomized dogs. Under these conditions the conjugates appear in the urine and plasma (85, 86). The glucuronide of T_4 has also been detected in the kidneys but not in the plasma of mice treated with I^{131} [Galton & Pitt-Rivers (89)]. Many derivatives of the thyroid hormones are also conjugated with glucuronic acid. The glucuronides of TA_3 and of the formic acid analogues of T_4 and T_3 have been detected in rat bile, and those of TA_4 and TA_3 in human bile following the administration of the parent compounds (90, 91, 92). Quantitative differences in the rate of conjugation of the various iodinated phenols have been demonstrated. Thus, in man, TA_3 is conjugated more rapidly than TA_4 and appears in greater concentrations in the bile [Green & Ingbar (92)]. Tapley et al. (93, 94) have obtained evidence suggesting that glucuronide formation is important for the transport of iodinated phenols across certain membranes.

The thyroid hormones can also undergo esterification with sulfate. The sulfate esters of T_4 (ST_4) and T_3 (ST_3) have been identified in bile and plasma following administration of the hormones to rats [Roche et al. (95, 96)]. However, the fate of the two hormones is dissimilar; T_3 is conjugated with sulfate in the liver and the ester is found in the plasma and bile (95). ST_3 has been identified in rats following the administration of minute amounts of T_3 (95). In the case of T_4, only small amounts of the sulfate appeared in the bile and none was detected in the plasma (96).

Similar findings have been reported in dogs. Injection of $3:5:3'-T_3$ resulted in the appearance of $3:5:3'-T_3$ sulfate and $3:3'-T_2$ sulfate in the bile (85, 97). The glucuronides were also formed, but to a lesser extent. The liver was not essential for esterification since $3:3'$-T_2 sulfate was found in the blood and urine of hepatectomized dogs. As in the rat, only small amounts of the sulfate ester were formed from T_4; the major conjugate was the glucuronide (86, 97). The formation of the sulfate ester of T_3 has also been demonstrated in the rabbit (98).

The physiological role of ST_3 is not known. It has been suggested that it is a storage form of T_3. The ester can be hydrolyzed by a suspension of intestinal contents, and also by homogenates of liver and kidney of the rat (99). Following administration of I^{131}- and S^{35}-labeled T_3, S^{35} sulfate appears in the urine before I^{131}, suggesting that hydrolysis may be a prerequisite for deiodination (100).

The first indication that oxidative deamination of the thyroid hormone molecule can occur *in vivo* was obtained by Roche *et al.* (101) who detected the ketoacid analogues in the bile of rats given large doses of I^{131}-labeled T_4 or T_3. Roche *et al.* later demonstrated the formation of the corresponding acetic acid analogues from $3:5:3'$-T_3, $3:3':5'$-T_3, and $3:3'$-T_2 in the same species (102, 103). Both TA_4 and TA_3 are formed *in vivo* from endogenous hormone; they have been detected in liver and kidney but not in the plasma of mice treated with I^{131} [Galton & Pitt-Rivers (104)]. However, the possibility that these compounds were the propionic acid analogues could not be excluded since the proprionic and acetic acid derivatives have identical mobilities in all the chromatographic solvent systems tested. Recently, the conversion of $3:5:3'$-T_3 to the corresponding lactic acid analogue has been demonstrated in the liver, kidney, and plasma of the rat [Roche *et al.* (105, 106, 107)].

The importance of oxidative deamination and decarboxylation as a pathway for the metabolism of the thyroid hormones and the physiological role of the deaminated derivatives *in vivo* is unknown. The pyruvic and acetic acid analogues are formed when the parent hormones are incubated with a snake venom L-amino acid oxidase [Nakano *et al.* (108)], and thus the possibility that oxidative deamination *in vivo* may result from the action of a similar nonspecific enzyme system cannot be excluded. Indeed, it is of interest that in both thyrotoxic patients and hyperthyroid rats, pyridoxal phosphate-dependent reactions such as decarboxylation are, in fact, diminished (109, 110).

Metabolism of thyroid hormones in vitro.—Theoretically, studies of thyroid hormone metabolism *in vitro* should provide a more direct insight into degradative mechanisms than studies performed *in vivo*. *In vitro*, the effects of extracellular binding interactions are minimized and competition for hormone between individual organs is eliminated. Finally, excretory mechanisms for the removal of products of hormonal metabolism are absent. On the other hand, studies *in vitro* are not without their own difficulties. In tissue slices, problems of cellular binding and penetration of the hormones as well as of added cofactors arise. In cell-free preparations, many of the interpretive difficulties cited earlier in connection with studies of the thyroidal organification mechanisms also appear in studies of deiodination. The technique of paper chromatographic analysis, while invaluable for assessing the products of hormonal degradation, may lead to erroneous conclusions since, in the single-dimensional analyses usually performed, poor resolution of hormonal derivatives may occur. Quantitative relationships may be disturbed by adsorption of hormone to incubating vessels (111). Perhaps the greatest difficulty, however, lies in the inability to distinguish between alterations in the hormone induced by tissue components, and those which result from the physiochemical properties of the hormone itself. First, self-irradiation of labeled hormone preparations, resulting in the generation of inorganic iodide or the corresponding lactic acid derivatives, may confuse the results of deiodination studies unless appropriate corrections are made. Such changes can be minimized by diluting the concentrated solution for storage (112, 113). Second, when labeled T_4 dissolved in an organic solvent is diluted into an aqueous medium and is then subjected to paper chromatography, there appears a compound which is not demonstrable in the original undiluted T_4 and which is chromatographically indistinguishable from inorganic iodide. This compound does not appear if the diluted T_4 is subjected to electrophoretic analysis. The appearance of this compound is completely prevented if the diluted T_4 is re-introduced into organic solvents, or if plasma or other thyroxine-binding proteins are present in or added to the aqueous solution before chromatographic analysis [Tata (114)]. Indeed, suppression of this effect can be utilized as an index of the hormonal-binding potency of protein preparations [Tata (115)]. A similar alteration of the molecule occurs in the case of other iodinated phenols, but to a lesser extent (114). While the nature of this alteration has not been clarified, it is apparent that the appearance of substantial proportions of a compound which is at least indistinguishable from inorganic iodide during chromatographic analysis can lead to erroneous conclusions in studies of hormonal deiodination. As would be expected, however, this source of error in studies of deiodination can be eliminated if plasma proteins are added into the reaction vessel, or if the iodinated compounds are extracted into organic solvents prior to chromatography (115, 116).

In general, the types of metabolic transformations which are observed *in vitro* are similar to those which occur *in vivo*, *viz.*, conjugation, oxidative deamination and decarboxylation, and deiodination. Conjugation has not been extensively studied, but both glucuronides and sulfates are formed *in vitro* (82, 117). In the authors' experience, conjugation occurs mainly in kidney, but also in liver, and is more marked in slices than in cell-free systems.

Although demonstrable in unfractionated preparations, deamination appears to be a property of mitochondria (118 to 122). Sonic disintegration diminishes deiodination and increases the deaminating activity of mitochondria derived from kidney, liver, heart, and brain (118, 119). In some preparations, activity is enhanced by the addition of DPN (119, 120, 121). Studies in soluble systems indicate that deamination yields the pyruvic or keto-acid derivatives which are then oxidatively decarboxylated to form the acetic acid analogues [Tomita & Lardy (120)]. The role of deamination as an alternate metabolic pathway to deiodination is indicated by the observations that both structural analogues of T_4 and hydroxylated derivatives of trypto-phan, which inhibit deiodination, increase the generation of deaminated products (116, 123). It has been reported that D-T_4 can not undergo deamina-tion, and this finding was correlated with the relative inactivity of this com-pound [Larson *et al.* (124)]. However, deamination of D-T_4 was subsequently observed in preparations of both tadpole and mouse liver, especially when supplemented with serotonin [Galton & Ingbar (116)].

Attempts to localize the deiodinating system intracellularly have pro-duced conflicting results. In early studies with liver, the highest activity was found in the microsomal fraction, although considerable deiodination also occurred in the soluble fraction [Maclagan & Reid (125)]. Others have dem-onstrated activity in microsomal preparations of liver and kidney (126), while Tata (127) found that the activity in brain and muscle was confined almost exclusively to the soluble fraction. In contrast, several workers em-ploying a variety of tissues, including muscle, have found that the highest activity resides in the mitochondrial fraction, although most cellular fractions possessed some activity (11, 128, 129).

Most of these studies have been performed with T_4 labeled exclusively in the phenolic ring. The major labeled product formed under these conditions is inorganic iodide. However, the generation of labeled material which re-mains at the point of application during chromatographic analysis (origin material) has been noted by many workers (82, 116, 119, 130). Origin ma-terial is not an artifact of deiodination *in vitro* since it has been detected in a variety of tissues obtained from animals given I^{131}-labeled T_4 or T_3 *in vivo* [Ford *et al.* (131)]. Origin material appears to consist of iodinated proteins. MIT has been identified following enzymic hydrolysis (132, 133), and the iodination of added egg albumin and lysozyme during the deiodination of T_4 has been demonstrated (132). It is thought to be formed by the iodination of tissue proteins during the deiodination of T_4 and its derivatives. However, it has been clearly demonstrated that origin material is not formed from the inorganic iodide which is liberated during deiodination [Galton & Ingbar (134)]. This indicates that the deiodinating mechanism must consist of at least two steps. Deiodination may either yield two products: iodide and a compound which leads to the formation of origin material; or it may yield a single product which can give rise to either iodide or origin material. Since iodide must be oxidized before it can iodinate a substrate, it seems probable that a relatively oxidized form of iodine is at least one of the products of hor-monal deiodination.

It is notable that, with two exceptions (135, 136), significant amounts of T_3 are not observed during the deiodination of T_4 by tissue systems (82), despite the finding that tissue preparations deiodinate T_3 more slowly than T_4 (128).

These studies with T_4 labeled exclusively in the phenolic ring have yielded no information concerning the fate of the iodine atoms in the inner ring, or of the deiodinated molecule. Only a few studies have been performed with T_4 labeled in the inner ring. In contrast to the findings *in vivo* (85, 86), experiments *in vitro* indicate that the iodine atoms in the inner ring are more stable than those in the phenolic ring [Plaskett (137)]. In a preparation of rat liver, $3:5:$-labeled T_4 is metabolized principally to a compound which yields DIT following alkaline hydrolysis. Formation of 4-hydroxy-3:5-diiodophenyl lactic acid was also demonstrated (137). These findings indicate that rupture of the ether bridge occurs during the metabolism of T_4. From studies employing tritiated T_3, Lissitzky has concluded that the hormone undergoes 0-hydroxylation and deamination as well as a splitting of the ether linkage during incubation with slices of rat liver (138). This author was unable to characterize iodinated products other than iodide and TA_4 following incubation of biosynthetically labeled T_4 with slices of rat liver (139). However, with the use of thyronine's property of fixing iodine specifically in the 3' and 5' positions, this compound was identified as an end product of hormonal metablism in this system (139). The formation of thyronine and tyrosine from T_4 and T_3 has been demonstrated in slices of rat liver and muscle and in rat kidney (140, 141).

A variety of compounds have been reported to stimulate the deiodination of T_4 in tissue preparations *in vitro*. These include ferrous ions (Fe^{++}), certain reducing agents such as ascorbic acid and sulfhydryl compounds, and flavin compounds (82, 126, 129, 130, 142). Recently, some doubt has been cast on the physiological significance of the role of these compounds in enzymic deiodination. For example, deiodination of T_4 has been demonstrated in tissue-free systems containing Fe^{++}, ascorbic acid, and oxygen (143), a system known to generate H_2O_2. Further, a heat-stable microsomal deiodinating system which requires Fe^{++} and oxygen has been described. This preparation is only active after heating at 100° for a few minutes and the activity is enhanced by cysteine or ascorbic acid. Dialysis also activates the system and renders it heat labile. Addition of Fe^{++} restores the heat stability. The deiodinating system is inhibited by cyanide and several substances which chelate Fe^{++} [Stanbury *et al.* (126)]. Other heat-stable deiodinating systems have been described (125, 128, 138, 141); in general, tissue slices appear to be less heat stable than homogenates (128). The nature of these latter systems is not clear, but the possibility that Fe^{++} may also play a role has not been excluded.

The significance of flavin compounds as cofactors for deiodinating systems has also been challenged [Galton & Ingbar (142)]. In the presence of light, flavin compounds can deiodinate T_4 and related substances during incubation in a tissue-free system. Iodide was identified as the major iodinated product by various techniques (142). The chemical degradation of T_4 by flavin mononucleotide in the presence of light has also been studied with concentrations of hormone sufficient to permit colorimetric identification of the products. Formation of iodide, $3:3':5'$-T_3, and DIT was demonstrated (144).

It is well known that H_2O_2 can be produced by auto-oxidation of flavin compounds in the presence of oxygen and light, and H_2O_2 is also generated by the Fe^{++}-ascorbic acid-oxygen system. Deiodination of T_4 has been observed during incubation with horseradish peroxidase (145). In a recent study, the possibility that a hydrogen peroxide-peroxidase system might play a role in enzymic deiodination was examined (146). The deiodination of T_4 by fresh and boiled homogenates of rat muscle was found to be inhibited in the presence of catalase. Supplementation of the homogenate system with a peroxide-generating source resulted in a marked increase in the deiodination of T_4, although under comparable conditions no deiodination occurred in the absence of tissue. It was also found that the enhanced deiodination observed in this system in the presence of added Fe^{++}, TPN, ATP, or certain other cofactors was reduced or inhibited by catalase [Galton & Ingbar (146)]. These findings strongly suggest that the deiodination of T_4 by the preparation used in this study is mediated by a peroxide-peroxidase system. To what extent peroxide generated from either chemical or enzymic sources participates in other deiodinating systems or in physiological deiodination remains to be shown.

The partial purification of the thyroxine dehalogenase from rabbit muscle has been achieved in two laboratories (147, 148). One of these preparations was stated not to be a peroxidase (147). In many respects these two preparations have similar properties. The unsupplemented enzymes are relatively inactive and activation can be achieved by the addition of flavin compounds. The enzyme systems are heat labile and are inactivated by $HgCl_2$. The same iodinated products are formed: iodide and origin material. Both preparations attack T_4 more readily than T_3 and have only a slight effect on iodotyrosines. However, certain differences have been demonstrated. In contrast to Lissitzky's preparation, Tata's enzyme does not require oxygen or light, is less stable on storage, and can be activated by Fe^{++} alone without flavins. In a subsequent study with one of these preparations, T_4-degrading activity as compared to that obtained in a simple buffer medium was difficult to demonstrate. No activity was observed in the dark, or in the light in the absence of flavin, and the results obtained in bright artificial light were identical in the two systems. However, a greater deiodination was observed in the presence of the enzyme during incubation in ambient light (142). These findings do not exclude the possibility that flavins participate in the deiodination mechanism. Perhaps the energy for the flavin-activated degradation of T_4 which, *in vitro*, is largely derived from light, is, in the intact animal, derived from metabolic sources.

In view of the foregoing observations, it is apparent that data obtained from studies of hormonal degradation *in vitro* are difficult to interpret and may lead to erroneous conclusions regarding enzymic metabolism; the observed deiodination may be a mixture of enzymic and direct chemical degradation. A greater knowledge of the nature of these processes is required before they can be satisfactorily dissociated.

A number of workers have described alterations in the peripheral metabolism of the thyroid hormones under certain conditions. Deiodination of T_4 is more rapid in slices of tissue from hyperthyroid than from hypothyroid rats [Larson et al. (149)], and similar observations have been made in vivo in man (150). Both the deiodinating activity and the oxygen consumption are increased in human white blood cells obtained from thyrotoxic patients and are decreased in those from myxedematous patients [Kurland et al. (151)]. Recently, it has been shown that the activity of "thyroxine-dehalogenase" is increased in hyperthyroid rats. The increased activity appears to be associated with the hypermetabolic state induced specifically by T_4 administration; a similar increase in activity was not achieved by treatment with dinitrophenol, or D-T_4 [Tata (152)], an isomer of T_4 which is a good substrate for the enzyme although it has little biological activity.

Many data indicate that certain thiouracils, when administered in vivo, alter the peripheral metabolism of T_4 and some of its derivatives, resulting generally in an increased fecal and a decreased urinary excretion of I^{131} (153 to 158). In thyroidectomized rats, propylthiouracil has been shown to increase the concentration of serum protein-bound iodine associated with the administration of standard doses of T_4 (155). These findings suggest that the thiouracils inhibit the metabolism of T_4. Evidence that thiouracils reduce deiodination in vitro has been presented (136, 149), but others were unable to demonstrate this effect (125, 128). However, recently it has been shown that both propylthiouracil administered in vivo and thiouracil in vitro inhibit the deiodination in vitro of T_4, TA_4, and to a lesser extent T_3; TA_3 is usually unaffected (159). The action of the thiouracils on the peripheral deiodination of T_4 is associated with a reduction in the metabolic effectiveness of the hormone (160, 161, 162), although thiouracil does not produce a similar change in the response to all T_4 analogues (162, 163).

The deiodination of T_4 and related compounds in vitro is inhibited by serotonin and other 5-hydroxylated derivatives of tryptophan (116). These compounds have also been found to interfere with an in vitro action of T_4 on the respiration of rat kidney slices (164). Deiodination of T_4 in vitro is also slowed in the presence of a number of T_4 analogues (123), including $3:3':5'$-T_3, a compound which antagonizes the metabolic effects of the thyroid hormones in vivo (165, 166, 167).

These data permit certain correlations to be drawn between hormonal activity and peripheral deiodination. In view of these observations, together with the finding that in certain amphibian species an apparent failure to respond metabolically to the thyroid hormones is associated with a decrease or loss of ability to deiodinate these agents [Galton & Ingbar (168, 169)], it has been suggested that certain metabolic actions of the hormones are closely linked to hormonal degradation (168). The evidence for and against this hypothesis has been discussed in detail elsewhere (168, 170).

During the period covered by this review, there has appeared a number of publications in which comprehensive consideration is given to diverse aspects of thyroid physiology (171, 172, 173). The following sources are also recommended for well-referenced reviews of areas of thyroid physiology not herein discussed: neuroregulation of thyroid activity (174), bioassay of TSH (175, 176), temporal aspects of thyroid function (177), thyroproteins and thyroid hormone-protein interactions (178, 179), effects of thyroid hormones on mitochondrial metabolism and general metabolic phenomena (180).

LITERATURE CITED

1. Lewitus, Z., Anbar, M., and Guttmann, S., *Advances in Thyroid Research*, 235–37 (Pergamon Press, London, 1961)
2. Anbar, M., Guttmann, S., and Lewitus, Z., *Nature*, **183**, 1517 (1959)
3. Anbar, M., Guttmann, S., and Lewitus, Z., *Endocrinology*, **66**, 888 (1960)
4. Halmi, N. S., *Vitamins and Hormones*, 133–63 (Academic Press, New York, 1961)
5. Wollman, S. H., *Am. J. Physiol.*, **186**, 453 (1956)
6. Lewitus, Z., *Endocrinology*, **70**, 295 (1962)
7. Wollman, S. H., *Ann. N.Y. Acad. Sci.*, **86**, 354 (1960)
8. Halmi, N. S., Granner, D. K., Doughman, D. J., Peters, B. H., and Müller, G., *Endocrinology*, **67**, 70 (1960)
9. Wollman, S. H., and Reed, F. E., *Am. J. Physiol.*, **196**, 113 (1959)
10. Halmi, N. S., Granner, D. K., Albert, H., and Doughman, J., *Endocrinology*, **65**, 101 (1959)
11. Wolff, J., *Biochim. Biophys. Acta*, **38**, 316 (1960)
12. Kanaya, R., *Endocrinol. Japon.*, **6**, 1 (1959)
13. Stanbury, J. B., and Chapman, E. M., *Lancet*, **I**, 1162 (1960)
14. Wolff, J., and Maurey, J. R., *Biochim. Biophys. Acta*, **47**, 467 (1961)
15. Brown-Grant, K., *Physiol. Rev.*, **41**, 189 (1961)
16. Halmi, N. S., and Pitt-Rivers, R., *Endocrinology*, **70**, 660 (1962)
17. Nagataki, S., Shizume, K., and Okinaka, S., *Endocrinology*, **69**, 199 (1961)
18. Rosenberg, I. N., Athans, J. C., Ahn, C. S., and Behar, A., *Endocrinology*, **69**, 438 (1961)
19. Taurog, A., Potter, G. D., and Chaikoff, I. L., *J. Biol. Chem.*, **213**, 119 (1955)
20. Serif, G. S., and Kirkwood, S., *J. Biol. Chem.*, **233**, 109 (1958)
21. Alexander, N. M., *J. Biol. Chem.*, **234**, 1530 (1959)
22. DeGroot, L. J., and Carvalho, E., *J. Biol. Chem.*, **235**, 1390 (1960)
23. Schussler, G. C., and Ingbar, S. H., *J. Clin. Invest.*, **40**, 1394 (1961)
24. Suzuki, M., Nagashima, M., and Yamamoto, K., *Gen. Comp. Endocrinol.*, **1**, 103 (1961)
25. Kondo, Y., *J. Biochem.*, **50**, 210 (1961)
26. Tong, W., and Chaikoff, I. L., *Biochim. Biophys. Acta*, **46**, 259 (1961)
27. Cunningham, B. A., and Kirkwood, S., *J. Biol. Chem.*, **236**, 485 (1961)
28. DeGroot, L. J., and Davis, A. M., *Endocrinology*, **70**, 492 (1962)
29. DeGroot, L. J., and Davis, A. M., *J. Biol. Chem.*, **236**, 2009 (1961)
30. DeGroot, L. J., and Berger, J. E., *Endocrinology*, **67**, 657 (1960)
31. Robbins, J., Wolff, J., and Rall, J. E., *Endocrinology*, **64**, 12 (1959)
32. Robbins, J., Wolff, J., and Rall, J. E., *Endocrinology*, **64**, 37 (1959)
33. DeGroot, L. J., and Davis, A. M., *Endocrinology*, **69**, 683 (1961)
34. Alexander, N. M., and Corcoran, B. J., *J. Biol. Chem.*, **237**, 243 (1962)
35. Galton, V. A., and Pitt-Rivers, R., *Endocrinology*, **64**, 835 (1959)
36. Iino, S., *Acta Endocrinol.*, **36**, 212 (1961)
37. Richards, J. B., and Ingbar, S. H., *Endocrinology*, **65**, 198 (1959)
38. Stanbury, J. B., Ohela, K., and Pitt-Rivers, R., *J. Clin. Endocrinol. Metab.*, **15**, 54 (1955)
39. Taurog, A., Tong, W., and Chaikoff, I. L., *Endocrinology*, **62**, 646 (1958)
40. Iino, S., Yamada, T., and Greer, M. A. *Endocrinology*, **68**, 582 (1961)
41. Ingbar, S. H., *J. Clin. Endocrinol. Metab.*, **21**, 128 (1961)
42. Haddad, H. M., and Rall, J. E., *Endocrinology*, **67**, 413 (1960)
43. McQuillan, M. T., Mathews, J. D., and Trikojus, V. M., *Nature*, **192**, 333 (1961)
44. Litonjua, A. D., *Nature*, **191**, 356 (1961)
45. Laughlin, R. E., McQuillan, M. T., and Trikojus, V. M., *Endocrinology*, **66**, 773 (1960)
46. Choufoer, J. C., Kassenaar, A. A. H., and Querido, A., *J. Clin. Endocrinol. Metab.*, **20**, 983 (1960)
47. Werner, S. C., Radichevich, I., Row, V. V., Mandl, R. H., and Block, R. J., *Advances in Thyroid Research*, 171–76 (Pergamon Press, London, 1961)
48. Dimitriadou, A., Fraser, T. R., Slater, J. D. H., and Turner, P. C. R., *Nature*, **187**, 691 (1960)

49. Beale, D., and Whitehead, J. K., *Clin. Chim. Acta*, **5**, 150 (1960)
50. Kono, T., van Middlesworth, L., and Astwood, E. B., *Endocrinology*, **66**, 845 (1960)
51. Dimitriadou, A., Manipol, V., and Fraser, T. R., *Biochem. J.*, **82**, 20P (1962)
52. Lissitzky, S., *Compt. Rend. Soc. Biol.*, **154**, 1567 (1960)
53. Triantaphyllidis, E., and Cukier, R., *Ann. Endocrinol. (Paris)*, **20**, 564 (1959)
54. Ermans, A. M., Bastenie, P. A., Galperin, H., and Beckers, C., *J. Clin. Endocrinol. Metab.*, **21**, 996 (1961)
55. Ingbar, S. H., Askonas, B. A., and Work, T. S., *Endocrinology*, **64**, 110 (1959)
56. Ui, N., Tarutani, O., Kondo, Y., and Tamura, H., *Nature*, **191**, 1199 (1961)
57. Mayberry, W. E., and Astwood, E. B., *J. Biol. Chem.*, **235**, 2977 (1960)
58. van Middlesworth, L., *Recent Progr. Hormone Res.*, **16**, 405 (1960)
59. Freinkel, N., *Biochem. J.*, **68**, 327 (1958)
60. Vilkki, P., *Advances in Thyroid Research*, 231–34 (Pergamon Press, London, 1961)
61. Kögl, F., and van Deenen, L. L. M., *Acta Endocrinol.*, **36**, 9 (1961)
62. Glock, G. E., and McLean, P., *Biochem. J.*, **56**, 171 (1954)
63. Field, J., Pastan, I., Herring, B., and Johnson, P., *Biochim. Biophys. Acta*, **50**, 513 (1961)
64. Dumont, J. E., *Biochim. Biophys. Acta*, **40**, 354 (1960)
65. Freinkel, N., *Endocrinology*, **66**, 851 (1960)
66. Dumont, J. E., *Biochim. Biophys. Acta*, **50**, 506 (1961)
67. Dumont, J. E., *J. Clin. Endocrinol. Metab.*, **20**, 1246 (1960)
68. Katz, J., and Wood, H. G., *J. Biol. Chem.*, **235**, 2165 (1960)
69. Brolin, S. E., and Thunberg, T., *Acta Physiol. Scand.*, **13**, 211 (1947)
70. Lindsay, S., and Jenks, P. R., *Advances in Thyroid Research*, 215–30 (Pergamon Press, London, (1961)
71. Bollet A. J., and Beierwaltes, W. H., *J. Clin. Endocrinol. Metab.*, **19**, 257 (1959)
72. Wollman, S. H., and Warren, L., *Biochim. Biophys. Acta*, **47**, 251 (1961)
73. Gregoire, J., Limozin, N., and Gregoire, J., *Biochim Biophys. Acta*, **47**, 27 (1961)
74. Lissitzky, S., Gregoire, J., Limozin, N., and Gregoire, J., *Biochim. Biophys. Acta*, **35**, 565 (1959)
75. Pastan, I., Herring, B., and Field, J. B., *J. Biol. Chem.*, **236**, PC 25 (1961)
76. Suzuki, M., and Nagashima, M., *Gunma J. Med. Sci.*, **10**, 168 (1961)
77. Field, J. B., Pastan, I., Johnson, P., and Herring, B., *J. Biol. Chem.*, **235**, 1863 (1960)
78. Dumont, J. E., *Biochim. Biophys. Acta*, **46**, 195 (1961)
79. Green, W. L., and Ingbar, S. H., *J. Clin. Invest.*, **40**, 1045 (1961)
80. Roche, J., Michel, R., and Gregorio, P., *Biochim. Biophys. Acta*, **47**, 398 (1961)
81. Klitgaard, H. M., Lipner, H. J., Barker, S. B., and Winnick, T., *Endocrinology*, **52**, 79 (1953)
82. Stanbury, J. B., *Ann. N.Y. Acad. Sci.*, **86**, 417 (1960)
83. Werner, S. C., Volpert, E. M., and Grinberg, R., *Nature*, **192**, 1193 (1961)
84. Roche, J., Michel, R., Jouan, P., and Wolf, W., *Endocrinology* **59**, 425 (1956)
85. Flock, E. V., Bollman, J. L., and Grindlay, J. H., *Endocrinology*, **67**, 419 (1960)
86. Flock, E. V., Bollman, J. L., Grindlay, J. H., and Stobie, G. H., *Endocrinology*, **69**, 626 (1961)
87. Taurog, A., *Brookhaven Symp. Biol.*, **VII** (1954)
88. Roche, J., Michel, R., and Tata, J., *Biochim. Biophys. Acta.*, **15**, 500 (1954)
89. Galton, V. A., and Pitt-Rivers, R., *Biochem. J.*, **72**, 314 (1959)
90. Michel, R., and Etling, N., *Compt. Rend. Soc. Biol.*, **151**, 36 (1957)
91. Culp, H. W., and Rice, C. N., *Endocrinology*, **67**, 563 (1960)
92. Green, W. L., and Ingbar, S. H., *J. Clin. Endocrinol. Metab.*, **21**, 1548 (1961)
93. Tapley, D. F., Herz, R., Ross, J. E., Denel, T. F., and Leventer, L., *Biochim. Biophys. Acta.*, **43**, 344 (1960)
94. Herz, R., Tapley, D. F., and Ross, J. E., *Biochim. Biophys. Acta*, **53**, 273 (1961)
95. Roche, J., Michel, R., Closon, J., and Michel, O., *Biochim. Biophys. Acta*, **33**, 461 (1959)

96. Roche, J., and Michel, R., *Ann. N.Y. Acad. Sci.*, **86**, 454 (1960)

97. Roche, J., Michel, R., Thieblemont, P., and Michel, O., *Bull. Soc. Chim. Biol.*, **43**, 1043 (1961)

98. Benard, H., Cruz, A., Michel, O., Michel, R., Roche, J., and Thieblemont, P., *Ann. Endocrinol (Paris)*, **22**, 429 (1961)

99. Roche, J., Michel, R., Closon, J., and Michel, O., *Biochim. Biophys. Acta*, **38**, 325 (1960)

100. Roche, J., Michel, R., and Closon, J., *Advances in Thyroid Research*, 497–504 (Pergamon Press, London, 1961)

101. Roche, J., Michel, R., and Tata, J., *Compt. Rend. Soc. Biol.*, **148**, 1545 (1954)

102. Roche, J., Michel, R., Jouan, P., and Wolf, W., *Endocrinology*, **59**, 425 (1956)

103. Roche, J., Michel, R., Nunez, J., and Jacquemin, C., *Endocrinology*, **65**, 402 (1959)

104. Galton, V. A., and Pitt-Rivers, R., *Biochem. J.*, **72**, 319 (1959)

105. Roche, J., Michel, R., Kanei, T., Drafha, D., and Cornie, A. Y., *Compt. Rend. Soc. Biol.*, **155**, 1454 (1961)

106. Roche, J., Michel, R., Varrone, S., and Michel, O., *Compt. Rend. Soc. Biol.*, **155**, 272 (1961)

107. Roche, J., Michel, R., Varrone, S., and Munoz de la Pena, A., *Compt. Rend. Soc. Biol.*, **155**, 231 (1961)

108. Nakano, M., Danowski, T. S., and Utsumi, A., *Endocrinology*, **65**, 242 (1959)

109. Litwak, G., *J. Biol. Chem.*, **228**, 823 (1957)

110. Labouesse, J., Chatagner, F., and Jollès-Bergeret, B., *Biochim. Biophys. Acta*, **39**, 372 (1960)

111. Lissitzky, S., Roques, M., and Benevent, M.-T., *Biochim. Biophys. Acta*, **41**, 252 (1960)

112. Tata, J. R., *Clin. Chim. Acta*, **4**, 427 (1959)

113. Van Zyl, A., *Clin. Chim. Acta.*, **7**, 20 (1962)

114. Tata, J. R., *Biochem. J.*, **72**, 214 (1959)

115. Tata, J. R., *Biochem. J.*, **72**, 222 (1959)

116. Galton, V. A., and Ingbar, S. H., *Endocrinology*, **68**, 435 (1961)

117. Etling, N., and Barker, S. B., *Endocrinology*, **64**, 753 (1959)

118. Tomita, K., Lardy, H. A., Larson, F. C., and Albright, E. C., *J. Biol. Chem.*, **224**, 387 (1957)

119. Albright, E. C., Tomita, K., and Larson, F. C., *Endocrinology*, **64**, 208 (1959)

120. Tomita, K., and Lardy, H. A., *J. Biol. Chem.*, **235**, 3292 (1960)

121. Yamamoto, K., Shimizu, S., and Ishikawa, I., *Japan. J. Physiol.*, **10**, 594 (1960)

122. Nakano, M., and Danowski, T. S., *Endocrinology*, **70**, 340 (1962)

123. Larson, F. C., and Albright, E. C., *J. Clin. Invest.*, **40**, 1132 (1961)

124. Larson, F. C., Tomita, K., and Albright, E. C., *Endocrinology*, **65**, 336 (1959)

125. Maclagan, N. F., and Reid, D., *Ciba Found. Colloq. Endocrinol.*, **10**, 190 (1957)

126. Stanbury, J. B., Morris, M. L., Corrigan, H. J., and Lassiter, W. E., *Endocrinology*, **67**, 353 (1960)

127. Tata, J. R., *Biochim. Biophys. Acta*, **28**, 95 (1958)

128. Yamazaki, E., and Slingerland, D. W., *Endocrinology*, **64**, 126 (1959)

129. Yamamoto, K., Shimizu, S., and Ishikawa, I., *Japan. J. Physiol.*, **10**, 610 (1960)

130. Tata, J. R., *Biochim. Biophys. Acta*, **35**, 567 (1959)

131. Ford, D. H., Corey, K. R., and Gross, J., *Endocrinology*, **61**, 426 (1957)

132. Tata, J. R., *Nature*, **187**, 1025 (1960)

133. Lissitzky, S., Benevent, M.-T., and Roques, M., *Bull. Soc. Chim. Biol.*, **43**, 743 (1961)

134. Galton, V. A., and Ingbar, S. H., *Endocrinology*, **69**, 30 (1961)

135. Albright, E. C., Larson, F. C., and Tust, R. H., *Proc. Soc. Exptl. Biol. Med.*, **86**, 137 (1954)

136. Cruchaud, S., Vanotti, A., Mahaim, C., and Deckelman, J., *Lancet*, **II**, 906 (1955)

137. Plaskett, L. G., *Biochem. J.*, **78**, 652 (1961)

138. Lissitzky, S., Benevent, M.-T., Nunez, J., Jacquemin, C., and Roche, J. *Compt. Rend. Soc. Biol.*, **154**, 267 (1960)

139. Lissitzky, S., Benevent, M.-T., Roques, M., and Roche, J., *Bull. Soc. Chim. Biol.*, **41**, 1329 (1959)

140. Nunez, J., and Jacquemin, C., *Compt. Rend. Acad. Sci.*, **252**, 802 (1961)

141. Etling, N., and Barker, S. B., *Endocrinology*, **65**, 95 (1959)

142. Galton, V. A., and Ingbar, S. H., *Endocrinology*, **70**, 210 (1962)

143. Lissitzky, S., and Bouchilloux, S., *Ciba Found. Colloq. Endocrinol.*, **10**, 135 (1957)
144. Lissitzky, S., Benevent, M.-T., and Roques, M., *Biochim. Biophys. Acta*, **51**, 407 (1961)
145. Mayrargue-Kodja, A., Bouchilloux, S., and Lissitzky, S., *Bull. Soc. Chim. Biol.*, **40**, 815 (1958)
146. Galton, V. A., and Ingbar, S. H., *Proc. Meeting Endocrine Soc.*, p. 26 (1962)
147. Tata, J. R. *Biochem. J.*, **77**, 214 (1960)
148. Lissitzky, S., Roques, M., and Benevent, M.-T., *Bull. Soc. Chim. Biol.*, **43**, 727 (1961)
149. Larson, F. C., Tomita, K., and Albright, E. C., *Endocrinology*, **57**, 338 (1955)
150. Ingbar, S. H., and Freinkel, N., *J. Clin. Invest.*, **34**, 914 (1955)
151. Kurland, G. S., Krotkov, M. V., and Freedberg, A. S., *J. Clin. Endocrinol. Metab.*, **20**, 35 (1960)
152. Tata, J. R., *Acta Endocrinol.*, **37**, 125 (1961)
153. Hogness, J. R., Wong, T., and Williams, R. H., *Metabolism*, **3**, 510 (1954)
154. Van Arsdel, P. P., and Williams, R. H., *Am. J. Physiol.*, **186**, 440 (1956)
155. Jones, S. L., and van Middlesworth, L., *Endocrinology*, **67**, 855 (1960)
156. Jagiello, G. M., and McKenzie, J. M., *Endocrinology*, **67**, 451 (1960)
157. Escobar del Rey, F., and Morreale de Escobar, G., *Endocrinology*, **69**, 456 (1961)
158. van Middlesworth, L., and Jones, S. L., *Endocrinology*, **69**, 1085 (1961)
159. Braverman, L. E., and Ingbar, S. H., *Program, Am. Goiter Assoc., Inc.*, p. 5 (1961)
160. Andik, I., Balogh, L., and Donhoffer, Sz., *Experientia*, **5**, 249 (1949)
161. Barker, S. B., Kiely, C. E., and Lipner, H. J., *Endocrinology*, **45**, 624 (1949)
162. Stasilli, N. R., Kroc, R. L., and Edlin, R., *Endocrinology*, **66**, 872 (1960)
163. Stasilli, N. R., Kroc, R. L., and Nemith, P. J., *Program, Am. Goiter Assoc., Inc.*, p. 4 (1961)
164. Lindsay, R. H., and Barker, S. B., *Endocrinology*, **65**, 679 (1959)
165. Pittman, C. S., and Barker, S. B., *Am. J. Physiol.*, **197**, 1271 (1959)
166. Pittman, J. A., Tingley, J. O., Nickerson, J. F., and Hill, S. R., *Metabolism*, **9**, 293 (1960)
167. Benua, R. S., Kumaoka, S., Leeper, R. D., and Rawson, R. W., *J. Clin. Endocrinol. Metab.*, **19**, 1344 (1959)
168. Galton, V. A., and Ingbar, S. H., *Endocrinology*, **70**, 622 (1962)
169. Galton, V. A., and Ingbar, S. H., *Program, Endocrine Soc. Meeting*, p. 28 (1961)
170. Barker, S. B., *Federation Proc.*, **21**, 635 (1962)
171. *Ann. N.Y. Acad. Sci.*, **86**, Art. 2 (1960)
172. *Brit. Med. Bull.*, **16**, No. 2 (1960)
173. Pitt-Rivers, R., and Tata, J. R., *The Thyroid Hormones* (Pergamon Press, London, 1959)
174. Bogdanove, E. M., *Federation Proc.*, **21**, 623 (1962)
175. McKenzie, J. M., *Physiol. Rev.*, **40**, 398 (1960)
176. Brown, J. R., *Acta Endocrinol.*, **32**, 289 (1959)
177. Soderberg, U., *Physiol. Rev.*, **39**, 777 (1959)
178. Ingbar, S. H., and Freinkel, N., *Recent Progr. Hormone Res.*, **16**, 353 (1960)
179. Robbins, J., and Rall, J. E., *Physiol. Rev.*, **40**, 415 (1960)
180. Hoch, F. L., *New Engl. J. Med.*, **266**, 446 (1962)

THE NEUROHYPOPHYSIS[1,2,3]

By C. R. Kleeman and R. E. Cutler[4]

Departments of Medicine, Mount Sinai Hospital, Wadsworth General Hospital, and the University of California Medical Center, Los Angeles, California

This review, covering the period from 1957 through the first quarter of 1962, encompasses the anatomy of the neurohypophysis; the active polypeptides produced, stored, and released from this area; the peripheral metabolism and end organ effects of these peptides; and, finally, pathological aspects of neurohypophyseal structure and function or clinical correlations. A definition of the neurohypophysis and a brief discussion of the present concept of neurosecretion and neurohumors initiate the review.

The neurohypophysis arises totally from neural tissue. In mammals it consists of: (*a*) a group of hypothalamic specialized nuclei, the best delineated being the supraoptic and paraventricular nuclei [while nuclei such as the lateral tuberal in primates and the nucleus arcuatus in rodents cannot be excluded (1), only the supraoptic and paraventricular nuclei are clearly capable of forming the active polypeptides to be discussed in this review (1 to 4)]; (*b*) the median eminence; (*c*) the neurohypophyseal tract [synonyms for which include the hypothalamohypophyseal, the supraopticohypophyseal tract, and the pituitary stalk], this tract containing the axons from the supraoptic and paraventricular nuclei and possibly those from tuberal nuclei (1, 2); and (*d*) the pars nervosa [synonyms—neural lobe, posterior lobe of the pituitary], in which the neurohypophyseal tract ends. In cyclostomes, elasmobranchs, and teleosts, there is no neural lobe as such. However, there is a neurohypophysis in the area of the floor of the diencephalon which functions as a neurosecretory structure delivering its secretion into the adenohypophyseal circulation (2). It is analogous to the median eminence of higher vertebrates. The neural lobe begins in lung fish and is present in Amphibia, reptiles, birds, and mammals (2, 5). The development of the neural lobe appears phyletically coincident with the acquisition of a semiterrestrial habitat (2, 5).

Welsh (6) has defined the chemical agents produced by neurons, which act on other neurons or other structures, as "neurohumors". They are short range, brief acting, and chemically identified as acetylcholine, epinephrine, norepinephrine, and 5-hydroxytryptamine (serotonin). The neurosecretory substances derived from the neurohypophysis serve as long range, long acting, co-ordinating agents. They are released into the circulation from storage

[1] The survey of literature pertaining to this review was concluded in March 1962.

[2] Among the abbreviations used in this review are: ACTH (adrenocorticotropic hormone) and ADH (antidiuretic hormone).

[3] Supported by United States Public Health Service Grant No. A-2972 "Experimental Adrenal Insufficiency".

[4] Present address: United States Naval Hospital, Oakland, California.

centers and are more stable after release than are the neurohumors. Neuro-secretory substances include oxytocin, vasopressin, and the other active polypeptides of the neurohypophysis. Ordinary neurons and neurosecretory cells have much in common. Clearly, the latter are derived from the former, hence the sharing of properties both structural and functional is to be expected. Neurosecretory cells have the following characteristics (7). (a) They elaborate secretory materials which can be demonstrated by histological techniques. (b) They can receive stimuli from other neurons. However, their own axons do not synapse with muscles, exocrine glands or, most important, with other neurons; usually they end at blood vessels. (c) They release physiologically active substances which affect organs lying at various distances from the central nervous system, and thus play an important role in the process of neuroendocrine integration.

The microscopic anatomy of the neurohypophysis.—During the past decade a number of studies and review articles on the microscopic anatomy of the neurohypophysis have appeared (1, 2, 4, 6 to 18). These studies have conclusively shown that the neural lobe is richly endowed with nerve endings of unmyelinated nerve fibers primarily derived from the supraoptic and paraventricular nuclei. The nerve cell bodies in these nuclei appear to be somewhat larger than those throughout most of the rest of the hypothalamus.

Their blood supply is considerably more extensive than that in other hypothalamic regions.

Neurosecretory granules identified in these neurons by standardized staining techniques appear in varying degrees of abundance in the perinuclear areas. From here the granules disperse distally in the direction of the axon and can be found along the entire axon, ultimately accumulating around the terminal nerve endings of the neural lobe. Most investigators have concluded that the neurosecretory granules are intra-axonal and that they are not derived from mitochondria throughout the axon or in the posterior lobe of the pituitary or, at least, that the neurosecretory granules can be readily distinguished from mitochondrial structures in electron-microscopic preparations. No data have appeared in the past decade to challenge seriously the concept that the neurosecretory granules are formed in the cells of the hypothalamic nuclei and are transported by axoplasmic "streaming" to the neural lobe.

Opinions differ as to whether the neurosecretory material in the median eminence is formed there or derived from a site above the median eminence (10). As previously mentioned, the tetrapod neurohypophysis differs from that of the fish in the development of the neural lobe or posterior pituitary gland. The median eminence is actually the rostral portion of the neurophypophysis and this retains in mammals an intimate relationship to the vascular supply of the anterior pituitary (19). Most, if not all, of the blood reaching the anterior pituitary passes first through the capillaries of this portion of the neurohypophysis by portal vessels.

Gregoretti (20) described the topography of the accessory supraoptic nuclei of 26 human hypothalami. The presence of these nuclei is apparent from the fifth month of intrauterine life; in all the hypothalami the nucleus was never absent. The paired supraoptic and paraventricular nuclei together contain about 100,000 neurons in the dog. Nuclei other than these two are of minor and ill-established significance. The supraoptic nuclei are the larger and more important. The volume of the supraoptic nuclei is surprisingly large, ranging from 5.75 to 6.80 mm^3 in three dogs weighing 12 to 20 kilos. In the same dogs the corresponding range of volume of the posterior lobe was 6 to 13 mm^3 (21).

Little has been added in the past decade to Green's original observations on the blood supply and interrelationships of the neurohypophysis and anterior lobe in a large number of species, starting with the most primitive vertebrates (9). In Amphibia, reptiles, and birds, it is easier to establish homologies with mammalian pituitaries. If the term "median eminence", as defined previously, is used, it has an exact topographical significance for all the vertebrates studied, since the primary capillary net of the portal system does not anastomose significantly with the vessels of the neural lobe or the hypothalamus. It appears that the portal vessels form the only possible functional link between the nervous system and the anterior pituitary.

It is apparent that the circulation to and from the posterior lobe of the pituitary is not connected with that of the anterior pituitary or the portal circulation and that blood draining the posterior lobe enters the systemic circulation. In none of the animals studied has an innervation of the pars distalis been found. This suggests that there are very few, if any, nerve fibers in the pars distalis or anterior pituitary. Various kinds of terminations in the neural lobe have been described; the most commonly found are the fine arborizations of the axons, derived from the supraoptic and paraventricular nuclei, which end around the capillaries.

Gregoretti (22), studying the circulation of the hypothalamus of normal adults, stained the capillary network with benzidine. He noted the unusual density of the very rich vascular plexus to the paraventricular and supraoptic nuclei, which is probably related to the large size of these cellular bodies and to their particular intense metabolism. In contrast, the vascular network of other hypothalamic nuclei is very much poorer.

Very little information has been gathered in recent years on the permeability characteristics of the blood vessels of the neurohypophysis. It has frequently been stated that a "blood brain barrier" does not exist in the posterior pituitary gland and that the permeability of the vascular bed in this part of the neurohypophysis is comparable to that in the rest of the body (17, 23). However, the permeability of the capillary bed surrounding the hypothalamic nuclei of the neurohypophysis now appears to have the same transport barrier which exists elsewhere in the central nervous system (23). These studies suggest that the neurosecretory material travels from very well vascularized areas in the hypothalamus which are within the normal blood brain barrier to reach equally well vascularized areas of the neurohypophysis which may be outside the blood brain barrier.

It is of great interest that urea, which enters the brain and spinal cord at about one tenth the rate at which it enters muscle (24), is not believed to be a stimulus to the release of antidiuretic hormone (194) yet it causes marked dehydration of the brain and cord (24). This suggests either that the permeability of the hypothalamic "osmoreceptors" to urea differs from that of central nervous system tissue in general, or that dehydration of these hypothalamic areas does not stimulate release of ADH.

The electron-microscopic studies do not disclose any unique characteristics of the capillaries of the neurohypophysis, other than their relative abundance (8, 12, 17, 23). The one exception is Gershenfeld's observation (12) of a lack of glial expansion around the capillaries of the neural lobe in contrast to that seen regularly in other parts of the central nervous system. This study (12) further indicates that the nerve endings terminate in extremely close apposition to the capillary beds in the posterior lobe.

The pituicyte.—The earlier concept that the pituicyte in the neural lobe was the site of origin of the active polypeptides has now been unanimously rejected by all workers in the field. However, the exact function of the pituicyte has not been conclusively determined. Leveque (11) and Noble (4) both believe the pituicytes to be modified astrocytic supporting elements. The large number of glial cells or astrocytes in the posterior pituitary, in the absence of a so-called "blood brain barrier", suggests that the glial elements here are not the site of any barrier to penetration of substances into the neural tissue. Stimulation of the neurohypophysis causes a progressive increase in mitotic activity of the pituicytes without comparable changes in other areas of the brain (11). Leveque proposes that the pituicytes may in some way assist in the release of the active peptides from the bulbus endings of the axon terminals.

Electron-microscopic studies.—The electron-microscopic studies delineate precisely the site of the neurosecretory granules in the neuron, in the axons, and within the posterior pituitary gland (2, 8, 12). The neurosecretory material which, with Gomori's stain, appears as dark-staining granules, is actually composed of dense vesicles with a surrounding plasma or enveloping membrane. In amphibians these vary in size from 620 to 1500 A and progressively enlarge as they extend from the hypothalamic nuclei down to the posterior pituitary gland (12). In the posterior pituitary gland, in addition to the secretory granules, the characteristic synaptic vesicles can be seen. These do not differ significantly from those observed at the terminal axon endings of many neurons. In addition, throughout the axon are bizarrely shaped mitochondria that bear no histologic relationship to the neurosecretory material. Gershenfeld and co-workers (12) feel that during the axoplasmic flow of this material toward the neural lobe it progressively increased in size, reaching chemical maturation near the endings within the posterior lobe. The electron-microscopic studies do not clarify the exact site of formation within the neuron of the neurosecretory material.

The median eminence.—The functional anatomy and histology of the median eminence are reviewed in great detail by Rinne (10). The neurosecretory nerve fibers entering the median eminence are either collaterals of the axons of the neurohypophyseal tract, or independent axons terminating in the region of the median eminence. It is not certain from the histological picture alone which alternative is correct. Nerve fibers which contain neurosecretory material at their perivascular endings, and are derived from the hypothalamohypophyseal tract, pass in the median eminence toward the capillaries of the hypophyseal portal vessels (9, 25, 26). Histologic preparations do not clarify the exact origin of these nerve fibers (27). It is still to be decided whether they derive from the supraoptic and paraventricular nuclei, or from the posterior hypothalamus as Fisher *et al.* (28) have found in mammals, and Wingstrand (29) in birds. Rinne (10) suggests that the only important nervous connections from other areas of the brain to the median eminence are those derived from the neurohypophyseal tract. However, destructive lesions of the supraoptic and paraventricular nuclei generally do not lead to impaired function of the adenohypophysis. This would seem to indicate that the nerve fibers running to the median eminence originate not from the supraoptic and paraventricular nuclei, but probably from other areas in the hypothalamus.

CHARACTERISTICS OF THE NEUROSECRETORY MATERIAL

Rinne (10) described in detail the chrome-alum-hematoxylin and aldehyde-fuchsin staining characteristics of the neurosecretory material and their relationship to the protein-bound S–H and S–S groups of the molecule. Barnett (30) confirmed that the disulfide-positive material found throughout the neurohypophysis of the rat and dog in colloidlike structures was the same as neurosecretory material stained selectively with chrome-alum-hematoxylin (Gomori's stain). The neurosecretory, or disulfide-positive material, is confined to the neural structures of the neurohypophysis. There is no conclusive evidence that the glial structures of any part of the neurohypophysis contain this material. However, we cannot categorically exclude the presence of some of it in the pituicytes of the posterior lobe (30, 31).

Bargmann (8, 17) presents an excellent chronologic summary of the histologic observations on the relationship between neurohypophyseal structure and function. Palay (16), in studies of men and monkey, noted neurosecretory material in the neurons and axons of the supraoptic and paraventricular nuclei. The size of the granules varies considerably from species to species; in man and monkey 0.25 to 0.55 μ in diameter, with man at the lower limit of this range; in the rat 0.5 to 0.15 μ (32, 33); in the cat, opossum, and pigeon 0.1 to 0.17 μ (14); in amphibians, 0.6 to 0.15 μ (12). Gershenfeld (12) suggested that the secretory granules progressively increase in size during axoplasmic flow, and that the largest granules noted in the neural lobe of the amphibians were equal to the small- or smallest-size granules optically visible by the light microscopic and staining procedure. Therefore, the granules of neurosecretory material vary in size from one species to another and from their sites of origin to their final storage in the neural lobe. Green (2, 14) suggests that it is equally possible that the neurosecretory material can be produced at all viable parts of the neuron rather than transported by axoplasmic streaming, hence its accumulation above a cut end of the hypophyseal stalk. He also suggests that the discrepancy between the assayable hormone and the apparent mass of the neurosecretion would disappear if the hormone is produced locally by mitochondria, which would then show a staining reaction or increased electron density when they contain the hormone. The failure to see an association between the granules and the mitochondria (12) does not unequivocally exclude the mitochondria as the source of the neurosecretory material. However, most investigators agree that the granules of this material arise within the cell bodies of the hypothalamic nuclei and reach the posterior lobe of the neurohypophysis by the process of axoplasmic streaming. It is not known whether gravity or activity of the neuron, mechanical or electrical, contributes to axoplasmic streaming of the granules (2, 4, 7, 8, 10, 11, 12, 14, 15, 17, 19, 23, 30, 31, 34 to 43). According to these authors the Herring bodies represent localized accumulations of the neurosecretory material. Within the neural lobe proper, this occurs within the smallest nonmyelinated neurofibrils which, in turn, are in intimate association with the capillaries of the posterior lobe. Distal movement of the granules within the living pituitary stalk has been observed *in vitro* by Hild (36) and by Carlyle (44).

Within the posterior lobe, in addition to the pituicytes and the Herring bodies, the neurofibrils with their coated particles of neurosecretory material, ranging from 600 to 3000 A in diameter, there can also be found vesicles of 300 to 400 A which appear to be analogous to the synaptic vesicles seen in all other axon terminals. Neurosecretory material and the synaptic vesicles are two essentially different components (2, 12, 32, 45). The synaptic vesicles are confined to the nerve endings and probably contain a chemical mediator which is released under the influence of the nerve impulse. These vesicles may in some way elicit the actual release of the neurosecretory material from the nerve endings in a manner analogous to the release of acetylcholine from the synaptic vesicles in the nerve endings of the adrenal medulla which in turn stimulate the release of catecholamines (12).

The physiological regulation of neurosecretory material release has been actively studied (2, 4, 8, 10, 12, 14, 17, 31, 34, 35, 42, 43). Dehydration or hypertonic saline administration in amphibians, rats, and dogs causes varying degrees of depletion of neurosecretory material from the neural lobe. The axons, the stalk, and the supraoptic and paraventricular nuclei under these circumstances may show either no alterations or varying degrees of depletion of this material. Howe & Jewell (34) found a distinct difference in depletion of neurosecretory material in the chronically dehydrated desert rat as compared with the laboratory rat: in ten days of dehydration no secretory material was present in the posterior lobe of the laboratory rat, whereas there was no such change in the desert rat. The supraoptic nuclei of both groups showed no significant change. This difference is obviously one of environmental adaptation and it is of interest that the posterior lobe of the desert rat is approximately twice as large as that of the laboratory rat. These findings indicate that the rate of synthesis and transport of the hormone in the desert rat is significantly greater than in the laboratory rat.

Ten days of chronic water loading in the dog cause the accumulation of neurosecretory material in the posterior lobe and descending tracts, while the cell bodies of the supraoptic and paraventricular nuclei are simultaneously depleted of such material (39). It appears that chronic water loading inhibits both synthesis and release of this substance. The fact that the neural lobe of the normal and the chronically hydrated dog contained similar amounts of neurosecretory material suggests that the neural lobe is always fully loaded with such stored material and that forced hydration does not lead to further storage. Dehydration in the dog and rat leads to depletion of the neural lobe, and if the pituitary stalk or descending tracts are then severed and the animals rehydrated, the proximal stumps on the hypothalamic side show progressive accumulation of neurosecretory material, whereas the peripheral fibers and the posterior lobe remain depleted (8, 12 17, 34, 35, 42). Adrenalectomized animals, not maintained on replacement steroid, show depletion of neurosecretory material as do those anesthetized with ether (14, 17, 43), but not with chloroform, pentobarbital, or chloralose (43).

Suckling is an important stimulus for the release of neurosecretory material from the neural lobe (46). This material appears in the neural lobe of the newborn rat between the first and second week after birth, at which the stalk and hypothalamic nuclei appear empty (8, 14, 17). Young rats (3 to 6 months) and old rats (12 to 24 months) show no difference in neurosecretory substance in the hypothalamic nuclei or neural lobe (40, 47). However, senile rats of 24 months show definite depletion. Therefore, the lesser concentration of the urine in the young, as compared with the old, rat cannot be explained by a difference in the neurohypophyseal hormonal content.

Gomori-positive material is found in degenerating tissue cultures of neural lobe even when the cultures are grown from transplants apparently free of this substance (14). However, degenerating tissue cultures of neural lobe may form a stainable material which is not related to actual active polypeptide or carrier substance. The neurosecretory material in the median eminence responds to dehydration, overhydration, and lactation in a manner similar to that in the neural lobe (10).

Sloper (38) studied the neurohypophysis in four patients with malignant disease at varying periods following total hypophysectomy. In three to ten days there was distinct accumulation of the secretory material above the cut end of the stalk and in the supraoptic and paraventricular nuclei. At 100 to 240 days the hypothalamic nuclei contained significant quantities, but the stalk itself contained very little. There was no overt diabetes insipidus in any of these patients despite adequate adrenal and thyroid replacement therapy. Sloper suggested that at least 85 per cent of the neurons of the supraoptic and probably of the paraventricular nuclei had to be destroyed before a patient or animal developed diabetes insipidus.

The amount of neurosecretory material in any portion of the neurohypophysis represents the balance between input and output. Therefore a histologic change in the material cannot be interpreted confidently without additional physiologic or kinetic data. It is unknown whether its presence within the axon, neural lobe, or median eminence can, by some feedback mechanism, decrease the rate of synthesis within the hypothalamic nuclear structures.

Chemical nature of neurosecretory material.—As pointed out by Sawyer (42): "Neurosecretion and the NSM in the hypothalamus and neurohypophysis is associated with active neurohypophyseal principles." Appropriate physiological stimuli, as mentioned above, deplete concurrently stainable neurosecretion and assayable neurohypophyseal activities. The active polypeptides that can be extracted from the neurohypophysis are probably not usually stained *in situ* by Gomori's method, although they may take the stain under certain conditions. It is more likely that the stain colors the protein to which the peptides are bound, the 'carrier substance'. The stainable component can be dissociated from the active polypeptides by treatment of tissue sections with appropriate solvents. That only the carrier protein is stained is consistent with the presence of similarly staining neurosecretory material in many invertebrates in which neurohypophyseal peptides are believed not to occur. The stain probably colors a carrier molecule associated with neurosecretory hormones that regulate many metabolic processes in invertebrates.

The interrelationship between extractable and assayable physiologic activity in various portions of the neurohypophysis, and the simultaneous parallel content of neurosecretory substance, suggest that the two are closely related. Acher (48) has extensively investigated and reviewed the chemical nature of this substance.

Modern techniques of fractionation, zonal electrophoresis, chromatography, and both column and starch gel, as well as paper electrophoresis, have considerably facilitated the isolation of active material from the neurohypophysis. Van Dyke *et al.* (49) isolated from the posterior pituitary gland of the ox a protein which had both antidiuretic and oxytocic activities. Its molecular weight was estimated to be about 30,000. This experiment suggested that in the posterior lobe of the ox both hormones were stored in association with the homogenous protein; similar conclusions were reached by Acher (50), who called the protein "neurophycine". The complex consisted of one molecule of vasopressin and one molecule of oxytocin per molecule of protein, both antidiuretic and oxytocin hormones being attached to the inert protein either by simple adsorption, or as a result of electrostatic force.

Acher showed that the neurophycine is probably the same substance as that which constitutes the Gomori granules. Little is known about the bonds by which the hormones are attached to the protein carrier. Some observations, however, suggest that the bond which fixes oxytocin is more labile than that which fixes vasopressin (51). In the posterior lobe of adults both hormones are stored in equal amounts. The presently accepted molecular weight for the inert protein is approximately 30,000. Chauvet (52) obtained from the sheep posterior pituitary gland a complex which contained 90 per cent of the oxytocic and vasopressin activity of the gland. The complex consisted of neurophycin, oxytocin, and vasopressin; it could be dissociated by trichloracetic acid and its three components, the protein and the two hormones, purified by chromatography. The reconstitution of the complex from the elements is realized under specified conditions. Analogous complexes were obtained from glands of cow, horse, and pig. It is possible to bring about associations between the hormones and the inert protein of different species (52).

VanDyke's original observation that neurosecretory material contained vasopressor and oxytocic activities in a one-to-one ratio reflected the source of his material (21). He worked with beef posterior pituitary lobes, and such equality of vasopressor and oxytocic activities is by no means always found in extracts of the hypothalamus or neurohypophysis (18, 42). The neurosecretory material in the median eminence may well be the same basic inert protein.

ACTIVE NEUROHYPOPHYSEAL PEPTIDES

During the period covered by this review a number of important papers and reviews have appeared which cover in extensive detail the extraction techniques, chemistry, and synthesis of the naturally occurring active neurohypophyseal peptides (3, 18, 48, 51 to 65), on the synthesis and activity of various analogues of the natural peptides (with emphasis on the relationship of activity to various structural modifications in the molecule), and on the extraction and identification of active principles from various vertebrates, mammalian and nonmammalian (42, 48, 63 to 75).

DuVigneaud et al. (76) and Tuppy (77) have simultaneously proposed the structure for oxytocin, which was at the same time proved by synthesis by the first author in 1953. Shortly afterwards the structures of hog vasopressin and beef vasopressin were established by duVigneaud et al. in 1953. In 1958 Katsoyannis and duVigneaud synthesized arginine-vasotocin in the expectation that its pharmacological properties would supply valuable information on the relationships between the molecular structure of the natural peptides and their biological activities (75). Comparison of its activities with those of neurohypophyseal extracts led to the conclusion that this analogue is a neurohypophyseal principle occurring naturally in most nonmammalian vertebrates. Its pharmacological properties suggest that it is identical with Heller's "amphibian water principle" and with the "natriferin" of Maetz (70).

Katsoyannis and duVigneaud had therefore synthesized a polypeptide hormone before its existence in nature had been recognized. Its chemical structure is shown in Figure 1.

Oxytocin, natural and synthetic.—Until now only one oxytocin has been found. The identical molecule, an octapeptide with amino acid sequence shown in the figure below, has been found in the posterior pituitary gland of all species so far investigated. Natural oxytocin from beef, highly purified by means of countercurrent distribution, has been found identical with the highly purified synthetic oxytocin by means of physical, chemical, and biological methods. This work was carried out by duVigneaud and collaborators.

Oxytocin

$$\underset{1\quad 2\quad 3\quad 4\quad 5\quad 6\ 7\ 8\ 9}{\overline{CyS} \cdot Tyr \cdot Ileu \cdot Glu(NH_2) \cdot Asp(NH_2) \cdot \overline{CyS} \cdot Pro \cdot Leu \cdot Gly(NH_2)}$$

Arginine vasopressin

$$CyS \cdot Tyr \cdot Phe \cdot Glu(NH_2) \cdot Asp(NH_2) \cdot CyS \cdot Pro \cdot Arg \cdot Gly(NH_2)$$

Lysine vasopressin

$$CyS \cdot Tyr \cdot Phe \cdot Glu(NH_2) \cdot Asp(NH_2)CyS \cdot Pro \cdot Lys \cdot Gly(NH_2)$$

Arginine vasotocin

$$CyS \cdot Tyr \cdot Ileu \cdot Glu(NH_2) \cdot Asp(NH_2) \cdot CyS \cdot ProArg \cdot Gly(NH_2)$$

FIG. 1. Amino acid sequence in the molecules of neurohypophyseal polypeptides.
[From Sawyer (42).]

Vasopressin.—In contrast to oxytocin, there are two vasopressins. One arginine-vasopressin has an arginyl group in position 8, and one lysine-vasopressin has a lysyl group in position 8. Arginine-vasopressin has been found in the posterior pituitary gland of cattle, beef, man, horse, camel, cat, dog, monkey, rabbit, rat, and sheep. Only the hog and hippopotamus neurohypophysis contain lysine-vasopressin (42).

Comparative endocrinology and evolution of the active neurohypophyseal peptides.—Sawyer (42) extensively reviews the papers on comparative endocrinology and evolution of the neurohypophyseal peptides, the majority by Sawyer, Munsick, and van Dyke in America, and Heller and his associates in Europe.

The relationship between structure of peptides and their pharmacological activities.—Little can be added to Sawyer's (42) extensive, meticulous, elaborate, and specific presentation of the relationship of structure to function of the various neurohypophyseal peptides and their analogues.

Formation and release.—It is apparent that the formation, distribution, and release of neurosecretory material are representative of comparable changes in the active neurohypophyseal hormones. Available evidence indicates that the active polypeptides of the neurohypophysis are formed within the nerve cell bodies of the supraoptic and paraventricular nuclei (2, 5, 7, 8, 12, 18, 21, 23, 42, 78, 79, 80), but apparently not within those of the tuberal nuclei or the median eminence.

No studies of the nature and rate of formation of active polypeptides from the hypothalamic nuclei of the neurohypophysis have been carried out *in vitro*. However, attempts have been made to determine the rate of incorporation of S^{35}-labeled cystine and methionine into the various areas of the neurohypophysis. The rate of uptake of total radioactivity, the specific activity of labeled material in the vasopressin of the hypothalamus and posterior pituitary, and the assessment of the relative radioactivity of different parts of the posterior pituitary and hypothalamus have been measured (38, 81, 82). The subarachnoid injection of S^{35}-labeled amino acid is followed by the rapid uptake and localization of radioisotope in the cell bodies of neurons in the nuclear regions and, in particular, the supraoptic and paraventricular nuclei. The uptake of the amino acid by the hypothalamus was greater when injected into the subarachnoid space than when injected intravenously. This suggests that the blood brain barrier impaired the transport of the amino acid to those neurons which were actively synthesizing the polypeptides, whereas this blood brain barrier was "bypassed" in injection into the subarachnoid space. Sachs, following continuous intravenous infusions of S^{35}-labeled cystine for 16, 24, and 36 hours, isolated S^{35}-labeled vasopressin in relatively pure form from the neurohypophysis (82). The mean ratios of the specific activity of hypothalamic to pituitary vasopressin were approximately 2.9, 2.0, and 3.1 respectively. The data are consistent with a more rapid and extensive rate of production of the active polypeptides in the hypothalamic area, but are not consistent with a simple two-compartment system (82). Unfortunately, no isotope data as to the exact localization of the earliest formation of hormone are available, and it is not possible to determine from these studies whether active polypeptide is synthesized solely in the hypothalamic nuclei. No studies on the intermediary stages of synthesis are available. The localization of neurosecretory granules in the perikaryon or perinuclear area of the cells of the supraoptic and paraventricular nuclei suggests that this region of the cell may be the site of formation of the active polypeptide or at least the carrier protein. It is not known whether carrier protein and active polypeptides are separately synthesized within the cell bodies.

Chronic stimulation of the neurohypophysis.—Chronic dehydration and chronic electrical stimulation are associated with or followed by increased synthesis of peptide hormones (34, 39, 83, 84). Chronic exogenous administration of vasopressin to rats does not inhibit their subsequent ability to release antidiuretic hormone during dehydration (85), nor cause an alteration in neurosecretory material in the neurohypophysis (14). These findings suggest that a feedback "mechanism" does not exist between the level of circulating hormone and its release or synthesis.

Vasopressin and oxytocic activities of the neurohypophysis of newborn rats, when expressed as mu per 100 g of body weight, mu per g of kidney weight or mu per 100 cm² of body surface, are significantly below the adult level and do not approach the adult level until the 28th day (47). The same relationship between age and neurophypophyseal hormone content is observed in the dog and in man (86). In the latter it approached the adult level by two to three years. The hormone content of the neural lobe of the guinea pig, which is much more developed at birth than that of the rat, dog, and man, includes amounts approaching the mature level. In general, at birth the neurosecretory material is scanty in those forms which are also immature by other criteria.

While the amount of hormone stored in the neural lobe of infant rats is very low as compared to that in adults, it seems possible that the mechanism for release by dehydration of the vasopressor-antidiuretic factor operates shortly after birth. Twenty-four hours of dehydration reduce antidiuretic activity in the hypophysis of young rats by about one fourth (47). However, the plasma of young rats (0 to 27 days old) displayed no antidiuretic activity after 24 hours of dehydration (87). In adult rats, withdrawal of food and water stimulates both the release and, as is shown by the concomitant increase in hormone storage, the rate of synthesis of the antidiuretic principle. In the young rat it is probable that ADH is released early in dehydration, but its release is not sustained (87).

Differences of opinion exist regarding the sites of synthesis of oxytocin. Olivecrona (88) suggested that the paraventricular nucleus secretes mainly oxytocin, and the supraoptic nucleus mainly vasopressin. Electrolytic lesions in the region of the paraventricular nuclei (80) or bilateral destruction of this nucleus in the cat (89) causes a decrease in the amount of oxytocin in the posterior pituitary gland with no change in its vasopressin content. Diabetes insipidus does not develop in these animals.

If these observations are correct, one would expect the paraventricular nuclei to contain oxytocin only or at least to have a low ratio of vasopressor-to-oxytocic activity. The investigations of the $V:O$ activity ratios in hypothalamic nuclei of the sheep, dog, and camel detect values varying from 3.3 in the supraoptic region to 0.26 in the paraventricular region (3, 18, 21, 90, 91). These suggest that the paraventricular nucleus, while not exclusively concerned with the formation of oxytocin, may, in some species, be of special importance for the synthesis of this peptide. Little of the synthesized neurohypophyseal hormone remains in the hypothalamus, but is ostensibly stored in the neural lobe (3, 18, 21, 78, 90). Rarely has a vasopressin-to-oxytocin ratio smaller than 1 been found in the posterior lobe. A $V:O$ ratio in the neural lobe of the human pituitary, obtained at autopsy, varied from 0.2 to 2.4 which suggests that the hormones in the human gland are not present in a fixed proportion bound to a protein (92). However, data obtained from autopsy material may not be representative of the ratio of these hormones in the healthy living subject, for the nature of their illness and death may have caused the varying ratios noted. A variation has been noted during embryonic development and growth in the mammal (53, 93), a high ratio being present in the embryo and immature animal, approaching unity in adulthood.

It is possible that the oxytocic principle is important only in reproduction and for this reason is synthesized somewhat later. The oxytocin level of the neurohypophysis is diminished following ovariectomy but increased following treatment with estrogen and progesterone (18, 94). Lactation in the dog decreases the relative amount of oxytocin in the neural lobe but not in the hypothalamic nuclei (21). Recent techniques for the isolation of purified oxytocin and vasopressin from the neurohypophysis (51, 54, 55, 57, 58, 59, 61, 95) will be of help in clarifying the relationship of the various neurohypophyseal peptides in different physiological states.

Release of Neurohypophyseal Hormones

The criteria for release are: (*a*) a decrease in neurosecretory material (as determined by electron or light microscopy) and a decrease in the hormonal content (by assay) of the neural lobe; (*b*) an increase in the amount of assayable material in blood or urine or both; and (*c*) end organ response.

When the neurohypophysis is intact, regardless of the stimulus, hormone is released into the systemic circulation only from the neural lobe (2, 4, 7, 8, 12, 23, 79). This may be true because of the permeability characteristics of the capillaries of the neural lobe (2, 30, 79). If the blood brain barrier is also capable of operating in the opposite direction, only in the neural lobe would the capillaries presumably be permeable to neurosecretory material or some component of it.

For the active peptide to pass from the axon to the circulation, it must pass through the 50 A "wall" of the neurosecretory vesicle, the plasma membrane of the axon, the minimal interstitial space, and the basement membrane of the capillary and either between or through the endothelial cells lining the basement membrane. The "pores" in the capillaries of the neural lobe have a diameter of approximately 30 to 75 mμ or 300 to 750 A (23). The intact granule in the neural lobe has a diameter from 1600 to as large as 5500 A. It is apparent that the so-called pores, described by Paley (23), are far too small to allow the passage through them of the intact granule. Stimuli evoking hormone release cause disappearance of the stainable component of the neural secretion. This suggests that the van Dyke protein or neurophysine, with or without its component of active polypeptide, is either transported into the circulation through the various barriers described or is metabolized prior to discharge of the active principles into the circulation.

Bargmann (97) in electron-microscopic studies on the teleost neurohypophysis demonstrated that pseudopodlike movement of the cytoplasm of the capillary endothelial cell through the pores in the basement membrane brings it into intimate apposition with the plasma membrane of the axon

terminal. The neurosecretory material is thus brought into close apposition
with the capillary endothelium. Granules have been seen within the capillary
lumen only under the influence of profound discharge of neurosecretory
material (8, 98). When such material is depleted, the dense granules seen on
electron microscopy disappear, leaving the intact empty vesicles within the
neural lobe (2, 4, 6, 7, 8, 12, 79).

The following calculations suggest that if the vasopressin-containing
neurosecretory material were discharged directly into the circulation it
should be readily seen by electron microscopy. Green & Maxwell (2) estimated that the normal neural lobe of the dog contains 3×10^{11} neurosecretory granules. If the neural lobe of the dog contains a maximum of 20 units,
or 20,000 mu, of vasopressin (78, 92), each granule should contain approximately 1×10^4 μu of active polypeptide. If maximal antidiuresis is achieved
by the discharge of approximately 300 μu per min (99, 100, 101), this would
require the release of 3×10^4 granules per min. Under these circumstances
electron microscopy would detect granules entering the circulation. Maximal
discharge of ADH, following stimuli such as acute hemorrhage or ether anesthesia, may attain rates 100 times the 300 μu per min (102 to 106). At this extreme rate of discharge it is conceivable that intact granules may be seen
occasionally in the capillary bed of the neurohypophysis (8, 98).

Although increased mitotic activity of the pituicytes (4, 11, 31) and the
accumulation of the synaptic vesicles (200 to 400 A in diameter) (12, 23)
parallel the disappearance of neurosecretory material, their exact contribution to release of the active peptide is unknown. The synaptic vesicles may
contain chemical mediators of release, possibly acetylcholine (12). However,
Felberg & Vogt (107), using choline acetylase, demonstrated no acetylcholine
synthesis in the neural lobe but a high level in the supraoptic nuclei. They
concluded that the neural lobe contained only noncholinergic nerve fibers
and that the levels in the supraoptic nucleus represented cholinergic fibers
which terminated in synaptic connection with the neurons of the supraoptic
nucleus. In other words, these neurons were acetylcholine-sensitive cells from
which noncholinergic fibers emerge. Conflicting results were obtained by
Koelle (108) and Abrahams (109). After studying the localization of acetylcholine esterase, they concluded that the fibers in the neural lobe were
cholinergic.

There is no conclusive evidence that stimulation or inhibition of release of
hormones from the neural lobe can occur in the absence of nervous stimulation by the axons of the neurohypophyseal tract. Although depletion of
neurosecretory material from the neural lobe can occur following section of
the stalk (4, 7, 8, 23), this probably represents nonphysiological liberation of
the hormone into the systemic circulation during degeneration of the axon
terminals. In support of this is the demonstration that the duration of the
"normal" interphase of experimental diabetes insipidus could not be appreciably influenced by dehydration, the infusion of hypertonic saline, or water
loading. It was concluded that the "normal" interphase of experimental

diabetes insipidus is a period of excessive and pathologic antidiuretic activity which is not affected by factors that regulate antidiuretic activity in normal animals (113). When permanent diabetes insipidus is produced in the chronically hypophysectomized rat, a "normal" interphase is not seen (110), indicating that the unphysiological release of ADH does not occur in the absence of the neural lobe.

In view of the secretory nature of the neurons of the paraventricular and supraoptic nuclei, and the probability that release of active peptides from the neural lobe occurs only following nervous stimulation, it is essential to demonstrate that the cells of these nuclei have electrical characteristics resembling those of typical neurons. Neurons of the nuclei exhibit typical action potentials following stimulation by injection of hypertonic solutions into the common carotid artery (111, 112). Similar injections increase the electrical activity of the neurohypophyseal-hypothalamic area (79, 114, 115). Intracellular recordings of the hypothalamic neuroendocrine cells demonstrate resting potentials of about 50 mv and action potentials up to 90 mv (116). These are comparable to those of non-hormone-producing vertebrate central neurons. Such a concept of electrical activity implies that there are receptor cells from which electrical discharge, directly or by synapse, brings about the release of active peptides from the neural lobe. Sunsten & Sawyer (115) carried out studies to determine if osmotically induced electroencephalographic changes are essential for neurohypophyseal hormone release and found that hypertonic saline injected into the internal carotid artery caused a simultaneous release of active peptide, as measured by milk ejection assay, and increased electroencephalographic activity in the osmosensitive areas. Ablation of the entire hypothalamus, with the exception of the supraoptic region, did not interfere with the electroencephalographic or milk ejection response. Removal of the supraoptic island eliminated the neurohypophyseal response despite the fact that the neural lobe itself could still discharge oxytocin when stimulated directly. Therefore, little more than the supraoptic nucleus with attached posterior pituitary is necessary for the osmotic release of oxytocin. Similar electroencephalographic and antidiuretic responses to intracarotid injections of hypertonic saline have been observed in the dog, rabbit, and cat in acute preparations (114). These data support the proposal that the osmoreceptors controlling hormone release exist in the basal hypothalamus, probably in the supraoptic nuclei (117).

Innumerable supra- and infranuclear stimuli and inhibitors of the release of neurohypophyseal hormones have been described. These can be classified into the following categories: osmotic (4, 11, 12, 34, 39, 87, 104, 111, 114 to 122); electrical (79, 111, 114, 115, 123, 124, 125); chemical (106, 118, 126 to 132); hydrostatic or volumetric (104, 131 to 141); and cortical (132, 142, 143, 144).

All these stimuli will evoke both vasopressin and oxytocin release. Additional stimuli which are physiologically related to oxytocin release, such as suckling, vaginal distention after natural mating, tactile stimulation of the external genitalia, and mechanical stimulation of the uterus or cervix, also cause release of vasopressin. Oxytocin may be liberated as an essential part of normal parturition.

The release of antidiuretic hormone follows electrical stimulation of the neurohypophyseal tract in the hypothalamus, in the median eminence, in the infundibular stalk, and in the neural lobe (79). The duration of the antidiuretic response could be correlated with the intensity of the stimulus, and the response in any one animal to a given stimulus remained remarkably constant over a period of weeks or months.

Baratz (133) attempted to evaluate the separate contribution of renal hemodynamic changes and ADH release to urinary volume and concentration changes following isotonic alterations in blood volume and distribution. Share (135) investigated the same problem. However, his technique did not adequately control osmotic changes, or large alterations in cerebral blood flow which could mask changes in the concentration of ADH in jugular vein blood. Transient bilateral occlusion of the common carotid arteries in dogs causes significant release of ADH (138, 139).

Numerous authors have reviewed the effect of variations in volume and distribution of the blood and extracellular fluids, without a change in tonicity, on the release of neurohypophyseal hormones (145 to 149). These reviews stress the extensive gaps still existing in our knowledge as to the receptor and arcs involved in such responses. However, it is generally agreed that a decrease in intrathoracic blood volume or hydrostatic pressure increases the release of antidiuretic hormone while an expansion of intrathoracic volume inhibits its release. Carbon dioxide inhalation in man causes a striking water-type diuresis (150). Ullman (151) has shown that this diuresis, caused by inhibition of ADH release, results from variations in ventilation and subsequent alterations in intrathoracic volume or pressure. The reviewers conclude that it is difficult to dissociate the effects of inhibition of antidiuretic hormone which follows the expansion of total plasma or extracellular volume from the effects of altered volume on renal hemodynamics and solute excretion.

Water intake in man and rats is closely regulated to provide nearly the minimal water necessary to cover excretory losses, that is, the physiological release of antidiuretic hormone is at a level approaching maximal. Radford (119) suggested that Pitressin might have a direct effect on the thirst mechanism; however, the dose he administered to rats would be equivalent to giving 50 to 70 units of Pitressin to a normal adult.

The synapses at the supraoptic and paraventricular nuclei may differ pharmacologically from those at autonomic ganglia since hexamethonium, in doses sufficient to block the pressor and convulsion action of nicotine, has no influence on its antidiuretic effect (106), which effect is also not blocked by atropine (136).

Intravenous infusion of nicotine (3–5 mg) in man elicits extremely variable release of ADH (152); a similar result has been seen by the authors of this review.

Electrical stimulation of the reticular formation in the region of periaqueductal grey and tegmentum brings about release of neurohypophyseal hormones which can only be explained by impulses transmitted from the reticular formation area of the medulla to the supraoptic and paraventricular nuclei of the hypothalamus (125). This might be part of the afferent limb of the reflex arc responsible for the antidiuretic effects of pain and emotional excitement.

SELECTIVE RELEASE OF OXYTOCIN AND VASOPRESSIN

Sawyer has stressed the difficulty in interpreting the data on the selective release of the individual hormones from the neurohypophysis (42). The difficulties arise: (a) from the varied types and intensity of the stimuli (18, 21, 103, 104, 105, 106, 153 to 156); (b) from the failure of many of the investigators to employ reproducible and valid biological assays for both hormones when these are simultaneously released into the circulation; (c) from equating the hormonal content in the neural lobe after stimulation with the rate of release; (d) from the use, under nonstressful or "normal" physiological states in which small amounts of either hormone may be released into the circulation, of assay techniques not sensitive enough to detect the complete absence of one and the presence of small amounts of the other. It may be noted that the range of sensitivity for oxytocin is in milliunits per milliliter in contrast to microunits per milliliter for ADH.

The apparent excess of circulating oxytocin could be attributed to inaccurate assay techniques, a markedly increased tissue sensitivity to oxytocin, a much more rapid rate of plasma clearing or degradation of vasopressin, and differential rates of release of these two hormones from the neural lobe. The latter seems the more reasonable hypothesis. However, the inert protein neurophysin seems to contain the two hormones in a one-to-one ratio, and the ratio of vasopressin to oxytocin in the neural lobe under all circumstances seems to be one or greater.

However, with the exceptions of acute hemorrhage [Ginsburg & Brown (102)] and the transfer of the rainbow trout from fresh to 60 per cent sea water (157), all the known stimuli listed above seem to cause a greater release of oxytocin than of vasopressin (vasotocin in the trout). This ratio of oxytocin to vasopressin release has been variously reported as from 4 to 100.

It is probable that certain axon terminals contain predominantly oxytocin rather than vasopressin and that these are stimulated much more readily and in a more sustained manner than the axons containing predominantly vasopressin. This assumes, as previously mentioned, that nervous stimuli coming from the hypothalamus are essential for the release of neurohypophyseal hormones from the neural lobe.

LaBella, Beaulieu et al. (158), following differential ultracentrifugation of the neural lobes, found different distributions of oxytocin and vasopressin in the various subcellular fractions. They concluded that their observations were best explained on the basis of the existence of separate particles in the neurosecretory system relatively specific for either oxytocin or vasopressin. However, the inclusion of both hormones in some neurosecretory granules is still a probability. Cross & Green (111) observed that hypertonic infusions in the internal carotid artery cause a simultaneous decrease in the electrical activity of the paraventricular neurons and an increase in the electrical activity of the supraoptic neurons. This only serves to emphasize the complexity of the problem and the confused state of our knowledge about the differential release of these hormones.

HORMONES IN THE BLOOD

Existing estimates of the levels of circulating antidiuretic hormone (87, 127, 159, 164) in mammals of various ages and under various stimuli seem to be fairly accurate and reasonable. Blood to be assayed was drawn from the animal or human subject and almost immediately injected into the assay rat.

The average antidiuretic activity in 1 ml of plasma from nonhydropenic normal man was equivalent to 1.67 μu/ml of vasopressin. No antidiuretic activity was detected in the plasma 30 to 60 min after three of the subjects ingested 800 cc of water. Heller concluded that antidiuretic activity in human plasma is normally less than 2 μu per cc (160). This plasma level is very similar to the estimate of Lauson (99). Heller could not detect significant antidiuretic activity in the plasma of human infants under the age of four months (162, 163). It approached the mean adult level at two to three years of age. He found further that the plasma antidiuretic activity of a number of normally hydrated mammalian species was inversely related to size (164): highest in the mouse, then rat, guinea pig, cat, rabbit, dog, and man, in that order. The average in the mouse was 8.8 μu per ml. No sex difference in antidiuretic activity of the plasma was noted in any of the species studied. After eight hours of moderate dehydration in normal humans the plasma level was approximately 12 μu per ml (160). In rats dehydrated for 24 hours the plasma contained on the average of 43.5 μu per ml (161). Morphine, urethane, and ether significantly increased the plasma antidiuretic activity of the rat; pentobarbital caused an insignificant increase; chloralose had no effect; and no antidiuretic activity was detected in the plasma after ethanol anesthesia (162). Following moderate dehydration and cigarette smoking, comparable levels of circulating hormone have been noted by others utilizing similar but slightly less sensitive assay techniques (3, 99, 129, 156, 165, 166, 167).

Fitzpatrick (168) has summarized the available information on the estimation of small amounts of oxytocin in blood. His review of previous work suggests that plasma concentration of 1.5 to 15 μu per ml would be appropriate normal levels of oxytocin in man and cattle.

In pregnant sheep, plasma activity of oxytocin increases from 4.2 μu per ml several days before parturition to as high as 3000 μu per ml at the time of parturition (168). Oxytocin levels of 200–300 μu per ml are found in peripheral venous human blood following overnight dehydration or intravenous injections of nicotine (117, 118).

The manner in which the active peptides are carried in the plasma has not been clarified but appears to differ from one mammalian species to another. Thorn (166) found that the active antidiuretic material in rat plasma was retained by a collodion ultrafilter and on electrophoretic analysis moved with the beta-globulin fraction. Dialysis against dilute 0.2 normal acetic acid appeared to dissociate the complex. The collodion membranes retained molecules with molecular weight greater than 70,000. The inert protein used by van Dyke, with a molecular weight of only 30,000, should have passed through the collodion membrane.

Starch-block electrophoresis of plasma, to which highly purified vasopressin and synthetic oxytocin had been added, disclosed the hormonal activity to be located in front of the major fraction of globulins (169). Lauson (99) states that there is general agreement that virtually all the hormone in the blood is confined to the plasma. Yet, purified vasopressin, added to dog serum and plasma, was found to be both readily diffusible and ultrafilterable and little was bound to plasma protein (99).

Antidiuretic hormone or vasopressin obtained from external jugular blood in an anesthetized dog subjected to hemorrhage was contained in the plasma; none was adsorbed by or permeated into the red cell, but three fourths of this ADH activity was ultrafilterable through cellulose tubing at 4°C (171).

Dingman (170) noted that Cohn's fraction 2 and 3 showed apparent antidiuretic activity when assayed in a dog with diabetes insipidus. However, Lauson (99) criticizes this work on two important counts: (*a*) that the free-water clearance and urinary osmolar concentration were so variable throughout as to make evaluation of of the assay difficult; and (*b*) that nonspecific vascular effects might have resulted from injection of human plasma protein concentrates into the dogs inasmuch as urine flow ceased altogether after an injection of the larger dose of fraction 2 and 3.

Numerous authors have estimated the rate of clearance and disappearance of active vasopressin and oxytocin from the plasma (42, 99, 118, 172 to 177). Lauson (99), assuming that exogenously administered vasopressin and endogenously secreted vasopressin behave similarly in attaining a steady-state plasma concentration, has calculated the total plasma clearance, the half-time of plasma disappearance, and the fractional turnover rates in man, dog, and rat.

Vasopressin clearance ranged from 3.4 cc per min in the rat to 250 cc per min in man or a fractional turnover rate (assuming that the volume of distribution is equivalent to plasma volume) of approximately 3 to 6 per min in man, 10 to 11 per min in the dog, and as much as 80 to 100 per min in the rat. The half life for vasopressin ranged from 10 to 20 min in man down to .5 to .7 min in the rat (171). Utilizing tritium-labeled arginine-vasopressin, Silver *et al.* (173) found the half-time of disappearance to be approximately the same in dog and man, ranging from 2 to $5\frac{1}{2}$ min. However, because of the low specific activity of their labeled hormone they had to inject 6 to 12 units of arginine-vasopressin intravenously. This unphysiologically large dose makes interpretation of their data difficult. Estimates based on the rate of disappearance of responses to injected hormones do not reflect the rate of disappearance of the hormone from the circulation, but the rate at which the tissue effect is dissipated. The latter, as Sawyer (42) stresses, may be considerably longer than the former.

Excretion and Inactivation

If the vasopressin clearance is approximately 200 cc per min in man (99), and the combined liver and kidney plasma flow is 1500 cc per min, it is evident that less than 15 per cent of the vasopressin is extracted in any given circulation through these organs. Despite this, the data available from renal and hepatic extirpation studies, and determination of arteriovenous differences of hormone concentration across the renal and hepatic circulations, indicate that these organs are the main sites of excretion and destruction of vasopressin and oxytocin, and that they extract about equal quantities of the hormone (3, 42, 99, 174 to 178). Approximately 10 per cent of the hormone circulating through the kidney appears in the urine (3).

With the exception of late pregnancy serum, inactivation of the active peptide occurs very slowly in plasma. Heller (178), utilizing a sensitive assay procedure, failed to demonstrate the presence of the antidiuretic hormone in extracts of kidney and liver of unanesthetized rats in normal water balance. The organs not only remove the hormone with great efficiency but they inactivate it quite rapidly. In the kidney, it is the tubules and not the glomeruli which are responsible for hormone inactivation (177, 180).

In lactating rats a tissue additional to the kidneys and the splanchnic region participates in a nonequilibrium uptake of the hormone. Since rats have no blood "oxytocinase" and since the puerperal uterus is unlikely to remove more oxytocin than in the uterus in late pregnancy, involvement of the mammary gland seems probable as the other site (178). The half life of oxytocin and vasopressin in rabbits is 3 to 5 min (180). The half-time of oxytocin in the blood of pregnant women after cessation of a "macro-infusion" was found to be between 1.2 to 4 min (181). When a similar student was made with more nearly physiological levels, the half-time of oxytocin was estimated to be 9 min. This is three times longer than the half-time of oxytocin measured directly in the blood after cessation of a macroinfusion.

Tissue slices did not completely inactivate the active peptides, whereas tissue homogenates do. This suggests that certain subcellular particles are involved in inactivation. Dicker & Greenbaum (192) also found that the supernatant fluid was the major inactivator, while Hooper (187) concluded that the supernatant inactivated oxytocin only and the mitochondria inactivated vasopressin. Smith & Sachs (188) found that organic mercurials and oxytocin itself inhibit the destruction of vasopressin in kidney slices *in vitro*. Adrenalectomy markedly decreases the clearance of vasopressin from the plasma, and it is not further decreased by nephrectomy. This suggests that adrenalectomy interferes with the kidneys' inactivating system (179). In rats Ginsburg (175) found the renal clearance of pitressin was 1.24 ± 0.06 times the clearance of inulin. In two rats in which urinary flow was unusually low, clearance of pitressin was respectively 0.16 and 0.32 times the inulin clearance. This may indicate that oliguric rats, with increased antidiuretic activity affecting the kidney, actually clear less or bind more of the hormone than is presented to the kidney.

Extensive series of papers have appeared during the period of this review relating to the inactivation *in vitro* of oxytocin and vasopressin by plasma, serum, tissue slices, and tissue homogenates (174, 176 to 192).

Except in the pregnant female, blood *per se* is not a site of inactivation of the hormone (176, 193). Oxytocinase in the plasma of pregnant females appears around 13 weeks, increases progressively to term, and disappears by ten days postpartum (176, 189, 193). There is no relationship to the level of oxytocinase and the presence or absence of uterine inertia. The serum enzymes inactivating oxytocin and vasopressin exist only in the plasma of primates, and their exact physiological functions are unknown (190). Electrophoretic isolation of these enzymes show that they move with the alpha-, 1-, and 2-globulin fractions of plasma (185). The peptidase qualities of oxytocinase make it possible for a synthetic substrate, cystine dibetanaphthylamide, to be used to detect the presence of the enzyme in the plasma of pregnant women (190). However, the specificity of this technique has been questioned (185). In addition to the presence of a vasopressinase in the serum of pregnant females, their plasma also contains a protein capable of binding vasopressin and protecting it from inactivation by vasopressin (184).

Heller stressed the fact that homogenates and tissue slice systems could not be extrapolated to inactivating systems in the intact organism and felt that perfusion studies in the various organs *in situ* were essential (176). Almost all tissue *in vitro* can inactivate oxytocin and vasopressin although the liver and kidneys are the main sites for inactivation and excretion *in vivo*. Oxytocinase and vasopressinase are both peptidases, while oxytocinase is also an esterase (183).

Response to the Hormones

Sawyer (42) discusses in detail the qualitative and quantitative characteristics of the responses to neurohypophyseal hormones, and incorporates a historical review of the earliest investigations of these responses in amphibian skin and bladder. Edelman (195) reviewed the action of antidiuretic hormone on the transport of water and electrolytes in biologic systems, while the reviews of Wirz (196) and Giebisch (197) more specifically cover the renal action of antidiuretic hormones. The reader is referred to these reviews for additional analysis.

Antidiuretic effect.—The antidiuretic effect of vasopressin has been

evaluated by many authors (196 to 205), who discuss in detail the relationship of the anatomy of the nephron and its circulation to the concentrating
and diluting functions of the kidney, and to the action of ADH. It is now
clear that the concentrating ability of the mammalian nephron is dependent
on the countercurrent exchange and multiplying function of the loop of
Henle. A hypertonic urine cannot be formed in the absence of the loop of
Henle (i.e., Amphibia). There is a direct correlation between the number and
length of the loops, the thickness and hypertonicity of the renal medulla, and
the maximal urinary concentration (206). During maximal antidiuresis the
urine leaving the collecting ducts has the same osmolality as the medullary
interstitium.

Localization of the site or sites of action of ADH on the mammalian
nephron has been investigated by clearance techniques, by stop-flow analysis, by collection of luminal fluid and vasa recti blood by micropuncture techniques, and by cryoscopic and chemical analysis of renal cortex and medulla.
These are summarized in the above reviews. There is no conclusive evidence
that ADH affects the transport of water in the proximal tubule or the descending or ascending limbs of the loop of Henle, the former being freely
permeable to water in both the presence or absence of ADH (199, 202, 203,
207 to 213).

Gottschalk et al. (202, 203), Lassiter et al. (207), and Ullrich et al. (199)
concluded that antidiuretic hormone, or vasopressin, acts primarily on more
distal portions of the nephron, although the latter authors, in particular, did
not exclude the possibility of an action on the descending limb of the loop of
Henle. The available evidence indicates that antidiuretic hormone does not
affect the permeability of the ascending limb of the loop of Henle to water.

All these studies indicate that the distal convolution and the collecting
tubule are made increasingly permeable to water by increasing doses of antidiuretic hormone and that these distal segments are relatively impermeable
to water in the absence of antidiuretic hormone. "Impermeability" here refers to the net movement of water from luminal fluid into the interstitium and
blood stream and not to the total flux of water in both directions across the
nephron. The impermeability, as defined, is influenced by the quantity of
solute remaining in the luminal fluid and by the rate of flow of the latter.

Although the degree of permeability of the collecting ducts to water is dependent on the level of circulating ADH, some net back diffusion continues
to occur in the absence of the hormone. This can be demonstrated by experimental conditions which delay the flow of luminal fluid along the collecting
ducts (211, 212, 213, 216).

The reduction of glomerular filtration rate in two patients with vasopressin-sensitive diabetes insipidus to levels of less than 10 per cent of normal
caused the production of significantly hypertonic urine in these patients.
However, the complete absence of ADH in these two cases could, of course,
not be proved (219).

A quantitative relationship between increasing doses of antidiuretic hormone (Pitressin), infused at rates from 0 to 15.5 mμ per hr and decreasing C_{H_2O}, or free-water clearance, has been demonstrated below levels of actual urinary hypertonicity in continuously water-loaded young men. As purified or synthetic arginine-vasopressin was not used, the quantitative relationship may pertain only to the conditions of this study (220). Similar observations have been made in the dog (101).

The original observations of Epstein (214) that high protein or high urea content in the diet augments the renal concentrating ability of normal subjects have now been confirmed by a large number of studies in other mammals (207, 208, 210, 215, 216, 217), which have demonstrated that the permeability of the distal convolution, and particularly the collecting tubule to urea, is influenced by the level of antidiuretic hormone (207, 208, 210, 214 to 217).

Urea contributes to the maximal concentration of the urine attained under the influence of antidiuretic hormone by augmenting the hypertonicity of the renal medulla. Bray (217) demonstrated that while vasopressin increased the permeability of the nephron to urea, it did not appreciably affect the permeability of the nephron to thiourea. A similar difference between urea and thiourea transport was noted by Maffly (218) in the bladder of the toad *Bufo marinus*. There is no evidence from the above studies that net movement of urea across the nephron requires an active transport mechanism as suggested by Schmidt-Nielsen (215).

The anatomy of the vasa recti and their function as a countercurrent exchange system have led to attempts to measure cortical and medullary blood flow simultaneously. Calculations of medullary blood flow have been made be measuring the mean transit time of Evans blue dye through the medulla of the kidney, and approximating the blood volume of the medulla from its hemoglobin and hematocrit content. Blood flow is assumed to equal the medullary blood volume divided by the mean transit time (199, 205). Utilizing this technique Ullrich & Achwadt concluded that antidiuretic hormone in physiologic doses decreased the rate of medullary blood flow, thus increasing the efficiency of the countercurrent exchange system. Contradictory results have been reported by Lillienfield *et al.* (221). It is unfortunate that it has not been possible as yet to measure medullary blood flow directly.

The mechanism by which antidiuretic hormone, vasopressin, increases the permeability of the nephron to water and urea is still unclear. From studies on amphibian skin and bladder, Ussing & Zerahn (222) and Koefoed-Johnsen & Ussing (223) postulated that neurohypophyseal hormone increases the pore size in some layer of these membranes, thereby increasing the total area available to water movement.

Equivalent pore radius has been estimated in red cells and other tissues by the rate of uptake of water from solutions containing varying concentrations of diffusible molecules (224, 225). Equivalent pore radius was increased by vasopressin.

Fong *et al.* (227, 228) studied the binding of tritiated labeled vasopressin, derived from beef Pitressin powder, to rat kidneys ten minutes after the injection and at the peak of antidiuretic activity. They observed that the binding of the labeled vasopressin to tissue protein was readily released by treatment with thiol compounds, and that larger doses of unlabeled hormone caused a diminution in the number of reactive sulfhydryl groups in the distal convoluted tubules of the rat kidney. They suggested that the antidiuretic action of the hormone was dependent upon the specific thiol disulfide exchange reaction at the hormone receptor site.

Darmady et al. (226) noted that the I^{131}-labeled Pitressin localizes in the area of the distal convoluted tubule and collecting tubule of the rat kidney. It is not possible to determine from the radioautographs whether this represents merely concentration of the labeled Pitressin in these areas, or actual adsorption on cellular membranes.

Ginetzinsky (229) attributes the action of antidiuretic hormone to activation of the hyaluronic acid-hyaluronidase system, which causes a dissolution of the metachromatic intracellular substance between epithelial cells, thus enhancing the intracellular transport of water in the distal tubules and collecting ducts. Dicker & Eggleton (230) concurred with the findings of Ginetzinsky. Antidiuresis has been produced in the ethanol-anesthetized rat by giving massive doses of bovine testicular hyaluronidase (35,000 IU per kilo) without producing visible toxic effects (231). We (unpublished observations) found no antidiuresis when 5000 IU were given intravenously to a patient with nephrogenic diabetes insipidus. Hyaluronidase in concentrations of 12 to 15 IU per ml did not affect the permeability of the toad or frog bladder to water, sodium, or urea in vitro (232). Berlyne (233, 234) was unable to confirm Ginetzinsky's observations, and he and Kaplan (235) raised serious objections to Ginetzinsky's technique for hyaluronidase assay.

Many of the investigations on the effect of oxytocin on urinary flow and electrolyte excretion have utilized single injections of the hormone plus large single oral water loads rather than sustained water diuresis. Only those papers in which the state of hydration was relatively sustained, therefore, are referred to (236, 237, 238). These suggest that in man oxytocin has mild antidiuretic properties with not more than one tenth the antidiuretic potency of commercial Pitressin (a mixture of lysine and arginine-vasopressin). Oxytocin did not affect renal hemodynamics or electrolyte excretion, and mixtures of oxytocin and vasopressin did not alter the antidiuretic effect of the latter.

Saluretic effect.—The available data indicate that the effect of neurohypophyseal hormones on electrolyte excretion is significantly influenced by both rates of urinary flow and species differences. The authors in at least 30 experiments, utilizing sustained water diuresis and doses of Pitressin of approximately 0.5 mu per kilo per hr, have not noted significant effects on sodium or potassium excretion (unpublished observations). We are unaware of any published or unpublished observations demonstrating a consistent increase in sodium or potassium excretion following the administration of commercial or purified antidiuretic hormone in acute experiments in man (237, 238).

In nonhydrated or dehydrated dogs, vasopressin or commercial Pitressin has no effect on renal hemodynamics, sodium, chloride, or potassium excretion (239, 240, 241). In contrast, the water-loaded dog, while urinary flow is decreasing, consistently demonstrates an augmentation in sodium and chloride excretion and frequently in potassium excretion when these preparations are administered (239 to 245). This augmented electrolyte excretion is not brought about by altered adrenocortical activity (111).

The latter studies have shown that oxytocin does not augment electrolyte excretion in the hydrated dog or a dog undergoing a significant water diuresis. Also, administration of oxytocin to dogs with diabetes insipidus, regardless of the state of hydration or urine flow, does not augment electrolyte excretion (239, 240, 241). On the other hand, the nonhydrated dog, or hydropenic dog, consistently demonstrates an augmented sodium, chloride, and, frequently, potassium excretion during intravenous infusions of commercial or purified oxytocin.

These observations suggest that for oxytocin to be saluretic, a certain amount of vasopressin must be circulating and acting on the nephron. In the hydropenic or hydrated animal, when vasopressin and oxytocin are administered concomitantly, a saluretic effect is noted. However, Brooks & Pickford (251) and Chan (243) demonstrated that doses of oxytocin large enough to cause antidiuresis can be saluretic in the water-loaded dog. They suggest that antidiuresis and not vasopressin *per se* is the essential prerequisite for the saluretic action of oxytocin. Intracarotid injections of doses of oxytocin (2.5–5 mu), which have no effect when injected intravenously, are saluretic (241, 243) as are minute doses of oxytocin injected into the third ventricle of conscious dogs (243). Vasopressin, however, has no greater saluretic effect when injected into the carotid than when injected intravenously. These studies suggest that the saluretic effect of oxytocin may be mediated through a central rather than a direct renal mechanism. However, the latter is difficult to reconcile with the conclusion that the saluretic effect of oxytocin is dependent on its antidiuretic effect (243). Intracarotid injections of oxytocin that produce saluresis are probably not antidiuretic, but this is not commented upon by Sawyer (42) or Brooks & Pickford (241).

Kinne (247) found that merino sheep, living in a hot environment, respond to Pitressin (12 mu per min) with a consistent augmentation of glomerular filtration rate and sodium, chloride, and potassium. Although saline-loaded rats respond to large doses (up to 100 mu) of vasopressin, oxytocin, or posterior pituitary extract with a chloruresis, renal hemodynamics and the effect of saline loads *per se* were not well controlled (249, 250). If water replaced the saline loads the chloruretic effect of the neurohypophyseal hormones was lost (250).

Thorn (244, 245) and Sawyer (42) discuss the effects of various analogues of vasopressin and oxytocin on the renal excretion of sodium and potassium in rats and dogs. The physiological significance of the saluretic effect of oxytocin and vasopressin in the dog and rat remains to be established. Thorn

(231, 252) has recently demonstrated that any dose of vasopressin or oxytocin capable of causing significant antidiuresis in the dog or rat can cause a simultaneous increase in calcium excretion. He postulated the release of calcium from membrane lipoprotein during antidiuresis. In this type of experiment it is important to determine whether this 200 or 300 μg per min increment in calcium excretion over a 20- to 30-min period could actually come from the tubules in the dog medulla or from inhibition of tubular reabsorption of filtered calcium.

As commercial Pitressin is a mixture of lysine and arginine-vasopressin, it is important to realize that with the exception of the pig and hog, in which lysine-vasopressin is the natural vasopressin, purified arginine-vasopressin has approximately six times the antidiuretic potency of lysine-vasopressin (60, 78, 253, 254, 255).

Effect on various membranes and enzyme systems—water and urea.— In the amphibian, vasotocin is significantly more potent than either oxytocin or the vasopressins; and while the skin and bladder of the toad are more responsive to vasopressin, these membranes in the frog are more responsive to oxytocin. However, despite these quantitative differences, the qualitative responses and the mechanism of the action of these various neurohypophyseal peptides are similar. Peachey & Rasmussen (256) have recently undertaken a light- and electron-microscopic study of the structural basis for the physiological response of the toad bladder to neurohypophyseal hormones. The serosal surface of the bladder epithelium was freely permeable to the net movement of water while the permeability of the mucosal surface was dependent upon the presence of these hormones. Water moved through the cytoplasm of the epithelial cells and not between them and was not transported by a process of pinocytosis. The amphibian skin, although considerably more complex histologically than the toad bladder, responds to neurohypophyseal hormones in a qualitatively similar manner. The relatively simpler histologic character of the bladder makes it a more appropriate structure for studies in which the correlation of active ion transport and water transport with biochemical events or electrical potential change is sought.

Studies on the amphibian skin and bladder have demonstrated that the neurohypophyseal hormones modify the penetration of three classes of molecules: water; a small group of uncharged organic molecules, such as urea; and sodium ions. In general, the techniques have involved mounting the amphibian bladder or skin in a lucite chamber enabling study of both water movement and ion transport simultaneously, or the separate halves of the isolated amphibian bladder have been mounted so that the rate of movement of water across the bladder wall could be determined by changes in the weight of the bladder "sac" and its contents.

In the absence of any net water transport, with isotonic solutions on both sides of the bladder, equal unidirectional fluxes of D_2O and T_3O indicate equal permeability to water in the two directions (257, 258). The effect of the neurohypophyseal hormones was to increase the unidirectional permeability of the bladder to water from the mucosal to the serosal side; but in the absence of an osmotic gradient, net water movement remains essentially zero. Water movement is passive and is proportional to the transmembrane osmotic gradient. The hormones are only effective when applied to the serosal side of the bladder. Leaf & Hays (257) tend towards the pore hypothesis to explain the action of the neurohypophyseal hormones on net transfer of water. By inserting their rates of water movement into the formulae for net transfer by diffusion, or by net transfer by bulk flow, according to the Poiseuille equation, they conclude that in the absence of the hormone, diffusion could account for only one sixth of the small net movement of water, while in the presence of the hormone, it could account for less than 1 per cent of the large net transfers of water. This entire calculation is based upon the conclusion that the nondiffusional component to water transfer is laminar flow through pores which follows Poiseuille's law, and that such pores are considered to be right circular cylinders positioned perpendicular to the surface of the membrane. The general conclusions and observations reviewed by Leaf (232, 257) had been previously and subsequently confirmed by numerous studies utilizing similar experimental designs (65, 218, 258 to 262).

Conclusions reached with respect to water movement are probably also applicable to urea transport. Changes in epithelial cell volume under the influence of the neurohypophyseal peptides indicate that the mucosal surface is the major site of action of the hormones (256, 257).

It is probable that the movement of water under the influence of the hormones is not dependent on the simultaneously active transport of sodium from mucosa to serosa (232, 261). However, the maximal rate of water transport may depend to some extent on sodium transport (263). The interaction of vasopressin with its receptor site on the amphibian bladder and its ability to increase the permeability of the bladder to water are not directly dependent upon metabolic energy or aerobic metabolism (232, 261), but the optimum rate of water transfer may still depend on an intact oxygen supply and sufficient substrate (258).

An extensive series of papers have appeared on the mechanisms by which the neurohypophyseal hormones are bound to the bladder and the relation of this binding to their physiological action. It has been concluded that one of the primary interactions between the hormone and the receptor involves the disulfide bond of the hormone and a sulfhydryl or related grouping in the receptor. Under control conditions the permeability of the bladder is maintained by a lipoprotein barrier rich in sulfhydryl groups, and disulfide bonds. These interact constantly so that a dynamic equilibrium is present. The introduction of vasopressin is followed by the interaction of the S–S bridge of the vasopressin with the SH group in the receptor. A new S–S bridge is formed between hormone and receptor and a new SH group on the hormone appears which reacts in turn with an S–S bridge in the receptor forming a second S–S bridge between hormone and receptor and liberating a new SH group on the receptor. The entire process is reversible; newly formed receptor SH can either interact with another vasopressin molecule or reversibly release the first. The amount of vasopressin molecules bound by the tissue will depend upon the vasopressin concentration. Sulfhydryl agents, such as N-ethylmaleimide, will competitively prevent the action of vasopressin. If added in critical concentrations between 10^{-4} and $10^{-5} M$ to the mucosal surface, such reagents as N-ethylmaleimide induce a change in permeability which is equalitatively similar to the effect of arginine-vasopressin (228, 260, 261, 264).

Bentley (258) clearly showed that, as the pH of the solution bathing the serosal side of the bladder was decreased, there was a progressive loss of activity of the hormone. The authors (unpublished observations) and Schwartz *et al.* (261) have confirmed Bentley's observations. A competition between protons (H^+) and hormones for the ionized group on the receptor may exist, and at the lower pH the ionization of the sulfhydryl group is diminished and conditions are unfavorable for the interchange reaction (261). It is of considerable interest that Lehninger & Neubert (265, 266), demonstrated that highly purified specimens of vasopressin and oxytocin, as well as insulin, reduced glutathione, and cystine, greatly accelerate water uptake by isolated rat mitochondria. On a molar basis these hormones are much more active than glutathione and cystine. Hormone concentrations were very effective at concentrations of $10^{-5} M$.

Orloff (262) tested the hypothesis that vasopressin altered permeability, by stimulating the production of cyclic adenosine monophosphate from adenosine triphosphate in toad bladder. The addition of $10^{-3} M$ cyclic adenosine monophosphate to the serosal surface of the bladder reproduced the effect of 500 μu per ml of vasopressin on water movement, short-circuit current, and electrical potential across the toad bladder. Theophylline had a similar effect. However, $10^{-2} M$ cysteine will inhibit the effect of various neurohypophyseal hormone analogues on water transport in the toad bladder without altering the action of cyclic adenosine monophosphate or theophylline (260).[5]

Edelman (259) carried out a kinetic analysis of the antidiuretic action of arginine-vasopressin on the toad bladder. Dose response curve revealed typical saturation kinetics at 10 mu per ml. He concluded that the rate of flow at a fixed osmotic gradient was linearly proportional to the number of vasopressin molecules bound per cm^2 of cell surface, and that the binding of the vasopressin to the cell membrane was a one-step reversible reaction.

Hays & Leaf (267), although concluding that the hydrodynamic calculations, previously discussed, support Ussing's view that the hormone acts to enlarge pores in the membrane permitting hydraulic flow, point out that such calculations assume that water moving across the membrane retains the

---

[5] Subsequent work by Handler and Orloff (unpublished observations) has demonstrated that cysteine interfered with the action of theophylline as well as vasopressin, but does not alter the action of cyclic adenosine monophosphate.

physical properties of ordinary water. Since there is much evidence that water in the vicinity of polar and nonpolar groups may undergo marked changes in structure, the degree of bonding of water in the toad bladder was determined by measurements of the activation energy for diffusion of tritiated water. They concluded that the results on variations in activation energy indicate that without hormone, water is in a highly bonded state which reverts to that of ordinary water with hormone. Studies at high temperature yielded the additional information that the extensive bonding in the absence of hormone is in large part between water and some component of the membrane phase. It appears from these experiments that vasopressin must enlarge channels in the membrane so that the central core of water they contain has the properties of bulk water.

Effects on sodium transport.—Neurohypophyseal hormones increase the short-circuit current and active transport of sodium across the toad bladder. The active transport continues despite reduction of the sodium content in the bladder lumen to levels of a fraction of a milliequivalent per liter (232, 257, 261, 268 to 275). These studies confirm and extend the original observations of Ussing *et al.* (222) and Fuhrman *et al.* (275) on isolated frog skin. The active transport of sodium under the influence of the hormone is dependent upon aerobic metabolism (232, 262, 269, 271). Leaf & Hays (257) suggested that the antidiuretic hormone did not in itself increase the active transport mechanism or the "pump" on the serosal side of the epithelial cells, but that the hormone increased the passive permeability of the mucosal surface to sodium. With increased amounts of intracellular sodium being available to the pump, a larger amount of sodium is actively transported. This has been confirmed by others (272, 273). Regardless of how low the concentration of sodium in the mucosal median, the sodium pool within the mucosal cells seems to be always less per gram of tissue water than the concentration in the mucosal median. Raising the concentration of sodium in the mucosal median to 30 to 60 meq per liter stimulated active transport as well as the sodium content of the tissue did. Further increase in concentration of the sodium failed to induce further changes, suggesting that although the entry of sodium across the mucosal surface of the epithelial cells may be passive it is not by free diffusion, but involves some interaction with the mucosal surface of the bladder and constitutes the major determinant of the rate of epithelial transport of sodium (271). Vasopressin increased the rate of transport of sodium without altering this relationship. A specific effect of neurohypophyseal hormones on the sodium transport across the mammalian or amphibian renal tubule has not been demonstrated.

EFFECT OF IONIC ENVIRONMENT ON HORMONE RESPONSE

The effects of changes in cationic composition on the serosal side of the bladder membrane or the outer surface of the amphibian skin have been studied in detail (257, 258, 261, 263, 276, 277). Calcium is necessary to maintain the normal low permeability of the amphibian bladder to water in the absence of vasopressin, but other divalent cations such as magnesium, strontium, and manganese, but not barium, can substitute for calcium in this regard (263). Low concentrations of calcium (0.27 mM) as well as high concentrations of calcium (9 mM) caused a reduction in water transfer across the bladder in response to vasopressin, and no other divalent cation could substitute for calcium (263). The inhibition with high calcium concentrations is overcome by raising the vasopressin concentration from 1 mu per ml to 66–100 mu per ml (276). While high concentrations of calcium have no effect on sodium transport in the isolated amphibian bladder system (276), high concentrations (11 mM per liter) on the outer surface of the amphibian skin cause a decrease in sodium permeability, pore size, and net sodium transport (272, 273). Calcium-free media markedly increase the passive permeability of kidney slices (equivalent pore radius) in the absence of vasopressin, while excess calcium (5 to 10 mM per liter) inhibits the pore-dilating effects of ADH (224, 225). This suggests that its action on membrane permeability may come from an interaction with membrane calcium. Bentley (263) noted that exclusion of potassium from the serosal side of the bladder reduced water transfer in the presence of vasopressin. This result could not be confirmed by Hays & Leaf (277) but they noted, in the absence of potassium, a significant impairment in the active transport of sodium under the influence of vasopressin. The action of oxytocin on the rabbit uterus *in vitro* is abolished when the muscle is depolarized by repeated washings with calcium-deficient solutions (278, 279, 280). When the bathing solution contained high potassium concentrations, the stimulatory action of oxytocin remained unchanged (278). Munsick (74) found that in a concentration of 0.5 mM per liter of magnesium ions the rat uterine response to USP Standard oxytocin and lysine and arginine-vasopressin was considerably augmented over the response in a magnesium-free solution. As the rat uterus is almost completely insensitive to arginine-vasopressin in the absence of magnesium, the bioassay for oxytocic activity using the rat uterus should be carried out in a magnesium-free media to eliminate any vasopressin effect (74).

Vasopressin in concentrations of 100 mu per ml causes a specific increase in phosphate flux and a decrease in rubidium flux across isolated rabbit mesentery, while lower concentrations of the hormone (10 mu per ml) have little effect on rubidium flux (281). As the authors point out, it is difficult to explain the difference between the flux noted by an alteration of pore geometry. Fishman (282) noted a significant decrease in the sodium exchange time between blood and cerebral spinal fluid in dogs after administrations of 5 units per kg, or greater, of Pitressin. These large doses increased arterial pressure, but comparable elevations with norepinephrine did not alter sodium transport into the cerebral spinal fluid. Despite this control, experiments utilizing these massive doses of Pitressin are of questionable physiological value. Large doses of Pitressin® (0.1 units per ml), when added to the serosal side of isolated everted segments of rat colon, cause an increase in net sodium transport (283).

Large doses of vasopressin (5 to 60 units), in contrast to large doses of oxytocin (10 to 40 units), when administered into the portal circulation of the dog, cause an appreciable increase in the concentrations of glucose in the hepatic vein. No measurements of portal hemodynamics were made (284). Oxytocin, in concentrations of 100 mu per ml, produced a highly significant increase in glucose oxidation in epididymal fat (285), and in mammary slices from lactating rats (286). The latter effect occurred in the presence of saturation concentrations of insulin, suggesting different sites of action of the two hormones. Vasopressin inhibited the oxidation of C^{14}-lactate in slices and homogenates of toad and mammalian kidney; oxytocin was inactive (287). These investigators concluded that vasopressin has the capacity to alter cellular metabolism independently of an effect on intact membranes. Pitressin® in doses of 0.4 units increased the specific activity of P^{32} in the phospholipids and sugar phosphate in rat brain slices, which may or may not indicate an effect on cellular permeability (288). The dibenzylene-blocked gastrocnemius muscle of the rat displays defective musuclar contraction, and abnormal transmembrane movements of sodium and potassium. Pitressin was able to antagonize the dibenzylene effect, possibly by enhancing depolarization (289). McCann & Taleisnik (290) confirmed previous observations of Parlow (291) that Pitressin administration to immature rats (like luteotropin) causes ovarian ascorbic acid depletion. Oxytocin has no appreciable activity. Their studies showed that endogenous vasopressin release did not deplete ovarian ascorbic acid and that the effect of Pitressin® was a direct one on the ovary.

OXYTOCIC AND GALACTAGOGUIC ACTIVITY OF NEUROHYPOPHYSEAL HORMONES

Two recent symposia (292, 293) extensively covered the biochemistry and physiology of oxytocin and the oxytocic effect of neurohypophyseal hormones. Sawyer (42) reviews in detail the rather controversial literature on oxytocic responses and milk ejection. One is impressed by the variations in response which are dependent on species differences (3, 21, 62, 294 to 300). The effect of progesterone in altering uterine response to oxytocin differs considerably depending upon the species study (301, 302). Estrogens generally increase the responsiveness of the mammalian uterus to oxytocin (62, 279, 298, 301). Despite its potent effect as a stimulator of uterine contraction, the exact role of oxytocin during labor and parturition is unknown (3, 42). No increased concentration of oxytocin has been found in the plasma of women during labor (3). In the hen, neurohypophyseal extract from the posterior lobe enhances the rate of oviposition. However, this effect is primarily from the arginine-vasotocin in the extract rather than its oxytocin content (303).

The essential role of oxytocin in the physiologic process of milk ejection is more clearly established (3, 112), as a result of the direct action of oxytocin on the myoepithelial cells of the breast. The reflex contraction of the myoepithelial cells is normally brought about by the stimulus of suckling or milking. The milk ejection reflex is a neurohumoral one, the efferent component being oxytocin (296, 304). The effect of various synthetic analogues of oxytocin on oxytocic and milk ejection have been extensively studied (42, 75, 294, 295, 305, 306). The exact mechanism by which the oxytocic and milk ejection activity of neurohypophyseal peptides is exerted is unknown. Alterations in the permeability of the plasma membrane of the sensitive cells, analogous to the effect of the antidiuretic activity of these hormones on the permeability to water, seem reasonable. By increasing membrane permeability in an excitable tissue (uterine muscle or breast myoepithelium), depolarization following electrical or chemical stimuli is generally enhanced (301, 307, 308). Excessive doses may actually produce sustained uterine contraction associated with continuous depolarization and absence of propagated action potentials (301, 307, 308, 309).

Vascular Responses

Vascular response to vasopressin.—The acute reduction in glomerular filtration rate, seen in amphibians, reptiles, and birds, which contributes to the water-conserving effect of vasopressin, is essentially an effect on the smooth muscle of the afferent glomerular arteriole. Sawyer (310) considers it the most primitive and the most widely distributed response to neurohypophyseal extract. Wooley (311) found that the sensitivity of peripheral vessels to mammalian posterior lobe extracts (Pitressin) has increased with the evolution of higher forms. The excitant dose could be supplied by endogenous secretion in mammals and birds, but probably not in reptiles, and certainly not in amphibians.

Kitchin (312) found that an infusion of Pitressin in man, in doses of 5 units every 30 min, caused an initial vasoconstriction in the hand accompanied by a slight increase in arterial pressure, both of which diminished as the infusion continued. Lysin-vasopressin, injected intravenously in doses of 20 to 300 mu to anesthetized cats, constricted the mesenteric and femoral vascular beds, had no significant effect on the pulmonary vascular bed, but caused a profound vasodilatation in the renal vascular bed, an effect also demonstrated by direct injection into the renal artery (313). Wagner & Braunwald (314) administered physiological doses of purified arginine-vasopressin and Pitressin® to patients with autonomic dysfunction and orthostatic hypotension. Infusions of 1 mu per min of purified vasopressin resulted in a 20 to 30 mm Hg rise in arterial pressure. Arterial pressures greater than 200 mm Hg systolic and 130 mm Hg diastolic were produced by a single intravenous injection of 1 unit of purified vasopressin, or by a continuous infusion of 10 mu per min. The increase in arterial pressure was related to a rise in total vascular resistance. Normal subjects with ganglionic blockade, who had previously shown no hypertensive response, showed a distinct rise when vasopressin was subsequently administered. The increased sensitivity to the pressor activity of vasopressin in patients with orthostatic hypotension may be related to increased reactivity of vascular smooth muscle and to the absence of normal depressor reflexes (314). For similar reasons in biological assays, pithing, decerebration, or adrenergic blocking drugs are employed in addition to deep anesthesia to enhance sensitivity to the vasopressor peptides (42). Prolonged elevation of arterial pressure in the rat and rabbit caused by Pitressin infusion increases the content of sodium in the aortic wall (315), but not the atrial content of sodium or potassium (316).

Lloyd and associates (317 to 320) studied the effect of sex castration and estrogen and progesterone administration on vascular responses to pitressin in rats. Females are more sensitive than males; an oophorectomy in the female reduces the response; castration in the male increases the vasopressor response or administration of estrogen, and administration of progesterone to the normal male increases the vasoconstrictor response; ovariectomy leads to a decrease in pressor response.

Vascular response to oxytocin.—Sawyer & Sawyer (310) felt that the vasodepressor effect of neurohypophyseal extract was traceable to its oxytocin content; van Dyke *et al.* (62) and Wooley (311) summarized the cardiovascular effect of oxytocin.

The continuous infusion of 2 to 10 mu per min to women caused no significant change in arterial pressure. Rapid intravenous injection of 0.2 unit produced a transient fall of 20 mm of Hg lasting 30 to 40 sec. Generalized peripheral vasodilatation follows the intravenous injection of 200 to 600 mu of Pitocin® (oxytocin) or Syntocinon® (oxytocin) to normal humans.

Brooks & Pickford (239, 241) have consistently demonstrated that oxytocin, administered to both the dehydrated and hydrated dog, causes an increase in renal plasma flow (iodopyracet or Diodrast clearance) without affecting glomerular filtration rate. This effect of oxytocin could be completely antagonized or prevented by simultaneous administration of vasopressin. However, Chan (243) has been unable to confirm these renal hemodynamic effects of oxytocin.

The direct brachial artery infusion of 20 mu causes a 98 per cent increase in blood flow to the hand and arm (321). Lloyd & associates (317 to 320) studied the effect of sex, castration, and gonadal hormones on vascular responses to oxytocin. Estrus, estrogens, progesterone, and pregnancy caused a vasopressor response to oxytocin in female rats; in male rats, castration caused a vasodepressor response, and estrogen caused a vasopressor response to oxytocin. Lloyd & Pickford (320) concluded that the vasodilator effect of oxytocin was traceable to a central neurogenic mechanism operating through the sympathetic nervous system. After sympathetic blockade and decerebration, oxytocin became vasopressor; and estrogens might depress sympathetic nervous activity or block the hypothetical central dilator action of oxytocin which masks a peripheral vasoconstrictor effect.

The physiological significance of the vascular effects of neurohypophyseal peptides in the mammalian organism is unclear. A number of investigators have directed their attention to the interactions of simultaneously circulating vasopressin and oxytocin, and found that intravenous administration of small amounts of vasopressin antagonized the effects of large doses of oxytocin on renal plasma flow (239, 241). The isoglutamine isomer of oxytocin can completely inhibit the pressor effect, in the anesthetized rat, of vasopressin in an $O:V$ dose ratio of 280 to 750:1 (67). The simultaneous intravenous infusion of one unit of oxytocin to 50 mu of vasopressin per minute inhibited the vasodilator effects of oxytocin on forearm and hand blood flow, as well as inhibiting any effect on arterial pressure (321). As an antagonist of oxytocin effect on the vasculature, lysine-vasopressin is one fifth as effective as arginine-vasopressin (3).

Mediator of Adenohypophyseal Hormones

While in the preterrestrial vertebrates, with the exception of the lung fish, a separate neural lobe and median eminence did not exist [Green and associates (2, 9)], the total neurohypophysis in these lower vertebrates, like the median eminence in tetrapods, appears to release neurosecretory material which regulates adenohypophyseal function by way of the hypophyseal portal system (2, 9, 16, 29, 42, 322, 323).

The results of innumerable experimental studies clearly indicate that neurohypophyseal secretions in mammals and other vetebrates can augment the release of ACTH and other tropic hormones from the anterior lobe. Destruction of the median eminence results in significant decreases in the release of ACTH following various stimuli (10, 42, 79, 324, 325, 326). Transplantation of the adenohypophysis to a site distant from the neurohypophysis, and particularly the median eminence, and conversely transplanting the isolated adenohypophysis to an area adjacent to the median eminence will decrease and increase, respectively, the release of ACTH (78, 79, 325, 327 to 343).

While it is clear that peptides produced in the neurohypophysis can stimulate release of tropic hormones from the anterior lobe, the exact nature of corticotropin-releasing factor (CRF), or other tropic releasing factors, is unknown. CRF is not now thought to be arginine- or lysine-vasopressin, or oxytocin, or vasotocin. Nichols (325) has reviewed in meticulous detail all the evidence for the role of antidiuretic hormone in corticotropin release. He concludes that neither antidiuretic hormone nor the vasopressins are corticotropin-releasing factors; van Dyke (78) concurs. Inhibition of antidiuretic hormone release by water loading, and stimulation of antidiuretic hormone release by nicotine and hypertonic mannitol, did not stimulate release of ACTH as measured by plasma cortisol in man (344).

Extensive recent studies involved with the purification of hypothalamic and posterior lobe extracts have clearly established that CRF is a polypeptide closely related to, but distinct from, the other active peptides of the neurohypophysis (41, 339, 345, 346, 347, 348).

It seems probable that to varying degrees all the neurohypophyseal peptides are capable of acting as neurohumoral mediators of adenohypophyseal secretion. Wilhelmi (349) demonstrated that the spawning reflex in fish could be initiated with extracts of beef and fish posterior pituitary proteins and that this same reflex could be elicited with purified arginine-vasopressin, natural vasopressin, and purified, natural oxytocin, in doses of 20 to 60 mu. The oxytocic vasopressor activity of fish pituitary preparations was in approximate proportion to their spawning reflex assay. Gonadotropin release could be elicited by the injection of Pitressin®, Pitocin®, lysine-vasopressin, and synthetic oxytocin to the female rabbit. The doses used were as large as four units given intravenously.

The involution of the mammary glands of lactating rats was greatly retarded by the chronic administration of oxytocin to the mothers following removal of the litters. No retardation of mammary involution occurred in the absence of the anterior pituitary gland (350, 351, 352).

The alterations of the bovine estrus cycle produced by 50 to 150 USP units of posterior pituitary extract or highly purified oxytocin (free of gonadotropic hormone contamination) demonstrated the role of oxytocin or a closely associated substance in the regulation of gonadotropic hormone secretion by the anterior pituitary (351, 353). Hypothalamic lesions near, or anterior to, the median eminence in lactating rats produced a block of both milk ejection and milk secretion (352). Electrical stimulation of various regions of the hypothalamus excites gonadotropic, adrenocorticotropic, and thyrotropic secretion (79). However, these probably do not involve Pitressin or oxytocin release, for Crosson and colleagues (354) were unable to demonstrate that doses of Pitressin or oxytocin in 200 to 500 mu every 8 hr to rats caused thyrotropin release. Andersson (355) demonstrated that local cooling of the preoptic region ("heat loss center") caused a conspicuous activation of the thyroid gland in unanesthetized goats.

INTERRELATIONSHIP WITH OTHER HORMONES

Large doses of Pitressin® (1 to 5 units) cause depletion of adrenal ascorbate in hypophysectomized rats (356) and potentiation of exogenous ACTH. The direct intra-arterial infusion of the adrenal glands of hypophysectomized dogs with synthetic lysine and arginine-vasopressin in doses of 100 to 400 mu per min causes a maximal increase of glucocorticoid secretion. Minimal activity could be detected with doses as low as 1 mu per min of arginine-vasopressin. Oxytocin, insulin, and glucagon did not show any cortisol-stimulating activity. The infusion of cyclic adenosine monophosphate caused an effect similar to that of arginine-vasopressin (357 to 361).

The interrelationships between glucocorticoids and the release, metabolism, and peripheral action of ADH are still unsettled. Certain observations in adrenal-insufficient men and animals have suggested that the absence of glucocorticoids increases neurohypophyseal release of antidiuretic hormones (362 to 371).

Other investigators have concluded that adrenal steroids do not alter the release, metabolism, or peripheral action of antidiuretic hormone in man, and that the effect of adrenal glucocorticoids on the renal handling of water is related to: (a) a direct action on the diluting segment of the nephron; and (b) a specific effect on renal hemodynamics and solute excretion (372). In the adrenal-insufficient dog with impaired water diuresis, we (unpublished observations) have been unable to improve the diuresis by sustained infusions of small doses of compound F into the carotid circulation, whereas systemic administration brings about an immediate improvement of the impaired diuresis. This suggests that a physiological level of glucocorticoid in the region of the neurohypophysis in the adrenal-insufficient animal does not improve the impaired diuresis. We have not been able to demonstrate an antagonism between Pitressin and adrenal glucocorticoids on the water transport across the isolated toad bladder (unpublished observations). Grage (373) studied the renal response to graded doses of Pitressin in conscious, hydrated, female dogs subjected to continuous infusions of epinephrine or norepinephrine, in doses of 0.25 to 1.5 μg per kg per min. Maximal antidiuresis could be completely abolished by simultaneous infusions of the pressor amines. It was concluded that epinephrine and norepinephrine directly inhibited the renal response to Pitressin and that epinephrine may affect the release of endogenous antidiuretic hormone.

The Effect of Certain Metabolic States on the Responsiveness to Antidiuretic Hormone

Chronic overhydration which is sustained in man for a period of three days causes a significant decrease in maximal urinary concentration and maximal negative free-water clearance in response to vasopressin (214, 374). The ability of high-protein diets to augment maximal urinary concentration and maximal negative free-water clearance is related to the urea content of the diet (214). However, Manitius et al. (375) suggest that high protein intake in contrast to high urea intake actually enhances the ability of dogs to concentrate urine by improving the efficiency of the process by which sodium and perhaps potassium are concentrated in the renal medulla. Hypercalcemia, of any duration or etiology, interferes with the renal concentrating mechanism in man, dog, and rat (376, 377, 378). The studies suggest that the impairment of the renal concentrating capacity results from a diminished ability to create and maintain a high concentration of sodium in the interstitial fluid of the medulla and papilla, and to an altered responsiveness of the distal portion of the nephron to ADH.

Assay Procedures

As yet no chemical method for the identification of specific neurohypophyseal peptides in biologic fluids is available. Reliance on bioassay techniques is still essential. Numerous reviews and articles have concentrated on the problem of assay of neurohypophyseal peptides (66, 99, 102, 121, 159, 160, 166, 245, 379 to 396).

From analysis of these various articles certain important trends are discernible: (*a*) an increasing emphasis on the use of plasma or whole blood rather than urine; (*b*) the fact that the assayable material is injected intravenously into the test animal rather than subcutaneously or intraperitoneally; (*c*) the fact that biochemical extraction procedures, such as chromatography, ion exchange, and electrophoresis, are being utilized to both concentrate and isolate specific hormones prior to assay, and to rule out the effects of nonspecific factors, such as histamine, 5-hydroxytryptamine, norepinephrine, and substance P (90); (*d*) utilization of thioglycollate, which specifically inactivates neurohypophyseal peptides; (*e*) the simultaneous utilization of multiple assay techniques to detect oxytocin; and (*f*) utilization of the synthetic or purified substance as standards in all bioassay procedures.

Although the various chemical extraction and concentrating procedures (61, 379, 381, 383, 393, 394, 395) will ultimately lead to the specific isolation of vasopressin or ADH from the blood for subsequent biochemical or bioassay detections, to date they have not been of greater value than the most sensitive bioassay procedures not involving extraction or concentration. The latter represent variations of the original technique of Jeffers *et al.* (397), subsequently improved in sensitivity and specificity by Dicker (159, 166, 384, 392). Heller's technique of utilizing the water-loaded ethanol-anesthetized rat with chronic ureteral fistulae seems to have produced the most sensitive bioassay procedure for antidiuretic hormone yet available. He has been able to detect as little as 0.625 μu of thioglycollate inactivable antidiuretic material. Heller (159) and Thorn (166) have stressed the importance of combining the measurement of urinary volume, urinary osmolality, or solute concentration and creatinine excretion on a single assay specimen, if possible, so that the effect of any change in glomerular filtration and solute excretion on urinary volume can be differentiated from a changing level of antidiuretic hormone.

Oxytocin.—Oxytocin is assayable by a combination of procedures both *in vivo* and *in vitro* and, as mentioned above, the emphasis has been on the simultaneous utilization of multiple assay techniques. The latter has been necessary because of the distinctly nonspecific nature of the assay techniques in their response to interfering substances (21, 90, 379). The most specific technique for assaying oxytocin seems to be the rabbit milk ejection (21). The sensitivity of this assay has been considerably increased by injection of the testing substance directly into the mammary artery (168). Even with the most sensitive technique for measurement of oxytocin, the range of minimal sensitivity is considerably above that for antidiuretic hormone, 50–500 μu per ml. However, a recent technique, using isolated mammary glands from lactating rats *in vitro* (386), may make it possible to detect concentrations of 5 to 50 μu per ml with considerable accuracy, the only major interfering substance being acetylcholine.

The rat uterus has largely replaced the guinea pig uterus in oxytocin assays. It is precise, sensitive, simple, and reliable, and if the bathing solution contains no magnesium the rat uterus is very insensitive to the vasopressins.

A major disadvantage of the rat uterus is that it is stimulated by 5-hydroxy-tryptamine, acetylcholine, substance P, bradykinin, potassium, and other substances which occur in plasma and tissue extracts, and is depressed by histamine (379).

A quotation from Sawyer (379) seems most appropriate.

Many methods for the biologic assay of oxytocin and vasopressin are available to the investigator. The nature of his problem must determine his choice. Standardization of neurohypophyseal extracts requires great precision, while high sensitivity is essential if material is limited. Tissue or blood extracts demand methods of great specificity. The assays discussed have useful individual characteristics. None, however, approaches the ideal that it be precise, specific, sensitive, economical, simple and reliable.

Some Clinical Pathologic States Involving Neurohypophyseal Hormones

Since the original description by Leaf *et al.* (398) of the physiological response in man to a sustained excess of Pitressin®, an increase in circulating antidiuretic hormone brought on by inappropriate release of ADH has been implicated in a number of clinical states (399 to 405).

Recently, Thorn (personal communication) has had the opportunity to measure the amount of antidiuretic material in the urine of a patient with bronchiogenic carcinoma and hyponatremia, and he was able to demonstrate a very large excretion of such antiduretic activity, much larger than could be ascribed to a physiological antidiuresis. This may represent the first direct demonstration of excess antidiuretic activity in the serum or urine of these patients.

Although antidiuretic hormone has frequently been implicated as an etiologic factor in edematous states, it is clear that marked edema and ascites can develop in the experimental animal in the complete absence of antidiuretic hormone (experimental diabetes insipidus in dogs).

Laragh *et al.* (406) and Buchborn (121) have found a significant correlation between plasma antidiuretic activity and serum osmolality in normal subjects and patients with various edematous states, but there was no evidence of excess levels in the clinical edematous subjects. Strauss (146) and Kleeman *et al.* (201) have outlined the possible role of antidiuretic hormone in water metabolism in normal and disease states. The Mayo Clinic group has recently classified the etiology of diabetes insipidus in more than 100 cases (407). The large number of idiopathic cases points to the deficiency of pathologic data in this disease. The difficulty in controlling diabetes insipidus during pregnancy, because of an increased requirement for ADH, has been noted by several investigators and is believed to be traceable to an increased inactivation, a change in the hormonal environment, or possibly a decreased renal responsiveness to circulating ADH (187, 191, 408, 409). A "new type of diabetes insipidus" caused by increased hormonal inactivation was recently described and, although it is an interesting concept, the data presented are inadequate to substantiate the conclusions drawn (410).

The effect of chlorothiazide and similar compounds in both nephrogenic diabetes insipidus and vasopressin-insufficient diabetes insipidus has received considerable attention (96, 127, 246, 411, 412, 413). The sustained antidiuretic effect of these drugs is most likely from slight depressions of renal hemodynamics secondary to a reduction in extracellular volume, and to a specific effect of the drug on the distal portion of the nephron producing a decrease in free-water clearance (248, 373). Recent studies by Cutler *et al.* (413) have shown that in patients with nephrogenic diabetes insipidus a severe reduction in renal hemodynamics did not cause the production of a concentrated urine as has been previously noted in physiological (213) and clinical diabetes insipidus (219). The lack of response of the patient with nephrogenic diabetes insipidus to antidiuretic hormone is ostensibly caused by an inability to "bind" and thereby utilize the hormone. Injection of vasopressin in two cases of nephrogenic diabetes insipidus was followed by the excretion of 50 to 80 per cent of the injected antidiuretic activity in contrast to normals or patients with vasopressin-sensitive diabetes insipidus who excreted 5 to 15 per cent (230).

LITERATURE CITED

1. Green, J. D., *Textbook of Endocrinology*, 883–98 (Saunders, Philadelphia, 1962)
2. Green, J. D., and Maxwell, D. S., *Comparative Endocrinology*, 368–92 (Wiley, New York, 1959)
3. Dicker, S. E., *J. Pharm. Pharmacol.*, **13**, 449–69 (1961)
4. Noble, R. L., *Can. J. Biochem. Physiol.*, **37**, 310–18 (1959)
5. Sawyer, W. H., *Recent Progr. Hormone Res.*, **17**, 437–65 (1961)
6. Welsh, J. H., *Comp. Endocrinol., Proc. Columbia Univ. Symp., Cold Spring Harbor, N. Y., 1958* (1959)
7. Scharrer, B., *Comp. Endocrinol., Proc. Columbia Univ. Symp., Cold Spring Harbor, N. Y., 1958* (1959)
8. Bargmann, W., *Endeavour*, **19**, 125–33 (1960)
9. Green, J. D., *Am. J. Anat.*, **88**, 225–90 (1951)
10. Rinne, U. K., *Acta Endocrinol.*, **35**, 5–108 (1960)
11. Leveque, T. F., and Small, M., *Endocrinology*, **66**, 641–62 (1960)
12. Gershenfeld, H. M., Tremezzani, J. H., and De Robertis, E., *Endocrinology*, **66**, 741–62 (1960)
13. Engelhardt, F. R., *Acta Neuroveget. (Vienna)*, **13**, 129 (1956)
14. Green, J. D., and VanBreeman, V. L., *Am. J. Anat.*, **97**, 177 (1955)
15. Diepen, R., *Pathophysiologia Diencephalica*, 122–33 (Springer-Verlag, Vienna, 1958)
16. Palay, S. L., *Am. J. Anat.*, **93**, 107 (1953)
17. Bargmann, W., *The Neurohypophysis*, 11–22 (Heller, H., Ed., Academic, London, 1957)
18. Heller, H., *Oxytocin*, 3–24 (Caldeyro-Barcia, R., and Heller, H., Eds., Pergamon, New York, 1961)
19. Sawyer, W. H., Munsick, R. A., and van Dyke, H. B., *Circulation*, Part II, **21**, 1027–37 (1960)
20. Gregoretti, L., *Acta Neuroveget. (Vienna)*, **10**, (1954)
21. van Dyke, H. B., Adamsons, K., Jr., and Engel, S. L., *Recent Progr. Hormone Res.*, **11**, 1–35 (1955)
22. Gregoretti, L., *Acta Neuroveget. (Vienna)*, **12**, 25 (1955)
23. Palay, S. L., *Progr. Neurobiol.*, **2**, 31–49 (1957)
24. Kleeman, C. R., Davson, H., and Levin, E., *J. Physiol. (London)* (In press, 1962)
25. Green, J. D., and Harris, G. W., *J. Endocrinol.*, **5**, 136 (1946/48)
26. Brettschneider, H., *Z. Mikroskop. Anat. Forsch.*, **62**, 30–39 (1956)
27. Sano, T., *Folia Anat. Japon.*, **27**, 345 (1955b)
28. Fisher, C., Ingram, H. W., and Ran-

son, S. W., *Am. J. Obstet. Gynecol.*, **36**, 1 (1938)

29. Wingstrand, K. G., *Comparative Endocrinology*, 393–403 (Wiley, New York, 1959)

30. Barnett, R. J., *Endocrinology*, **55**, 484–501 (1954)

31. Rennels, E. G., and Dreiger, G. A., *Anat. Record*, **122**, 193 (1955)

32. Palade, G. E., and Palay, S. L., *Anat. Record*, **118**, 129 (1954)

33. Hartmann, J., *Z. Zellforsch. Mikroskop. Anat.*, **48**, 291–308 (1958)

34. Howe, A., and Jewell, P. A., *J. Endocrinol.*, **18**, 118–24 (1959)

35. Hild, W., Guillemin, R., and Carton, C. A., *Hypothalamic Hypophyseal Interrelationships*, 17–26 (Fields, W. S., Ed., Thomas, Springfield, Ill., 1956)

36. Hild, W., *Texas Rept. Biol. Med.*, **12**, 474–88 (1954)

37. Pardoe, A. F., and Weatherall, M., *J. Physiol.* (*London*), **127**, 201–12 (1955)

38. Sloper, J. C., and Adams, C. W. M., *J. Pathol. Bacteriol.*, **72**, 587–602 (1956)

39. Andersson, B., and Jewell, P. A., *J. Endocrinol.*, **15**, 332/38 (1957)

40. Rodeck, H., Lederis, K., and Heller, H., *Endocrinology*, **21**, 225–28 (1960)

41. Schindler, W. J., *Proc. Roy. Soc.* (*London*), **55**, 125–30 (1962)

42. Sawyer, W. H., *Pharmacol. Rev.*, **13**, 225 (1961)

43. Rothballer, A. B., *Acta Neuroveget.* (*Vienna*), **13**, 179 (1956)

44. Carlyle, D. B., *Intern. Symp. Neurosekretion*, *2nd*, *Lund*, 18–19 (Springer-Verlag, Berlin, 1958)

45. De Robertis, E., and Bennett, H. S., *J. Biophys. Biochem.*, *Cytol.*, **2**, 307 (1955)

46. Stutinski, K., *Ann. Endocrinol.* (*Paris*), **14**, 722 (1953)

47. Heller, J., and Lederis, K., *J. Physiol.* (*London*), **147**, 229–314 (1959)

48. Acher, R., *Ann. Rev. Biochem.*, **29**, 547–76 (1960)

49. van Dyke, H. B., Chow, B. F., Greep, R. O., and Rothen, A., *Am. J. Pharmacol.*, **74**, 190–209 (1941)

50. Acher, R., and Fromageot, C., *Ergeb. Physiol.*, **48**, 286–327 (1955)

51. Acher, R., Light, A., and du Vigneaud, V., *J. Biol. Chem.*, **233**, 116–19 (1958)

52. Chauvet, J., Lenci, M. T., and Acher, R., *Biochim. Biophys. Acta*, **38**, 266–72 (1960)

53. Acher, R., and Fromageot, C., *The Neurohypophysis*, 39–48 (Butterworths, London, 1957)

54. Schally, A. V., and Porath, J., *Federation Proc.*, **21**, 208 (1962)

55. Light, A., Studer, R., and du Vigneaud, V., *Arch. Biochem. Biophys.*, **83**, 84–87 (1959)

56. Bartlett, M. F., Johl, A., Roeshe, R., Steodman, R. J., Stewart, F. H. C., Ward, D. N., and du Vigneaud, V., *J. Am. Chem. Soc.*, **78**, 2905 (1956)

57. Ward, D. N., and Guillemin, R. *Proc. Soc. Exptl. Biol. Med.*, **96**, 568–70 (1957)

58. Light, A., Acher, R., and du Vigneaud, V., *J. Biol. Chem.*, **288**, 633 (1957)

59. Light, A., and du Vigneaud, V., *Proc. Soc. Exptl. Biol. Med.*, **98**, 692–96 (1958)

60. Thorn, N. A., *Acta Endocrinol.*, **32**, 134–41 (1959)

61. Saffran M., Kaplan, B. U., Mishkin, M., and Muhlstock, B., *Endocrinology*, **70**, 43–46 (1962)

62. van Dyke, H. B., *Oxytocin*, 48–67 (Pergamon, New York, 1961)

63. du Vigneaud, V., Weinstock, G., Murti, V. V. S., Hope, D. B., and Kimbrough, R. D., Jr., *J. Biol. Chem.*, **235**, 64–66 (1960)

64. Boissonnas, R. A., *Polypeptides Which Affect Smooth Muscles and Blood Vessels*, 7–19 (Schachter, M., Ed., New York, 1960)

65. Sawyer, W. H., *Endocrinology*, **66**, 112–20 (1960)

66. Konzett, H., *Polypeptides Which Affect Smooth Muscles and Blood Vessels* 20–23 (Pergamon, New York, 1960)

67. Ressler, C., and Rachele, J. R., *Proc. Soc. Exptl. Biol. Med.*, **98**, 170–74 (1958)

68. Sawyer, W. H., *Nature*, **187**, 1030–31 (1960)

69. Sawyer, W. H., Munsick, R. A., and van Dyke, H. B., *J. Gen. Comp. Endocrinol.*, **1**, 30–60 (1961)

70. Maetz, J., Morrell, F., and Lahlouk, B., *Nature*, **184**, 1236–37 (1959)

71. Pickering, B. T., Heller, H., Sawyer, W. H., Munsick, R. A., and van Dyke, H. B., *Nature*, **184**, 1463–65 (1959)

72. Heller, H., and Pickering, B. T., *J. Physiol.* (*London*), **155**, 98–114 (1961)

73. Sawyer, W. H., Munsick, R. A., and van Dyke, H. B., *Endocrinology*, **67**, 137–38 (1960)

74. Munsick, R. A., Sawyer, W. H., and

van Dyke, H. B., *Endocrinology*, **66**, 860–71 (1960)

75. Katsoyannis, P. G., and du Vigneaud, V., *J. Biol. Chem.*, **233**, 1352–54 (1958)

76. du Vigneaud, V., Ressler, C., and Trippett, S., *J. Biol. Chem.*, **205**, 949 (1953)

77. Tuppy, H., *Biochim. Biophys. Acta*, **11**, 449 (1953)

78. van Dyke, H. B., *Vasopressins, Intern. Congr. Physiol. Sci., 21st, Buenos Aires, 1959*, 61–70

79. Harris, G. W., *Handbook of Physiology* Sec. 1, Chap. 39 (1960)

80. Boggan, A. W., and Reed, G. W., *Nature*, **181**, 1278–79 (1958)

81. Ford, D. H., and Hirschmann, A., *Anat. Record*, **130**, 302 (1958)

82. Sachs, H. *J. Neurochem.*, **5**, 297–303 (1960)

83. Dicker, S. E., and Nunn, J., *J. Physiol. (London)*, **136**, 235–47 (1957)

84. Kivalo, E., and Rinne, U. K., *Ann. Med. Exptl. Biol. Fenniae (Helsinki)*, **39**, 50–56 (1961)

85. Hollander, W., Jr., and Blythe, W. B., *Am. J. Physiol.*, **198**, 1129 (1960)

86. Capek, K., and Heller, J., *Physiol. Bohemoslov.*, **10**, 522–28 (1961)

87. Heller, J., *Physiol. Bohemoslov.*, **9**, 289–93 (1960)

88. Olivecrona, H., *Nature*, **173**, 1001 (1954)

89. Nibbelink, D. W., *Am. J. Physiol.*, **200**, 1229–32 (1961)

90. Lederis, K., *Gen. Comp. Endocrinol.*, **38**, 1589 (1962)

91. Adamson K., Jr., Engel, S. L., vans, Dyke, H. B., Schmidt-Nielsen, B., and Schmidt-Nielsen, K., *Endocrinology*, **58**, 272 (1956)

92. Currie, A. R., *J. Clin. Endocrinol. Metab.*, **20**, 947–51 (1960)

93. Dicker, S. E., and Tyler, J., *J. Physiol. (London)*, **121**, 206–14 (1953)

94. Fendlar, K., *Acta Physiol. Hung.*, **20**, 89–92 (1961)

95. Chauvet, J., Tenco, M. T., and Acher, R., *Biochim. Biophys. Acta*, **38**, 571–75 (1960)

96. Kaplan, S. A., Yuceoglu, A. M., and Strauss, J., *J. Diseases Children*, **97**, 308–13 (1959)

97. Bargmann, W., and Knoop, A., *Z. Zellforsch. Mikroskop. Anat.*, **52**, 256–77 (1960)

98. Rothballer, A. B., *Anat. Record*, **115**, 21 (1953)

99. Lauson, H. D., *Hormones in Human Plasma*, 225–93 (Antoniades, H. N., Ed., Churchill, London, 1960)

100. Noble, R. L., *The Neurohypophysis*, 97–106 (Butterworths, London, 1957)

101. Orloff, J., Wagner, H. N., Jr., and Davison, D. G., *J. Clin. Invest.*, **37**, 458 (1958)

102. Ginsburg, M., and Brown, L. M., *Brit. J. Pharmacol.*, **11**, 236–44 (1956)

103. Bisset, G. W., Lee, J., and Bromwich, A. F., *Lancet*, 1129–32 (Dec. 1, 1956)

104. Ginsburg, M., and Brown, L. M., *The Neurohypophysis*, 107–30 (Butterworths, London, 1957)

105. Walker, J. M., *The Neurohypophysis*, 221–32 (Butterworths, London, 1957)

106. Bisset, G. W., and Walker, J. M., *Brit. J. Pharmacol.*, **12**, 461–67 (1957)

107. Feldberg, W., and Vogt, M., *J. Physiol. (London)*, **107**, 372–81 (1948)

108. Koelle, G. B., and Geesey, L., *Proc. Soc. Exptl. Biol. Med.*, **106**, 625–28 (1961)

109. Abrahams, V. C., Koelle, G. B., and Smart, P., *J. Physiol. (London)*, **139**, 137–44 (1957)

110. Gale, C. C., Taleisnik, S., and McCann, S. M., *Am. J. Physiol.*, **201**, 811–14 (1961)

111. Cross, B. A., and Green, J. D., *J. Physiol. (London)*, **148**, 554–69 (1959)

112. Cross, B. A., *Oxytocin*, 24–27 (Pergamon, New York, 1961)

113. Mudd, R. H., Dodge, H. W., Jr., Clark, E. C., and Randall, R. V., *Proc. Staff Meetings Mayo Clinic*, **32**, 99–108 (1957)

114. Sawyer, C. H., and Fuller, G. R., *Electroencephal. Clin. Neurophysiol.* **12**, 83–93 (1960)

115. Sunsten, J. W., and Sawyer, W. H., *Exptl. Neurol.*, **4**, 548–61 (1961)

116. Kandel, E. R., *Federation Proc.*, **21**, 361 (1962)

117. Jewell, P. A., and Verney, E. B., *Proc. Roy. Soc. (London)*, **240**, 197–324 (1957)

118. Chaudhury, R. R., and Joplin, G. F., *J. Endocrinol.*, **21**, 125–28 (1960)

119. Radford, E. P., Jr., *Am. J. Cardiology*, **8**, 863–69 (1961)

120. Sawyer, W. H., and Gernandt, D. E., *Am. J. Physiol.*, **185**, 209–16 (1956)

121. Buchborn, E., *Endocrinology*, **61**, 375–79 (1957)

122. MacFarlane, W. V., and Robinson,

K. W., *J. Physiol.* (*London*), **61**, 375–79 (1957)

123. Fang, H. S., Lin, H. M., and Wang, S. C., *Am. J. Physiol.*, **202**, 212–16 (1962)

124. Dingman, J. F., and Gaitan, E., *J. Clin. Endocrinol. Metab.*, **19**, 1346–49 (1959)

125. Sharpless, S. K., and Rothballer, A. B., *Am. J. Physiol.*, **200**, 909–15 (1961)

126. Heller, H., *Physiol. Bohemoslov.*, **9**, 203 (1960)

127. Crawford, J. D., and Kennedy, G. C., *Nature*, **183**, 891–92 (1959)

128. Grewal, R. S., Lu, F. C., and Allmark, M. G., *J. Pharmacol. Exptl. Therap.*, **135**, 84–88 (1962)

129. Bisset, G. W., and Lee, J., *Lancet*, II, 715–19 (1958)

130. Fingl, E., Arnovitz, M. S., Carson, D. R., Datt, S. B., and Shurtleff, L. F., *Federation Proc.*, **14**, 339 (1955)

131. Kleeman, C. R., Rubini, M., Lamdin, E., and Epstein, F. H., *J. Clin. Invest.*, **34**, 448 (1955)

132. DeWied, D., and Jinks, R., *Proc. Soc. Exptl. Biol. Med.*, **99**, 44–45 (1958)

133. Baratz, R. A., and Ingraham, R. C., *Am. J. Physiol.*, **198**, 565–70 (1960)

134. Murdaugh, H. B., Jr., Sieker, H. O., and Manfredi, F., *J. Clin. Invest.*, **38**, 834–42 (1960)

135. Share, L., *Endocrinology*, **65**, 925–33 (1961)

136. Ledsome, J. R., Linden, R. J., and O'Connor, W. J., *J. Physiol.* (*London*), **159**, 87–100 (1961)

137. Hulet, W. H., and Smith, H. W., *J. Clin. Invest.*, **38**, 1972–80 (1959)

138. Perlmutt, J. H., *Federation Proc.*, **21**, 207 (1962)

139. Usami, S., Peric, B., and Chien, S., *Federation Proc.*, **21**, 207 (1962)

140. Gauer, O. H., Henry, J. P., Sieker, H. O., and Wendt, W. E., *J. Clin. Invest.*, **33**, 287–96 (1954)

141. Vera, R., and Croxatto, H., *J. Appl. Physiol.*, **7**, 172 (1954)

142. Hulet, W. H., *Federation Proc.*, **21**, 429 (1962)

143. Andersson, B., and Larsson, S., *Acta Physiol. Scand.*, **32**, 19–27 (1954)

144. Hawker, R. W., and Roberts, V. S., *Brit. Vet. J.*, **113**, 459–64 (1957)

145. Smith, H. W., *Am. J. Med.*, **23**, 623–52 (1957)

146. Strauss, M. B., *Body Water in Man*, 286 (Little, Brown, Boston, 1957)

147. Heller, H., and Eckstein, P., *Mem. Soc. Endocrinol.*, 25–37 (1956)

148. Welt, L. G., *Circulation*, **21**, 1002–8 (1960)

149. Gauer, O. H., Henry, J. P., and Sieker, H. O., *Progr. Cardiovascular Diseases*, **4**, 21–26 (1961)

150. Barbour, A. Bull, G. M., Evans, B. M., Hughes Jones, N. C., and Logothelopoulos, J., *Clin. Sci.*, **12**, 1–13 (1958)

151. Ullman, T., *J. Physiol.* (*London*), **155**, 417–37 (1961)

152. Baratz, R. A., Doig, A., and Adatto, I. J., *J. Clin. Invest*, **39**, 1539–45 (1960)

153. Hawker, R. W., *J. Clin. Endocrinol. Metab.*, **18**, 54–50 (1958)

154. Andersson, B., *The Neurohypophysis* 131–40 (Butterworths, London, 1957)

155. Abrahams, V. C., and Pickford, M., *J. Physiol.* (*London*), **126**, 329 (1954)

156. Chaudhury, R. R., and Walker, J. M., *J. Physiol.* (*London*, **143**, 16 (1958)

157. Carlson, I. H., and Holmes, W. N., *J. Endocrinol.*, **24**, 23–32 (1962)

158. LaBella, F. S., Beaulieu, G., and Reiffenstein, R. J., *Nature*, 173–74 (Jan. 13, 1962)

159. Heller, J., and Stulc, J., *Physiol. Bohemoslov.*, **8**, 558–64 (1959)

160. Heller, J., and Stulc, J., *Physiol. Bohemoslov.*, **9**, 5–12 (1960)

161. Heller, J., and Stulc, J., *Physiol. Bohemoslov.*, **9**, 93–98 (1960)

162. Heller, J., *Physiol. Bohemoslov.*, **9**, 283–88 (1960)

163. Heller, J., and Hradvoca, L., *Physiol. Bohemoslov.*, **9**, 351–59 (1960)

164. Heller, J., *Physiol. Bohemoslov.*, **10**, 167–72 (1961)

165. Chaudhury, R. R., *Clin. Sci.*, **19**, 641–44 (1960)

166. Thorn, N. A., *J. Exptl. Med.*, **105**, 585–90 (1957)

167. Blackmore, W. P., and Chester, H. T., *Endocrinology*, **59**, 493–94 (1956)

168. Fitzpatrick, R. J., *Oxytocin*, 358–79 (Pergamon, London, 1961)

169. Thorn, N. A., *Acta Endocrinol.*, **30**, 472–76 (1959)

170. Dingman, J. F., *Am. J. Med. Sci.*, **235**, 79–99 (1958)

171. Lauson, H. D., and Bocanegra, M., *Am. J. Physiol.*, **200**, 493–98 (1961)

172. Lauson, H. D., *Hormones in Human Plasma*, 316, 352 (Churchill, London, 1960)

173. Silver, L., Schwartz, I. L., Fong, C. T. O., Debons, A. F., and Dahl, L. K., *J. Appl. Physiol.*, **16**, 297–99 (1961)

174. Ginsburg, M., *Polypeptides Which Af-*

fect Smooth Muscles and Blood Vessels, 91 (Pergamon, New York, 1960)

175. Ginsburg, M., *J. Endocrinol.*, **16**, 217–26 (1957)

176. Heller, H., *The Neurohypophysis*, 77–96 (Academic, London, 1957)

177. Heller, H., and Zaidi, S. M., *Brit. J. Pharmacol.*, **12**, 284–92 (1957)

178. Heller, H., *Polypeptides Which Affect Smooth Muscles and Blood Vessels*, 59–69 (Pergamon, New York, 1960)

179. Ginsburg, M., and Smith, M. W., *Brit. J. Pharmacol.*, **14**, 345–52 (1960)

180. Chaudhury, R. R., and Walker, J. M., *J. Endocrinol.*, **19**, 189–92 (1959)

181. Gonzalez-Panizza, V. H., Sica-Blanco, Y., and Mendez-Bauer, C., *Oxytocin*, 347–59 (Pergamon, New York, 1961)

182. Hooper, K. C., *Polypeptides Which Affect Smooth Muscles and Blood Vessels*, 83–86 (Pergamon, New York, 1960)

183. Hooper, K. C., *J. Physiol. (London)*, **148**, 238 (1959)

184. Hipsley, E. H., and McKellar, J. W., *J. Endocrinol.*, **19**, 345 (1960)

185. Riad, A. M., and Scandrett, F. J., *Nature*, **193**, 372–73 (1962)

186. Dicker, S. E., *Polypeptides Which Affect Smooth Muscles and Blood Vessels*, 79–82 (Pergamon, New York, 1960)

187. Hooper, K. C., *Biochem. J.*, **74**, 297–300 (1960)

188. Smith, M. W., and Sachs, H., *Biochem. J.*, **79**, 663–69 (1961)

189. Dicker, S. E., and Whyley, G. A., *J. Obstet. Gynaecol. Brit. Commonwealth*, **66**, 605–9 (1959)

190. Tuppy, H., *Polypeptides Which Affect Smooth Muscles and Blood Vessels*, 49–58 (Pergamon, New York, 1960)

191. Hawker, R. W., *Quart. J. Exptl. Physiol.*, **41**, 301–8 (1956)

192. Dicker, S. E., and Greenbaum, A. L., *J. Physiol. (London)*, **132**, 199–212 (1956)

193. Hawker, R. W., *J. Exptl. Physiol.*, **41**, 301–8 (1956)

194. Verney, E. B., *Proc. Royal Soc. (London), B*, **135**, 25–107 (1947–48)

195. Edelman, I. S., *Ann. Rev. Physiol.*, **23**, 37–70 (1961)

196. Wirz, H., *Ann. Rev. Physiol.*, **23**, 577–606 (1961)

197. Giebisch, G., *Ann. Rev. Physiol.*, **24**, 357–420 (1962)

198. Berliner, R. W., Levinsky, N. G., and Davidson, D. G., *Am. J. Med.*, **24**, 730–44 (1958)

199. Ullrich, K. J., Kramer, K., and Boylan, J. W., *Progr. Cardiovascular Diseases*, **3**, 395–431 (1961)

200. Leaf, A., and Frazier, H. S., *Progr. Cardiovascular Diseases*, **4**, 47–64 (1961)

201. Kleeman, C. R., and Maxwell, M. H., *Clinical Disorders of Fluid and Electrolyte Metabolism* (McGraw-Hill, New York, 1962)

202. Gottschalk, C. W., *The Physiologist*, **4**, 35–55 (1961)

203. Gottschalk, C. W., *Circulation*, **21**, 861–69 (1960)

204. Lamdin, E., *Arch. Internal Med.*, **19**, 644–71 (1959)

205. Ochwadt, B., *Progr. Cardiovascular Diseases*, **3**, 501–10 (1961)

206. Schmidt-Nielsen, K., and Pennycuik, P., *Am. J. Physiol.*, **200**, 746–50 (1960)

207. Lassiter, W. E., Gottschalk, C. W., and Mylle, M., *Am. J. Physiol.*, **200**, 1139–47 (1961)

208. Jaenike, J. R., *J. Clin. Invest.*, **40**, 144–51 (1961)

209. Kiil, F., and Aukland, F., *Scand. J. Clin. Lab. Invest.*, **12**, 277–89 (1960)

210. Jaenike, J. R., *Am. J. Physiol.*, **199**, 1205–10 (1960)

211. Ullrich, K. J., *Circulation*, **21**, Part II, 869–74 (1960)

212. Jaenike, J. R., and Berliner, R., *J. Clin. Invest*, **39**, 481–90 (1960)

213. Berliner, R. W., and Davidson, D. G., *J. Clin. Invest.*, **36**, 1416–27 (1957)

214. Epstein, F. H., Kleeman, C. R., Pursel, S., and Hendrix, A., *J. Clin. Invest.*, **36**, 635–41 (1957)

215. Schmidt-Nielsen, B., O'Dell, R., and Osaki, H., *Am. J. Physiol.*, **200**, 1125–32 (1961)

216. Kiil, F., and Aukland, K., *Scand. J. Clin. Lab. Invest*, **12**, 290–99 (1960)

217. Bray, G. A., *Am. J. Physiol.*, **199**, 1211–14 (1960)

218. Maffly, R. H., Hays, R. M., Lamdin, E., and Leaf, A., *J. Clin. Invest.*, **39**, 630–41 (1960)

219. Kleeman, C. R., Maxwell, M. H., and Rockney, R. E., *Clin. Res. Proc.*, **6**, 295 (1958)

220. Hollander, W., Jr., Williams, T. F., Fordham, C. C. III, and Welt, L. G., *J. Clin. Invest*, **36**, 1059–71 (1957)

221. Lilienfield, L. S., Maganzini, H. C., and Bauer, M. H., *Federation Proc.*, **19**, 363 (1960)

222. Ussing, H. H., and Zerahn, A., *Acta Physiol. Scand.*, 23, 110–27 (1951)

223. Koefoed-Johnsen, V., and Ussing, H. H., *Acta Physiol. Scand.*, 28, 60–76 (1953)

224. Whittembury, G., Sugino, N., and Solomon, A. K., *Nature*, 187, 699–701 (1960)

225. Solomon, A. K., *Membrane Transport and Metabolism, Proc. Symp.*, 94–99 (Academic, London, 1961)

226. Darmady, E. M., Durant, J., Matthews, E. R., and Stranack, F., *Clin. Sci.*, 19, 228–43 (1960)

227. Fong, C. T. O., Schwartz, I. L., Popenoe, E. A., Silver, L., and Schoessler, M. A., *J. Am. Chem. Soc.*, 81, 2592 (1959)

228. Fong, C. T. O., Silver, L., Christman, D. R., and Schwartz, I. L., *Proc. Natl. Acad. Sci. US*, 46, 1273–77 (1960)

229. Ginetzinsky, A. G., *Nature*, 182, 1218–19 (1958)

230. Dick, S. E., and Eggleton, M. G., *Amer. J. Physiol.*, 154, 378–84 (1960)

231. Thorn, N. A., Knudsen, P. J., and Koefoed, J., *Acta Endocrinol.*, 38, 571–76 (1961)

232. Leaf, A., *J. Gen. Physiol.*, 43, 175–89 (1960)

233. Berlyne, G. M., *Nature*, 185, 389 (1960)

234. Berlyne, G. M., *Clin. Sci.*, 19, 619–29 (1960)

235. Kaplan, D., Meyer, R., Chan, W. L., and Sawyer, W. H. [Unpublished observations quoted in Sawyer's article in *Pharmacol. Rev.*, 13, 225–27 (1961)]

236. Abdul-Karim, R., and Assali, N. S., *J. Lab. Clin. Med.*, 57, 522–32 (1961)

237. Thomson, W. B., *Am. J. Physiol.*, 145, 12–13 (1958)

238. Cross, R. B., Dicker, S. E., Kitchin, A. H., Lloyd, S., and Pickford, M., *Am. J. Physiol.*, 153, 553–61 (1960)

239. Brooks, F. P., and Pickford, M., *The Neurohypophysis*, 141–56 (Butterworths, 1957)

240. Anslow, W. P., Jr., and Wesson, L. G., Jr., *Am. J. Physiol.*, 182, 561–66 (1955)

241. Brooks, F. P., and Pickford, M., *Am. J. Physiol.*, 142, 468–93 (1958)

242. Pickford, M., *Oxytocin*, 68–86 (Pergamon, New York, 1961)

243. Chan, W. Y., *Pharmacol. Rev.*, 13, 225–27 (1961)

244. Thorn, N. A., and Milewski, B., *Proc. Soc. Exptl. Biol. Med.*, 100, 276–29 (1959)

245. Thorn, N. A., *Danish Med. Bull.*, 7, 113–18 (1960)

246. Cross, R. B., *Am. J. Physiol.*, 148, 55–56 (1959)

247. Kinne, R., MacFarlane, W. V., and Budtz-Olsen, O. E., *Nature*, 192, 1084–85 (1961)

248. Orloff, J., and Burg, M., *Metabolic Basis of Inherited Diseases*, 1274–94 (McGraw-Hill, New York, 1960)

249. Kellogg, R. H., Burack, W. R., and Isselbacher, K. J., *Proc. Soc. Exptl. Biol. Med.*, 81, 333–38 (1952)

250. Jacobson, H. N., and Kellogg, R. H., *Am. J. Physiol.*, 184, 376 (1956)

251. Brooks, F. P., and Pickford, M., *Pharmacol. Rev.*, 13, 256 (1961)

252. Thorn, N. A., *Danish Med. Bull.*, 7, 108–12 (1960)

253. Ali, M. N., *Brit. J. Pharmacol.*, 13, 131–37 (1958)

254. van Dyke, H. B., Engel, S. L., and Adamson, K., *Proc. Soc. Exptl. Biol. Med.*, 91, 484–86 (1956)

255. Munsick, R. A., Sawyer, W. H., and van Dyke, H. B., *Endocrinology*, 63, 688–93 (1958)

256. Peachey, L. D., and Rasmussen, H., *J. Biophys. Biochem. Cytol.*, 10, 529–53 (1961)

257. Leaf, A., and Hays, R. M., *Recent Progr. Hormone Res.*, 17, 467–92 (1961)

258. Bentley, P. J., *J. Endocrinol.*, 17, 201–9 (1958)

259. Edelman, I. S., and Petersen, M. J., *Proc. Ann. Meeting Am. Soc. Clin. Invest.*, 54th, 21, (1962)

260. Rasmussen, H., and Schwartz, I. L., *Proc. Ann. Meeting, Am. Soc. Clin. Invest.*, 54th, 58, (1962)

261. Rasmussen, H., Schwartz, I. L., Schoessler, M. A., Silver, L., and Fong, C. T. O., *Proc. Natl. Acad. Sci. US*, 46, 1278–98 (1960)

262. Orloff, J., and Handler, J. S., *Biochem. Biophys, Res. Commun.*, 5, 63–66 (1961)

263. Bentley, P. J., *J. Endocrinol.*, 18, 327–33 (1959)

264. Marc-Aurele, J., Holliday, M. A., Christman, D. R., Schoessler, M. A., Rasmussen, H., and Schwartz, I. L., *Clin. Res.*, 10, 253 (1962)

265. Lehninger, A. L., and Neubert, D., *Proc. Natl. Acad. Sci. US*, 47, 129–36 (1961)

266. Neubert, D., and Lehninger, A. L., *J. Biol. Chem.*, 237, 952 (1962)

267. Hays, R. M., and Leaf, A., *J. Gen. Physiol.*, **45**, 602A (1962)

268. Leaf, A., and Dempsey, E., *J. Biol. Chem.*, **235**, 2160–63 (1960)

269. Leaf, A., and Page, L. B., *J. Gen. Physiol.*, **41**, 657–58 (1958)

270. Bentley, P. J., *Endocrinology*, **21**, 161–70 (1960)

271. Frazier, H. S., Dempsey, E. F., and Leaf, A., *J. Gen. Physiol.*, **45**, (1962)

272. Curran, P. F., Herrara, F. C., and Flanigan, W. J., *Federation Proc.*, **21**, 145 (1962)

273. Herrera, F. C., and Curran, P. F., *J. Gen. Physiol.*, **45**, 602 (1962)

274. Wright, J., *J. Physiol. (London)*, **152**, (1960)

275. Fuhrman, F. A., and Ussing, H. H., *J. Cellular Comp. Physiol.*, **38**, 109–30 (1951)

276. Petersen, M. J. and Edelman, I. S., *Federation Proc.*, **21**, 146 (1962)

277. Hays, R. M., and Leaf, A., *Ann. Internal Med.*, **54**, 700–9 (1961)

278. Berger, E., and Marshall, J. M., *Am. J. Physiol.*, **201**, 931–34 (1961)

279. Marshall, J. M., and Csapo, A. I., *Endocrinology*, **68**, 1026–35 (1961)

280. Coutinho, E., and Csapo, A. I., *J. Gen. Physiol.*, **43**, 13–28 (1959)

281. Berndt, W. O., and Gosselin, R. E., *Science*, **134**, 1987–88 (1961)

282. Fishman, R. A., *J. Clin. Invest.*, **38**, 1698–707 (1959)

283. Aulsebrook, K. A., *Endocrinology*, **68**, 1063–65 (1961)

284. Bergen, S. S., Jr., Sullivan, R., Hellon, J. G., Willis, S. W., Jr., and Van Itallie, T. B., *Am. J. Physiol.*, **199**, 136–38 (1960)

285. Mirsky, I. A., and Perisutti, G., *Biochem. Biophys. Acta*, **50**, 603–4 (1961)

286. Goodfriend, T. L., *J. Biol. Chem.*, **236**, 1241–43 (1961)

287. Goodfriend, T. L., and Kirkpatrick, J., *Clin. Res.*, **10**, 248 (1962)

288. Canfer, J., and Titus, E., *Biochim. Biophys. Acta*, **54**, 601–3 (1961)

289. Sréter, F. A., and Friedman, S. M., *Proc. Soc. Exptl. Biol. Med.*, **106**, 10–13 (1961)

290. McCann, S., and Taleisnik, S., *Am. J. Physiol.*, **199**, 847–50 (1960)

291. Parlow, A. F., *Federation Proc.*, **17**, 402 (1958)

292. Symposium held in the Univ. of Montevideo, in *Oxytocin* (Symposia) (Pergamon, London, 1961)

293. Pernow, B., *Polypeptides Which Affect Smooth Muscles and Blood Vessels*, 171–78 (Pergamon, London, 1960)

294. Boissonnas, R. A., Guttman, S. T., Jaquenoud, P. A., Waller, J. R., Konzett, H., and Berde, B., *Nature*, **178**, 206–11 (1956)

295. Berde, B., Doepfner, W., and Konzett, H., *Brit. J. Pharmacol.*, **12**, 209–14 (1957)

296. Cowie, A. T., and Folley, S. J., *The Neurohypophysis*, 183–97 (Butterworths, London, 1957)

297. Cowie, A. T., and Folley, S. J., *Oxytocin*, 198, 201 (Pergamon, London, 1961)

298. Schofield, B. M., *J. Physiol. (London)*, **138**, 1–10 (1957)

299. Pose, S. V., and Fielitz, C., *Oxytocin*, 229–46 (Pergamon, London, 1961)

300. Muller, H. M., *Oxytocin*, 137–57 (Pergamon, London, 1961)

301. Csapo, A., *Oxytocin*, 100–26 (Pergamon, London, 1961)

302. Caldeyro-Barcia, R., and Sereno, J. A., *Oxytocin*, 177–202 (Pergamon, London, 1961)

303. Tanaka, K., and Nakajo, S., *Endocrinology*, **70**, 453–58 (1962)

304. Linzell, J. L., *Physiol. Rev.*, **39**, 534–76 (1959)

305. Katsoyannis, P. G., *J. Am. Chem. Soc.*, **79**, 109–11 (1957)

306. Ressler, C., and du Vigneaud, V., *J. Am. Chem. Soc.*, **79**, 4511–15 (1957)

307. Evans, D. H., Schild, H. O., and Thesleff, S., *J. Physiol. (London)*, **143**, 474–85 (1958)

308. Jung, H., *Oxytocin*, 87–99 (Pergamon London, 1961)

309. Poseiro, J. J., and Noriega-Guerra, L., *Oxytocin*, 158–76 (Pergamon, London, 1961)

310. Sawyer, W. H., *Physiol. Zool.*, **25**, 84–89 (1952)

311. Woolley, J., *J. Exptl. Biol.*, **36**, 453 (1959)

312. Kitchin, A. H., *Clin. Sci.*, **16**, 639–44 (1957)

313. Barer, G. R., *J. Physiol. (London)*, **156**, 49–66 (1961)

314. Wagner, N., Jr., and Braunwald, B., *J. Clin. Invest.*, **35**, 1412–18 (1956)

315. Daniel, E. E., Dodd, A., and Hunt, J., *Arch. Intern. Pharm. Pharmacol. Dyn.*, **119**, 43–55 (1959)

316. Hansen, K. M., and Johnson, J. A., *Am. J. Physiol.*, **190**, 81–83 (1957)

317. Honore, L. H., and Lloyd, S., *J. Physiol. (London)*, **159**, 183–90 (1961)

318. Lloyd, S., *J. Physiol. (London)*, **148**, 625–32 (1959)

319. Lloyd, S., *J. Physiol. (London)*, 149, 586–92 (1959)

320. Lloyd, S., and Pickford, M., *J. Physiol. (London)*, 155, 161–74 (1961)

321. Kitchin, A. H., Lloyd, S. M., and Pickford, M., *Clin. Sci.*, 18, 399–407 (1959)

322. Arko, H., and Kivalo, E., *Acta Endocrinol.*, 29, 9–14 (1958)

323. Jorgensen, C. B., and Larsen, L. O., *Ergeb. Biol.*, 22, 1–29 (1960)

324. Hume, D. M., *Pathophysiologica Diencephalica*, 217–28 (Springer-Verlag, Vienna, 1958)

325. Nichols, B. L., Jr., *Yale J. Biol.*, 33, 415–34 (1961)

326. Jorgensen, C. B., Larsen, L. O., Rosenhilde, P., and Wingstrand, K. G., *Comp. Biochem. Physiol.*, 1, 38–43 (1960)

327. Martini, L., and Dipoli, A., *J. Endocrinol.*, 13, 229 (1956)

328. Nikitovitch-Winer, M., and Everett, J. W., *Pathophysiologica Diencephalica*, 217–28 (Springer-Verlag, Vienna, 1958)

329. Earley, L. E., Kahn, M., and Orloff, J., *J. Clin. Invest.*, 40, 857–65 (1961)

330. Saffran, M., and Schally, A. V., *Endocrinology*, 57, 439 (1955)

331. McDonald, R. K., and Weise, V. K., *Proc. Soc. Exptl. Biol. Med.*, 92, 107 (1956)

332. Saffran, M., and Schally, A. V., *Can. J. Biochem. Physiol.*, 33, 408 (1955)

333. Sayers, G., and Burks, R., *J. Clin. Endocrinol.*, 15, 840 (1955)

334. Sobel, H., Levy, R., Marmorston, J., Schapiro, S., and Rosenfeld, S., *Proc. Soc. Exptl. Biol. Med.*, 89, 10 (1959)

335. McDonald, R. K., Wagner, H. N., Jr., and Weise, V. K., *Proc. Soc. Exptl. Biol. Med.*, 96, 652–55 (1957)

336. McCann, S. M., *Endocrinology*, 60, 664 (1957)

337. Martini, L., Depoli, A., and Curri, S., *Proc. Soc. Exptl. Biol Med.*, 91, 490 (1956)

338. Shibusawa, K., Saito, S., Fukuda, M., and Yoshimura, F., *Endocrinol. Japon.*, 2, 47 (1955)

339. Nichols, B., Jr., and Guillemin, R., *Endocrinology*, 64, 914–20 (1959)

340. DeWied, A., *Endocrinology*, 68, 956–70 (1961)

341. Rumsfeld, H. W., Jr., and Porter, J. C., *Endocrinology*, 70, 62–67 (1962)

342. Brizze, K. R., and Eik-Nes, K. B., *Endocrinology*, 68, 166–69 (1961)

343. Martini, L., *Pathophysiologica Diencephalica*, 229 (Springer-Verlag, Vienna, 1958)

344. Schuster, S., *J. Endocrinol.*, 21, 171–76 (1960)

345. Saffran, M., *Methods Med. Res.*, 224–29 (1961)

346. Porter, J. C., and Rumsfeld, H. W., Jr., *Endocrinology*, 58, 359 (1956)

347. Saffran, M., *Can. J. Biochem. Physiol.*, 37, 319–29 (1959)

348. Guillemin, R., Dear, W. E., Nichols, B., Jr., and Lipscomb, H. S. *Proc. Soc. Exptl. Biol. Med.*, 101, 107–11 (1959)

349. Wilhelmi, A. E., Pickford, G. E., and Sawyer, W. H., *Endocrinology*, 57, 243–52 (1955)

350. Martini, L., Mira, L., Pecile, A., and Saito, S., *J. Endocrinol.*, 18, 245–50 (1959)

351. Benson, G. K., and Folley, S. J., *J. Endocrinol.*, 16, 189–201 (1957)

352. McCann, S. M., Mack, R., and Gale, C., *Endocrinology*, 63, 870–89 (1959)

353. Armstrong, D. T., and Hansel, W., *Federation Proc.*, 17, 6 (1958)

354. Crosson, J., Falch, J., and Reichlin, S., *Endocrinology*, 66, 777–79 (1960)

355. Andersson, B., *Life Sciences*, 1 (1960)

356. Royce, P. C., and Sayers, G., *Proc. Soc. Exptl. Biol. Med.*, 98, 70–74 (1958)

357. Hilton, J. G., *Circulation*, 21, Part II, 1038–46 (1960)

358. Hilton, J. G., Scian, L. F., Westermann, C. D., and Kruesi, O. R., *Science*, 129, 971 (1959)

359. Hilton, J. G., Scian, L. F., Westermann, C. D., Nakano, J., and Kruesi, O. R., *Endocrinology*, 67, 298–310 (1960)

360. Shultin, J. G., Kruesi, O. R., Nedeljkovic, R. I., and Scian, L. F., *Endocrinology*, 68, 908–13 (1961)

361. Bohus, B., and Endroczi, E., *Acta Physiol.*, 20, 285–92 (1961)

362. Dingman, J. F., and Despointes, R. H., *J. Clin. Invest.*, 39, 1851–63 (1960)

363. Dingman, J. F., *Am. J. Med. Sci.*, 235, 79–99 (1958)

364. Dingman, J. F., Despointes, R. H., Laidlaw, J. C., and Thorn, G. W., *J. Lab. Clin. Med.*, 51, 690–700 (1958)

365. Gaunt, R., Lloyd, C. W., and Chart, J. J., *The Neurohypophysis*, 233–49 (Butterworths, London, 1957)
366. Gaunt, R., Birnie, J. H., and Eversole, W. J., *Physiol. Rev.*, 29, 281 (1949)
367. Ginsberg, M., *J. Endocrinol.*, 11, 165 (1954)
368. Kleeman, C. R., Maxwell, M. H., and Rockney, R. E., *J. Clin. Invest.*, 37, 1799 (1958)
369. Kleeman, C. R., Koplowitz, J., Maxwell, M. H., Cutler, R. E., and Dowling, J. T., *J. Clin. Invest.*, 39, 472–80 (1960)
370. Lindeman, R. D., VanBuren, H. C., and Raisz, L. G., *J. Clin. Invest.*, 40, 152–58 (1961)
371. Raisz, L., McNeely, G., Saxon, W. F., and Rosenbaum, J. D., *J. Clin. Invest.*, 36, 767 (1957)
372. Cutler, R. E., Kleeman, C. R., Koplowitz, J., Maxwell, M. H., and Dowling, J. T., *J. Clin. Invest.* (July 1962 issue)
373. Grage, T. B., *Federation Proc.*, 21, 208 (1962)
374. Yoong, M. C., and Hong, S. K., *J. Appl. Physiol.*, 16, 815–18 (1961)
375. Manitius, A., Pigeon, G., and Epstein, F. H., *Clin. Res.*, 10, 252 (1962)
376. Zeffren, J. L., *J. Clin. Invest.*, 39, 1042 (1960)
377. Epstein, F. H., Beck, D., Carone, F. A., Levitin, H., and Manitius, A., *J. Clin. Invest.*, 38, 1214–21 (1959)
378. Manitius, A. Levitin, H., Beck, D., and Epstein, F. H., *J. Clin. Invest.*, 39, 693–97 (1960)
379. Sawyer, W. H., *Methods Med. Res.*, Chap. 15 (1961)
380. Bisset, G. W., *Oxytocin*, 380–99 (Pergamon, New York, 1961)
381. Jessup, D. C., Carroll, K. K., and Nobel, R. L., *Can. J. Biochem. Physiol.*, 39, 1647–49 (1961)
382. Walker, J. M., *Polypeptides Which Affect Smooth Muscles and Blood Vessels*, 3–48 (Pergamon, New York, 1961)
383. Weinstein, H., Berne, R., and Sachs, R., *Endocrinology*, 66, 712–18 (1960)
384. Dicker, S. E., *J. Physiol.*, (*London*), 122, 149–57 (1953)
385. Thorn, N. A., *Physiol. Rev.*, 38, 169–95 (1953)
386. Sjoholm, I., *Nature*, 193, 77–78 (1962)
387. Bisset, G. W., *Polypeptides Which Affect Smooth Muscles and Blood Vessels*, 87–89 (Pergamon, New York, 1961)
388. Baratz, R. A., *Proc. Soc. Exptl. Biol. Med.*, 100, 296–99 (1959)
389. Arimura, A., and Dingman, J. F., *Nature*, 184, 878–81 (1959)
390. Hunter, J., Kalant, H., and Ogilvie, J. C., *Can. J. Biochem. Biophys.*, 37, 1215–25 (1959)
391. Andersson, B., and Persson, N., *Acta Physiol. Scand.*, 42, 257–61 (1958)
392. Dettelbach, H. R., *Am. J. Physiol.*, 192, 379–86 (1958)
393. Thorp, R. H., *Methods in Hormone Research*, 495–519 (Academic, New York, 1962)
394. Walker, J. M., *Hormones in Blood*, 149–76 (Academic, New York, 1962)
395. Walker, J. M., *Hormones in Blood*, Chap. 5 (Academic, New York, 1962)
396. MacFarlane, W. V., *Clinical Endocrinology*, 637–48 (Grune & Stratton, New York, 1960)
397. Jeffers, W. A., Livezey, M. M., and Austin, J. H., *Proc. Exptl. Biol. Med.*, 50, 184–86 (1942)
398. Leaf, A., Bartter, F. C., Santos, R. F., and Wrong, O., *Ann. Internal. Med.*, 51, 1420 (1959)
399. Schwartz, W. B., Bennett, W., Curelop, S., and Bartter, F. C., *Am. J. Med.*, 23, 529 (1957)
400. Schwartz, W. B., Tassel, D., and Bartter, F. C., *New Engl. J. Med.*, 262, 743 (1960)
401. Roberts, H. J., *Ann. Internal Med.*, 51, 1420–26 (1959)
402. Carter, N. W., Rector, F. C., Jr., and Seldin, D. W., *New Engl. J. Med.*, 264, 67 (1961)
403. Williams, M. J., and Sommers, S. C. (In press)
404. Rees, J. R., Rosalki, S. B., and McLean, A. D. W., *Lancet*, II, 1005 (1960)
405. Epstein, F. H., Levitin, H., Glaser, G., and Lavietis, P., *New Engl. J.* 265, 513–18 (1961)
406. Laragh, J., van Dyke, H. B., Jacobson, J., Adamsons, K., Jr., and Engel, S. L., *J. Clin. Invest.*, 35, 897–903 (1956)
407. Randall, R. V., Clark, E. C., and Bahn, R. C., *Proc. Staff Meetings Mayo Clinic*, 34, 299–302 (1959)
408. Scheer, R. L., Raisz, L. G., and Lloyd,

C. W., *J. Clin. Endocrinol. Metab.*, 19, 805–11 (1959)

409. Assali, N. S., Dingman, W. J., and Longo, L., *J. Clin. Endocrinol. Metab.*, 20, 581–92 (1960)

410. Hankiss, J., Keszthelyi, M., and Siro, B., *Am. J. Med. Sci.*, Ser. II, 242, 125–605—139–619 (1961)

411. Kovacs, K., David, M. A., and Laszlo, F. A., *Acta Med. Hung. Acad. Sci.*, 17, 301–10 (1961)

412. Kennedy, G. C., and Crawford, J. D., *J. Endocrinol.*, 22, 77–86 (1961)

413. Cutler, R. E., Kleeman, C. R., Koplowitz, J., and Dowling, J, T., *J. Clin. Endocrinol. Metab.*, 22, 827 (1962)

PHYSIOLOGY OF VISION: RETINAL STRUCTURE AND VISUAL PIGMENTS[1]

By H. J. A. Dartnall and Katharine Tansley

Institute of Ophthalmology, London

In preparing this review the authors have been mindful of the editorial exhortation that it be "a critical presentation that will give the reader a broad view of the progress, direction, and purpose of current research", but that "coverage must be selective rather than comprehensive". Since the literature of vision is so extensive this has meant that we have had to concern ourselves with only a part of it. We have in fact elected to give a presentation of recent events in two subjects only, namely, the fine structure of the vertebrate visual cell, and the visual pigments. In both of these ultimately related topics we have delved back beyond the normal three-year period whenever the development of an argument or the explanation of a present position has seemed to demand it.

The Fine Structure of the Vertebrate Visual Cell

Since Sjöstrand (1), in 1949, published his first paper on the fine structure of the rods of the guinea pig, much work has been done with the electron microscope on visual cells in fishes, amphibia, reptiles, birds, and mammals. The general picture that has emerged is very similar in all vertebrates—and for both rods and cones, with a few special features which will be dealt with in detail below. All vertebrate visual cells have an outer segment with a laminated structure that is in close association with the processes of the cells of the pigment epithelium. With very few exceptions the outer and inner segments are connected by a typical cilium. The inner segment has a concentration of mitochondria in its distal part, the ellipsoid, which is more marked in the cones than in the rods, while the proximal part contains the Golgi complex. Some nonmammalian cones contain two additional structures—an oil droplet and a paraboloid: the first near the junction of the inner and outer segments, the second in the proximal part of the inner segment. The inner segments of both rods and cones are enclosed in a complex of microvilli derived from the Müller's fibres. A fibre, resembling a nonmyelinated nerve fibre in structure, connects the inner segment to the cell body, which is, in turn, connected to the first synapse by another fibre of similar appearance. The rod synapse receives dendrites from one bipolar cell and, in at least some cases, is also associated with processes from other rods and cones. The cone synaptic pedicle is more complex than that of the rod, and it probably makes contact with several bipolar and horizontal cells as well as with other visual cells. The main structural differences between rods and cones appear to be in the relative diameters of the two segments (in the rods the diameters

[1] The survey of literature pertaining to this review was concluded in July 1962.

of the two are about the same; in the cones the inner segment usually has about four times the diameter of the outer), in the greater concentration of mitochondria in the inner segment of the cone, and in the very much greater complexity of the cone synapse.

The outer segment.—The close association of the outer segment with the processes of the pigment epithelial cells and sometimes with the pigment granules contained in these processes has been described in the cat by Bernstein (2), in the mouse (3) and monkey (4) by Cohen, in the turtle by Yamada (5), in the frog by Fernandez-Moran (6), and in the gecko by Pedler & Tansley (7).

In most studies, and in all the earlier work, the tissue was prepared for electron microscopy by fixation in osmium tetroxide. This method of preparation shows the outer segment to be composed of a pile or stack of double membrane discs or sacs, enclosed in a cell membrane which also stains with osmic acid. In the rods these discs are usually not in apparent contact with the cell membrane (1, 3, 8 to 11) although there are exceptions that will be mentioned later. In transverse section each rod disc can usually be seen to have a deep incision running from its surface near the cell membrane to the centre of the disc (1, 3, 6, 8, 9, 12 to 16). Sjöstrand & Elfvin (17) found several such incisions in each disc of the toad rod, while Cohen (4) reported that they were not present in the monkey rod where the edges of the discs were lobulated. The individual discs are arranged in the rod outer segment so that all the incisions are in line with one another—making a groove up one side of the outer segment. In some animals, such as the guinea pig (8), rat (12), and rabbit (15), the discs have tubular connections which are located at the inner end of the incision near the centre of the disc. It seems probable that these tubules are, in fact, a fairly constant feature of the rod outer segment architecture, although Cohen (4) was unable to find either incisions or connecting tubules in the monkey rod.

When we come to consider the cone outer segment we have a rather different picture. No worker has seen the incisions nor the connecting tubules between the discs of the cones of the many animals examined with this point in mind—the perch (8, 9), the frog (16), the toad (17), and the rabbit (18). A striking feature of the cone outer segment is that the membranes bounding individual discs can often be seen to be continuous with the surface membrane of the cell, giving the impression that the discs are made up of actual infoldings of this membrane. This appearance has been described by Sjöstrand (8, 9) in the cones of the perch, by de Robertis & Lasansky (10) in the toad, by Moody & Robertson (16) and Yamada (20) in the frog, by Cohen (4, 21) in the monkey, by Lanzavecchia (11) in *Xenopus*, and by Yamada (20) in the turtle. On the other hand, de Robertis & Lasansky (18) observed no connection between the discs and surface membrane in the rabbit cone. Moody & Robertson (16) have described some evidence of surface membrane infolding in the frog rod and Cohen (4) has described similar evidence at the base of the monkey rod outer segment.

The suggestion that the discs of the outer segment are really not enclosed sacs but are infoldings of the surface membrane, at least in cones, is of special interest when one considers the development of the visual cell. The morphogenesis of the outer segment has been studied in the mouse rod by de Robertis (22), in the cat rod by Tokuyasu & Yamada (23) and Sjöstrand (9), and in the chicken cone by Ueno (24). All these workers are agreed that, after the inner segment has developed its typical structures, such as the mitochondria of the ellipsoid and the Golgi complex, a cilium grows out of its distal end. The tip of the plasma membrane covering the cilium then enlarges and, at the distal end of the enlargement, invaginations appear, forming tubules orientated parallel to the long axis of the visual cell. As the outer segment develops further, these tubules are transformed into sacs, which flatten and gradually become orientated in their adult position at right angles to the long axis of the outer segment. In his first study de Robertis (22) thought that the sacs were formed by the coalescence of primitive tubules and vesicles in the undeveloped outer segment, but he has now accepted (10) that they are produced by invaginations of the surface membrane. Sjöstrand (9) suggests that the connecting tubules seen in the majority of rod discs represent the bases of the original folds, which have been narrowed down and displaced towards the centre of the disc to leave an open slit or incision extending from the edge to the centre. In the cone outer segment, on the other hand, the disc membranes have remained in contact with the surface membrane and with each other at their edges.

The classical picture of the visual cell outer segment as being made up of a stack of double membrane discs was based on material fixed in osmic acid. Sjöstrand (1) noticed that, whereas the width of the spaces between the discs was very variable in such material, the spaces within the discs between the two osmiophilic membranes tended to be fairly constant. He suggested that the intradisc spaces contained a substance which kept the disc membranes glued together at a constant distance. On the basis of Schmidt's (25) polarization optical analysis of the outer segments of frog visual cells, Sjöstrand proposed that the osmiophilic membranes represented protein molecules with their long axes orientated at right angles to the long axis of the outer segment and separated by a double layer of lipoid molecules orientated parallel to the visual cell axis. The individual discs were thought to be separated by an ionic aqueous medium. Later work by Moody & Robertson (16), however, revealed that the disc structure is more complex than this. Fixation with potassium permanganate instead of osmic acid showed another electron-dense layer lying in the middle of the disc and separated from the disc membranes by two clear interspaces. This new layer was twice the thickness of the disc membranes (40 A as opposed to 20 A) and was shown actually to be made up of two layers in contact with one another, joined at their edges by a hairpin loop and separated from the disc membranes by a light interspace 35 A thick. Moody & Robertson made no suggestions as to the chemical nature of these layers; they merely described the outer segment discs as made up of two "membranes" each 75 A thick in contact with one another. It was thought that the two "membranes" were identical with one another and that each consisted of two parallel dense layers 20 A thick separated by a light interspace 35 A thick. These workers pointed out that this is the usual structure of the plasma (surface) membrane and that these two "membranes" were often continuous with the surface membrane of the cell. They considered, therefore, that the double membrane disc was a derivative of the cell membrane, and this idea fits very well with what we already know about the process of development of the outer segment.

Fernandez-Moran (6, 13), using an elegant method of fixation involving freeze-drying, also demonstrated a central dense layer between the disc membranes that was separated from them by a lighter interspace. Accepting and confirming the results with potassium permanganate fixation, Sjöstrand (9) has proposed a chemical structure for the plasma membrane and, by extension, for the two membranes described by Moody & Robertson. In appearance, the structure of the outer segment discs is similar to that of the myelin sheath of peripheral nerve fibres (26), which tissue has been much studied not only by electron microscopy but also by X-ray diffraction and polarization optical methods. In addition it has been shown (27) that the myelin sheath is probably developed from the plasma membrane of the Schwann cells. Using these different data, one can make reasonable assumptions as to the chemical nature of the myelin sheath (28), and thus of the plasma membrane. Sjöstrand (9), therefore, suggests that the plasma membrane consists of two layers of protein molecules with extended peptide chains orientated along the length of the membrane and separated by a double layer of lipoid molecules orientated across it. In addition, according to Sjöstrand, there is in the plasma membrane another layer of protein abutting onto the cytoplasm of the cell. He suggested that the enzyme molecules, which are assumed to be present in most cell membranes, are located in this layer. He observed (1, 8) that the osmiophilic layers of the disc membranes were thicker at the end loops than over the flat central portion and suggested that this extra thickness is attributable to the globular proteins and enzyme molecules of the plasma membrane that have been lost from the rest of the disc membranes.

De Robertis, in collaboration with Lasansky (10, 29), used another method of preparation based on prolonged treatment of the tissue with bichromate after fixation in formalin. Chromation is known to stabilize some lipoid fractions by making them insoluble in organic solvents (30), and this method was therefore used in an attempt to obtain more information about the lipoid constituents of visual cells. After preparation in this way, electron micrographs of visual cell outer segments presented quite a different picture from that obtained after osmic acid fixation. The layers appeared to be more compact and there were no light interspaces. Within this continuous background there were two denser lines named l_1 and l_2; of these l_1 is thicker (70 A) and has less density than l_2, which is approximately 30 A thick. Line

l_1 may in reality be a double layer, but l_2 is definitely single. As pointed out by these authors, it is difficult to fit this picture into the pattern revealed by osmic acid fixation, but they are inclined to think that both l_1 and l_2 are lipoid in nature, that l_1 lies between the double membrane discs stained by osmic acid, while l_2 lies within them, and that the disc membranes themselves are unstained by this method. Some confirmation of the idea that l_1 and l_2 represent lipids was obtained by the use of lipid solvents after formalin fixation but before the application of bichromate. This treatment completely removes the lines l_1 and l_2 but makes practically no difference to the picture after osmic acid fixation, a fact suggesting that the lipoid structures are lost anyway with this method.

When we consider the location of the visual pigment within the structure of the outer segment, we meet differences of opinion among the workers concerned. Sjöstrand (9) is not prepared to express a definite view but is inclined to think that the pigment is located within the double membrane discs. Fernandez-Moran (6) is roughly of the same opinion. Using his low temperature technique he got a picture very similar to those found after potassium permanganate fixation but, in addition, he observed that the spaces within the discs contained dense particulate constituents organized within the plane of the layers. These particles were closely associated with the outer and intermediate disc layers, and perhaps actually contributed to their formation. The spaces between the discs were more uniform and filled with a homogeneous substance of varying density often associated with the interstitial matrix round the visual cells. This worker experimented with various procedures which could be expected to affect the visual pigment. For instance, after application of a combination of platinum chloride and osmic acid, which, he claims, would preserve the interaction of the former reagent with visual pigment while stabilizing the underlying lipoprotein matrix, he found that dark-adapted rods and cones showed a characteristic compact appearance due to enhanced staining and conservation of the intradisc structures, the interdisc spaces, and the enveloping interstitial material. The intermediate layers in the middle of the discs became more prominent and wider, occupying more of the middle zone, while the interdisc spaces were reduced and uniformly packed with a substance full of dense particles. In light-adapted material the granular components disappeared completely from the interdisc spaces leaving a low density homogeneous substance, while within the discs they were usually less numerous and slightly reduced in size. The light-adapted retinae had been completely bleached, and Fernandez-Moran suggests that the generally depleted appearance of their visual cell outer segments may be due to a loss of vitamin A, which might modify the pigment complex making it more susceptible to extraction by the fixation and dehydration procedures. After digitonin extraction of dark-adapted retinae, pretreated with alum-formalin, there was extensive fenestration and general disruption of the outer segments. The membranes of the discs were preserved but the intradisc granules, particulate matrix, and intermediate layer were completely removed. As a result of these observations on material subjected to procedures (light adaptation or extraction with digitonin) designed to affect or remove the visual pigment, Fernandez-Moran suggests that the intradisc structures are either directly related to or in some way associated with the pigment complex. It must be pointed out, however, that these treatments also appear to affect the layers between the discs.

Wolken (31, 32, 33), on the other hand, believes that the disc membranes represent the lipoprotein, presumably opsin, and that the retinene part of the visual pigment is located on the outer surface of these structures in the interdisc spaces. This view appears to be based on some experiments with frog rod outer segments isolated from the retina and suspended in physiological saline. When dark-adapted outer segments so prepared were subjected to white light they swelled and began to break transversely as though the plates composing them had fallen apart. This observation seems to have suggested to Wolken that the bleaching of visual pigment caused the outer segment discs to become separated from one another. However, the appearances during bleaching illustrated in his paper (33) are indistinguishable from those caused by the ordinary deterioration of an outer segment that has been separated from the retina. This deterioration is often observed in complete darkness while it is also quite possible to light-adapt such isolated outer segments without its occurring (34). However, the identification by Wolken of the lipoprotein complex which apparently makes up the outer segment discs is supported by Dowling & Gibbon's observations on vitamin A-deficient rats (12). These workers found that no histological changes could be seen in the outer segments during the early stages of the deficiency when the level of rhodopsin was falling; the degeneration they observed, a swelling and breakdown of the discs, appeared instead concurrent with the loss of opsin which occurs at a later stage.

There seems to be little agreement as to whether the thickness of the disc layers and interdisc spaces varies between rods and cones. De Robertis & Lasansky (10) found very similar measurements in the toad, while Sjöstrand & Elfvin (17) reported that the dense layers of the double membrane disc of the single cone of this animal were thicker and more widely separated than in the rod. In the toad double cone they found that one member had an outer segment resembling that of the rod but without the incision, while the other member resembled the single cone. Yamada, Tokuyasu & Iwaki (35) observed in man that the dimensions of the outer segment discs of cones were generally smaller than in rods, while Moody & Robertson (16) reported that in the frog the thickness and separation of the membranes were similar in both rods and cones. Cohen (4) observed that the disc thickness in monkey rods and cones appeared to be similar, but he points out that there was too much artefact in his preparations for certainty.

Fernandez-Moran (6) has described what he calls "condensation zones" in dark-adapted frog rods and cones after treatment with heavy metal salts. These look like distorted and displaced abnormal discs, and are usually found in the cone outer segment. He reported transitions between these and dense paracrystalline inclusion bodies which were usually in the rods. He suggested that these latter may be related to Kolmer's droplets (36). Pedler & Tansley (7) observed structures rather like Fernandez-Moran's condensation zones (but none like his inclusion bodies) at the base of the outer segment of some gecko cones. They attributed these structures to incomplete or imperfect development which might be associated with the absence of a typical cilium in these cells.

The connecting cilium.—The cilium which connects the outer segment to the inner has a structure typical of cilia throughout the animal kingdom. The cilium is eccentrically placed and enters the outer segment of the rod at the base of the groove formed by the series of disc incisions (15), its surface membrane making contact with the surface membrane of the outer segment (15, 17, 37). Within the cilium are at least nine filaments. Usually there are eighteen filaments arranged in pairs forming two concentric circles.' Such paired filaments have been described in guinea pig rods (28), in rabbit rods (15) and cones (18), and in human rods (14, 35) and cones (35). The outer nine filaments are commonly fused with the plasma membrane (17, 28). Cohen (3) reported that he could not see the nine inner filaments in the mouse rod. These filaments penetrate deeply into the groove of the outer segment in rods and may, indeed, run throughout the length of the groove (15). De Robertis (15) reported that in cross section the filaments have a core which is less dense than the edge and suggests that they may in fact be tubules. Tokuyasu & Yamada (23) came to the same conclusion in the developing rod of the cat. Occasionally two central filaments can be seen in addition to the nine (15, 24). These ciliary filaments penetrate the apical portion of the inner segment, making contact with its plasma membrane (17) and ending there in a centriole or basal body (4, 15, 18, 21, 28, 35). A second centriole, sometimes orientated at right angles to the basal body, has been described in human rods and cones by Yamada, Tokuyasu & Iwaki (35) and in monkey rods and cones by Cohen (4, 21).

Pedler & Tansley (7) found that in the cones of a diurnal gecko the cilium was practically nonexistent; they could see no filaments, basal body, or second centriole in this material although all were present in the cones of a closely related lizard. Yamada and his colleagues (35, 38) noticed some abnormal visual cells in man, mouse, and rabbit that also showed no connecting cilium. In these there was a direct contact between outer and inner segments, the discs of the outer segment going down to the level of the inner segment mitochondria. In these abnormal visual cells the orientation of the outer segment discs was sometimes disturbed, a phenomenon also observed by Pedler & Tansley in the gecko. The ciliary filaments or tubules can be seen in the developing visual cell before the differentiation of the outer segment begins (23, 24). Tokuyasu & Yamada (23) are of the opinion that during morphogenesis the ciliary filaments may act as a site of intracellular induction for the plasma membrane invaginations that form the outer segment discs.

The inner segment.—Perhaps the most striking feature of the visual cell inner segment is the concentration of mitochondria in the ellipsoid, which makes up the outer part of the structure. These mitochondria are markedly denser and more numerous in the cones than in the rods and this appears to be a universal difference between the two. The number of mitochondria reported in the rod ellipsoid varies from five to six in the mouse (3) to twenty to thirty in man (14). In the rod they are orientated in relation to the basal body with their long axes parallel to the long axis of the cell (15, 20, 39). There appears to be no such orientation in the cone (18). Pedler & Tansley (7) have described three distinct types of mitochondria in the gecko cone: one in which there are few cristae, a second which is larger with dense cristae, and a third, apparently specialized, type with the cristae arranged in regularly spaced lamellae. This third type was always found close to the junction with the outer segment; the first type was situated in the proximal part of the ellipsoid with the second type in an intermediate position. Mitochondria of the second and third types were more tightly packed and often in contact with one another. Fernandez-Moran (6) found numerous spherical or polyhedral bodies within the mitochondria of frog rods. These contained densely packed granules in fairly regular patterns similar to the intra-mitochondrial granules described by Sjöstrand (19) and other authors in various types of cell. These granules were much more numerous in dark-adapted material.

In the cone ellipsoid there appears to be little endoplasmic reticulum between the mitochondria (18) but, in the rod, endoplasmic reticulum between the mitochondria has been observed by Missotten (14) in man, by de Robertis (15) in the rabbit, and by Yamada (39) in the frog. The two latter authors also found dense particles, such as those described by Palade (40) in other cells, in the endoplasmic reticulum, which, according to Yamada, is of two types. One of these is rough-surfaced, shows some orientation parallel to the long axis of the segment, and is in partial continuity with the plasma membrane of the cell surface. The other is a smooth-surfaced membrane system which is sometimes in continuity with the rough-surfaced endoplasmic reticulum. Yasuzumi, Tezuka & Ikeda (41), studying the visual cells of a bird, *Uroloncha striata*, were unable to find any endoplasmic reticulum between the mitochondria even in the rods.

One or two ciliary rootlet bundles arising in apparent relationship with the basal body and located between two systems of vacuoles have been described by Cohen in mouse (3) and monkey rods (4). These bundles run the entire length of the inner segment finally losing their identity in the neighbourhood of the Golgi complex. Cohen suggests that these ciliary rootlets may be concerned with the conduction of the excitation. De Robertis (15) mentions neuroprotofibrils in the inner part of the inner segment of the rabbit rod. These penetrate into the rod fibre.

A typical Golgi complex is situated in the myoid region, sometimes extending below the external limiting membrane (4). This part of the cell contains a well-marked endoplasmic reticulum.

Two specialized structures may be present within the inner segments of some nonmammalian cones—the oil droplet situated at the apex of the inner segment and the paraboloid found just proximal to the ellipsoid between it and the Golgi complex. Oil droplets were found by Sjöstrand & Elfvin (17) in some single cones of the toad, and by Pedler & Tansley (7) in certain cones of the lizard and a diurnal gecko. In all these species the oil droplet was closely surrounded by mitochondria. Pedler & Tansley were unable to see any significant structure in the lizard oil droplet but were struck by the intimate association between its substance and the cristae of adjacent mitochondria. The structure of the paraboloid has been described by Yamada (20) in the turtle and by Pedler & Tansley (7) in a gecko, and the two descriptions are very similar. The paraboloid is a spherical or oval body made up of a dense outer rim and a lighter centre, with the latter taking up the greater part of the total volume. The central region contains an accumulation of particles, which, towards the periphery, give way to a tight network of tubules, some of which are continuous with the surrounding endoplasmic reticulum. The paraboloid contains glycogen and, apparently, almost nothing else.

In birds (41) and reptiles (7, 20) the base of the cone inner segment is formed into a series of "fins" projecting at right angles to the long axis of the cell and becoming shorter towards the outer part of the inner segment until they disappear altogether. There are forty to fifty of these "fins" on each visual cell. Yasuzumi, Tezuka & Ikeda (41) thought that they were glial in origin, but Yamada (20) and Pedler & Tansley (7) have shown that they are formed by the surface membrane of the inner segment and that they interdigitate with glial processes from the radial fibres. Both Yamada, and Pedler & Tansley, assumed that these structures facilitate the transport of glycogen or other metabolites between the glial fibres, which are the chief source of glycogen in the retina (42) and the cones. The retinae of both reptiles and birds are completely nonvascular. Yasuzumi, Tezuka & Ikeda (41) also saw "fins" on the inner segments of about half the rods in the bird retina (the remaining rods showed the usual smooth profile) and Carasso (43) described them on the rods of a nocturnal gecko.

Yamada (39), Yamada, Tokuyasu & Iwaki (35), Cohen (3), Missotten (14), and Sjöstrand (9) have all described processes of the glial fibres in the form of slender unbranched microvilli surrounding the base of the inner segment of the visual cell. Sjöstrand has suggested that these processes represent the outside of the excitable membrane.

The concentration of mitochondria in the inner segment of the visual cell indicates that this is a region of high activity. There appear to be two views as to their exact function. It is generally thought that the presence of so many mitochondria means an important metabolic activity in the inner segments that may be concerned with maintaining the integrity of the outer segments. On the other hand, Sjöstrand (9) has suggested that the excited state may arise in the inner segment having been "triggered" by events in the. outer. This excitation might then be conducted to the synapse either as in nonmyelinated nerve fibres or by means of electrotonic decremental conduction, for no spike potentials have ever been recorded from this region of the retina. This view would, perhaps, fit the recent observations of Brown & Watanabe (44) on the isolated receptor potential of monkey cones. These workers concluded that, on stimulation, depolarization occurs at the level of the synapse and that this draws current from the further end of the cell. It should be pointed out, however, that contact with the inner segment appears to be important in maintaining the integrity of the outer segment. When a retina is removed and suspended in physiological saline, those outer segments which become detached break up much more readily than those which remain attached to the retina (45).

It is not at all clear why there should be so much greater a concentration of mitochondria in the cone than in the rod. We have, at present, no good reason to expect that the energy requirements of the cone should be greater than those of the rod. Cohen (4) has suggested that some aspect of the mean frequency of discharge of impulses is reflected in this difference, but against this view is the fact that spike potentials have never been recorded from this part of the retina. Brown & Watanabe (44) suspect that the receptor potential recorded by them at the level of the visual cell synapses is identical with Granit's PIII (46). It is well known that PIII is better developed in cone retinae, and the higher concentration of mitochondria in cones may reflect this finding—especially if Sjöstrand (9) is right in supposing that the excited state arises in the inner segment of the visual cell.

The nucleus and cell body.—The visual cell body is connected to the inner segment by means of a fibre that has all the appearance of a nonmyelinated nerve fibre, while a similar fibre connects it to the synapse (47). Yamada, Tokuyasu & Iwaki (35) and Missotten (14) have described a single mitochondrion in each of these fibres in man, but mitochondria generally appear to be absent from this part of the visual cell. There is nothing remarkable in the structure of the nucleus, and there is little surrounding cytoplasm. However, that which is present does contain the usual endoplasmic reticulum and Golgi complex (35). Rod nuclei are often packed very close together with no obvious cell constituents between them, suggesting the possibility of interaction between rods at the nuclear level (3). Where the nuclei are separated, processes of Müller's fibres lie between them—their plasma membranes being closely applied to the plasma membrane of the cell body (4). In some purecone retinae in reptiles the fibre connecting the cell to the synapse is very short (7), while occasionally in mammals a few rod cells have no fibre at all, the synapse being actually within the cell body (3, 47, 48).

The synapse.—It is not our intention to give a complete description of the visual cell synapse. Detailed descriptions and reconstructions have been published by de Robertis and Franchi (47) for the rabbit, by Sjöstrand (9, 49) for the guinea pig, and by Ladman (48) for the rat.

The rod synapse is formed by an approximately spherical enlargement of the proximal end of the conducting fibre from the cell body (the rod spherule) into which the dendrites of a single cell (assumed to be a bipolar cell) penetrate. A single mitochondrion has been found in the distal part of the rod spherule in the rat (48) and the mouse (3). Mitochondria have also been reported in both rod and cone synapses of the monkey, although they are not always evident (4); they appear to be definitely absent from the guinea pig, oppossum (48), and rabbit (47) synapses. Certain rod synapses have one synaptic ribbon associated with the penetrating bipolar dendrites at the synaptic junction (4, 47, 48, 49, 50), although Missotten (14) reported that several might be present in man. Ladman (48) and Cohen (4) described another lamellar structure related to the synaptic ribbon, and called by Ladman the "rod arciform density". All workers have found, as might be expected, that there are many synaptic vesicles in the rod spherule, although, in his first description of the guinea pig synapse in 1953, Sjöstrand (51) called them granules. The synaptic vesicles are present throughout the presynaptic part of the rod spherule. Opinions differ as to whether synaptic vesicles are present in the postsynaptic structures, but most workers consider that they are. Yamada (39) could find none in the bipolar dendrites of the frog and neither could Carasso (50) in the toad. Ladman (48) also failed to see them in the woodchuck though he reported their presence in the rat, the grey squirrel, and the oppossum. He remarked, however, that their presence appears to depend on the fixation method used. Sjöstrand (49) did not see synaptic vesicles in the bipolar dendrites of the guinea pig, but he did find them on the postsynaptic side in the processes of the β rods where they make contact with the spherule of the α rod (see below). Ladman (49) believes that the synaptic vesicles may well contain acetylcholine, but Sjöstrand (9) apparently thinks it unlikely that they contain transmitter substances. If they do he suggests that the postsynaptic vesicles in the β rod processes are involved in antidromic inhibitor effects. De Robertis & Franchi (47) found that keeping rabbits in the dark for twenty-four hours increased the concentration of vesicles round the synaptic membrane, but that longer periods of dark adaptation (nine days) reduced their size and number. These workers found that prolonged exposure to darkness had a similar, but more pronounced, effect on the synaptic vesicles of the cone pedicle. In addition to the association with bipolar dendrites, the rod synapse may also show contacts with processes from other cells. Sjöstrand (49) describes two sorts of rod in the guinea pig which he calls α and β rods. There are contacts between these two types at the synaptic level so that processes of the conducting fibres of four β rods make surface contact with the spherule of one α rod. It is these rod processes which contain synaptic vesicles and which Sjöstrand suggests may exert an inhibitory effect on the responses of the α rod. In the human retina Missotten (14) found that there was occasionally a connection between processes from the cone pedicle and the rod spherule. In these cases the cone processes were enclosed within invaginations of the rod spherule similar to those formed by the bipolar dendrites. In addition, this worker reported that all cone pedicles had processes which made surface contact with a rod spherule. This arrangement might be the basis of the inhibition of rods by cones, postulated by Elenius & Heck (52) to explain some of their results on human dark adaptation. .

The cone synapse has not been so thoroughly investigated as that of the rod, but all authors agree that it is much more complex, receiving processes from a number of cells instead of only from one (4, 7, 35, 47). Pedler & Tansley (7), studying the cone synapse of a diurnal gecko, found connections with processes from the horizontal cells as well as from the bipolar cells, and were of the opinion that there were also connections with other cones, and possibly with glial fibres. Cohen (4) saw desmosomes on the cone pedicle after potassium permanganate fixation, which suggested that there were surface contacts with the pedicle that might be glial attachments. Multiple synaptic ribbons have been reported in the cone pedicle by Carasso (50) and by Pedler & Tansley (7), also indicating synaptic contacts with the processes of several cells, rather than with only one as seems to be the case in the rod.

The Visual Pigments

Since the publication in 1957 of Dartnall's *The Visual Pigments*, which reviewed the literature up to August 1955, a great deal of work has been done in this field. One of the theses of this book (53) was the probable multiplicity of visual pigments and, as a corollary, the need for testing the homogeneity of retinal extracts from a wide variety of animals. Events in the last few years have certainly supported this thesis for, in a recent review completed in August 1961, Dartnall (54) lists the visual pigments of over 100 animals, 80 per cent of which have been investigated since 1957. This list includes upwards of 30 distinct visual pigments.

In spite of this rich harvest yielded by the recent, more catholic approach to the subject, the picture is still a simple one, at least in certain respects. Thus, each and every one of the pigments so far reported is a chromoprotein with prosthetic group based either on vitamin A_1 or on vitamin A_2. This remains as a natural dichotomy in the subject and one that will, presumably, continue to be valid until such time as a "vitamin A_3" may be discovered. Another, and this time wholly unifying feature is that the extinction spectra of all the known visual pigments—whether "A_1" or "A_2"—are closely similar in shape when plotted to a frequency (reciprocal wavelength) scale. The "visual pigment nomogram", devised in 1953 (55) on the basis of the four visual pigments then adequately characterized, is thus still applicable and is widely used. Originally, the congruence of extinction spectra was inferred (56) from the similarity between the "positive" portions of difference spectra, the direct comparison of spectra generally being vitiated to a greater or lesser degree by the presence of yellow impurities in retinal extracts. Recently, however, a direct comparison (54) has been made between the spectra of cattle rhodopsin, or pigment 498_1 (57); iodopsin, or pigment 562_1 (58); and the syn-

thetic cyanopsin, or pigment 620_2 (59), showing that the inference was justified. Indeed the shape agreement between spectra appears to extend to the
β band in the ultraviolet as well as to the α or main band in the visible (54).
This is not surprising, for the β band is probably an "overtone" of the main
band, depending on the same molecular group or chromophore (53).

Yet a further generalization has been made—this one concerning the
cis-trans conformation (shape) of the prosthetic group. It is now a decade
since the classic experiments of Hubbard & Wald (60) showed that, in the
synthesis of cattle rhodopsin (498_1) from opsin (the protein moiety of the pigment) and retinene$_1$, only a particular isomer of the latter would react to
form the natural pigment. Six isomers of retinene$_1$ (and of vitamin A_1) are
now known. These have the configurations of all-*trans*, 13-*cis* (*neo-a*),
11-*cis* (*neo-b*), 11:13-di-*cis* (*neo-c*), 9-*cis* (*iso-a*), and 9:13-di-*cis* (*iso-b*). [For the
"tangled story" allocating these configurations to the isomers, formerly
known by the trivial names "*neo-a*", etc., see the admirable review by
Morton & Pitt (61)]. The *neo-b* (11-*cis*) isomer has been shown by Wald and
his collaborators to be concerned in the structure of a few natural visual
pigments, and no other isomer of retinene has yet appeared in this context.
Wald (62) has recently summarized his conclusions concerning isomerization
and the visual pigments in the statement that "the retinene precursor of a
visual pigment is always *neo-b*, whether one is dealing with vitamin A_1 or
A_2, or the corresponding retinenes; and whether vertebrate or invertebrate
visual pigments" (62). Wald's assumption in this statement that the stereo-
chemical requirements of A_2 pigments are identical with those of A_1 pigments is not an unreasonable one, considering that the isoprenoid chain is
the same in both vitamin A_1 and A_2, and that visual pigment "analogues"
have been made by combining an undetermined isomer of retinene$_2$ with
opsin from two retinene$_1$ visual pigments [viz. the 517_2 analogue (63) produced with the opsin of cattle rhodopsin (498_1) and the 620_2 analogue called
"cyanopsin" (59) produced with the opsin of chicken iodopsin (562_1)].
Nevertheless, it should not be overlooked that the stereo-structures of the
retinene$_2$ isomers in the A_2 series of visual pigments have not yet been elucidated.

According to Wald's present views (62) there are only three isomers of
each of the retinenes that are of interest from the visual chemistry aspect.
These are the *neo-b* (11-*cis*) form involved in the actual pigment structure,
the all-*trans* form in which the retinene leaves the molecule after bleaching,
and the *iso-a* (9-*cis*) form which combines with opsin to form photosensitive
pigments, which Wald regards as artefacts (the "iso-pigments") since they
have not so far been detected in retinae. Since these conclusions are based on
observations with a relatively small number of visual pigments and since, as
mentioned above, the A_2 series of pigments has been included more by analogy than by demonstration, further work may complicate the picture.
Nevertheless, these views form a useful temporary hypothesis, though it is,
perhaps, premature to re-define "rhodopsin" [as Wald (62) does] as any

visual pigment derived from rods and involving *neo-b* retinene₁—particularly since the term "rhodopsin" is freely used, mostly in cases where the fact of these new requirements has not been established.

These several generalizations suggest rather strongly that all the visual pigments are built to the same pattern fundamentally, and encourage us to hope that the chemical task before us may be reduced to that of unraveling the structure of one pigment, rather than of many. Thus, Hubbard's conclusion (64) that in cattle rhodopsin (498_1) there is only one prosthetic group (retinene₁) to each opsin (protein) molecule is often regarded as applicable to all the visual pigments.

On the other side of the coin, however, this very similarity of pattern poses a difficult problem—that of accounting for the remarkable range in λ_{max} of the visual pigments. This range extends from 430 mμ to 562 mμ in the A_1 series, and from 510 mμ to 620 mμ in the A_2 series. If all the visual pigments are based on *neo-b* isomers of the two retinenes, if every pigment has but one prosthetic group, and if each such group fits an identically shaped niche in its opsin bed, what is the secret of this diversity? It hardly seems likely that it resides in the molecular weight of the opsin, for cattle and frog rhodopsins have quite different molecular weights and yet very similar λ_{max}.

The problem of the λ_{max} of the visual pigments has so far been tackled only in relation to the explanation of the λ_{max} of classical rhodopsin (500 mμ) in terms of its precursor retinene₁ ($\lambda_{max} = 385$ mμ). Originally Collins & Morton (65, 66) thought that such a large difference in λ_{max} could best be explained by supposing that there was a doubling of the retinene molecule in the prosthetic group of the pigment. Later work (67, 68) convincingly showed, however, that in the "indicator yellow analogues" formed by reacting amines with retinene₁ only one molecular contribution from the latter was involved.

Indicator yellow (*N*-retinylidene-opsin) has $\lambda_{max} = 365$ mμ in the alkaline form, and $\lambda_{max} = 440$ mμ in the acid form. It has hitherto been assumed (e.g., 53), on grounds of λ_{max}, that the acid form (quadrivalent nitrogen) is structurally closer to rhodopsin than is the alkaline form (tervalent nitrogen). Thus, Hubbard (69) has suggested that in rhodopsin the otherwise unstable resonance hybrids of the acid form of *N*-retinylidene-opsin are stabilized through interaction with the protein moiety, the consequent lowering of energies thus accounting for the shift of λ_{max} to longer wavelengths. This being so, one might expect that, in the photodecomposition of rhodopsin, *N*-retinylidene-opsin would first make its appearance in the acid form, and only subsequently would it convert to the alkaline form (should the pH of its environment so demand). Bridges (70) has now reported, however, that when rhodopsin is bleached, in solution or in the photoreceptor, the alkaline form of *N*-retinylidene-opsin is produced at first, whatever the pH condition. From this he concludes that the prosthetic group of rhodopsin is based on the alkaline and not the acid form of the substance.

Although at first sight this conclusion presents us with an even greater problem than before—that of accounting for the λ_{max} displacement of visual pigments from 365 mμ, rather than from 440 mμ—it at least unifies the situation when we consider the retinene$_1$ visual pigments as a whole instead of concentrating on a 500 mμ rhodopsin alone. For, as already noted, the λ_{max} of the known visual pigments in this series range from 430 to 562 mμ. With the acid form of N-retinylidene-opsin as our starting point we would have to account for λ_{max} displacements in both directions. With the alkaline form we have to consider only displacements to longer wavelengths.

As regards a crude "formula" for rhodopsin (and visual pigments in general) there is a satisfying measure of agreement. Dartnall (53) and Hubbard (69) have independently made virtually identical proposals. In Dartnall's schematic "formula" the *neo-b* (11-*cis*) form of the prosthetic group was regarded as in a lock and key relationship with the protein (opsin). Conversion of the prosthetic group to the all-*trans* form destroys this correspondence. The change of configuration from 11-*cis* to all-*trans* was envisaged as a possible origin of the visual response.

Thus when the chromophore of visual purple [rhodopsin] absorbs a quantum of energy, the consequent raising of the electronic levels must cause an alteration to the shape of the chromophore so that it no longer has the "lock and key" correspondence to protein. The effect of this is two-fold: the electric tension between chromophore and protein disappears (giving rise, perhaps, to excitation processes in the retinal rod) and the parts of the protein which were "covered" by the chromophore are now revealed (sulph-hydryl groups) (53).

In Hubbard's pictorial formula, the surface of the opsin molecule was similarly shown as complementing the shape of the active 11-*cis* isomer of retinene. She also pointed out that the only other isomer which, because of its similarity in shape to the 11-*cis* form, would be a near fit to this surface is the 9-*cis* form. This accounts for the existence of iso-rhodopsin.

In subsequent developments of these ideas in order to account for the photoproducts, Hubbard & Kropf (71) have suggested that the change to all-*trans* form, undergone by the prosthetic group as a result of light absorption, results in corresponding changes in the opsin—as though the two components had been holding each other together. Thus

the polypeptide chain of opsin can fluctuate between different configurations, one of which prevails in the presence of the 11-*cis* chromophore (visual pigment), another when combined with the all-*trans* chromophore (meta-pigment) and perhaps a third one in the absence of a chromophore (opsin). However, when the *cis* chromophore of the visual pigment is isomerised to all-*trans* (lumi-pigment) in a rigid solvent at low temperatures, the configuration of the protein, although unstable, is unable to rearrange until the temperature is raised sufficiently to render the system more fluid (71).

The change in protein form (which at ordinary temperatures follows isomerization of the chromophore) is supposed to expose sulphhydryl or other active groups. Hubbard & Kropf regard this exposure, rather than the actual isomerization of the chromophore, as the origin of visual excitation.

The next stage, according to Hubbard and Kropf's scheme (71), is hydrolysis of meta-rhodopsin to free retinene and opsin, the intervening stage of N-retinylidene-opsin (indicator yellow) being inexplicably omitted. The formula that they assign to meta-rhodopsin could have been more reasonably given to indicator yellow.

The structures so far proposed for rhodopsin and its derivatives are not capable of explaining all the facts. For example, rhodopsin and (vertebrate) meta-rhodopsin are not pH indicators, whereas N-retinylidene-opsin is. Another, possibly related, difference is in the effect of hydroxylamine on these substances. Indicator yellow, as one would expect of an azo-methine (—C=N—)derivative, is decomposed by hydroxylamine to yield retinene oxime; rhodopsin and meta-rhodopsin—presumably also azo-methine derivatives—are not affected, however.

Morton & Pitt (72) consider that the stability of rhodopsin and meta-rhodopsin arises because in them the azo-methine link is shielded. They have suggested the possibility that meta-rhodopsin is a retinylidene ammonium derivative of the structure

where R is the polypeptide chain as in N-retinylidene-opsin and R' is "an unknown grouping (possibly on another polypeptide chain) joined by a link which is hydrolyzed when meta-rhodopsin is converted to N-retinylidene opsin" (72). In support of this suggestion they point out that the only known substance of this type, namely, retinylidene-dimethylammonium iodide ($R = R' = CH_3$) (67), resembles meta-rhodopsin in having a similar λ_{max} and in being unstable in water and decomposed by alkali. Against this proposal is the recent conclusion of Bridges (70), mentioned above, that the prosthetic group of rhodopsin is based on the alkaline (tervalent nitrogen) form of indicator yellow. Further work is clearly required before these delicate points can be elucidated.

NEW VISUAL PIGMENTS

In the following paragraphs we briefly mention the new visual pigments that have been extracted into solution since the last review in this series (73).

Invertebrates.—Hubbard & Wald (74) have extracted the visual pigment of the horseshoe crab *Limulus polyphemus*. The pigment has $\lambda_{max} = 520$ mμ, and is based on retinene$_1$. On exposure to light it bleaches to a mixture of retinene and opsin, and in this respect differs from certain other invertebrate pigments—those of the squid (493_1), octopus (475_1), cuttle fish (492_1), and lobster (515_1)—which yield relatively stable "metarhodopsins" when irradiated. The *Limulus* pigment, which has an extinction spectrum in good agreement with the spectral sensitivity (electrophysiological) measurements of Hartline & Graham (75), is the seventh invertebrate pigment to be extracted. The λ_{max} range of invertebrate pigments now extends from 440 mμ (honey-bee) to 520 mμ. All are retinene$_1$ pigments.

Vertebrates (mammals).—The visual pigments of some 25 mammalian species have now been recorded. The pigments are all based on retinene$_1$, and have λ_{max} ranging between 491 mμ and 502 mμ. The latest additions since Crescitelli's 1958 observations (76, 77) on eleven new species are listed below.

Species	Pigment	Reference
Rat (*Rattus rattus*)	498$_1$	Bridges (78)
Mouse (*Mus musculus domesticus*)	498$_1$	Bridges (78)
Guinea pig (*Cavia porcellus*)	497$_1$	Bridges (78)
Rabbit (*Lepus cuniculus*)	502$_1$	Bridges (78)
Hamster (*Cricetus auratus*)	502$_1$	Bridges (78)
Rhesus monkey (*Macaca mulatta*)	497$_1$	Bridges (78)
Hump-back whale (*Megaptera nodosa*)	495$_1$	Dartnall (54)
Grey squirrel (*Sciurus carolinensis leucotis*)	502$_1$	Dartnall (79)

In all cases except one, the pigments obtained from mammalian retinae are definitely or presumably related to scotopic, or rod, vision. The exception is the grey squirrel which is reputed, on very good evidence (e.g., 80), to have a pure-cone retina. From this retina a pigment ($\lambda_{max} = 502$ mμ) has been extracted that is indistinguishable in light-absorbing properties from the pigment 502$_1$ obtained from the pure rod retina of the hamster. Dartnall (81) had earlier questioned the usefulness of describing rod pigments as "scotopsins" (rhodopsins or porphyropsins) and cone pigments as "photopsins" (iodopsins or cyanopsins) (59, 82), and had suggested there were no grounds for supposing that a given pigment could not function as a rod pigment in one case, and as a cone pigment in another. The squirrel pigment seems to lend point to this view and to expose a semantic paradox in the classical nomenclature, for according to this system the hamster (rod) pigment is a "rhodopsin", and the apparently identical squirrel (cone) pigment is an "iodopsin".

Vertebrates (birds).—Visual pigments have now been extracted from eight species of birds. In all cases the pigments are based on retinene$_1$, and all but two of them have λ_{max} within the narrow range 500 to 503 mμ.

The two birds of outstanding interest are the chicken (*Gallus gallus*) and the pigeon (*Columba livia*). Both species have yielded two visual pigments. The two chicken pigments have λ_{max} at 502 and 562 mμ respectively ("rhodopsin" and "iodopsin"). Since pigments with λ_{max} around 500 mμ are known to occur in many pure-rod or mainly rod retinas, the 562 mμ pigment is assumed to be the pigment of the cones (with which the chicken retina is generously supplied). This assumption is supported by the approximate agreement between the light-absorbing properties of the two chicken pigments and Hönigmann's old measurements (83) of the scotopic and photopic sensitivity functions of the chicken.

Most of the information about the two chicken pigments has come from the brilliant study by Wald, Brown & Smith (58). In addition to a careful spectrophotometric characterization of the pigments both were synthesized by incubation of their respective opsins with 11-*cis* (*neo-b*) retinene$_1$. (At 10°C the velocity constant for the iodopsin synthesis was over 500 times that for the rhodopsin synthesis.)

By using similar methods of extraction, Bridges (84, 85) has now obtained two pigments from the pigeon retina. One of these has $\lambda_{max} = 502$ mμ and is similar to chicken rhodopsin. The other, presumptively cone, pigment has $\lambda_{max} = 544$ mμ. These pigments were characterized by the partial bleaching technique, and [because of an oblique reference in the literature (62) to the pigeon retina's containing iodopsin] particular regard was paid to the possibility that the difference spectrum of the red-sensitive pigment (544$_1$) might have been "contaminated" by concurrently bleached rhodopsin. In fact Bridges was able to demonstrate that the red light (720 mμ) used for bleaching the red-sensitive component was without effect on the rhodopsin. Thus the 544 mμ pigeon pigment can not be dismissed as a "contaminated" 562 mμ iodopsin.

The extinction spectrum of the pigeon 502$_1$ pigment is in satisfactory agreement with Donner's (86) electrophysiological, and with Blough's (87) behavioural measurements of the scotopic sensitivity of this bird. The spectrum of the 544$_1$ pigment, on the other hand, does not agree with the photopic curve (86, 87, 88) which, like the corresponding curve for the chicken (83), is maximal at about 580 mμ. Exact correspondence would not be expected, of course, because the cones of the pigeon retina, as of most birds, contain coloured oil droplets (chromatophanes). Bridges (85) has identified two of the stable pigments extracted by petroleum ether from dried pigeon retinae as astaxanthin and (possibly) sarcinin or sarcinoxanthin. The effect of such pigments, intervening between the incident light and the visual pigment, would be to depress the bird's sensitivity to short-wave light, and hence to displace its sensitivity function to longer wavelengths. It is extremely doubtful, however, whether such a disparity in spectral position as that between the pigeon photopic curve (580 mμ) and the pigment 544 curve can be explained in terms of preabsorption by such pigments as are found in the petroleum ether extract. It is even doubtful whether the similar chromatophane pigments of the chicken (89) can resolve the more modest discrepancy between the photopic curve (580 mμ) and visual pigment (562$_1$) of that bird.

The resemblance between the photopic functions of the chicken and the pigeon, and the similarity of their chromatophane pigments, render the more surprising the differences between their presumptively cone visual pigments (562$_1$ and 544$_1$). Whether both birds possess other cone visual pigments (as yet undetected), or whether the comparison between photopic curves and visual pigments involves unsuspected subtleties, remains to be seen. In the meantime these results only serve to emphasize that no photopic sensitivity curve has yet received an entirely satisfactory interpretation in visual pigment terms.

Vertebrates (amphibians and reptiles).—No further additions to the visual pigments of animals in these two classes have been made during the period under review. Wilt (89), however, has studied the visual pigments in metamorphosing larvae of *Rana catesbeiana*. He found that prior to metamorphosis, the retinas contained 70 to 85 per cent porphyropsin (523_2) and 15 to 30 per cent rhodopsin (502_1). By inducing metamorphosis (in unfed animals) with thyroxine he obtained photopigment conversion, the postmetamorphic animals having rhodopsin only.

Some years ago Collins, Love & Morton (90) reported that the tadpoles of *Rana esculenta* and *Rana temporaria* had visual pigments with $\lambda_{max} = 500$ and 502 mμ, i.e., virtually identical with those of the adult frogs. In a recent reassessment of these results, however, Dartnall (54) has pointed out that allowance for the presence of yellow impurities in their extracts would place the corrected λ_{max} for the tadpole extracts at 510 mμ and 508 mμ, respectively —thus suggesting that they were mixtures of rhodopsin and porphyropsin. It seems, therefore, that Collins, Love & Morton's results no longer stand as an exception to Wald's general thesis for amphibia (91, 92) of a metamorphic shift from a larval retinene$_2$ to an adult retinene$_1$ visual system.

Vertebrates (fishes).—Over the years, the visual pigments of more fishes have been investigated than of any other single class of animal. With the application of the partial bleaching technique it has become increasingly evident that fishes exhibit an exceptional diversity (and frequent multiplicity) in their visual pigments. This is undoubtedly traceable in the main to the great variation in their radiation climate. Thus the discoveries (93 to 97) reported in the previous review in this series (73) that deep-sea fishes have golden-coloured retinae apparently adapted for the reception of the predominantly blue light that penetrates deep oceanic waters (or that is emitted by certain luminous organisms) have revived the idea (98) of a correlation of visual pigment with depth of habitat (99) or, more exactly, with environmental demands (95, 100). In a penetrating survey of bathypelagic, surface pelagic, rocky shore, sandy shore, and fresh-water fishes, Munz (95) has established a connection between the spectral location of visual pigment and fhe λ_{max} of transmitted sunlight.

The most interesting recent developments in this field relate to species in which the visual pigments are not constant, but change in response to a change of environment which may, or may not, be coincident with some metamorphic change in the animal itself.

The first of these is the sea lamprey *Petromyzon marinus* which starts life in fresh water, where it develops from the egg into a larval form (ammocoete) that is blind. After a few years it metamorphoses, whilst still in fresh water, and develops eyes. After this change it normally migrates to the sea where it spends its adult life, eventually returning to the river to spawn. Crescitelli

(101) studied specimens of a population of *P. marinus* that had been land-locked in the upper Great Lakes region. He found that his specimens ("recently transformed downstream migrants") possessed a homogeneous retinene$_1$ pigment of $\lambda_{max} = 497$ mμ. This was an unexpected result for "if fresh water habitat is the primary determinant, these animals should possess the porphyropsin system" (101). Wald (102), using downstream migrants from the same source, confirmed Crescitelli's observations. On the other hand Wald found that sexually mature *P. marinus*, taken from the Oyster River, New Hampshire, whilst they were on their spawning run upstream from the ocean, possessed a substantially homogeneous retinene$_2$ pigment (porphyropsin) of $\lambda_{max} = 518$ mμ.

To explain these interesting results, Wald (92) has postulated that the return to the natal environment for spawning requires changes that may be regarded as a second metamorphosis. "It is of the essence of a second metamorphosis to reverse in part the changes which accompanied the first metamorphosis" (92). Thus the downstream migrants, newly metamorphosed from the blind larval ammocoete form, have a rhodopsin in preparation for their marine existence; the sexually mature upstream migrants have a porphyropsin because this "represents the true, albeit missing larval type". "Both the first and second metamorphoses *anticipate* changes in environment. Ordinarily they occur in the old environment and are completed there. They are preparations for the new environment, not responses to it" (92).

Another instance of visual pigment changes associated with metamorphosis is provided by the European eel *Anguilla anguilla*. The larva (leptocephalus), as it makes its way from the deep Atlantic grounds, where it was spawned, to the coasts of Europe, changes into a juvenile eel (yellow eel). After some years in this form, feeding and growing in fresh or estuarine water, the eel undergoes a second change; gonads appear, the eyes enlarge, and the livery alters to silver. The silver eel then returns to the Atlantic to spawn the next generation. The visual pigment of the larval leptocephalus has not been examined, but Carlisle & Denton (103) have inspected yellow and silver (immature and adult) specimens of *Anguilla anguilla* taken together in fresh water. They found that the mature eels had golden-coloured retinae ($\lambda_{max} = 485$ mμ) while the immature, yellow eels had purple retinae (515 mμ). Extracts of these pigments were not made. However, according to Wald (92, 104), P. K. and P. S. Brown, working from the Stazione Zoologica in Naples, have found that the retinae of immature eels yield mixtures of vitamin A$_1$ and A$_2$ in various proportions and have visual pigment with λ_{max} ranging correspondingly from 504 to 513 mμ. Partial bleaching and regeneration experiments have shown the pigments to be mixtures of 523$_2$ and 502$_1$. The retinae of adult eels on the other hand yield only vitamin A$_1$.

This change seems to antedate the transition from ordinary to deep sea opsin, for in various silver eels that had already lost their vitamin A$_2$ the λ_{max} of the visual pigment range between 500 and 487 mμ, as though the opsin were in various stages of transition (104).

This interesting work by the Browns has not yet been published. Wald considered that "the deep sea rhodopsin" (487_1) of the ocean-bound mature silver eel represents a return to the larval type visual pigment (as yet undetermined).

Changes in visual pigment have also been observed in a nonmigratory and nonmetamorphosing fish. This is the rudd *Scardinius erythrophthalmus*, a common British fish that lives in ponds and sluggish rivers. Dartnall, Lander & Munz (105) have made a study of a uniform population of some 2000 to 3000 rudd which were kept in a small spring-fed pond. These rudd had had an identical history and were between three and four years old at the beginning of the investigations. Over the ensuing 14 months, samples of this population were taken from time to time and examined immediately, and also after periods under various laboratory conditions. In all, over forty extracts of visual pigment were made. The λ_{max} of these extracts ranged between 513 and 532 mμ depending on the time of the year and the conditions to which the fish had been subjected after sampling from the pond. It was established that all extracts contained the same pair of pigments—a retinene$_2$ pigment of $\lambda_{max} = 543$ mμ and a retinene$_1$ pigment of $\lambda_{max} = 510$ mμ—but in varying proportions. Thus in the winter months it is the 543_2 pigment that preponderates while in the summer months it is the 510_1 pigment. There was indeed found to be a rough correlation between the composition of the retinal pigment and the "daylight hours" curve for latitude 52°N. Confirmation that the light environment is in some way directly concerned with these changes was provided by further experiments in which some fish, after removal from the pond, were kept in darkness and others of the same batch kept in an aquarium under brighter conditions than the natural environment. It was found that the fish kept in darkness increased their 543_2 pigment at the expense of the 510_1 pigment, and that the fish kept in the bright aquarium reacted conversely. Such interconversions of visual pigments could be reversed by reversing the environments.

The extremes of visual pigment composition in this fish were 15 per cent 543_2+85 per cent 510_1 and 85 per cent 543_2+15 per cent 510_1. The retinal vitamins A_1 and A_2 showed changes corresponding to the visual pigment changes but the liver vitamins (predominantly A_1) did not change.

PROPERTIES OF VISUAL PIGMENTS IN PHOTORECEPTORS

Do visual pigments have the same light-absorbing properties after extraction into solution as they had in the photoreceptors? This question was first raised forty years ago by Hecht & Williams (106), who found that their measurements of the human scotopic curve (expressed as the reciprocal energies of the light incident on the cornea) did not correspond as well as expected with the extinction curve of extracted "visual purple" in solution.

They suggested that the differences observed might be the result of the operation of Kundt's rule, viz., that in the more refractive medium of the rod substance, the spectrum of the pigment is displaced to longer wavelengths.

The discrepancies in the data were successively whittled down, however, by Dartnall & Goodeve (107), who pointed out that sensitivity should be expressed as the reciprocal of quantum intensity; by Wald (108), who took into account the absorption of light by the preretinal ocular media (lens); and by Crescitelli & Dartnall (109), who reported that extracted human visual pigment ($\lambda_{max} = 497 \pm 2$ mμ) was slightly different from extracted frog pigment ($\lambda_{max} = 502$ mμ). (The data for frog pigment had normally been used in the past for such comparisons.) When the comparison is made on a proper basis (55), and with relevant data, there is very good agreement between the absorption spectrum of extracted human pigment and the human scotopic curve, except at the extreme short-wave end of the spectrum where there are uncertainties about the correction for preretinal absorption. This and like comparisons with data from other animals strongly suggest that there can be little difference between *in situ* and extracted pigment, and hence that the properties of extracted pigment (as measured in solution) are relevant for the interpretation of visual functions. Nevertheless, interest in the question has been recently revived (110 to 114).

Dartnall (81, 115) has compared the light-absorbing properties of visual pigments before and after extraction from their visual cells. The properties before extraction were ascertained with suspensions of the visual cells in equal-density sucrose solution, using an adaptation of an "opal-glass" method, attributed to Shibata (116), so that the light truly absorbed by the pigment in these suspensions could be characterized separately from the light scattered by them. The validity of the method was proved experimentally by correctly deriving the absorption spectrum of known dyestuffs after adding them to highly scattering emulsions or suspensions. The properties of the visual pigments after extraction were determined in the usual way, viz., in 2 per cent digitonin solution.

Dartnall found for all three pigments studied (pigment 502_1 from the frog *Rana temporaria;* pigment 487_1 from the eel *Conger conger;* pigment 523_2 from the carp *Cyprinus carpio*) that there was no detectable change in light-absorbing properties when the pigments were extracted from their natural environment into solution. On the other hand, the photoproducts formed when the visual pigments were bleached *in situ* were significantly different from the photoproducts ordinarily found in solution. In fact the products formed in the visual cells bore a resemblance to those found by Bridges (117) in cold ($-5°C$) solution.

Since the photoproducts formed *in situ* absorb in the visible spectrum, the difference spectra of suspensions of visual cells are substantially displaced to longer wavelengths (115). Thus the difference spectrum of the conger pigment (487_1) is maximal at 501 mμ *in situ*. Likewise, the difference spectra of the frog and carp pigments are displaced 8 mμ and 12 mμ, respectively, from the λ_{max} of the pigments concerned (502_1 and 523_2, respectively). Wald & Brown's observation (113) that a suspension of human retinal rods has a difference spectrum ($\lambda_{max} = 500$ mμ) displaced 7 mμ from the difference spectrum of the extracted pigment ($\lambda_{max} = 493$ mμ) is also in line with these results. It seems reasonable to conclude that this displacement is the result of the formation *in situ* of photoproducts that absorb in the visible (as in the case of frog, conger, and carp suspensions) rather than—as Wald and Brown supposed—to the operation of Kundt's rule. If this interpretation (115) is correct, then the measurements in solution ($\lambda_{max} = 493$ mμ) are the ones that should be used for interpreting the human scotopic curve. This would be an embarrassment, for the scotopic data are already well fitted by Crescitelli & Dartnall's (109) measurements of the human pigment in solution, placing the λ_{max} at 497 ± 2 mμ. Because of the special interest concerning the human pigment it is to be hoped that the discrepancy between these estimates— small though it may seem—will be soon resolved.

These observations on suspensions of visual cells suggest that difference spectra of intact retinae, whether obtained directly or by fundus reflectometry, are to be interpreted with caution. The stability in the cell of visual pigment photoproducts that ordinarily have only a fleeting existence in solution raises several questions. It is possible, for example, that the course of bleaching of the same visual pigment could be different in a cone from its course in a rod (81). Thus, although the difference spectra, obtained by fundus reflectometry, of several (rod) "rhodopsins" agree reasonably well with the same function of the extracted pigment, the all-cone retina of the grey squirrel (which likewise contains a 502_1 pigment) gives a fundus difference spectrum, according to Weale (118), that is narrow and peaks at 535 mμ. Dartnall (79) has interpreted this result by supposing that, in the cone, the 502_1 visual pigment bleaches to a 480 mμ photoproduct.

Another possible consequence of the presence of "unusual" photoproducts in the visual cell is that they might actively participate in the visual reaction. If, as seems probable, the isomeric chromoprotein photoproducts of visual pigments are relatively stable in photoreceptors—or, perhaps, stable in some (cones) if not in others (rods) (81)—then the interconvertibility (119) of the *cis-trans* forms of the chromoprotein may have an important bearing on the interpretation of spectral sensitivity functions (54). "Under the conditions of normal photopic vision we should have to consider the implications of there being a mixture of chromoproteins as 'visual pigment' rather than the single 11-*cis* chromoprotein extractable from the fully dark-adapted retina" (54).

LITERATURE CITED

1. Sjöstrand, F. S., *J. Cellular Comp. Physiol.*, **33**, 383–97 (1949)
2. Bernstein, M. H., *The Structure of the Eye*, 139–50 (Smelser, G. K., Ed., Academic Press, Inc., New York, 1961)
3. Cohen, A. I., *Am. J. Anat.*, **107**, 23–48 (1960)
4. Cohen, A. I., *Exptl. Eye Res.*, **1**, 128–36 (1961)
5. Yamada, E., *The Structure of the Eye*, 72–84 (Academic, New York, 1961)
6. Fernandez-Moran, H., *The Structure of the Eye*, 521–56 (Academic, New York, 1961)
7. Pedler, C. M. H., and Tansley, K., *Exptl. Eye Res.* (In Press)
8. Sjöstrand, F. S., *J. Cellular Comp. Physiol.*, **42**, 15,44 (1953)
9. Sjöstrand, F. S., *The Structure of the Eye*, 1–28 (Academic, New York, 1961)
10. de Robertis, E., and Lasansky, A., *The Structure of the Eye*, 29–49 (Academic, New York, 1961)
11. Lanzavecchia, G., *Arch. Ital. Anat. Embriol.*, **65**, 417–35 (1960)
12. Dowling, J. E., and Gibbons, I. R., *The Structure of the Eye*, 85–99 (Academic, New York, 1961)
13. Fernandez-Moran, H., *Science*, **129**, 1284–85 (1959)
14. Missotten, L., *Ophthalmologia*, **140**, 200–14 (1960)
15. de Robertis, E., *J. Biophys. Biochem. Cytol.*, **2**, 319–30 (1956)
16. Moody, M. F., and Robertson, J. D., *J. Biophys. Biochem. Cytol.*, **7**, 87–92 (1960)
17. Sjöstrand, F. S., and Elfvin, L. G., *Proc. Intern. Conf. Electron Microscopy, 4th, Stockholm, 1956*, 194–96 (1956)
18. de Robertis, E., and Lasansky, A., *J. Biophys. Biochem. Cytol.*, **4**, 743–46 (1958)
19. Sjöstrand, F. S., *Rev. Mod. Phys.*, **31**, 301–18 (1959)
20. Yamada, E., *J. Electronmicroscopy (Tokyo)*, **9**, 1–14 (1960)
21. Cohen, A. I., *The Structure of the Eye*, 151–58 (Academic, New York, 1961)
22. de Robertis, E., *J. Biophys. Biochem. Cytol.*, **2**, Suppl. (No. 4, Part II), 209–18 (1956)
23. Tokuyasu, K., and Yamada, E., *J. Biophys. Biochem. Cytol.*, **6**, 225–30 (1959)
24. Ueno, K., *Japan. J. Ophthalmol.*, **5**, 114–22 (1961)
25. Schmidt, W. J., *Z. Zellforsch. Mikroskop. Anat.*, **22**, 485–522 (1935)
26. Finean, J. B., Sjöstrand, F. S., and Steinmann, E., *Exptl. Cell Res.*, **5**, 557–59 (1953)
27. Ben Geren, B., *Exptl. Cell Res.*, **7**, 558–62 (1954)
28. Sjöstrand, F. S., *Experientia*, **9**, 68–69 (1953)
29. Lasansky, A., and de Robertis, E., *J. Biophys. Biochem. Cytol.*, **7**, 493–98 (1960)
30. Baker, J. R., *Principles of Biological Microtechnique* (Wiley, New York, 1958)
31. Wolken, J. J., *J. Cellular Comp. Physiol.*, **48**, 349–69 (1956)
32. Wolken, J. J., *Trans. N. Y. Acad. Sci.*, **19**, 315–27 (1957)
33. Wolken, J. J., *The Structure of the Eye*, 173–92 (Academic, New York, 1961)
34. Dobrowolski, J. A., Johnson, B. K., and Tansley, K., *J. Physiol. (London)*, **130**, 533–42 (1955)
35. Yamada, E., Tokuyasu, K., and Iwaki, S., *J. Kurume Med. Assoc.*, **21**, 1979–2027 (1958)
36. Detwiler, S. R., and Zwemer, R. L., *Anat. Record*, **67**, 295–302 (1937)
37. Sjöstrand, F. S., *J. Cellular Comp. Physiol.*, **42**, 45–70 (1953)
38. Tokuyasu, K., and Yamada, E., *J. Biophys. Biochem. Cytol.*, **7**, 187–89 (1960)
39. Yamada, E., *Kurume Med. J.*, **4**, 127–47 (1957)
40. Palade, G. E., *J. Biophys. Biochem. Cytol.*, **1**, 59–68 (1955)
41. Yasuzumi, G., Tezuka, O., and Ikeda, T., *J. Ultrastruct. Res.*, **1**, 295–306 (1958)
42. Eichner, D., and Themann, H., *Z. Zellforsch. Mikroskop. Anat.*, **56**, 231–46 (1962)
43. Carasso, N., *Compt. Rend. Acad. Sci.*, **242**, 2988–91 (1956)
44. Brown, K. T., and Watanabe, K., *Nature*, **193**, 958–60 (1962)
45. Tansley, K. (Unpublished observations)
46. Granit, R., *Sensory Mechanisms of the Retina* (Oxford Univ. Press, 1947)
47. de Robertis, E., and Franchi, C. M., *J. Biophys. Biochem. Cytol.*, **2**, 307–18 (1956)
48. Ladman, A. J., *J. Biophys. Biochem. Cytol.*, **4**, 459–66 (1958)

49. Sjöstrand, F. S., *J. Ultrastruct. Res.*, **2**, 122–70 (1958)

50. Carasso, N., *Compt. Rend. Acad. Sci.*, **245**, 216 (1957)

51. Sjöstrand, F. S., *J. Appl. Phys.*, **24**, 1422 (1953)

52. Elenius, V., and Heck, J., *Nature*, **180**, 810 (1957)

53. Dartnall, H. J. A., *The Visual Pigments* (Methuen, London, Wiley, New York, 1957)

54. Dartnall, H. J. A., *The Photobiology of Visual Processes*, in *The Eye*, 2 (Davson, H., Ed., Academic, London & New York, 1962)

55. Dartnall, H. J. A., *Brit. Med. Bull.*, **9**, 24–30 (1953)

56. Dartnall, H. J. A., *J. Physiol. (London)*, **116**, 257–89 (1952)

57. Collins, F. D., Love, R. M., and Morton, R. A., *Biochem. J.*, **51**, 292–98 (1952)

58. Wald, G., Brown, P. K., and Smith, P. H., *J. Gen. Physiol.*, **38**, 623–81 (1955)

59. Wald, G., Brown, P. K., and Smith, P. H., *Science*, **118**, 505–8 (1953)

60. Hubbard, R., and Wald, G., *J. Gen. Physiol.*, **36**, 269–315 (1952)

61. Morton, R. A., and Pitt, G. A. J., *Fortschr. Chem. Org. Naturstoffe.*, **14**, 244–316 (1957)

62. Wald, G., in *Visual Problems of Colour*, Natl. Phys. Lab., Gt. Brit., *Symp. No. 8*, 7–61 (1958)

63. Wald, G., *Ann. Rev. Biochem.*, **22**, 497–526 (1953)

64. Hubbard, R., *J. Gen. Physiol.*, **37**, 381–99 (1954)

65. Collins, F. D., and Morton, R. A., *Biochem. J.*, **47**, 10–17 (1950)

66. Collins, F. D., and Morton, R. A., *Biochem. J.*, **47**, 18–24 (1950)

67. Pitt, G. A. J., Collins, F. D., Morton, R. A., and Stok, P., *Biochem. J.*, **59**, 122–28 (1955)

68. Morton, R. A., and Pitt, G. A. J., *Biochem. J.*, **59**, 128–34 (1955)

69. Hubbard, R., in *Visual Problems of Colour*, Natl. Phys. Lab., Gt. Brit., *Symp. No. 8*, 151–69 (1958)

70. Bridges, C. D. B., *Vision Res.*, **2**, 201–14 (1962)

71. Hubbard, R., and Kropf, A., *Ann. N. Y. Acad. Sci.*, **81**, 388–98 (1959)

72. Morton, R. A., and Pitt, G. A. J., *Fortschr. Chem. Org. Naturstoffe.*, **14**, 244–316 (1957)

73. Crescitelli, F., *Ann. Rev. Physiol.*, **22**, 525–78 (1960)

74. Hubbard, R., and Wald, G., *Nature*, **186**, 212–15 (1960)

75. Hartline, H. K., and Graham, C. H., *J. Cellular Comp. Physiol.*, **1**, 277–95 (1932)

76. Crescitelli, F., *Ann. N. Y. Acad. Sci.*, **74**, 230–55 (1958)

77. Crescitelli, F., in *Photobiology*, 30–51 (Oregon State College, Corvallis, 1958)

78. Bridges, C. D. B., *Nature*, **184**, 1727–28 (1959)

79. Dartnall, H. J. A., *Nature*, **188**, 475–79 (1960)

80. Arden, G. B., and Tansley, K., *J. Physiol. (London)*, **127**, 592–602 (1955)

81. Dartnall, H. J. A., in *Mechanisms of Colour Discrimination*, 147–61 (Gallifret, Y., Ed., Pergamon, London, 1960)

82. Wald, G., *Federation Proc.*, **12**, 606–11 (1953)

83. Hönigmann, H., *Arch. Ges. Physiol.*, **189**, 1–72 (1921)

84. Bridges, C. D. B., *Nature*, **195**, 40–42 (1962)

85. Bridges, C. D. B., *Vision Res.*, **2**, 125–37 (1962)

86. Donner, K. O., *J. Physiol. (London)*, **122**, 524–37 (1953)

87. Blough, D. S., *J. Opt. Soc. Am.*, **47**, 827–33 (1957)

88. Granit, R., *Acta Physiol. Scand.*, **4**, 188–24 (1942)

89. Wilt, F. H., *Develop. Biol.*, **1**, 199–233 (1959)

90. Collins, F. D., Love, R. M., and Morton, R. A., *Biochem. J.*, **53**, 632–36 (1953)

91. Wald, G., *Harvey Lecture Ser.*, **41**, 117–60 (1947)

92. Wald, G., *Circulation*, **21**, 916–38 (1960)

93. Denton, E. J., and Warren, F. J., *Nature*, **178**, 1059 (1956)

94. Denton, E. J., and Warren, F. J., *J. Marine Biol. Assoc. U. K.*, **36**, 651–62 (1957)

95. Munz, F. W., *The Photosensitive Retinal Pigments of Marine and Euryhaline Teleost Fishes* (Doctoral thesis, Univ. of California Los Angeles, 1957)

96. Munz, F. W., *Science*, **125**, 1142–43 (1957)

97. Munz, F. W., *J. Physiol. (London)*, **140**, 220–35 (1958)

98. Bayliss, L. E., Lythgoe, R. J., and Tansley, K., *Proc. Roy. Soc. (London)*, B, **120**, 95–113 (1936)

99. Wald, G., Brown, P. K., and Brown, P. S., *Nature*, 180, 969–71 (1957)

100. Munz, F. W., *J. Gen. Physiol.*, 42, 445–59 (1958)

101. Crescitelli, F., *J. Gen. Physiol.*, 39, 423–35 (1956)

102. Wald, G., *J. Gen. Physiol.*, 40, 901–14 (1957)

103. Carlisle, D. B., and Denton, E. J., *J. Marine Biol. Assoc. U. K.*, 38, 97–102 (1959)

104. Wald, G., in *Comparative Biochemistry*, 1 (Academic, New York, 1960)

105. Dartnall, H. J. A., Lander, M. R., and Munz, F. W., in *Progress in Photobiology*, 203–13 (Christensen, B. C., and Buchmann, B., Eds., Elsevier, Amsterdam, 1961)

106. Hecht, S., and Williams, R. E., *J. Gen. Physiol.*, 5, 1–34 (1922)

107. Dartnall, H. J. A., and Goodeve, C. F., *Nature*, 139, 409–11 (1937)

108. Wald, G., *J. Gen. Physiol.*, 21, 795–832 (1938)

109. Crescitelli, F., and Dartnall, H. J. A., *Nature*, 172, 195–96 (1953)

110. Rushton, W. A. H., *J. Physiol.*, 134, 11–29 (1956)

111. Rushton, W. A. H., *J. Physiol. (London)*, 134, 30–46 (1956)

112. Denton, E. J., and Walker, M. A., *Proc. Roy. Soc. (London)*, 148, 257–69 (1958)

113. Wald, G., and Brown, P. K., *Science*, 127, 222–26 (1958)

114. Dartnall, H. J. A., *J. Physiol.*, 145, 630–40 (1959)

115. Dartnall, H. J. A., *Proc. Roy. Soc. (London)*, B, 154, 250–66 (1961)

116. Shibata, K., *J. Biochem.*, 45, 599–623 (1958)

117. Bridges, C. D. B., *Nature*, 186, 292–94 (1960)

118. Weale, R. A., *J. Physiol. (London)*, 127, 587–91 (1955)

119. Hubbard, R., Brown, P. K., and Kropf, A., *Nature*, 183, 442–50 (1959)

SOMATOSENSORY MECHANISMS[1]

By Edward R. Perl

Department of Physiology, University of Utah, College of Medicine,
Salt Lake City, Utah

The reviewer has chosen to present a view of current work on somatosensory mechanisms by describing a selected group of papers in some detail. The topics considered deal with the mechanisms, particularly in the mammal, concerned with detection of either the state of the musculoskeletal apparatus or those environmental changes which affect the body skin. The special and cutaneous sensory systems of the head are not treated.

To make the result manageable and in the hope of giving a thread of continuity, the material was selected so as to permit some correlation. For each major reference, an attempt was made to state the problem attacked, some of its implications, the type of method used, and pertinent conclusions. The articles receiving emphasis appeared after January 1, 1961 and were available by July 1962. An obvious drawback is that only a fraction of the publications on matters relating to the topic have been cited and, therefore, a number of important contributions are not mentioned. Additional descriptions of contemporary work are given in the papers discussed, some of which are summaries or have appeared in symposia.

RECEPTORS

INITIATION OF IMPULSES

The first step in a sensory process, that is, the conversion of stimuli into neuronal activity by a sense organ, continues to receive active attention. Two articles concerned with the properties of the nerve membrane participating in such a transformation in the Pacinian corpuscle lead to somewhat different conclusions. Loewenstein (1) believes that the unmyelinated nerve terminal of the Pacinian corpuscle is specialized for the production of a potential change following mechanical distortion and is incapable of initiating a regenerative and conducted action potential. Evidence for these conclusions stems from the results of several kinds of experiments on the unmyelinated receptor nerve terminal after removal of the outer lamina. A microelectrode placed close to the nerve ending was found to record a slow potential change or generator potential after a brief mechanical stimulus delivered by a small probe some ten times the diameter of the unmyelinated axon. This generator potential decremented with distance from the stimulus site and summated with the potential evoked by a stimulus applied by another probe of similar size to a different place along the receptor axon. These observations, and the assumption that the change in a resistive element of an equivalent network

[1] Preparation of this review was supported by Research Grant B-1576 (C4) from the National Institutes of Health.

for the membrane was all-or-none during mechanical excitation for every functional subunit of the receptor membrane, led Loewenstein to conclude that the area of the receptor membrane excited determines the size of the generator potential and that the generator potential process can be a localized phenomenon. Additional support for this concept is presented: (*a*) by a description of the relation between area of the membrane excited (estimated from the size of the probe used as a stimulator) and generator potential size, and (*b*) from a relation between amplitude of generator potential and stimulus intensity required to activate terminals which had been damaged to various degrees. On the basis of the deduction that the area of membrane involved is the important factor in the production of generator potential, fluctuations in its size are related to fluctuations in active membrane area, and postactivation depression also is attributed to a spatially localized process.

Variations in the area of a receptor membrane stimulated certainly could explain the changes in generator potential which were described, but this hypothesis is only one of several reasonable possibilities. Much of Loewenstein's evidence hinges on the assumption, for which no direct evidence exists, that the point of stimulus application determines the place of activation of the receptor membrane; it is quite possible that mechanical spread of the stimulus occurs. Effects ascribed to area changes alone could be the result of partial excitation of the membrane at a given place plus an unknown contribution from other regions. Furthermore, as Loewenstein points out (1, p. 518), conductance change in each patch of receptor membrane representing a functional unit need not be all-or-none and may vary as the stimulus intensity does. Thus, an alternative working hypothesis is that the physiological changes over much of the susceptible receptor membrane leading to a generator potential are graded according to the relative degree of change in conductance produced by mechanical distortion.

The view that the portion of a sense organ responsible for transforming the stimulus into neural activity does not and cannot produce regenerative, conducted impulses is challenged by the findings of Hunt & Takeuchi (2, 3) on the electrical activity of the unmyelinated ending of the Pacinian corpuscle. From records secured with fine wire leads at various positions along the terminal of a corpuscle free of its outer lamellae, they found that the more distal portions of the unmyelinated axon can be an all-or-none sink of electrical activity to a more centrally located source. This distal sink or negativity appeared both after antidromic stimulation of the myelinated nerve at some distance central to the corpuscle and in the course of orthodromic initiation of impulses by mechanical stimuli. The duration of the rising phase and period of current flow were similar to those noted for the impulse in the more proximal myelinated nerve. The latency of the impulsive current flow varied linearly with distance along the terminal segment without showing recognizable changes in the time of the rising phase. During refractoriness of the myelinated segment or under the influence of procaine, the potential change associated with the all-or-none event in the unmyelinated terminal could be initiated alone. These experiments strongly suggest that the unmyelinated terminal of the Pacinian corpuscle can conduct impulses since the timing, all-or-none appearance, and polarity in each instance were appropriate only for such an event. On the other hand, this conclusion does not imply that the impulse must be initiated in the unmyelinated region of the receptor axon (3), and therefore does not necessarily conflict with the suggestions offered by Diamond, Gray & Sato (4), or Loewenstein (1), that conducted activity begins at the first node of Ranvier in the myelinated stretch of nerve. The fact that impulse initiation or conduction into the unmyelinated terminal of the corpuscle has not previously been reported may be related to the recording situation in other studies, because the presence of entire lamellar structure or even the inner core of the corpuscle undoubtedly leads to shunting. It thus appears that the geographical portion of the sensory nerve fiber capable of producing a generator type of potential can also produce a regenerative type of impulse although, with the present evidence, it is still possible that different patches of the receptor membrane are responsible for each phenomenon.

An unusual approach to the problem of impulse initiation in afferent fibers is offered by Murray's (5) work on the cutaneous nerve plexus of elasmobranch fishes. In the ray, unitary impulses can be detected by recording with a monopolar wire electrode on the cutaneous surface, apparently because of the existence of a high-resistance barrier (stratum compactum) some 300 μ below the surface which is penetrated by the nerve fibers. The recorded impulses indicate initiation central to the barrier with subsequent antidromic invasion of the terminals. The fact that an impulse is initiated in a receptor some place central to the mechanical-sensitive terminal is consistent with many previous interpretations. However, in this case Murray presents arguments, based upon the long temperature-sensitive latency between mechanical stimulus and the recordable impulse, that a conducted prepotential precedes it. Here then is another situation in which the receptor structure transforming the stimulus into a neural signal may give rise to conducted activity. Of importance was the apparent refractoriness after mechanical stimulation which ran a time-course similar to accommodation during a prolonged stimulus. Both the refractoriness and accommodation were explained as consequences of the viscoelastic properties of the tissue surrounding the nerve terminals, a mechanism worthy of greater consideration in analyzing activity of mammalian receptors.

THE NEUROMUSCULAR SPINDLE

Several studies on the structure, innervation, and functional behavior of the muscle spindle have emphasized its complexity while offering insight into possible differences in the afferent signals transmitted over its large (Group I) and smaller (Group II) dorsal root fibers. This double afferent innervation of the spindle has been particularly perplexing because of the separate and occasionally opposing central connections of the two kinds of dorsal root fibers.

From extensive microscopic examination of single spindles teased after staining with methylene blue or gold chloride, Boyd (6, 7) concludes that each muscle spindle contains two distinct types of intrafusal muscle fibers which differ in structure and motor innervation. In muscle of the cat hind-limb, Boyd usually found two large-diameter intrafusal muscle fibers, usually running the length of the spindle, which were distinguished by a number of nuclei grouped in the equatorial region (nuclear bag fibers), numerous myo-fibrils evenly distributed in cross section, and a slow rate of atrophy after section of the ventral root. A second kind of intrafusal muscle fiber, found to be more numerous (commonly four) in each spindle, was shorter and smaller in diameter and was further characterized by a single row of nuclei spread along the equatorial region (nuclear-chain fibers), fewer and more irregularly distributed myofibrils, and relatively rapid atrophy after ventral root sec-tion. The motor innervation to the two types of intrafusal fibers is reported to be separate: larger-diameter (2.5 to 6 μ) gamma$_1$ ventral root fibers sup-plying the nuclear-bag muscle fibers with several end plate (extrafusal-type endings) near the spindle pole, while the nuclear-chain fibers had a distributed network of endings in areas other than the nuclear region from small, very thinly myelinated (1–2 μ), gamma$_2$ ventral root fibers. The one large afferent fiber from the spindle (Group I) arises around both the nuclear-bag fibers and from the nuclear-chain fibers. The smaller afferent fiber(s), Group II, are said to originate predominantly on the nuclear-chain intrafusal muscle fibers. It would appear that the two types of afferent nerve fibers from the muscle spindle might respond differently to stretch and to modulation by intrafusal muscle activity.

Some disagreement with this interesting concept of the structural organ-ization of the muscle spindle is expressed by Barker (8) in describing results obtained in his laboratory, largely from reconstructions of serial sections of silver-impregnated material (9). In these investigations there was not in-frequently seen an intrafusal muscle fiber of an intermediate type, different from both the nuclear-bag fiber and the nuclear-chain fiber. On occasion such intermediate-type fibers were noted to bifurcate and then become a nuclear-bag fiber and a nuclear-chain fiber. Similarly, in tandem spindles (spindles linked at a polar region), a nuclear-chain fiber of one of the pair was found to continue as a nuclear-bag fiber in the other. Further, the myofibril struc-ture of the intrafusal fibers was said to change along their length, perhaps because of different degrees of contraction at the time of fixation. This latter point is most unusual because Hess (10) has found that the basic pattern of myofibril distribution and size in extrafusal muscle fibers was not signifi-cantly affected by contraction or relaxation. Barker was also unable to con-firm separate innervation by large fusimotor (gamma$_1$) and small fusimotor (gamma$_2$) fibers to the nuclear-bag and nuclear-chain intrafusal muscle elements, although he agrees with Boyd that the Group I afferent innervation encircles the nuclear-bag fibers and also has endings on the nuclear-chain fibers while the Group II afferent fibers largely innervate the nuclear-chain intrafusal fibers. Support for Boyd's contention that two types of intrafusal muscle fibers have different types of motor endings is present in Hess's (11) study of the motor innervation to the intrafusal muscle fibers using cholinesterase stains. The regions of motor innervation delineated by the presence of cholinesterase were found to be of two types, one a concentrated or motor-plate variety, the other a distribution or *en grappe* variety. Unfortunately, Hess was not able to tell whether the two types of motor endings were on the same or different fibers. Possibly Boyd's construction of a double and separate efferent control of only two types of intrafusal contractile elements is an over-simplification; however, it is an attractive suggestion and amenable to functional test.

If there are different kinds of intrafusal muscle fibers and different ways in which the afferent fibers are distributed to them, it might be expected that the discharge of the two kinds of afferent fibers will vary during the course of physiological excitation. Early observations did not distinguish remarkable variation in the response of the Group I and Group II dorsal root fibers from spindles of the same muscle to steady applied stretch of the muscle or to fusimotor (gamma efferent) activity (12, 13). On the other hand, more extensive study of the activity of the large-diameter and small-diameter spindle afferent fibers under a variety of conditions shows that they have dissimilarities in behavior. The responses of fast-conducting Group I (over 72 m per sec), and slower-conducting afferent fibers from spindles of the de-efferented soleus muscle of the cat were differentiated by Harvey & Matthews (14) with slow phasic and constant stretch. In recording the discharge of single dorsal root fibers, it was found that, on the average, the Group I fibers had a significantly lower threshold and were appreciably more sensitive to the dynamic component of stretch than the Group II fibers. On the other hand, the discharge frequency of the Group II fibers changed much less in passing from the dynamic to the static phase of stretch than did that of the larger fibers, and during the release of tension the pause in discharge was also less pronounced in the Group II fibers. Furthermore, Harvey & Matthews confirmed Kuffler, Hunt and Quilliam's (15) observation that the sensitivity of spindle endings was changed by intrafusal muscle fiber contraction.

An elegant method which may provide an appropriate functional test for the anatomical concepts of the spindle organization has been devised by Bessou & Laporte (16). It consists of identification of single Group I and Group II afferent fibers in a dorsal root from the same muscle spindle of the cat's tenuissimus, a muscle with spindles arranged in a chainlike fashion with little overlap. The muscle was de-efferented and isolated, except for vascular and nerve pedicles, in an oil pool. Single dorsal root fibers of widely different conduction velocity were located which discharged to stretch of the muscle but not during its contraction. Electrical stimulation of the muscle surface by closely spaced electrodes, moved in small steps over the surface, served to show whether two afferent fibers, one conducting above and one below 60 m per sec, were excited by the same placement of the stimulating cathode. When such fibers were found, a further test of their origin from the same sense organ was that both fibers discharged simultaneously on application of slight, localized pressure over a length substantially less than that occupied by a spindle. With this method, Group I fibers were found to have a lower threshold than the "secondary" (Group II) fiber from the same spindle. Once threshold was reached for the Group II fiber, the increase in frequency of discharge for unit changes in length was more rapid than for the larger fiber. The Group I fiber was found to adapt more rapidly during the dynamic phase of stretch and at subsequent static positions than the smaller fiber. Sudden stretch evoked a burst of impulses in the Group I fiber but not in the Group II fiber. During and following elastic shortening, the Group I discharge stopped while the Group II fibers showed little slowing. Stimulation of some fusimotor fibers in a shortened muscle produced a more marked acceleration of Group I than of the Group II discharge. In one case, three different fusimotor fibers evoked divergent changes of discharge in a Group I and Group II fiber from the same tenuissimus spindle. All of these effects were thought to be consistent with separate viscoelastic properties of the "primary" (Group I) fiber and "secondary" (Group II) fibers, perhaps traceable to their origin on dissimilar structures within the spindle. In addition, there is a preliminary suggestion that the two afferent fibers are subject to unlike effects by fusimotor (gamma) excitation. Thus there is some physiological evidence which is consistent with the kind of Group I and Group II afferent innervation of the spindle that is observed in morphological studies.

The studies by Harvey & Matthews (14) and Bessou & Laporte (16) were performed on muscle spindles in which the contraction of the intrafusal muscle fibers was not under control of the central nervous system. Possible effects of central control of spindle characteristics were obtained by Cooper (17) in a study of the discharge of afferent fibers (in the dorsal root) from an extensor muscle, soleus, of a decerebrate cat. Cooper's cats in general showed good decerebrate rigidity and therefore, to a certain degree, the extrafusal fibers of the soleus were tonically active. Small extensions of the soleus muscle excited the Group I afferent fibers, the response generally displaying the characteristics described above for spindles deprived of motor innervation. On the other hand, the Group II fibers from the same muscle frequently did not change significantly in their discharge to similar stimulation. These effects may have resulted from the limited degree of stretch that Cooper employed and the lower sensitivity of the secondary endings, but in view of Boyd's analysis (6), it is tempting to suggest that the existing fusimotor activity had further modified the sensitivity of the endings by independent modulation of the nuclear-bag and nuclear-chain fibers. The reflex connections in decerebrate animals are so set as to depress many flexor-directed mechanisms (18, 19) and this may include not only the central effect of Group II impulses but also factors altering the initiation of Group II activity.

GROUP III MUSCLE RECEPTORS

Muscle nerves contain a number of small-diameter (1–4 μ) myelinated fibers of dorsal root origin, Group III. These are known to initiate divers reflex effects and to have centrally directed connections reaching supraseg-mental regions at several levels. Bessou & Laporte (20) have examined the response to various stimuli of single fibers in dorsal root filaments arising from the ankle extensor muscles in the cat with conduction velocities appropriate for Group III. The majority of fibers studied were excited by pressure while few behaved as if they arose from muscle spindles or tendon organs, results comparable to those independently obtained by Paintal (21). Slowly adapting pressure-sensitive units were found at the musculotendinous junction and in the main body of the muscle. Fibers adapting rapidly to pressure occurred at the soleus insertion and on the surface of the muscle. Certain units were found to have receptive fields covering large fractions of the muscle, indicating extensive branching of the nerve fiber. A small fraction of the pressure-sensitive fibers discharged with marked stretch or muscle contraction. Paintal (21) had found that some fibers which respond to pressure, but not those from stretch receptors, also were effectively excited by injection of hypertonic saline, a procedure that produces pain in humans. This response to a form of noxious stimulation suggests a relationship between the higher-threshold, slowly adapting pressure fibers of Group III and the sensation of muscle pain (21). On the other hand, the low sensitivity and rapid adaptation to mechanical stimuli of other Group III receptors make it reasonable to believe that they have another perceptual significance such as signaling the degree of contraction (force of handgrip) or deep pressure.

"SPECIFICITY" OF RECEPTORS

Recently, doubt has arisen anew regarding the anatomical and functional specificity of the nerve endings responsible for initiating impulses which eventually lead to cutaneous sensation. Weddell, a leading proponent of the group challenging the concept that sense organs distinct in structure and sensitivity are used to signal each of the cutaneous "modalities" recognized by man, has summarized some of the experimental and clinical evidence supporting his position (22). He and his colleagues have found only two morphologically distinguishable types of nerve terminals in the hairy skin of man, apart from that on the back of the fingers: those endings at the base of hairs and "free" nerve endings. Complex nerve end-formations were found only in exposed mucous membranes and in the hairless skin of the hands and feet. With use of vital stains in human subjects, solely nonspecialized endings were observed in the conjunctiva of young people while complicated end-bulb-type structures were seen in the later decades of life. Further, in the conjunctiva of a living man, the disappearance of "frustrated" growth cones from time to time was apparently related to degeneration and regeneration of nerve fibers. Thus, in the hands of these investigators complex endings in the skin innervated by sensory nerve fibers are not common, and, when present, seem to be a product of growth processes rather than some stable organization. They also argue the impossibility of exciting only one nerve fiber with a physiological stimulus: because of the complicated branching and intertwining of endings from several stem axons, a pattern of "impulses" from even discrete stimuli would automatically result. Weddell (22) bases part of his case upon the fact that in psychophysiological experiments a variety of sensory experiences were reported for different stimuli delivered to the cornea, a region considered to be innervated by only "free" nerve endings. He recapitulates other experiments in which action potentials were led from small bundles of the ciliary nerve and it was found that individual axons had specific and varying sensitivities to certain kinds of stimuli such as heat, cold, mechanical deformation, and intense mechanical stimuli. On the basis of these various considerations, Weddell concludes that "although 'modality' specific nerve receptors must certainly exist, there are others which are less specific in relation to the four primary sensory modalities, and that the cutaneous sensory modalities as generally understood depend upon patterns of activity which, for a given report, must be highly reproducible." He further deduces that at least two complementary somatosensory systems must subserve cutaneous sensation: a highly specialized one with discrete multiple-innervated terminals and a more complex system served by widespread overlapping terminals which conveys a greater range of information on the state of the skin and its environment.

Supporters of the pattern theory frequently cite other investigators' results. Certainly, in Sergeev's (23) findings, clear support exists for the relation of many kinds of sensory experience in man to relatively unspecialized receptors. At other times, data said to be consistent with nonspecificity of receptors can, viewed from a different vantage, be interpreted as indicating that the signaling of cutaneous environmental changes and sensation are related to distinct structures. Thus, Douglas & Ritchie (24), in a review of the properties and afferent functions of nonmyelinated nerve fibers, emphasize that many C fibers respond well to both mechanical and thermal stimuli of moderate intensity. However, as seen below, this may not mean that the function of fibers having this dual sensitivity is to signal both changes in heat transfer and mechanical deformation of the skin or that the receptor is not specialized. On the other hand, Iggo's experiments (25), and the evidence given by Weddell and by Douglas and Ritchie, show clearly that the plexus of nerve fibers in the skin connected to finely myelinated or unmyelinated stem axons transduces more than tissue-damaging or noxious stimuli. The alternative for separate receptors, separate afferent fibers, and separate central pathways in the identification by the nervous system of the kind of cutaneous stimulus is at this date purely a hypothesis. Hensel (26) has discussed theoretical means by which receptors sensitive to more than one stimulus might signal different kinds of stimuli. Such schemes involve different numbers of discharges per unit time for each kind of stimulus; however, he stresses that the only well-documented relationship between impulse frequency and stimulus is the one for intensity. He further summarizes the evidence for kinds of specifically sensitive cutaneous receptors (mainly mechanical or temperature) and nonspecific receptors (largely mechanical plus temperature).

VIBRATION, TOUCH, AND TENSION RECEPTORS

In connection with the question of receptor specificity, it is interesting that within the period covered by this review a special sensitivity to particular stimuli has been suggested for two cutaneous receptors and one deep sense organ. The afferent nerve fibers supplying these were of relatively large diameter (over 5 μ). Thus, the relation between distinct anatomical features and stimulus sensitivity does not necessarily contradict evidence in favor of the "pattern theory", much of which is derived from studies concerned with the sensory endings of smaller-diameter nerve fibers.

Vibration receptors.—Hunt & McIntyre (27) had noted a group of afferent fibers of the interosseus nerve of the cat's lower hindlimb which responded particularly well to sinusoidal vibration. Hunt (28) subsequently traced this nerve and found that it received many fibers from clusters of Pacinian corpuscles. Recordings of the nerve's electrical activity showed that when these corpuscles were subjected to sinusoidal vibratory stimuli, a multifiber discharge of impulses was initiated for each cycle of the mechanical stimulation at frequencies between 50 and 800 cps. If the spread of stimulus was limited, regions not containing Pacinian corpuscles did not respond in this way. Recordings of single afferent fibers taken from the interosseus nerve, or from a dorsal root fiber which supplied this nerve, showed that the response initiated by sinusoidal vibration of a single corpuscle ordinarily consisted of one impulse for each cycle over the same frequency range. When the uniqueness of the response was tested, muscle receptors and a variety of cutaneous receptors were found not to respond to the higher vibration frequencies of this range. Further, low-amplitude sinusoidal vibration (above 200 cps) applied to the skin supplied by the sural nerve evoked a discharge in the nerve at the frequency of vibration only from certain discrete foci. Pacinian corpuscles were found to be located near such foci. Because the corpuscle was particularly sensitive to high-frequency vibration and other receptors were not, Hunt concluded that it must be responsible for signaling vibratory changes of the skin and deeper structures.

Taking cognizance of this suggested relationship, Sato (29) examined the behavior of Pacinian corpuscles from the mesentery of cat, *in vitro* and *in vivo*, using vibratory stimuli delivered by a transducer with known characteristics. He confirmed the observation that the Pacinian corpuscle is effectively excited by sinusoidal vibratory stimuli at frequencies beyond that initiating similar activity in other receptors. Temperature changes affected the threshold and frequency characteristics of the response. A distinct generator potential in response to each cycle of sinusoidal mechanical disturbance could be recorded and an impulse would be initiated every time this was of the appropriate size. The vibration-frequency sensitivity of the Pacinian corpuscle matches the usual figures given for vibratory perception when stimuli of reasonable intensity are employed (28, 29), a fact emphasized by a recent determination of the vibration threshold-frequency relationship in man (30). It is of historical interest that earlier studies on the Pacinian corpuscle had noted the effectiveness of vibratory stimuli (31, 32) without implicating it in the signaling of vibratory sensation. Despite these facts and correlations, the important direct confirmation in man is still missing.

Touch receptors.—Previously, several investigators had reported afferent fibers of large diameter in cat and man which discharged to both skin pressure and skin temperature changes (33, 34, 35). The spotlike characteristic of the receptive field described by Hunt & McIntyre (36) has aided in subsequent study of the structural relationships. Iggo (37) has found in the hairy skin on the cat's hindlimb small raised areas (200 μ in diameter). Stimulation of these by localized slight pressure or by cooling initiated a slowly adapting response in afferent fibers supplying the region. These raised areas or domes were characterized by the presence of a vascular glomus and ordinarily were innervated by a single axon which had divided 200 to 300 μ centrally. Additional branching of the axon occurred as it entered the structure, and these branches took a radial course toward the epithelium. The terminals of the axons were characteristic and unique, being roughly circular plates or disks some 10 μ in diameter and 1 μ thick. Each disk appeared to be a terminal expansion of the axon.

Iggo & Muir (38) portray in detail the histological features of structures within these hemispherical "touch" domes. In sections examined by electron microscope, they noted that the terminal nerve blade or disk was not a free ending but was invested in a sheath, possibly of Schwann cells, and that there were no myelin lamellae present. [Enclosure of certain sensory terminals in a Schwann-like structure also has been described by Weddell for the so-called "free" nerve axons (22).] The terminal nerve disk seemed to be in close contact with certain specialized epithelial cells in the center of the dome and it was hypothesized that these specialized epithelial cells are related to the functional response of the sense organ.

Tension receptors.—The correlation of a structure with the discharge of afferent fibers of the interosseus nerve to tension upon or deformation of the interosseus membrane (27) is based upon exclusion. The conduction velocity of the nerve fibers exhibiting this kind of response was quite high, falling, with two exceptions, into the Group I range (over 72 m per sec). Barker (8) found that the structures associated with afferent fibers of the interosseus nerve of cat and supplied by large myelinated fibers were largely of two types,

Pacinian corpuscles and Golgi tendon organs. Response of the "tension" afferent fibers was slowly adapting, and tap or vibratory stimuli were not effective in evoking their discharge. This would eliminate the Pacinian corpuscles (28) leaving the Golgi tendon organs located in the fascia of the adjacent flexor digitorum longus muscle. The functional significance of such tendon organs in this location is of some importance, particularly in view of the diverse opinions on the kind of connections made by afferent fibers from the tendon organs (i.e., Group Ib). It is possible that tendon organs not excited specifically by tension of a given muscle may have reflex effects and central connections different from those which are located so as to signal contraction or marked stretch of a particular muscle.

SYNAPTIC TRANSMISSION

It has been recognized for some time that synaptic transmission to the most intensively studied neuron of the mammalian central nervous system, the spinal motoneuron, may not be representative of synaptic action at other sites. For example, a number of authors have documented the fact that a single volley of impulses in primary afferent fibers may initiate multiple impulses recurring at high frequency (over 500 per sec) in nuclear regions of sensory projections, a kind of response which is exceptional in most studies of motoneuron discharge (39, 40, 41). Some of the factors or the mechanisms responsible for the repetitive firing of neurons were previously discussed by McIntyre, Mark & Steiner (42). On the other hand, the properties of the cells exhibiting this type of activity have only been examined in spinal interneurons of unknown destination (43) although some may well have been associated with ascending systems. Considering the common occurrence of multiple discharges after sensory system synapses, one might expect that the widespread use of intracellular recording would be extended to examine this question. Two recent and detailed investigations of synaptic action on cells of the spinocerebellar tracts help to explain the paucity of intracellular recordings from such neurons. Eccles, Hubbard & Oscarsson (44) point out that impalement of cells identified as belonging to the ventral spinocerebellar tract was usually accompanied by deterioration of the cells' resting potential and ability to generate "spike" potentials; apparently these cells do not readily tolerate insertion of a microelectrode. In cats under light barbiturate anesthesia, transmembrane potentials were recorded from cells identified by antidromic invasion following stimulation of the appropriate portion of the rostral spinal cord and short-latency or "monosynaptic" activation by ipsilateral Group I muscle afferent fibers. The action potential of ventral spinocerebellar cells has two components but these cannot be easily separated by repetitive activation as in many neurons. Following the impulse, a period of hyperpolarization is present, somewhat shorter in duration than that seen in lumbar motoneurons. Excitatory postsynaptic potentials were obtained from cells in which the impulsive event was suppressed because of damage. As judged by central latency, these potentials were generated in the cells by monosynaptic action from the large myelinated afferent fibers of muscle nerves. An increase in size (up to 100%) during repetitive stimulation at frequencies above one second was an unusual feature of the excitatory potentials. Such potentiation with repetitive stimulation is much more marked than the effect seen in dorsal spinocerebellar cells (45) and is in contrast to changes following similarly repeated Group I monosynaptic excitation in motoneurons. In addition, Group I and smaller muscle afferent fibers evoked inhibitory postsynaptic potentials (hyperpolarization). The potentiating effect of repetitive activation of presynaptic fibers on the excitatory synaptic potentials was suggested as one of the mechanisms important in allowing ventral spinocerebellar tract neurons to follow high frequencies of primary afferent activity for long periods of time. A comparison of synaptic action in these cells and motoneurons indicates some difference in synaptic contact, transmitter release, or presynaptic termination in the two situations.

Dorsal spinocerebellar cells (Clarke's column) are known to respond to a single volley of primary afferent impulses with repetitive activity, and Eccles, Oscarsson & Willis (45) describe some findings apparently related to this type of response. They noted that after the first impulse evoked by large Group I volleys, the synaptic depolarization (excitatory potential) reappeared and incremented up to 5 msec after its initial onset, at times being associated with a second impulse. Further, the excitatory synaptic potential evoked by a monosynaptic linkage with the Group I fibers showed a two-step decay, a rapid initial phase and a slower later one. The more slowly declining phase lasted for 30 to 40 msec and therefore is considerably longer than that found in motoneurons following similar short-latency (monosynaptic) excitation. Repetitive stimulation of the primary afferent fibers causing excitatory postsynaptic potentials prolonged the synaptic potentials to an even greater degree. These features led to the conclusion that the transmitter substance is persistent, perhaps as a consequence of the very large synaptic endings on cells of Clarke's column described by Szentágothai & Albert (46). Therefore, the explanation for the multiple response of Clarke's column cells is different from that suggested for similar discharge of spinal interneurons where an important feature is asynchrony of excitatory activity (43).

ASCENDING PATHWAYS

The usual description of ascending pathways in the spinal cord of mammals includes tracts destined to reach the suprasegmental nervous system at several levels. These are the two cerebellar tracts ordinarily recognized, one in the dorsolateral and one in the ventrolateral funiculus; at least two pathways long believed to reach thalamic neurons, the dorsal column system and the spinothalamic pathways in the ventrolateral funiculus; and the spinoreticular, spino-olivary, and spinotectal pathways, considered to run in the ventrolateral funiculus. The nature and organization of spinal sensory tracts have been actively studied during the past year and one-half, resulting in a considerable increase of information.

Spinocerebellar Pathways

Oscarsson (47) had demonstrated that the cells of origin of the ventral spinocerebellar tract were considerably more caudad than Clarke's column, the accepted source of the dorsal spinocerebellar tract. Hubbard & Oscarsson (48) mapped the spinal cord for cell somata monosynaptically excited by Group I muscle afferent fibers and antidromically invaded from axons of the opposite ventrolateral funiculus. These were located in the lateral part of the intermediate zone and dorsolateral portion of the ventral horn of the spinal gray column several segments cephalad of the afferent root entrance. In the report mentioned earlier, Eccles, Hubbard & Oscarsson (44) detailed some of the afferent connections to ventral spinocerebellar cells, using post-synaptic potentials as evidence. Group I afferent fibers of the most rapidly conducting group from a given muscle evoked a short-latency depolarization (monosynaptic), and Group I fibers from muscles other than that producing the excitatory synaptic potentials caused increased (inhibitory) membrane potentials. A complex pattern of convergence of the Group I muscle afferent excitation and inhibition was described and this was interpreted as indicating that ventrospinal cerebellar tract neurons "carry information, not concerning changes of tension in single muscles or muscle groups acting at single joints, but concerning stages of movement or position of the whole limb." In addition to the afferent connections, effects on the ventrolateral tract neurons were recognized following rostral spinal stimulation. Inhibition was evoked by stimulation of the ipsilateral dorsolateral funiculus, possibly the pyramidal tract, and excitation was produced by stimulation of the ipsilateral ventral quadrant.

In other experiments Lundberg & Oscarsson (49) examined the projection of ventral spinocerebellar tract neurons to the cerebellar cortex. With micropipettes inserted into the ventrolateral funiculus of the cord, records were obtained from single fibers of the tract. The appropriate units were selected by demonstrating Group I muscle afferent excitation and by antidromic invasion from more rostral portions of the ventral quadrant. The conduction velocity of the tract fibers was high, ranging from 70 to 120 m per sec with an average of 94 m per sec. Such fibers were monosynaptically discharged only from contralateral Group I muscle afferent fibers but were also influenced after a longer latency by cutaneous and muscle afferent fibers of smaller diameter from both sides of the body. The termination of the fibers was tested by mapping the area of cerebellar cortex from which they could be antidromically discharged by electrical stimulation. Fibers of the ventral tract were found to end in longitudinal zones on the intermediate cortex of the cerebellum and on a lateral strip of the vermal cortex. The majority of fibers had recrossed the midline and some apparently projected bilaterally. It was concluded from the area of cerebellar cortex involved that profuse preterminal branching occurred so that single ascending fibers made synaptic contact with large areas of the cortex. The observed response of tract fibers to nerve volleys was interpreted to indicate that afferent fibers from Golgi tendon organs were the source of the Group I excitaiton. A small group of neurons otherwise meeting the criteria for the tract were also discharged by cutaneous or muscle afferent fibers of smaller diameter.

A past study by Lundberg & Oscarsson (50), which described features of the dorsal spinocerebellar tract, used the above methods, but applied them to elements of the lateral spinal funiculus. The ascending fibers reaching the cerebellar cortex via the dorsal spinocerebellar tract had conduction velocities from 30 to 120 m per sec, and could be classified according to the nature of the exciting sensory input. The termination in the cerebellar cortex was different from that of the ventral tract, dorsal spinocerebellar neurons ending largely if not exclusively in a position ipsilateral to the tract, with an individual fiber supplying only a small cortical area. In their intracellular recordings from neurons giving rise to the dorsal spinocerebellar tract (Clark's column), Eccles, Oscarsson & Willis (45) concluded that some of these cells receive excitatory convergence via a monosynaptic pathway from both high- and low-threshold (to electrical stimulation) afferent Group I fibers of a particular muscle and occasionally also for Group II diameter fibers. Since they attribute the low-threshold Group I afferent fibers from muscle to spindles and the high-threshold Group I fibers to tendon organs, it was concluded that both spindle- and tendon-organ afferent fibers converge upon the same Clarke's column cell. The validity of the assumption that a complete separation of afferent fibers from different receptors can be accomplished by stimulating muscle nerves with various intensities of electrical shock has been questioned (51). Direct evidence obtained by Laporte & Bessou (52) showed that while, on the average, a difference exists between the conduction velocity of afferent fibers from muscle spindle and Golgi tendon organs, significant overlap occurs even in animals selected for marked separation of Group I volley components. The overlap is recognized by Eccles *et al.* (44) as a possible "contaminate" of the volleys. One might question if the evidence given by electrical stimulation of nerve is sufficient to disregard other studies which failed to find convergence from different stretch receptors on dorsal cerebellar tract neurons [(53, 54); see below].

ASCENDING PATHWAYS DESTINED FOR MEDULLARY, MIDBRAIN, AND THALAMIC REGIONS

Not all of the ascending fibers of the lateral funiculus are destined for the cerebellum. Lundberg & Oscarsson (55) have analyzed the afferent connections of dorsolateral funiculus neurons which orginate below the caudal level of Clarke's column. The activity of single fibers was recorded with a microelectrode inserted into the lateral column. Those units which responded to stimulation of the column more rostrally were considered part of an ascending tract. The neurons discussed could not be antidromically excited by stimulation of the cerebellar culmen; however, this may not have been an adequate test of cerebellar projection since peripheral receptors are known to excite more rostral portions of the cerebellum and the paramedian lobules (56, 57). After single volleys initiated in peripheral nerves, one group of fibers were excited at short latency by the lowest-threshold cutaneous afferent fibers. Such cells were also discharged by light touch applied to restricted ipsilateral receptor fields but not by pressure or pinching of the skin. The axons were located quite close to the entrance line of the dorsal roots and could not be influenced by a variety of supraspinal excitations shown to affect transmission in other ascending pathways. Other dorsolateral funiculus fibers also responded to tactile stimuli but the receptive fields were large and additional kinds of afferent input were excitatory. Evoked responses of a third group of fibers were initiated from bilateral afferent input after a long latency. Stimulation of the rostral spinal cord or anterior cerebellum changed the response of the latter two groups to afferent stimulation. Lundberg & Oscarsson point out that the first-mentioned or "tactile" group of fibers resembles that previously described by Morin (58) and these fibers probably reach the cerebral cortex (see later). Neurons of the ventrolateral funiculus not antidromically excitable from the anterior cerebellum were found by Lundberg & Oscarsson (59) to separate into two main classes: those discharged by small-diameter muscle afferent fibers and cutaneous afferent fibers from bilaterally located nerves, and a group responding to similar afferent fibers from contralateral hindlimb nerves only. Both classes also responded to touching or pinching the skin innervated by the excitatory nerve. Cells with bilateral receptive fields could be excited (or inhibited) by electrical stimulation of the exposed anterior cerebellar lobe while the group of neurons connected mainly to contralateral receptors could not be influenced from the cerebellum. The suprasegmental projection of cells excited by bilateral afferent stimulation was traced in the ventral midbrain to about the level of the inferior colliculus. It is impossible to say yet which kind of ventrolateral fiber group belongs to the spinoreticular, spino-olivary, or spinothalamic pathways.

The physiological importance of reported effects on ascending systems initiated by electrical stimulation of more centrally located structures is obscure. It is often assumed that these changes are mediated by mechanisms changing excitability of either an ascending neuron or an interstitial cell intercalated between it and a primary afferent fiber. There seems ample evidence that descending systems can alter excitability of spinal interneurons (18, 19); however, changes initiated by electrical stimulation of the central nervous system might produce complex effects having little relation to control mechanisms. One possibility is that incidental antidromic excitation of neurons with ascending processes could set up potential fields which in turn might polarize primary afferent terminals, a suggested cause of "presynaptic inhibition" (60). Some reports on certain ascending pathways in the spinal cord likewise bring up the question of the proper definition of an ascending tract. Groups of ascending fibers are sometimes separated into one or another functional category without due consideration for the possibility that these may represent pathways carrying messages from different somatic receptors to some common destination and may have a functional and structural unity.

INFLUENCE OF SYNAPTIC RELAYS UPON SIGNALS FROM PERIPHERAL RECEPTORS

An obvious and pertinent problem is the fate of signals from primary afferent neurons, particularly when initiated by "natural" stimuli, in the transfer to second-order neurons. This question, of course, could be asked after each successive synaptic station and, in a sense, represents an objective of much of the research on the higher levels of sensory systems. Over the past ten years, many studies have pointed out that in some of the ascending somatosensory systems the responses of a higher-order neuron can be related to one or another general class of stimulus; i.e. "tactile", joint rotation, noxious, etc. In the projections destined for the cerebral cortex, such characteristics can be recognized at thalamic recording stations and again for some neurons of the somatosensory receiving areas of the cerebral cortex. However, in most instances, the correlations are relatively crude because the exact nature of the signals being transmitted to the central nervous system following adequate stimuli was not known. Therefore, a close comparison between input and response is difficult. A clearer situation exists in the spinocerebellar pathways. The responses of the large afferent fiber from the muscle-spindle and the Golgi tendon-organ afferent fiber have been examined in some detail, and the recorded response of a second-order neuron can be related to the expected input coming from the stretch receptors. McIntyre & Mark (54) reported that some cells of the dorsal spinocerebellar tract give responses mimicking the activity of muscle-spindle or tendon-organ afferent fibers during muscle contraction or stretch. The careful investigation by Lundberg & Winsbury (53) also demonstrated that certain of the dorsal spinocerebellar tract neurons behaved as if they were excited by either muscle-spindle afferent fibers or muscle tendon-organ afferent fibers, the discharge in each case representing a typical kind of response for one or the other receptor. This kind of data suggests no significant change in the sensory information forwarded by the spinocerebellar tracts compared to what it received from a specific muscle. Comparisons of sensitivity and adaptation during various kinds of stretch might affect this inference.

A systematic analysis of the change in signals from cutaneous receptors after synaptic transfer has been developed by Gray and co-workers at University College, London. Study of some factors concerned with the linkage between a mechanical stimulus and response of receptors of the cat's pads has been one step. Armett & Hunsperger (61) excited the central pad of a cat paw with a small probe attached to a Rochelle salt crystal. Displacement of the pad was measured by an optical system, and the properties of the mechanical wave transmitted across the pad after stimuli applied at various locations were determined. Impulses from the receptors innervating the pads were recorded from fibers of the dorsal root or the nerve supplying the pad itself, and the nerve responses were then compared to the known spread of the mechanical disturbance across the pad's surface. The displacement at the beginning and the restoration after a mechanical pulse both contributed to excitation of the receptors. The amount and rate of displacement required to reach threshold increased with distance from the center of a receptor's excitatory field. Further, the initiation of impulses from a receptor was delayed at the periphery of the receptive field as compared to its center. Changes in excitability following a subthreshold pulse in the intact pad and after surgical removal and replacement of a portion of the pad were similar. Armett & Hunsperger concluded that the properties of a receptive field and certain interactions that occur within it may be caused by mechanical transmission of stimuli. Therefore, caution should be used before all interactions are attributed to central factors. Armett, Gray & Palmer (62) located a group of cells in the spinal cord which apparently are excited from these primary afferent fibers. The cells were situated in the medial portion of the dorsal horn and if they are somata of neurons forming an ascending sensory tract should project ipsilaterally, according to the hypothesis advanced by Magni & Oscarsson (63). Thus, it is possible that these neurons are the source of the lateral column tactile pathway described above. The latest step in this analysis appears in experiments by Armett *et al.* (64). The area and time-course of the population response from the whole nerve innervating a cat's foot pad were compared with the predicted distribution of activity from the data obtained by Armett & Hunsperger (61) and from a knowledge of the number of fibers involved. On the basis of a reasonably good agreement between the predicted and recorded activity following mechanical stimulation, it was concluded that only one impulse is transmitted by any one fiber following a single mechanical deformation of short duration. On recording from the spinal neurons identified by Armett, Gray & Palmer (62) at low repetition rates of a constant stimulus, (*a*) many second-order cells were activated by the input signal, (*b*) activity in only a very few primary afferent fibers was required to set up a second-order response, and (*c*) suprathreshold stimuli gave rise to prolonged variable bursts of impulses. On the other hand, at high repetition rates, more convergence was apparently needed to discharge a given second-order neuron and the responses were stable, consisting of one or two discharges. Estimation of the input to the second-order cells in terms of the number of primary active units using double-pulse stimulation led to the deduction that considerable convergence of excitatory activity from primary afferent fibers occurred within the first few milliseconds with no evidence of inhibition from regions outside the excitatory field. This pattern of convergence was hypothesized to give the same result, in a "phasic" system, one might obtain in the case of lateral inhibition or "surround" in a "tonic" system.

Probably the changes associated with sensory nuclear relays vary from one projection to another. Investigation of the difference in signals in primary afferent fibers and those in second-order neurons of the dorsal column system has been made by Perl, Whitlock & Gentry (65). The electrical activity of single elements of the gracilis was recorded with small electrodes in decerebrate cats. The gracilis neurons were divided into various groups depending upon the nature of the response to "natural" forms of stimulation known to be effective in exciting one or another receptor supplied by primary afferent fibers of relatively large diameter. Neurons of one type responded to hair deflection with a rapidly adapting discharge and were located largely in the midportion of the nucleus. Responses evoked from such hair-driven units could be inhibited by stimulation of nerves or receptors from surrounding skin. A second group of gracilis units were excited by light skin pressure, adapted relatively slowly, and routinely showed a distinctive background discharge which changed with skin temperature. A third class of gracilis units responded to light taps or vibratory stimuli with a discharge related to each cycle of sinusoidal vibratory stimuli between 70 and 350 cps. In addition to these, smaller numbers of units were found, particularly in the more rostral portions of the nucleus, which responded to joint manipulation alone, pressure on a foot pad, or pressure on a joint capsule. The area of skin (peripheral receptive field) effective in exciting either a hair or "touch" unit varied with location on the body surface: the smallest receptive fields were situated most distally on the hindlimb. The receptive fields for those cells responding to skin pressure and temperature changes were regularly larger than for those excited by hair deflection and for many units involved almost the entire lateral or medial surface of the hindlimb as well as nearby portions of the trunk. Each of these three types of gracilis units gave responses consistent with the projection from only one type of receptor (see above). The relation of the second-order responses to those in primary afferent fibers suggested that a major change in sensory signals after a synapse in this nucleus was a consequence of a systematic excitatory convergence of receptors of one type upon a given neuron. In addition, in the pathway for hair receptors the excitatory effects were modified by a form of lateral or "surround" inhibition. Thus, the discharge characteristics as determined by the adaptation and sensitivity of the receptor are transmitted relatively unchanged through the second-order neuron. The peripheral receptive field demonstrated a spatial "code"; however, a repetitive response of single elements to a single volley in primary afferent fibers suggested superimposition of some temporal "coding" as well. "Surround" inhibition was evident only in the rapidly adapting hair receptor pathway, illustrating that it is not only a property of "tonic" systems. In man, temperature sense is apparently not dependent upon the dorsal column so the touch projection to the gracilis may have nothing to do with the temperature "modality"; however, Weber's illusion whereby cold weights appear heavier than warm ones may have an origin here (26).

ORGANIZATION OF DORSAL COLUMN NUCLEI

In the study by Perl et al. (65), some congregation of units excited by specific receptors was noted in certain portions of the nucleus, for example, the common occurrence of hair-excited elements in the middle third of the longitudinal dimension. Other investigators have methodically studied the topographic organization of the gracilis nuclei in cat and rat. Gordon & Seed (66) recorded the activity of single gracilis elements in barbiturate-anesthetized cats and correlated the caudal-rostral location of gracilis cells with central structures from which they could be antidromically discharged. They discovered that not all of the cells responding to tactile stimulation of the hindfoot could be driven antidromically from the medial lemniscus. The proportion of cells demonstrated to project centrally over the lemniscus by this technique was highest in the middle third of the nucleus and considerably lower in the more rostral regions. Some of the cells in the rostral third of the nucleus, apparently not projecting over the lemniscus (of the opposite side), could be excited from the ipsilateral anterior cerebellar cortex. Evidence was offered that stimulation in the vicinity of the medial lemniscus discharged some of the rostral pole units after a synapse. The latter finding brings to mind the anatomical (67, 68) and electrophysiological (69) data suggesting that higher centers, such as the cerebral cortex, have descending pathways via the pyramidal tract reaching cells of the dorsal column nuclei. Even weak stimulation in the vicinity of the medial lemniscus conceivably could excite nearby pyramidal fibers. The responses of variously located gracilis cells to antidromic excitation appear to confirm a caudal rostral functional organization in the dorsal column nuclei of the type originally described by Gordon & Paine (70). Further evidence along this line appears in McComas' work on the rat gracilis nucleus (71). When the hairless skin on the hindpaw of the rat was stimulated mechanically, the rostrally located gracilis cells tended to have large receptive fields, high thresholds, and long latencies while more caudally located cells also had relatively large fields, but with relatively low thresholds, and responded at short latencies. Cells from the middle third of the rat gracilis were characterized by small receptive fields. Although the receptors excited by Gordon & Paine (70), and by McComas (71), have not been determined, it is clear that the gracilis nucleus has a complex organization.

Kruger, Siminoff & Witkovsky (72) have detailed somatotopic features of the projection to the dorsal column nuclei by recording unitary activity in deeply anesthetized animals. A rostral-caudal and medial-lateral position arrangement was found in which different portions of the body were projected to the different portions of the nuclei. The size of the receptive fields for a given neuron was apparently related to the region of peripheral innervation, small receptive fields being located distally on the limb. Kruger et al. did not find segregation of projections from different kinds of receptors at different parts of the nucleus although they noted some tendency for groups of units responding to a common form of peripheral stimulus, i.e. joint rotation or "tactile", to be located in close proximity.

Kuypers, Hoffman & Beasley (73) report cytoarchitectural differences in the dorsal column nuclei of the cat that are pertinent to the functional findings. Based upon Golgi and Nissl material, several different kinds of cells are found and their concentration varies in the rostral-caudal dimension. Cells with very large dendritic arborizations are common more rostrally and other similar cells are prevalent in the caudal pole. In the intermediate region, clusters of cells, with intertwining dendrites, are most obvious. It has been suggested that the cell clusters may be related to the "surround" inhibition evident in this portion of the nucleus associated with the dense hair receptor projection (65, 73). Kuypers *et al.* also examined the descending projection from the cerebral cortex and noted that the cells with larger dendritic ramifications receive the greatest descending projection. Obviously, further correlations between functional and structural data in the dorsal column nuclei might prove very illuminating.

In an attempt to reconcile the various studies on the dorsal column nuclei, it could be emphasized that some form of somatotopic pattern exists and that the sizes of the receptive fields for cells excited from distal regions are smaller than those for cells excited from more proximal portions of the limb or trunk. Different kinds of receptors (hair, touch) concentrating in different skin areas might then impose the kind of caudal-rostral organization described above. On the other hand, it is possible that these nuclei are no more homogeneous than the medial geniculate body, with the rostral pole having a functional significance different from that of the more caudal regions.

HIGHER SUPRASEGMENTAL PROJECTIONS
The Thalamus

Using material from a human cordotomy case, Mehler (74) has traced ascending pathways of the ventrolateral spinal quadrant to their termination at various levels of the brainstem by the Nauta stain of degenerating fibers. This careful morphological analysis, with an extensive supporting bibliography, stresses the fragmentary state of our understanding of higher nervous mechanisms related to sensory phenomena. In the course through the medullary and midbrain regions, the ascending ventrolateral spinal tracts not only lose fibers destined for cerebellar termination, but also the fibers to nuclei of the reticular regions, the midbrain tectum, and the periaqueductal grey. In the past, the effect of afferent activity on neurons of the "reticular formation" has been described with noticeably rare attempts to locate and specify carefully the nuclei or cells giving rise to the responses recorded. It is clear that before the functional organization of the spinal projections to medullary and midbrain regions can be deciphered, it will be necessary to perform controlled experiments in which cell groups involved are identified in regard to their input and other connections with the same care Mehler has given to his anatomical description.

A somewhat more hopeful situation exists in the thalamic regions where a number of studies have correlated physiological data to the anatomical location. Mehler (75) has demonstrated that the number of fibers in the ventrolateral spinal cord reaching the thalamus without synapse increases in the progression from lower mammals such as rabbit or cat to primate, but otherwise termination within the thalamus is fairly similar. These more rostral terminations concern three or four nuclear divisions of the thalamus. One is to the classical "sensory" nucleus of the thalamus, the ventrobasal complex, and specifically its lateral division, the nucleus ventralis posterior lateralis, where are found (75, 76, 77) endings of spinothalamic fibers related to some groups of ventrobasal cells but not others. The fibers of ventrolateral spinal origin end primarily on cells of fairly large diameter (77). Thus scattered bursts of degenerating spinothalamic endings are found in the ventrobasal complex in contrast to the more uniform distribution of endings from those fibers of the medial lemniscus originating from the dorsal column nuclei (76, 77). In man the same lateral division of the pathway which ends in the ventrobasal complex also has a distribution somewhat posterior to it in the immediate vicinity of the medial geniculate body. Mehler believes that the cell group involved is the dorsomedial cap of the magnocellular portion of the medial geniculate body. This restricted type of termination has been also found by Bowsher (77), who notes that the majority of endings in this region are axosomatic in contrast to the axodendritic endings in the ventrobasal complex. Several authors (78, 79, 80) have suggested that the suprageniculate body is involved as well. Part of the spinothalamic pathway takes a medial course, and while it consists of a relatively small group of fibers, it has repeatedly been shown to end in the intralaminar nuclei of the thalamic midline group. The medial distribution of fibers then represents a third point of termination of ventrolateral spinal tracts and, as will be seen, one that may have considerable physiological significance. On the basis of cytoarchitectonic evaluation, Mehler (74) and Bowsher (77) conclude that the medial bundle does not reach the centrum medianum. A fourth region receiving spinothalamic fibers is the nucleus reticularis, though here agreement is not complete (74, 77).

A different approach to analysis of sensory projections to the thalamus has been taken by Mountcastle (81), who suggests that duality of function exists in the somatic afferent systems. This concept arose from earlier experiments on cats by Poggio & Mountcastle (79) in which responses from neurons of the ventrobasal complex were compared to those obtained in more caudal regions adjacent and rostral to the medial geniculate body. In animals with intact spinal cords, the behavior of single neural elements in these two thalamic regions differed according to the kind of stimulus and its effective loci. In the ventrobasal complex, there is a separation of the projection from receptors, those from cutaneous regions and those from structures as joints reaching different cells, all within a somatotopic arrangement. Mountcastle (81) emphasizes that this does not mean that only one or a few cells are related to receptors of a specific portion of the body, but that a whole population of cells receive projections from one class of receptors from a given body region. Stimulation at the center of its peripheral receptive field or "excitatory angle" of a joint yields the maximum number of discharges from a cell. A given stimulus would tend to activate a population of cells with a maximum response from the (geographical) center of this population. In simultaneous stimulation of separate skin areas, several populations of cells might be excited with areas of lesser activation in parts of the nucleus located between them. Such groups would in turn project to the cortex giving rise to spatially separated cortical activity. It was hypothesized that this kind of sensory projection to the ventrobasal complex is important for perceptually distinguishing both the nature and location of the stimulus. Furthermore, in unanesthetized preparations single ventrobasal neurons and cortical neurons can follow repeated stimulation as rapidly as signals enter the central nervous system from receptors, so that little information would be lost in transmission of a signal from receptor to cortex. As Mountcastle points out, the temporal capabilities of the somatosensory system are important for signaling the temporal pattern of stimulation encountered by the skin as it moves across an object. The projection to the ventrobasal complex is identified as "lemniscal" because its properties were believed to result largely from excitation by the dorsal column-medial lemniscus system.

In contrast to this "lemniscal" system, Mountcastle (81) describes a projection to individual neurons in more posterior portions of the thalamus where the separation of the kind of stimulus and its location is not clear. "Tactile", vibration, temperature change, and noxious stimuli delivered to various portions of the body, it was reported, each excited a given neuron of the posterior region. A conspicuous group of cells were found to discharge only after noxious stimuli. In part, this posterior region includes the projection mentioned above of the spinothalamic tracts to the magnocellular division of the medial geniculate body; however, neurons distributed over a much larger region (including parts of the pulvinar, the lateral posterior nucleus, and the suprageniculate nucleus) were also classified as part of the same system. Poggio & Mountcastle (79) did not find somatotopic organization in the receptive fields of neurons from this region, and for many cells there also appeared to be convergence of input from the auditory system. The difference between unitary responses recorded from the ventrobasal complex and from this posterior region were taken to indicate that the projection to the latter must be a source other than the medial lemniscus. Arguing from this, Mountcastle deduces that a second kind of afferent input arrives to the thalamus from peripheral receptors via the spinothalamic system, one which is important for some sensory function other than distinguishing the nature and location of the stimulus. The hypothesis of double function in the projections from the somatic receptors to the higher portions of the brain has great appeal because it has long been known that there are some generalized types of perceptual and motor reactions which are not necessarily dependent upon the ability to recognize the nature and place of origin of the stimulus. In the arrangement just suggested, the duality is expressed in the character of the information transmitted by the ascending fibers. If these exhibited spatial localization and stimulus specificity, the projection would be labeled "lemniscal". But if spatial localization and stimulus specificity were not evident, the projection would be "spinothalamic" in character, the terms being applied without regard to the anatomical location of the spinal tract since some overlap was recognized. Considering the evidence presented below, this choice of nomenclature introduces difficulties for it implies separation of ascending sensory information into two classes prior to the thalamic termination as the principal mechanisms.

Previously, two kinds of projection to thalamic regions of the cat via the ventrolateral spinal tracts alone were recognized by Whitlock & Perl (78, 82) from electrophysiological experiments on preparations with subacute spinal lesions which had divided the dorsal columns and at least one lateral tract. Identification of functional termination of the remaining pathway was then possible without confusion or coloring by overlap from dorsal column-medial lemniscus effects. The ventrolateral pathways contributed an input to the ventrobasal complex which was organized in the somatotopic manner, the pattern fitting the relationship between peripheral body and portion of the nucleus obtained in intact animals. A second region of projection was distributed posterior to the ventrobasal complex and included the magnocellular portion of the medial geniculate body and a small area immediately adjacent. Recently, Whitlock & Perl (80) outlined the ventrolateral pathway to the primate thalamus in a similar manner, the loci of projection being taken as the position of single units which could be discharged by afferent stimulation of an "adequate" type. Their results closely correspond to the anatomical findings of Mehler (74) and Bowsher (77). In the ventrobasal complex of the monkey as in the cat, responses were found to be evoked from the contra-lateral side of the body and arranged in a somatotopic pattern. In addition to this crossed pathway from peripheral receptors, three regions received an input without clear somatotopic organization: the magnocellular division of the medial geniculate body and a region immediately superior to it, a portion of the intralaminar nuclei, and neurons belonging to the reticular nuclei just lateral to the ventrobasal complex.

In another report, Perl & Whitlock (83) describe the nature of somatic stimuli capable of exciting neurons in the thalamus in animals with spinal lesions, usually with only ventrolateral tracts spared. Recordings obtained from single elements in cat and monkey indicated that a given unit of the ventrobasal complex was excited by receptors located in the restricted portions of the contralateral body, the effective stimulus being hair displacement, light mechanical disturbance of the skin, distortion of muscle-fascial position, joint rotation, muscle or "deep" pressure, or stimuli of tissue-damaging intensity. Convergence to one unit from receptors sensitive to distinctly different kinds of stimuli was not demonstrated. The effects produced by muscle pressure and fascia displacement are quite interesting if it is recalled that most Group III muscle afferent fibers respond to pressure or fascial distortion. [A good number of spinothalamic neurons are excited by peripheral fibers of small diameter (83). Group III fibers project to the somatic I area of cortex (84).] Thus, at first glance, there appears no qualitative difference between the kind of input to the ventrobasal complex via "spinothalamic" pathways and that recognized in intact animals. However, in the absence of the powerful contribution from the medial lemniscus, a projection excited only by localized intense stimuli was observed. In contrast to the ventrobasal input, units in the vicinity of the magnocellular medial geniculate body of both the cat and monkey regularly had large and frequently bilateral, scattered receptive fields. The usually effective stimulus was a transient mechanical stimulation of the skin, or "tap". In the intralaminar nuclei of the monkey, but not in the posterior group region, units responded only to noxious stimulation of receptive fields with wide geographical distribution. The absence of observations indicating noxious excitation of posterior group neurons represents a departure from the results described by Poggio & Mountcastle (79). The discrepancy possibly comes from the use of different anesthetic levels and/or the latter's observations on neurons located in regions outside of that shown by anatomical methods to have direct spinothalamic terminations.

Two types of somatosensory input to the thalamus seen from another point of view appeared in Albe-Fessard & Kruger's (85) experiments on single centrum medianum-intralaminar elements of cats. In view of the long controversy on fast and slow pain, it appears quite significant that the responses evoked in neurons of this medial thalamic region by somatic nerve stimuli were distinct in timing, one being short in latency and the other occurring after a very long delay (over $\frac{1}{2}$ sec). Albe-Fessard & Kruger could not identify the kinds of receptors for either type but did note that localized pin prick to skin, articular capsules, periosteal tissues, and the cornea would all excite the same cells. Their units did not respond to hair bending, light touch, or muscle stretch; but noxious stimuli to any part of the body provoked discharges. Evoked responses of the intralaminar-centrum medianum region of the cat depend on ventrolateral tracts and not on the dorsal columns (86). Therefore, a similar pathway from afferent fibers discharged by noxious stimuli exists in both cat and monkey (83, 85). Mehler (74) argues against inclusion of the centrum medianum as a termination point of ventral quadrant tracts, and unfortunately Albe-Fessard and Kruger's technique for identification of recording loci may not have been adequate for distinguishing the centrum medianum from the intralaminar nuclei.

The relation of the intralaminar nuclei to sensory function is obscure; however, it seems that these nuclei are innervated directly only from one (spinothalamic) of the several ascending sensory systems. Studies reported by Ervin & Mark (87) on people with thalamic lesions indicate a possible relationship between the medial region and the conscious perception of pain.

Patients suffering from terminal carcinoma of the head and neck were relieved of discomfort by medial lesions while others did not receive relief following more lateral lesions in the vicinity of the ventrobasal complex. Of possible significance is the kind of afferent input to the midline nuclei and the ability to "activate" diffusely the cerebral cortex from them.

The diverse data on the nature of thalamic input from somatosensory systems can not easily be reconciled with a clear separation of function according to ascending pathways. Morphological and functional evidence has established that the spinothalamic pathway ends in the ventrobasal nucleus with all the spatial and stimulus specificity repeatedly demonstrated for this structure, as well as having other terminations without a clear somatotopic pattern. In primates the dorsal column-medial lemniscus system contributes to both a somatotopically organized nucleus (ventrobasal) and a region not so characterized (posterior nuclear group) in anatomical material (77), supporting deductions from physiological data (65, 83). A complicating fact in evidence for the latter is the presence of a third cortically destined tract in the dorsolateral spinal white matter that signals cutaneous events with relays at undetermined points. Thus, it may be argued that in addition to some differences of somatotopic and receptor connections of neurons afferent to thalamic sensory regions, one projection cell may distribute terminals to neurons of several nuclei. This suggestion would place importance upon the type of convergence of presynaptic fibers in different regions as well as on the make-up of ascending pathways and represents an alternative to Mountcastle's (81) proposal for the mechanism underlying "duality" in sensory function.

The Cerebral Projection of Somatic Receptors

With few exceptions, the material presented so far has been derived from studies in which the electrical activity of neurons was used as the sign of neuronal function and the criterion of features of functional organization. The organization of the cerebral cortex is appropriately introduced by considering a discussion, based largely on theoretical considerations of an anatomical and embryological nature, by Bishop (88), one of the first workers to exploit electrical recording techniques on nervous tissue extensively. He approached the analysis of cerebrocortical organization from the standpoint of the diameter of the fibers in ascending systems reaching it and the subcortical projection nuclei. Building on Herrick's embryological studies, Bishop suggests that the evolutionary elaboration of afferent pathways can be related to some of the following features. (a) There has been a succession of "brains" and this succession has progressed from caudal to cephalic levels in phylogenetic history. (b) Higher levels in turn dominate those below with respect to both afferent co-ordination and motor control. (c) Several processes are employed in the extension upward of afferent pathways including a simple relay of activity from a lower to higher level as well as parallel paths from the periphery that bypass a given synaptic station reaching higher levels more directly. (d) The specificity of central co-ordination and motor control of lower centers by higher centers is correlated with the addition of the parallel pathways. (e) The organization of primate sensory systems still carries more primitive and earlier-developed afferent components existing in the nervous systems from which it was evolved. After presenting these generalities, Bishop considers the relationship between ascending pathways and regions of termination. In summary, he hypothesizes that phylogenetically older areas receive input from smaller-diameter fibers which presumably signal less discrete kinds of sensory input while the newer regions receive input largely from larger-diameter peripheral afferent fibers and larger-diameter centrally projecting pathways. The cortex develops in relation first to projections from small-diameter systems and later achieves greater specificity and complexity as the large-diameter pathways reach the thalamus and thence project to the cortex. Finally, he suggests that some of the specific evoked responses of the cerebral cortex from primary relays are mainly related to input from the large-diameter afferent fibers and that cerebral activity from the diffuse or nonspecific projection systems is a consequence of input associated with small-diameter fibers. While some objections to details of this proposal can be found in the material discussed in this review, the suggestion that the phylogenetically new systems contain primarily large-diameter fibers seems valid. Moreover, ample evidence has been presented herein on the presence of parallel pathways. In addition, Bishop's theoretical framework explains the existence and possible functional significance of those centrally located systems in the reticular portions of the lower brainstem and midline nuclei of the thalamus which receive many afferent inputs and can cause diffusely distributed changes in cerebral electrical activity.

Turning to the question of specific pathways and the afferent input involved in the somatesthetic projection to the cerebral cortex, McIntyre (89) has re-examined the question of the diameter and source of afferent fibers from muscle capable of evoking responses in the cerebral cortex. He stresses that the Group I fibers from muscles of the hindlimb do not ascend in the dorsal columns above the lower thoracic segments, but end there and excite the neurons of the dorsal spinocerebellar tracts. In recording the antidromic response from muscle nerve following excitation of the cervical dorsal column, no Group I and only a very small amount of Group II activity were observed. From cortical surface recordings in deeply anesthetized cats, McIntyre found that a small evoked response resulted from stimulation of Group II fibers provided that a number of different muscle and deep nerves were combined. The cortical response became apparent when the Group I afferent volley reached approximately 35 per cent of maximum, a stimulus just strong enough to recruit a few of the largest Group II fibers. If less than a combination of nerves were used, stimulus strengths well above that completing the Group I volley were required to produce a cortical evoked potential. The marked increase in cortical response with addition of Group III afferent fibers to the input volley was confirmed (84). McIntyre's data would again suggest that the pressure receptors of muscle described by Paintal (21) and by Bessou & Laporte (20) reach the cerebral level since they form the bulk of the Group III fibers. Two Group II volleys, a few milliseconds apart and subliminal for the cortical response, were shown to summate in evoking a cortical potential, indicating a threshold in the projection between Group II primary afferent fibers of muscle and cortical neurons. Inasmuch as Group II afferent fibers apparently project to the cortex, the question arises as to whether these fibers are of muscle-spindle origin, like the majority in muscle nerves, or whether they arise from other sense organs. The Pacinian corpuscles supplied by fibers of Group II or even larger diameter were suggested as a possible source of cortical response to transient muscle stretch. As support for this, the cortical potential evoked by a nerve almost exclusively supplying a muscle, the lateral flexor digitorum longus, was shown to be very small. In contrast, stimulation of the mesial flexor digitorum longus nerve, which contains fibers from many Pacinian corpuscles (27), gave rise to a much larger response. If Pacinian corpuscles do represent the source of relatively large-diameter muscle afferent projection to the cerebral cortex, then the fact that McIntyre apparently evoked the best cortical responses from somatosensory II becomes particularly significant, because this area is thought to receive part of its afferent input from the posterior nuclear region of the thalamus, certain neurons of which are excited by vibration, tap, and sound (79, 83).

Observations on the "antidromic" reaction initiated in the cerebral cortex by stimulation of the pyramidal medullary tract have reopened the question of afferent pathways to the cerebral cortex in the immediate vicinity of the pyramids. In cats, Kennedy & Towe (90) demonstrated that the distribution of the various components of the surface cortical response initiated by electrical stimulation of the bulbar pyramids was different. The earliest component was maximal in the pericruciate or "motor" region while the next deflection appeared largest in the vicinity of the coronal sulcus. Both components have short latency and must be rapidly transmitted. Through study of interaction between surface-recorded potentials initiated by pyramidal tract stimulation and by electrical excitation of superficial receptors by needle electrodes, the primary afferent activity was demonstrated to interfere with the second and later components of the response evoked from the pyramids. Furthermore, such interaction was also present in recordings from the white matter immediately subjacent to the cerebral cortex after complete removal of the cerebral mantle. Reasoning from these results, Kennedy & Towe suggest that the second peak of the complex response initiated by pyramidal tract stimulation is produced by orthodromically conducted impulses. A relay at which interaction with cutaneous excitation can take place apparently occurs between the point of stimulation of the pyramids in the medulla and the cerebral cortex. Whether the rapidly conducting orthodromic pathway in the vicinity of the pyramids is different from the medial lemniscus must still be determined, particularly since different portions of the dorsal column nuclei may not project rostrally in a strictly localized bundle of fibers. However, evidence has been presented earlier in this review that a fast-conducting system other than the dorsal columns and ventrolateral tracts is present in the spinal cord. This pathway is excited by cutaneous stimulation and has been localized in the dorsolateral spinal funiculus (55, 58). Norrsell & Voorhoeve (91) found that the dorsolateral cutaneous tract seems to take a ventral course in the medulla (see below). Moreover, Mark & Steiner (92) suggested that a group of cutaneous afferent fibers of lowest threshold project to the cerebral cortex via a fast route in the ipsilateral lateral column, since destruction of both the dorsal columns and the contralateral ventral column did not abolish the cortical response initiated by cutaneous nerve stimulation. Thus, it might be deduced that the ascending tract located near the pyramids represents the continuation of a lateral column spinal pathway for cutaneous afferent fibers. The possible implications of a third route to the cortex for cutaneous impulses are not clear; however, this input coupled with different recording locations may explain certain variations in the results obtained by different workers examining the convergence of sensory input upon single cortical elements (90, 93, 94, 95). A background to the latter question as well as to the type of research on the cerebral cortex described below can be found in Amassian's (96) scholarly review and critique of the methods, previous findings, and past conflicts.

Direct evidence for a gradation in cortical cell behavior comes from work by Brooks, Rudomin & Slayman (97, 98) on activity of single units in the general motor-sensory cortical region of cat. Recording with microelectrodes, Brooks *et al.* classified cells according to whether or not they were "antidromically" excited by stimulation of the medullary pyramids; but some doubt is cast upon this technique by Kennedy & Towe's demonstration of an orthodromic component (90). Surprisingly, the characteristics of the cells that responded to pyramidal tract stimulation were generally similar to those not so activated except that more posteriorly located, nonpyramidal cells were more likely to be excited by only one kind of peripheral stimulus from a stable receptive field. The stimuli effective for "unimodal" cortical cells included hair bending, "touch" pressure, or passive joint movement. Different classes of cutaneous receptive fields could be distinguished: small and fixed in dimension, large and fixed, small and variable in size and fixed in dimension, large and variable. Neurons exhibiting "labile" receptive fields at first were responsive to one form of stimulation over a given area of skin but, as stimulation continued, responded to other manipulations applied to a larger area. The units displaying local and stable receptive fields remained specific as to stimulus type while those with large receptive fields or labile receptive fields could frequently be excited by several kinds of stimuli and these stimuli were frequently effective when applied ipsilateral to the cortical recording site. In general, neurons which were located close together, as evidenced by simultaneous recordings from one position within the cortex, tended to have fields of the same classification. In addition to the excitatory effects described, several kinds of inhibitory effects were observed including the "surround" type of inhibition mentioned earlier, inhibition by stimulation of more distant points, and inhibition by a different kind of stimulus. In considering these findings, it must be remembered that the animals studied by Brooks *et al.* were not systemically anesthetized while a majority of previous studies on the somatosensory projection area were performed on preparations depressed by general anesthesia. Therefore, it appears that within the somatosensory cortex of the cat, an animal in which the sensory areas and the "motor" regions are not clearly separated, a gradation is present which progresses from a fixed field type posteriorly to more labile fields in the anterior regions. Brooks *et al.* suggest that the labile neuron of the anterior areas may be an indication of integrative functions. Since different skin receptors may have differently organized projections (see above), it is unfortunate that the cutaneous stimuli were not of the type useful in distinguishing receptor responses. The report by Angel & Dawson (99) on variation of the response of ventrobasal neurons to a constant stimulus may be pertinent to the "labile" neurons. Rubbing or stroking of the skin of distant regions, which of itself did not produce detectable changes in the neuronal activity under consideration, significantly increased the number of discharges and the stability of the evoked response. Alteration in activity of a thalamic projection nucleus undoubtedly would be reflected in the response of cortical neurons.

Using the classical technique of recording evoked potentials on the cortical surface, Berman (100, 101) has re-studied the organization of the cortical somatic II region and its overlap with the auditory region. He confirms that the second somatic area of the cat exhibits a somatotopic pattern and that the region excited by auditory stimuli overlaps a large portion of the area responding to somatic stimuli. In testing for interaction between responses to an auditory transient and a nerve volley, an effect occurred which was dependent upon the interval between stimuli and the order in which they were presented, and which could not be accounted for by algebraic summation of potentials. The interaction was most marked in the region of overlap between somatic II and the auditory fields with the effects apparently resulting from neurons common to both pathways. Berman's results are striking in relation to the suggestions that the posterior nuclear region might be the exclusive relay for the afferent pathway to both the somatic II and the auditory II areas. In the first place, no evidence exists that the thalamic posterior nuclear region has a somatotopic organization. Furthermore, deep anesthesia markedly depresses this portion of the thalamus (79), yet under these circumstances the somatic II region gives rise to large responses and a somatotopic organization.

Some help in resolving this apparent conflict can be gained by a consideration of Andersson's (102) extensive analysis of the source and type of input to single elements of the cat's somatic II area. Recording the electrical activity of area II cells with extracellular microelectrodes, he determined the kind and location of receptors evoking responses in animals with or without systematic spinal lesions. A striking finding was that a stimulus-specific projection from small regions of the contralateral body goes to some units, and in addition other units were excitable from large, sometimes bilateral receptive fields. In electrode penetrations made perpendicular to the cortical surface, a columnar arrangement was often found, cells of one column being related by the characteristics of receptive field and excitatory stimuli, an organizational feature described some time ago by Mountcastle (94). Bilateral receptive fields were more prevalent posteriorly where the somatic II area abuts the auditory fields. In area II, as in the more rostral portions of somatic I (see above), there is an apparent topographic gradation in the characteristics of units as determined by their sensory activation, the more anteriorly located cells displaying features similar to those existing in somatic I. A major point in Andersson's report is the contribution of different ascending pathways to excitation of somatic II neurons. In particular, he established the importance of an input from the dorsal column system to area II and demonstrated "surround" inhibition from cutaneous regions outside of the excitatory field for this linkage. His experiments also indicated a role for the dorsolateral spinal tract (see above) which apparently transmits information rapidly from restricted regions but without related inhibitory interaction. From such findings, Andersson logically concludes that the somatic area II must receive part of its input via the ventrobasal thalamic system, but that the large bilateral fields with less stimulus specificity may be related to a pathway from the posterior thalamic region. The ventrolateral spinal systems were believed to mediate solely long-latency responses and only from receptors responding to strong stimuli. In emphasizing the dorsally placed spinal pathways, Andersson leans heavily on a study by Norrsell & Voorhoeve (91) because they showed that the pathway for tactile activity evoking short-latency cortical responses was interrupted by the section of the dorsal columns and the dorsolateral tract. However, Norrsell & Voorhoeve dealt only with responses from somatic I, while Andersson's own experiments (102), in which spinal pathways were limited to ventrally located white matter, involved lesions so extensive that part of the tactile portion of the spinothalamic pathway may have been affected. Evidence for an excitatory spinothalamic projection to the ventrobasal nuclei has been given above; in view of the intimate relation between this structure and the cerebral somatic regions, continuation to the cortex is most likely. Moreover, direct evidence for such a termination was given earlier by Gardner & Haddad (103) and subsequently confirmed (78). The ventrobasal fraction of the spinothalamic projection may not reach somatic II, but even its component to the posterior nuclear group consists of some rapidly conducting fibers discharged by comparatively low-threshold cutaneous receptors. All factors considered, it appears likely that part of the ventrolateral spinal projection to somatic II was missed, probably because of its relative paucity in the cat.

CONCLUSION

"Feedback" systems in ascending sensory pathways have received considerable attention recently. Such systems are considered to exist when a more rostral region has descending pathways terminating upon neurons whose axons form ascending sensory tracts (67, 68, 69, 73). Zanchetti's excellent article in the previous volume in this series (104) discusses this question in detail. As one example, Nauta (105), using a staining method specific for degenerating fibers, noted axons from the somatosensory cortex that end in the ventrobasal nucleus. As yet, definitive proof is lacking that the intra-thalamic axon degeneration does not represent retrograde alterations of thalamic neurons. Other evidence for cortical connections to the ventrobasal nucleus comes from Iwama & Yamamoto (106) who showed that the electrical activity of the ventrobasal nucleus evoked from the dorsal columns was altered by conditioning stimulation of the somatosensory cortex. The conditioning was demonstrated to be more than the result of antidromic invasion of thalamic cells, because opposite effects were produced by removal of the somatosensory cortex. With the present data, the significance of recurrent or feedback connections to sensory nuclei is a matter of conjecture. Interconnections of this type may function to set the sensitivity of ascending systems in a manner appropriate for the animal's actions and the functional state of the cortex. Another possibility is that rostrally directed messages may be filtered in some manner. Obviously, before a workable hypothesis on the role of such connections can be formulated, considerably more information is needed.

It would be desirable to close a discussion of current work on somatic sensory systems by correlating the physiological factors with perception in man. Unfortunately, here the gap in our understanding is very large. In this regard, two publications by Stevens (107, 108) on the relation between perceptual magnitude and stimulus magnitude are interesting. Stevens marshals his experimental results in attempting to "repeal Fechner's law" whereby the estimated magnitude of a sensation is said to be logarithmically related to the physical change. The relationship Stevens reports is best described by a power function $(a = b^n)$ whose exponent varies with the stimulus type. The power function seems to hold in experiments requiring a subject to compare the relative intensity of different kinds of stimuli (i.e., sound and light) as well as in studies using direct estimates of stimulus magnitude. These psychophysical experiments are relevant to reports by Mountcastle (109) and Poggio et al. (110) on the responses of single units of the monkey ventrobasal complex to rotation of a joint. The steady-state discharge of such thalamic units was found to be related to the angle of the joint. When this relationship was expressed in terms of a number of discharges for each of a series of positions within the "excitatory angle", a power function was found to give the best fit. These and Stevens' results led to the suggestion that mechanisms operating among thalamus, cortex, and perception may be linear.

ACKNOWLEDGMENT

The author is grateful to several colleagues for helpful suggestions. Mrs. E. Eyzaguirre's assistance with the bibliography was invaluable.

LITERATURE CITED

1. Loewenstein, W. R., *Ann. N. Y. Acad. Sci.*, 94, 510–34 (1961)
2. Hunt, C. C., and Takeuchi, A., *J. Physiol. (London)*, 160, 1–21 (1962)
3. Hunt, C. C., and Takeuchi, A., *Symposium on Muscle Receptors*, 143–53 (Hong Kong Univ. Press, 292 pp., 1962)
4. Diamond, J., Gray, J. A. B., and Sato, M., *J. Physiol. (London)*, 133, 54–67 (1956)
5. Murray, R. W., *J. Physiol. (London)*, 159, 546–70 (1961)
6. Boyd, I. A., *Phil. Trans., B*, 245, 81–136 (1962)
7. Boyd, I. A., *Symposium on Muscle Receptors*, 185–90 (Barker, D., Ed., Hong Kong Univ. Press, 292 pp., 1962)
8. Barker, D., *Symposium on Muscle Receptors*, 227–40 (Hong Kong Univ. Press, 292 pp., 1962)
9. Barker, D., and Cope, M., *Symposium on Muscle Receptors*, 263–69 (Hong Kong Univ. Press, 292 pp., 1962)
10. Hess, A., *Am. J. Anat.*, 107, 129–52 (1960)
11. Hess, A., *Anat. Record*, 139, 173–82 (1961)
12. Merton, P. A., *Acta Physiol. Scand.*, 29, 87–88 (1953)
13. Hunt, C. C., *J. Gen. Physiol.*, 38, 117–31 (1954)
14. Harvey, R. J., and Matthews, P. B. C., *J. Physiol. (London)*, 157, 370–92 (1961)
15. Kuffler, S. W., Hunt, C. C., and Quilliam, J. P., *J. Neurophysiol.*, 14, 29–54 (1951)
16. Bessou, P., and Laporte, Y., *Symposium on Muscle Receptors*, 105–19 (Hong Kong Univ. Press, 292 pp., 1962)
17. Cooper, S., *Quart. J. Exptl. Physiol.*, 46, 389–98 (1961)
18. Eccles, R. M., and Lundberg, A., *J. Physiol. (London)*, 147, 565–84 (1959)
19. Kuno, M., and Perl, E. R., *J. Physiol. (London)*, 151, 103–22 (1960)
20. Bessou, P., and Laporte, Y., *Arch. Ital. Biol.*, 99, 293–321 (1961)
21. Paintal, A. S., *J. Physiol. (London)*, 152, 250–70 (1960)
22. Weddell, G., *Brain and Behavior*, I (Brazier, M. A. B., Ed., Am. Inst. Biol. Sci., Washington, 1961)
23. Sergeev, K. K., *Arkh. Anat. Gistol. Embriol.*, 39, 70–77 (1960)
24. Douglas, W. W., and Ritchie, J. M., *Physiol. Rev.*, 42, 297–334 (1962)
25. Iggo, A., *J. Physiol. (London)*, 152, 337–53 (1960)
26. Hensel, H., *Arch. Ges. Physiol.*, 273, 543–61 (1961)
27. Hunt, C. C., and McIntyre, A. K., *J. Physiol. (London)*, 153, 74–87 (1960)
28. Hunt, C. C., *J. Physiol. (London)*, 155, 175–86 (1961)
29. Sato, M., *J. Physiol. (London)*, 159, 391–409 (1961)
30. Plumb, C. S., and Meigs, J. W., *Arch. Gen. Psychiat.*, 4, 611–14 (1961)
31. Scott, D., Jr., *Federation Proc.*, 10, 123 (1951)
32. Gray, J. A. B., and Matthews, P. B. C., *J. Physiol. (London)*, 114, 454–64 (1951 b)
33. Witt, I., and Hensel, H., *Arch. Ges. Physiol.*, 268, 582–96 (1959)
34. Wall, P. D., *J. Neurophysiol.*, 23, 197–210 (1960)
35. Hensel, H., and Boman, K. K. A., *J. Neurophysiol.*, 23, 564–78 (1960)
36. Hunt, C. C., and McIntyre, A. K., *J. Physiol. (London)*, 153, 88–98 (1960)
37. Iggo, A., *Symp. Vol. Acta Neuroveget.* (Springer, Vienna, 1962)
38. Iggo, A., and Muir, A. R., *J. Anat.* (In press, 1962)
39. Alvord, E. C., Jr., and Fuortes, M. G. F., *J. Physiol. (London)*, 122, 302–21 (1953)
40. Alvord, E. C., Jr., and Fuortes, M. G. F., *J. Physiol. (London)*, 123, 251–59 (1954)
41. Eccles, J. C., *The Physiology of Nerve Cells* (Johns Hopkins Press, Baltimore, Md., 1957)
42. McIntyre, A. K., Mark, R. F., and Steiner, J., *Nature*, 178, 302–4 (1956)
43. Hunt, C. C., and Kuno, M., *J. Physiol. (London)*, 147, 364–84 (1959)
44. Eccles, J. C., Hubbard, J. I., and Oscarsson, O., *J. Physiol. (London)*, 158, 486–516 (1961)
45. Eccles, J. C., Oscarsson, O., and Willis, W. D., *J. Physiol. (London)*, 158, 517–43 (1961)
46. Szentágothai, J., and Albert, A., *Acta Morphol. Hung.*, 5, 43–51 (1955)
47. Oscarsson, O., *Acta Physiol. Scand.*, 40, 222–31 (1957)
48. Hubbard, J. I., and Oscarsson, O., *Nature*, 189, 157–58 (1961)

49. Lundberg, A., and Oscarsson, O., *Acta Physiol. Scand.*, **54**, 252–69 (1962)

50. Lundberg, A., and Oscarsson, O., *Acta Physiol. Scand.*, **50**, 356–74 (1960)

51. Eyzaguirre, C., Rapporteur, Discussion of Sir John Eccles' paper, *Symposium on Muscle Receptors*, 103–4 (Hong Kong Univ. Press, 1961)

52. Laporte, Y., and Bessou, P., *J. Physiol. (Paris)*, **49**, 1025–37 (1957)

53. Lundberg, A., and Winsbury, G., *Acta Physiol. Scand.*, **49**, 165–70 (1960)

54. McIntyre, A. K., and Mark, R. F., *J. Physiol. (London)*, **153**, 306–30 (1960)

55. Lundberg, A., and Oscarsson, O., *Acta Physiol. Scand.*, **51**, 1–16 (1961)

56. Snider, R. S., and Stowell, A., *J. Neurophysiol.*, **7**, 331–58 (1944)

57. Snider, R. S., *Res. Publ., Assoc. Nervous Mental Disease*, **30**, 267 (1952)

58. Morin, E., *Am. J. Physiol.*, **183**, 243–52 (1955)

59. Lundberg, A., and Oscarsson, O., *Acta Physiol. Scand.*, **54**, 270–86 (1962)

60. Eccles, J. C., Eccles, R. M., and Magni, F., *J. Physiol. (London)*, **159**, 147–66 (1961)

61. Armett, C. J., and Hunsperger, R. W., *J. Physiol. (London)*, **158**, 15–38 (1961)

62. Armett C. J., Gray, J. A. B., and Palmer, J. F., *J. Physiol. (London)*, **156**, 611–22 (1961)

63. Magni, F., and Oscarsson, O., *Acta Physiol. Scand.*, **54**, 53–64 (1962)

64. Armett, C., Gray, J. A. B., Hunsperger, R. W., and Lal, K. B., *J. Physiol. (London)* (In press, 1962)

65. Perl, E. R., Whitlock, D. G., and Gentry, J. R., *J. Neurophysiol.*, **25**, 337–58 (1962)

66. Gordon, G., and Seed, W. A., *J. Physiol. (London)*, **155**, 589–601 (1961)

67. Walberg, F., *Brain*, **80**, 273–87 (1957)

68. Kuypers, H. G. J. M., *Brain*, **93**, 161–84 (1960)

69. Magni, F., Melsack, R., Moruzzi, G., and Smith, C. J., *Arch. Ital. Biol.*, **97**, 357–77 (1959)

70. Gordon, G., and Paine, C. H., *J. Physiol. (London)*, **153**, 331–49 (1960)

71. McComas, A. J., *J. Physiol. (London)*, **161**, 21P–22P (1962)

72. Kruger, L., Siminoff, R., and Witkovsky, P., *J. Neurophysiol.*, **24**, 333–49 (1961)

73. Kuypers, H. G. J. M., Hoffman, A. L., and Beasley, R. M., *Proc. Soc. Exptl. Biol. Med.*, **108**, 634–37 (1961)

74. Mehler, W. R., in *Recent Contributions of Basic Research to Paraplegia* (French, J. D., and Porter, R. W., Eds., Thomas, Springfield, Ill., 1961)

75. Mehler, W. R., *Anat. Record*, **127**, 332 (1957)

76. Mehler, W. R., Feferman, M. E., and Nauta, W. J. H., *Brain*, **83**, 718–50 (1960)

77. Bowsher, D., *Comp. Neurol.*, **117**, 213–28 (1961); (Personal communication, 1962)

78. Whitlock, D. G., and Perl, E. R., *J. Neurophysiol.*, **22**, 133–48 (1959)

79. Poggio, G. F., and Mountcastle, V. B., *Bull. Johns Hopkins Hosp.*, **106**, 266–316 (1960)

80. Whitlock, D. G., and Perl, E. R., *Exptl. Neurol.*, **3**, 240–55 (1961)

81. Mountcastle, V. B., in *Brain and Behavior*, **I** (Am. Inst. Biol. Sci., Washington, 1961)

82. Whitlock, D. G., and Perl, E. R., *Anat. Record*, **127**, 388 (1957)

83. Perl, E. R., and Whitlock, D. G., *Exptl. Neurol.*, **3**, 256–96 (1961)

84. Mountcastle, V. B., Covian, M. R., and Harrison, C. R., *Res. Publ. Assoc. Nervous Mental Disease*, **30**, 339–70 (1952)

85. Albe-Fessard, D., and Kruger, L., *J. Neurophysiol.*, **25**, 1–20 (1962)

86. Kruger, L., and Albe-Fessard, D., *Exptl. Neurol.*, **2**, 442–67 (1960)

87. Ervin, F. R., and Mark, V. H., *Federation Proc.*, **20**, 345 (1961)

88. Bishop, G. H., *Ann. N. Y. Acad. Sci.*, **94**, 559–69 (1961)

89. McIntyre, A. K., *Symposium on Muscle Receptors*, 19–29 (Hong Kong Univ. Press, 292 pp., 1962)

90. Kennedy, T. T., and Towe, A. L., *J. Physiol. (London)*, **160**, 535–47 (1962)

91. Norrsell, U., and Voorhoeve, P., *Acta Physiol. Scand.*, **54**, 9–17 (1962)

92. Mark, R. F., and Steiner, J., *J. Physiol. (London)*, **142**, 544–62 (1958)

93. Mountcastle, V. B., Davies, P. W., and Berman, A. L., *J. Neurophysiol.*, **20**, 374–407 (1957)

94. Mountcastle, V. B., *J. Neurophysiol.*, **20**, 408–34 (1957)

95. Patton, H. D., and Towe, A. L., *Federation Proc.*, **16**, 99 (1957)

96. Amassian, V. E., *Intern. Rev. Neurobiol.*, **3**, 67–136 (1961)

97. Brooks, V. B., Rudomin, P., and Slayman, C. L., *J. Neurophysiol.*, **24**, 286–301 (1961)

98. Brooks, V. B., Rudomin, P., and Slayman, C. L., *J. Neurophysiol.*, **24**, 302–25 (1961)

99. Angel, A., and Dawson, G. D., *J. Physiol. (London)*, **156**, 23P–24P **(1961)**

100. Berman, A. L., *J. Neurophysiol.*, **24**, 595–607 (1961)

101. Berman, A. L., *J. Neurophysiol.*, **24**, 608–20 (1961)

102. Andersson, S. A., *Acta Physiol. Scand.*, **56**, Suppl. 194, 1–74 (1962)

103. Gardner, E., and Haddad, B., *Am. J. Physiol.*, **172**, 475–82 (1953)

104. Zanchetti, A., *Ann. Rev. Physiol.*, **24**, 287–324 (1962)

105. Nauta, W. J. H. (Personal communication)

106. Iwama, K., and Yamamoto, C., *Japan. J. Physiol.*, **11**, 169–82 (1961)

107. Stevens, S. S., in *Sensory Communications*, 1–33 (Rosenblith, W. A., Ed., M. I. T. Press and Wiley, New York and London, 1961)

108. Stevens, S. S., *Science*, **133**, 80–86 (1961)

109. Mountcastle, V. B., *Proc. I.U.P.S.*, **I**, Part II, 930 (Leiden, 1962)

110. Poggio, G. F., Werner, G., Viernstein, L. J., and Mountcastle, V. B., *Proc. I.U.P.S.*, **II**, 1044 (Leiden, 1962)

CONDUCTION AND TRANSMISSION IN THE NERVOUS SYSTEM

By R. Stämpfli

First Department of Physiology, University of Saarland Medical School, Homburg/Saarland, Germany

This review gives many of the author's personal views. It is therefore far from a complete account of all the literature published in the field between July 1961 and about June 1962. Some topics will be treated rather briefly, as last year's excellent review by Terzuolo & Edwards (198) treated transmission at synaptic junctions very extensively. On the other hand, questions of the peripheral nerve, being within the field of the author's own research, will find more extensive and critical appreciation. Apologies are made in advance to all the authors whose work may have been overlooked.

THE MEMBRANE

Membrane structure.—There is almost general agreement that excitable membranes consist of a bimolecular surface layer of lipid and phospholipid coated with protein on both sides (159). The protein part seems less important for electrical activity than the lipid-phospholipid layer. Goldman (79) describes the structure of some of the phosphatides contained in the membrane (phosphatidylserine, -choline, and -ethanolamine and diphosphoglyceroinositide) showing that shape and orientation of fixed ions and dipoles attached to the end groups will strongly depend on the electric field across the membrane. Calcium is supposed to combine with the membrane elements at specific sites controlling the availability of ion-passing "channels". Two layers of sites are suggested which become permeable to sodium when they are not occupied by calcium. However, by collision processes their configuration would rapidly change and a potassium-permeable channel would be formed. Here again formal agreement with experimental findings of Hodgkin & Huxley (96) can be found with high-speed computer analysis, if the adsorption energy of calcium on the sites is assumed as linearly depending on membrane potential and if the penetration process is taken to be governed by electrical and diffusion gradients. A similar formal agreement is claimed by Shanes (169, 170) based on experimental findings with octadecanol or stearic acid monolayers and on theoretical considerations of "surface pressure" in fatty monolayers governing the relative permeability of such membranes to water and other molecules without assuming homogeneous rigid pores. A further view on this subject is given by Mullins (145). He sees the membrane composed of ion-permeable pores and of other, ion-impermeable parts which are responsible for the condenserlike properties. The field across the membrane is assumed to be discontinuous. Ions are thus not driven across the membrane by the continuous action of an electric field as in the constant field theory of Goldman (78) but they are submitted to the action of the field when entering or leaving the membrane. Again agreement between experimentally found ionic fluxes and calculations based on variable field formulation is obtained and assumption made as to how narrow the membrane pores would have to be for the passage of singly hydrated ions if it is assumed that penetration depends on a close fit between the hydrated ion and the pore. The rate of penetration of different ions into frog sartorius muscle leads to the suggestion of pores of the order of 4 A in radius. "The discrimination between Na⁺, K⁺, and other ions appears to be on the basis of size" is the conclusion.

Still another approach is used by Tasaki (187, 188), relying upon tracer experiments reported last year (191), using the microinjection technique with squid axons (20).

The finding of anionic fluxes slower than cationic fluxes out of the squid axon is believed to reveal fixed negative charges in the membrane, possibly carboxyl and phosphate radicals in dissociated form. Divalent and univalent ions would compete for negative sites in the membrane. Experiments showing increased cation effluxes during repetitive stimulation are thought to reveal a sudden removal of mobile divalent cations under the influence of depolarization, increasing the number of negative sites available for univalent cations. Although a certain resemblance to the views of Goldman (79) and much earlier assumptions of Brink (21) can be seen up to this point, Tasaki comes to completely different conclusions as to the validity of the Hodgkin-Huxley sodium and potassium currents, assuming that the inward membrane current during the rising phase of the action-potential could be carried by sodium ions on the external surface of the membrane when at the same moment it could be carried by potassium ions in the vicinity of the inner membrane surface. The equation $I_{Na} = G_{Na}(E_{Na} - V)$ (where I_{Na} = net sodium current through membrane; G_{Na} = sodium conductance of membrane; $E_{Na} - V$ = potential difference between sodium potential where no sodium current flows and membrane potential at which I_{Na} is measured) would then have little physical meaning. It is difficult to follow such views when one accepts the experimental proof of an actual transfer of sodium which corresponds roughly to the sodium current (111, 114). There is a very recent attempt to measure sodium and potassium fluxes under voltage-clamp conditions with tracer techniques and to compare them with the actual transfer of electric charge. The early current during activity is found to be carried by sodium. The delayed and sustained current, however, is not carried by potassium alone (146).

Membrane models.—Electrophoresis of a homogeneous electrolyte solution across layers of ion exchange gels acting functionally as a membrane gives under certain conditions oscillatory behavior caused by "negative" conductance. This instability obviously has a certain similarity with excitatory phenomena in living tissues but does not imply that excitable membranes are made up of similar types of ion exchangers (195). The oscillatory behavior resembles that observed in nodes of Ranvier in isotonic potassium chloride solutions (211).

Teorell continues to stress the importance of electro-osmosis for the rectifying properties of excitable membranes. The experimentally found current-voltage relation of *Nitella* can be reproduced by computer analysis, using the formulation of the electrohydraulic theory (196). But experimental proof of the paramount importance of electro-osmosis is still not available. A review of Teorell's recent work has been published (197).

An attempt has been made to reconstitute a cell membrane structure *in vitro* from solubilized lipids, extracted from membrane structures of white matter under addition of a yet unidentified heat-stable molecule obtained from bacterially desugared egg whites. This water-soluble macromolecule adsorbs to the single, stable bimolecular lipid and proteolipid membrane and lowers its resistance to about 10^3 ohms cm². Polarizing this membrane induces at a distinct threshold voltage a sudden resistance increase, similar to that in potassium-depolarized Ranvier nodes or in *Valonia*. It remains to be seen whether this membrane, as the authors claim, is really a reconstituted biological membrane structure (143).

Mathematical models.—Mathematical formulation of the behavior of excitable membranes continues. A mathematical model of the nerve membrane has been obtained by generalizing Van der Pol's equation for a relaxation oscillator by adding terms to produce a pair of nonlinear differential equations with either a stable singular point or a limit cycle (65).

There is now excellent mathematical treatment of the electrical properties of myelinated nerve based on the Hodgkin-Huxley differential equations for the nodes and a partial differential cable equation for the internodes (66). Furthermore, computed responses for Ranvier nodes obtained with a slightly modified Hodgkin-Huxley formulation also agree very well with most of the experimental data (43). The mathematical theory concerning the stability conditions of a space-clamped axon has been developed (30) showing the reasons for the oscillations described by certain authors in voltage-clamp experiments.

Lengthening of squid fiber action potentials after tetraethylammonium and nickel treatment proves to be consistent with the Hodgkin-Huxley equations if the potassium-carrying mechanism is slowed down by a factor of 100 (74). Experimental work on frog Ranvier nodes confirms this view (137).

The effect of raised potassium concentrations and hyperpolarizing responses can also be computed in a satisfactory agreement with experimental results in terms of the Hodgkin-Huxley model with appropriate modifications (75). A bi-stable state hypothesis such as that presented by Tasaki and co-workers (186, 189, 190) seems unnecessary.

The Hodgkin-Huxley formulation has also been successfully modified and applied to mathematical treatment of Purkinje fiber and pacemaker region potentials (150, 151).

The author of this review is impressed by the unfailing success of the now ten-year-old Hodgkin-Huxley mathematical model. It still remains the most successful one, having the great advantage of not committing itself to too many unproved assumptions. Should it ever prove to contain errors one should remember the tremendous impetus it gave to development of nerve and muscle physiology of the last decade. In this respect, it can well be compared to the Hill-Meyerhof lactic acid theory of muscle contraction. But the Lundsgaard-type of experiment disproving its basic concept has still not been performed.

The perfused giant axon.—Important support for the ionic theory is now obtained by Baker, Hodgkin & Shaw (8, 9, 10), and Shaw (173) by extruding the axoplasm of giant axons with a rubber-covered roller and then refilling and perfusing the axon with a buffered isotonic potassium solution. Excitability of such perfused axons remains for hours without notable changes in action and resting potentials. Replacement of intracellular potassium by sodium abolishes resting and action potential. Substitution by rubidium, however, gives prolonged action potentials for a certain time. Excitability ceases when the internal potassium concentration is reduced to less than 90 meq per l. The potassium permeability of the perfused squid axon falls as the resting potential increases, determining the saturation effect observed in the curve relating the logarithm of the external potassium concentration and membrane potential in the range of low external potassium concentrations (cf. 180). An increase of internal sodium concentration invariably reduces the overshoot. Delayed rectification is reversibly abolished if the internal potassium sulfate solution is replaced with isotonic sodium sulfate, thus it seems to result from a change of potassium permeability.

Extrusion of the axoplasm does not harm the sodium-pumping mechanism. The method of the perfused giant axon will therefore be useful for a better understanding of the basic processes of active transport.

The chloride permeability of the membrane is low. The intra-axonal anion is not critical for normal function of the membrane. This finding is somehow puzzling, as Keynes (113) has clearly established that in squid axons the intra-axonal chloride concentration is not 36 mM per kg axoplasm as found by Steinbach (184) but at least three times as much and that chloride ions are accumulated by active transport in squid axoplasm. The inhibition of chloride influx after treatment with 0.2 mM dinitrophenol, and probably also by ouabain, suggests a link between chloride uptake and activity of the sodium pump. As this accumulation of chloride in the axoplasm of squid seems to have little importance for excitability, one could consider it as by-product of active sodium transport, although high intra-axonal chloride could also have a relative importance for conduction by keeping the conductivity of the axoplasm core high.

The relatively low chloride permeability of the membrane should prevent chloride from influencing the membrane potential. The high intra-axonal chloride furthermore excludes the assumption of a simple Donnan equilibrium for chloride ions, especially as the activity coefficient of chloride ions in axoplasm is not reduced (134).

For comparison it may be mentioned that in frog muscle the intracellular chloride concentration in Ringer's of 3.1 to 3.8 mM per kg fiber water is consistent with a purely passive distribution. Also, NO_3^- and SCN^- in the external fluid reduce the chloride permeability of the membrane. Inward and outward movements of chloride across the membrane seem not to be independent (3).

Another perfusion technique for squid giant axons gives very different results (153). This same method has been used on a Japanese squid giant fiber, with strikingly small membrane potential changes caused by variation of intracellular potassium or sodium (192). Intra-axonal tetraethylammonium, however, prolongs and increases the action potential within 30 to 60 sec. Changes in intracellular pH to more than 8 or less than 7 reduce the time of survival. Excess calcium or magnesium tends to block conduction after an initial depolarization. These results are presented as favoring the "two stable states" theory of Tasaki (186). The writer of this review hesitates to accept such conclusions before it is clearly established why the method of perfusing without having extruded the bulk of axoplasm gives such a marked insensitivity to changes of intracellular potassium concentration. It looks as if the impossibility of reproducing this widely accepted prerogative of the Hodgkin-Huxley formulation, corroborated some years ago by good indirect evidence (e.g., 2), may be partly due to methodological shortcomings.

Other work on squid giant axons.—Sodium and potassium activity within the axoplasm of the squid giant axon were determined at rest and during activity by means of cation-selective glass microelectrodes (95). Average activities are for sodium $(A_{Na})_i = 0.037 \pm 0.0019$, for potassium $(A_K)_i = 0.203 \pm 0.0046$. After electrical stimulation $(A_{Na})_i$ increases, $(A_K)_i$ decreases, and the average net fluxes calculated from these changes are in good agreement with estimates from isotope studies. The potassium potential exceeds the resting potential by about 20 mv. The action potential, on the other hand, never exceeds the sodium potential. If at least 90 per cent of the axoplasm potassium is free, about 70 per cent of sodium must be present in free solution as well. All these results confirm the Hodgkin-Huxley explanation of membrane potentials at rest and during activity.

Electronic measurements of intracellular sodium concentrations of squid axons by determining the inflection point of early ionic current in voltage-clamp steps agree satisfactorily with directly determined sodium concentrations. The increase of intracellular sodium obtained by this method permits the calculation of net sodium entry per hour, and its change because of stimulation gives figures for the net sodium influx per impulse. Both are in close agreement with the results obtained by conventional methods. Electronic measurement of E_{Na} therefore gives advantages over chemical methods, as successive determinations permit calculation of fluxes while the electrical characteristics of the membrane as well as changes because of membrane active substances or activity can still be measured (140).

Reduction of external calcium and magnesium concentration to one tenth of the normal values nearly doubles the sodium influx by increasing the resting sodium conductance of the squid giant axon membrane (1).

Efflux of ^{14}C-glycerol from giant nerve fibers of the squid is shown to have three components: (a) a very rapid one, probably caused by contamination with extracellular fluid; (b) a less rapid one (disappearing if 10 μM copper chloride is present), attributed to a facilitated diffusion from an external compartment through the endoneurium membrane; (c) a slow one, attributed to diffusion from the axoplasm according to measurements of radioactivity of extruded axoplasm. The suggestion is made to identify the periaxonal compartments of others (27, 171) with this newly reported ^{14}C-glycerol compartment (202).

Lobster axons.—The temperature effects on membrane potentials of lobster axons differ from those in squid. It is suggested that there is a temperature-dependent fraction of the resting potential in lobster axons which is either not present or inactive in the squid axon, where the resting potential remains constant between 3 and 20°C. In the lobster axon within the same range, the resting potential increases from 72 to nearly 82 mv (40).

The electrical properties of small areas of excitable membrane of lobster axons can be measured by using two "sucrose gaps" (178, 182) leaving between them an artificial "node". Membrane potential changes and membrane characteristics can then be measured with external electrodes by using the techniques developed for myelinated fibers, even though there are adjacent membrane compartments, and the membrane is bathed in isotonic, high-resistance sucrose solutions (108). The method has also been used for voltage-clamp experiments with the lobster giant axon (109). Although the voltage-clamp results are in excellent agreement with those from squid axons and frog and toad nodes, some doubts persist whether the sucrose gap is a completely reliable method with nonmyelinated nerve fibers. During the experiments, the membrane potential within the "nodal" region increases by 20 to 60 mv after beginning of the sucrose flow on both sides of it. This polarizing action is confirmed with the double sucrose-gap method in artificial "nodes" of striated muscle fiber membrane (24). Its origin is not yet fully explained. Washing of large membrane surfaces with practically ion-free isotonic sucrose solutions is likely to remove intracellular ions as well and to change their concentration. Because of the different diffusion rates of chloride and sodium one expects a liquid junction potential between sucrose and the test solution around the node, making the external nodal compartment positive with respect to the sucrose compartment. The continuous flow of the external solutions would maintain this junction potential and hence its polarizing action on the nodal area. On the other hand, a rubber membrane (cf. 13, 119, 165) or a vaseline seal between the solutions will considerably reduce the power of this polarizing battery, as is confirmed by our own experiments (13, 182).

SYNAPSES

Reviews.—Eccles has most competently reviewed within one year the effect of frequency of activation on transmission across synapses (46), the membrane time-constants of cat motoneurons and time-courses of synaptic action (50), the synaptic mechanism for postsynaptic inhibition (49), inhibitory pathways to motoneurons (48), and the mechanism of synaptic transmission (47). He deserves full admiration for his almost miraculous working power, particularly if one realizes how prolific his laboratory has been with most valuable new experimental developments during the same period.

General physiology and pharmacology of junctional transmission are discussed by Grundfest (84). The methods of identifying mammalian inhibitory transmitters are reviewed by Curtis (37), the varieties of inhibitory processes by Grundfest (85). Excitatory and inhibitory processes in crustacean sensory nerve cells have been treated (63). An admirable review on transmission from nerve to muscle and the subcellular unit of synaptic action has been written by Katz (110).

Mollusc ganglia.—Studies of the pathways between the different large ganglia of the mollusc *Aplysia* have been based on electrophysiological results (104, 105). Evidence now suggests acetylcholine as the inhibitory transmitter in the giant ganglion cells of *Aplysia depilans* (194). Two types of cells are distinguished: the H type which is hyperpolarized and inhibited and the D type which is depolarized and excited by acetylcholine. This latter type has only excitatory input; the H type has both inhibitory and excitatory input. The effect of acetylcholine applied electrophoretically to different parts of the soma and proximal axon membrane is the same although the axonal regions seem to be more sensitive than the soma membrane. The more distant axonal parts are insensitive. The inhibitory postsynaptic potentials and the action of acetylcholine on H cells are reduced by *d*-tubocurarine and atropine but not by hexamethonium. On the other hand, the acetylcholine effects on D cells are blocked by hexamethonium. Physostigmine reinforces and prolongs the acetylcholine action. Carbamylcholine, which is not hydrolyzed by acetylcholinesterase, is more efficient than acetylcholine which speaks for the presence of a specific cholinesterase in the ganglia of *Aplysia*. The threshold of immediate acetylcholine action in H neurons is about 10^{-12} g per cm^3, which is probably a high estimate as the accessibility to the membranes is delayed by protective membranes. It compares well with the estimate for the vertebrate neuromuscular junction of 10^{-15} mole (41). There is a reversal of hyperpolarizing action of acetylcholine on H neurons if the membrane potential is hyperpolarized to more than about -60 mv. This conforms to findings on spinal motoneurons (35). All the evidence presented in this paper is very convincing and corroborated by excellent records. It is interesting that long-lasting inhibition of the D-type ganglia can be obtained by orthodromic stimulation. This secondary effect of the excitatory input resembles presynaptic inhibition. The transmitter substance for either excitatory action on H cells or long-lasting inhibition of D cells is not known. Inhibition of H cells and excitation of D cells is, however, clearly cholinergic (193).

Trigeminal nucleus.—Transmission through the trigeminal nucleus of rat has been studied with extracellular electrodes (62). It remains to be seen whether the inhibitory effects obtained by longer stimulation of remote skin areas do not come from presynaptic inhibition (p. 496).

Electrophysiological investigation of the caudal part of the spinal nucleus of cat trigeminal nerve makes it possible to distinguish between two types of cells. The numerous cells belonging to an A group respond to hair movement or tactile stimuli of skin and mucous membranes of the ipsilateral face and antidromically to lemniscal stimulation (40 per cent of A cells only). Mechanical stimulation of neighboring hairs can inhibit the response of some A cells, possibly by presynaptic inhibition. The less numerous B cells respond with longer latency to stimulation of larger receptive areas of the ipsilateral face. Only one of ten B cells responds antidromically to lemniscal stimulation (80).

Motoneurons.—A histological survey of the volume distribution of moto- and interneurons in the peronaeus-tibialis neuron pool of the cat spinal cord has been made (164). The nerve cell body of motoneurons has a mean volume of 29000 μ^3, that of interneurons 75000 μ^3 if reconstructed from measurements in different planes. Among the cells of smaller volume are also about 10 per cent of small motoneurons. After severing of the tibialis-peronaeus nerve, about 25 per cent of the cells show retrograde degeneration. These motoneurons have a nearly Gaussian volume distribution between 3000 and 64000 μ^3 with a maximum around 30000 μ^3.

Direct stimulation of cat spinal motoneurons with linearly increasing currents applied through an intracellular micropipette makes it possible to distinguish between two groups of motoneurons, as follows.

(*a*) Fast or phasic motoneurons with relatively high accommodation. At lowered rate of current rise, the threshold current intensity increases to a final value. Spikes are generated at the initial segment for rapid rise and in the soma membrane during slow rises.

(*b*) Tonic or slow motoneurons with little accommodation, showing nearly constant threshold current within a wide range of slopes, the spikes being always generated at the initial segment and being frequently repetitive. Further hypotheses concerning the possibility of a transitional zone between the initial segment and the soma to explain the particular shape of the threshold latency curves of the fast motoneurons need more experimental corroboration (163).

The anion permeability of motoneurons was estimated from the reversal and the subsequent recovery of inhibitory postsynaptic potentials in cat motoneurons after intracellular electrophoretical injection. From the recovery of such potentials after injection, the following sequence for their relative ability to penetrate the cell membrane was established:

$$Br^- = SCN^- > Cl^- > NO_2^- > BF_4^- > I^- > NO_3^- > ClO_3^- > HCO_2^-$$

which is only more or less in accordance with the relative hydrated size and is thus not convincing evidence for a pore-structure hypothesis for the activated inhibitory postsynaptic membrane (6).

There is agreement that inhibitory postsynaptic potentials in frog motoneurons are mediated through oligosynaptic pathways (73, 120). The same conclusion is reached about cat motoneurons, where the synaptic delay for excitatory and inhibitory synapses is the same (61).

Rectangular current steps of 2 to 6×10^{-9} amp applied to motoneurons of the lumbosacral spinal cord of the cat by means of single microelectrodes are shown to hyperpolarize or depolarize the membrane with a summit reached after 16 msec and a decline of about 30 per cent of the peak value within about 100 msec. The change in membrane threshold is an accurate image of the membrane-potential change. The phenomenon thus can not be identified with accommodation. The equivalent circuit for such a behavior is not a resistance-capacitance model. It includes an inductive component as well, as was proposed for other excitable structures. At the end of steady current pulses the membrane potential swings in the opposite direction. The large undershoot after repetitive postsynaptic potentials may be a summation of such potential swings (7).

Spinal interneuron activity seems to be facilitated in cats by intravenous injection of 1 μg norepinephrine per kg body weight. This effect is believed to be a direct action on the nerve cells (174).

Other neurons.—Synaptic potentials of lateral geniculate neurons have been recorded extracellularly after ortho- or antidromic activation. They generate three kinds of nonpropagating potentials: (*a*) slow rhythmic oscillations, (*b*) synaptic potentials, and (*c*) afterpotentials after a cell-body spike. This last potential may originate in the cell body alone; the other two probably involve dendrites as well(14).

The influence of direct currents on activity of optical cortex neurons in the cat has again been studied. Extracellular recording of neuron activity has confirmed that a surface anode which tends to raise the physiological steady-potential difference between the pial surfaces and the ventricles has a stimulating, a cathode an inhibiting, effect. The question whether the physiological potential difference between the cortex and the ventricles has a regulatory influence on cortical activity is answered negatively. It is observed that this potential difference is shifting in the opposite direction, i.e., physiological activation of cortical neurons is accompanied by a diminished positivity of the surface and inhibition by increased positivity (36). But this conclusion may be wrong as nobody knows how complex the potential-producing mechanism within the cortex is and which of the potential-producing elements is the main current-pathway. It is further likely that glia cells and neurons both contribute to the potential and interact in every respect, physically and chemically. Therefore, much more refined intracellular measurements are needed before a final answer to this question can be given.

A similar problem of complex behavior of central nervous tissue is encountered in the study of water and electrolyte distribution. There again it is impossible to deal with one tissue component without considering the others. There is reasonable evidence that, after arrest of normal oxygenation of the cerebral cortex, a rapid shift of water from extracellular space into the cellular compartment takes place. Histologically there is a swelling of apical dendrites and Bergmann fibers. These cells show also an increased chloride content. This observation is corroborated by impedance measurements (90). It is, however, uncertain how the differences in swelling of different cells can be explained—particularly the very rapid swelling of glial elements in certain cases. There seems to be a still unknown interaction of cortical elements for osmotic regulations, which may well be linked to ionic changes and to the steady-potential changes mentioned afore.

Autonomic ganglia.—A scheme concerning the origin of synaptic potentials in the superior cervical ganglion has been elaborated on the basis of electrophysiological and pharmacological evidence. Preganglionic fibers are believed to release acetylcholine. This release can be inhibited by botulinus toxin. The acetylcholine elicits the primary depolarizing synaptic response by immediately acting on subsynaptic sites (N-potential) which are readily blocked by curariform agents but not by atropine in low concentrations. The chromaffin cells also receive preganglionic released acetylcholine at postsynaptic sites which, however, are very sensitive to atropine. They release epinephrine if adequately excited by acetylcholine, and this epinephrine interacts with special receptor sites on the ganglion cell membrane (P-potential). Dibenamine [*N*-(2-chloroethyl)dibenzylamine] prevents this interaction. The late negative potential which is attributed to another more remote type of postsynaptic ganglionic acetylcholine receptors can also be blocked by atropine but also by relatively low concentrations of Dibenamine. This seems one of the points of this investigation which needs further explanation (59).

Presynaptic inhibition.—Presynaptic inhibition, briefly mentioned in last year's review, is likely to become one of the inhibitory mechanisms of paramount importance within the central nervous system of vertebrates and invertebrates. It is almost unbelievable that it remained undiscovered despite the numerous facts pointing in this direction [for earlier literature see (47)]. It was shown by Frank & Fuortes (67, 68) that muscle afferent volleys diminish the size of the monosynaptic excitatory postsynaptic potential of motoneurons without producing any change of postsynaptic permeability which should have been observed, had the inhibition been postsynaptic. Frank called this effect "remote" inhibition, supposing that the inhibitory action was exerted on dendrites too far away from the electrode in the soma of the motoneuron to give a measurable influence, although he and Fuortes in their original paper had designated the phenomenon as "presynaptic inhibition". There is now full evidence proving a presynaptic inhibitory mechanism, starting with two preliminary reports in 1960 and full publication in 1961 (48, 53, 57, 58). The essential fact is a long-lasting (200 msec and more) depolarization of the primary afferents by group I afferent volleys. This depolarization affects the amplitude of the primary afferent impulse and the amount of excitatory transmitter substance released at the synaptic endings. It also increases the likeliness that "dorsal root reflexes" (56) occur by means of ephaptic transmission from one afferent to another. Furthermore, this presynaptic depolarization is powerful enough to produce a field potential within the spinal cord with a maximum negativity at or near the ventral ends of the afferents (verified with extracellular electrodes) and a relative positivity at and around the dorsomedial entry of the dorsal roots. These slow potential changes, generated on the spinal cord surface by muscle or cutaneous afferent volleys, have not been observed by previous researchers interested in the changes of the spinal cord surface (57) mostly because single afferent volleys had been used and the gastrocnemius nerve had been taken as the standard muscle afferent, whereas it is a particularly inefficient one. It is now found that a single volley from other muscle afferents (for instance, biceps and semitendinosus nerve) is followed by a small positive potential of the cord dorsum which is very much amplified by successive volleys.

The same time-course of potential change is also reflected by intracellular recording of the depolarization of Ia and Ib afferent fibers in the cord and by the excitability changes observed with the double impulse method of Wall (203) and of course by the depression of monosynaptic excitatory postsynaptic potentials. The depression has a latency of about 4 msec, 15 to 20 msec rise time, and a total duration of at least 300 msec.

The morphological correlate to presynaptic inhibition might be a special type of synaptic knob superimposed on a large synaptic knob that is associated with monosynaptic activation of motoneurons (82, 115). Activation of this special type of inhibitory ending should depolarize the afferent ending of the Ia fiber and reduce its synaptic efficacy by reducing the amplitude of the conducted impulse and the amount of transmitter liberated (55). The resulting depression of excitatory postsynaptic potentials can then produce failure of the reflex discharge.

Whether the reduced output of transmitter during presynaptic inhibition is caused by the depolarization directly or by the reduced spike amplitude is still not certain. Results with presynaptic depolarization of neuromuscular junctions have led to the suggestion that the depolarizing currents may act by reducing the amount of transmitter available for release by the nerve impulse by slowing the replenishment of transmitter at the terminal membrane. The release of transmitter would then be a matter of availability rather than of amplitude of the releasing impulse (103).

With respect to the possible mechanism of transmitter release, it is of interest that this release is shown to increase at the diaphragm end-plate of the rat in the presence of calcium and to decrease in the presence of magnesium, as judged from the change of frequency of the miniature end-plate potential. It is suggested that the transmitter release during activity is obtained by the same mechanism that releases transmitter during rest, responding to calcium (102).

Presynaptic inhibition is not only observed with Ia afferents but also with Ib afferents. They receive the largest part of their presynaptic inhibition from Ib impulses of either flexor or extensor muscles. A similar negative feedback control on central actions is observed with large cutaneous fibers. Here the negative feedback action of presynaptic inhibition is mainly brought about by all other cutaneous afferents from the same limb, but also to a lesser extent by groups Ib, II, and III—not, however, by Ia fibers.

Presynaptic inhibition is also produced in primary Ib and cutaneous afferents (but not in Ia afferents) by stimulation of the sensorimotor region of the cerebral cortex. This stimulation activates all synaptic actions, excitatory and inhibitory, transmitted by one or several interneurons. This action is mediated by the pyramidal tract (132).

Electrical stimulation of the medulla oblongata or of the caudal pons produces presynaptic inhibition of Ia, Ib, and flexor reflex afferents in the lumbar cord (28).

Presynaptic inhibition is likely to be the basis of some recent observations (100, 131). It has been clearly described in crayfish where a similar presynaptic inhibitory effect can be obtained by applying γ-aminobutyric acid (45). Presynaptic inhibition forms, according to Eccles, a means of suppressing by negative feedback all trivial sensory inputs in favor of a powerful sensory input having an implication of urgency.

Recurrent inhibition.—Further confirmation of distribution of Renshaw inhibitory postsynaptic potentials as given by Wilson and co-workers (207) has been published (51). Chloralose seems to reduce the Renshaw inhibition specifically (88); succinylcholine is believed to increase recurrent Renshaw inhibition (93). Intracellular recording from Renshaw cells permits an analysis of the time-course of the synaptically induced excitatory postsynaptic potentials. An initial depolarization of 36 mv lasting about 2 msec is followed by a slowly declining tail of 60-msec duration. These two phases correspond to a sudden rapid burst of impulses, followed by a longer phase of low-discharge frequency (52).

Quantitative relations between normal reflex discharge frequency of motoneurons of gastrocnemius nerve and discharge frequency during antidromic tetanization of the rest of the motor root, causing a constant amount of recurrent inhibition, have been established. The difference between these two frequencies given in impulses per second is constant and is furthermore directly proportional to the rate of antidromic tetanization within about 10 to 30 shocks per sec (81).

Further support of cholinergic transmission of Renshaw cells has been published but it is still not certain that acetylcholine is the only excitatory transmitter agent activating them (38).

Crossed spinal reflexes evoked by volleys in somatic afferents have been studied extensively (99). The importance of the brainstem for control of reciprocal actions of excitation to flexor and inhibition to extensor motoneurons from the flexion reflex afferents is demonstrated (100). Some of these results will probably be explained by presynaptic inhibition.

Intracellular recording from cells of the ventral spinocerebellar tract has been accomplished. Their spike potentials are similar to those of motoneurons. The cells are monosynaptically excited by descending fibers of the ipsilateral ventral quadrant of the spinal cord and bisynaptically inhibited by descending fibers of the ipsilateral dorsal funiculus (54).

Two ascending pathways in the ventral part of the spinal cord have been identified by the impossibility of exciting them antidromically from the cerebellar cortex. Both pathways are activated from flexor reflex afferents, but the receptive field for one pathway is bilateral and under strong excitatory and inhibitory influence from the anterior cerebellar lobe. The other pathway is polysynaptically activated from the contralateral receptive field and not controlled from the cerebellum (131). Inhibitory effects from stimulation of flexor-reflex afferents observed in this paper may well be explained by presynaptic inhibition. Descending activity of the dorsolateral funiculus evokes large dorsal root potentials and may therefore cause depolarization of primary afferents or presynaptic inhibition.

Transmission in crayfish.—Impulse transmission across the septal and commissural junctions of crayfish lateral giant axons is ephaptic and bidirectional. It is, however, unidirectional but possibly ephaptic as well from the cord lateral giant axon to the root motor giant fiber. The ephaptic transmission between homologous segments of two lateral giant fibers and from one segment to another within the same fiber gives way to reverberatory repetitive activity of both axons (205).

Between the "colossal" nerve cells of the leech ephaptic and reverberating transmission is also found, with an attenuation factor of only two to three, corresponding to the one in earthworm commissural connections (89).

The inhibitory action of 3-hydroxytyramine, γ-aminobutyric acid, and some other compounds on crayfish stretch receptor neurons has been studied. There seems to be more than one receptor site involved in the inhibitory effects observed (135).

MYELINATED NERVE FIBERS AND RANVIER NODE

Myelinated nerve fibers.—With excised frog sciatic nerves, epinephrine bitartrate in concentrations up to 10^{-3} is shown to have no action on threshold, strength-duration curve, conduction velocity, or intensity response curves which could be distinguished from the action of changed pH, because of the marked acidity of epinephrine bitartrate (172). Unpublished experiments of the author of this review have also never shown any direct action of epinephrine on membrane properties of single Ranvier nodes. Recent *in vitro* investigations, however, confirm earlier *in vivo* findings of Bülbring & Whitteridge (23) which show an increase of excitability and of the action potential caused by epinephrine concentrations between 2×10^{-6} and 2×10^{-5} in myelinated nerve. The experiments were made with the sucrose-gap technique (77). This difference of results is hard to explain. The author of this review rather favored the idea that the findings of Bülbring & Whitteridge, showing strong increases of the compound action potential of *in situ* sciatic nerves of the cat, were ascribable to epinephrine-induced changes of circulation rather than to its actual influence on nerve properties (23). But on account of these sucrose-gap experiments this conclusion is inadmissible.

Weight changes of the nerves in epinephrine with pH variations of several units did not exceed 5 per cent, although hypotonic Ringer's solutions of 50 per cent normal produce about 20 per cent, and 10 per cent hypotonic Ringer's produced 40 per cent weight increase within one hour [growing to a limiting value of 50 per cent in two hours (172)].

Efforts to stimulate single myelinated nerve fibers mechanically have been made (213). The method does not allow conclusions as to where the pressure acts and which absolute pressure is necessary to obtain a response. Furthermore, no attempt is made to explain mechanical excitability in terms of electrical changes within the membrane.

Ranvier node.—Frankenhaeuser (69, 70, 71) has further developed his voltage-clamp technique with single Ranvier nodes of large isolated fibers from the sciatic nerve of the African toad *Xenopus laevis*. In order to keep the node completely independent of other nodal membranes, he cuts the isolated fiber on both sides of the node. It is important to notice that such a drastic procedure has little effect. Intra-axonal hydrostatic pressure can therefore not be essential for membrane function. As in squid fibers, the delayed voltage-clamp currents seem to be mainly carried by potassium ions, moving down their electrochemical gradient. At high external potassium concentrations, inward potassium currents are found in a membrane-potential range between 60 and 10 mv (outside positive) with a maximum between 30 and 40 mv. This confirms previous and recent findings of a negative resistance part in the current-voltage relation of potassium-treated Ranvier nodes (11, 179, 183) that permits regenerative potential changes similar to action potentials (127, 128, 141). The delayed steady state membrane currents measured at various external potassium concentrations agree with those calculated according to the independence principle in the Hodgkin-Huxley formulation. The concept of a potassium transport system which undergoes partial inactivation under prolonged action of depolarizing voltage steps (127) is again confirmed (70). The quantity P_K (permeability constant for potassium) rather than G_K (membrane conductance for potassium) is the adequate magnitude to be used in analyzing the potassium transport system except for equal values of inside and outside potassium concentrations, where both can be used; P_K is found to increase to a limiting steady value with step membrane-potential changes of about +100 mv or more. This limiting value is about 1.2×10^{-3} cm per sec. The delayed membrane currents are not influenced by replacing chloride by methylsulfate or isethionate. The small depolarization of the unclamped resting membrane by substitution for chloride of methylsulfate is believed to demonstrate a slight chloride permeability of the resting membrane (but see objections below). The corresponding small membrane currents cannot yet be measured with the voltage-clamp technique. An increase of the sodium concentration increases the delayed outward currents; replacement of sodium by choline reduces them. Choline chloride added in substance also reduces, but to a smaller extent, the delayed currents (71). Recent experiments with bundles of myelinated fibers support the P_K-increasing action of sodium (167).

Other attempts to apply voltage clamp to Ranvier nodes are less convincing, because of technical shortcomings and wrong explanations (154). It is rather distressing to see that the boards of editors of well-known journals of physiology accept papers which are full of basic errors, and inaccurate and misspelled quotations as well (e.g. 155, 212).

One of the uncertain points in the work with single nodes is the influence of the myelin-covered regions which are also in contact with the test solutions. Changes of external sodium and chloride cencentrations have been shown to affect the transmyelin potential and resistance. Both are reduced by an excess of sodium or chloride and increase if nonpenetrating ions are substituted for them. Changes of external potassium concentration, however, have little effect (149). The thoughts of Lüttgau & Straub, discussed below, have therefore to be kept in mind.

After previous depolarization with KCl-rich solutions, a hyperpolarization of myelinated nerve fiber bundles is observed if tetraethylammonium (TEA) is added (15, 186). This action resembles the one of increased calcium concentration (cf.166). Both hyperpolarizing effects are also observed if the $[K]_0 \cdot [Cl]_0$ product is kept constant. They vanish under prolonged action of potassium-rich solutions. Treatment with normal Ringer's solution restores the effect within about 20 min. An increase of membrane resistance is observed with TEA (cf. 127) and under excess calcium treatment as well (cf. 181). As the Donnan mechanism may not be operating in nerve (113), the existence of the effect in constant $[K]_0 \cdot [Cl]_0$ product does not contradict the possibility of a readjustment of the chloride potential to a new membrane equilibrium. If addition of calcium ions reduces P_K and P_{Na}, the potassium-induced depolarization will shift towards the chloride potential under the influence of a raised external calcium concentration. This shift will vanish progressively during the passive redistribution of chloride. The calcium-induced repolarization is considerably reduced when chloride is replaced by methylsulfate (168). The TEA repolarization, however, is unaffected by such substitutions. Lüttgau (127) suggested that such hyperpolarization in potassium-rich solution caused by TEA could be explained if one assumed that the solution only affects the nodal membrane parts which are not covered by the spiral endings of the mesaxon. The covered parts would only slowly depolarize after an increase of the external potassium concentration within the mesaxon cleft by diffusion. This process would take many minutes, possibly up to one hour or more. If within this time a TEA-induced increase of the resistance of the "free" membrane parts took place, the "covered" parts would discharge into them and raise the membrane potential. Straub has taken up this suggestion and postulates that the whole internode discharges into the nodal membrane and lifts its membrane potential if the membrane resistance is increased by TEA (15). Experimental proof of this hypothesis with single nodes and various lengths of internodes exposed to potassium-rich solutions should be relatively easy but has not yet been performed. This assumption might explain why moderate increases of external potassium concentration have small and slow effects on membrane potential (180). The change of nodal membrane resistance would not be strong enough to allow sufficient current flow through the nodal membrane battery to overcome the adjacent transmyelin potentials. Only after about an hour would the transmyelin potential have adjusted itself to the nodal potential by intramesaxonal or possibly intra-Schmidt-Lautermann-cleft diffusion. There is another implication of this idea. Recovery of the membrane potential of single nodes after application of potassium-rich solutions has a two-step time-course. After an initial fast repolarization, there is suddenly a much slower one. The membrane-potential level, where this sudden inflection of repolarization occurs, depends on duration of contact with potassium-rich solutions. The longer it is, the nearer the inflection is to the potassium-equilibrium potential. In this case, in spite of an immediate rise of the nodal membrane potential to the normal resting level after restoration of normal potassium concentration, the transmyelin potential would keep the potential down until potassium would have gradually diffused back. The hyperpolarizations observed with excess calcium, cocaine, hypertonic solutions, etc., in a potassium-rich medium may be explained by this mechanism as all these agents increase the resistance of the nodal membrane. Furthermore, the difficulties in lowering the membrane potential by substitution of nonpenetrating anions for chloride may find a similar explanation. Before conclusive evidence for or against this mechanism is available, one should avoid accepting statements that the chloride potential is not important for the resting membrane. There is an urgent need for further experimental work in this field.

Ionic theory.—An excellent review on ionic transport is presented by Wilbrandt & Rosenberg (206), a discussion of transport problems by Tasaki (187), and a review of potassium and sodium distribution of nerve fibers by Hurlbut (107).

Comparison of the passive sodium- and potassium-transporting system of Ranvier nodes by means of current-voltage characteristics, resistance measurements, and action-potential recordings in solutions with different cations makes it likely that rubidium and cesium use the potassium-transporting system. However NH_4 ions pass through sodium channels during the initial phase of activity and later through potassium channels (129).

Voltage-clamp experiments in ammonium Ringer's led to the conclusion that NH_4-Ringer's is about equivalent to 25 per cent sodium Ringer's and that the potassium current is slightly larger than the controls in normal Ringer's, which favors the views expressed above. The equilibrium potential with sodium inside and ammonium outside is about $+13$ mv (outside negative) (43).

Desheathed sciatic nerves of *R. pipiens* take up hydrazinium ions as found previously by Lorente de Nó and remain excitable in sodium-free solutions containing this onium ion. Recent analysis of this uptake suggests that hydrazine quantitatively replaces sodium during activity but is not "pumped" out again. The extra uptake of the onium ion is 4.5 mM per hr per g wet nerve which is only 10 per cent of the initial content of nerves after soaking in hydrazinium Ringer's overnight. But this extra uptake is more injurious to the fibers which irreversibly fail to conduct impulses of 50 per sec after 1.2 to 1.5 hr. It is not yet known whether a slow release of ammonium ions is at the basis of this phenomenon (33).

The action of increased hydrogen ion concentration (from pH 7 to 6.5) on action potentials of single nodes is supposed to be mainly indirect through increased activity of calcium ions in the nodal membrane. At still lower pH values, however, there seems to be a delay and reduction of the P_K change during the action potential which can be attributed to a direct membrane action of hydrogen ions. This conclusion is drawn from comparing the action of calcium and hydrogen ion concentration and from combining experiments with both ions (91, 92).

With repetitive stimulation (500 to 2500 pulses of 90 μsec duration per sec), single or repeated action potentials of nodes are obtained. Their size and shape and time of appearance can well be explained by accepting the view that the local response and inactivation of the sodium transport system undergo summation in successive stimuli and that, according to the prevalence of one or the other of these two opposed phenomena of different time-course, all kinds of activity, subthreshold and other, can be obtained. Differing assumptions by the author of two recent papers are difficult to accept (116, 117).

Anelectrotonus is found to increase the width of the myelin-free gap at the node of Ranvier; catelectrotonus reduces it. The whole myelin sheath seems to move in the direction of the cathode (144).

Role of acetylcholine in Ranvier nodes.—The controversy concerning the role of acetylcholine in bioelectrogenesis is still going on. Conduction of Ranvier nodes is claimed to be blocked by physostigmine (200 to 300 μg per ml) and by curare (10^{-3} moles), more or less reversibly (42). One should avoid speaking of conduction block if one has only observed that one single node, treated with a substance, stopped to produce an action potential. A block of impulse conduction is possible, even when action potentials of single nodes can still be recorded. Conduction depends not only on amplitude, but on rate of rise of the action potential, threshold of the neighboring node, and current losses within the internode, none of which was measured. Furthermore, as pointed out by one of the discussants of the paper mentioned above, the action potential looked bad even before the enormous concentrations of inhibitors were applied. The RC amplifier used did not permit the recording of resting-potential changes of the single node preparation which very likely have taken place. Disappearance of action potentials or changes of threshold and time-course are almost meaningless if no further membrane properties are measured. One should at least have indications concerning the membrane resistance, the absolute value of resting potential, rectifier properties, percentage of sodium transport system inactivation, and response to high external potassium concentrations. Only such indications would permit specific conclusions concerning the reason of the disappearance of excitability.

Application of a detergent (0.1 per cent Triton X-100) during the histochemical test for acetylcholine-esterase with acetylcholine gives a strongly stained ring at each node of Ranvier which seems to be composed of fine lamellae. Esterase-inhibitors prevent the staining. The axoplasm shows inconstant staining of smaller intensity (76). Even if this result suggests a possible concentration of the enzyme at the nodes, the author of this review can so far see no conclusive proof that acetylcholine is essential to the activity of the nodal membrane.

Posttetanic hyperpolarization.—The posttetanic hyperpolarization of C fibers seems to be caused by metabolic extrusion of sodium ions (34, 97, 158). The original concept that the hyperpolarization is caused by removal of potassium by a coupled potassium pump from a compartment outside the axon is now given up in favor of an uncoupled sodium extrusion, i.e., an electrogenic sodium pump (16, 97, 185). The great increase of the posttetanic hyperpolarization of both myelinated (136) and unmyelinated (158) fibers in potassium-free solutions is then explained as the result of uncoupling of the pump rather than of a summation of potassium permeability increases during a long train of impulses, as suggested by Meves (136).

Posttetanic hyperpolarization of nonmyelinated and myelinated fibers is most powerfully inhibited by antimycin A, a compound with a specific site of action in the cytochrome system even in concentrations of only a few micrograms per liter (lowest active concentration is $1.8 \mu M$). Treatment with nitrogen, sodium fluoride, sodium fluoroacetate, hydroxylamine, mersalyl, and maleic acid is much less effective. Removal of glucose either decreases or increases the hyperpolarization. Addition of acetate, pyruvate, malonate, or alcohol is associated with an increase, oxalacetate with a decrease, of posttetanic hyperpolarization (83). Even if these results favor a relation of the posttetanic hyperpolarization with metabolic events, one should remember that dinitrophenol poisoning reducs posttetanic hyperpolarizations of mammalian C fibers, but has been found inactive (136) in myelinated frog fibers where the posttetanic hyperpolarization clearly reflects a cumulative increase of the potassium permeability of the nodal membrane and nothing which could be related to active transport.

Recent important results show that posttetanic hyperpolarization is inconstant in mammalian nonmedullated nerve fibers if they are in Krebs solution of pH 7.4 (97). If the pH is lowered to 6.4 by using Locke's solution, there is a constant and strong hyperpolarization after repetitive stimulation. The time-constant of this change is about half an hour which is believed to show the time-constant of hydrogen ion penetration into the nerve fibers (98). Blocking of the intermediate metabolism by iodoacetate, cyanide, and dinitrophenol abolishes the hyperpolarization. All this confirms earlier findings on C fibers and gives rather strong support to a metabolic origin of the phenomenon, probably caused by active and electrogenic extrusion of sodium. Whether the impossibility of obtaining a similar effect in myelinated nerve is caused by an unfavorable pH remains to be seen. It is important to know that the polarity of posttetanic electrogenic activity in C fibers is pH-dependent. In a high pH a posttetanic depolarization can be obtained. It is not known whether this phenomenon is abolished by inhibition of intermediate metabolism as well. As the time-course of the posttetanic potential is the same, it seems probable that the same agent, set free during tetanic activity of the nerve fibers, produces either hyperpolarization or depolarization. But it is also quite new that single action potentials elicited after the phase of tetanic activity have a marked negative and a long-lasting positive afterpotential, independent of pH and hence of the direction of the posttetanic membrane potential change. These afterpotentials are, however, sensitive to inhibitors of active transport and thus connected with it. One needs no prophetic mind to foresee most interesting developments in this field of electrophysiological investigations, made possible by the much better measurement of C fiber potentials with the sucrose gap.

Hyperpolarizing response.—The negative resistance part of the current-voltage curves of squid axons in high external potassium concentrations is also found in the single motor axon rapidly closing the claw of the crayfish. The hyperpolarizing response at high potassium concentrations sometimes becomes repetitive (200) as can be observed in Ranvier nodes as well (own published observations). This hyperpolarizing response should not be mixed up with the "action potential" of Mueller (142) and Lüttgau (128) in potassium-rich solutions. These authors have, to begin with, repolarized the fiber by anelectrotonus and given a short cathodal stimulus which produces a regenerative fall of membrane potential followed by potassium carrier inactivation and a subsequent repolarization. The author of this review interpreted the hyperpolarizing responses of Tasaki (186) and of his own as the result of a membrane "breakdown". Hyperpolarizing responses are, however, also obtained with single frog muscle fibers (24) in a very reproducible way which makes a breakdown unlikely. Membranes of crayfish axons and Ranvier nodes in high potassium and skeletal frog muscle fibers in normal Ringer's seem to reach a point of inflection of the current-voltage relation at very high membrane potentials where they become permeable to potassium again. Hence during a polarizing impulse the potassium permeability is first shut off and the potential drop across the membrane grows until the membrane potential region is reached where the potassium permeability increases again. Then a regenerative fall of the potential takes place which is the descending phase of the hyperpolarizing response or the rising phase of the "action potential" going in the usual direction. The repolarizing phase of the "action potential" is thus nothing but the ascending phase of the hyperpolarizing response. Hyperpolarizing responses may not always be obtained in Ranvier nodes and in muscle membranes. An increased potassium permeability resulting from hyperpolarization occurs at a lower membrane potential if the fiber has been frequently polarized with strong currents and is not in a very good state. In this case, repetitive hyperpolarizing responses can be more easily obtained (own unpublished observations).

A review by Grundfest (156) on ionic transport across neural and non-neural membranes contains some interesting unpublished data on hyperpolarizing responses in muscle membranes and chloride-transient responses in crayfish muscle fibers, and their modification by picrotoxin (87).

Metabolism and Active Transport

An excellent review on energy sources for active transport in nerve and muscle is given by Keynes (112).

The adenosine triphosphatase discovered by Skou (175, 176) in crab nerve is sensitive to cardiac glycoside and activated by sodium and potassium. It is a part of the active sodium-potassium transport mechanism in erythrocyte membranes. This enzyme has now been found in sheaths of squid axons and in smaller concentration in the axoplasm; it is believed to be an integral part of the active sodium-potassium transport mechanism in the squid axon (17).

The contents of adenosine di- and triphosphate and creatine phosphate in frog sciatic nerves are found to be 0.3, 0.9, and 2.02 μM per g wet nerve, respectively (31). Iodoacetic acid affects the electrical activity of chicken vagus nerve long before any changes of ATP or CrP can be measured. On the other hand, anoxia diminishes both ATP and CrP without significantly altering the electrical activity. The energy cost of activity therefore is not directly related with breakdown of high-energy phosphates (39). Accordingly there is little or no increase of oxygen consumption and little or no decrease of CrP if frog nerve is excited during two hours with 50 impulses per second (32). Immature sciatic nerve fibers of chick have also no significant activity respiration. Their ability to carry impulses, however, depends on the amount of glucose present in the suspension medium. The average time to extinction of the response during repetitive stimulation is proportional to this glucose concentration. The metabolic requirement during activity is thus supported by carbohydrate (29).

Oxidation of glucose in a sympathetic ganglion at rest and during activity has been measured in the rat with a flow respirometer for measuring labeled carbon dioxide production when the ganglion was bathed in a solution containing labeled glucose (101). Eighty-seven per cent of the measured oxygen uptake appears as carbon dioxide, $260 \pm 6 \, \mu M$ per g dry weight per hr with an increase during supramaximal stimulation at a frequency of 5 per sec of $55 \pm 11 \, \mu M$ per g dry weight per hr. Oxidation of glucose therefore accounts fully for the increase of oxygen uptake during activity of sympathetic neurons.

MOVEMENT OF AXOPLASMIC CONTENTS ALONG THE AXON

If labeled amino acids are placed on the floor of the fourth ventricle, an extensive synthesis of labeled protein occurs in the medulla oblongata of rabbits whilst Schwann cells and other components of encephalic nerves incorporate only small amounts of tagged amino acids. The synthetized proteins can then be shown to travel with the movement of the axoplasm to the distal parts of the hypoglossal and vagus nerves (138). Similar experiments with phosphorus-32 orthophosphate show that the radioactive phospholipids extracted from peripheral segments of the same nerves increased and that there was a gradient of activity within these segments, indicating a velocity of lipid transport along the nerves of about 1.7 mm per hr. Crushing of nerves causes an abrupt fall of radioactivity just underneath the injury. This is against the possibility of migration of phospholipids between the interstices and incorporation in Schwann cells, and other structures. After crushing, this migration would still have taken place (139).

Similar experiments with phosphorus 32 injected into the spinal cord of cats give a velocity of radioactive phosphorus transport along the ventral roots of about 4.5 mm per day and much lower activity in the dorsal roots. This velocity is reduced by pressure asphyxiation of the cord. Reduction is also found with cyanide poisoning or lowered temperature of the cord. The activity declines exponentially along the fibers. A "pumping" mechanism along the axis cylinder is postulated to explain the measured axoplasmic flow (152).

A recent motion picture of single nerve fibers by Paul Weiss (personal communication) shows tremendous mechanical activity of the Schwann cells, recalling peristalsis. Even if axoplasmic movements may not be unilateral, they must have a strong mixing effect and must speed up diffusion along the axoplasm.

Electronmicrographs of frog sciatic nerve seem to show two or even three myelinated fibers within one single Schwann cell or three to four unmyelinated fibers included in one Schwann cell. This is taken as evidence against the theory of formation of the myelin sheath by rotation (18).

DEGENERATION AND REGENERATION

Crushing myelinated nerve fibers of the rabbit produces demyelination of the internodes proximal to the site of damage. The demyelination gradually disappears and does not stretch further than 5 mm proximally. As a result of demyelination the Schwann cells which normally are sedentary, i.e. fixed to each internode, begin to divide. There is an accumulation of Schwann cytoplasm and nuclei within the nude part of the axon. During regeneration all nuclei except one disappear and a new "intercalated" internode (123) is formed which forms a new myelin sheath. The thickness of the newly formed myelin depends on the length of the intercalated internode. The longer it is, the thicker the myelin sheath grows (124). The agent which is postulated as cause of demyelination is unknown. Recent experiments show that demyelination of the ends of an internode is observed if anelectrotonus is applied (144). The author of this review suggests therefore the following explanation of demyelination after crushing: after sealing up of the injured nerve segment, the still intact proximal segments would tend to restore the lost ionic equilibrium near the site of crushing by feeding current into the depolarized nodes. Demyelination would be strongest where the strongest anelectrotonus is to be expected, i.e., at the nodes which are adjacent to the crushed portion. This is actually observed by Lubinska (124).

During Wallerian degeneration the water-soluble hexosamine fraction within the myelin increases between the fourth and tenth day after transection (209). Retrograde degeneration of spinal ganglia of the rat has been extensively studied by electron microscopy (5).

Acetylcholinesterase activity decreases along peripheral nerves of dogs, the terminal part having only 60 to 70 per cent of the activity measured in proximal segments (125, 126). Nerve section gives a reduced activity in the most proximal segments and accumulation of the enzyme proximal to the site of section. Crushing of sciatic nerves of rats, rabbits, and dogs leads to an accumulation of the enzyme on both sides, proximal and distal from the site of crushing. If two crushes are applied far enough apart from each other, there will be four zones of accumulation. These findings are interpreted in terms of bidirectional flow of axoplasm (214) (see also comments under heading "Movement of Axoplasmic Contents along the Axon").

STRUCTURE

Boyd has written an excellent review on the structure and innervation of the nuclear-bag muscle fiber system and the nuclear-chain muscle fiber system in mammalian muscle spindles (19).

The perineurium rather than the epineurium must be considered as difiusion barrier according to recent electron-microscope studies on rat sciatic nerves (160). Excellent electron micrographs of the fine structure of rat spinal ganglia have been published (4).

There is new anatomohistological evidence for a great number of C fibers contained in the carotid nerve ranging from 0.1 to 0.3 μ diam besides a smaller number of myelinated fibers from 1 to 9 μ diam. Electrophysiological investigations distinguish between two groups of C fibers, one originating from the superior cervical ganglion, the other one probably from the intracranium (64).

Human vocal muscles possess spiral nerve endings, probably mechanoreceptors, similar to the spiral endings in extrinsic eye muscles (162). Vocal muscle fibers frequently have multiple innervation, i.e., two to five end-plates which are usually innervated by the same motor fiber. This type of innervation is believed to facilitate rapid over-all contraction of one fiber (161).

STRUCTURE AND BIOCHEMISTRY OF MYELIN

Histochemical investigations on neurokeratine network of dog-, cat-, and rat-myelinated fibers show that adenosine triphosphatase, 5-nucleotidase, creatinephosphatase, and other phosphatases are localized in the faces of hexagonal prisms in the myelin sheath of the nerve fiber. The prisms have a diameter of 1 to 2 μ and extend radially from the axon to the neurilemmal sheath. The faces of the prisms are believed to be important for the passage of sodium, potassium, or chloride, having the necessary metabolic equipment to facilitate it (199). Peripheral nerve neurokeratin can be isolated virtually free of collagen and mucopolysaccharides. Protein-bound tryptophan is only present in myelin, not in the axis cylinder. The tryptophan containing protein is resistant to trypsin digestion. White matter contains more than three times the proteolipid and neurokeratin of spinal roots. This may be explained by admitting another myelin protein, which is not tryspin resistant. There is, however, no evidence for this suggestion yet (208). Mipafox (bismonoisopropylaminofluorophosphine oxide), a potent cholinesterase inhibitor, is known to produce a peripheral neuropathy in man. In rats and hens a similar neuropathy develops with concomitant depression of the sciatic nerve indicating a subtotal degeneration of the nerves. No evidence is found that Mipafox is a specific myelin poison, as postulated by others. It is rather thought to exert its action through a primary central lesion (133). Just before the formation of myelin in human white matter starts, there is a sudden increase in the number of glial cells and an increase of dinitrophenol diaphorase activity in them. After myelination, thick fibers of the white matter contain more enzyme than the glial cells, thin fibers much less than the glial cells. A strong enzyme reaction in the axon is always accompanied by small glial activity and vice versa (72). Extracts from cerebral white matter contain a complex of polysaccharide, cerebroside, cholesterol phospholipid, and protein. This complex cannot be found in peripheral-nerve myelin (210).

MISCELLANEOUS

General aspects of neurophysiology have been reviewed by Lüttgau (130), ionic mechanisms in electrogenesis by Grundfest (86), mammalian nonmyelinated nerve fibers by Douglas & Ritchie (44), and modes of operation of electric organs by Bennett (12).

Electrophysiological properties of glia and Schwann cells.—Neurons and neuroglia of young cat and rat, grown in tissue culture, are accessible to intracellular electrophysiological investigation. The neurons fire spontaneously. Somata and dendrites are found to be excitable and capable of producing all-or-none responses. Neuroglia is shown to have a potassium-dependent resting potential, a membrane resistance of about 10 ohm cm², and even an "electric response" accompanied by an impedance reduction of 3 to 5 sec duration (94). It is important to note that such behavior cannot be found in fibroblasts and macrophages and that some of the glial cells undergo contraction in response to an electrical stimulus. There is, however, no discrete threshold and no all-or-none response in glia. Schwann cells of the giant squid fiber of *Sepioteuthis sepioidea* which are unusually thick (2 to 5 μ) are shown to have a membrane potential of their own, being independent of the actual axonal membrane potential. Proof of this is given by simultaneous impalement with three microelectrodes, 100 to 150 μ apart, one in the Schwann cell and two in the axon. The axonal membrane potential can be shifted at will by feeding current into one of the axonal electrodes without changing the Schwann cell potential of about −40 mv inside at all. This suggests that currents applied to the axon find a pathway around the Schwann cells, without traversing them, and that the axolemma is the actual site of the membrane-potential difference of squid axons. Had the polarizing current passed through the Schwann cells, a considerable asymmetry of their potential should have occurred. It is thus probable that the Schwann cell potential is not recorded in series with the axonal potential and that each one can be recorded independently. No data concerning the electrical characteristics of the Schwann cell membranes have been published (201).

Decremental conduction.—Decremental conduction is once more advocated by Lorente de Nó (122). It seems to occur, as one would expect, only when graded responses are observed, caused by unphysiological substituents for sodium. Another possibility for decremental conduction is a gradient of excitability, established by unequal treatment of the impulse-conducting stretch with such substituents or other agents, mechanical pressure, etc. In physiological situations, however, it is unlikely to occur.

Back response.—Synchronous volleys of motor fibers produce a powerful synchronous muscle fiber activity which in turn excites terminal ramifications of the fibers, producing a "back response". This response is shown to be a "physiological artifact" which will never occur with the less synchronized normal motor impulses. The possibility of a "back response" and its tetanizing effect on the muscle contraction has to be kept in mind if one measures contraction amplitudes as a function of stimulus intensity (22).

Role of acetylcholine in the nervous system.—Bioelectrogenesis and the possible role of acetylcholine are reviewed by Nachmansohn (147). Neurohumoral functions of acetylcholine are extensively reviewed by Koelle, particularly with respect to a possible participation of acetylcholine in sensory reception (118). There are still doubts that the so-called acetylcholine "receptor" protein isolated from electric tissue of the electric eel, shown to bind curare, acetylcholine, and related compounds, is actually the molecule responsible for physiological action of these substances in the electroplax or anywhere else (60).

Tissue culture of anterior horn cells.—Anterior horn cells of the guinea pig spinal cord have been successfully maintained in tissue culture for use in investigations on neurotropic diseases (204).

Local anesthetics.—The influence of local anesthetics on C fiber potentials of rabbits, measured with the sucrose-gap method, was studied in dependence of pH. The cationic form is found to be the active one for blocking impulse conduction, because an increase of the pH in the perfusing solution after pretreatment of the fibers with the anesthetic unblocks, and going back to normal pH blocks, conduction again (157). The question whether it is the undissociated base or the cation which exerts the anesthetic action is also reviewed by Skou (177) with special reference to results obtained with frog skin, where both the undissociated base and the cationic form have easily distinguishable actions. The concentration of local anesthetics necessary to block myelinated fibers of cat spinal roots is higher for large than for small fibers. Small myelinated fibers are also blocked when the minimum concentration for blocking all nonmyelinated fibers is applied, but still lower concentrations will only block small myelinated fibers without blocking the nonmyelinated ones (148).

Nerve endings, autonomic nervous system.—By means of microelectrode impalements in sympathetically innervated smooth muscle fibers such as the isolated vas deferens of the guinea pig, it has been possible to record spontaneous potentials, similar to miniature end-plate potentials (25), and to analyze their origin pharmacologically (26). The conclusion is that like the slow muscle fibers of the frog these smooth muscle fibers are activated by a compound discharge of many small potentials and that norepinephrine is the transmitter, released spontaneously and with better synchronization in response to nerve stimulation.

Receptors.—Pacinian corpuscles from the cat's mesentery are found to have a double innervation. There is a C fiber which can be traced by histological and electrophysiological means, responding only when the stimulus strength is raised by a factor of 3 to 6 above threshold of the large A fiber (121). The nonmyelinated end of this large fiber has been found to conduct impulses both in response to above-threshold mechanical stimulation and to antidromic stimulation (106).

LITERATURE CITED

Books

The following books of interest have been published during the period covered by this review:

Bioelectrogenesis, Proc. Symp. Comp. Bio-electrogenesis (Chagas, C., and Paes de Carvalho, A., Eds., Elsevier, Amsterdam, XVI+414 pp., 1961)

Membrane Transport and Metabolism, Proc. Symp. Prague (Kleinzeller, A. and Kotyk, A., Eds., Academic, London and New York, 608 pp., 1961)

Nervous Inhibitions, Proc. Intern. Symp. (Florey, E., Ed., Pergamon, Oxford, XV+475 pp., 1961)

Proc. Intern. Union Physiol. Sci., 22nd Intern. Congr., Leiden, 1962 (Duyff, J. W., Ed., **I**, *Lectures and Symposia*, Part I, 484 pp., Part II, 940 pp., **II**, *Abstr. Free Commun., Films Demonstrations*, 1254 Abstr., Intern. Congr. Ser. No. 47 and No. 48, Excerpta Med. Found., Amsterdam, 1962)

Symp. Muscle Receptors (Barker, D., Ed., Hong Kong Univ. Press, 293 pp., 1961)

The Visual System, Neurophysiology and Psychophysics, Sym. Freiburg/Br. (Jung, R., and Kornhuber, H., Eds., Springer, Berlin, 524 pp., 1961)

Journals

1. Adelman, W. J., and Moore, J. W., *J. Gen. Physiol.*, **45**, 93–103 (1961)
2. Adrian, R. H., *J. Physiol.* (*London*), **133**, 631–58 (1956)
3. Adrian, R. H., *J. Physiol.* (*London*), **156**, 623–32 (1961)
4. Andres, K. H., *Z. Zellforsch.*, **55**, 1–48 (1961)
5. Andres, K. H., *Z. Zellforsch.*, **55**, 49–79 (1961)
6. Araki, T., Ito, M., and Oscarsson, O., *J. Physiol.* (*London*), **159**, 410–35 (1961)
7. Araki, T., Ito, M., and Oshima, T., *Nature*, **191**, 1104–5 (1961)
8. Baker, P. F., Hodgkin, A. L., and Shaw, T. I., *Nature*, **190**, 885–87 (1961)
9. Baker, P. F., Hodgkin, A. L., and Shaw, T. I., *J. Physiol.* (*London*), **157**, 25 P (1961)
10. Baker, P. F., Hodgkin, A. L., and Shaw, T. I., *Proc. Intern. Union Physiol. Sci., 22nd Intern. Congr. Leiden, 1962*, **I**, Part II, 559–60 (Excerpta Med. Found., Amsterdam, 1962)
11. Balk, O., and Müller-Mohnssen, H., *Naturwissenschaften*, **49**, 303–4 (1962)
12. Bennett, M. V. L., *Ann. N. Y. Acad. Sci.*, **94**, 458–509 (1961)
13. Berger, W., *Proc. Intern. Union. Physiol. Sci. 22nd, Intern. Congr., Leiden, 1962*, **II**, Abstr. No. 872 (Excerpta Med. Found., Amsterdam, 1962)
14. Bishop, P. O., and Davis, R., *J. Physiol.* (*London*), **154**, 514–46 (1960)
15. Böhm, H. W., and Straub, R. W., *Arch. Ges. Physiol.*, **274**, 28–29 (1961)
16. Böhm, H. W., and Straub, R. W., *Arch. Ges. Physiol.*, **274**, 468–79 (1962)
17. Bonting, S. L., and Caravaggio, L. L., *Nature*, **194**, 1180–81 (1962)
18. Borovyagin, V. L., *Doklady Akad. Nauk SSSR*, **133**, 214–17 (1960)*
19. Boyd, I. A., *Phil. Trans. Roy. Soc. London, B*, **245**, 81–136 (1962)
20. Brady, R. O., Spyropoulos, C. S., and Tasaki, I., *Am. J. Physiol.*, **194**, 207–13 (1958)
21. Brink, F., *Pharmacol. Rev.*, **6**, 243–98 (1954)
22. Brown, M. C., and Matthews, P. B. C., *J. Physiol.* (*London*), **150**, 332–46 (1960)
23. Bülbring, E., and Whitteridge, D., *J. Physiol.* (*London*), **99**, 201–7 (1941)
24. Burke, W., and Stämpfli, R. (Unpublished observations)
25. Burnstock, G., and Holman, M. E., *J. Physiol.* (*London*), **160**, 446–60 (1962)
26. Burnstock, G., and Holman, M. E., *J. Physiol.* (*London*), **160**, 461–69 (1962)
27. Caldwell, P. C., and Keynes, R. D., *J, Physiol.* (*London*), **154**, 177–89 (1960)
28. Carpenter, D., Engberg, I., and Lundberg, A., *Experientia*, **18**, 450–51 (1962)
29. Carpenter, F. G., *Am. J. Physiol.*, **202**, 845–48 (1962)
30. Chandler, W. K., Fitzhugh, R., and Cole, K. S., *Biophys. J.*, **2**, 105–27 (1962)
31. Cheng, S. C., *J. Neurochem.*, **7**, 271–77 (1961)
32. Cheng, S. C., *J. Neurochem.*, **7**, 278–88 (1961)
33. Cheng, S. C., *Nature*, **193**, 691–92 (1962)

34. Connelly, C. M., *Rev. Med. Phys.*, **31**, 475–86 (1959)

35. Coombs, J. S., Eccles, J. C., and Fatt, P., *J. Physiol. (London)*, **130**, 326–73 (1955)

36. Creutzfeldt, O. D., Fromm, G. H., and Kapp, H., *Exptl. Neurol.*, **5**, 436–51 (1962)

37. Curtis, D. R., *Nervous Inhibitions, Proc. Intern. Symp.*, 342–49 (Pergamon, Oxford, 1961)

38. Curtis, D. R., Phillis, J. W., and Watkins, J. C., *J. Physiol. (London)*, **158**, 296–323 (1961)

39. Dahl, N. A., Samson, F. E., and Balfour, W. M., *Federation Proc.*, **21**, 363 (1962)

40. Dalton, J. C., and Hendrix, D. E., *Am. J. Physiol.*, **202**, 491–94 (1962)

41. Del Castillo, J., and Katz, B., *Proc. Roy. Soc. (London)*, *B*, **146**, 339–56 (1957)

42. Dettbarn, W. D., *Bioelectrogenesis, Proc. Symp. Comp. Bioelectrogenesis*, 262–87 (Elsevier, Amsterdam, 1961)

43. Dodge, F. A., Jr., *Biophysics of Physiological and Pharmacological Actions*, 119–43 (Am. Assoc. Advan. Sci., Washington, D.C., 1961)

44. Douglas, W. W., and Ritchie, J. M., *Physiol. Rev.*, **42**, 297–334 (1962)

45. Dudel, J., *Arch. Ges. Physiol.*, **274**, 30 (1961)

46. Eccles, J. C., *Bioelectrogenesis, Proc. Symp. Comp. Bioelectrogenesis*, 297–309 (Elsevier, Amsterdam, 1961)

47. Eccles, J. C., *Ergeb. Physiol., Biol. Chem., Exptl. Pharmakol.*, **51**, 299–430 (1961)

48. Eccles, J. C., *Nervous Inhibitions, Proc. Intern. Symp.*, 47–60 (Pergamon, Oxford, 1961)

49. Eccles, J. C., *Nervous Inhibitions, Proc. Intern. Symp.*, 71–86 (Pergamon, Oxford, 1961)

50. Eccles, J. C., *Exptl. Neurol.*, **4**, 1–22 (1961)

51. Eccles, J. C., Eccles, R. M., Iggo, A., and Ito, M., *J. Physiol. (London)*, **159**, 479–99 (1961)

52. Eccles, J. C., Eccles, R. M., Iggo, A., and Lundberg, A., *J. Physiol. (London)*, **159**, 461–78 (1961)

53. Eccles, J. C., Eccles, R. M., and Magni, F., *J. Physiol. (London)*, **159**, 147–66 (1961)

54. Eccles, J. C., Hubbard, J. I., and Oscarsson, O., *J. Physiol. (London)*, **158**, 486–516 (1961)

55. Eccles, J. C., Kostyuk, P. G., and Schmidt, R. F., *J. Physiol. (London)* (In press)

56. Eccles, J. C., Kozak, W., and Magni, F., *J. Physiol. (London)*, **159**, 128–46 (1961)

57. Eccles, J. C., Magni, F., and Willis, W. D., *J. Physiol. (London)*, **160**, 62–93 (1962)

58. Eccles, J. C., Oscarsson, O., and Willis, W. D., *J. Physiol. (London)*, **158**, 517–43 (1961)

59. Eccles, R. M., and Libet, B., *J. Physiol. (London)*, **157**, 484–503 (161)

60. Ehrenpreis, S., *Bioelectrogenesis, Proc. Symp. Comp. Bioelectrogenesis*, 379–96 (Elsevier, Amsterdam, 1961)

61. Eide, E., Lundberg, A., and Voorhoeve, P., *Acta Physiol. Scand.*, **53**, 185–95 (1961)

62. Erickson, R. P., King, R. L., and Pfaffmann, C., *J. Neurophysiol.*, **24**, 621–32 (1961)

63. Eyzaguirre, C., *Nervous Inhibitions, Proc. Intern. Symp.*, 285–317 (Pergamon, Oxford, 1961)

64. Eyzaguirre, C., and Uchizono, K., *J. Physiol. (London)*, 268–81 (1961)

65. Fitzhugh, R., *Biophys. J.*, **1**, 445–66 (1961)

66. Fitzhugh, R., *Biophys. J.*, **2**, 11–21 (1962)

67. Frank, K., *IRE (Inst. Radio Engrs.) Trans. Med. Electron. ME*, **6**, 85–88 (1959)

68. Frank, K., and Fuortes, M. G. F., *Federation Proc.*, **16**, 39–40 (1957)

69. Frankenhaeuser, B., *J. Physiol. (London)*, **160**, 40–45 (1962)

70. Frankenhaeuser, B., *J. Physiol. (London)*, **160**, 46–53 (1962)

71. Frankenhaeuser, B., *J. Physiol. (London)*, **160**, 54–61 (1962)

72. Friede, R. L., *J. Neurochem.*, **8**, 17–30 (1961)

73. Fukami, T., *Japan. J. Physiol.*, **11**, 596–604 (1961)

74. George, E. P., and Johnson, E. A., *Nature*, **194**, 874–75 (1962)

75. George, E. P., and Johnson, E. A. (Private communication)

76. Gerebtzoff, M. A., *Arch Intern. Physiol. Biochim.*, **70**, 418–20 (1962)

77. Goffart, M., and Holmes, O., *J. Physiol. (London)*, **162**, 18–19P (1962)

78. Goldman, D. E., *J. Gen. Physiol.*, **27**, 37–60 (1943)

79. Goldman, D. E., *Proc. Intern. Union Physiol. Sci., 22nd Intern. Congr., Leiden, 1962*, **I**, Part II, 583–85

(Excerpta Med. Found., Amsterdam, 1962)

80. Gordon, G., Landgren, S., and Seed, W. A., *J. Physiol. (London)*, **158**, 544-59 (1961)

81. Granit, R., and Renkin, B., *J. Physiol. (London)*, **158**, 461-75 (1961)

82. Gray, E. G., *Nature*, **193**, 82 (1962)

83. Greengard, P., and Straub, R. W., *J. Physiol. (London)*, **161**, 414-23 (1962)

84. Grundfest, H., *Biophysics of Physiological and Pharmacological Actions*, 329-89 (Am. Assoc. Advan. Sci., Washington, D. C., 1961)

85. Grundfest, H., *Nervous Inhibitions*, *Proc. Intern. Symp.*, 326-41 (Pergamon, Oxford, 1961)

86. Grundfest, H., *Ann. N. Y. Acad. Sci.*, **94**, 405-57 (1961)

87. Grundfest, H., *Properties of Membranes and Diseases of the Nervous System*, 71-102 (Springer Publ. Co., New York, 1962)

88. Haase, J., and Meulen, J. P. van, *Arch. Ges. Physiol.*, **274**, 272-80 (1961)

89. Hagiwara, S., and Morita, H., *Federation Proc.*, **21**, 361 (1962)

90. Harreveld, A. van, *Federation Proc.*, **21**, 659-64 (1962)

91. Heene, R., *Arch. Ges. Physiol.*, **274**, 27 (1961)

92. Heene, R., *Arch. Ges. Physiol.*, **275**, 1-11 (1962)

93. Henatsch, H. D., Langrehr, D., Schulte, F. J., and Kaese, H. J., *Arch. Ges. Physiol.*, **274**, 511-27 (1962)

94. Hild, W., and Tasaki, I., *J. Neurophysiol.*, **25**, 277-304 (1962)

95. Hinke, J. A. M., *J. Physiol. (London)*, **156**, 314-35 (1961)

96. Hodgkin, A. L., and Huxley, A. F., *J. Physiol. (London)*, **117**, 500-44 (1952)

97. Holmes, O., *Arch. Intern. Physiol. Biochim.*, **69**, 397-400 (1962)

98. Holmes, O., *Arch. Intern. Physiol. Biochim.*, **70**, 211-45 (1962)

99. Homquist, B., *Acta Physiol. Scand.*, **52**, Suppl. 181 (1961)

100. Holmquist, B., and Lundberg, A., *Acta Physiol. Scand.*, **54**, Suppl. 186 (1961)

101. Horowicz, P., and Larrabee, M. G., *J. Neurochem.*, **9**, 1-21 (1962)

102. Hubbard, J. I., *J. Physiol. (London)*, **159**, 507-17 (1961)

103. Hubbard, J. I., and Willis, W. D., *Nature*, **193**, 1294-95 (1962)

104. Hughes, G. M., and Tauc, L., *Nature*, **191**, 404-5 (1961)

105. Hughes, G. M., and Tauc, L., *J. Exptl. Biol.*, **39**, 45-69 (1962)

106. Hunt, C. C., and Takeuchi, A., *J. Physiol. (London)*, **160**, 1-21 (1962)

107. Hurlbut, W. P., *Biophysics of Physiological and Pharmacological Actions*, 97-118 (Am. Assoc. Advan. Sci., Washington, D. C., 1961)

108. Julian, F. J., Moore, J. W., and Goldman, D. E., *J. Gen. Physiol.*, **45**, 1195-216 (1962)

109. Julian, F. J., Moore, J. W., and Goldman, D. E., *J. Gen. Physiol.*, **45**, 1217-38 (1962)

110. Katz, B., *Proc. Roy. Soc. (London), B*, **155**, 455-77 (1962)

111. Keynes, R. D., *J. Physiol. (London)*, **114**, 119-50 (1951)

112. Keynes, R. D., *Symp. Membrane Transport and Metabolism*, 131-39 (Czech. Acad. Sci. Prague, 1961)

113. Keynes, R. D., *Proc. Intern. Union Physiol. Sci.*, *22nd Intern. Congr.*, *Leiden, 1962*, **I**, Part II, 563-64 (Excerpta Med. Found., Amsterdam, 1962)

114. Keynes, R. D., and Lewis, P. R., *J. Physiol. (London)*, **114**, 151-82 (1951)

115. Kidd, M., *J. Anat.*, **96**, 179-87 (1962)

116. Kitamura, S., *Japan. J. Physiol.*, **11**, 410-18 (1961)

117. Kitamura, S., *Japan. J. Physiol.*, **11**, 419-26 (1961)

118. Koelle, G. B., *J. Pharm. Pharmacol.*, **14**, 65-90 (1962)

119. König, K., *Arch. Ges. Physiol.*, **275**, 452-60 (1962)

120. Kubota, K., and Brookhart, J. M., *Federation Proc.*, **21**, 361 (1962)

121. Loewenstein, W. R., Goto, K., and Noback, C., *Experientia*, **18**, 460 (1962)

122. Lorente de Nó, R., *Bioelectrogenesis*, *Proc. Symp. Comp. Bioelectrogenesis*, 229-36 (Elsevier, Amsterdam, 1961)

123. Lubinska, L., *Nature*, **181**, 957-58 (1958)

124. Lubinska, L., *Exptl. Cell Res.*, Suppl. 8, 74-90 (1961)

125. Lubinska, L., Niemierko, S., and Oderfeld, B., *Nature*, **189**, 122-23 (1961)

126. Lubinska, L., Niemierko, S., Oderfeld, B., and Szwarc, L., *Science*, **135**, 368-70 (1962)

127. Lüttgau, H. C., *Arch. Ges. Physiol.*, **271**, 613-33 (1960)

128. Lüttgau, H. C., *Arch. Ges. Physiol.*, **272**, 67-68 (1960)

129. Lüttgau, H. C., *Arch. Ges. Physiol.*, **273**, 302–10 (196

130. Lüttgau, H. C., *Fortschr. Zool.*, **15**, 92–124 (1961)

131. Lundberg, A., and Oscarsson, O., *Acta Physiol. Scand.*, **54**, 270–86 (1962)

132. Lundberg, A., and Voorhoeve, P. E., *Experientia*, **17**, 46–47 (1961)

133. Majno, G., and Karnovsky, M. L., *J. Neurochem.*, **8**, 1–16 (1961)

134. Mauro, A., *Federation Proc.*, **13**, 96 (1954)

135. McGeer, E. G., McGeer, P. L., and McLennan, H., *J. Neurochem.*, **8**, 36–49 (1961)

136. Meves, H., *Arch. Ges. Physiol.*, **272**, 336–59 (1961)

137. Meves, H., *Proc. Intern. Union Physiol. Sci.*, *22nd Intern. Congr.*, *Leiden*, *1962*, **I**, Part II, 581–82 (Excerpta Med. Found., Amsterdam, 1962)

138. Miani, H., *Nature*, **185**, 541 (1960)

139. Miani, H., *Nature*, **193**, 887–88 (1962)

140. Moore, J. W., and Adelman, W. J., *J. Gen. Physiol.*, **45**, 77–92 (1961)

141. Mueller, P., *J. Gen. Physiol.*, **42**, 137–62 (1958)

142. Mueller, P., *J. Gen. Physiol.*, **42**, 163–91 (1958)

143. Mueller, P., Rudin, D. O., Tien, H. T., and Wescott, W. C., *Nature*, **194**, 979–80 (1962)

144. Müller-Mohnssen, H., *Z. Zellforsch.*, **54**, 468–98 (1961)

145. Mullins, L. J., *Ann. N. Y. Acad. Sci.*, **94**, 390–404 (1961)

146. Mullins, L. J., Adelman, W. J., and Sjodin, R. A., *Biophys. J.*, **2**, 257–74 (1962)

147. Nachmansohn, D., *Bioelectrogenesis*, *Proc. Symp. Comp. Bioelectrogenesis*, 237–61 (Elsevier, Amsterdam, 1961)

148. Nathan, P. W., and Sears, T. A., *J. Physiol. (London)*, **157**, 565–80 (1961)

149. Neher, G., and Stämpfli, R., *J. Physiol. (Paris)*, **51**, 544–45 (1959)

150. Noble, D., *J. Physiol. (London)*, **160**, 317–52 (1962)

151. Noble, D., *Proc. Intern. Union Physiol. Sci.*, *22nd Intern. Congr.*, *Leiden*, *1962*, **I**, Part I, 177–82 (1962)

152. Ochs, S., Dalrymple, D., and Richards, G., *Exptl. Neurol.*, **5**, 349–63 (1962)

153. Oikawa, T., Spyropoulos, C. S., Tasaki, I., and Teorell, T., *Acta Physiol. Scand.*, **52**, 195–96 (1961)

154. Ooyama, H., and Wright, E. B., *Am. J. Physiol.*, **197**, 1247–54 (1959)

155. Ooyama, H., and Wright, E. B., *J. Neurophysiol.*, **25**, 67–93 (1962)

156. Reuben, J. P., Werman, R., and Grundfest, H., *J. Gen. Physiol.*, **45**, 243–65 (1961)

157. Ritchie, J. M., and Greengard, P., *J. Pharmacol. Exptl. Therap.*, **133**, 241–45 (1961)

158. Ritchie, J. M., and Straub, R. W., *J. Physiol. (London)*, **136**, 80–97 (1957)

159. Robertson, J. D., *Progr. Biophys. Biophys. Chem.*, **10**, 343–418 (1960)

160. Röhlich, P., and Knoop, A., *Z. Zellforsch.*, **53**, 299–312 (1961)

161. Rudolph, G., *Experientia*, **16**, 551–53 (1960)

162. Rudolph, G., *Nature*, **190**, 726–27 (1961)

163. Sasaki, K., and Otani, T., *Japan. J. Physiol.*, **11**, 443–56 (1961)

164. Schadé, J. P., and Harreveld, A. van, *J. Comp. Neurol.*, **117**, 387–98 (1961)

165. Schmidt, H., *Arch. Ges. Physiol.*, **274**, 632–41 (1952)

166. Schmidt, H., *Proc. Intern. Union Physiol. Sci.*, *22nd Intern. Congr.*, *Leiden*, *1962*, **II**, Abstr. 775 (Excerpta Med. Found., Amsterdam, 1962)

167. Schmidt, H., cited in Stämpfli, R., *Proc. Intern. Union Physiol. Sci.*, *22nd Intern. Congr.*, *Leiden*, *1962*, **I**, Part II, 574–76 (Excerpta Med. Found., Amsterdam, 1962)

168. Schmidt, H. (Unpublished observations)

169. Shanes, A. M., *Proc. Intern. Union Physiol. Sci.*, *22nd Intern. Congr.*, *Leiden*, *1962*, **I**, Part I, 93–102 (Excerpta Med. Found., Amsterdam, 1962)

170. Shanes, A. M., *Proc. Intern. Union Physiol. Sci.*, *22nd Intern. Congr.*, *Leiden*, *1962*, **I**, Part II, 586–87 (Excerpta Med. Found., Amsterdam, 1962)

171. Shanes, A. M., and Berman, M. D., *J. Gen. Physiol.*, **39**, 279–300 (1955)

172. Shapiro, H., *J. Cellular Comp. Physiol.*, **59**, 15–30 (1962)

173. Shaw, T. I., *Proc. Intern. Union Physiol. Sci.*, *22nd Intern. Congr.*, *Leiden*, *1962*, **I**, Part I, 103–5 (Excerpta Med. Found., Amsterdam, 1962)

174. Skoglund, C. R., *Acta Physiol. Scand.*, **51**, 142–49 (1961)

175. Skou, J. C., *Biochim. Biophys. Acta*, 23, 394–401 (1957)
176. Skou, J. C., *Biochim. Biophys. Acta*, 42, 6–23 (1960)
177. Skou, J. C., *J. Pharm. Pharmacol.*, 13, 204–17 (1961)
178. Stämpfli, R., *Experientia*, 10, 508–9 (1954)
179. Stämpfli, R., *Helv. Physiol. Pharmacol. Acta*, 16, 127–45 (1958)
180. Stämpfli, R., *Ann. N. Y. Acad. Sci.*, 81, 265–84 (1959)
181. Stämpfli, R., *Actualités Neurophysiol.*, 64 (Masson, Paris, 1959)
182. Stämpfli, R., *Proc. Intern. Union Physiol. Sci.*, *22nd Intern. Congr.*, *Leiden*, *1962*, II, Abstr. No. 871 (Excerpta Med. Found., Amsterdam, 1962)
183. Stämpfli, R., *Proc. Intern. Union Physiol. Sci.*, *22nd Intern. Congr.*, *Leiden*, *1962*, I, Part II, 574–76 (Excerpta Med. Found., Amsterdam, 1962)
184. Steinbach, H. B., *J. Cellular Comp. Physiol.*, 17, 57–64 (1941)
185. Straub, R. W., *J. Physiol. (London)*, 159, 19–20P (1961)
186. Tasaki, I., *J. Physiol. (London)*, 148, 306–31 (1959)
187. Tasaki, I., *Properties of Membranes and Diseases of the Nervous System*, 100–2 (Springer Publ. Co., New York, 1962)
188. Tasaki, I., *Proc. Intern. Union Physiol. Sci.*, *22nd Intern. Congr.*, *Leiden*, *1962*, I, Part II, 588–89 (Excerpta Med. Found., Amsterdam, 1962)
189. Tasaki, I., and Hagiwara, S., *J. Gen. Physiol.*, 40, 859–85 (1957)
190. Tasaki, I., and Spyropoulos, C. S., *Am. J. Physiol.*, 193, 318–27 (1958)
191. Tasaki, I., Teorell, T., and Spyropoulos, C. S., *Am. J. Physiol.*, 200, 203–8 (1961)
192. Tasaki, I., Watanabe, A., and Takenaka, T., *Proc. Natl. Acad. Sci. US*, 48, 1177–84 (1962)
193. Tauc, L., and Gerschenfeld, H. M., *Nature*, 192, 366–67 (1961)
194. Tauc, L., and Gerschenfeld, H. M., *J. Neurophysiol.*, 25, 236–62 (1962)
195. Teorell, T., *Arkiv Kemi*, 18, 401–8 (1961)
196. Teorell, T., *Acta Physiol. Scand.*, 53, 1–6 (1961)
197. Teorell, T., *Biophys. J.*, 2, Suppl., 27–52 (1962)
198. Terzuolo, C. A., and Edwards, C., *Ann. Rev. Physiol.*, 24, 325–56 (1962)
199. Tewari, H. B., and Bourne, G. H., *Bibl. Anat.*, 2, 111–27 (1961)
200. Tomita, T., Saimi, T., and Toida, N., *Nature*, 190, 271–72 (1961)
201. Villegas, R., Gimenez, M., and Villegas, L., *Biochim. Biophys. Acta*, 62, 610–12 (1962)
202. Villegas, R., and Villegas, G. M., *Biochim. Biophys. Acta*, 60, 202–4 (1962)
203. Wall, P. D., *J. Physiol. (London)*, 142, 1–21 (1958)
204. Walsh, J. W., *Federation Proc.*, 21, 362 (1962)
205. Watanabe, A., and Grundfest, H., *J. Gen. Physiol.*, 45, 267–308 (1961)
206. Wilbrandt, W., and Rosenberg, T., *Pharmacol. Rev.*, 13, 109–83 (1961)
207. Wilson, V. J., Talbot, W. H., and Diecke, F. P. J., *J. Neurophysiol.*, 23, 144–53 (1960)
208. Wolfgram, F., and Rose, A. S., *J. Neurochem.*, 8, 161–68 (1961)
209. Wolman, M., *Chemical Pathology of the Nervous System*, 254–60 (Pergamon, Oxford, 1961)
210. Wolman, M., *J. Neurochem.*, 9, 59–62 (1962)
211. Wright, E. B., and Ooyama, H., *J. Neurophysiol.*, 25, 94–109 (1962)
212. Wright, E. B., and Tomita, T., *Am. J. Physiol.*, 202, 856–64 (1962)
213. Yamada, M., and Sakada, S., *Japan. J. Physiol.*, 11, 378–84 (1961)
214. Zelená, J., and Lubinska, L., *Physiol. Bohemoslov.*, 11, 261–68 (1962)

* English translation will be announced in *Technical Translations*, issued by the Office of Technical Services, U. S. Department of Commerce, and will be made available by the Photoduplication Service, Library of Congress, and by the SLA Translation Center at the John Crerar Library, Chicago, Illinois.

COMPARATIVE PHYSIOLOGY: INTEGRATIVE ACTION OF THE NERVOUS SYSTEM[1]

By G. Adrian Horridge

The Gatty Marine Laboratory, St. Andrews, Scotland

INTRODUCTION

Scope.—This review considers the main trends, outstanding themes, and lines of exploitation of the past decade in a rapidly expanding, diversely radiating, and technically complex area. Emphasis will be upon the results of analysis of neurons and ganglia as organs of co-ordination, mainly of movements, and as organs of integration of sensory stimuli. Mechanisms of excitation of nerve, stimulation of sense organs, theories of conduction, and properties of neuron membranes are considered to be out of range in the direction of biophysics. The emphasis is upon accounts of behavior in terms of neuron activity; therefore, chemical, secretory, and growth mechanisms which may underlie the slower aspects of control by central nervous systems are not considered. These limitations are similar to those of a much larger review now in press (1). Effort has been concentrated on the invertebrates, because recent reviews on vertebrate material are available. There are the reviews on the physiology of synapses (2, 3), on general integrative action of the central nervous system in vertebrates (4), on cortex (5, 6, 7), on cerebellum (8), on vision (9), and a variety of important articles in the *Handbook of Physiology* (10). Also relevant are the as yet unpublished proceedings of R. W. Gerard's special meetings at the 1962 International Congress at Leiden. Accounts of nervous co-ordination in some groups of invertebrates, Crustacea (11, especially Vol. 2), and cephalopods (12) are available.

This review is not intended for the few tens of individuals who are actively engaged on the more intricate aspects of the subject, but for the few thousands who wish to see general trends over the past decade.

Progress in the subject.—Two bandwagons have carried most of the performers. One has been the exploitation of new electronic techniques which became available in the 1950's, the other has been the discovery and analysis of certain favorable preparations by a variety of appropriate techniques. The generalities and over-all concepts have sometimes, as in the case of the discovery and analysis of excitatory and inhibitory postsynaptic potentials, depended on surprisingly few and highly specialized preparations and have sometimes, as in the case of the distinction between central and peripheral control of locomotory movements, been allowed to accrue haphazardly by many diverse and initially unrelated observations. The chief physiological techniques have been the use of intracellular microelectrodes on preparations with few large cells, the isolation of units in ganglia recording with extra-

[1] The survey of literature pertaining to this review was completed in May 1962.

cellular microelectrodes (13), and the teasing out of axons and small bundles from central connectives of crustaceans (14). The outstanding new preparations for internal recording have been the stretch receptor sensory cells of crustacean abdomens (15, 16, 17), the visceral ganglia of the mollusc *Aplysia* [mainly in a series by Tauc (18 to 21) and others (22, 23)], the giant fibers of annelids (24) and arthropods and their synapses (25), and the crustacean heart ganglion [Hagiwara (26)]. These are relatively simple preparations which have been partly described by anatomists using specific stains; they have large fibers or cells, and are the most convenient preparations for analysis. They yield information at the most detailed level about synaptic potentials.

It is important to note that complex central ganglia with many small cells and fibers have produced no new phenomena which might be correlated with complexity. Optic lobes of insects (27), central ganglia of one or two molluscs (23) and of several arthropods (28, 29), and heart ganglion of crustaceans (26) have been probed with microelectrodes and analysed for input-output relations; but essentially all electrophysiological results can be explained in terms of anatomy of synapses and summation of various types of synaptic potentials (3); see below. The study of input-output relations has only just begun to reveal what other types of interaction, if any, there may be (30). Long-term phenomena concerned with origin of long sequences, pattern recognition after delays in presentation, hormonal or neurosecretory control of behavior, behavioral control of neurosecretion and tropic influences, and maturation of connexions are virtually unexplored. Over the same period the finding of progressively greater complexity of integrating activity within regions of neurons has, among some students, led to a fall in interest in studies of impulse frequency in relation to information theory. It has been realized that it is more profitable to discover what actually is happening in ganglia rather than discuss the possibility of optimum systems. Transmission capability is limited by junctions, not by impulses.

The Neuronal Level

Basis of integrative action.—Integrative action of an isolated part of the nervous system is said to occur when a response is not equal to the input and, in particular, when several simultaneous or successive inputs are taken into account. Astonishingly enough there is only one level of complexity at which the process of integration can actually be provided with a mechanism. This is on regions of the membrane of single neurons. On simultaneous stimulation of neighboring areas of a neuron membrane, the responses to the two stimuli are added by virtue of the storage properties of the membrane as a capacitor, along which charge can spread with decrement to neighboring regions. Worked out for mammalian sensory dendrites (31) and for mammalian spinal neurons, the process of partial summation of neighboring stimuli on adjacent dendrites has turned up wherever postsynaptic cells or fibers have been penetrated. It is equally true for potentials aroused in receptors, or at the postsynaptic side of chemical or electrical synapses (3, 32, 33). When two or more stimuli are presented successively in time, the response of the first (or as much of it as remains, for it decays with a time constant of some milliseconds in most neurons) can be added by simple summation to later responses, again by virtue of the capacitative storage properties of the membrane. However, more commonly and of much greater interest, the response to the second or later stimuli is not necessarily the same as to the first. The effect of the first stimulus is to change the property of the membrane, a process called facilitation when the second response is abnormally great and antifacilitation when the second response is reduced as a consequence of the first. Thus, at the anterior cells of the crustacean heart ganglion, the acceleratory axons of the regulatory cardiac nerve produce facilitating postsynaptic potentials while the axon arborizations of pacemaker cells of the posterior end of the ganglion produce antifacilitating postsynaptic potentials on the same membrane (26). In this instance, at any rate, the nature of the change (over and above simple summation) depends on the identity of the presynaptic neurons as well as the responsiveness of the postsynaptic one.

Excitation and inhibition.—In the period of 1952–60, microelectrode studies on cat spinal neurons (3), crustacean muscle cells [reviewed by Hoyle (34), modified by later papers (35, 36)], crustacean stretch receptor cells (37, 38), crustacean heart ganglion cells (26), and *Aplysia* visceral ganglion cells (18 to 23), with less information from some giant fibers (3, 39) and some other neurons, particularly of giant cell bodies in the central nervous system of the puffer fish (40), led to the general agreement that there are two possible responses of the postsynaptic cell, namely, excitatory postsynaptic potentials and inhibitory postsynaptic potentials. The former are always depolarizations and tend to pull the membrane potential towards the threshold at which spikes are initiated; the latter may be depolarizations or hyperpolarizations, depending on whether the membrane potential is previously greater or less, respectively, than an equilibrium potential called the reversal potential. The stimulus from the presynaptic cell can be either chemical, from transmitter substance, or electrical, from the presynaptic action current; and either type of presynaptic stimulus can lead to excitation or inhibition (3).

Several inhibitory responses in different preparations have been shown to depend on an increase in the conductance of the membrane, and inhibition then acts on the integrating membrane by two mechanisms: (*a*) the cancelling effect of hyperpolarizing responses which pull the membrane away from spike threshold and (*b*) the clamping effect of the increased conductance of the membrane to ions so that the membrane tends to be held near the reversal potential. Summation of many short-lived excitatory and inhibitory postsynpatic potentials has come to be accepted as the normal cause of depolarization leading to initiation of impulses. But it has also been realized that the region where this summation occurs in the dendrites, or (in some vertebrate neurons, in the soma) of sensory, inter- or motoneurons, cannot itself be the region where the spikes are actually initiated because it is not repolarized after a spike. This mechanism of a generator potential with electrotonic spread remains as the principal means of generation of spikes, but grafted to it we now have a variety of other less familiar phenomena which are not so directly connected with spike initiation. These are spontaneity, long latency, direct anastomosis, presynaptic inhibition (and probably presynaptic excitation), repolarization without spikes, and existence of more than one equilibrium state of the membrane.

Spontaneity.—In its commonest form, spontaneity consists of a depolarizing drift of the membrane towards the threshold at which spikes are initiated. One region of the neuron drifts fastest and therefore becomes the pacemaker region. One neuron can have two such regions, with differing rates (26). This type of spontaneity is closely related to the generation of impulses at receptors, in which the drift towards spike initiation is driven by the pacemaker potential spreading from the sensory region (3, 30, 37). However, a spike is not always necessary for repolarization (18, 30). Less commonly, spontaneity may be seen as slow undulatory potentials, not necessarily sinewave (18); these are best known in mollusc neurons and may be related to oscillations in squid giant axons in reduced calcium solutions and to the dropping out of impulses from an otherwise regular sequence when crab axons are stimulated with direct current [discussion in (41)]. Spikes may be generated by undulatory potentials but do not necessarily appear on the peaks (18, 26, 28, 40)

Latency.—Long delay in the response of a neuron, a ganglion, or a whole animal must in part arise from the necessity of summating many excitatory postsynaptic potentials before a spike is initiated, as in numerous preparations studied, but it is by no means clear that such is always the explanation. On stimulation of a crab motor axon by constant current of about 10^{-8} amp, utilization times up to a second are encountered [references to crab axon studies in (42)]. Jellyfish ganglia show delays up to several seconds after the arrival of a sensory impulse before a motor impulse is initiated (43). Intervals between beats show signs of regulation of the interval length, apparently without intervening impulses. Intervals between bursts in examples of centrally controlled rhythms in annelids and arthropods, and especially in pacemaker cells of arthropod hearts, and even longer delays, during which the effect of a repeated stimulus accumulates over hours or even days before a threshold to a whole-animal response is reached, can provide many examples where the known time constants of synaptic potentials seem to set limitations that are thousands of times too short. The possibility has not been sufficiently explored that the long delays of these wildly differing responses may belong to the same class of phenomena as secretion.

Nonsynaptic connexions.—Direct anastomosis between nerve cells has been seen structurally in a few examples, notably *Amphioxus* atrial sensory cells, peculiar coelenterate nerve nets, neurons in Nematoda, and giant fibers to which more than one cell body contributes (1, 44). However, in many preparations there is now physiological evidence of continuity of a different kind between large neurons. Forced change of membrane potential of one neuron causes appropriate following by another cell as if a long thin nerve fibre ran directly between the two cells. This evidence is now available for crab heart neurons (26), supermedullary neurons of puffer fish (45), and central cells in leech ventral cord (Hagiwara, personal communication). Only slow changes in potential are conducted between the cells; synaptic potentials and spikes do not pass. Therefore, the structure could well serve to equilibrate membrane potentials over long periods. No function is known, but students of brain waves have long ago suggested that their potentials may arise by influences between neurons without impulses.

Presynaptic interaction.—To date presynaptic inhibition is known in few examples, but to record it at all requires special conditions so far attained in few preparations. When inhibition can be demonstrated by stimulation of presynaptic pathways without inhibitory synaptic potentials being observed at the neuron under observation, we may postulate that the inhibition occurs in remote dendrites or consists of a depression on the presynaptic side of the input to the neurons. The conclusion that the effect takes the form of a depression of presynaptic excitatory terminals must be based on considerable anatomical knowledge so that possible effects of intervening interneurons can be eliminated (3, 46). At a crustacean neuromuscular junction, the frequency of occurrence of miniature potentials is reduced by impulses in the inhibitory axon. The miniature potentials are thought to signal the release of transmitter substance in small packets from the motor (excitatory) axons, and the decrease in their frequency could be shown to be a primary effect on the rate of their inititation rather than a reduction in the responsiveness of the muscle fiber membrane (36). Other examples which may well be in the same class of phenomenon are known in mammalian spinal cord (46), in *Aplysia* visceral ganglion, and possibly commonly, though this is difficult to demonstrate (20).

Presynaptic excitation (i.e., enhancement of the excitatory power of presynaptic axon arborizations) is as yet undescribed. A site for presynaptic effects has been suggested by the finding of sequential synapses, i.e., fiber A synapsing with fiber B which in turn immediately synapses with fiber C. These occur in mammalian cortex and postretinal layers (47). They may also be typical of amacrine neurons, which could take the middle place (B above). Having no axon, amacrine cells have so far been enigmatic.

Repolarization without spike.—In records from crustacean heart ganglion cells (26) and from *Aplysia* neurons, cells that fire spontaneously perform a saw-tooth oscillation in which each upward wave is terminated by a spike. But the spike is evidently not necessary, or at least it cannot be recorded from the soma on some occasions in the sequence. Some factor other than a spike can reset the rhythm, but there is no certainty that one cell only is involved.

Diverse aftereffects.—In Bullock's useful short reviews (30, 48) and in Shane's long one (42), post-spike phenomena such as negative or positive aftereffects are listed with references. Of unknown function, they occur in preparations in various degrees but the recent tendency is to neglect them as a factor in behavior and to regard with suspicion all results with extracellular recording. Little new work with intracellular electrodes is available.

Extension of all-or-none theory.—Partial independence of spike activity in the processes of multipolar or branched neurons increases the complexity of recordings from multipolar cell bodies. Different regions of one neuron can show independent pacemaker potentials and can even initiate spikes independently. Spikes originating in different branches of one cell may be separated by a region (usually the cell body) which cannot support spike conduction, so that two all-or-none spikes of different height can be recorded intracellularly from this critical region (26, 28). A different phenomenon, on the other hand, occurs when spikes originate separately in branches of one neuron in different ganglia and then spread over the whole spike-bearing main part of the neuron (49). Spike-initiating regions can be numerous in one neuron and can be labile (28). The neuron doctrine, being based on the embryological discreteness of neurons as cells, is not affected by these findings.

Synaptic importance.—A waning of the importance of the synapse, formerly considered as the only site of integrative activity, has necessarily accompanied the discovery of the diverse integrating activities within regions of the neurons. Numerous reviews by Grundfest cite details of these regional differences (32, 33). Clearly one important type of integration is that by summation at transition zones between different types of membrane, each with its own diverse forms of responsiveness (1, 2, 3, 30, 32, 33, 48). Spontaneously active regions may lie adjacent to others on which excitatory and inhibitory synapses impinge, and these again may be separated to various extents by membrane regions which are mainly passive or may have various proportions of active response, and the whole of this input system to the neuron can be near or far from the nearest spike-initiating region. When this system is excited there can be various degrees of invasion of the dendritic regions by the spike, considerable in crayfish stretch receptor cells (15, 16, 37) and vertebrate motor neurons (3), but small in crustacean heart neurons (26). When we consider these possibilities of physiological regionalization and diversity together with the multitude of possibilities which spring from the known diversity of histological arrangement of dendrites, we can understand how the superficially similar ganglia and neuropiles of different animals could provide the immense diversity actually seen in their behavior.

Glial participation.—A trend which reduces the importance of synapses, and even of the neurons themselves, in integrative activity is a hesitance to attribute only nutritive and supporting functions to the glial cells. Apart from coelenterates (50), all nervous systems contain numerous glial cells. These ramify among the neurons, forming sheaths round single larger axons (and round bundles of fine axons) in all invertebrate groups studied (1). Glial cells can be diverse (51) but almost nothing is known of their activity.

Recordings from some vertebrate glial cells have shown slow, long-maintained (20 sec) responses to electrical stimuli (52). A suggestion by Galambos (53) that glial cells are important in co-ordination, and even in learning, will no doubt set in motion studies which will eventually produce more definite evidence of glial participation.

Transmitter diversity.—Diversity of transmitter substances and neuron responsiveness to them adds a possibility of complexity at the chemical level. Undoubted examples are as yet few, and the present tendency is to think of only a limited number of small-molecule transmitters (54). However, there are indications that two inhibitory axons to crustacean muscles have different transmitters (35). Acceleratory axons which form facilitating synapses on crustacean heart cells probably have a different transmitter from those which form antifacilitating synapses on the same cells (26), and the two inhibitory fibers on lobster stretch receptors may have two transmitters (55). Different cortical cells (56) and *Aplysia* neurons (21) react differently to pharmacological agents; for *Helix* cells, see (126).

Synapse structures.—Consistency in general plan, combined with variety in spatial arrangement, has marked all new anatomical descriptions of synapses. Membranes of two neurons are applied closely together with a narrow but regular cleft between. A number of synapses in which the presynaptic action current has been shown to be adequate to excite the postsynaptic neuron (electrical, as opposed to chemical, transmission) have synaptic clefts less than 20 mμ and synaptic vesicles on both sides (57). Known chemically transmitting synapses have wider clefts up to 50 mμ and vesicles only presynaptically (except for rare exceptions in mammalian sensory transducer cells). On this basis, it has been feasible to infer that narrow clefts indicate electrical transmission (3), but why electrically transmitting synapses should have vesicles remains a puzzle (50). Evidently the theory of the function of electrical synapses of the vesicles as the containers of transmitter substance is not complete. Synapses are now known from electron-micrograph studies of many phyla (1). Coelenterates have axon-axon symmetrical synapses with 20 mμ cleft and vesicles on both sides (50). The transverse septa of earthworm and crayfish giant fibers which are segmentally divided up are double membranes with a narrow synaptic cleft down to 7.5 mμ and vesicles on both sides. Synapses between giant fibers and motor fibers of crustacea are superficially axon-axon but the postsynaptic fiber has minute dendrites which invade the sheath of the presynaptic fiber. Vertebrate central synapses can have associated with them a variety of rods, bars, or thickening of the cleft membranes (58) which suggest physiological specialization, but most synapses of invertebrate neuropile are of simple axon-to-dendrite contact with presynaptic vesicles and a cleft which suggest chemical transmission. From the point of view of physiological integrating mechanisms, the feature of importance in synaptic structure is the spatial arrangement of synapses on the postsynaptic neuron in relation to the spatial decay of electrotonic spread. This determines whether or not spatial summation (and hence integration of several stimuli) will occur. We have not yet advanced beyond this to long-term properties of synaptic junctions as influenced by secretions or lasting changes in the membranes (see below, learning).

THE GANGLIONIC LEVEL

The processing of sensory information.—The past decade has seen analysis of numerous sense organs (1). The parameters of the stimulus which are passed on to the central nervous system consist primarily of changes, because almost all sense organs adapt, and we do not understand how an animal constantly makes adjustments of the zero, if indeed this is possible. Each sensory neuron, of which there is an enormous physiological and anatomical variety, responds to a certain class of environmental changes. Primary sensory neurons usually initiate spikes. Photoreceptor neurons have three different spectral sensitivities in insect compound eye (59) and contra earlier papers can initiate spikes (60). Crustacean ganglion cells (61) and molluscan central cells (62) can be light sensitive. Apparent spikes (63) in *Limulus* retinula cells (contra most interpretations) could have spread from eccentric cells. Primary photoreceptors of insects ocellus have an inhibitory effect on second-order cells (64). Chemoreceptor neurons respond either to sugars, salts, or protein (possibly some respond to water), and some are sensitive only to certain chemicals in insects (65, 66), *Limulus* (67), or crustaceans (68). Mechanoreceptors, especially hair sensilla in crustaceans (69) and insects (70), hair plates (71) of which the importance has been fully appreciated (72), joint receptors [refs. are in (73, 74)], water wave detectors in crustaceans (75), and campaniform sensilla of insects [nothing since (76)] are some of the receptors which provide the central ganglia with a fantastic array of information. When we consider that a segmental nerve of a worm $\frac{1}{2}$ cm in diameter, a large insect, or a reasonably sized crustacean has about 2000 sensory neurons, we can see that most of the available information must be wasted on arrival at the central nervous system.

How much of this incoming information from primary sensory axons is effective in arousal of interneurons in invertebrates is hardly known. Inputs to giant fibers in worms (77) and a cockroach [all refs. in (78)] show that here most detailed information is lost and only sudden stimuli are effective. Interaction such that neighboring receptors mutually inhibit each other reduces the total information without loss of the one main feature—the location of a contrasting edge moving across the receptor field. The most informative results come from isolation of units by microelectrodes or by teasing out interneurons. Isolation of units with microelectrodes has led to the description of (for example) "on" and "off" and "on-off" receptors in optic lobes of insects (27). In crustacean ganglia, microelectrodes have so far been less effective than the teasing out of interneurons in adjacent connectives (49, 79) although they have shown normal postsynaptic potentials in larger dendrites (28, 61). In vertebrates, studies of units isolated by probing are continually appearing. From the point of view of pattern reception, outstanding results come from following the visual and auditory pathways (80, 81). The frog retina projects to the tectum units which can be picked out as follows: (*a*) detectors of sustained contrast, not responding to general change in illumination but with a strong response when a contrasting source is switched on, (*b*) detectors of the nett convexity of the edge of a dark object, (*c*) large units which detect any moving edge, (*d*) detectors of nett dimming, (*e*) general darkness detectors. In the order given, the visual fields of these units increase and the first two types are by far the most numerous. In the optic tectum the retina is projected spatially, with the arborizations of these fibers at different depths (82).

According to published results, the retinal units of the frog eye must work on different principles from those of the fish (83) and mammal (84) in which postretinal units are much less complex. Complexity of responses of frog third-order (optic nerve) fibers is equalled only by sixth-order mammalian units and therefore the latter are available for more generalized responses at a surprisingly high level. Even in the cat cortex, many of the units are relatively simple, i.e., resemble "on" or "off" responses of sensory units with small visual fields although certain stimulus configurations such as long rectangles are particularly effective stimuli. Complex units of the cortex differ from those in the geniculate body in that they respond most strongly to a particular stimulus orientation wherever it may occur in the visual field of the units, and again slits and edges are most effective stimuli (84). By comparison with integrating interneurons of crustacea which occur at a low level (even as second-order neurons) in the ventral cord, we can see that a great deal of detail is integrated in the mammal cortex, and it must be carried so far to be available there. Cortical units are not individually complicated in their responses; it is their combination which becomes so formidable.

Crustacean interneurons which run between ventral ganglia up and down the cord, and eventually to the brain, have proved to be of several types with differing degrees of sensory convergence on to them. A large number have been isolated and their (mainly mechanoreceptor) inputs noted (49, 85). Integration of similar sensory input occurs more frequently than that of dissimilar output. Overlap of similar sensory inputs, in that they influence many interneurons, leads to the simultaneous stimulation of many interneurons from one sensory field, and similar sensory fields act on similar overlapping groups of interneurons. Two homologous sensory fields on different segments can have a considerable number of interneurons in common and only one not so. The records suggest that most of the connexions studied were monosynaptic. Interneurons which collect from sensory fields in different ganglia have branching dendrites in each, and impulses in such neurons do not carry information as to the ganglion of their origin. This example, which is likely to be typical for arthropods and perhaps all invertebrates, gives a picture of many partially integrated sensory fields conveying information simultaneously and integrated to different extents in a variety of combinations.

A general understanding of ganglionic function emerges when we consider the past paragraphs in relation to the commonest highly branched form of the dendrites of the interneurons and motoneurons. They have dendrites which arborize widely through the neuropile of one or more ganglia. Where accessible, as in crustacea, these dendrites show summation of postsynaptic potentials and a variety of types of response which show that they sum many diverse inputs and are individually recognizable and diverse. Evidently they pick up appropriate patterns of excitation in the the ganglia by virtue of their functional connectivity patterns with other neurons. We need nothing more to explain the abstraction of instantaneous patterns so long as a hypothetical connectivity of patterns of dendrites can be invoked to provide the necessary analysis or selectivity (85).

That this much is generally accepted is indicated from many sources, e.g., by an attempt to explain pattern discrimination by the octopus as a function of the asymmetries of dendritic fields (12). Independence of responses from the apparent size of an object is similarly considered as a function of funnel-shaped dendritic fields in the octopus. In no instance so far has it been possible to correlate dendritic form directly with function, but if this proves possible the question is where do we go from there? I think that the answer lies towards the study of the chemical basis of the connectivity or mechanism of addressing in neuropile (85) and towards a study of the long latencies and delays in drawn-out responses which are of much longer time scale than events such as postsynaptic potentials. The point is that pattern abstraction is not only an instantaneous process, but necessarily involves memory which can be built innately into the dendritic connectivity at every stage.

At the behavioral level, pattern recognition is best analysed either from training experiments, as in shape or tune recognition, or by evocation of a specific response. The concept of a minimal adequate trigger (86) is useful because the necessary parameters of the trigger can be worked out behaviorally, and the responses to these parameters by the many parallel nervous inputs can then be analysed. This is the aim of much work on visual pathways in the frog (82) and the octopus (12); and the stereotyped responses of birds will be a rich field for this type of analysis. Knowledge of responses from interneurons in a wide range of animals (except for giant fibers and very rapid responses) suggests that activity in many differently acting pathways in parallel is necessary before a complex response is initiated. There need not necessarily be a single neuron structure or simple reflex system which could be isolated as having the inherited disposition to act upon receiving a given sensory pattern. Many neurons, however, must act as "decision units" in that they respond by firing only when a threshold feature of their combined input is reached (1). So far as we know, this feature in neurons is the (fluctuating) threshold voltage at the spike-initiating region and there are no other demonstrated capabilities (such as multiplication of effects of inputs, measurement of ratios, or estimation of equalities) which can be given a physiological basis for a single neuron. Therefore, whatever other more complicated integrative features are observed must, on present knowledge, be attributed to the organization of groups of neurons.

Despite promising attacks on the relation between behavioral activities and the recording of responses of neurons, some of the simplest observations obtained from the two disciplines seem irreconcilable. For example, puffs of air, shadows moving across the eye, or rustling sounds repeatedly excite large neurons which run abundantly through the ventral cord and brain in a locust, but they rarely elicit behavioral responses. Many insects rotate with minute slow rotations of their visual fields, but an asymmetrically placed stroboscope causes no response at all although a great number of units in the optic lobes and brain are excited thereby. A bee collecting nectar is almost insensitive to the mechanical or visual disturbances to which it would respond if in flight or guarding the hive. Although the neuronal units are firing, the information they convey is not necessarily utilized. We are, in fact, still at a loss to explain the attention-directing mechanism in neuronal terms; yet fundamentally this is the crux of the whole problem of sensory inflow.

Learning.—One type of long-term response which can be separated for study is learning, defined as the formation of an association between two stimuli. At its simplest level an association requires only one interneuron which changes its responses so that one sensory input to it becomes associated with another not previously associated with the first. An example so elementary as this is not known, but there has been a drift away from theories of learning which invoke feedback reiterative circuits in complex massive arrays of continually active neurons. The retention of learning during freezing and the transfer of learning between two hemispheres by several possible fractions of the available paths (87) have contributed to this change of attitude. Important recent reviews by Morrell, and others, on learning in mammalian cortex (refs. in 89) and in octopus discrimination (12) recently appeared, and one advocate in this field suggests that glial cells may be involved in long-term changes (53). At St. Andrews we have tried to develop a preparation of a brainless insectan ventral cord which can learn to place a residual leg in such a position as to avoid getting electric shocks (88). Compared with a vertebrate or octopus brain, the total number of cells is here relatively small and presumably most of them are concerned with other activities. There seems to be no reason why any isolated ganglion should not be able to form an association if the appropriate test circumstances can be found. The way is then open for detailed analysis at the neuronal level, and classes of new phenomena may appear.

Central sequences controlling movements.—Impulse sequences of purely nervous origin were first analysed at the unit level in the crustacean heart ganglion. There are conveniently few (nine) neurons, and a relatively simple regulation by one pair of inhibitory and two pairs of excitatory axons from the ventral cord. Stretch of the heart ganglion or of dendrites from some of the intrinsic cells also influences (accelerates) the rhythm. Thus central rhythm, external control from other ganglia, and proprioceptive effects are exemplified in this model nervous system. In detail, however, the actual pattern of the burst seems not critical because each burst causes only a twitch in the one muscle (26, 90).

In the last decade there have come to light a number of preparations which have demonstrated for the first time an undoubted central origin of sequence of motor impulses in the absence of the corresponding muscles, thereby eliminating proprioceptive control. Comparison of Weis-Fogh, 1956 (91), with Wilson, 1961 (92), both writing on locust flight control, reveals the change in attitude towards acceptance of central control. Alternate impulses in the motor nerves of the two sides to the sound-producing tymbal muscles of a cicada are initiated in short bursts from the isolated ganglion, as in normal song. In a mantis, patterned bursts of impulses emerge along the phallic nerve when the deafferentated last abdominal ganglion is finally isolated from the rest of the cord. From the ventral cord of the locust, the bursts of impulses which normally co-ordinate the ventilatory movements continue with little modification when their ganglia of origin are separated from the effective muscles. Similarly, the sequences of impulses which control spiracular movements of insects do not depend on the performance of the action for their continued pattern. The alternating bursts of motor impulses to the antagonistic direct wing muscles of the locust continue when all the thoracic muscles are removed so long as a stream of impulses arrives at the thoracic ganglia in axons from head sensory hairs which are normally stimulated by wind on the head [refs. to all the above in (93)].

The sequence of motor impulses which control swimmeret movements of the crayfish can be recorded in swimmeret nerve stumps even though all the corresponding movement is obliterated. Even the isolated cord initiates such sequences, which run anteriorwards from ganglion to ganglion. They can be switched on or off by stimulation of identifiable long interneurons of the cord (94). In all these examples the experiment has been essentially the same —to record little difference in impulse pattern from motor nerves before and after removal of the muscles. The impulse sequence of central origin is only relatively predetermined and in all examples is modified by sensory impulses aroused by normal extraneous stimuli and by the consequences of the movement itself. The former, of immense variety, can sometimes be separated off as discrete reflexes; the latter have been called reafferent effects (see below).

Formal models of nervous integrative mechanisms.—Prospective critics and those experimenters who wish to interpret purely behavioral results in terms of how the nervous system works would do well to peruse a commentary on types of explanation in the first chapter of a book by Deutsch (95). Any explanation of a particular case as being an example of a more general case is suspect unless the particular case can be inferred as a consequence of interacting components in a system, mechanism, or structure. Even the latter explanatory devices are by necessity usually hypothetical constructs but are none the worse for that. They are still testable so long as the intervening variables which are related together refer to something more than tendencies or dispositions which are theoretically unobservable except in terms of the original observations. Deutsch accentuates the validity of models in terms of structural relationships between hypothetical components which work together in a mechanism. He attaches less attention to information about the physical location of the parts in space or to the detailed activity of a single neuron whose place in any system we do not fully know. Yet localization by lesions and probing of units in the central nervous system are the subjects of intense current research (10).

Three examples of formal explanations which have had a wide influence on the interpretation of invertebrate behavior have appeared in the past few years, in part inspired by current expansion of the subject of servomechanisms. Ten years ago the concept of reafferent excitation was introduced (96). Excitation is reafferent when it is the consequence of the animal's own movement. The problem was, then, to understand how an animal compensates for its reafferent excitation, for example, not making compensatory responses to apparent movement in its visual field caused by its own movements; and so the idea of an efferent copy was proposed. The latter is a hypothetical automatic cancellation of reafferent impulses by a duplication or copy of centrally initiated patterns of movements. However, no actual examples of a compensatory copy appeared, and the postulation of cancellation by a copy came to appear as another way of describing the original data. One example has recently appeared in the crustacean abdomen; this is the initiation of impulses in the inhibitory axons to the stretch receptor neurons by giant fiber impulses which also excite motor axons and eventually cause a tail flick. The inhibitory impulses cut off the reafferent sensory response which would arise from the stretch receptor neurons (97). There are no doubt different explanations for other examples of the problem of "efferent copy" at the neuronal level.

The feeding behavior of the mantis, which accurately grabs small moving prey from a wide variety of angles and positions, has been analysed in detail in terms of feedback loops depending on proprioceptors which sense the position of the head, and the directional sense of the compound eye. By loading the parts or by removing them piece by piece, it is possible to infer a number of necessary central interactions. Leg control by the angle subtended on the eye is more important in this animal than that depending on motion of the head on the neck. Once the foreleg is in rapid motion towards the prey at the correct strike angle, it is probably still controlled. An excellent account in English (98) contains details of the control of the rapid eye movements by a high-gain feedback loop with intermittent action.

The beetle *Chlorophanus* tends to turn with the direction of rotation of its visual field. By ingenious analysis the effects of various combinations of stimuli show the following principal results. Stimuli, such as changes of light intensity, are correlated as a time sequence occurring successively on adjacent and subadjacent ommatidia on the eye, but not over wider areas. The autocorrelation leads to a measure of the extent and direction of apparent movement of the visual field. The structure of the formal model which has been proposed depends fundamentally on two facts. (*a*) Nett excitation from two ommatidia depends on the excitation of one multiplied by that of the other, taking the sign of the change into account. (*b*) The animal makes a superficially apparent error in judgment of the direction of a moving sequence that runs across alternating brightening and dimming of successive lights arranged in a row round it (99). The error is only an apparent one, because autocorrelation between ommatidia is still maximized.

INVERTEBRATE PHYLA

Coelenterate nerve nets.—In 1952 our general idea of a nerve net as the basis of behavior in sea anemones and jellyfish was derived mainly from Pantin's analysis of *Calliactis*. The critical experiment was based on the fact that the second of two shocks could be placed on the column at a distance from the first and still elicit a symmetrical shortening of the column. Therefore, the effect of the first shock spread over the whole animal. Because it is followed by a refractory period, the first shock must cause a single nerve impulse. Two shocks cause a much greater contraction of the anemone's longitudinal mesenteric muscles when separated by a short interval than when separated by a long interval. This is facilitation, in which the passage of an impulse facilitates the effect of succeeding impulses. This concept accounts for much of the behavior. First, near the boundary (possibly the neuromuscular junction) between conducting and contracting elements, excitation at one impulse per ten seconds in the column nerve net excites only the circular muscle while impulses at higher frequency cause contraction in the longitudinal mesenteric muscles. Secondly, the decay of the response of tentacles in transmission of impulses across the disc could be explained as a consequence of hypothetical facilitation at neuron-neuron junctions, such that for a short time an impulse cleared a way to allow for progressively further spread of later impulses. Thus the concept of facilitation could explain a wide range of phenomena. The strength of the contraction of the bell muscle of the jellyfish *Aurelia* also fitted the same scheme [refs. for this paragraph will be found in (100)].

However, during the past decade this simple picture has been overlaid by a variety of more complex themes. The demonstration that each beat of the jellyfish bell is achieved by a single nerve impulse accompanied by an electrical spike of the usual form showed that two separate nerve nets must be present because other excitation can cross the bell unaccompanied by a contraction wave (101). This "other excitation" consists of waves of tentacle co-ordination, and asymmetrical feeding and steering movements, all long known, which were now inferred to be co-ordinated by a second or diffuse nerve net containing multipolar cells (102). The "giant-fiber" net of bipolar cells which co-ordinates the symmetrical beat by a single through-conducted impulse was shown to meet and interact with the diffuse net at the marginal ganglia in an arrangement which bears some resemblance to a reflex arc except that the diffuse net, or sensory side, contains elements which also act on muscles in the feeding responses. Hydromedusans, with two ring nerves and at least one subumbrellar nerve net, can at one time perform two independent actions which involve transmission of two types of excitation simultaneously in two different directions through the one subumbrellar epithelium. There must be at least two nets to achieve this; in most hydromedusans, excitation of the nerve net which performs feeding movements actually inhibits the spontaneous excitation which arises in the net co-ordinating the symmetrical beat (refs. in 101, 102). That the spontaneous beats must arise within the giant-fiber net in jellyfish was inferred because antidromic impulses reset the rhythm so that the next interval is as long as a normal interval. Old accounts of a compensatory pause following an extra beat of this kind cannot be vindicated; the interval following an extra beat can, in a variety of species and different preparations of jellyfish, be longer or shorter than, or similar to, normal depending on the state of the ganglion and the stimulation of the diffuse net (43).

Finally it is possible to obtain electrical records which show separately the electrical activity of the two nerve nets in jellyfish (103). Similarly, *Cerianthus* has two systems (104). In anemones which swim by simultaneous tentacle twitching (*Boloceroides*), the movement is co-ordinated by one form of excitation which can be transmitted across the animal but arrested by another form, following electrical shocks. Here again, and in the spontaneously beating heads of the soft coral *Heteroxenia*, and in a variety of colonial hydrozoans [refs. in (105, 106)], there must be two conducting systems which are probably separate nets. In *Porpita* the two nets are histologically separable and one has anastomosing neurons (44). Since so many coelenterates seem to have two or more separate nerve nets and since transmission properties of nerve nets can be extremely diverse, we are now in the situation of having many available factors to explain new behavioral observations; the problem is to design experiments to choose among the large number of possibilities.

The various types of transmission in a single nerve net are nowhere better illustrated than in corals, where the spread of excitation between individuals of the colony may be negligible, localized, or through-conducting. Where localized it may be pushed progressively further by repeated stimulation or, in some instances, limited no matter how often a stimulus is repeated on one spot (105, 107). Explanatory models show that: (*a*) one-dimensional nets with some conducting junctions scattered at random give a too variable spread of excitation and are probably thereby ruled out; (*b*) progressively greater or negligible further spread at successively later stimuli can be explained in terms of long- or short-lived facilitation. A study of nets with a computer serves to sharpen up the details which should be looked for by future coral gazers. The mathematical analysis leads to the conclusion that repetitive discharge to a single shock is the most likely explanation of the consistent and symmetrical spread of excitation in random nets which contain a random distribution of conducting connexions. In fact, direct evidence of repetitive responses to single short stimuli is available in a hydrozoan *Cordylophora* (108). Thus, models of spread of excitation cannot assume a single impulse from a single shock, and further complexity is added.

Apart from the rapid protective closure responses of anemones and corals, the beating, feeding, and tentacle movements of medusae and food catching in the hydroid *Syncoryne*, and probably the swimming movements in anemones such as *Stomphia* (109), there is little direct evidence of co-ordination by nerves in coelenterates. However, there is a relatively rich variety of slow co-ordinations of great complexity, with immensely long latencies and summation periods. The specific response of the anemone *Calliactis* to *Buccinum* shells, on to which it hoists itself in part by control of nematocyst discharge (110), is only one of many examples. During the past decade there have been numerous descriptions of cyclic and slow co-ordinated movements in anemones, perhaps related to the nervous system (111, 112), and nervous control of nematocyst discharge (113). The trend is towards positive evidence of differentiated separate pathways some of which may be nervous, some from muscle fiber to fiber, some perhaps humoral, and some by mechanical traction; but the critical experiments have yet to be done with direct microtechniques.

Peripheral nerves in annelids.—From the present point of view there are many issues still in doubt, especially in relation to the controversial peripheral connexion between neurons. Few studies by recording from annelid sensory nerves have been attempted. Early work (114) is not to be relied upon because the nerves were connected to the central cord, and impulses may have been of central origin. The parapodial nerve in the polychaete *Harmothoë* has recently been found to contain about 2000 axons whereas polychaete segmental nerves have previously been thought to contain relatively few axons (Horridge, unpublished). The number of segmental axons in *Harmothoë* corresponds with the number of peripheral cells, and on reviewing all the old work I have come to the conclusion that the description of peripheral connexions between neurons could all be attributed to vagaries of the specific staining methods. At the same time, however, it is clear that physiological evidence from stimulation of body wall strips in the earthworm cannot be dismissed without careful repetition to test whether direct response by muscle to stretch, spread of the stimulus, or direct conduction from fiber to fiber of the muscle could be responsible. For such an analysis direct physiological micromethods would be necessary, as in *Golfingia* (Sipunculid) muscles (115). At present it seems safest to suppose that annelid sensory neurons have axons which run to the central nervous system.

On the motor side, there is still uncertainty as to the relations between the relatively few central motor cells and the numerous muscle fibers. A peripheral motor plexus has never been demonstrated; a synapse to second-order motor neurons was proposed (116) but has not been demonstrated by either anatomical or physiological preparations, although looked for in polychaetes (117). However, local reflexes of parapodia isolated from the central ganglia are real enough and suggest that peripheral synapses to motor axons must exist in the parapodia, perhaps in the parapodial ganglia. The hodological anatomy of the peripheral neurons is not known sufficiently well for useful experiments to be devised. By a combination of following motor axons in methylene blue preparations (77) and stimulation of segmental nerves (117), it is now clear that the fast motor axons are few and run direct to the muscles; some slow axons are probably similar but are less well substantiated, though certainly present.

Giant fibers and central ganglia of annelids.—Startle responses of worms are invariably co-ordinated by central giant axons, but many more of the latter are known (they are numerous in some species) than can be explained at present in terms of responses. The giant fibers are interneurons, except in *Myxicola*, where they may run direct to the muscles. The rapid decay of the twitch response to repeated stimuli is in part at the synapse between sensory axons and giant fiber, mainly at the synapses between giant fiber and motor axons, and negligibly at the neuromuscular junction, at least in the only form analysed, *Nereis* (77). Distribution of giant fibers was last reviewed in 1948 (118) and little new has been added except that the varied types of connexions between giant fibers have been subject to a new appraisal in the light of the finding of nonrectifying direct electrical connexions between the two lateral giant fibers of *Lumbricus* (119). Maybe some of the formerly described quasi-artificial synapses will prove to be of the same nature.

Large ganglion cells of molluscs.—The visceral ganglion of *Aplysia* is a new preparation where several large cells can be penetrated separately (18 to 23). Spontaneous activity may be an irregular stream of impulses or may appear in bursts at intervals. Some spontaneously active cells show no synaptic potentials to any kind of sensory stimulation. Most cells penetrated in this ganglion are inactive in the resting animal but become excited when the animal is touched or otherwise stimulated, but some spontaneous cells are then inhibited. Activity in at least one giant cell of the abdominal ganglion is associated with retraction. Antidromic stimulation of a neuron (without invasion of the cell body by the spike) can be distinguished from synaptic stimulation because the former is reduced and the latter increased by hyperpolarization of the cell body. Many neurons have two or more axons in different nerve trunks and there are many instances of direct axon pathways from one nerve trunk to another via such branched neurons (23). The large neurons differ in their sensitivity to drugs; thus neurons from which inhibitory synaptic potential can be recorded are inhibited (with a reversal potential, typical of inhibition by nonspecific increase in membrane conductance) on application of acetylcholine while other cells are activated by the same application of the drug, without intermediate activity of other neurons which would be revealed by postsynaptic potentials (21). For *Helix*, see (126).

Ganglionic action in arthropods.—Aspects new to the past decade, but already covered, are the ubiquity of typical summation of synaptic potentials in recordings from dendrites (28, 29), the occurrence of centrally initiated rhythms (90, 92, 93, 94), and the characteristic long interganglionic interneurons with diverse types of sensory convergence on to them (120). A new example of the latter is the ascending auditory interneurons which run up each side of the cord to the brain in the locust. Primary sensory auditory fibers from the typanum at the posterior side of the thorax make connexions (perhaps directly) with these interneurons. The point of interest is that the ipsilateral interneuron is excited whereas the contralateral one is inhibited so that a directional sense of the sound is enhanced (79, 121, 122). Ganglionic transmission in crustaceans has been reviewed up to 1959 (123), and the more recent work in (14, 28, 49, 73, 97) has been mentioned in this review.

Stimulation of local regions of the brain, in particular in an insect, the cricket, has led to new understanding of the control of co-ordinated movements. Depending on its position, local stimulation will arouse specific identifiable patterns of normal activity such as walking, turning, flight, jumping, and especially stridulation. The frequency of stimulation is not very critical and it is not likely that these readily repeatable results are obtained by the fortuitous stimulation of an appropriate group of neurons. It is much more likely that arousal of a behavior pattern can be achieved by stimulation of the appropriate single neuron. From the distribution of effective points in the insect brain it can be seen that most responses can be elicited from a wide area but stridulation of the normal song is only released when corpora pedunculata are stimulated. It is postulated that command fibers or premotor descending interneurons are sensitive to particular patterns of sensory input to the brain. The action of these neurons is not to control the muscles directly but to put the lower ganglia of the ventral cord into an appropriate state so that the specific movement is co-ordinated at the lower level (124). Fibers acting similarly have been found in crustaceans (14) and this is a pattern of co-ordination which is likely to be common. Most central giant fibers are premotor interneurons.

Analyses of reflex responses at the neuronal level are beginning to appear. Two such in crustaceans show how convenient are these animals for this type of analysis. In keeping with the trend shown by workers on vertebrate central nervous system, the use of combinations of natural rather than electrical stimuli throws most light on normal co-ordination. Stretch receptor neurons of the crustacean abdomen (125) have inhibitory axons running out to their peripheral sensory cell bodies. Sensory impulses in stretch receptor axons reflexly activate the efferent inhibitory axon to the stretch receptors and their muscles up to three segments away and inhibit extensor motor axons. The segmental extensor motor neuron excites the stretch receptor muscle, taking up slack. Impulses in the giant fibers also excite efferent inhibitory axons to the stretch receptors, preventing their action except at the end of the tail flick (97). Analysis of leg nerve reflexes shows that specific inhibitors to muscles (rather than antagonistic muscles) are effective in stopping reflexly excited movements of the claw, but most other movements are stopped reflexly by central inhibition of motor axons. Central coupling between motor and inhibitor axons remains speculative. Joint receptors are coupled centrally to motoneurons in such a way that passive movements of joints are resisted (73). No function has been found for the common inhibitor axon to all muscles of the crustacean leg.

In conclusion, one must contemplate the fact that we are still at the stage of discovering sense organs, neuromuscular patterns, and types of reflexes. The invertebrates offer unique examples of relatively simple ganglia and responses from which one can hope to discover a large fraction of the relevant mechanisms of co-ordination, but studies at the neuron level have hardly started.

LITERATURE CITED

1. Bullock, T. H., and Horridge, G. A., *Structure and Function in the Nervous Systems of Invertebrates* (W. H. Freeman, San Francisco and London, in press, 1963)
2. Eccles, J. C., *The Physiology of Nerve Cells* (Johns Hopkins Press, Baltimore 1957)
3. Eccles, J. C., *Ergeb. Physiol., Biol. Chem. Exptl. Pharmakol.,* 51, 299–430 (1961)
4. Katsuki, Y., Ed., *Electrical Activity of Single Cells* (Igaku Shoin Ltd. Tokyo, Japan, 312 pp., 1960)
5. Burns, B. D., *The Mammalian Cerebral Cortex* (Arnold, London, 119 pp., 1958)
6. Jasper, H. H., Proctor, L. D., Knighton, R. S., Noshay, W. C., and Costello, R. T., Eds., *Reticular Formation of the Brain* (Little, Brown, Boston, 766 pp., 1958)
7. Magoun, H. W., *The Waking Brain* (Charles C Thomas, Springfield, Ill., 138 pp., 1958)
8. Dow, R. S., and Moruzzi, G., *The Physiology and Pathology of the Cerebellum* (Univ. Minnesota Press, Minneapolis, Minn., 675 pp., 1958)
9. Brindley, G. S., *Physiology of the Retina and Visual Pathway* (Arnold, London, 298 pp., 1960)
10. Field, J., Magoun, H. W., and Hall, V. E., *Handbook of Physiology,* 1–3 (Am. Physiol. Soc., Washington, D.C., 2013 pp., 1960, 1962)
11. Waterman, T. H., *The Physiology of Crustacea,* 1 and 2 (Academic Press, New York and London, 670 pp. and 681 pp., 1961)
12. Young, J. Z., *Biol. Revs. Cambridge Phil. Soc.,* 36, 32–96 (1961)
13. Gesteland, R. C., Howland, B., Lettvin, J. Y., and Pitts, W. H., *Proc. I.R.E. (Inst. Radio Engrs.),* 47, 1856–62 (1959)
14. Wiersma, C. A. G., *J. Comp. Neurol.,* 110, 421–71 (1958)
15. Eyzaguirre, C., and Kuffler, S. W., *J. Gen. Physiol.,* 39, 87–119 (1955)
16. Kuffler, S. W., and Eyzaguirre, C., *J. Gen. Physiol.,* 39, 155–84 (1955)
17. Burkhardt, D., *Biol. Zentr.,* 78, 22–62 (1956)
18. Tauc, L., *Colloq. Intern. Centre Natl. Rech. Sci. (Paris),* 67, 91–119 (1955)

19. Tauc, L., *J. Physiol.* (*Paris*), **47**, 769–92 (1955)

20. Tauc, L., *Inhibitions in the Nervous System and γ-Aminobutyric Acid*, 85–89 (Pergamon Press, Oxford, 591 pp., 1960)

21. Gerschenfeld, H., and Tauc, L., *Nature*, **189**, 924–25 (1961)

22. Kerkut, G. A., and Walker, R. J., *Comp. Biochem. Physiol.*, **3**, 143–60 (1961)

23. Hughes, G. M., and Tauc, L., *J. Exptl. Biol.*, **39**, 45–70 (1962)

24. Wilson, D. M., *Comp. Biochem. Physiol.*, **3**, 274–84 (1961)

25. Watanabe, A., and Grundfest, H., *J. Gen. Physiol.*, **45**, 267–308 (1961)

26. Hagiwara, S., *Ergeb. Biol.*, **24**, 284–311 (1961)

27. Burtt, E. T., and Catton, W. T., *J. Physiol.* (*London*), **154**, 479–90 (1960)

28. Kennedy, D., and Preston, J. B., *J. Gen. Physiol.*, **43**, 655–70 (1960)

29. Maynard, D. M., *Anat. Record*, **137**, 380–81 (1960)

30. Bullock, T. H., *Science*, **129**, 997–1002 (1959)

31. Katz, B., *J. Physiol.* (*London*), **111**, 261–82 (1950)

32. Grundfest, H., *Evolution of Nervous Control*, 43–86 (Am. Assoc. Adv. Sci., Washington, D.C., 231 pp., 1959b)

33. Grundfest, M., *Biophysics of Physiological and Pharmacological Actions* (Shanes, A. M., Ed., Am. Assoc. Adv. Sci., Washington, D.C., 1961)

34. Hoyle, G., *Comparative Physiology of the Nervous Control of Muscular Contraction* (Univ. Press, Cambridge, 147 pp., 1957)

35. Hoyle, G., and Wiersma, C. A. G., *J. Physiol.* (*London*), **143**, 441–53 (1958)

36. Dudel, J., and Kuffler, S. W., *J. Physiol.* (*London*), **155**, 543–62 (1961)

37. Edwards, C., and Ottoson, D., *J. Physiol.* (*London*), **143**, 138–48 (1958)

38. Wiersma, C. A. G., and Pilgrim, R. L. C., *Comp. Biochem. Physiol.*, **2**, 51–64 (1961)

39. Bullock, T. H., and Hagiwara, S., *J. Gen. Physiol.*, **40**, 565–77 (1957)

40. Bennett, M. V. L., Crain, S. M., and Grundfest, H., *J. Gen. Physiol.*, **43**, 221–50 (1959)

41. Wright, E. B., and Coleman, P. D., *J. Cellular Comp. Physiol.*, **43**, 133–64 (1954)

42. Shanes, A. M., *Pharmacol. Rev.*, **10**, 59–273 (1958)

43. Horridge, G. A., *J. Exptl. Biol.*, **36**, 72–91 (1959)

44. Mackie, G. O., *Quart. J. Microscop. Sci.*, **101**, 119–31 (1960)

45. Bennett, M. V. L., *Federation Proc.*, **19**, 298 (1960)

46. Eccles, J. C., Kostyuk, P. G., and Schmidt, R. F., *J. Physiol.* (*London*), **161**, 258–81 (1962)

47. Gray, E. G., *Nature*, **193**, 82–83 (1962)

48. Bullock, T. H., *Exptl. Cell Res.*, **5**, 323–37 (1958)

49. Hughes, G. M., and Wiersma, C. A. G. *J. Exptl. Biol.*, **37**, 291–307 (1960)

50. Horridge, G. A., Chapman, D. M., and MacKay, D., *Nature*, **193**, 899–900 (1962)

51. Wigglesworth, V. B., *Quart. J. Microscop. Sci.*, **100**, 299–314 (1959)

52. Hild, W., Chang, J. J., and Tasaki, I., *Experientia*, **14**, 220–21 (1958)

53. Galambos, R., *Proc. Natl. Acad. Sci. US*, **47**, 129–36 (1961)

54. Florey, E., *Ann. Rev. Physiol.*, **23**, 501–28 (1961)

55. Burgen, A. S. V., and Kuffler, S. W., *Nature*, **180**, 1490 (1957)

56. Elkes, J., *Neurological Basis of Behaviour*, 303–36 (Wolstenholme, G. E. W., and O'Connor, C. M., Eds., J. & A. Churchill Ltd., London, 400 pp., 1958)

57. Hama, K. *Science of the Living Body* (Engl. Transl. title of Japanese journal), **12**, 72–84 (1961)

58. Gray, E. G., *J. Anat.*, **95**, 345–56 (1961)

59. Autrum, H., and Burkhardt, D., *Nature*, **190**, 639 (1961)

60. Naka, K. I., and Eguchi, E., *J. Gen. Physiol.* (In press)

61. Kennedy, D., *Am. J. Ophthalmol.*, **46**, 19–26 (1958)

62. Kennedy, D., *J. Gen. Physiol.*, **44**, 277–99 (1960)

63. Fuortes, M. G. F., *J. Physiol.* (*London*), **148**, 14–28 (1959)

64. Ruck, P., *J. Gen. Physiol.*, **44**, 641–57 (1961)

65. Evans, D. R., *Anat. Record*, **132**, 433–34 (1958)

66. Dethier, V. G., *Survey of Biological Progress* (Avery, G. S., Ed., Academic Press, Inc., New York, 332 pp., 1957)

67. Barber, S. B., *J. Exptl. Zool.*, **131**, 51–73 (1956)

68. Laverack, M. S., *Comp. Biochem. Physiol.* (In press)

69. Case, J., and Gwilliam, G. F., *Biol. Bull.*, **121**, 449–55 (1961)

70. Wolbarsht, M. L., *J. Gen. Physiol.*, **44**, 105–22 (1960)

71. Lindauer, M., and Nedel, J. O., *Z. Vergleich. Physiol.*, **42**, 334–64 (1959)

72. Wendler, G., *Naturwissenschaften*, **48**, 676–77 (1961)

73. Bush, B. M. H., *J. Exptl. Biol.*, **39**, 71–106 (1962)

74. Cohen, M. J., *Anat. Record*, **137**, 346 (1960)

75. Laverack, M. S., *Comp. Biochem. Physiol.*, **6**, 137–45 (1962)

76. Pringle, J. W. S., *J. Exptl. Biol.*, **15**, 114–31 (1938)

77. Horridge, G. A., *Proc. Roy. Soc. (London)*, **150**, 245–62 (1959)

78. Roeder, K. D., *Smithsonian Inst. Misc. Collections*, **137**, 287–306 (1959)

79. Suga, M., and Katsuki, Y., *J. Exptl. Biol.*, **38**, 759–70 (1961)

80. Grüsser, O. J., and Grüsser-Cornehls, U., *Neurophysiologie und Psychophysik des Visuellen Systems*, 314–24 (Jung, R., and Kornhuber, H., Eds., Springer-Verlag, Berlin, 1961)

81. Rosenblith, W. A., Ed., *Sensory Communication* (John Wiley & Sons, Ltd., New York, 844 pp., 1961)

82. Maturana, H. R., Lettvin, J. Y., McCulloch, W. S., and Pitts, W. H., *J. Gen. Physiol.*, **43**, 129–75 (1960)

83. Wagner, H. G., MacNichol, E. F., and Wolbarsht, M. J., *J. Gen. Physiol.*, **43**, 45–62 (1960)

84. Hubel, D. H., and Wiesel, T. N., *J. Physiol. (London)*, **160**, 106–54 (1962)

85. Horridge, G. A., *Nervous Inhibition*, 395–409 (Florey, E., Ed., Pergamon Press, Oxford, 475 pp., 1961)

86. Bullock, T. H., *Physiological Triggers and Discontinuous Rate Processes* (Bullock, T. H., Ed., Am. Physiol. Soc., Washington, D.C., 179 pp., 1957)

87. Sperry, R. W., *Biological and Biochemical Bases of Behaviour*, 401–24 (Harlow, H. F., and Woolsey, C. N., Eds., Univ. Wisconsin Press, Madison, Wis., 476 pp., 1958)

88. Horridge, G. A., *Nature*, **193**, 697–98 (1962)

89. Deutsch, J. A., *Ann. Rev. Physiol.*, **24**, 259–83 (1962)

90. Maynard, D. M., *Nervous Inhibition*, 144–78 (Florey, E., Ed., Pergamon Press, Oxford, 475 pp., 1961)

91. Weis-Fogh, T., *Phil. Trans. Roy. Soc. London*, **239**, 553–89 (1956)

92. Wilson, D. M., *J. Exptl. Biol.*, **38**, 471–90 (1961)

93. Horridge, G. A., *J. Physiol. (London)*, **155**, 320–36, 553–72 (1960)

94. Hughes, G. M., and Wiersma, C. A. G., *J. Exptl. Biol.*, **37**, 657–70 (1960)

95. Deutsch, J. A., *The Structural Basis of Behavior* (Univ. Chicago Press, Chicago, 185 pp., 1960)

96. Holst, E. von, and Mittelstaedt, H., *Naturwissenschaften*, **37**, 464–76 (1950)

97. Eckert, R. O., *J. Cellular Comp. Physiol.*, **57**, 149–74 (1961)

98. Mittelstaedt, H., *Transactions of the Fifth Conference on Group Processes* (Schaffner, B., Ed., Josiah Macy Foundation, New York, 196 pp., 1960)

99. Hassenstein, B., and Reichardt, W. I., *Die Umschau in Wissenschaft und Technik*, **10**, 302–5 (1959)

100. Pantin, C. F. A., *Proc. Roy. Soc. (London)*, **140**, 147–68 (1952)

101. Horridge, G. A., *J. Exptl. Biol.*, **33**, 366–83 (1956)

102. Horridge, G. A., *Quart. J. Microscop. Sci.*, **97**, 59–74 (1956)

103. Passano, L. M., and McCullough, C. B., *Federation Proc.*, **20**, 338 (1961)

104. Horridge, G. A., *J. Exptl. Biol.*, **35**, 369–82 (1958)

105. Horridge, G. A., *Phil. Trans. Roy. Soc. London*, **240**, 495–529 (1957)

106. Josephson, R. K., *J. Exptl. Biol.*, **38**, 559–77 (1961)

107. Josephson, R. K., *J. Theoret. Biol.*, **1**, 460–87 (1961)

108. Josephson, R. K., *J. Exptl. Biol.*, **38**, 579–93 (1961)

109. Robson, E. A., *J. Exptl. Biol.*, **38**, 685–94 (1961)

110. Ross, D. M., and Sutton, L., *Proc. Roy. Soc. (London)*, **155**, 266–81 (1961)

111. Ross, D. M., *J. Exptl. Biol.*, **37**, 753–74 (1960)

112. Ewer, D. W., *J. Exptl. Biol.*, **37**, 812–31 (1960)

113. Davenport, D., Ross, D. M., and Sutton, L., *Vie et Milieu*, **12**, 197–209 (1961)

114. Prosser, C. L., *J. Exptl. Biol.*, **12**, 95–104 (1955)

115. Prosser, C. L., and Sperelakis, N., *J. Cellular Comp. Physiol.*, **54**, 129–33 (1959)

116. Smith, J. E., *Phil. Trans. Roy. Soc. London*, **240**, 135–96 (1957)

117. Wilson, D. M., *J. Exptl. Biol.*, **37**, 46–56 (1960)

118. Nicol, J. A. C., *Quart. Rev. Biol.*, **23**, 291–323 (1948)

119. Wilson, D. M., *Comp. Biochem. Physiol.*, **3**, 274–84 (1961)

120. Fielden, A., and Hughes, G. M., *J. Exptl. Biol.*, **39**, 31–44 (1962)

121. Suga, N., and Katsuki, Y., *J. Exptl. Biol.*, **38**, 545–58 (1961)

122. Horridge, G. A., *Proc. Roy. Soc. (London)*, **155**, 218–31 (1961)

123. Wiersma, C. A. G., *The Physiology of Crustacea*, **II**, 191–279 (Waterman, T. H., Ed., Academic Press, New York, 681 pp., 1961)

124. Huber, F., *Z. Vergleich. Physiol.*, **44**, 60–132 (1960)

125. Pilgrim, R. L. C., *Comp. Biochem. Physiol.*, **1**, 248–57 (1960)

126. Kerkut, G. A., and Walker, R. J., *Comp. Biochem. Physiol.*, **3**, 143–60 (1961)

HIGHER NERVOUS FUNCTIONS:
THE ORIENTING REFLEX

By E. N. Sokolov

Moscow University, Moscow, USSR

The investigation of higher nervous functions demands detailed analysis of the orienting reflex as a part of the complex exploratory behavior of animals and man. The classical characterization of the orienting reflex was given by Pavlov (1, p. 27), the first to study it physiologically:

> It is this reflex which brings about the immediate response in man and animals to the slightest changes in the world around them, so that they immediately orientate their appropriate receptor-organ in accordance with the perceptible quality in the agent bringing about the change, making full investigation of it. The biological significance of this reflex is obvious. If the animal were not provided with such a reflex its life would hang at every moment by a thread. In man this reflex has been greatly developed in its highest form by inquisitiveness—the parent of that scientific method through which we hope one day to come to a true orientation in knowledge of the world around us.

Pavlov's studies of the orienting reflex have recently begun again to attract the attention of neurophysiologists. Several recent books deal with this problem (1–8), and the role of the orienting reflex in conditioning has been touched on in several reviews (9, 10, 11).

The following main problems present themselves:

(*a*) the relation of the orienting reflex to activation mechanisms in general: the changes of intrinsic brain waves, the facilitation of evoked potentials, and posttetanic potentiation;

(*b*) the relationship of the orienting reflex to natural or artificial shifts in the steady potential of the cortex;

(*c*) the organization of the orienting reflex at the neuronal level;

(*d*) the participation of the memory trace in the orienting reflex mechanism.

THE ORIENTING REFLEX AT THE MACROLEVEL

Criteria for Distinguishing the Orienting Reflex

The orienting reflex as an independent functional system.—Individual motor, vascular, or EEG reactions can appear not only as components of the orienting reflex but also as components of other unconditioned reflexes. At the same time, various combinations of the different reactions which share certain properties can be considered orienting reflexes. Special criteria are required which enable us to characterize a given reaction as a component of the orienting reflex.

[1] The survey of literature pertaining to this review was concluded in September 1962.

Three main principles are involved: (*a*) Nonspecificity with regard to the quality of the stimulus. (*b*) Nonspecificity with regard to the intensity of the stimulus. (*c*) Selectivity of extinction of various properties of the stimulus with repeated presentation. These properties characterize such responses as turning of the head and eyes in the direction of stimulation and pricking up the ears, which have been regarded by all the authors as somatic components of the orienting reflex. With the criteria mentioned above, it is possible to study other reactions whose relationship to the orienting reflex has been disputed—vegetative, electroencephalographic, and sensory components of this reflex.

Nonspecificity of the orienting reflex with regard to the quality of stimulus makes it possible to differentiate the orienting reflex from adaptation and defensive reflexes, as, for example, with plethysmographic changes. The simultaneous dilatation of cerebral blood vessels and constriction of peripheral vessels, which is observed in response to the first few presentations of such diverse stimuli as sound, light, electrical or thermal stimulation of the skin, demonstrates that no special modality gives rise to the orienting reflex. It is distinguishable from the adaptation reflex which depends upon the quality of the stimulus: for instance, warmth evokes dilatation of both cerebral and peripheral vessels, while cold evokes constriction of both. The defensive reflex in response to painful stimulation is characterized by a nonhabituating constriction of both peripheral and cerebral vessels (12, 13). Recently, further data concerning the dilatation of brain vessels as a component of the orienting reflex have been obtained by Kanzow (14), working alone and with Krause (15), using a new thermal conductivity method for the measurement of blood flow in the cerebral cortex of the cat. With simultaneous EEG recording it was shown that when a sudden attention reaction occurred, cerebral blood flow rapidly increased. As soon as attention to a novel stimulus decreased, the blood flow dropped. The significance of the cerebrovascular reaction for the activation of cortical neurons has been described by Klossovsky & Kosmarskaya (16). They state that the degeneration of cortical neurons resulting from transection of their connections with peripheral receptors is accompanied by a decrease in the density of the capillary net in the same cortical area. The authors suggest that the angioarchitechtonics of the brain mirror the cytoarchitechtonics. They believe the activating function of the reticular formation is carried out through certain vegetative functions: regulation of glandular activity, respiratory activity, and vascular activity of the brain and body as a whole. This mechanism takes part in behavior indirectly, by producing the shifts in vegetative function which anticipate and make possible the execution of certain reflexes by the animal.

Nonspecificity of the orienting reflex with regard to the intensity of the stimulus.—The responses to turning a stimulus off or on are identical. This phenomenon is related also to disappearance of this reflex against the background of a long-lasting stimulus. An example of the effective application of this criterion is found in a paper by Soltysik *et al.* (17) who found that the heart rate of dogs increases in response to sound-on and decreases in response to sound-off; thus such changes of heart rate cannot be regarded as components of the orienting reflex. It is important for this discussion that heart rate decreased with the switching-off of a sound which was a constant component of the acoustical environment. The authors suppose that this is an "acousticocardiac reflex," specifically dependent upon the intensity of the sound. Careful analysis of their papers, however, shows that, besides the acousticocardiac reflex, there was an enhanced response at the very beginning of sound stimulation, probably reflecting summation of the acoustico-cardiac and the orienting reflex.

The selectivity of extinction of the orienting reflex with regard to a repeatedly presented stimulus is seen in the character of the recovered reflex, which does not depend upon which property of the stimulus is changed, whether it be intensity, quality, or some temporal characteristic. Although its ability to undergo extinction is often considered the main quality, the independence of the character of the reaction from the type of stimulus modification is more essential. The ability to be extinguished has been demonstrated, however, on such specific adaptation reflexes as pupillary constriction to light (7) and the constriction of vessels to cold (5). In the paper by Soltysik (17) metnioned above, extinction of the acousticocardic reflex was also observed although it could not be classified as an orienting reflex.

The above criteria enable us to describe the orienting reflex as a functional system which becomes inactivated with repeated presentation of a standard stimulus and is then reactivated by any change in that stimulus. The reaction is the same no matter what quality of the stimulus undergoes change. According to such criteria, it is possible to regard a number of motor, vegetative, and electroencephalographic reactions as components of the orienting reflex, an integrated reaction which is specifically evoked by the novelty of a stimulus.

Modifications of Intrinsic Brain Waves as a Component of the Orienting Reflex

Differentiation of the orienting reflex from the defensive reflex.—The comparison of EEG reactions with known components of the orienting reflex indicates special EEG components of this reflex. It is difficult, however, to distinguish these EEG components from changes related to the defensive reflex. One solution is to study responses of the midpontine pretrigeminal preparation, the advantages of which lie in the combination of complete immobilization of the animal and exclusion of pain sensitivity with preservation of a high level of wakefulness. In experiments conducted by Affani, Marchiafava & Zernicki (18), using visual stimuli and electrical stimulation (100 per sec) of the hypothalamus, three components of the orienting reflex in cats were recorded: pupillary dilatation, eye movements towards the light source, and EEG activation. A flickering light evokes pupillary dilatation accompanied by movement of the eyes in the direction of the light stimulus. The pupillary dilatation is transient, i.e. it disappears in the same way as other orienting reflex components with continuation of the flicker stimulus. Simultaneously, the EEG pattern becomes desynchronized. With repeated stimulus presentation, all responses decrease and after the twentieth trial disappear; they recur after a rest period, but not so effectively as before. A tonic orienting reflex was evoked by such biologically significant stimuli as motion of the experimenter's hand in the visual field and by electrical stimulation of the hypothalamus. These were always accompanied by pupillary dilatation and EEG activation. The relationship of EEG activation and pupillary dilatation to such a typical component of the orienting reflex as eye movement was demonstrated by the dependence of eye movements upon the level of EEG arousal and the degree of dilatation of the pupil. Thus, when the EEG was synchronized and the pupils constricted, orienting eye movements to the light stimulus were absent. The experimenters have shown the difference between the pupillary response as a component of the orienting reflex and as a component of the adaptation reflex. In darkness, light evokes adaptive pupillary constriction, which precludes observation of the orienting pupillary dilatation. With constant illumination, however, when the pupil is partially constricted, a new light stimulus can evoke orienting dilatation of the pupil, which coincides with EEG activation and orienting eye movements. Since pain perception is excluded, this EEG activation cannot be interpreted as being a component of the defensive reflex.

Even during the elaboration of a defensive conditioned reflex, EEG changes are determined by activation of the orienting reflex. In experiments on rats with chronically implanted electrodes, Kelemen et al. (19) compared the EEG reactions accompanying extinguishable and nonextinguishable avoidance conditioned responses. The latter were established by the pairing of sound with a strong pain stimulus. The animal avoided the pain stimulation by jumping onto a glass cylinder. After several days of training, the conditioned response was maintained for months without further reinforcement. If the animal was placed in new surroundings, it responded to the sound by exploratory behavior as though it were searching for the cylinder; this was accompanied by EEG desynchronization which was not extinguished even after 100 to 200 nonreinforced trials. In untrained rats or rats with extinguishable avoidance responses, sound ceased to evoke EEG desynchronization after 20 to 30 trials, coincident with extinction of the exploratory behavior. This was accompanied by synchronization and spindling in the background EEG. Since the orienting-exploratory behavior of the rat coincides with changes in the EEG rhythm, the authors conclude that even in the case of such defensive behavior EEG activation is related to the orienting reflex. Similar results have been observed by Doty (20). With the development of defensive conditioned responses in cats, the intensity of the EEG activation reaction diminished after the conditioning became stabilized, and with continuation of training no alteration in EEG appeared.

Anokhin (21, 22), studying EEG desynchronization during the elaboration of defensive and alimentary conditioned responses, succeeded in selectively depressing behavioral and EEG manifestations of the defensive reflex by administration of chlorpromazine. He concluded that different mechanisms may underlie apparently identical desynchronization phenomena. Thus desynchronization in response to defensive stimuli and that in response to alimentary stimuli differ in physiological significance and constitute the cortical representation of two antagonistic systems: defensive and alimentary. Anokhin emphasizes three main activating mechanisms: activation for the preservation of wakefulness, activation underlying the orienting reflex, and activation in response to nociceptive stimuli.

The problem of the relationship between EEG activation and various reflexes has not yet been settled, but the role of the orienting reflex should not be underestimated.

The nonspecificity of the EEG as an orienting reflex component.—EEG activity in different species reflects the nonspecificity of EEG reactions. Thus, although the repertoire of specific reflexes varies greatly from species to species, responses recorded by the EEG are quite similar. This is confirmed by harmonic analysis of brain waves which shows the frequency spectra of the EEG to be similar for all vertebrates (23). Voronin (23) showed that with the repeated application of external stimuli, EEG changes can be observed which in their dynamics and temporal sequence are similar in man and animals (fish, frog, lizard, pigeon, rabbit, and dog). Voronin concluded that such changes represent a component of the orienting reflex which is related to the activity of the reticular formation: the responses to various stimuli in normal animals are usually accompanied by shifts in the frequency spectrum of the EEG. This generalized EEG reaction is eliminated by pentobarbital in all species tested, and by midbrain transection in all but the fish and frog (24).

The nonspecificity of EEG changes in various brain structures with the application of different stimuli has recently been pointed out by Galambos (25), who draws attention to slow wave activity in the white matter similar to activity usually seen in the gray matter. This similarity involves both the intrinsic rhythms and induced changes. Similar effects are produced by stimuli of different modalities and by indifferent and signal stimuli. This nonspecifiity of EEG changes holds with regard to recording site, stimulus modality, and significance of the stimulus. The latter has been emphasized by John (9); variations in EEG reactions were observed for the most part only in the duration, degree of spreading, and resistance to extinction. EEG reactions were more stable in the structures corresponding to the stimulus modality. Longer-lasting, generalized, and slowly extinguishing EEG responses occur with application of biologically significant stimuli, application of highly novel stimuli, and differentiation of stimuli, requiring increased orienting activity.

Tuge & Shima (26), in experiments on pigeons, showed similar types of EEG reactions with the application of indifferent and conditioned stimuli.

The differences between the responses lay in their duration and resistance to extinction. Thus, the generalized depression of slow waves observed in the EEG from the occipital lobe was more stable following light and electrical stimuli and less stable in response to sound stimulation. With repeated application of such stimuli, the reaction extinguished but reappeared during elaboration of differentiation and at the very beginning of the extinction of the conditioned reflex. Similar results in dogs were obtained by Naumova (27) on the changes of brain waves in response to sound as a nonsignal or signal stimulus. She studied the responses of cortical and subcortical structures of the auditory and motor analyzers as well as of the medullary reticular formation.

Rabinovich (28) has also reported the similarity of EEG activity and its modifications in various layers of the cortex as recorded from chronically implanted electrodes in dogs. Reactions involving increased amplitude and frequency of EEG rhythms extinguish most rapidly in the areas not related to the cortical projection of the stimulated analyzers. Localization of EEG responses to specific cortical layers occurs during elaboration and stabilization of conditioned reflexes.

The nonspecificity of EEG responses with regard to indifferent, positive, and negative (differentiated) stimuli is manifested by the EEG arousal that may accompany either excitation or inhibition of a conditioned reflex. In Ivanova's (29) experiments on people, as differentiated signals were made more complex the latency of the motor response to the positive signal increased. This inhibition of the conditioned reflex was accompanied by prolongation of alpha-rhythm depression to both positive and negative stimuli, indicating the presence of an excitatory process. If EEG desynchronization is regarded as a component of the orienting, rather than of the conditioned, reflex, a number of apparent contradictions in the EEG changes accompanying behavioral excitation and inhibition can be explained. Thus, an external stimulus may evoke external inhibition of a conditioned reflex, as indicated by increased latency of the motor response, and simultaneously evoke excitation of the orienting reflex, as expressed in EEG activation. With repeated presentation this external stimulus gradually loses its effectiveness for evoking either reflex.

The significance of EEG activation for processes in the conditioned reflex depends upon interrelations between it and the orienting reflex, which has a positive influence as an activator of the conditioned reflex and also a negative influence in the form of external inhibition, described by Pavlov (1).

There is, therefore, no simple relationship between the spontaneously arising alpha-rhythm depression and the motor conditioned reflex. Fedio et al. (30) describe the increased latency of a motor response during spontaneous alpha-rhythm blockade. On the other hand, experiments by Fraisse, Durup & Voillaume (31) showed a lack of correlation between spontaneous alpha blockade and the latent period of a motor response. No correlation has been found (32) between the alpha-rhythm blockade and efficiency in reproducing a matrix of numbers exposed tachistoscopically.

Comparison of EEG changes with the vegetative and motor components of the orienting reflex indicates that the EEG reaction represents an efferent part of the orienting reflex arc (7). This statement may appear to be paradoxical. Orbeli (33), in his theory of adaptive-trophic function of the vegetative nervous system, pointed out its role in the regulation of cortical metabolism. From this point of view the EEG changes result from efferent mechanisms of the vegetative system. This idea is supported by observations of Shevelyeva (34) who finds that in the very first days of postnatal development the increase of discharges in the sympathetic nervous system causes the spread of waves throughout the central nervous system.

Steady-Potential Shift and the Orienting Reflex

The relations between the steady potential and intrinsic brain waves.—Caspers (35) has developed a theory according to which the EEG constitutes amplitude modulation of the steady potential, so that this potential in a given cortical area determines the peculiarities of the intrinsic brain waves and evoked potentials recorded from that area. Following this line of investigation, Caspers & Stern (36) studied the inhibitory influence of factor P (a polypeptide extracted from the brain). On local application to the cortex it produces a positive shift of the steady potential accompanied by decreased frequency and increased amplitude of the EEG recorded from that area. The effect of factor P summates with the activity level of the animal. Thus, with the onset of sleep, slow waves appear some seconds earlier at the site of factor P application than in other areas of the cortex. On the other hand, negativity of the cortex and the arousal reaction can diminish or abolish its effect. Caspers concludes that slow waves cannot be explained as the summation of spikes. Instead he suggests that the slow waves represent oscillations of the local stationary potential, whose function is to regulate electrotonically the potential of the cell membrane which generates spikes.

The theory that the slow wave is an instance of stationary excitation has been developed further by Rusinov (37), who showed that the elaboration of the temporary connection is accompanied by a cortical steady potential shift, which becomes more localized during the stabilizing of the connection.

A shift in steady potential can be evoked by the orienting reflex and thus be accompanied by the blockade of slow waves (37, 38). In experiments on cats, Gumnit (39) has shown that with sound stimulation a very localized negative shift of steady potential can be recorded from one area of the auditory cortex. The duration of the shift coincides with the stimulus duration and is not an artifact of eye or body movements. One indication that the steady-potential shift is related to the orienting reflex is its susceptibility to habituation. By means of calomel nonpolarizing electrodes, Gumnit and Grossman (40) studied the interaction of the evoked- and the steady-potential shift. Normally the auditory cortex is positive relative to an indifferent point on the animal. The potential evoked by the onset of a tone consists of phases of primary positivity, primary negativity, and secondary positivity. With prolongation of the tone the secondary positivity is followed by negativity persisting throughout the total period of presentation. It is thought that the negative steady potential increases the cells' firing rates.

The steady-potential shift is a phenomenon common to different analyzers. Meshchersky & Smirnov (41), recording the evoked potentials in occipital cortex of the rabbit with calomel electrodes, observed the steady-potential shift during flickering light stimulation. The role of this shift in the elaboration of conditioned reflexes has been studied by Mnukhina (42). She notes that a negative shift can be evoked in the rabbit by indifferent stimuli and is followed by a train of slow waves in the EEG. The shift in steady potential is larger at the beginning of elaboration of a conditioned reflex to such stimuli. During stabilization of this reflex the negativity shift in response to the conditioned stimulus may give way to a positive shift which itself finally disappears.

The steady potential and the functional state of the cortex.—Under the influence of a localized artificial shift in steady potential, the functional state of a given cortical area can be significantly changed. The application of positive polarization to a cortical area, presumably by blockading the inhibitory cortical interneurons and thus increasing the excitability of pyramidal neurons, induces a "dominant focus" (38) so that, for instance, even though the polarization current is so low that it does not alter the intrinsic rhythm, previously indifferent stimuli come to evoke movements of the extremities.

Subsequent experiments demonstrated the importance of the orienting reflex in this mechanism. Novel stimuli evoked persistent EEG depression and paw movement. If a stimulus was applied to which the orienting reflex had previously been extinguished, however, it evoked only a slight depression of the EEG and no motor reaction at all. Simultaneous polarization of the reticular formation summated with cortical polarization, increasing the effectiveness of both types of stimuli. Nonhabituated stimuli came to evoke stronger responses, and habituated stimuli came to produce greater desynchronization and paw movement (43).

The steady potential and fixation of the stimulus trace.—The properties of the dominant focus are not limited to summation effects. Focal polarization can produce effects which outlast its own duration and thus may play a role in the fixation of traces. Polarization by a potential oscillating about a given mean leads to the fixation of a trace of this rhythmical stimulation. After the current has been switched off, rhythmical movement of the paw may continue to be evoked by extraneous stimuli. The "pulsating dominant focus" is highly stable and can be preserved for several days.

Simultaneous rhythmical polarization of the reticular formation enhances the paw movement. The site of trace fixation is the cortex, however, since after polarization is discontinued at both sites, a spontaneous rhythm matching that of the polarization oscillation frequency is seen only in the EEG of the cortex (37).

The functional role of steady-potential oscillations has been studied by Sologub (44). In the formation of stereotype motor responses in man, the EEG during intermediate stages of learning shows slow wave potentials coinciding in frequency with the performed motor reactions. This slow activity subsequently arises when the subject comes into the experimental surroundings. It seems that these oscillations arise on the basis of a rhythmical memory trace and participate in reproduction of the learned motor response.

Similar phenomena have been observed in dogs by Majkowski & Jasper (45). In elaborating a conditioned reflex to a sound paired with rhythmic electrical stimulation of the paw (5 impulses per sec), they observed that sound elicited the same rhythm in the EEG of the sensorimotor .cortex whether the shocks were given or not. This rhythm coincided with a twitching of the paw ("conditioned tremor").

Analysis of the steady-potential shift in response to indifferent stimuli shows that it may play a role in the mechanisms of EEG activation and participate in the fixation of traces. As a response to novel stimuli, this shift is a component of the orienting reflex.

THE ORIENTING REFLEX AND IMPROVEMENT OF THE FUNCTIONAL STATE OF BRAIN STRUCTURES

Facilitation of the evoked potential.—Kupalov (46) distinguishes two groups of nervous processes: those involved in performing the reaction, and those of general activation which only establish the tonus of different structures of the brain.

The activating effect is produced both by the novelty of the stimulus and by succeeding afferent impulses. Thus, the total effect of a new light stimulus includes both "orienting" activation and the activation, continuously evoked by light. Darkness as a novel stimulus produces the nonspecific activation which characterizes the orienting reflex but, at the same time, has an inactivating effect by limiting the visual input (47). In darkness the magnitude of conditioned reflexes is reduced (48), the latent period of motor reactions increases (49), and the level of cutaneous sensitivity drops (50). The same authors observed that all of these changes were reversed in the light. Changes of the functional state, which are not directly observable in background activity, can be detected and evaluated only by comparing evoked potentials recorded at different levels of the analyzers.

Activation is expressed indirectly in the facilitation of the cortical evoked potential produced by electrical stimulation of the optic chiasm and optic radiation fibers. Dumont & Dell (51) distinguish "nonspecific facilitation", consisting in the enhancement of cortical potentials evoked by single shocks in the visual system with high-frequency electrical stimulation

of the brainstem reticular formation, and "specific facilitation" referring to
the same effect when produced by light stimulation. That the mechanisms
of the two types of facilitation are identical is suggested by the facts that
the evoked potential changes are similar and the effects of light and reticular
formation stimulation are summative.

Facilitation of the evoked potential is not the only indication of improved
functional state. Dumont & Dell (51) report that when the EEG is desynchronized, reticular formation stimulation depresses the evoked potentials.
The difference between these two forms of modification becomes obvious
when the effects on such potentials evoked in a given analyzer by stimuli
of the same modality are compared with those evoked by electrical stimulations. In an experiment on curarized cats Moniava, Kadshaya & Narikashvili
(52) investigated the influence of reticular formation activation induced by
pain stimulation upon the potentials evoked in different parts of the visual
system by light and electrical impulses. Following the onset of cutaneous
pain stimulation, potentials evoked, by flashing light, in the cortex of the
hemisphere homolateral to the pain stimulation were depressed. The evoked
potentials in the geniculate body were depressed slightly. Those in the optic
tract, however, did not change. The depression of the cortical evoked
potential persisted for some time after the end of cutaneous stimulation.
Pain stimulation, on the other hand, increased the potentials in the cortex
evoked by low-frequency electrical shocks of the chiasm and failed to change
them in the geniculate body. The considerably greater change of cortical
potentials shows that nonspecific activation has its influence directly at the
cortical level rather than along the afferent pathways.

In attempting to explain why reticular activation has different effects
on the form of cortical potentials evoked by external stimuli and by direct
stimulation of the afferent pathways, Bremer (53) suggests that reticular
formation excitation may induce a partial refractoriness of the cortical
interneurons, which cannot be overcome by the relatively nonsynchronized
afferent volleys evoked by external stimuli. The highly synchronized afferent
discharge produced by electrical stimulation can, however, overcome this
refractoriness and reveal the activation effect induced by reticular formation
stimulation. Analysis of evoked potentials shows that even with a depression
of amplitude, there is acceleration of the processes underlying the potential.
That is, the activation effect may be expressed either in the reduction or in
the enhancement of the amplitude of evoked potentials. The crucial point is
that orienting reflex activation of the EEG is accompanied by a decrease in
duration of the evoked potential.

Dumont & Dell (51) have pointed out that the nonspecific facilitation
of cortical evoked potentials is related to the orienting reflex: during the
moment when an animal turns its head and eyes towards an unexpected
stimulus, the mechanism transmitting the new signals to the brain is facilitated. The analogy between facilitation of the cortical evoked potential by
stimulation of the reticular formation and by elicitation of the orienting

reflex has been noted also by Moruzzi (54), who suggests that the mechanisms of facilitation include: sympathetic facilitation, depolarization of apical dendrites and cell bodies in the cortex, and activation of intrinsic brain waves. Bremer's (53) hypothesis indicates that the orienting reflex involves an increase in the rate of nervous processes. This is supported by experiments of Lindsley (55) on the *cerveau isolé* preparation of the cat. Applying paired light flashes with 50-msec intervals between single flashes, he stimulated the reticular formation for 5 sec with electrical impulses (100 per sec). Before and during this stimulation, each pair of flashes evoked a single cortical evoked potential. During a 10-sec interval after this stimulation, however, each flash evoked a separate cortical potential. Lindsley concluded that the reticular stimulation enhanced the power of the cortex to differentiate closely spaced stimuli, and thus the transmission of sequences at signals was facilitated.

Caspers (35) states that the amplitude of the negative wave of the evoked potential depends upon the steady potential and the "indifferent level" of cortical negativity. Cortical activation associated with the orienting reflex shifts the steady potential towards negativity and diminishes the distance between it and the indifferent level, thus the negative wave of the evoked potential is reduced. When the cortical negativity becomes equal to the "indifferent level" the evoked potential altogether disappears.

Fessard's laboratory has studied changes in the evoked potential in response to radial nerve stimulation immediately following presentation of attention-provoking stimuli. Working with chronic preparations the authors have found depression of (a) the secondary response in the cortical association areas, (b) evoked potentials of the medial thalamic nuclei, and (c) the negative component of the primary potential. The positive wave of the primary response and of the response in specific nuclei is not affected (56, 57). The suggestion concerning different pathways responsible for different components of the evoked potential expressed by these authors coincides with results of studies by Anokhin (21, 22) which have demonstrated physiologically that such pathways do exist.

The mechanisms underlying changes in the evoked potential at various points along the afferent pathway during the orienting reflex have been explored in Gershuni's laboratory. Maruseva (58) concludes that the most significant modification accompanying this reflex is not the change in amplitude of the evoked potential but the rate of signal transmission in the central nervous system. The orienting reflex evoked by the appearance of a mouse before a cat's eyes does not change the microphonic effect to clicks but reduces the amplitude of the evoked potential in the medial geniculate body and in the auditory cortex. Most depressed are the negative components. Suppression of the evoked potential is accompanied by the appearance of fast waves in the EEG. The coincidence of the depression of this potential with a statistically significant increase in the excitability of the auditory system is attributed to lack of synchronization of nerve impulses under the influence of the activating mechanisms of the brain (59). Maruseva's interpretation is based upon studies by Gershuni (60) who distinguishes two types of summated electrical responses: summated axon spikes and summated synaptic potentials.

That reduced amplitude of evoked potentials may be caused by a lack of synchronization of afferent impulses is suggested by Gershuni's finding that the amplitude of summated potentials depends upon the rise time of the stimulus. Thus, if the rise time of the sound is more than 15 to 40 msec, no summated spike potential is recorded from the round window, but the cortical evoked potential is still present. If the rise time is increased to 100 to 175 msec the latter potential also disappears. Thus the form of the evoked potentials along the auditory pathway depends upon the transition characteristic of the stimulus. If the slope of the stimulus rise determines the degree of synchronization of discharges at the receptor and the synchronization of impulses is of importance for the evoked potential amplitude, any factor which tends to decrease the synchronization of spike activity probably lowers the amplitude of the response. Such desynchronization of spikes reaching the cortex, i.e., the more sparse distribution of spikes in time, also enables us to explain certain additional late components of the evoked potential recorded in the central parts of the analyzers during arousal.

Maruseva (58) states that the orienting reflex is accompanied by generalized excitation of the analyzers. The corollary is true also: the lowering of functional state produced by pentobarbital, for instance, is accompanied by a slowing of signal transmission.

In experiments by Altman & Maruseva (61) on cats with chronically implanted electrodes, it was shown that in anesthetized animals the latencies of the neural components of the cochlear response and of evoked potentials in the medial geniculate and, more pronounced, in cortex were increased with pentobarbital; increases in amplitude also occurred. Simultaneous lowering of the auditory threshold was apparently related to the disappearance of noises produced earlier by movement of the animal. The authors attributed the increased latencies to the slowing of synaptic transmission. The increase in amplitude, according to their view, is caused by the exclusion of the influence of nonspecific structures, which would otherwise induce desynchronization of spike volleys. Other data concerning the velocity of signal transmission as an important index of the brain's functional state have been reported by Mey Ley (62). When light flashes were presented to cats and rabbits subjected to hypoxia, he observed an increase in the latent periods of the "a" wave of the EEG and of the cortical evoked potential, an increase of retinocortical transmission time, and a decrease in the amplitude and the number of afterdischarges in the cortex. In normal cats with extended presentation of repetitive clicks, there occurred a reduction in the amplitude of the cochlear neural response and in evoked potentials of the medial geniculate body and cortex; the microphonic effect was unaltered. This indicates that the central changes are not dependent upon the muscles of the middle ear. Following electrical cutaneous stimulation, the responses recovered their original characteristics. Under barbiturate narcosis no decrease in evoked potentials takes place, suggesting the participation of central mechanisms in the habituation of the responses (63).

The decrease in amplitude of evoked potentials during habituation is regarded by Hernández-Péon (64) as a result of excitation of the reticular formation leading to the blockade of afferent impulses in the specific pathways. This view is contradicted by the fact that with repetitive stimulation and habituation EEG becomes synchronized rather than activated. Habituation is observed and occurs even more rapidly in the *cerveau isolé* preparation. This makes it questionable that the reticular formation plays an important role in habituation (65, 66).

The modification of the evoked potential with repeated stimulation can be characterized not only by a decrease in amplitude but also by an increased amplitude during early stages of habituation. Roitbak (67, 68), in a detailed study on cats of the "metamorphosis" of evoked potentials during extinction of the orienting reflex to a train of clicks (10 per sec), has observed that the disappearance of the behavioral orienting reflex coincided with the appearance of alpha-like slow waves in the EEG. At first these slow waves were localized in the ectosylvian gyrus; then they irradiated over the whole cortex. At this stage the evoked potentials were enlarged. Subsequent presentation of another stimulus evoked EEG activation accompanied by reduced evoked potential amplitude. Similar phenomena occurred with repetitive cutaneous stimulation and introduction of a novel stimulus. The author's main conclusion was that EEG activation and the behavioral orienting reflex represent a reversal of the extinction process. Regarding the low-frequency EEG waves as arising in the thalamic reticular formation and having an inhibitory function, Roitbak believes that the slow negative wave of the evoked potential represents the excitation of pyramidal cell dendrites, which according to Beritov (8) leads to the inhibition of the pyramidal cell bodies. Thus, summarizing findings on the mechanism of activation and inactivation, Maruseva (59) concludes that the amplitude of the evoked potential is not a simple indicator of the functional state of the analyzer. A drop in amplitude can reflect an increase or a decrease in reactivity. On the other hand, the time constant of evoked potentials is always reduced in the presence of the orienting reflex or at the beginning of the elaboration of a conditioned reflex indicating an increase in the reactivity of the analyzer. The facilitation of the evoked potential is in some aspects similar to the effect of posttetanic potentiation. Thus a question arises whether the orienting reflex plays a role in the regulation of synaptic transmission (69).

Modification of the frequency-specific reaction.—The ability of activation process to enhance or reduce evoked potentials is analogous to its ability to alter EEG responses to rhythmical stimulation. The effect of activation depends to a large degree upon the frequency of the test stimulus; a decrease in amplitude occurs in response to low-frequency stimulation, and an increase sometimes with a high test frequency. Ilyanok (70), studied the occipital EEG in people and showed that preliminary light adaptation leads to increased amplitude of response to a flickering light (20 to 60 cps). In the lower-frequency range (below 20 cps), enhancement was never observed and even a drop in amplitude often took place. Similar differences between the responses to high- and low-frequency visual and auditory stimulation have been demonstrated on pigeons (71) and men (72).

Thus, the amplitude of the low frequency-specific reaction is not the only criterion of the functional state of brain structures. Sometimes a reduction in the amplitude of the low-frequency response suggests a drop in functional state. But in such cases a high-frequency stimulus produces an increased amplitude of response.

Sensitization of receptors.—In addition to the clearly expressed effects of activation at cortical and subcortical levels, changes accompanying the orienting reflex are also observed in the receptors. The mechanism of such changes is closely related to the adaptive system described by Orbeli (33).

The participation by the vegetative system in the activation of receptors has been demonstrated by Beidler (73) in rabbits. The responses of the olfactory nerve to odors was increased immediately following the presentation of a loud noise, light flash, cutaneous stimulation, electrical stimulation of cervical sympathetic nerve, or increased activity of sympathetic fibers in the ethmoidal nerve.

The relationship of skin receptor sensitivity to vegetative responses in man has been demonstrated by Edelberg (74). By continuously measuring the threshold to vibratory stimulation, he discovered an increase in sensitivity of the tactile receptors during spontaneous or artificially induced orienting reflexes as demonstrated by the appearance of the galvanic skin response and constriction of the peripheral vessels. The galvanic response is thought to arise as a by-product of impulses of the sympathetic nervous system whose primary function is to sensitize the tactile receptors.

The facilitation of the functional state of the visual receptors has been studied by Sokolov (69) in unanesthetized rabbits. Frequency analyses were performed on the rhythmical electroretinograms evoked by flickering light (40 cps). Two forms of enhancement of the retinal response to the flashing light have been shown: modality-specific facilitation induced by a light stimulus and modality-nonspecific facilitation induced by a sound stimulus. The rate of extinction with repetition of the latter was much higher than that of the former. Similar specific and nonspecific facilitation in the visual system were also demonstrated in pentobarbitalized cats by Dulenko & Sokolov (75 to 78).

Modifications of the evoked potentials accompanying extinction and disinhibition of the orienting reflex.—The participation of peripheral receptor mechanisms in modifying the evoked potential has not been elucidated. Direct contradictions exist in experimental findings. Thus, Gershuni (70) and Galambos (25), in experiments on cats with transection of the muscles

of the middle ear and with curarized preparations, have demonstrated that
the decrease and the recovery of the evoked potential do not depend upon
peripheral mechanisms. However, other experiments demonstrate quite the
opposite. Guzman-Flores, in remarks following a paper by Neff (79),
directly raises an objection to Galambos' conclusions. Recording the evoked
potential to clicks from the auditory cortex simultaneously with orienting
movements of the ears in cats, he showed that, after complete extinction of
the motor orienting reflex, the evoked potential did not change; only later
did it decrease and undergo extinction. Thus he feels that extinction of the
motor orienting reflex and habituation of the evoked potential have essentially different mechanisms. On the basis of studies of the selectivity of
habituation to the frequency of a sound stimulus, Guzman-Flores suggests
that extinction of the evoked potential involves an "anticipatory increase
of the tonus" in the muscles of the middle ear. The anticipation may arise
from elaboration of a conditioned reflex regulating the tonus of the middle
ear muscles.

Similar results for the visual system are offered by Mancia (80) in a
discussion of pupillary responses. The presentation of 1-sec light flashes to
an *encéphale isolé* preparation of the cat leads to the disappearance of responses in the visual pathway and a synchronization of the EEG. After a
series of flashes lasting two hours, stimulation of the reticular formation
increases the amplitude of evoked potentials even in the optic tract and
lateral geniculate body. This increase is accompanied by pupillary dilatation and eye movements. Dilatation of the pupil by atropine or destruction
of the third nerve nuclei abolishes the habituation of the evoked potential.
In these cases, reticular stimulation has no magnifying effect at any level
and even depresses the cortical evoked potentials. It appears that the decrease in amplitude of the evoked potential during habituation depends
directly upon the intensity of the light falling on the retina; this in turn is
regulated by the size of the pupil. The situation is more complicated, however, as Fernández-Guardiola (65, 66) states that the amplitude of the
evoked potential depends upon the intensity of the stimulus; the magnitude
of pupil diameter; and the level of background activity of the structure,
from which the potential is recorded.

The cortical evoked potential does not depend directly upon either the
intensity of the light or the diameter of the pupil. With atropinized pupils,
partial habituation still takes place in the form of decreased amplitude of the
potential; at the same time, atropinization abolishes the habituation of this
potential caused by electrical stimulation of the optic chiasm. The intensity
of such stimulation does not depend, of course, upon the diameter of the
pupil.

Microelectrode recordings show that the activity of retinal neurons increases during dilatation of the pupils and decreases when the pupils become
constricted. This leads to deactivation of cortical and reticular structures
which regulate the level of wakefulness and to decreased EEG activity and

reduced evoked potential amplitude. The central deactivation abolishes the centrifugal facilitatory action upon the retina, which further inactivates the receptors. Thus, the pupil participates in habituation insofar as it influences the spontaneous neural activity of the retina. The diminution in the evoked potential is related to the system of reflex mechanisms by which the cortex influences retinal neurons. The participation of cortical regulation of receptor mechanisms thus may explain the selectivity of habituation of evoked potentials along the afferent pathways to certain stimulus characteristics.

Modification of the evoked potential as a manifestation of the orienting reflex in conditioned reflex elaboration.—If modification of evoked potentials is considered to be closely related to the orienting reflex, it is possible to explain the similarity of the evoked potential changes which take place during habituation of the orienting reflex and during stabilization of a conditioned reflex. This similarity is based upon the extinction of the first during the stabilization of the second reflex.

Recording the potential evoked by clicks (5 per sec) in auditory, sensory, and motor cortex of dogs, Majkovski & Jasper (45) observed habituation with repetition of the clicks 30 to 50 times per day. Insofar as the experimental conditions were preserved, the evoked potential continuously diminished from day to day. At the beginning of elaboration of an avoidance conditioned reflex (unconditioned stimulus = 5 per sec electrical shock to the paw), the evoked potential regained its initial magnitude. When the level of correct avoidance responses reached 90 to 95 per cent, the potential's amplitude became low again. The responses recovered again at the beginning of extinction of the conditioned reflex. The authors concluded that the evoked potential is related to the level of general excitement of the animal to the orienting reflex and not to the conditioned reflex itself.

Similar results have been reported by Galambos (25). Monkeys with bipolar implanted electrodes became habituated to clicks (6 per min) which were presented for several days. When the click was paired with an air puff in the face, the original responses were recovered. In ten minutes the responses to click disappeared again, but could be re-established by a subsequent air puff. Marsh *et al.* (81), in experiments on cats, also observed depression of the amplitude of the evoked potential in specific and nonspecific structures. The elaboration of defensive conditioned reflexes produced increased responses in 30 of 32 leads.

Similar results were obtained by Chow (82) who used flashing light of different frequencies to illuminate the test object. He demonstrated the weakening of the frequency-specific reaction during conditioned reflex stabilization and elaboration of consistent differentiation of the signals. Changes in the frequency-specific EEG reaction did not correlate with the learning curve; they reflected the functional state of the organism during learning more than the stage of learning. It is especially interesting that every time the animal started to solve a new problem, recovery of the frequency-specific response occurred.

The structure of the orienting reflex; conditioned inhibition as the mechanism of orienting reflex extinction.—The main method in the study of the orienting reflex involves selective habituation to certain characteristics of the stimulus and subsequent change of those characteristics. Thus it is possible to discover factors in the excitation and the inhibition of this reflex. Insofar as the form of the orienting reflex, as manifested in the EEG, depends upon the background EEG activity, the most reliable form of orienting reflex extinction is that which takes place without marked changes in background brain waves. If background EEG activity does not change, disappearance of the orienting reflex cannot be attributed to a simple lowering of functional state. Also, since a new stimulus will evoke the same type of response as before, extinction cannot be attributed to a decrease in the excitability of the efferent paths of this reflex. The absence of reaction cannot be explained by lowered excitability of the peripheral afferents, because a drop in intensity of the stimulus to near threshold level will evoke the orienting reflex just as any other change of the stimulus will (83, 84).

Extinction of the orienting reflex consists in a gradual decrease in the duration of response with little or no change in its latent period. After complete extinction it can recur immediately when the pattern of stimulation is changed. The type of response is the same whether evoked by a new stimulus or by the omission of a signal which has been presented repeatedly at fixed intervals. Both extinction of the orienting reflex and conditioned inhibition develop proportionally to the number of times the stimulus is applied (1). Presumably, the arrival of afferent impulses to the centers from which different component reactions of the orienting reflex arise is regulated by a conditioned mechanism which modifies synaptic transmission (13).

The fact that after complete extinction of the orienting reflex to a regularly repeated signal the reaction reappears at the moment the signal is omitted cannot be explained by a lack of a conditioned blockade. Thus a second, internal, source of impulses must be postulated. It is assumed that the applied stimulus evokes excitation which travels by two pathways: the first leads directly to the center responsible for a given orienting reflex component and can be blocked by conditional inhibition. The second leads to the mechanism of memory trace fixation. On the basis of this memory trace, impulses of mismatch are produced which are proportional to the difference between the arriving signals and the trace. These impulses can also reach the centers responsible for the orienting reflex. The trace has been referred to as a "nervous model of the stimulus" (85).

The nervous model of stimulus.—The concept of the "nervous model of stimulus" is closely related to the concept of "acceptor of action" (6). Only in terms of such a concept is it possible to explain the appearance of the orienting reflex upon the very first presentation of the altered stimulus. Since the intensity of the orienting reflex is assumed to be proportional to difference between the stimulus and the nervous model, the reflex can become a tool for investigating the model. The minimal change of a given

parameter of the stimulus required to evoke the orienting reflex characterizes the precision with which this parameter is registered in the central
nervous system. Consecutive change of the stimulus parameters allows
determination of the multidimensional "form" of the model. The following
characteristics of the nervous model of stimulus can be distinguished:

(a) Following multiple presentation of a constant stimulus, the nervous
model coincides with the parameters of the stimulus within limits near to
the just noticeable difference.

(b) After repeated presentations of stimuli with characteristics varying
within given limits, the nervous model is generalized to match the limits of
stimulus variation.

(c) Since it simultaneously represents the intensity, quality, and
temporal characteristics of signals, the nervous model can be thought of as
a multidimensional model of the stimulus.

(d) Appearance of the orienting reflex in response to omission of one of
the components of a complex stimulus (a stimulus affecting more than one
analyzer) shows that complex sets of stimuli are registered in the nervous
model.

(e) Appearance of the orienting reflex in response to a change in the
sequence of a repeated set of signals shows that the nervous model involves
extrapolation in time of the expected value of the stimulus (86).

The study of motor conditioned reflexes has shown that the nervous
model is of importance for conditioning (87, 88).

The conditioned orienting reflex.—If the orienting reflex to an unconditioned stimulus is one which takes a long time to extinguish, it can be used
to study the conditioned orienting reflex, elaboration of which follows essentially the same laws as the formation of other conditioned reflexes. In
this regard, the experiments of Affani *et al.* (89) involving the elaboration of a
"conditioned OR" in pretrigeminal cats are of special interest. After a number of applications of a train of flashes, all components of the orienting
reflex disappeared. Subsequently, pairing of the light stimulation with
electrical stimulation of the hypothalamus (which evokes nonhabituating
pupillary dilatation, EEG desynchronization, and eye movement) led to
the appearance of all these responses to the flickering light alone. That this
orienting reflex to light resulted from the elaboration of a conditioned reflex
and not from a potentiation effect is shown by the following facts: (a) while
the background EEG soon returned to normal, the response to light flashes
persisted for several hours, and (b) the response was specific to the flicker
frequency which had been paired with hypothalamic stimulation.

Evidence of participation of the cortex in initiation of the activation is
to be found in experiments on cats conducted by Buchwald *et al.* (90). Their
work has demonstrated a specific role of the integrative visual areas in
activating the visual system. Ascher *et al.* (91) showed in cats under chloralose anesthesia that light and sound stimuli produced pronounced discharges
in the ventral spinal roots. That this response is facilitated by a cortical

mechanism was demonstrated by the fact that strychninization of the visual cortex increased the ventral root discharges. Application of potassium chloride to the visual cortex eliminated both the visual cortex evoked potential and the motor response to light.

Thus, in addition to the inhibitory conditioned mechanism manifested in extinction of the orienting reflex, a conditioned mechanism for its excitation has been demonstrated. Such conditioning may explain the enhancement of the orienting reflex by verbal instruction (92, 93).

Conditioned regulation of the level of sleep-wakefulness.—In analyzing the conditioned mechanism of orienting reflex extinction, we have concentrated on cases not accompanied by changes in EEG background activity. It is possible, however, to condition changes in functional state.

The conditioned lowering of functional state can be demonstrated in man using a repetitive flickering light stimulus. In the beginning the light evokes a frequency-specific reaction. Then a gradual drop in functional state takes place and the flickers evoke only frequency-nonspecific EEG activation. In later experiments a complex response appears: the onset of a train of flashes evokes the activation response, which quickly gives way to a sequence of slow waves. The process ends with complete disappearance of the activation response and the appearance of slow waves immediately following the onset of light. That these slow waves are related specifically to the applied stimulus is shown by the fact that any change in flicker frequency or (even more effective) the application of a stimulus of a different modality immediately evokes the typical EEG arousal (94). The change in response from one of desynchronization to one of the enhancement of slower alpha waves is also observed with repeated presentations of a tactile stimulus. These phases appear as a result of extinction of the orienting reflex. The introduction of sound as a novel stimulus at any point will evoke generalized depression of the alpha rhythm (95). Apparently the repeatedly applied stimulus itself becomes the signal for inactivation. This inhibitory conditioned reflex can be elaborated within one analyzer, and the beginning of the stimulus becomes a signal for the development of EEG inactivation.

This conditioned inactivation is closely related to conditioned sleep. Most interesting is the sleep which is evoked by repetitive application of an indifferent stimulus following extinction of the orienting reflex. Such an agent induces sleep more rapidly with each succeeding experiment. Eventually it becomes a conditional stimulus for sleep inhibition (1).

Kupalov (46) has shown that the functional state can be regulated by the conditioned reflex mechanism. In Asratian's laboratory, Sakhiulina (96) observed the conditioning of tonically enhanced electrical activity in dogs. After several conditioned reflex experiments, enhancement of the EEG was observed as the dog was brought into the experimental room. Fast waves were observed during the whole experiment only in the cortical area which was most involved in the motor behavior under study.

The interrelations of the activating and inactivating mechanisms involved in the orienting reflex.—The integrative efferent center of the orienting reflex has been suggested to be the reticular formation. The arguments supporting this assumption include the facts that the arousal reaction to direct electrical reticular stimulation does not extinguish, and prolonged drowsiness follows lesions of the reticular formation.

More recently, concepts concerning the activating system have been altered by new studies showing extinction of the arousal reaction to electrical stimulation of the brainstem and the recovery of the arousal reaction after chronic lesions of the brainstem reticular formation.

Glickman & Feldman (97) stimulated this brainstem formation through chronic electrodes to produce arousal reactions in sleeping unanesthetized cats. After a few presentations of 2-sec trains of impulses (50 to 400 per sec) applied at 1-min intervals, the arousal reaction was extinguished. It recovered after a 33-min interval, with prolongation of the train of impulses from 2 to 4 sec or with change of the stimulating frequency. Usually the shifts from low to high frequency evoked the full reaction while shifts from high to low frequency evoked weaker responses or none. This extinction could not be explained by a decrease in excitability of the reticular formation since various external stimuli (claps, etc.) readily evoked the response. The authors concluded that either a mechanism performing the inhibition of the responses exists in the reticular formation itself or inhibition is achieved by means of corticoreticular feedback.

Indirect evidence for such cortically mediated feedback has been obtained in other experiments by the same authors. Cats under chloralose anesthesia required an unusually large number of reticular stimulations for orienting reflex extinction; the extinction was never complete, and it lacked frequency-specific selectivity. The fact that the orienting reflex evoked by such electrical stimulation can be extinguished indicates that such stimulation is not acting on the final efferent link in the orienting reflex arc. There must be a synaptic junction between the reticular formation site stimulated and the orienting reflex center, for only at such a junction could the inhibition which is responsible for extinction of the response be brought about.

Further evidence that the reticular formation is not the only effector center of the orienting reflex has come from experiments involving serial lesions. Moruzzi (54) states that after chronic transection of the midbrain at a high level (especially when the transection was performed in several steps) gradual recovery of the normal EEG was observed in cats and dogs. A question arises concerning the participation of rostral parts of the reticular formation and the hypothalamus in the tonic activation observed in such preparations.

The role of higher levels of the central nervous system in the regulation of reticular formation excitability is attracting more and more interest (98). Thus, experiments by Adey & Lindsley (99, 100) have demonstrated that the functional state of the brainstem reticular formation is dependent upon its interaction with the subthalamus. In cats, subthalamic lesions lower the tonus of the reticular formation as reflected in decreased spontaneous firing rate of single cells and decreased amplitude of evoked potentials in that area. A temporary recovery of excitability can be obtained by tetanic electrical stimulation of the brainstem. The drop in functional state of the reticular formation occurs simultaneously with the decrease of phasic inhibition. This leads to the shortening of the recovery cycle of the evoked potentials.

The concept of the reticular formation as surrounded by inhibitory systems of thalamus and lower brainstem seems to be giving way to a model in which activating and inactivating systems operate compatibly in the same structures. Moruzzi (54) has shown that low-frequency stimulation of the reticular formation can give rise to slow waves in the cortical EEG and thus be a source of a direct inhibitory process. Buchwald *et al.* (101), studying the caudate nucleus, have come to similar conclusions concerning the topographical compatibility of activating and inactivating systems. Low-frequency caudate stimulation evokes inactivation, expressed in EEG spindling and reduced behavioral activity. High-frequency stimulation at this site abolishes the spindles and inhibition of behavioral responses.

The mechanism of local cortical activation.—The possibility of a multiple representation of the activating and inactivating functions in different brain structures raises a question concerning the existence of such mechanisms in the cortex itself. The suggestion of a cortical arousal mechanism independent of activation mechanisms of other structures has been expressed by Kupalov (46). His hypothesis is based upon the study of conditioned changes of the functional state of the cortex.

Of most interest for the further testing of this hypothesis is the search for a local orienting response confined to the analyzer stimulated. Such are the local changes in rolandic rhythm which occur in response to proprioceptive stimulation or the change in alpha rhythm of the occipital cortex to light stimulation. The question of the local EEG reaction is discussed in a paper by Tsuy Chgi-Pin (102). Working with normal human subjects, he placed electrodes at regular intervals from the motor area to the occipital area. During the elaboration of a motor conditioned reflex to a sound stimulus he observed the so-called "funnel effect", i.e., the depression of alpha rhythm in the motor region began earlier and lasted longer than in areas nearer to occipital pole. The difference in responses in the latter areas was regarded as a consequence of the spreading of EEG blockade to other parts of the cortex, while the local cortical arousal is caused by greatly limited irradiation of excitation in the cortex.

Important data concerning local cortical activation are contained in a paper by Roitbak & Buthkusi (103). With electrical stimulation (impulses 40 to 70 per sec) of the medial geniculate body, local activation of the auditory area was observed, followed by all the usual manifestations of the orienting reflex, but occurring more slowly. During local cooling of auditory cortex, electrical stimulation of the medial geniculate body failed to elicit the arousal reaction, indicating that in this situation local activation of the auditory cortex is necessary for elicitation of the orienting reflex.

The relative independence of cortical and reticular activation mechanisms was suggested by observations of Beteleva & Novikova (104) on the EEG of rabbits after olfactory deafferentation. A lowering of activity in all cortical areas occurred, accompanied by increased electrical activity in the brainstem reticular formation. Thus, in the normal rabbit, olfactory input apparently makes a contribution to cortical activity which is not mediated by the reticular formation.

The possibility of local cortical activation has further been demonstrated in experiments by Karimova on dogs (105), in which ear movements, respiratory changes, and EEG changes in the motor and occipital cortices and the reticular formation of the thalamus and brainstem were recorded. After extinction of all components of the orienting reflex to a 500 cps tone in light natural sleep, a change in frequency of the tone by 100 cps evoked EEG desynchronization, ear movements, and a change in respiratory rhythm. In pentobarbital sleep, however, the arousal reaction to sound was sometimes observed only in the cortical structures with no sign of reticular activation. During deeper sleep, when changes in tone frequency failed to evoke any response, the name of the animal could evoke a high-frequency rhythm in the cortex, again with no change of rhythm in the reticular formation. The local cortical arousal to tone was most pronounced in the temporal region (105) in pentobarbital and natural sleep.

Suggestions of an independent cortical component of arousal accord with data obtained by Kogan (106) with cats. Undercutting of the cortical area of the visual and motor analyzers did not altogether prevent desynchronization in the isolated part to visual, auditory, and mechanical cutaneous stimulations, but total isolation of the same area abolished the responses. It thus appears that excitation can irradiate, at least partially, transcortically. Studies by Kogan (1961) indicate that even after a cut around a given cortical area, direct electrical stimulation evokes the orienting reflex in all its components, which indicates the role which corticofugal connections can play in evoking this reflex.

The relation of local cortical activation to cortical mechanisms of the memory trace is involved in experiments of Purpura (107). Stimulation of the intralaminar thalamic nuclei by electrical impulses (25 per sec) evoked synchronized waves (10 to 14 per sec) in the suprasylvian gyrus of three-day-old kittens. With prolonged electrical stimulation such waves steadily decreased and finally disappeared. The rhythm was re-established, however, when the stimulating frequency was changed to 50 per sec. Purpura relates these experiments to familiar habituation phenomena. He believes that mechanisms producing increased or decreased "meaningfulness" of stimuli are to be found in the synaptic organization of the cortex.

Purpura's experiments do not rule out the participation of thalamic activating structures in the generation of the cortical EEG. Direct demonstration of local cortical activating mechanisms is to be found in subsequent investigations of electrical activity of the chronically isolated cortical slab by Purpura & Housepian (108). The auditory cortex was surgically isolated in kittens, two days after birth. Seven days later, direct stimulation of this isolated area evoked a rhythm (8 to 14 per sec) similar to the waves evoked in the intact animal by stimulation of the intralaminar thalamus. These data indicate that, in addition to the activating influences entering the cortex from the reticular formation of the brainstem, thalamus, and hypothalamus, the possibility exists of an intracortical activating mechanism evoked by impulses entering directly via the specific pathway.

ORIENTING REFLEX AT THE LEVEL OF THE SINGLE NEURON
Mechanisms of the Memory Trace and Arousal

The memory trace.—The concept that the orienting reflex results from a mismatch of incoming signals with a neuronal model of the stimulus makes it important to consider the possible nature of this model or "memory trace".

One hypothesis considers that the neuron is the elementary unit of memory mechanisms, and that the formation of the memory trace involves the integrated activity of groups of neurons. This viewpoint is supported by Hubel & Wiesel (109) concerning the organization of the receptive fields of individual visual cortical neurons of the cat. There are two types of receptive field: simple and complex. The simple field differs from the circular receptive field of the neurons of lateral geniculate body; thus cortical neurons receive integrated impulses from circular receptive fields. The stimulus to which neurons with such fields respond is a line whose axis of orientation is the same as that of the field. The simple receptive field is localized on the retina. Cortical neurons with complex receptive fields respond to stimuli with special orientation but independent of areas of the retina on which the image falls. The complex receptive field depends for its specificity upon complex spatial characteristics (the slope of a line). The excitation of neurons with such properties must result from their involvement by numerous connections with other neurons. In terms of this theory the elaboration of the nervous model of a complex stimulus depends upon the complexity of the receptive fields. So far, the receptive field studies do not explain the representation of complex time sequences of stimuli in the central nervous systems.

A second hypothesis, suggested by Hydén (110, 111), involves intracellular mechanisms of stimulus trace preservation. Hydén's concept of the molecular mechanism of memory is based upon the fact that the rate of production of nerve cell RNA and the level of activity of its oxidative enzymes are dependent upon the level of nervous activity. The sequences of amino acid in protein molecules of the cell are determined by the sequences of bases in its RNA molecules. Assuming frequency modulation of impulses to be the principal form of coded information in the nervous system, Hydén proposes that the first step in the establishment of the intraneuronal engram is a specific change of the RNA structure according to the temporal pattern of entering nervous impulses. He suggests that the pattern of nervous impulses may change the order of bases in the RNA molecule by altering the ionic milieu in which these molecules are synthesized. Certain patterns of impulses would lead to the production of corresponding stable RNA molecules.

The second step in the formation of the engram would consist in the formation of a protein specific to the RNA molecule. The third step, it is suggested, is the rapid dissociation of the specific protein when the pattern of impulses responsible for synthesis of the specific RNA is repeated. The fourth step in Hydén's theory requires that the products of dissociation of the protein take part in the formation of substances which facilitate synaptic transmission. Thus a given cell comes to respond selectively to the pattern of impulses received in the past. This molecular hypothesis suggests that information arriving in the brain is simultaneously fixed in a multitude of neurons, thus explaining the well-known fact that memory may remain unimpaired even after extirpation of large areas of the hemispheres.

This theory concerning the molecular mechanism of trace fixation has aroused a number of objections regarding the hypothetical selective influence of patterned nerve impulses on the synthesis of RNA molecules (112). On the basis of such a hypothesis, however, it is possible to explain the formation of a nervous model of stimulus, which registers all aspects of a signal including its temporal sequential properties.

Habituation of local cortical arousal.—It is difficult to explain the extinction of local cortical arousal, where the mechanisms of the formation of the nervous model and the activation mechanism are present in the same cortical structure. Of special interest is the selective extinction of the response to a sequence of stimuli, such that the response reappears if one of the stimuli is omitted or if the order of presentation is changed. This phenomenon suggests that the nervous model should not be conceived of simply as a passive stable engram, but as a mechanism which can extrapolate the patterning of future nervous impulses. To explain this type of extinction, a hypothesis has been proposed involving the interaction of three functionally different types of neurons (86):

(*a*) afferent neurons which are always responsive to the stimulus, even with repeated presentation;

(*b*) extrapolatory neurons which tend to respond as they have responded in the past;

(*c*) comparator neurons which respond quantitatively according to the degree of asimilarity between signals coming to them from the afferent and extrapolatory neurons. Local activation is suggested to occur as a result of the activity of comparator neurons, with the participation of glial cells. This activating function of glial cells may be attributable to neurosecretory effects (113) on the polarization of neurons which influence synaptic transmission.

With repetition of a stimulus there occur: (*a*) fixation of the sequence of afferent signals by molecular mechanisms in the extrapolatory neurons; (*b*) generation by the extrapolatory neurons of a sequence of nervous impulses, which anticipates the future stimulus and represents an elementary form of conditioning at the single neuron level; (*c*) disappearance of the reactions of the comparator neurons as soon as the impulses, coming to the comparator neurons from afferent and extrapolatory neurons, coincide; (d) disappearance of the local cortical EEG arousal with the disappearance of comparator neuron responses; (e) changes in spike background activity because of changes in the level of local arousal; (f) recovery of the activation response to a change of the stimulus, when a new mismatch between the input of afferent and extrapolatory neurons leads to renewed activity of the comparator neurons; (g) corresponding increase in the functional state of the cortical area involved in the arousal (83).

This theory regarding the neuronal mechanisms of extinction and recovery of the local cortical activation reaction receives indirect support in a number of papers devoted to the study of the properties of single neurons.

Afferent neurons.—Jung's studies (114) present convincing evidence that certain neurons in the visual cortex always respond to light flashes, i.e., do not habituate. Such afferent neurons may respond to specific stimulus properties. According to Jung's modified classification, B (brightness) neurons and D (darkness) neurons, responses of which are reciprocally related, are responsible for the perception of simultaneous and successive visual contrasts (115). The activity of these afferent neurons can depend upon very complex stimulus properties, especially in the case of cortical neurons, but even at the retinal level in the frog.

As shown by Lettvin et al. (116), certain retinal neurons respond selectively to complex properties of visual stimuli. Such cells include "boundary detectors", which react only if a boundary falls on the receptive field; "convexity detectors", which respond to appearance in the visual field of an angle but do not respond to straight lines; "contrast detectors", which respond to changes in the degree of contrast between two objects but not to changes in general illumination.

Hubel & Wiesel (109) have demonstrated cells in the visual cortex of the cat which respond to stimuli specially oriented in space. Katsuki (117) has shown cells in the auditory cortex whose firing rates increase if two simultaneously presented tones are harmonically related. The chief characteristics of the afferent neurons are their specificity to the modality of stimulation and the stability of their responses with repeated presentation of the stimulus.

Extrapolatory neurons.—The concept of a specialized extrapolatory type of cell is supported by Lettvin et al. (116) who describe so-called "sameness neurons" in the tectum of the frog. Such neurons begin to respond only some time after the appearance of a stimulus in the visual field. Once a sameness neuron has "caught" the stimulus, however, it responds to the stimulus no matter where it may be located in the visual field. The fact that the sameness neuron "follows" a given stimulus may indicate that it has an extrapolatory function. This locking in on a given stimulus appears to be very selective, since the appearance of a second stimulus in the visual field does not alter its responsiveness to the first object. A sameness neuron will start to follow another stimulus only after the first one has disappeared.

The suggestion that the extrapolatory neurons simply represent a specific state of the afferent neurons is supported by experiments of Morrell (118, 119). During anodal polarization of the rabbit visual cortex, he observed "imprinting" of the rhythm of a 3-per-sec flickering light. After presentation of the flicker, when spontaneous firing of a given neuron was absent, the presentation of a single flash evoked 3-per-sec bursts of spikes. This rhythmic response to a single flash might last for several hours.

Comparator neurons.—These should closely resemble the "attention units" found by Hubel *et al.* (120) in the auditory cortex of the cat. The special characteristic of these cells is that with repetition of a given signal, they cease to respond. A new, unexpected stimulus re-establishes the response of such a cell. A small number (2 out of 77 cells studied) were found by Huttenlocher (121) in the brainstem reticular formation of cats. Very characteristic of these cells were rapid habituation to a repetitive stimulus and great sensitivity to new stimuli of any modality.

In their work in the frog tectum, Lettvin *et al.* (116) describe "novelty cells" which appear to be similar to Hubel's attention units. These cells ceased to respond to the movement of an object so long as it moved repeatedly along a given track in the visual field. A change in the direction of movement, however, evoked the response anew. The novelty neurons were shown to be efferent: the cell body lies in the tectum, while the axon running in the optic nerve ends in the retina.

Neuronal mechanisms of the orienting reflex.—These are discussed in a monograph by Beritov (8), who makes a distinction between cortical "sensory neurons" and cortical efferent neurons especially involved in execution of the orienting reflex. On the basis of his own work and that of Shkolnik-Yarros (122), Beritov concludes that the stellate cells, located in the second and fourth layers of the primary sensory projection areas, provide the morphological elements responsible for the integration and differentiation of stimuli.

He has given the name "sensory neurons" to one type of stellate cell, whose axon does not extend beyond the sphere of its own dendritic arborization. He suggests that it participates in local neural mechanisms underlying sensation. A second type of stellate cell, characterized by short dendrites and a long axon, is presumed to conduct impulses from the afferent thalamic neurons to association and interneurons of the cortex. The integration of sensory neurons by means of the long-axoned stellate cells occurs after a single perception and may be preserved for months or even years without repetition. This type of integration of sensory neurons differs greatly from the establishment of a conditioned reflex. The latter involves the participation of the projection pyramids and requires repeated reinforcement for its formation and to prevent its extinction.

The perception of new objects and the reproduction of images are accompanied by the orienting reflex. The efferent mechanism of this reflex includes the pyramidal Meinert cells, which are responsible for head movement, and the Cajal cells, terminating in oculomotor centers. The sensory neurons, which Beritov believes to be responsible for the subjective conscious aspect of perception, are not influenced by extinction inhibition. According to his theory, however, the weakening of impulses entering via the reticular formation can lead to the cessation of activity in stellate neurons.

Extinction of the orienting reflex, according to Beritov, is based on inhibition which develops in the following way: excitation arising in the dendrites of pyramidal cells cannot give rise to impulses because of the sharp decrement in membrane potentials but spreads electrotonically toward the cell body. Because of the glial covering of the neuron, the current flows only through the synaptic knobs, evoking there electrotonic blockades which prevent the further activation of the dendrites by subsequent impulses arriving at these synapses. Thus, during the period of general "desynchronization" of the EEG when there is increased stimulation from the reticular formation, the slow dendritic potentials become weaker and disappear. With blockade of its synapses the cell body fails to respond to impulses from the reticular formation, and its initial depolarization diminishes. The cell body becomes hyperpolarized and thus less excitable. The first cortical layer in which the majority of apical dendrites of the pyramidal cells are located is thought to be the source of inhibition, since activation of these dendrites is assumed to inhibit the responses of such cells.

The function of glia in the arousal reaction.—Contemporary electron microscopy demonstrates very close connections between neurons and surrounding oligodendroglia. Luse (123), noting that the extracellular space is no more than 3 to 5 per cent of the total space in neural tissue, believes that the oligodendroglia, by separating vessels and neurons, acts as a pathway for the transport of electrolytes in the nervous system. In experimentally induced edema or dehydration of the rabbit brain, the only changes observed are in the oligodendrocytes. According to Hydén (110, 111), the entire surface of a neuron, except for that covered by synaptic contacts, is covered with glia which are thought to constitute the blood-brain barrier. In experiments on rabbits held in a revolving case (130 rotations per min, for 25 min per day), Hydén discovered increases in the RNA and cytochrome oxidase activity of neurons of Deiters' nuclei coincident with decreased RNA content and cytochrome oxidase activity in the glial cells of these nuclei. Aleksandrovskaya (124), in a systematic study of the reactions of brain tissues to chronically implanted electrodes, noted a rapid increase in the number of microglia and astrocytes oriented radially from the track of the electrode: according to her data, the implanted electrode is in direct contact only with glial cells after several weeks. The similarity of potentials recorded by implanted electrodes and surface electrode indicates that glial cells participate in the generation of EEG.

According to Kornmüller (113), the EEG may be nonspecific for different structures because it is a bioelectrical representation of neurosecretory activity of glial cells. Substances secreted by glial cells may regulate the excitability of neighboring neurons and, if in such quantity as to reach the vascular system, would also evoke distant effects. The neurosecretory function of the gray matter has been demonstrated in perfusion experiments. The application of an extract obtained from the brain of an animal with an abnormal EEG to the brain of a normal one elicits a corresponding change in the EEG of the normal. Kornmüller believes that the factor responsible for these changes may originate in the glial cells.

Heller & Hesse (125), studying oxygen exchange in the sciatic nerve of normal rats and of rats whose sciatic nerves had been sectioned 12 weeks previously, observed that direct electrical stimulation of the sciatic nerve led to an increase in exchange rate of up to 60 per cent in both cases. The increase was observed although degeneration of the axis cylinders was demonstrated morphologically in the sectioned nerves, The authors conclude that the "activating substance", preserved after nerve section, is not related to the axis cylinders but to the Schwann cells, which are a type of glial cell. It is tempting to generalize their conclusion to include the function of glial cells in the cortex.

A systematic presentation of questions concerning the function of glia has been offered by Galambos (126) who suggests the possibility of glial participation in the shift of steady potential, changes in EEG, modification of evoked potentials, and slow waves which are similar in different brain structures. He especially emphasizes that besides neuron-neuronal contacts there exist contacts between glial cells and neurons and between glial cells themselves. The functional unit of the nervous system is not the simple neuron, but the neuron united with its neighboring glial cells. Artemyev (127), in referring to certain pilot experiments, has attributed slow waves (6 to 25 per sec) to units which fulfill metabolic functions, presumably glial cells.

Comparing electron micrographs of hippocampal cells with the results of microelectrode recording from such cells, Green and co-workers (128, 129) suggest that the astrocytes play a role in the generation of theta waves and the production of evoked potentials. Eidelberg (130) also concludes that there may be participation by glial cells in the generation of hippocampal slow potentials; Sokolov & Dulenko (77) in experiments on pentobarbitalized cats observed spontaneous slow waves in the optic chiasm and tract which resembled cortical alpha waves and, like them, may be attributable to glial cells. Hild & Tasaki (131), studying cortical neurons and glial cells in tissue culture, have obtained direct evidence that the single glial cell produces a slow potential. Further, they have shown that spikes may originate in dendrites as well as in nerve cell bodies.

THE ORIENTING REFLEX AND THE FUNCTIONAL STATE

The state of sleep.—This is not accompanied by an absolute decrease in functional activity at the neuronal level, as indicated by the observations of Jasper (132), Lehmann & Koukkou (133), and Evarts, Fleming & Huttenlocher (134).

Creutzfeldt (80) showed that when the EEG is desynchronized, the spontaneous firing rate of single neurons of the cat's visual cortex is 10 to 20 per sec. During spindle activity, when the animal is sleeping, the spontaneous discharges of individual neurons are irregular and slightly less frequent. Hypoxic animals show slow wave EEG activity accompanied by bursts of neuronal discharges. Under extreme hypoxia the EEG almost disappears, spontaneous unit discharges are absent, and the unit responses to light are reduced. During the slow wave activity induced by barbiturate anesthesia, impulses come in short bursts and many neurons stop firing altogether.

The influence of arousal upon neuronal discharges.—Arousal may be acompanied by any one of the following changes in the activity of a given cell: (a) an increased frequency and change in pattern of firing, (b) a decreased frequency and even complete cessation of impulses, or (c) absence of marked change in pattern of firing.

Even in cases of decreased spontaneous firing accompanying the depression of slow waves, however, there may be increased responsiveness of the neuron to afferent stimuli-to-noise ratio. Thus the transmission of information from the periphery to cortical neurons is improved following arousal.

Similar conclusions hold for the reticular formation. Huttenlocher (121) has shown in a study of reticular formation neurons that the activity of the majority of neurons increases during sleep and that of only a small proportion of neurons decreases. The evoked firing becomes weaker with the onset of slow waves and disappears altogether during sleep; the reverse occurs with waking. Fuster (135, 136), studying neurons of the rabbit visual cortex during stimulation of the reticular formation, showed that such stimulation slowed the spontaneous firing of some neurons and increased the firing rate of others. In half of the neurons studied, no observable changes occurred. Reticular stimulation considerably enhanced the responses of both B and D neurons.

Katsuki, Murata & Kameda (137) analyzed simultaneous recordings of EEG and single-unit activity in auditory, somatic, and visual cortex and showed that natural arousal and arousal evoked by reticular stimulation are comparable. The most common effect of the orienting reflex on a single-unit activity is the increase of the responsiveness of neurons during attention, waking, or stimulation of the reticular formation (138).

Observing unit responses in the visual cortex during deepening of sleep induced by pentobarbital, Hubel & Wiesel (109) report that the number of spikes per flash is reduced and eventually spike activity altogether disappears. But even after all responses to a flashing stimulus have disappeared, the movement of an object in the visual field can evoke discharges in a cortical unit. Despite the changes in EEG activity and the magnitude of neuronal responses, the shape of the receptive field of each neuron remained unchanged during sleep and arousal. Similar data are presented in a paper by Jung (114), who states that reticular stimulation increases the responsiveness of neurons, but does not modify the type of neuron, i.e., B neurons do not turn into D neurons, etc. Arden & Söderberg (138) have observed that with reticular stimulation there is a decrease in the latency of responses in neurons of the lateral geniculate body, an increased number of spikes per volley, and increased synchronization of the spikes in response to the applied stimulus.

Further study of the changes in unit activity accompanying the generalized orienting reflex is presented in a paper by Jung (114). He studied critical fusion frequency, measured from single neurons of the visual cortex of the cat, as an indicator of the functional state of the analyzer. High-frequency stimulation of the midbrain reticular formation or intralaminar thalamic nuclei produced an increase in the critical fusion frequency for flickering light, perhaps by simultaneous increases of both excitatory and inhibitory influences on single neurons, which allow a shorter time constant of the burst response to each light flash. This phenomenon fits with the increase in subjective fusion frequency which occurs when a person pays close attention to a flickering light. The increase in critical fusion frequency means that the nervous system can handle more signal changes per unit time. Insofar as the amount of information which can be transmitted by a communication channel is a function of maximum frequency of transmitted signal, it is possible to say that the orienting reflex facilitates the transmission of information in the central nervous system.

The involvement of new units in the response to stimuli and facilitation of responses with evocation of the orienting reflex is thought to take place through synaptic mechanisms. Working with the curarized cat preparation, Akimoto and co-workers (139) observed the facilitation of single-neuron responses in the somatosensory and motor cortex to electrical stimulation of the specific thalamic nuclei during electrical stimulation of the midbrain or thalamic reticular formation.

With electrical impulses applied directly to the motor cortex, it was possible to distinguish short- and long-latency responses of neurons in the medulla oblongata. Reticular stimulation facilitated the long-latency, but not the short-latency response, indicating that the facilitation occurs at synaptic junctions. Activation of cortical neurons is observed not only with reticular stimulation, but with stimuli applied to the peripheral receptors. Thus, with extended rhythmic light stimulation the number of neurons which respond to the light increases (140).

Multisensory Convergence of Impulses

Specific sensory interaction.—Only in recent years has the convergence of nervous impulses from different analyzers on single neurons been studied intensively (141). This problem is related to three different aspects of the neuronal organization of the orienting reflex: (*a*) specific convergence as a mechanism underlying formation of neuronal models of multimodality stimuli; (*b*) convergence of specific and nonspecific impulses in the mechanism of activation; (*c*) nonspecific convergence on attention units.

The first problem concerns the development of a neuronal model of a complex stimulus which acts on several different analyzers. Investigation in human subjects by Voronin & Sokolov (142) has shown that after extinction of the orienting reflex to a complex multimodality stimulus, the omission of one component leads to evocation of this reflex. This shows that the nervous model involves the integration of components of different modalities; its development does not involve a simple summation of stimuli, but rather the elaboration of a system in which every component preserves its specific significance. The development of multimodality nervous models may be explained by the existence not only of neurons sensitive to stimuli of one modality, but also of neurons which can respond to stimuli of several modalities.

This aspect of the multimodality convergence of impulses on a single neuron is considered by Jung (114) in his attempt to explain the constancy of visual perception. Visual constancy involves the participation of proprioceptors of the eye muscles and vestibular receptors as well as the retinal receptors. Jung has shown that neurons of the cat visual cortex respond to vestibular stimulations.

The question arises whether this convergence may not occur in lower nonspecific systems and the results be transmitted to the cortex. Polarization of the vestibular portion of the cochlear nerve enhances the activity of most neurons in the area 17 of the cat visual cortex; this cannot represent a nonspecific increase in the excitability level of all cortical neurons, as supported by the fact that different neurons of the visual cortex respond to labyrinthine stimulation in different ways.

The convergence of specific and nonspecific impulses.—The convergence of specific (visual) and nonspecific (reticular) impulses on a single neuron in the visual cortex of the cat has been demonstrated in Jung's laboratory (114). This type of convergence apparently results in the activation of specific neurons, which leads to an increased critical fusion frequency. The distinction between these two types of convergence has been investigated by Kornhuber & Da Fonseca (143). They studied the neurons in primary and secondary fields of the visual, auditory, and somatosensory cortex of the *encéphale isolé* cat preparation. By stimulating with diffuse light, sound, and polarization of the round window, they were able to distinguish two types of unit response. The first type, which includes the excitations evoked by onset and end of stimulus, has a very short latency and is usually observed in the primary areas. The second type of response is characterized by a long-latency increase of firing rate during the period of stimulus presentation and apparently originates in the nonspecific activating system. During application of flickering light stimulation, interaction of the first and second types took place in single neurons of the secondary areas of the visual cortex.

Highly synchronized nonspecific impulses acting on a specific neuron can evoke the same response as normal impulses transmitted by the specific pathway, and perhaps can produce a sensation corresponding to the modality of the neuron. Jung suggests that this type of convergence can explain why an unexpected strong click can evoke a sensation of light stimulation. Usually, however, only the enhancement of specific responses under the influence of nonspecific stimulation is observed.

The convergence of specific impulses on nonspecific neurons.—The third aspect of the convergence of impulses lies in the fact that the orienting reflex is one and the same, regardless of the modality of the stimulus which evokes it. One can speak of convergence of stimuli in the sense that the specific properties of the stimuli are lost and a common response occurs. Thus, the simultaneous application of two stimuli of different modalities produces a response larger than but of the same form as that evoked by either stimulus separately. The mechanism of such a reaction seems to involve neurons which respond to stimuli from various modalities. Such a type is mentioned above: the attention units in the cortex and reticular formation.

The ability of individual reticular formation neurons to respond equally to light, sound, and touch stimuli was recently shown by Huttenlocher (121). An analogous nonspecificity is seen in neurons which respond to all stimuli of a given modality without regard to quality. Katsuki (117), studying the responses of reticular formation neurons to acoustic stimuli, has shown that for all sound frequencies the threshold of evoked firing in certain neurons is the same.

Buser & Imbert (144) have recorded from similar multisensory neurons in the motor cortex of the cat. With simultaneous stimulation of different analyzers, the total number of spikes is greater than the arithmetical sum of responses evoked by stimuli when applied separately. If the different stimuli are presented at 20-to-50-msec intervals, an inhibition or delay of the second response is observed. The authors distinguish such multisensory neurons from the polyvalent neurons which respond to different parameters of stimulation of a single modality. They conclude that the multisensory neurons are similar to neurons of the reticular formation and that thus the motor cortex to a certain extent shares the function of this region in sensorimotor integration. Besides the major types of convergence on reticular neurons of afferent impulses of different modalities, convergence of afferent impulses and corticofugal impulses occurs (145).

SUMMARY

The orienting reflex as a complex functional system includes the integrative activities of different brain areas. Its distinguishing characteristic is that it arises in response to novelty. It depends upon elaboration of a nervous model of stimulus and the mismatch between the model and a new stimulus. The elaboration of the neuron model consists in fixation by the nervous system of stimulus traces. The origin of the orienting reflex apparently lies in a mismatch of extrapolatory impulses and afferent signals reaching common efferent neurons.

The modifications of the EEG, the shift in steady potential of the cortex, and the increase in functional state represent components of the orienting reflex arising in response to any change of a repetitive stimulus. A special component of this reflex is a local intracortical activation, arising as a result of cortical stimulation by meaningful specific sensory information in the absence of reticular formation activation.

To explain both the appearance and the extinction of local cortical activation, a hypothesis involving interaction of afferent, extrapolatory, and comparator neurons with glial cells is offered (86). The molecular mechanism of the memory trace is discussed.

The orienting reflex at the neuronal level converts nonresponsive into responsive neurons, produces facilitation and enhancement of unit responses, and increases critical flicker fusion frequency. Analysis of this reflex indicates that it facilitates the transmission of information at all levels of the analyzers.

LITERATURE CITED

1. Pavlov, I. P., *Complete Collection of Works*, **IV**, 351 (Moscow-Leningrad, USSR, 1947) (Russian)
2. Voronin, L. G., and Leontiev, A. N., Eds., *The Orienting Reflex and Exploratory Behavior*, 350 (Moscow, 1958) (Russian)
3. Sokolov, E. N., Ed., *The Orienting Reflex in Normal and Pathological Cases*, 350 (Moscow, 1959) (Russian)
4. Berlyne, D. E., *Conflict, Arousal, and Curiosity*, 350 (McGraw-Hill, New York-Toronto-London, 1960)
5. Vinogradova, O. S., *The Orienting Reflex and its Neurophysiological Mechanisms*, 207 (Moscow, 1960) (Russian)*
6. Anokhin, P. K., *Internal Inhibition as a Problem of Physiology*, 471 (Medgiz, Moscow, 1958) (Russian)*
7. Sokolov, E. N., *Perception and the Conditioned Reflex*, 330 (Moscow Univ. Press, Moscow, 1958) (Russian)*
8. Beritov, I. S., *Nervous Mechanisms of Behavior in Higher Vertebrates*, 349 (Acad. Sci. USSR Press, Moscow, 1961) (Russian)*
9. John, E. R., *Ann. Rev. Physiol.*, **23**, 451–84 (1961)
10. Morrell, F., *Physiol. Rev.*, **41**, 443–94 (1961)
11. Buser, P., and Rougeul, A., *Ann. Rev. Physiol.*, **23**, 387–418 (1961)
12. Vinogradova, O. S., and Sokolov, E. N., *Fiziol. Zhur. USSR*, **43**, 47–51 (1957) (Russian)*
13. Sokolov, E. N., *Central Nervous System and Behavior*, 187–239 (Brazier, M. A. B., Ed., Josiah Macy, Jr., Found., New York, 1960)
14. Kanzow, E., *Intern. Congr. EEG Clin.*
Neurophysiol., 5th, Rome, Italy, 1961, 14
15. Kanzow, E., *Arch. Ges. Physiol.*, **274**, 447–58 (1962)
16. Klossovsky, E. N., and Kosmarskaya, E. N., *Active and Inhibitory States of the Brain*, 345 (Medgiz, Moscow, 1961) (Russian)*
17. Soltysik, S., Jaworska, K., Kowalska, M., and Radom, S., *Acta Biol. Exptl.*, **21**, 335–52 (1961)
18. Affani, J., Marchiafava, P. L., and Zernicki, B., *Arch. Ital. Biol.* (In press, 1962)
19. Kelemen, K., Longo, V. G., Knoll, J., and Bovet, D., *Electroencephal. Clin. Neurophysiol.*, **13**, 745–51 (1961)
20. Doty, R. W., *Ann. N. Y. Acad. Sci.*, **92**, 939–45 (1961)
21. Anokhin, P. K., *Ann. N.Y. Acad. Sci.*, **92**, 899–938 (1961)
22. Anokhin, P. K., *Brain and Behavior*, 139–70 (Brazier, M. A. B., Ed., Washington, 1961)
23. Voronin, L. G., *Pavlov J. Higher Nervous Activity*, **11**, 795–805 (1961)*
24. Guselnikov, V. S., *Fiziol. Zhur. USSR*, **46**, 537–43 (1960)*
25. Galambos, R., *Brain and Behavior*, 171–204 (Brazier, M. A. B., Ed., Washington, 1961)
26. Tuge, H., and Shima, J., *Physiol. Bohemoslov.*, **9**, 465–71 (1960)
27. Naumova, T. S., *Pavlov J. Higher Nervous Activity*, **12**, 119–27 (1962) (Russian)*
28. Rabinovich, H. Ya., *Pavlov J. Higher Nervous Activity*, **11**, 463–73 (1961) (Russian)*
29. Ivanova, M. P., *Bull. Exptl. Biol. Med. USSR*, **53**, 27–31 (1962) (Russian)*

30. Fedio, P., Mirsky, A. F., Smith, W. J., and Parry, D. *Electroencephal. Clin. Neurophysiol.*, **13**, 923–26 (1961)

31. Fraisse, P., Durup, G., and Voillaume, C., *Ann. Psychol.*, **59**, 345–53 (1959)

32. Fraisse, P., and Voillaume, C., *Ann. Psychol.*, **61**, 53–57 (1961)

33. Orbeli, L. A., *Problems of Higher Nervous Activity*, 448 (Acad. Sci., USSR Press, Moscow-Leningrad, 1949) (Russian)

34. Shevelyeva, V. S., *Proc. Acad. Sci. USSR*, **142**, 249–52 (1962)*

35. Caspers, H., *Arch. Ges. Physiol.*, **269**, 157–81 (1959)

36. Caspers, H., and Stern, P., *Arch. Ges. Physiol.*, **273**, 94–110 (1961)

37. Rusinov, V. S., *Pavlov J. Higher Nervous Activity*, **11**, 776–94 (1961) (Russian)*

38. Rusinov, V. S., *Problems of Liability, Parabiosis and Inhibition*, 188–92 (Moscow, 1962)*

39. Gumnit, R. J., *Electroencephal. Clin. Neurophysiol.*, **13**, 889–95 (1961)

40. Gumnit, R. J., *Am. J. Physiol.*, **200**, 1219–25 (1961)

41. Meshersky, R. M., and Smirnov, G. D., *Proc. Acad. Sci. USSR*, **139**, 245–48 (1961) (Russian)*

42. Mnukhina, R. S., *Pavlov J. Higher Nervous Activity*, **11**, 346–53 (1961) (Russian)*

43. Kalinin, P. I., and Sokolova, A. A., *Pavlov J. Higher Nervous Activity*, **11**, 112–19 (1961) (Russian)*

44. Sologub, E. B., *Fisiol. Zhur. USSR*, **48**, 3–10 (1962) (Russian)*

45. Majkowsky, J., and Jasper, H. H., *Intern. Congr. EEG Clin. Neurophysiol.*, *5th, Rome, Italy, 1961*, 16

46. Kupalov, P. S., *Pavlov J. Higher Nervous Activity*, **11**, 769–75 (1961) (Russian)*

47. Sokolov, E. N., *Pavlov J. Higher Nervous Activity*, **11**, 394–401 (1961) (Russian)*

48. Kupalov, P. S., *Gagra Conf.*, III, *The Mechanism of Elaboration of Temporary Nervous Connection*, 9–42 (Tbilisi, 1960) (Russian)

49. Kamchatnov, V. P., *Pavlov J. Higher Nervous Activity*, **12**, 208–12 (1962) (Russian)*

50. Kamchatnov, V. P., *Pavlov J. Higher Nervous Activity*, **12**, 37–39 (1962) (Russian)*

51. Dumont, S., and Dell, P., *Electroencephal. Clin. Neurophysiol.*, **12**, 342–67 (1960)

52. Moniava, E. S., Kadshaya, P. B., and Narikashvili, S. P., *Pavlov J. Higher Nervous Activity*, **11**, 368–77 (1961) (Russian)*

53. Bremer, F., *Sensory Communication*, 675–98 (Rosenblith, W. A., Ed., MIT Press; John Wiley, New York-London, 1961)

54. Moruzzi, G., *Intern. Congr. EEG Clin. Neurophysiol.*, *5th, Rome, Italy, 1961*, 16

55. Lindsley, D. B., *Brain and Behavior*, 359–92 (Brazier, M. A. B., Ed., Washington, 1961)

56. Albe-Fessard, D., Mallart, A., and Aléonard, P. *J. Physiol. (Paris)*, **53**, 244–45 (1961)

57. Albe-Fessard, D., Mallart, A., and Aléonard, P., *Compt. Rend.*, **252**, 1060–62 (1961)

58. Maruseva, A. M., *Proc. Conf. Problems Physiol. Analysers (Sense Organs)*, 44 (Leningrad, 1961)*

59. Maruseva, A. M., *Fisiol. Zhur. USSR*, **48**, 542–50 (1962) (Russian)*

60. Gershuni, G. V., *Fisiol. Zhur. USSR*, **48**, 241–50 (1962)*

61. Altman, Ya. A., and Maruseva, A. M., *Fisiol. Zhur. USSR*, **46**, 1345–55 (1960) (Russian)*

62. Mey Ley, *Fisiol. Zhur. USSR*, **48**, 11–15 (1962) (Russian)*

63. Altman, Ya. A., *Fisiol. Zhur. USSR*, **46**, 526–35 (1960) (Russian)*

64. Hernández-Péon, R., *Sensory Communication*, 497–520 (Rosenblith, W. A., Ed., MIT Press; John Wiley, New York-London, 1961)

65. Fernández-Guardiola, A., Roldán, E. R., Fanjul, M. L., and Castells, S. C., *Bol. Inst. Estud. Med.*, **18**, 1–28 (1960)

66. Fernández-Guardiola, A., Roldán, E., Fanjul, L., and Castells, C., *Electroencephal. Clin. Neurophysiol.*, **13**, 564–74 (1961)

67. Roitbak, A. J., *Electroencephal Clin. Neurophysiol.*, *Suppl.*, **13**, 91–100 (1960)

68. Roitbak, A. J., *Major Problems of Electrophysiology of the CNS*, 232 (Makarchenko, A. F., and Vorontsov, D. C., Eds., Kiev, 1962)

69. Sokolov, E. N., *Pavlov J. Higher Nervous Activity*, **12**, 145–54 (1962) (Russian)*

70. Ilyanok, V. A., *Proc. Acad. Sci. USSR*, **139**, 729–32 (1961) (Russian)*

71. Guselnikov, P. S., and Polansky, V. B., *Biol. Sci., Proc. Higher School*, I, 83–86 (1962) (Russian)*

72. Danilova, N. N., *Pavlov J. Higher*

Nervous Activity, **11**, 12–21 (1961)
(Russian)*

73. Beidler, L. M., *Sensory Communication*, 143–57 (Rosenblith W. A., Ed., MIT Press; John Wiley, New York-London, 1961)

74. Edelberg, R., *J. Exptl. Psychol.*, **62**, 187–95 (1961)

75. Dulenko, V. P., and Sokolov, E. N., *Proc. Conf. Problems Physiol. Analyzers (Sense Organs)*, 78 (Leningrad, 1961) (Russian)*

76. Dulenko, V. P., and Sokolov, E. N., *Proc. Acad Ped. Sci. RSFSR*, **3**, 105–10 (1961) (Russian)*

77. Sokolov, E. N., and Dulenko, V. P., *Proc. Acad. Ped. Sci. RSFSR*, **3**, 101–4 (1961) (Russian)*

78. Sokolov, E. N., *in Major Problems of Electrophysiology of the CNS*, 157–88 (Makarchenko, A. F., and Vorontsov, D. C., Eds., Kiev, 1962)

79. Neff, W. D., *Brain and Behavior*, 205–62 (Brazier, M. A. B., Ed., Washington, 1961)

80. Creutzfeldt, O. D., *Brain and Behavior*, 299–358 (Brazier, M. A. B., Ed., Washington, 1961)

81. Marsh, J. T., and McCarthy, D. A., *Electroencephal. Clin. Neurophysiol.*, **13**, 224–334 (1961)

82. Chow, K. L., *J. Neurophysiol.*, **24**, 377–90 (1961)

83. Sokolov, E. N., and Paramonova, N. P., *Pavlov J. Higher Nervous Activity*, **11**, 206–15 (1961) (Russian)*

84. Zimkina, A. M., Ed., *Neurophysiological Investigations* (Leningrad, 1961)

85. Voronin, L. G., and Sokolov, E. N., *Electroencephal. Clin. Neurophysiol.*, Suppl. 13, 335–46 (1960)

86. Sokolov, E. N., *Gagra Conf.*, **IV** (1962) (Russian)

87. Voronin, L. G., *Pavlov J. Higher Nervous Activity*, **11**, 358–93 (1961) (Russian)*

88. Paramonova, N. P., *Pavlov J. Higher Nervous Activity*, **11**, 409–14 (1961) (Russian)*

89. Affani, J., Marchiafava, P. L., and Zernicki, B., *Arch. Ital. Biol.* (In Press, 1962)

90. Buchwald, N. A., Rakic, L., Wyers, E. J., Hull, C., and Henser, G., *Exptl. Neurol.*, **5**, 1–20 (1962)

91. Ascher, P., Jassik-Gerschenfeld, D., and Buser, P., *Compt. Rend.* 252, 1383–85 (1961)

92. Hyomskaya, G. D., *Proc. Acad. Ped. Sci. RSFSR*, **I**, 117–22 (1961) (Russian)*

93. Klimkovsky, M. K., *Proc. Acad. Ped. Sci. RSFSR*, **2**, 109–13 (1961) (Russian)*

94. Danilova, N. N., *Biol. Sci., Proc. Higher School*, **3**, 86–92 (1962) (Russian)*

95. Roeva, S. N., *Fisiol. Zhur. USSR*, **48**, 264–70 (1962) (Russian)*

96. Sakhiulina, T. T., *Pavlov J. Higher Nervous Activity*, **11**, 450–62 (1961) (Russian)*

97. Glickman, G. E., and Feldman, S. M., *Electroencephal. Clin. Neurophysiol.*, **13**, 703–9 (1961)

98. Magoun, H. W., *Ann. N.Y. Acad. Sci.*, **92**, 818–29 (1961)

99. Lindsley, D. F., and Adey, W. R., *Exptl. Neurol.*, **4**, 358–76 (1961)

100. Adey, W. R., and Lindsley, D., *Exptl. Neurol.*, **I**, 407–26 (1959)

101. Buchwald, N. A., Wyers, E. J., Lauprecht, C. W., and Heuser, G., *Electroencephal. Clin. Neurophysiol.*, **13**, 518–25 (1961)

102. Tsuy Chgi-Pin, *Pavlov J. Higher Nervous Activity*, **11**, 225–31 (1961) (Russian)*

103. Roitbak, A. J., *Proc. Acad. Sci. USSR*, **139**, 1502–4 (1961) (Russian)*

104. Beteleva, T. G., and Novikova, L. A., *Pavlov J. Higher Nervous Activity*, **11**, 525–34 (1961) (Russian)*

105. Karimova, M. M., *Pavlov J. Higher Nervous Activity*, **11**, 1065–73 (1961) (Russian)*

106. Kogan, A. B., *Pavlov J. Higher Nervous Activity*, **11**, 651–58 (1961) (Russian)*

107. Purpura, D. P., *Ann. N.Y. Acad. Sci.*, **92**, 840–59 (1961)

108. Purpura, D. P., and Housepian, E. M., *Exptl. Neurol.*, **4**, 377–401 (1961)

109. Hubel, D. H., and Wiesel, T. N., *J. Physiol. (London)* **160**, 106–54 (1962)

110. Hydén, H., *The Cell*, **IV**, *Biochemistry, Physiology, Morphology*, 216–308 (Brachet, J., and Mirsky, A. E., Eds., Academic, New York-London, 1960)

111. Hydén, H., *Sci. Am.*, **205**, 62–70 (1961)

112. Deutsch, J. A., *Ann. Rev. Physiol.*, **24**, 259–86 (1962)

113. Kornmüller, A. E., *Intern. Congr. EEG Clin. Neurophysiol., 5th, Rome, Italy, 1961*, 24

114. Jung, R., *Sensory Communication*, 627–74 (Rosenblith, W. A., Ed.,

MIT Press; John Wiley, New York-London, 1961)

115. Baumgartner, G., and Hakas, P., *Arch. Ges. Physiol.*, **274**, 489–510 (1962)

116. Lettvin, J. Y., Maturana, H. R., Pitts, W. H., and McCulloch, W. S., *Sensory Communication*, 757–76 (Rosenblith, W. A., Ed., MIT Press; John Wiley, New York-London, 1961)

117. Katsuki, Y., *Sensory Communication*, 561–84 (Rosenblith W. A., Ed., MIT Press; John Wiley, New York-London, 1961)

118. Morrell, F., *Ann. N.Y. Acad. Sci.*, **92**, 860–76 (1961)

119. Morrell, F., *Fisiol. Zhur. USSR*, **48**, 251–63 (1962)*

120. Hubel, D., Henson, C., Rupert, A., and Galambos, R., *Science*, **129**, 279–84 (1959)

121. Huttenlocher, P. R., *J. Neurophysiol.*, **24**, 452–68 (1961)

122. Shkolnik-Yarros, E. G., *Pavlov J. Nervous Activity*, **11**, 680–89 (1961) (Russian)*

123. Luse, S. A., *Anat. Record*, **138**, 461–92 (1960)

124. Aleksandrovskaya, M. M., *Proc. Acad. Sci. USSR*, **143**, 1442–44 (1962)*

125. Heller, I. H., and Hesse, S., *Exptl. Neurol.*, **4**, 83–90 (1961)

126. Galambos, R., *Proc. Natl. Acad. Sci. US*, **47**, 129–36 (1961)

127. Artemyev, V. V., *Proc. Acad. Sci. USSR*, **142**, 1424–27 (1962) (Russian)*

128. Green, J. D., and Maxwell, D. S., *Electroencephal. Clin. Neurophysiol.*, **13**, 837–46 (1961)

129. Green, J. D., Maxwell, D. S., and Petsche, H., *Electroencephal. Clin. Neurophysiol.*, **13**, 854–67 (1961)

130. Eidelberg, E., *J. Neurophysiol.*, **24**, 521–32 (1961)

131. Hild, W., and Tasaki, I., *J. Neurophysiol.*, **25**, 277–304 (1962)

132. Jasper, H. H., *Intern. Congr. EEG Clin. Neurophysiol.*, *5th, Rome, Italy, 1961*, 1–2

133. Lehmann, D., and Koukkou, M., *Intern. Congr. EEG Clin. Neurophysiol.*, *5th, Rome, Italy, 1961*, 6

134. Evarts, E. V., Fleming, C. T., and Huttenlocher, P. R., *Am. J. Physiol.*, **199**, 373–76 (1960)

135. Fuster, J. M., *Proc. Intern. Congr. EEG Clin. Neurophysiol.*, *5th, Rome, Italy*, 17

136. Fuster, J. M., *Science*, **133**, 2011–12 (1961)

137. Katsuki, Y., Murata, K., and Kameda, K., *Proc. Intern. Congr. EEG Clin. Neurophysiol.*, *5th, Rome, Italy, 1961*

138. Arden, G. B., and Söderberg, U., *Sensory Communication*, 521–44 (Rosenblith, W. A., Ed., MIT Press; John Wiley, New York-London, 1961)

139. Akimoto, H., Saito, Y., Nakamura, Y., and Moekawa, K., *Proc. Intern. Congr. EEG Clin. Neurophysiol.*, *5th, Rome, Italy, 1961*

140. Smirnov, G. D., *Brain and Behavior*, 263–98 (Brazier, M. A. B., Ed., Washington, 1961)

141. Fessard, A., *Sensory Communication*, 585–606 (Rosenblith, W. A., Ed., MIT Press; John Wiley, New York-London, 1961)

142. Voronin, L. G., and Sokolov, E. N., *Gagra Conf.*, **III**, *The Mechanism of Elaboration of Temporary Nervous Connections*, 213–37 (Tbilisi, 1960) (Russian)

143. Kornhuber, H. H., and Da Fonseca, J. S., *Proc. Intern Congr. Clin. Neurophysiol.*, *5th, Rome, Italy, 1961*, 12

144. Buser, P., and Imbert, M., *Sensory Communication*, 607–26 (Rosenblith, W. A., Ed., MIT Press; John Wiley, New York-London, 1961)

145. Limansky, Yu. P., *Fisiol. Zhur. USSR*, **48**, 126–33 (1962)*

* English translation will be announced in *Technical Translations*, issued by the Office of Technical Services, U. S. Department of Commerce, and will be made available by the Photoduplication Service, Library of Congress, and by the SLA Translation Center at the John Crerar Library, Chicago, Illinois.

COMPARATIVE PHYSIOLOGY: DIURNAL RHYTHMS[1,2,3]

By Juergen Aschoff[4]

Max-Planck-Institut für Verhaltensphysiologie,
Seewiesen und Erling-Andechs, Germany

INTRODUCTION

At the very beginning of the period to be covered in this review, Cole (1) published his paper on metabolism of the unicorn. He demonstrates (*a*) the universal occurrence of "biological clocks" (!); (*b*) possible pitfalls in the analysis of time series data; and (*c*) the caution necessary in interpreting a special frequency as more than noise, even if its amplitude has been statistically shown to be different from zero. In keeping with Cole's implied skepticism, an attempt will be made to differentiate between rigorously established conclusions and more or less possible interpretations. Particular emphasis will be placed on animal experimental work which contributes to the questions: (*a*) is there an endogenous (self-sustained) oscillation behind the overt rhythm and (*b*) if endogenous, how does a rhythm become synchronized with the periodic environment? Lesser emphasis will be given to ecological aspects of rhythms, and to problems of diurnal rhythms in mammalian physiology.

Extensive surveys have been published during the last 4 years—some of them including also tidal, lunar, and other periodicities (2, 3, 4). More specialized summaries deal with diurnal rhythms in unicellular organisms (5) and mammals (6 to 9), others with the implications of these rhythms in space and time orientation of insects (10) and in human performance (11). In addition, two monographs (12, 13) and the reports of two symposia (14, 15) give an idea of both the diversity of phenomena and the growing interest in this field. The interrelations between photoperiodism [cf. Farner (16)] and diurnal rhythms are discussed in some recent publications (12, 17, 18; cf. also 14) and will not be treated here.

DEFINITIONS, NOMENCLATURE

As has been stated several times (19 to 24), there is good reason to consider diurnal rhythms as oscillations in a technical sense. In doing this, one has to differentiate between (*a*) autonomous systems whose oscillations decay if the inevitable losses of energy are not restored periodically from outside the system (damped oscillations) and (*b*) autonomous systems which are

[1] The survey of literature pertaining to this review was concluded in April 1962.

[2] The following symbols are used: LL, DD (continuous light, continuous darkness); τ (spontaneous period); τ_{LL}, τ_{DD} (spontaneous period in LL or in DD); τ_n (the "natural period" of a driven oscillation, not overtly measurable, but determining the phase-angle difference).

[3] Dedicated to the sixtieth birthday of Professor Konrad Lorenz.

[4] I am greatly indebted to Dr. J. T. Enright and Dr. R. Wever for their critical comments, and to Dr. J. T. Enright for his untiring efforts in correcting the English text.

capable of auto-oscillations (self-sustained oscillations). Both of them have been designated as endogenous by Klotter (25). From the facts so far at hand it seems probable that living organisms in general belong to one or the other of these autonomous systems. The question of whether diurnal rhythms are really self sustained or not is more difficult to answer (see below).

The frequency of an autonomous oscillation is a property of the system ("natural frequency" in technical terms), although it always depends to some degree on environmental conditions, e.g., on temperature. These influences upon the natural frequency may be very small or nearly negligible, as with the majority of physical systems, or they may result in conspicuous variations of the frequency. An oscillating system can be entrained by another periodic source of energy. The resulting forced oscillation always has the same frequency as the driving agent when the system is not capable of self-sustained oscillations. For self-sustained systems several ranges of entrainment exist, the limits of which depend both on the properties of the driven system and on the strength of the driving agent. Implicit in the existence of more than one range of entrainment is the statement that an autonomous, self-sustained oscillation can become sychronized not only with a frequency near its own natural frequency but also with multiples and submultiples (19, 24, 25). Especially good examples for frequency demultiplication in circadian systems are cited by Bruce (23).

The steady state of entrainment, both for damped and for self-sustained oscillations, is characterized by a special phase-relationship between the driven and the driving oscillation. This phase-angle difference is the result of the relation between the (virtual) "natural frequency" of the driven system and its (overt) forced oscillation (24, 26, 27). A natural frequency becomes overt only when there is no periodic driving agent. In reference to diurnal rhythms in living systems, such overt oscillations have been called free running (20) or spontaneous (3). Because their period may deviate from 24 hours, Halberg (8) has proposed the term "circadian" instead of diurnal. The periodic factors of the environment, by which free-running circadian oscillations can be synchronized, have been variously designated as entraining agents (19), synchronizers (8) or *Zeitgebers* (22).

CIRCADIAN RHYTHMS AS AUTONOMOUS OSCILLATIONS

ENDOGENOUS VERSUS EXOGENOUS

To prove that a circadian rhythm is autonomous, it must be demonstrated that it exhibits a frequency not in synchrony with any environmental periodic signal. Although the temperature, light, and other commonly controlled variables in the laboratory are kept constant, one may still have some "residual periodic variables" (20)—e.g., air ionization, cosmic ray showers, and so on. Therefore, an oscillation which continues to oscillate under such conditions with a period of exactly 24 hours may or may not be autonomous. But, as Pittendrigh has pointed out, "the existence of persistent daily rhythms with periods different from 24 hours is truly crucial evidence against their control by residual periodic variables associated with the earth's 24 hour rotation" (20, p. 247).

Autonomous oscillations have been shown to exist in all kinds of living systems, from unicellular organisms (5, 28, 29) to man (30). Frequently, the overt rhythm damps out under constant conditions, which does not necessarily deny the possibility of self-sustained oscillations (cf. 22, 26). But, in other cases, free-running periods have often persisted with a remarkable constancy over weeks and months—e.g., Rawson (31) has followed the activity rhythm of a bat *Eptesicus fuscus* for a period of five months—and rhythms can persist even in hibernation (32) or in successive generations of mice (33). In populations of *Gonyaulax polyedra*, spontaneous frequencies for several functions within the same species have been shown, including luminescence, cell division, luminescent glow, and photosynthesis (34, 35, 36). Only two studies have been made wherein two or more functions have been followed simultaneously in the same individual under constant conditions. Hoffmann (37) measured the rhythm of activity and of sun-compass orientation of starlings in continuous light, and both rhythms showed a similar spontaneous period of about 23.4 hours. In men, synchronous free-running periods of body temperature and urine excretion have been demonstrated (30).

At this point, it is necessary to discuss arguments advanced several times by F. A. Brown in favor of the hypothesis of an exogenous control of circadian rhythms under "constant conditions". The historic foundation of this hypothesis lies in Brown's earlier observations "that organisms in constant conditions may retain unaltered phase relationship with the external physical cycles even for periods of months" (38, p. 131). Nevertheless, Brown himself has occasionally recognized circadian (free-running?) periods, once in the fiddler crab (39) and more often in rats and mice (40, 41). Including these facts and the accumulated data from other workers in his hypothesis, Brown postulated what he has called "autophasing":

The organism reaching a "light-sensitive" phase in its daily cycle, and encountering the illumination of a constantly illuminated environment, would be given a shifting stimulus whose strength, within limits, would be a function of the level of the illumination. Though physically the light is held constant, in stimulative effectiveness for the organism it is rhythmic as a consequence of rhythms in the organism's own responsiveness (42, p. 1542).

This definition of autophasing does not contain any periodic input from the environment, as the observed frequency results from a repetition of phase-shifts produced by the periodically changing sensitivity of the organism in a genuinely constant environment. One year later Brown explained "all the odd-lengthed periods between 20 and 30 hours in terms of, first, an input of a 24-hour periodic signal followed by the generation of a different frequency within the organism, but one whose generation depends upon the 24-hour periodic informational inflow. The means I have termed autophasing . . . " (43, p. 70). As a further support to this last version of the hypothesis, it has been stated that even animals with an overt period deviating from 24 hours "possess simultaneously a fundamental underlying periodism not perceptibly different from 24 hours" (41, p. 36).

This viewpoint of Brown has not been accepted by other workers in the field for several basic reasons which concern (a) methods of data accumulation, (b) data analysis, and (c) interpretation.

(a) Data accumulation. Studies of the chromatophore rhythm of fiddler crabs have usually involved light signals at regular intervals (e.g. every four hours), raising the question of frequency demultiplication (cf. p. 582). By using randomly timed observations of isolated individuals, Stephens (44) elegantly avoided this danger and demonstrated truly circadian rhythms in Uca. Thus, with adequate experimental methods, the "precision" of the fiddler crab disappears. Other experiments have involved the changing of experimental animals every third or fourth day (e.g. 45). Since the reserve animals were under natural conditions of day and night, one must expect a clear 24-hour periodicity in the average results from animals freshly synchronized every few days.

(b) Data analysis. The danger of using moving averages is now well established (1, 46). Furthermore, it is pertinent that in living systems one is dealing with an essentially continuous spectrum of frequencies. All periods, including one of 24 hours, exist in, and can be extracted from, continuously registered biological data. It has not been demonstrated that such a 24-hour period, in cases of free-running overt periods, is present with any significantly greater amplitude than one with 23.9 or with 24.1 hours, i.e., that it is more than "noise" (18). The study of such periodic phenomena, obscured by random fluctuations especially with regard to autocorrelation and power spectrum analysis, has been discussed in some recent publications (46, 47, 48).

(c) Interpretation. A periodically changing sensitivity to light is indispensable for any autonomous system which can be synchronized by light, using phase control (see below). In conditions of constant illumination, all other factors being truly constant, such a system oscillates between maximal and minimal sensitivity to light. As Schmitt (49) has pointed out, the mathematical model one has in mind dictates whether one uses the phase-shift nomenclature or the variable-frequency nomenclature. In any case, the cause for the periodicity in such a system is endogenous since there is no periodic signal in the environment; the actual value of the realized frequency depends on the respective constant conditions (e.g. on light intensity).

If, on the other hand, there is a periodic source of energy in the environment, to which the system has a periodically changing sensitivity (as the final definition of autophasing requires), the autonomous oscillation will be either synchronized with the driving agent or out of the range of entrainment, showing a spontaneous (endogenous) frequency (22). Even when an organism under prolonged exposure to a periodically fluctuating environment exhibits a steady frequency which differs from that of the environment, the particular fluctuating environmental agent may still, under other circumstances (different amplitude or period of the driver, e.g.), act as a synchronizing agent and the period of the rhythm may still be affected by the fluctuating environmental agent. However, this steady frequency, deviating from that of the environment, does prove that the organism is exhibiting spontaneous, self-sustained oscillations which could persist in the absence of fluctuations in the environment [cf. the special problems of self-sustained oscillations just outside the range of entrainment (26, 50)].

Summarizing, it appears that there is no convincing evidence in favor of the hypothesis that the circadian rhythms in constant conditions are controlled by unknown periodic variables in the environment. All facts are in good agreement with the hypothesis that the circadian rhythms are autonomous and mostly self-sustained oscillations.

Spontaneous Frequencies

As Pittendrigh has pointed out in his many sided survey of circadian organization of living systems, an individual organism cannot be characterized by a special spontaneous period but rather by "a range of realizable spontaneous τ values. The system can be pushed within this range to any one of, presumably, many frequencies where it is stable, at least for a while" (21, p. 167). He also has shown that the period occasionally changes without a recognized outside cause. Examples of such sudden or gradual frequency shifts have occurred in experiments with mice (51), flying squirrels (52), lizards (53), cockroaches (54), and other animals. There are also increasing indications that the free-running periods can be altered by pretreatment (21). Thus the spontaneous frequency is evidently labile. Nevertheless, one gets similar values for τ under similar constant conditions in one species; and these values can be ordered in a special sense, at least for different levels of illumination.

Period depending on light intensity.—An accumulating variety of data supports the following generalization: in constant conditions with continuous light of different intensities, light-active animals shorten and dark-active animals lengthen their periods with increasing intensities of illumination. In brief: for light-active animals $\tau_{DD} > \tau_{LL}$, for dark-active animals $\tau_{DD} < \tau_{LL}$. To determine whether an animal conforms to this generalization, one has to measure τ in at least two different constant conditions, either in continuous light and in continuous darkness or in two intensities of constant illumination. The rule has been shown to be valid for the dark-active species *Peromyscus leucopus* (51, 55, 56), *Sigmodon hispidus* (57), *Mus musculus* (22, 58), *Mesocricetus auratus* (22), *Glaucomys volans* (52, 59), *Leucophaea maderae* and *Brysotria fumigata* (60), *Velia currens* (61); and for the light-active species *Phyrulla phyrulla* (62), *Sturnus vulagris* (22, 63), *Fringilla coelebs* (22), *Lacerta sicula* (63).

Exceptions for the rule have been claimed for the spider *Arctosa perita* (64) and the beetle *Geotrupes silvaticus* (65); more data are desirable. In *Drosophila*, which as an adult organism is clearly light active, the rhythm of pupal emergence has a shorter period in continuous darkness than in continuous light (21). This seems to violate the rule. One should, however, consider the possibility that the pupae of *Drosophila* are dark active instead of light active. Changes from light- to dark-activity during ontogeny have been observed in other species (cf. 9).

Period depending on temperature.—There is clear adaptive value in the remarkable independence of the spontaneous period from environmental and tissue temperatures (18, 66). The variation of this period in constant conditions with different constant temperatures is seldom more than 10 per cent which is not much different from the effects of light intensity. Thus, a comparable relative "independence" of the free-running period from both temperature and light could be claimed. Generalizations, similar to those for light- and dark-active animals, have been tentatively formulated about the changes of spontaneous period with temperature for warm- and cold-active animals (22). The available data for Q_{10} are summarized in a review by Sweeney & Hastings (67).

Innate versus learned rhythms.—Circadian rhythms are neither learned, nor imprinted on the organism by immediate experience of a periodic environment, as Pittendrigh has pointed out (18). He uses *Drosophila* cultures as an example: "Raised in constant temperature and darkness, the population is aperiodic in its eclosion activity, but promptly becomes periodic if exposed to a single, unrepeated light-signal that is effective when as brief as 1/2000 second. The signal gives no information on periodicity, much less on a specific frequency. The oscillation, and its frequency, evoked by the signal are innate to the system; they are specified in the genotype" (18, p. 116). This conclusion holds true whether one follows Pittendrigh in his argument that the individuals raised in continuous darkness had already developed a rhythm and only became synchronized by the single light-signal or whether one prefers the interpretation that the rhythm was genuinely initiated, an alternative stressed by Sweeney & Hastings (67), particularly for rhythms that have been started by pulses or steps of temperature. The effectiveness of short light- and temperature-signals and of steps in intensity level to start an overt rhythm in an aperiodic culture has been shown in *Drosophila* (19, 66, 68) and *Gonyaulax* (34) among others.

Convincing evidence for an innate rhythmicity is also given in instances when a free-running period developed spontaneously in vertebrates, raised from the egg in constant conditions [chickens (69); lizards (70)].

PROBLEMS OF ENTRAINMENT

PREFACE

As Bruce explained in his elegant treatise at the Cold Spring Harbor Symposium (23), there are several possibilities of entrainment with either direct or indirect coupling of the driven to the driving oscillator. In general, the goal of synchronization in circadian systems is not simply "synchrony"

—i.e., equal "speed" in the two systems—but "phase control": a clearly defined and stable phase-angle difference between the biological oscillation and the *Zeitgeber*. The prerequisite for such a phase control is a periodically changing sensitivity of the organism toward the effective agent, which then corrects the phase of the oscillation at least once during each period (24, 26). This can be done in two ways: (*a*) by changing one of the parameters which determine the frequency of the system (parametric entrainment) and (*b*) by direct action of the exogenous source of energy on the oscillation (nonparametric entrainment). Nonparametric entrainment has been much used in technology, leading to the normal so-called forced oscillation, while parametric entrainment has a briefer history in technical fields.

If one takes a light-dark cycle as an example of a *Zeitgeber*, one is confronted with two possibilities in regard to modes of action: (*a*) only the transitions from light to darkness and/or darkness to light are effective; (*b*) there is a continuous action of light on the oscillating system. It seems reasonable to consider the action of transitions as an instance of nonparametric entrainment. On the other hand, although parametric entrainment could be most easily accomplished by a continuous action of light on the frequency, continuous action is not synonymous with parametric entrainment: the influence of light between the two transitions could act on an element in the oscillation which itself does not directly determine the frequency, but which nevertheless allows entrainment, e.g., the "level", or average value of all instantaneous values during one period (24, 27), of the oscillation. [This does not imply, however, that the frequency may not be indirectly influenced by the level, as seems to be the case in nonlinear oscillations (26).] With either parametric or nonparametric entrainment, a changing sensitivity of the oscillation to light is implicit in terming light a *Zeitgeber*. Some of these problems will be discussed in more detail in the following sections.

THE *ZEITGEBER*

Light.—Light is the most common and most important *Zeitgeber* for circadian rhythms. If one imposes on an organism that is free-running under constant conditions of continuous light or continuous darkness an artificial light-dark cycle with 12 hours of light and 12 hours of darkness, the organism may become synchronized within a few days, as in birds (22), or it may require 10 or more periods until a stable phase-relationship has been reached, as in flying squirrels (71). There are wide ranges of light-dark ratio to which circadian systems can be entrained. To synchronize the oviposition rhythm of *Aedes aegypti*, 15 minutes of light every 24 hours are enough, but not 5 minutes (72). In hamsters, 50 minutes of light (15 Lux) have been shown to be effective (51). In *Pilobolus sphaerosporus* the rhythm of spore formation could be entrained to all light-dark ratios from 21:3 to 1:23; one hour of darkness was not sufficient, but a 1/200 sec of light was effective (73). In general, one can say that in varying the light-dark ratio, light can become shorter than darkness before losing the *Zeitgeber* effectiveness (23); perhaps this holds true, however, only for dark-active animals. The "amplitude"—or, better, the range (25) or the "intensity ratio"—of light between hours of light and hours of darkness may be small, 250:50 Lux being enough to entrain the incubation relief schedule in pigeons (74).

Temperature.—In two mammalian species tested, 12 hours of higher and 12 hours of lower temperature were ineffective as a *Zeitgeber* [hamster (23); flying squirrel (69)]. But a great variety of other organisms can be entrained with a temperature cycle or with temperature pulses every 24 hours [*Drosophila* (23, 66); the cockroaches *Leucophaea* and *Byrsotria* (54, 54a); the lizard *Sceloperus* (23)]. In some experiments very small variations have been used. The spore formation rhythm of *Pilobolus* has been entrained with a 4°C temperature range (75), but not with one of only 1°C; a 5°C increase of temperature during one hour was also effective (73). The eclosion rhythm of the dung fly *Trichopoda pinnipes* was reported to be entrained in continuous darkness by a temperature cycle with a range of only 0.6°C (76).

Other Zeitgebers.—Pittendrigh states that light and temperature are "the only two variables known to be coupled to the living oscillation" (18, p. 98). His co-worker Bruce considers the possibility that "a periodically repeated stimulus of some other type causes an overt persistent rhythm to become periodic with the same period as the entraining cycle" (23, p. 29). Although there are indications in favor of Bruce's opinion (3), it must be admitted that the effectiveness of a *Zeitgeber* other than light and temperature has not been adequately demonstrated. Some earlier statements about synchronization are open to question because the crucial experiment—comparison of the subsequent free running with the entrained situation—was not executed. Also what has been called "masking" (22)—suppression or accentuation of the observed function (e.g. locomotor activity) by the environmental stimulus—may simulate entrainment, although the "clock" is still free running [cf. DeCoursey's experiment with a temperature cycle on *Glaucomys* (59, Fig. 7)]. Some factors such as periodic noise in the building or from animals in the vicinity of the experimental animals are said to be without influence (52). But at least in some species there remains a possibility of mutual entrainment between individuals. Statements to the contrary with regard to *Gonyaulax* (34) are not conclusive on the basis of the data presented. And the differences between results, obtained by Stephens (44) when observing individually isolated crabs and groups of individuals, can be explained most easily by the assumption of mutual entrainment between the grouped animals. Furthermore, the synchronization of blind mice, which were previously free running, following the addition of normal seeing mice under cyclic light-dark conditions (77), suggests that social *Zeitgebers* (3) exist.

Phase-shifts with a Zeitgeber.—If one entrains a circadian system with a light-dark cycle of 12 hours:12 hours (or any other light-dark ratio or with a temperature cycle) and then shifts the phase of the artificial light-dark cycle with regard to local time—e.g., by adding or subtracting once six hours of light or darkness (phase-shift of 90°)—the entrained organism seldom follows immediately. More often it takes several days until the organism is resynchronized and reaches again its characteristic phase-relationship to the shifted *Zeitgeber*. The time necessary for such a resynchronization can be estimated from several recent publications. An over-all calculation indicates that many organisms need three to six days for a six-hour phase-shift— i.e., one to two hours shift per day. Figures in this order of magnitude have been found for the following species and functions: orientation rhythm of the starling (37, 78) and of the amphipod *Talitrus saltator* (79); feeding time of the bee (80); incubation relief schedule, orientation, and homing in the pigeon (74); orientation and activity in the lizard *Lacerta viridis* (81); urine excretion in man (82). The amount of daily shift seems to vary during the time of resynchronization (83). Furthermore, the advance-shift (subtracting once a few hours of light or darkness) seems to produce stable phase in a shorter time than the delay-shift (74, 81).

Other species follow a six- or twelve-hour phase-shift of the *Zeitgeber* on only one or two days, as demonstrated for the orientation rhythm of the water skater *Velia currens* (84) and the spider *Arctosa perita* (85) and also for the activity rhythms of the same two species (61, 64). This may indicate, together with other facts, that the rhythm in these species is not really autonomous but instead is exogenously controlled (3).

TRANSITION VERSUS CONTINUOUS ACTION APPROACH

Phase-angle difference in light-dark cycles.—As several workers have recognized, the phase-angle difference between organism and *Zeitgeber* can convey information about the mechanism of entrainment (21 to 24). Experiments with light-dark cycles of 24 hours, with varying photoperiods, are of special interest in this regard. But interpretation must be made with caution: parametrically entrained systems may have characteristic phase-angle differences which are not obviously different from those of a system which is entrained by transitions. The problem becomes even more difficult if both types of entrainment are combined or if both transitions are effective but with different and (depending on photoperiod) varying intensities. When it is stated: "The phase may depend primarily on dawn . . . or on the dusk . . ." (23, p. 31), the reader could conclude that the examples cited necessarily imply an action of one of these transitions. This conclusion, however, does not necessarily follow, because in a fully parametrically entrained system (where transitions have no influence) the phase may also be apparently bound to dawn (or dusk) over a wide range of light-dark ratios [cf. (24, Fig. 4)]. Generalizations about the changes of phase-angle differences with changing photoperiods in light- and dark-active animals have been attempted (86), but it is clear that we need more information on the behavior of more species before firm conclusions are warranted.

Transition effects.—Pittendrigh executed an experiment in which he released *Drosophila* cultures from a light-dark cycle of 12 hours:12 hours into continuous darkness, the last light signal being of different duration varying from 1 to 32 hours (21, Fig. 17). The peak of emergence in the following steady state always occurred 15 hours after dusk, whenever the last light signal was longer than 12 hours. "This transition . . . is thus an absolute phase-giver provided it is not followed by a dark/light transition within the next 24 hours. When this happens the transitions interact; and the steady-state phase resulting from their interaction is a sensitive function of the phase-angle between them. It is, in short, a function of the photoperiod" (21, p. 178). Other experiments support these statements for *Drosophila* (68), and comparable results have been obtained for the rhythm of cell division in *Chlorella* cultures (87) and for the spore formation rhythm of *Pilobolus sphaerosporus* (88). In summary, there is no doubt that in some species the transitions are phase-givers par excellence.

Response curves.—To show the periodically changing sensitivity of the oscillating system, free-running organisms have been systematically disturbed by single stimuli at all phases of their cycle. The resulting phase-shifts have been found to depend in both their direction (advance, delay) and amount on the phase at which the original rhythm was perturbed. The graphic representations of such experiments have been called "response curves" by the Cold Spring Harbor group. Response curves for light have been measured in *Peromyscus* (51), *Drosophila* (17, 20, 21, 89), *Glaucomys* (71, 90), *Euglena* (91), *Gonyaulax* (34), and *Paramecium* (92, 93). In most cases the phase of the circadian system has been advanced by the stimulus during parts of the period and delayed during others; sometimes, no response could be found during parts of the period (51, 90, 94). Theories of entrainment are based on such response curves (21, 59). One should keep in mind also the possible connections between photoperiodic effects and response curves, both showing a diurnally changing sensitivity (cf. 95, 96). Just as with light, one must expect a response curve for temperature whenever temperature is a *Zeitgeber*. Experiments in this direction have been executed on *Uca pugnax* (97), *Periplaneta americana* (98), *Paramecium bursaria* (93), *Oedogonium cardiacum* (99), and *Leucophaea maderae* (54a). More general problems of synchronization in rhythmically dividing cell cultures, also with regard to the periodic changing sensitivity of the system toward single stimuli, are discussed in an excellent review by Zeuthen (100).

Continuous action approach.—If there are genuinely constant conditions in the environment, an observable influence of the environment on the circadian system cannot be caused by transitions. It seems reasonable, therefore, to call the influence of different levels of illumination intensity (or of temperature) on the free-running period (cf. p. 585) a continuous action. Such effects are, at least, parametric by definition: the frequency of the system is determined by their influence. Furthermore, the continuous action certainly does not imply that there is always the same effect during the whole period; there has to be a "response curve", but this need not be identical with the response curve for transitions (24). Is there any indication for a continuous action in entrained systems? Pittendrigh has demonstrated in his already mentioned experiment (21, Fig. 17) that for *Drosophila*, released from a light-dark cycle into continuous darkness, continuous action could be excluded. However, his own laboratory published results of another experiment with the same species, which, in my opinion call for an explanation by continuous action (23, Fig. 6). Two cultures of *Drosophila* had been entrained to a temperature cycle, one in continuous darkness, the other in continuous light. For *Drosophila* pupae, τ_{DD} is shorter than τ_{LL} (21). From this one should expect that the continuous-darkness culture (with its shorter "natural period" τ_n) would show a smaller positive—or larger negative—phase-angle difference to the *Zeitgeber* than the continuous light culture. Exactly this has been shown to happen. There are two other experiments in which light-active animals have been entrained to a light-dark cycle of 12 hours: 12 hours with different average intensities of illumination [finches (22); pigeons (74)]. In both cases, the negative phase-angle difference became greater with an increase in average light intensity, as one would expect when τ_n shortens because of a continuous action of light intensity. Predictions have also been made about changes of the phase-angle of activity in free living birds with changing daylight hours during the year, based on a theory of mainly parametric entrainment; they seem to be in qualitative agreement with the observed behavior of birds (27).

In brief, there is always a "natural period" τ_n which deviates more or less from 24 hours, depending on environmental conditions. To become entrained, this natural period has to be corrected through advancing or delaying phase-shifts by the *Zeitgeber*. This may be accomplished by (a) the effect of one transition, (b) the difference of the effects of two transitions, (c) by the net (integrated) effects of continuous actions, or (d) by some combination of these possibilities. It seems probable that in the majority of organisms the fourth possibility is realized (22, 26, 86).

THE MULTI-OSCILLATOR SYSTEM

It has been stated that several observations on circadian systems "elude any obvious one-oscillator treatment" (21, p. 165). The 2-oscillator scheme, developed by Pittendrigh & Bruce (17), is based on the following observations. (a) The "phase-jump" over a forbidden zone in animals, which are entrained by two conflicting *Zeitgebers* with a varying phase-relation (as Pittendrigh agrees, however, this would also be expected of a single oscillator). (b) The behavior of transients after single signals and the final subsequent phase. Klotter (101) has shown, in this regard, that a single oscillator may behave in a similar manner; but in the mathematical model he used, the transients are the result of an interaction of two linear oscillations, a decaying "old" one and a signal-produced new one. It could be argued, therefore, that this is not strong evidence against a 2-oscillator system. The behavior of a (nonlinear) self-sustained oscillation during transients after a single stimulus has not yet been theoretically studied. (c) The "memory" of *Drosophila* cultures which were entrained to two conflicting *Zeitgebers* and which returned to the old (light-determined) phase when released in constant conditions (21, Fig. 5). This results seems quite significant, although there are still unexplained complications concerning the behavior of the A oscillator. (*d*) Experiments in continuous darkness and in light-dark cycles with *Drosophila* cultures, both exposed to temperature drops from 26° to 16° C (21, Fig.6). These experiments support the 2-oscillator hypothesis.

Whatever the final interpretation may be of the specific phenomena in *Drosophila* that led Pittendrigh and Bruce to their generalized coupled-oscillator scheme for circadian rhythms, there is clear evidence that an organism is a system of coacting multi-oscillations, not only in the area of circadian rhythms but as a hierarchy of frequencies (9, 19, 102). The problems of mutual entrainment within these oscillations are of special interest "as a base of the system's integrity and temporal order" (18, p. 122). There is, for example, an increase in stability of oscillation by mutual entrainment (20, 103, 104) which has been discussed with regard to possible advantages of the hierarchy of frequencies in biological systems (50).

The most striking example for the multi-oscillator scheme has been presented by Swade [cf. (18, Fig.7)]: in the free-running activity rhythm of a ground squirrel in continuous light, a low-frequency component "broke loose" from the system and was re-entrained seven weeks later when it regained phase with the rest of the system. Reports on possible dissociations of several functions in the same organism (3) point in the same direction. Observations on mice in continuous light and in continuous darkness suggest a dissociation even of functions in the same organ (mitosis and phospholipoid metabolism in the liver) (105). Furthermore, it should be noted that in body temperature and urine secretion of men living on artificial time schedules, both a 24-hour and a 21- or 27-hour period have been observed simultaneously (106).

MISCELLANEOUS

Biochemical aspects.—The possibilities of phase-shifting by chemicals have been reviewed by Hastings (107). Generalizations do not seem possible at this time. Further studies are encouraged by the observation that heavy water lengthens the free-runing period of phototactic response in *Euglena gracilis* (108). Ethyl alchohol has been reported to lengthen the period in *Phaseolus multiflorus* (109). The phase-angle difference of *Chlorella* in light-dark cycles is said to be a function of salt concentration (110); one could, therefore, expect varying free-running periods depending on salt concentration. Other biochemical aspects have been discussed by Ehret, especially with regard to action spectra and nucleic acid metabolism (94) and to the possibilities of a realistic model for circadian systems (111). The persistence of a photosynthetic rhythm in enucleate algae (*Acetabularia major*) (112), however, raises doubts about assigning a central role in all circadian rhythms to the cell nucleus.

Endocrine organs.—Endocrine factors in insect circadian rhythms have been discussed by Harker (113). From her own studies with cockroaches, she concluded that the oscillation in neurosecretion in the subesophageal ganglion is controlled by a distinct second oscillator (114). Most intriguing are her reports that the implantation of a subesophageal ganglion, shifted in its secretion rhythm by light or by cooling, into a headless cockroach induces an activity rhythm and determines its phase in the formerly arrhythmic animal (115). Roberts, however, was unable to confirm these transplantation experiments (54). Some recent publications deal with the diurnal variations of neurosecretion in *Carausius morosus* (116) and changes in the diameter of the corpora allata in *Pieris brassica* (96).

There are few observations concerning the role of endocrines in mammalian circadian rhythms. In mice after hypophysectomy, for example, free-running rhythms have been shown to exist for eosinophiles (117) and for activity (58). The diameter of cell nuclei in the hypothalamus of mice is said to have a diurnal rhythm (118).

Compass orientation rhythm.—The Cold Spring Harbor volume on biological clocks (14) contains several review articles on solar, lunar, and star orientation to which few comments may be added. As mentioned above, the orientation rhythm can be shifted with an appropriate *Zeitgeber*, as can all other functions investigated (cf. p. 589). Free-running orientation rhythms have been demonstrated in fish (119), *Arctosa perita* (85), and in starlings, concurrent with locomotor activity (37). From phase-shift experiments with fish, Braemer (120) concluded that the sun's altitude as well as the azimuth may have an influence on direction finding. In sunfish (121) and starlings (122) the ability to compute the sun's movement seems to be inherited, but not in bees (123) and in lizards (81).

Hibernation.—Free-running circadian rhythms persist in the body temperature of hibernating bats (32). If the environmental conditions are not rigorously constant, the hibernating animals remain entrained; the continuation of diurnal rhythms in such cases has been demonstrated for regular arousals of hamsters and squirrels (124, 125), for body temperature in the birch mouse (126), and for metabolism in the dormouse (127). Of special interest are the experiments of Strumwasser (128) who followed the course of brain temperature in squirrels which were entering hibernation. Diurnal rhythms of torpidity have been studied in the California pocket mouse (129) and the swift (130).

CIRCADIAN RHYTHMS IN MAMMALS

System phase.—For three species of laboratory animals, viz. mice, rats, and hamsters, we now have quite a good "map" of the interrelationships between several circadian functions. Halberg's versatile and instructive studies on *Mus musculus* present the most elaborate treatment available (6, 7, 8). These relations between the rhythms of several functions are called "system phases" (49). They are described for mice in some recent publications which include not only blood constituents (sugar, eosinophiles, corticosterone, etc.) and mitosis in several tissues (131) but also metabolic changes, particularly of nucleic acids (132), and hormone secretion (133). The rhythm of mitotic activity has been extensively studied in the corneal epithelium by Vasama (134) and by Movchan (135), in cortical adrenal parenchyma (131), and also in the kidney, together with diuresis (136). Bullough (137) emphasized the relation of mitotic activity to stress and epinephrine.

In the rat, rhythms of mitosis have again been studied in the corneal epithelium (135) and in the liver (138); diurnal changes in the function of the pancreatic islets (139) and in adrenal ascorbic acid concentration (140) were also observed. Heusner (141, 142) demonstrated that there is, concurrent with body temperature change, a diurnal rhythm in basic oxygen consumption, calculated for equal amounts of locomotor activity. The system phases for body temperature, mitosis, and blood eosinophiles in the hamster are now well established (143, 144); onsets of estrus and ovulation are also diurnally timed (145). In wild mammals, diurnal rhythms of oxygen consumption (146) and of blood coagulation times (147) have been described.

Diurnal sensitivity.—Of great clinical as well as physiological interest are the observations that toxic agents and disturbing stimuli have different effects at different phases of diurnal rhythms. Usually, the sensitivity of an animal is higher when the animal is active. When mice are kept in a light-dark cycle, audiogenic convulsions produced by the sound of a "bell-tub" occur most frequently during darkness, and this rhythm can be shifted with the light-dark cycle, as can all other circadian rhythms (148). Diurnal rhythms in susceptibility have also been demonstrated for a toxic dose of ethanol (149), for *E. coli* endotoxin (150, 151), for the psychotherapeutic drug Librium [7-chloro-2-(methylamino)-5-phenyl-3-H-1,4-benzodiazepine-4-oxide HCl] (152), and for barbiturates (153).

Human physiology.—The studies of Hellbruegge, summarized in his Cold Spring Harbor lecture (154), demonstrate that during ontogeny of the human infant diurnal rhythms develop one after another, not only for several organs, but also as a sequence of events in one organ, e.g. the kidney. This leads to the question of "period dissociation" (see above), which has been best demonstrated by Lewis & Lobban (155, 156) in their ingenious Spitzbergen experiment. Subjects living in an artificial 21- or 27-hour day, partly adapted to this regime, showed in some cases a dissociation of functions in one organ, e.g., between water and potassium excretion. Lobban & Simpson (157) obtained comparable results during a 3-week walk from Bergen to Tromsø during arctic summer. To observe human excretory rhythms during phase-shift, Flink & Doe used a long distance flight (82) and Sharp (158) used a reversed time schedule for subjects living in Spitzbergen during midsummer. Free-running rhythms could be demonstrated in isolated human subjects, as already mentioned (30). The results suggest (a) influences of light on length of period and (b) dissociations in the rhythmicity of different functions.

One could now make a map of system-phases for men as well as for mice: more than 50 rhythmically changing constituents, functions, and behavior elements have been studied. Three selected papers may be cited as examples for many others. Graf (159) measured the liver temperature continuously, using biopsy needles. The telephone has been used to show a fluctuating hum frequency (160). Hampp (161) submitted an extensive questionnaire to 400 people about their diurnal changes in mood and "drive". Furthermore, Richter's broadly applied and theoretically supported paper on biological clocks in medicine and psychiatry is worthy of attention (162); it includes a wide variety of rhythmic phenomena.

ECOLOGY

The general patterns of activity in caged and free living mammals have been recently discussed in an extensive review (9). It does not mention the ethological studies of Bubenik (163) on the Przewalski horse (also observed during night by use of infrared light) and of Graefe (164) on the flying squirrel. Pearson (165, 166, 167) followed the habits of the meadow mouse *Microtus californicus* and of the harvest mouse *Reithrodontomys megalotis* for two years with an automatic photographic recording technique. His results indicate that different patterns of activity characterize different seasons. A miniature transmitter has been used to observe activities of the badger *Meles meles* (168).

A review on awakening and roosting times of birds presents six generalizations which are interpreted in terms of parametric circadian entrainment (27). Two recent papers, not mentioned there, deal with the daybreak and evening songs of 20 species, recorded over a four-year period (169) and the morning and evening song of the robin in different latitudes (170). Hoffmann (171) observed the diurnal rhythms of song birds in the continuous daylight of the arctic summertime. The varying relation between the day and night fauna in the course of the year, sampled by pitfall traps, is described by Williams (172). Haddow and co-workers have continued their extensive work on biting habits of African mosquitoes (72, 173, 173a); new laboratory observations include the oviposition cycle (174), feeding activity (175), and emergence (176). The diurnal pattern of biting activity has been especially studied in *Aedes aegypti* (177), *Glossina pallidipes* (178), *Chrysops silacea* (179, 180), and *Simulium venustum* (181). Extensive studies on fruit leaf tortricids have been published by Sylvén, with special reference to species differences in periodicity (182). Remmert (183) demonstrated that there is a diurnal rhythm in preference for temperature and light in some insects.

CLOSING REMARKS

New interest in the field grew up since one recognized (a) the significance and adaptive value of free-running rhythms, (b) the characteristic features of self-sustained oscillations and their entrainment as applicable to biological rhythms, and (c) the more general problems of temporal organization in living systems, which depend on a hierarchy of coupled oscillators. Future research may follow two directions: one leading to the physicochemical basis of the oscillation, and its representation at the cell level; the other one applying the generalized rules of entrainment and time measurement to a wide variety of processes in ecology, including functional taxonomy, and to photoperiodic effects. The time may also come when one recognizes the oscillating nature of living systems as one of their major prerequisites, the disturbance of which one has to consider as a cause for damage to the organism and as a tool in the studies of environmental influences on organisms.

LITERATURE CITED

1. Cole, L. C., *Science*, **125**, 874–76 (1957)
2. Harker, J. E., *Biol. Rev. Cambridge Phil. Soc.*, **33**, 1–52 (1958)
3. Aschoff, J., *Z. Tierpsychol.*, **15**, 1–30 (1958)
4. Webb, H. M., and Brown, F. A., Jr., *Physiol. Rev.*, **39**, 127–61 (1959)
5. Hastings, J. W., *Ann. Rev. Microbiol.*, **13**, 297–312 (1959)
6. Halberg, F., *Z. Vitamin-, Hormon-Fermentforsch.*, **10**, 225–96 (1960)
7. Halberg, F., *Perspectives Biol. Med.*, **3**, 491–527 (1960)
8. Halberg, F., Halberg, E., Barnum, C. P., and Bittner, J. J., in *Photoperiodism and Related Phenomena in Plants and Animals*, 803–78 (Am. Assoc. Advan. Sci., Washington, 1959)
9. Aschoff, J., *Handbuch der Zoologie*, **VIII**, Part 11, 1–76 (1962)
10. Renner, M., *Ergeb. Biol.*, **20**, 127–58 (1958)
11. Ray, J. T., Martin, O. E., Jr., and Alluisi, E. A., *Natl. Acad. Sci.— Natl. Res. Council, Publ. 882* (1961)
12. Bünning, E., *Die physiologische Uhr* (Springer-Verlag, Berlin, Göttingen, Heidelberg, 1958)
13. Cloudsley-Thompson, J. L., *Rhythmic Activity in Animal Physiology and Behaviour* (Academic, New York and London, 1961)
14. *Cold Spring Harbor Symp. Quant. Biol.*, **25**, (1960)
15. *Circadian Systems, Rept. Ross Pediat. Res. Conf.*, **39**, (1961)
16. Farner, D. S., *Ann. Rev. Physiol.*, **23**, 71–96 (1961)
17. Pittendrigh, C. S., and Bruce, V. G., in *Photoperiodism and Related Phenomena in Plants and Animals* (Am. Assoc. Advan. Sci., Washington, 1959)
18. Pittendrigh, C. S., *Harvey Lectures*, *Ser. 56*, 93–125 (1961)
19. Pittendrigh, C. S., and Bruce, V. G., in *Rhythmic and Synthetic Processes in Growth*, 75–109 (Princeton Univ. Press, 1957)
20. Pittendrigh, C. S., in *Symp. Perspectives Marine Biol.*, 239–68 (Univ. of Calif. Press, Berkeley, Calif., 1958)
21. Pittendrigh, C. S., *Cold Spring Harbor Symp. Quant. Biol.*, **25**, 159–84 (1960)
22. Aschoff, J., *Cold Spring Harbor Symp. Quant. Biol.*, **25**, 11–28 (1960)
23. Bruce, V., *Cold Spring Harbor Symp. Quant. Biol.*, **25**, 29–47 (1960)
24. Wever, R., *Cold Spring Harbor Symp. Quant. Biol.*, **25**, 197–206 (1960)
25. Klotter, K., *Cold Spring Harbor Symp. Quant. Biol.*, **25**, 185–87 (1960)
26. Wever, R., *Kybernetik*, **1**, 139–54. (1962)
27. Aschoff, J., and Wever, R., *J. Ornithol.*, **103**, 2–27 (1962)
28. Hastings, J. W., and Sweeney, B. M., in *Photoperiodism and Related Phenomena in Plants and Animals*, p. 567–87 (Am. Assoc. Advan. Sci., Washington, 1959)
29. Bruce, V. G., and Pittendrigh, C. S., *Proc. Natl. Acad. Sci. US*, **42**, 676–82 (1956)
30. Aschoff, J., and Wever, R., *Naturwissenschaften*, **49**, 337–42 (1962)
31. Rawson, K. S., *Cold Spring Harbor Symp. Quant. Biol.*, **25**, 105–13 (1960)
32. Menaker, M., *J. Cellular Comp. Physiol.*, **57**, 81–86 (1961)
33. Aschoff, J., *Arch. Ges. Physiol.*, **262**, 51–59 (1955)
34. Hastings, J. W., and Sweeney, B. M., *Biol. Bull.*, **115**, 440–58 (1958)
35. Sweeney, B. M., and Hastings, J. W., *J. Protozool.*, **5**, 217–24 (1958)
36. Hastings, J. W., Astrachan, L., and Sweeney, B. M., *J. Gen. Physiol.*, **45**, 69–76 (1961)
37. Hoffmann, K., *Cold Spring Harbor Symp. Quant. Biol.*, **25**, 379–87 (1960)
38. Brown, F. A., Jr., *Am. Naturalist*, **91**, 129–33 (1957)
39. Webb, H. M., Brown, F. A., Jr., and Sandeen, M. I., *Anat. Record*, **120**, 796 (1954)
40. Brown, F. A., Jr., Shriner, J., and Ralph, C. L., *Am. J. Physiol.*, **184**, 491–96 (1956)
41. Terracini, E. D., and Brown, F. A., Jr., *Physiol. Zoöl.*, **35**, 27–37 (1962)
42. Brown, F. A., Jr., *Science*, **130**, 1535–44 (1959)
43. Brown, F. A., Jr., *Cold Spring Harbor Symp. Quant. Biol.*, **25**, 57–71 (1960)
44. Stephens, G. C., *Circadian Systems, Rept. Ross Pediat. Res. Conf.*, **39**, 83–85 (1961)
45. Webb, H. M., and Brown, F. A., Jr., *Biol. Bull.*, **121**, 561–71 (1961)
46. Mercer, D. M. A., *Cold Spring Harbor Symp. Quant. Biol.*, **25**, 73–85 (1960)

47. Halberg, F., and Panofsky, H., *Exptl. Med. Surg.*, **19**, 284–309 (1961)

48. Panofsky, H., and Halberg, F., *Exptl. Med. Surg.*, **19**, 323–38 (1961)

49. Schmitt, O., *Cold Spring Harbor Symp. Quant. Biol.*, **25**, 148 (1960)

50. Aschoff, J., and Wever, R., *Oeynhausener Gespräche V.*, 1–15 (Delius, L., Ed., Springer-Verlag, Berlin, Göttingen, Heidelberg, 1962)

51. Rawson, K. S., *Homing Behavior and Endogenous Activity Rhythms* (Doctoral thesis, Harvard, 1956)

52. DeCoursey, P. J., *Daily Activity in the Flying Squirrel*, Glaucomys volans (Doctoral thesis, Univ. of Wisconsin, Madison, 1959)

53. Hoffmann, K., *Z. Vergleich. Physiol.*, **42**, 422–32 (1959)

54. Roberts, S. K., *Circadian Activity Rhythms in Cockroaches* (Doctoral thesis, Princeton Univ., 1959)

54a. Roberts, S. K. de F., *J. Cellular Comp. Physiol.*, **59**, 175–86 (1962)

55. Johnson, M. S., *J. Exptl. Zool.*, **82**, 315–28 (1939)

56. Stinson, R. H., *Can. J. Zool.*, **38**, 51–55 (1960)

57. Calhoun, J. B., *Ecology*, **26**, 250–73 (1945)

58. Müller, M., and Giersberg, H., *Z. Vergleich. Physiol.*, **40**, 454–72 (1957)

59. DeCoursey, P. J., *Cold Spring Harbor Symp. Quant. Biol.*, **25**, 49–54 (1960)

60. Roberts, S. K. de F., *J. Cellular Comp. Physiol.*, **55**, 99–110 (1960)

61. Rensing, L., *Z. Vergleich. Physiol.*, **44**, 292–322 (1961)

62. Aschoff, J., *Z. Vergleich. Physiol.*, **35**, 159–66 (1953)

63. Hoffmann, K., *Z. Vergleich. Physiol.*, **43**, 544–66 (1960)

64. Tongiorgi, P., *Arch. Ital. Biol.*, **97**, 251–65 (1959)

65. Geisler, M., *Z. Tierpsychol.*, **18**, 389–420 (1961)

66. Pittendrigh, C. S., *Proc. Natl. Acad. Sci. US*, **40**, 1018–29 (1954)

67. Sweeney, B. M., and Hastings, J. W., *Cold Spring Harbor Symp. Quant. Biol.*, **25**, 87–104 (1960)

68. Brett, W., *Ann. Entomol. Soc. Am.*, **48**, 119–31 (1955)

69. Aschoff, J., and Mayer-Lohmann, J., *Arch. Ges. Physiol.*, **260**, 170–76 (1954)

70. Hoffmann, K., *Naturwissenschaften*, **44**, 359–60 (1957)

71. DeCoursey, P. J., *Z. Vergleich. Physiol.*, **44**, 331–54 (1961)

72. Gillett, J. D., Corbet, Ph.S., and Haddow, A. J., *Ann. Trop. Med. Parasitol.*, **53**, 132–36 (1959)

73. Uebelmesser, E. R., *Arch. Mikrobiol.*, **20**, 1–33 (1954)

74. Schmidt-König, K., *Z. Tierpsychol.*, **15**, 301–31 (1958)

75. Schmidle, A., *Archiv. Mikrobiol.*, **16**, 80–100 (1951)

76. Wilson, F., and Snowball, G. J., *Australian J. Zool.*, **7**, 1–6 (1959)

77. Halberg, F., Visscher, M. B., and Bittner, J. J., *Am. J. Physiol.*, **179**, 229–35 (1954)

78. Hoffmann, K., *Z. Tierpsychol.*, **11**, 453–75 (1954)

79. Pardi, L., *Boll. Ist. Museo Zool. Univ. Torino*, **4**, (1–8) No. 9 (1953/54)

80. Renner, M., *Cold Spring Harbor Symp. Quant. Biol.*, **25**, 361–67 (1960)

81. Fischer, K., *Z. Tierpsychol.*, **18**, 450–70 (1961)

82. Flink, E. B., and Doe, R. P., *Proc. Soc. Exptl. Biol. Med.*, **100**, 498–501 (1959)

83. Halberg, F., Albrecht, P. G., and Barnum, C. P., Jr., *Am. J. Physiol.*, **199**, 400–2 (1960)

84. Birukow, G., and Busch, E., *Z. Tierpsychol.*, **14**, 184–207 (1957)

85. Papi, F., Serretti, L., and Parrini, S., *Z. Vergleich. Physiol.*, **39**, 531–61 (1957)

86. Aschoff, J., *Proc. Intern. Congr. Photobiology, 3rd, Amsterdam*, 50–62 (1961)

87. Pirson, A., and Lorenzen, H., *Z. Botan.*, **46**, 53–66 (1958)

88. Bruce, V. G., Weight, T., and Pittendrigh, C. S., *Science*, **131**, 728–30 (1960)

89. Pittendrigh, C. S., Bruce, V. G., and Kaus, P., *Proc. Natl. Acad. Sci. US*, **44**, 965–73 (1958)

90. De Coursey, P. J., *Science*, **131**, 33–35 (1960)

91. Bruce, V. G., and Pittendrigh, C. S., *Am. Naturalist*, **92**, 295–306 (1958)

92. Ehret, Ch. F., *Federation Proc.*, **18**, 1232–40 (1959)

93. Ehret, Ch. F., in *Photoperiodism and Related Phenomena in Plants and Animals* (Ann. Assoc. Advan. Sci., Washington, 1959)

94. Ehret, Ch. F., *Cold Spring Harbor Symp. Quant. Biol.*, **25**, 149–57 (1960)

95. Bünning, E., *Cold Spring Harbor Symp. Quant. Biol.*, **25**, 249–56 (1960)

96. Bünning, E., and Joerrens, G., *Z. Naturforsch.*, **17b**, 57–61 (1962)
97. Stephens, G. C., *Physiol. Zoöl.*, **30**, 55–69 (1957)
98. Bünning, E., *Z. Naturforsch.*, **146**, 1–5 (1959)
99. Bünning, E., and Ruddat, M., *Naturwissenschaften*, **47**, 286 (1960)
100. Zeuthen, E., *Archiv. Biol. Med. Physiol.*, **6**, 37–73 (1959)
101. Klotter, K., *Cold Spring Harbor Symp. Quant. Biol.*, **25**, 189–96 (1960)
102. Aschoff, J., *Naturwissenschaften*, **44**, 361–67 (1957)
103. Barlow, J. S., *Cold Spring Harbor Symp. Quant. Biol.*, **25**, 54 (1960)
104. Schmitt, O. H., *Cold Spring Harbor Symp. Quant. Biol.*, **25**, 207–10 (1960)
105. Halberg, F., and Barnum, C. P., *Am. J. Physiol.*, **201**, 227–30 (1961)
106. Lobban, M., *Cold Spring Harbor Symp. Quant. Biol.*, **25**, 325–32 (1960)
107. Hastings, J. W., *Cold Spring Harbor Symp. Quant. Biol.*, **25**, 131–40 (1960)
108. Bruce, V. G., and Pittendrigh, C. S., *J. Cellular Comp. Physiol.*, **56**, 25–31 (1960)
109. Bünning, E., and Baltes, J., *Naturwissenschaften*, **49**, 19 (1962)
110. Soeder, C. J., *Flora*, **148**, 489–516 (1959/60)
111. Ehret, Ch. F., and Barlow, J. S., *Cold Spring Harbor Symp. Quant. Biol.*, **25**, 217–20 (1960)
112. Sweeney, B. M., and Haxo, F. T., *Science*, **134**, 1361–62 (1961)
113. Harker, J. E., *Cold Spring Harbor Symp. Quant. Biol.*, **25**, 279–87 (1960)
114. Harker, J. E., *J. Exptl. Biol.*, **37**, 154–63 (1960)
115. Harker, J., *J. Exptl. Biol.*, **37**, 164–70 (1960)
116. Mothes, G., *Zool. Jahrb., Abt. Allgem. Zool. Physiol. Tiere*, **69**, 133–62 (1960)
117. Ferguson, D. J., Visscher, M. B., Halberg, F., and Levy, L. M., *Am. J. Physiol.*, **190**, 235–38 (1957)
118. Niebroj, T., *Naturwissenschaften*, **45**, 67 (1958)
119. Schwassmann, H. O., *Cold Spring Harbor Symp. Quant. Biol.*, **25**, 443–50 (1960)
120. Braemer, W., *Cold Spring Harbor Symp. Quant. Biol.*, **25**, 413–27 (1960)
121. Hasler, A. D., and Schwassmann, H. O., *Cold Spring Harbor Symp. Quant. Biol.*, **25**, 429–41 (1960)
122. Hoffmann, K., *Naturwissenschaften*, **40**, 148 (1953)
123. Lindauer, M., *Z. Vergleich. Physiol.*, **42**, 43–62 (1959)
124. Folk, G. E., Jr., *Am. Naturalist*, **91**, 153–66 (1957)
125. Folk, G. E., Meltzer, M. M., and Gindeland, E., *Nature*, **181**, 1598 (1958)
126. Johansen, K., and Krog, J., *Am. J. Physiol.*, **196**, 1200–4 (1959)
127. Pohl, H., *Z. Vergleich. Physiol.*, **45**, 109–53 (1961)
128. Strumwasser, F., *Am. J. Physiol.*, **196**, 8–14 (1959)
129. Tucker, V. A., *Science*, **136**, 380–81 (1962)
130. Koskimies, J., *Vogelwarte*, **21**, 161–66 (1961)
131. Halberg, F., Peterson, R. E., and Silber, R. H., *Endocrinology*, **64**, 222–30 (1959)
132. Barnum, C. P., Jardetzky, Ch., and Halberg, F., *Am. J. Physiol.*, **195**, 301–10 (1958)
133. Halberg, F., Albrecht, P., and Bittner, J. J., *Am. J. Physiol.*, **197**, 1083–85 (1959)
134. Vasama, R., *Ann. Univ. Turku., Ser. A, II*, No. 29 (1961)
135. Movchan, O. T., *Bull. Exptl. Biol. Med.*, **52**, 845–48 (1961)
136. Zakharov, M. K., *Bull. Exptl. Biol. Med.*, **51**, 715–17 (1961)
137. Bullough, W. S., and Laurence, E. B., *Proc. Roy. Soc. (London), B*, **154**, 540–56 (1961)
138. Jackson, B., *Anat. Record*, **134**, 365–77 (1959)
139. Hellman, B., and Hellerström, C., *Acta Endocrinol.*, **31**, 267–81 (1959)
140. Rinne, U. K., and Kytömaki, O., *Experientia*, **17**, 512–13 (1961)
141. Heusner, A., *J. Physiol. (Paris)*, **49**, 205–9 (1957)
142. Heusner, A., *Compt. Rend. Soc. Biol.*, **153**, 1258–60 (1959)
143. Chaudhry, A. P., Halberg, F., Keenan, C. E., Harner, R. N., and Bittner, J. J., *J. Appl. Physiol.*, **12**, 221–24 (1958)
144. Halberg, F., and Chaudhry, A. P., *Am. J. Physiol.*, **199**, 807–8 (1960)
145. Harvey, E. B., Yanagaimachi, R., and Chang, M. C., *J. Exptl. Zool.*, **146**, 231–35 (1961)
146. Grodzinski, W., *Bull. Acad. Polon. Sci.*, **9**, 493–99 (1961)
147. Everson, R. A., *Physiol. Zoöl.*, **33**, 281–87 (1960)

148. Halberg, F., Jacobson, E., Wardsworth, G., and Bittner, J. J., *Science*, **128**, 657–58 (1958)

149. Haus, E., and Halberg, F., *J. Appl. Physiol.*, **14**, 878–80 (1959)

150. Halberg, F., and Stephens, A. N., *Federation Proc.*, **17**, 439 (1958)

151. Halberg, F., Johnson, E. A., Brown, B. W., and Bittner, J. J., *Proc. Soc. Exptl. Biol. Med.*, **103**, 142–44 (1960)

152. Marte, E., and Halberg, F., *Federation Proc.*, **20**, 305 (1961)

153. Davis, W. M., *Experientia*, **18**, 235 (1962)

154. Hellbrügge, Th., *Cold Spring Harbor Symp. Quant. Biol.*, **25**, 311–23 (1960)

155. Lewis, P. R., and Lobban, M. C., *Quart. J. Exptl. Physiol.*, **42**, 371–86 (1957)

156. Lewis, P. R., and Lobban, M. C., *Quart. J. Exptl. Physiol.*, **42**, 356–70 (1957)

157. Lobban, M. C., and Simpson, H. W., *J. Physiol.* (*London*), **155**, 64P (1961)

158. Sharp, G. W. G., *Nature*, **193**, 37–41 (1962)

159. Graf, W., *Acta Physiol. Scand.*, **46**, Supply. 160 (1959)

160. Rubenstein, L., *Science*, **134**, 1519–20 (1961)

161. Hampp, H., *Arch. Psychiat. Z. Ges. Neurol.*, **201**, 355–77 (1961)

162. Richter, C. P., *Proc. Natl. Acad. Sci. US*, **46**, 1506–30 (1960)

163. Bubenik, A. B., *Proc. Intern. Symp. Przewalski Horse, Prag, 1959*, 122–40 (Prag, 1961)

164. Graefe, G., *Z. Tierpsychol.*, **18**, 84–90 (1961)

165. Pearson, O. P., *J. Mammalogy*, **40**, 169–80 (1959)

166. Pearson, O. P., *J. Mammalogy*, **41**, 58–74 (1960)

167. Pearson, O. P., *Ecol. Monographs*, **30**, 231–49 (1960)

168. Canivenc, R., Croizet, J., Blanquet, P., and Bounin-Laffargue, M., *Comp. Rend. Acad. Sci.*, **250**, 1915–27 (1960)

169. Leopold, A., and Eynon, A. E., *Condor*, **63**, 169–93 (1961)

170. Miller, R. C., *Condor*, **60**, 105–7 (1958)

171. Hoffmann, K., *J. Ornithol.*, **100**, 84–89 (1959)

172. Williams, G., *J. Animal Ecol.*, **28**, 1–13 (1959)

173. Haddow, A. J., *Bull. Entomol. Res.*, **50**, 759–79 (1960)

173a. Haddow, A. J., Corbet, P. S., and Gillett, J. D., *Trans. Roy. Entomol. Soc. London*, **113**, 249–368 (1961)

174. Haddow, A. J., Corbet, P. S., and Gillett, J. D., *Ann. Trop. Med. Parasitol.*, **54**, 392–96 (1960)

175. Gillett, J. D., *Nature*, **191**, 881–83 (1961)

176. Haddow, A. J., Gillett, J. D., and Corbet, Ph. S., *Ann. Trop. Med. Parasitol.*, **53**, 123–31 (1959)

177. McClelland, G. A. H., *Bull. Entomol. Res.*, **50**, 687–96 (1960)

178. Leggate, B. M., and Pilson, R. D., *Bull. Entomol. Res.*, **51**, 697–704 (1960/61)

179. Duke, B. O. L., *Ann. Trop. Med. Parasitol.*, **52**, 24–35 (1958)

180. Wolfe, L. S., and Peterson, D. G., *Can. J. Zool.*, **38**, 489–97 (1960)

181. Duke, B. O. L., *Ann. Trop. Med. Parasitol.*, **54**, 147–55 (1960)

182. Sylvén, E., *Swed. State Plant Protection Inst. Contrib.*, **11**, 74, 135–296 (Statens Växtskyddsanstalt, Meddelanden, Stockholm, 1958)

183. Remmert, H., *Biol. Zentr.*, **79**, 577–84 (1960)

TRANSPORT THROUGH BIOLOGICAL MEMBRANES[1,2]

BY WALTHER WILBRANDT

Department of Pharmacology, University of Bern, Switzerland

This review covers, essentially, material published in the years 1960 and 1961. For reasons of space, work on plant cells, physicochemical studies on inanimate membranes, and most of the work on electrophysiology (even if it touched transport problems) had to be excluded. A number of symposia were held dealing wholly or partly with transport problems (25, 112, 173, 256, 282) and several surveys were published (43, 82, 242, 331, 333, 338a). Some reviews of more restricted scope will be mentioned below. A number of contributions to the symposia mentioned (particularly 173) also have the character of reviews.

Developments of special interest, in the opinion of the reviewer, include the growing amount of valuable information gained from bacteria (especially from studies on permease systems for which mutants lacking enzymes or permeases are especially favorable), the increasing evidence for the operation of carrier systems, the approach towards better understanding of the alkali cation transport based on the study of membrane ATPase, and the growing knowledge about the types of functional membrane polarity in transporting cells, mainly of epithelia.

GENERAL ASPECTS OF MEMBRANE PASSAGE

Porosity and experimental determination of pore sizes in cell membranes.— A number of papers, mainly from Solomon's laboratory, deal with the determination of pore sizes in cell membranes [summaries: (288, 289)], from measurements of the osmotic pressure developed across a membrane permeable for a solute. From the "reflection coefficient" of Staverman (the ratio of the observed pressure to the theoretical osmotic pressure according to Van't Hoff's law) and from the molecular radius of the solute, the equivalent pore radius can be assessed by graphical methods. The equations used have been tested by Durbin (88) on collodium membranes. In the human red cell (110), measurements with nine solutes yielded an equivalent pore radius of 4.2 A, as compared to 3.5 A determined previously by means of the Pappenheimer-Ussing method of comparing the rates of water movement under concentration and osmotic pressure gradients. In the resting axolemma of the squid axon (319, 320), a value of 4.25A was found by Villegas & Barnola, as

---

[1] The survey of literature pertaining to this review was concluded in December 1961 (occasional references are made to papers published in the first half of 1962).

[2] Abbreviations used repeatedly in this review are: ADP (adenosine diphosphoric acid); ATP (adenosine triphosphoric acid); DNP (2,4-dinitrophenol).

compared to $1.5-8.5$ A from water fluxes; and a value of 4.0 A in the luminal surface of intestinal mucosal cells was found by Lindemann & Solomon (199). Kidney slices from *Necturus* (327) yielded 5.6 A in the absence, and 6.5 A in the presence of Pitressin. For comparison, "effective hydrodynamic molecular radii" were determined by Schultz & Solomon (277) from viscosimetry following Einstein's treatment. The values for 11 solutes agreed with the results of measurements on molecular models. They ranged from 1.9 A for urea to 6.0 A for raffinose.

Poorly permeable porous membranes.—Starting from his observations on the loss of aldolase from muscle cells, Zierler (347) deals with the properties of porous membranes with small numbers of holes he describes as "small compared to the number of molecules capable of diffusing through the apertures." He deduces that such a membrane should show saturation and competition and presents experiments on a macroscopic model system in accordance with this prediction. He argues correctly that competition or saturation constitutes no conclusive evidence for a carrier mechanism. Counter transport is not included in his discussion.

Carrier systems.—The general features of carrier transport systems, both equilibrating and transporting uphill, were reviewed by Wilbrandt & Rosenberg (337) and compared to reported observations. It was pointed out that a number of kinetic features are shared by "adsorption systems" which involve binding of substrate at fixed sites rather than on mobile carriers, but that counter transport and competitive activation are criteria for mobile binding sites. (Competitive activation—termed counter acceleration previously—is acceleration of downhill movement of a substrate A by the presence of a competitive substrate B in low concentrations.) A number of pertinent observations reported in the literature were discussed (336). Recent observations mentioned here, concerning counter transport (48, 180, 228, 234, 253, 262, 307, 334) and competitive activation (148, 165, 172, 228), which were not interpreted by all authors along the same lines, are also pertinent in this context. Further treatments of carrier systems were given by Jacquez (147) and by Reiner (251). Heinz & Patlak (126) have treated the energetics of uphill carrier systems.

Uphill transport.—Reviews were given by Netter (224) dealing with possible mechanisms and by Ussing (312) treating biological significance and possible experimental evidence. Mitchell (213, 215) pursues his interpretation of uphill transport in terms of membranes containing "anisotropic" enzymes with orientated accessibility for substrates and coenzymes. He suggests (214) a scheme, based on this principle, for oxidative phosphorylation consisting of an anisotropic reversible ATPase with oriented accessibility for H^+ and OH^-, located in a membrane next to a redox pump. Katchalsky & Kedem (160, 161, 162) deal with uphill transport in terms of irreversible thermodynamics.

The "leak and pump" scheme.—The concept of a steady state, in accumulating cells, which involves a metabolically driven pump and a spatially separated diffusion leak, has been questioned from two directions. Results (see below) which indicate that in certain permease systems exit is slowed by metabolic inhibitors (165) and displays counter transport (228), and that agents stimulating uphill transport may do so by slowing exit (44, 230), question the assumption of diffusion for the leak. The observation, made in several different systems (228, 259, 321), that DNP blocks accumulation by increasing efflux rather than by decreasing influx questions the assumption of two components as outlined above.

The sorption theory.—To explain unequal distribution of solutes by specific binding rather than by specific penetration or transport has repeatedly been attempted in recent years. Surveys are given by Troshin (306), Kurella (178, 179), and Ling (200). From studies in smooth muscle, Bozler (29) had concluded in 1958 that the distribution of a number of nonelectrolytes studied was "not determined by a semipermeable membrane" and that "water is contained in segregated spaces which are so narrow that diffusion of molecules of moderate size is severely hindered." In recent work on frog sartorius and stomach muscle (30) he finds again that the distribution volume of some nonelectrolytes, for example, erythritol, are larger than inulin space but smaller than total water (yet constant over 24 hours). Stolkowski (296), in an extensive review on cellular potassium, refers potassium accumulation to binding of this ion to ribonucleic acid without participation of an active transport system, enhanced by corticosteroids. As evidence, data are presented showing an increase of total potassium in the hearts of *Helix pomatia*, in the presence of cortisone, from 58.6 to 64.4 meq per g dry weight. The sorption view is also held by Joseph *et al.* (158) and by Aschheim (9).

Contractile proteins.—In support of his theory of transport by contractile proteins, Goldacre (109) describes new observations on *Nitella*. He finds contraction of the surface area of cytoplasm at various places where the cytoplasma layer thickens.

Pinocytosis.—Chapman-Andresen (40) has found that salt-induced pinocytosis in *Amoeba proteus* has a temperature optimum of 22–24°C and a pH optimum of about 7. Pinocytotic uptake of fluorescent albumin in the same organism led to formation of many fluorescent vacuoles at pH 4.2–4.5 while surface binding and uptake was slight or absent at pH 6.5–6.9 (41).

Holtzer & Holtzer (139), also using labeled plasma proteins, have studied pinocytotic uptake in a large variety of mature normal cells from rabbit, mouse, and chick. Binding of proteins by injured cells and other cytological artifacts are discussed. Pinocytosis was observed in reticuloendothelial cells (macrophages, Kupffer cells, reticular cells, granular and nongranular leukocytes), intestinal cells from 6- to 10-day old mice, and kidney proximal tubule cells; it was not, however, in normal uninjured liver cells, stomach, bladder, lung, colon, cornea, amnion cells, cardiac and skeletal muscle fibers, thyroid, cartilage and fat cells, red cells, L cells, and a variety of fibroblasts. Some capacity for pinocytosis was also found in malignant cells

(HeLa, Ehrlich, and DBA ascites tumor cells). Undamaged yeast cells (*S. Carlsbergiensis*) did not take up labeled proteins (138).

SUGARS AND RELATED SUBSTANCES

Results of work on a number of different types of cells including red cells, muscle fibers, heart muscle fibers, yeast cells, and bacteria, as well as on transcellular transport mainly across the intestinal epithelium, have been interpreted in terms of carrier systems. New experimental support for this concept has mainly come from a number of observations demonstrating counter transport in red cells (180, 334), in L cells (253), heart muscle fibers (234), intestine (262), yeast cells (48), and bacteria (228). Numerous carrier parameters, mainly Michaelis constants, have been determined.

Rosenberg (258) has reviewed published work on various cell types. He pointed out that, with the exception of uphill transport in the intestine, in no case could an individual hydroxyl group of the sugar molecule be made responsible for a transport reaction. He suggests binding of the sugar molecule to the carrier by multiple hydrogen bonds.

Red cells.—LeFèvre (191) has given an extensive review on structure-activity relationship in red-cell sugar transport. He also showed (192) that ghosts retain transport capacity and he made use of their lack of catabolism to study the sugar capacity of the membrane. Finding no detectable binding of sugar from concentrations as low as 0.05 mM, he estimates the maximum number of reactive sites as 500,000 per ghost which would imply a minimal turnover number per site of 500 per second.

LeFèvre & McGinniss (193) showed that in red cells the rate ratio of glucose isotope exchange to net movement is about 50 to 100, in reasonable accordance with the value of 35 as predicted on the basis of a carrier system with $k_M = 1$ mM, but differing widely from 1.65 as predicted for diffusion.

Sen & Widdas have determined maximal rates and Michaelis constants k_M of glucose transport in human red cells as a function of temperature and pH (280). Both values increased with rising temperature, k_M giving a linear Van't Hoff plot corresponding to an energy of dissociation of 10,000 calories per mole. In the presence of inhibitors, the apparent half-saturation concentration was increased in the case of phloretin and polyphloretin phosphate in accordance with prediction for competitive inhibition, while dinitrofluorobenzene (noncompetitive) lowered the constant (281).

Faust (93) interprets glucose penetration as "altered diffusion".

Stein (293) interprets glycerol transport as brought about by dimer formation at a fixed membrane receptor and by penetration of the free dimers without reaction with a carrier. The evidence includes concentration dependence of inhibition by H^+ and by Cu^{++} from which the existence of a divalent receptor is concluded. Since application of the same scheme to other cases is considered by the author (293a), it may be pointed out that in cases showing counter transport the mechanism cannot be operative.

Muscle fibers.—Muscle is of special interest in view of a number of studies dealing with the effect of insulin. Battaglia & Randle (14) observed in rat diaphragm that a first group of sugars including D-glucose, D-mannose, and D-xylose compete with each other for the transport, but this was not true with a second group including D-galactose and D-fructose. D-Xylose transport is inhibited by SH reagents. Insulin increases the rate of glucose uptake. Randle (250) assumes the operation of a carrier, presumably a protein. Bhattacharya (20) reports that the insulin effect in the diaphragm depends on the presence of Mg and alkali metal ions (Li > Na > K > Rb > Cs).

A number of studies on perfused hearts of rats were reported from Park's laboratory (129, 216, 217, 246) and summarized by Morgan, Post & Park (218). It was found that insulin increases the rate of glucose uptake severalfold. In alloxan diabetic as well as in hypophysectomized animals, the rate was reduced and could be normalized by insulin. An analysis in terms of carrier parameters and parameters of enzymatic phosphorylation system was performed. The results indicated that insulin increases both k_M (3- to 5-fold) and maximal rate (5- to 13-fold) of the transport.

Fisher (96), in similar experiments with L-arabinose and D-xylose, likewise noted an increased rate of sugar uptake in the presence of insulin. The result of his analysis, however, differed from that of Park's group: according to Fisher, insulin decreases maximal rate by 80 per cent and 50 per cent, respectively, but increases k_M (400-fold and 30-fold, respectively). The latter effect, in a saturated carrier system, is bound to lead to an increase of the rate. The discrepancy between the results of the two studies appears too large to be referred only to the different sugars used.

Cadenas, and associates (34), also working with perfused hearts of rats, found that the accelerating effect of insulin on glucose uptake is reduced by N-ethyl maleimide and that this SH reactor diminishes binding to the tissue of insulin labeled with I^{131}. They consider a reaction of an S-S group of insulin with an SH group of the receptor in the muscle membrane.

Mammalian tissue cultured cells (L cells).—Rickenberg & Maio (253) report that L cells take up glucose and galactose by a system resembling that of the red cells in that it displays Michaelis-Menten kinetics, competition, counterflow, and inhibition by phlorizin and more strongly by phloretin, but not by azide, dinitrophenol, and iodoacetate. The transport does not lead to accumulation.

Yeast cells.—Sugar transport in microorganisms was reviewed by Cirillo (47). He finds (48, 49) that uptake of monosaccharides by yeast cells proceeds in two steps, the first of which is interpreted as adsorption, the second as a carrier transfer showing stereospecificity, saturation kinetics, and counterflow. Since uranyl inhibits sorbose influx and downhill efflux as well as counterflow, its effect is taken to be on the carrier system rather than on energy supply.

Scharff (270) presents evidence that freeze-dried, acetone-treated yeast cells maintain a glucose transfer mechanism inhibited by 2-deoxyglucose.

Sols & Fuente (99, 291) studied the disaccharide uptake in yeast cells

and distinguished two types of disaccharides. The first, sucrose and meli-
biose, are hydrolyzed outside the membrane, followed by transport of the
liberated hexoses into the cells. Trapping the hexoses by addition of ATP
interferes with fermentation in these cases. The second group, maltose and
lactose, apparently enter unhydrolyzed by specific transport systems. Their
fermentation is not influenced by ATP trapping and may proceed faster
than that of their constituent hexoses.

At pH values at which maltose is not utilized, it is accumulated in the
cells (119), an observation similar to those on permeases in bacteria. A further parallelism is the inducibility of the transport system.

Bacteria.—Progress in the field of bacteria has been fast. The concept of
permeases as introduced by Monod & Cohen, that of stereospecific transport
systems with saturation kinetics, partly constitutional and partly inducible,
was reviewed by Kepes (164). The original interpretation of accumulation
was that of a two-way system, with entry proceeding through a pump mechanism following Michaelis-Menten kinetics, and exit passively by diffusion.
In his kinetical study of galactoside permease (165), Kepes shows that exit
is inhibited by p-chloromercuribenzoate, questioning the assumption of exit
by passive diffusion. His observation that methylthio-β-D-galactoside (TMG)
inhibits entry of galactosylthio-D-galactoside (TDG) competitively only in
high concentrations ($>10^{-4}M$) while it accelerates in low concentrations
($2\times10^{-5}M$) agrees with prediction for carrier systems (competitive transport activation, compare above). He proposes a model involving only one
carrier which undergoes an activating reaction with ATP externally. Kepes
assumes the reaction to be rate limiting; this condition, however, would not
lead to the prediction of counterflow.

Rotman & Guzman (259) devised a method of studying exit directly,
rather than by kinetic analysis on the "pump and leak" assumption. They
use C^{14}-o-nitrophenyl-β-D-galactopyranoside (ONPG), which is hydrolyzed
rapidly inside the cells because of excess of galactosidase. This enables the
authors to measure the rate of entrance directly by the rate of hydrolysis.
In a galactokinase-less mutant, then, galactose is accumulated and the
accumulation can be followed by counting the intracellular radioactivity.
The authors find that exit is not linear but rises with increasing steepness as
the internal concentration is increased. Further, dinitrophenol and azide,
contrary to expectation on the basis of the pump and leak interpretation but
in accordance with Horecker's results (see below), affect the transport by
increasing the rate of exit rather than by lowering the rate of entrance rate.

Wiesmeyer & Cohn (332) describe an inducible azide-sensitive maltose
permease in *E. coli* which appears to be somehow related to sensitivity towards bacteriophage γ, since phage-resistant mutants lack the permease.

Horecker and his group reported several studies on galactose permease
(141, 142, 228) in a mutant strain of *E. coli* lacking galactokinase and therefore accumulating galactose. Their work was partly summarized by Horecker

and associates (140). Accumulated radioactive galactose is rapidly displaced by excess of galactose or glucose or by DNP. The higher exit rate in the displacement by glucose is suggestive evidence of counterflow. Stereospecificity is considered high by the authors, although 7 out of 13 sugars tested inhibited at equal, and 9 out of 13 at 100 times higher, concentration, as compared to the concentration of galactose. The quantitative data given are suggestive of competitive activation. The exit mechanism was found to be inducible [confirmed by Rotman & Guzman (259)] and inhibited by succinate as well as by α-methyl glucoside. As in the case of ONPG for galactose, the effect of DNP was found to be an acceleration of exit rate rather than a slowing of entrance. All these observations constitute evidence against the concept that exit is a passive diffusion process.

Intestinal absorption.—Much work has been done in the field of intestinal absorption. Reviews have been given by Crane (59, 63). Further surveys including substrates other than sugars will be mentioned later.

Crane & Mandelstam (62) have shown that intact strips of hamster intestine, isolated mucosal sheets or isolated villi, accumulate various sugars building up concentration ratios tissue-to-medium ($T:M$) up to 200 (in the case of glucose 1 mM in intact strips). The accumulation is inhibited by azide, phlorizin, and 4,6-dinitrocresol. Paralleling the observations on transintestinal absorption, only hexoses having an unsubstituted hydroxyl group at carbon 2 were accumulated. In frozen dried sections of hamster intestine, which were 15 μ–40 μ in thickness and prepared by Lowry's methods, galactose accumulation was shown to be highest in the epithelia as compared to the core of the villi and to the whole tissue (208). It was concluded that the site of active transport process is at or near the brush-border end of the epithelial cells.

As to mechanism of absorption, a number of observations point to a carrier system. Crane (61) described mutual inhibition between members of a group comprising glucose, galactose, 1,5-anhydro-D-glucitol and 6-deoxy-D-glucose. Inhibition calculated from k_M values agreed with observation for glucose and galactose but not for 1,5-anhydroglucitol. The structural specificity of absorption was tested by Wilson & Landau (339). They compared 49 sugars and sugar derivatives, 20 of which were newly tested. Out of the 49 compounds, 14 were transported uphill. The main requirement for uphill transport is concluded to be intact OH at C_2 (in the glucose configuration). Further, there appear to be limitations with respect to substitution, mainly as to size of the substituting groups. Rummel & Stupp (261) found that L-glucose is not transported uphill in the rat intestine, in agreement with results of Csaky & Fernald (66) in the frog. The latter authors find further that 3-o-methyl-glucose is transported uphill at 30°C, but not at 0°C in the frog intestine. Lee & Lifson (190) confirmed lack of exchange of O^{18} and H^2 between H_2O and glucose during glucose absorption. Salomon *et al.* (262) describe counter transport of D-xylose induced by a D-glucose gradient in the small intestine of the guinea pig. The finding of Tzur & Shapiro (307) that galactose absorption is enhanced by glucose on the serosal side, but slowed by glucose on the mucosal side, likewise suggests counter transport.

Inhibitors of glucose absorption are uranyl, antagonized by ethylene-diaminetetraacetic acid (202), Fe^{++}, Cu^{++}, Ce^{++}, and Hg^{++} (201), dinitro-phenol, dinitrocresol, and K attractilate (243). Phloretin is weaker than phlorizin (8, 181). Matthews & Smyth (207) find that phlorizin inhibits not only uphill transport, as DNP does, but also entry into the cells, which is not affected by DNP. It is concluded therefore that two distinct mechanisms exist, an "entry" mechanism, not dependent on metabolic energy, and an accumulation mechanism. Bihler et al. (24) reach the same conclusion. Alvarado & Crane (8) report further that according to kinetic analysis, phlorizin inhibition is competitive.

For a test of the phosphorylation theory of glucose absorption, Janke et al. (150), using paper chromatographic methods and radiophosphorus, studied the metabolism of 13 organic phosphates, including those of adenosine, guanosine, and uridine in the intestinal mucosa during the absorption of water and of glucose. No differences were found except that during glucose absorption the P^{32} incorporation into all organophosphates was 30 to 65 per cent faster than during water absorption. This fact was referred by the authors to action of insulin, because the effect was observed in other tissues as well.

Interesting observations concern the role of alkali cations in sugar absorption first described by Riklis & Quastel (255). Csaky and co-workers found, with sodium-free media on the mucosal side, reversible suppression of uphill transport of 3-o-methylglucose in the toad intestine (67) and of glucose in the rat intestine (68). Csaky (64) further reports that cardiac glycosides inhibit glucose absorption. Crane and co-workers (23, 24, 63), confirming these observations, find that Na^+ is indispensable both for "entry" and for uphill transport, whereas cardiac glycosides only inhibit uphill transport. The authors suggest that glucose entry into the epithelial cell occurs in a Na-glucose-carrier complex, that the complex dissociates inside the cell, and that Na^+ is removed from the cell by a sodium pump, inhibited by cardiac glycoside. Thereby the gradient for the complex is steepened and glucose moves faster and against its concentration gradient. The uphill transport of glucose thus would be driven by the sodium pump.

Absorption of disaccharides, according to Crane and co-workers (209, 210, 211), does not, as commonly assumed, require extracellular hydrolysis; unhydrolyzed disaccharides are taken up and hydrolyzed inside the cell. The evidence offered includes the observation that glucose accumulation in intestinal strips from sucrose or maltose solutions is faster than from solutions containing the same concentration of glucose without disaccharide. Isolated epithelial brush-border membranes, obtained by a newly developed method (212), were found to contain virtually all of the invertase and maltase activities of the unfractionated homogenate (211). Dahlqvist & Borgström (74) present experiments on disaccharide absorption in man from which they reach essentially the same conclusion.

In alloxan diabetic rats Crane (60) found sugar absorption more than twice as rapid as in normal rats. Insulin did not reverse this change, when added either *in vitro* or *in vivo*.

Kidney.—In kidney cortex slices Krane & Crane (176) found that accumulation of galactose against a concentration gradient was inhibited by dinitrocresol, and by phlorizin. Kleinzeller & Kotyk (174) report that here again Na^+ is indispensable for, and ouabain $5.10^{-4}M$ inhibits, the transport.

The inhibition by phloretin-2'-galactoside of tubular glucose reabsorption in the dog was found by Diedrich (81) to be much weaker than that by phlorizin in the form of phloretin glucoside, illustrating again the importance of the sugar moiety for renal action, indicated also by the stronger renal action of phlorizin as compared to phloretin.

AMINO ACIDS AND PEPTIDES

Most of the work on amino acids has been done on tumor cells and microorganisms, some on intestinal absorption. While the biological significance of amino acid transport systems so far appeared evident, mainly in the preparation of protein synthesis, there is now evidence for an additional role, namely, in osmoregulation.

Reviews and discussion were given by Christensen (42) and Heinz (125). Christensen stresses the viewpoint of binding, that is, fixed sites vs. mobile carriers with a shift of preference towards fixed groups; Heinz's report (125), contains a number of new observations.

Tumor cells.—Quastel (248), in a review of the biochemistry of Ehrlich ascites tumor cells (all experiments reported here have been carried out on this cell type), includes a discussion of amino acid transport.

Tenenhouse & Quastel (301) confirm earlier kinetic findings of Heinz for glycine uptake. The uptake rate of S-ethyl-cysteine, however, departs distinctly from Michaelis-Menten kinetics at high concentration, the rate increasing more steeply than expected. S-ethylcysteine inhibited the uptake of other amino acids without mutual inhibition, which might be expected if the affinities differ markedly. In two papers Johnstone & Quastel describe inhibitory effects of indole and skatole as well as of several anesthetics on amino acid uptake (156) and on influx in the steady state (157). The latter being independent of energy supply, the results are interpreted as coming from association with lipid components of the transport system.

From the structural specificity of amino acid uptake, Paine & Heinz (232) conclude that a three-point attachment of the amino acids to the receptor involving —COOH, —NH_2, and α-C is essential. According to Heinz (125) the pH dependence of glycine influx (increase with rising pH) resembles closely a dissociation curve with $pK = 7$.

The interrelationship between amino acid uptake and potassium movements described by Christensen has been taken up again. Heinz (125) finds neither an effect on potassium efflux of preloading the cells with glycine nor a change in glycine influx with varying intracellular K, but a decrease at low values of external Na. Hempling & Hare (128) observe, during accumulation of glycine, an increase both of potassium influx and efflux without net change. Both authors conclude that amino acid accumulation cannot be driven by potassium efflux. Heinz discusses the possibility of a relationship to sodium, resembling that in glucose absorption from the intestine (see above).

The role of pyridoxal and its possible carrier function were discussed in several papers. Christensen & Oxender (46) report interesting experiments on a model membrane consisting of tumor cells embedded in a millipore filter. They observe that establishing a gradient of pyridoxal induces glycine movement in the direction of the gradient, while a gradient of potassium induces oppositely directed glycine movement. Although these effects would agree with the carrier assumption, Christensen (42) gives reasons for questioning this concept. They include the observation of Oxender & Royer (230) that aldehyde reagents do not block the transport. Further, these authors find that pyridoxal appears to slow amino acid efflux rather than to increase influx. They consider the possibility of a "carrier mediated exodus". Hempling (127) reports that pyridoxal increases both influx and efflux of potassium, but only in the absence of glycine.

Jacquez (146, 148, 149) studied transport of the amino acid analogues o-diazoacetyl-L-serine (azaserine) and 6-diazo-5-oxo-L-norleucine (DON) and their relationship to the transport of amino acids. Both analogues are concentrated intracellularly, reaching higher accumulation ratios than all "normal" amino acids. The uptake is inhibited by glycine, glutamine, glutamic acid, and tryptophan (148). A resistant line of an ascitic form of a lymphocytic leukemia did not differ in the uptake of azaserine from a normal line (149). In competition experiments on L-tryptophan uptake, azaserine, L-2,4-diamino-isobutyric acid, L-histidine, and L-leucine all increased uptake at 1 mM, but inhibited at 5mM, whereas other amino acids including glycine, alanine, and lysine inhibited in both concentrations. This is reminescent of competitive activation and inhibition in a carrier system with substrates of higher affinities, corresponding to glycine, and with lower affinities, corresponding to azaserine. Cells pretreated with azaserine took up more L-tryptophan than controls without azaserine, losing simultaneously more azaserine than controls with tryptophan, again in accordance with expectation in carrier systems.

Muscle.—Akedo & Christensen (5) report that insulin enhances the uptake of at least eight amino acids in the diaphragm. Battaglia *et al.* (13), finding phlorizin to inhibit amino acid uptake in the cut diaphragm only, not the intact, conclude that it acts inside the cell.

Various mammalian cells.—With respect to uptake in *L*-strain fibroblasts (177), three groups of amino acids were distinguished by Kuchler & Grane. Group I acids (glycine, alanine, glutamic acid, aspartic acid, proline, and threonine) are concentrated in the pool; group II acids (leucine, isoleucine, valine, methionine, phenylalanine, and tyrosine) are not concentrated; group III acids (arginine, histidine, lysine) are only taken up in traces.

In slices of rat brain cortex Scholefield & Abadom (273) found a correlation between amino acid uptake and the level of ATP under conditions varied as to substrate and inhibitors and under conditions of high K^+ or low Ca^{++}. Both these latter conditions, besides lowering ATP and decreasing amino acid uptake, increased oxygen consumption. Also, in rat brain cortex slices Vardanis & Quastel (317) studied the effects of tetraethyl lead (4 EL) and of tetraethyl tin (4 ET). Both agents, at low concentrations which did not affect basal respiration, abolished potassium-stimulated respiration. Slices from animals poisoned with tetraethyl lead or tetraethyl tin were unable to accumulate amino acids. This change was paralleled by the onset of neuropathological symptoms. Phospholipase A diminished uptake of alanine.

The effect of two hormones was correlated with transport changes. Riggs & Walker, in earlier studies, had demonstrated increased uptake of α-aminoisobutyric acid (AIB) in the presence of growth hormone. They showed now (254) that hypophysectomy raises the blood level of α-aminoisobutyric acid and diminishes its uptake into cells. Both effects are counteracted by growth hormone. Noall (226) showed that the enhancing effect of estradiol on protein synthesis in the uterus appears to come (partly at least) from increased amino acid uptake: α-aminoisobutyric acid penetration in the rabbit uterus *in vivo* (not *in vitro*) rises rapidly after the administration of estradiol.

Osmoregulation in euryhaline invertebrates.—A number of studies from Florkin's laboratory (84, 152 to 155) show that osmoregulation in euryhaline crustacea, worms, echinoderms, and shrimps makes use of changes in amino acid transport. This is observed both in fresh-water and in sea-water organisms, when they are transferred to dilute salt media. *Arenicola marina* and *Perinereis cultrifera*, marine annelids, rely on changes of intracellular amino acid concentrations alone (Type I), the annelid *Nereis diversicolor* (154, 155) on osmoregulation of the blood combined with changes in the intracellular amino acid concentration (Type II). *Asterias rubens*, when transferred from sea water ($\Delta = -2.1°C$) to diluted sea water ($\Delta = -1.23°C$), lowers its intracellular amino acid level by nearly 50 per cent. By means of increased intracellular concentration, partly caused by an increase of free amino acids, the freshwater crayfish *Astacus astacus* survives in brackish water, although other osmoregulatory mechanisms maintain blood concentration higher than the concentration of the external medium. *Leander saratur L.* and *Leander squilla L.* (shrimps) belong to Type II (152).

Yeast cells.—Halvorson & Cowie (117) review the evidence for the existence of two distinct amino acid pools in yeast cells. The "expandable pool" has amino acid levels exceeding those in the medium. It is, however, capable of exchange with the medium—more easily in the presence of external amino acids. The "internal pool" has no exchange with the medium, is insensitive to osmotic shock, and appears to be the immediate source of amino acids for protein synthesis. Entry into the expandable pool shows saturation kinetics, competition, energy dependence, and inhibition by azide and DNP, and may lead to concentration ratios up to 200-900. According to Kempner & Cowie (163), α-fluorophenylalanine is transported into the expandable pool at a slower rate than phenylalanine. The preference for phenylalanine is maintained in the entry into the inner pool but not in protein synthesis: in the synthesized protein the ratio of the two compounds is the same as in the internal pool (163).

Eddy & Indge (90) give $k_M = 8.10^{-4}M$ for glycine uptake and confirm competition with graded affinities. They find uptake to be stimulated by K^+.

Bacteria.—In *Lactobacillus casei*, Leach & Snell (188) observe that uptake of glycine and alanine from media containing appropriate peptides proceeds faster than from media containing the free amino acids. From competition experiments the authors conclude that peptides, glycine, and alanine use three different pathways, respectively.

In *E. coli*, Boezi & de Moss (27) describe an inducible transport system for tryptophan that is Mg-stimulated and DNP-inhibited; and Lubin *et al.* (167, 204) report on mutants requiring high proline, histidine, or glycine that apparently lack the respective transport systems.

Hancock (118) reports that in *E. coli*, during exponential growth, when protein synthesis is blocked by chloramphenicol, the accumulation of three amino acids proceeds at about the same rate as during normal protein synthesis, leading to higher internal concentrations under these conditions. Parafluorophenylalanine uptake in *E. coli* was found to be retarded until phenylalanine is used up (163).

Intestinal absorption.—Quastel (249) and Smyth (287) review absorption of sugars and of amino acids in the intestine. Like the absorption of sugars, that of amino acids appears to be preceded by accumulation in the intestinal tissue (94, 196, 223). The accumulating uptake can be followed in isolated segments of intestine. It is inhibited by DNP, with the possible exception of L-arginine and L-lysine, follows Michaelis-Menten kinetics, and shows competition. Finch & Hird (95) have undertaken a comparative study of the uptake of 17 amino acids. They find Michaelis constants ranging from 0.55 mM for L-lysine to 80 mM for aspartic acid. The more lipophilic compounds tend to have higher affinities. The order of uptake rates at 10 mM is reversed as compared to 1 mM, the amino acids with higher affinity penetrating more slowly at 10 mM and faster at 1 mM, in accordance with predictions for carrier systems. Observed intensities of inhibition in general agreed well with calculation from k_M values, with the exception of the diaminocarboxylic acids which inhibited less than predicted. It was concluded that they do not compete for a common mechanism with other amino acids. Hagihira *et al.* (115) report competition experiments *in vivo*, indicating higher affinity of L-methionine as compared to L-histidine (inhibition not mutual) and affinities of approximately the same order for L-valine, L-leucine, and L-isoleucine (mutual competition), in accordance with the results of Finch & Hird. Another observation in harmony with carrier mechanism is the inhibition of tryptophan absorption in high concentrations of this amino acid (292).

The effect of pyridoxine, pyridoxal, and pyridoxal phosphate on intestinal absorption of amino acids was studied in rats by Jacobs et al. (144, 145) and by Akedo et al. (6). It was found that pretreatment of the animals with deoxypyridoxine or with DNP reduced the rate of methionine absorption. The effect of DNP was antagonized by pyridoxal phosphate but not by pyridoxine (when given after DNP), while that of deoxypyridoxine was counteracted by pyridoxine also (144). Given before DNP, pyridoxal and pyridoxine antagonized DNP (145). The authors conclude that the inhibitory block is linked to the phosphorylation of the vitamin cofactor. In B_6-deficient rats, treated with penicillamine, Akedo et al. (6) found a reduction of absorption rate of methionine counteracted by B_6 in vivo.

Akedo & Christensen (4) introduced a new group of nonmetabolized "model amino acids": 1-aminocyclopentane carboxylic acid and 1-aminocyclohexane carboxylic acid (cf. below). They find low affinity to the transport system of glycine (concordant with Finch & Hird) and of α-aminoisobutyric acid.

In the isolated intestinal epithelium of the Greek tortoise, Baillien & Schoffeniels (10) measured transmucosal electrical potential differences and unidirectional fluxes of amino acids. They conclude that glycine, alanine, and histidine are actively transported, while glutamic acid is not. Alanine inhibited glycine influx. Csaky (65) finds reduced intestinal absorption of amino acids, uracil, and 3-o-methylglucose from Na-free media in the frog.

Kidney tubules.—The above mentioned nonmetabolized amino acids, 1-aminocyclopentane carboxylic acid, 1-aminocyclohexane carboxylic acid, and α-aminoisobutyric acid, were shown by Christensen & Jones to be reabsorbed from kidney tubules so effectively that their half-times in mice are several months (45). This leads to considerable toxicity since α-aminoisobutyric acid imitates glycine and the cycloderivatives imitate valine or leucine.

In kidney cortex slices of the rat, α-aminoisobutyric acid and L-fluorophenylalanine were found to be accumulated against concentration gradients. The transport is oxygen dependent and blocked by DNP (257). Phlorizin $10^{-5}M - 3 \times 10^{-3}M$ (inhibiting glucose uptake in the slices by 50 per cent) was found to increase the slice-to-medium ratio of amino acids nearly twofold (278).

Cell nuclei.—The exchange of amino acids across the membrane of thymus nuclei is reported by Allfrey et al. (7) to show many parallelisms to that across cell membranes: specificity for L-isomers, energy dependence, particularly with respect to ATP synthesis, competition. Similar conditions appear to prevail for the transfer of thymidine, adenosine, and adenine. Both systems are dependent on Na^+.

PURINES AND PYRIMIDINES

Specific transport systems appear to exist for this group, displaying some uncommon features.

Red cells.—In erythrocytes the transport systems have been studied mainly by Lassen & Overgaard-Hansen (182 to 186, 229). It was first shown that uric acid uptake in human red cells is inhibited by hypoxanthine (229). The inhibition, however, did not increase with rising hypoxanthine concentration at levels higher than 1.0 mM. Later (183, 184) the same concentration dependence was found for inhibition by hypoxanthine of uric acid efflux but no more for influx. The latter appeared to follow Michaelis-Menten kinetics (182) and to be inhibited competitively in a normal manner. Two coexisting mechanisms of uric acid transport were assumed, only one of which is inhibited by hypoxanthine. Hypoxanthine itself was found to be concentrated slightly, reaching intracellular concentrations about 50 per cent higher than those in the medium (184). From increased influx rate at lower pH values, a "nonionic transfer" for uric acid was concluded (182). Besides hypoxanthine, purine and a number of other purine derivatives including azapurine, adenine, 6-chloropurine and 6-mercaptopurine inhibited the transport. Adenine and hypoxanthine were mutually inhibitory while uric acid did not appear to inhibit hypoxanthine transfer, presumably reflecting graded affinities. In contrast to the reabsorption of uric acid in the kidney tubule, influx in erythrocytes was not affected by probenecid, salicylic acid, and pyrazinamide (186).

Christensen & Jones (44) report stimulation of net inward movement of uric acid by estrogens, leading to slight accumulation in the cells (while in the absence of estrogens uric acid appears not to be concentrated). Unidirectional flux analysis reveals efflux to be diminished rather than influx to be increased.

Intestine.—In everted sacs of intestine from rat, hamster, and frog, Schanker & Tocca (269) find uphill transport of uracil from mucosa to serosa, inhibited by thymine, 5-fluorouracil, 5-bromouracil, 6-azauracil and 6-azathymosine.

Kidney.—Kidney cortex slices accumulate uric acid by a system resembling that of p-aminohippuric acid accumulation (241).

ORGANIC ACIDS

Transfer interpreted both as "passive" and specific transport systems was studied.

Red cells.—Giebel & Passow (104) compared rate of entrance into horse and beef erythrocytes of nine monocarboxylic acids, nine dicarboxylic acids, and four benzoate derivatives. Monocarboxylic acid penetrated fast (90 per cent exchange being completed in about 1 min in most cases), dicarboxylic acids with much lower and more variable rates ($t_{0.5}$ ranging from 1 to 2200 min). It is assumed that the former migrate as undissociated molecules through the lipoid phase, the latter through pores of the membrane. From the molecular volumes and the rate of penetration, an estimate of the pore radius of 3.8 to 4.5 A is derived.

Bacteria.—Durham & Hubbard (89) find in flavobacteria that p-amino-salicylic acid inhibits oxidation of p-aminobenzoic acid by competition for the transport.

Renal tubules.—Despopoulos (77) finds accumulation of p-aminohippuric acid (PAH) in rabbit kidney cortex slices inhibited both by salicylate and salicylurate, while only salicylurate—not salicylate—is accumulated itself. Another group of inhibitors of p-aminohippuric acid accumulation is composed of oxypyrimidines (78). Since they do not depress oxygen utilization, their effect is interpreted in terms of competition for "appropriate reactive loci on a cellular receptor molecule." In concordance with his interpretation of structure-activity relationships for the transport of organic acids (76), the author interprets these effects in terms of a three-point interaction between the three oxygens of the inhibitor, oxypyrimidine, or of the substrate, organic anion, and the receptor molecule. Absence of any one of the three oxygens in the oxypyrimidine structure eliminates potency.

Kinter & Cline (172) find the rate of runout of iodopyracet from pre-loaded isolated goldfish kidney to be either increased or decreased in the presence of various competitors including p-aminohippuric acid and pro-benecid, suggesting competitive activation and inhibition.

Huang *et al.* (143) find p-aminosalicylic acid in the dog to be either re-absorbed or secreted, depending on the conditions. Both K accumulation and p-aminohippuric acid accumulation in kidney slices are reduced by stro-phanthidin (33).

Ciliary body.—Failure of certain organic anions, including penicillin, to reach the posterior chamber of the eye led to the discovery that the ciliary body accumulates these acids and secretes them out of the eye (15, 19, 298). Studies *in vitro* of the accumulation of iodopyracet revealed tissue-to-medium ratio of 10–15, O_2- and glucose dependence and saturation kinetics. The transport is depressed by metabolic inhibitors including DNP, iodoacetic acid, and phlorizin and by competitive substrates including fatty acids, salicylate, p-aminohippuric acid probenecid, and penicillin. A study *in vivo* of the loss from the rabbit eye of iodopyracet injected into the vitreous humor (97) led to similar results.

Plexus chorioideus.—Pappenheimer *et al.* (233) find active transport of diodrast from cerebrospinal fluid to blood (with a well-defined T_M) presumably located in the plexus of the fourth ventricle.

Alkali Cations

Developments in this field were outstanding in the convergence of studies along different lines, resulting in an approach to closer understanding of the more intimate details of the transport mechanism. A monographic treatment of the biology of alkali metal ions has been presented by Ussing *et al.* (313). Reviews on alkali transport were given by Conway (53, 54), Ussing (310,

311), and Wilbrandt (335). Ion movements in the eye were surveyed by Kinsey (171).

Nerve.—Keynes reviewed mechanism (169) and energy source (168) of ion transport in nerve and muscle. Caldwell & Keynes (37) report that total K^{42} influx from sea water into squid fibers is $1-6\times10^{-8}$ mole per cm axon and that a large part of the K is taken up by a superficial region, presumably the Schwann cell. Influx into the axoplasm was 16 pmole per cm^2 sec. Potassium-42 efflux from the axoplasm had a half-time of 50 hr and was increased twelvefold by stimulation.

Caldwell (35), studying the phosphorus metabolism of squid axons, found considerable fall in ATP and arginine phosphate in the presence of 0.2 mM DNP, reversed by resynthesis after removal of DNP (depending on pH in details). Ouabain 10^{-5} M, although inhibiting Na transport, did not affect ATP and arginine phosphate. In the presence of DNP, Caldwell *et al.* (36) were able to reactivate Na efflux by injection into the fiber (not, however, by external application) of ATP, arginine phosphate, or phosphoenol pyruvate. The molar ratio of transported sodium to injected organophosphate was about 0.7. "K sensitivity", however (drop of Na efflux in potassium-free medium), was only restored by arginine phosphate and phosphoenol pyruvate.

Striated muscle.—Rudolph (260) has reviewed the subject. Adrian (2), varying the KCl concentration in the medium surrounding frog sartorius, observed equilibrium values of K_i and Cl_i in accordance with prediction for a Donnan system according to Boyle & Conway. The rate of change from one equilibrium to another depended on the direction: inward movement of KCl was considerably faster than outward movement. He concluded that under conditions of outward movement of potassium the potassium permeability falls.

Conway *et al.* (52, 56, 57) report that sodium extrusion from Na-rich muscles depends both on membrane potential and external sodium concentration in such a manner as to indicate the existence of a critical energy barrier which cannot be overcome by the secretion. Steinbach's results on K-depleted and Na-enriched muscle (294) are at variance with this concept.

Renkin (252) finds for choline entrance into frog muscle a rate similar to that of Na, but a much slower rate of exit.

Kernan (166) reports that the membrane potential of frog sartorii under conditions of facilitated sodium loss (sodium-enriched muscles, immersed in Ringer or in choline-Ringer) is considerably higher than that calculated from potassium equilibrium, as long as marked sodium extrusion continues. He concludes that the sodium pump is not electroneutral.

Heart muscle.—Weidmann (323) and Carmeliet (39) review ion movements underlying the action potential. Page & Solomon (231), in an analysis of various parameters of cat papillary muscle, find that this tissue, in contrast to frog muscle, swells very little if the K concentration is increased at the expense of Na.

Weatherall (321) analyzes the unidirectional fluxes of K^{42} in rabbit auricles. He finds two intracellular K fractions, presumably in series, comprising 79 and 21 per cent of total K. At rest the main fraction exchanges at rates of 1.07 per cent and 0.37 per cent per minute with the medium and with the slow fraction, respectively, in the beating auricle at 2.25 and 0.20 per cent, respectively. Dinitrophenol 10^{-4} M had no immediate effect on potassium uptake but raised the efflux rate coefficient reversibly from 0.0164 ± 0.0004 to 0.0229 ± 0.014 min^{-1}. Fractionation of auricles (274, 322) revealed the sarcosome fraction to resemble the "slow fraction" as to exchange parameters, but to contain only 2 per cent of total K. Dinitrophenol inhibited K^{42} influx into the sarcosomes.

Smooth muscle.—Bülbring (31), reviewing the physiology of smooth muscle, discussed potassium and sodium fluxes in this tissue. Sodium content is higher, potassium content lower than in striated muscle (111). Sodium exchange is exceedingly fast, being 90 per cent completed in less than one minute. Reasons are given for rejection of the possibility that this rate might refer to extracellular Na only. The sodium pump is considered to be electrogenic, and the hyperpolarizing effect of epinephrine is attributed to stimulation of the pump by way of activation of phosphorylase.

Red cells.—Giebel & Passow (105) report potassium loss from red cells poisoned with N-ethyl maleimide and they present evidence for an "all or none effect" in that 10 per cent of the cells do not respond at all, regardless of the concentration of N-ethyl maleimide. In a number of papers Passow *et al.* deal with potassium loss from fluoride-treated human red cells (194, 195, 197, 198, 235). The effect appears to be complex. It is suppressed by ethylenediaminetetraacetic acid and reactivated by Ca^{++} or Mg^{++}, with a lag period at low concentrations of the divalent ions (effect A) and rapidly at high concentration (effect B). Effect A appears to depend on ATP, the duration of the lag period showing a distinct correlation to ATP levels. Effect B shows "all or none" features (cf. above). Sheep red cells with high K content were shown to have a K pump mechanism four times more powerful than in sheep red cells with low K (305). Red cell ghosts, according to Hoffman, Tosteson & Whittam (131), retain the capacity to accumulate K.

The inhibitory effect of *g*-strophanthin on uphill movements of Na and K in red cells was found by Pfleger *et al.* (240) to be 15 times stronger in human cells than in rat cells. Kahn (159) finds the effect of ouabain on Rb entry stronger than on K entry. He assumes higher carrier affinity of Rb.

Membrane adenosine triphosphatase, phosphatidic acid, and alkali cation transport in erythrocytes and in other cell types.—A new line of approach was opened by Skou's work on Mg-dependent membrane ATPase of crab nerve and by his finding that this enzyme is activated by Na^+ (286) and additionally by K^+ and, furthermore, that the activation is abolished by ouabain.

Dunham & Glynn (86) and Post *et al.* (244, 245, 247) reported similar studies on an erythrocyte ATPase (fragmentated ghosts) and compared the enzyme activity with membrane transport. Striking parallelisms were found in the concentrations of half maximal action of internal sodium, of external potassium, of external NH_4^+ (which substitutes for K but not for Na in both systems), and of ouabain, and further parallelisms in the structure-activity relationships of cardiac glycosides, in their antagonism against K and in the action of Ca. It was concluded that ATPase is part of the coupled transport system for Na and K, activated inside the cells by Na and outside the cells by K. These postulated specific sites of activation were confirmed in experiments on nonfragmentated ghosts by Glynn (108) and by Whittam (324).

Alkali-dependent membrane ATPase has since been found in other cells and cell fractions including bacteria (1, 290), liver (92), gills (272), brain (79, 151), and kidney (247, 324) and, furthermore, in a variety of other tissues (27a).

Hokin & Hokin consider that phosphatidic acid is the sodium carrier (135, 137). This suggestion is mainly based on work on the Na-secreting avian salt gland and on erythrocytes. It is assumed that phosphatidic acid is formed on one side of the membrane from diglyceride by an ATP-activated kinase, that it takes up sodium, crosses the membrane, and is hydrolyzed by a phosphatase at the other side of the membrane, releasing sodium.

The evidence offered (133, 134, 136) includes a severalfold increase, in the microsome fraction, of P^{32} incorporation into phosphatidic acid (reaching a maximum after one to two minutes) in slices of the cholinergic salt gland (133, 136) "stimulated" by acetylcholine. The two postulated enzymes were demonstrated in both salt gland and red cells. The kinase was found to be alkali activated, more strongly by Na^+ than by K^+. Although the parallelism appears somewhat inconclusive in this point, it is taken by the authors to indicate a possible relationship to the ATPase work discussed above. Unanswered are the questions of K transport and of the fate of the inorganic phosphate.

Yoshida & Nukada (346) describe stimulation of phosphatidic acid turnover by K in brain slices, only in the presence of Na and suppressed by DNP.

Bacteria and yeast cells.—*E. coli*, in the logarithmic growth phase, was shown by Schultz & Solomon (276) to accumulate K^+ and to extrude Na^+ against the gradients. These authors (275) as well as Lubin & Kessel (203) described mutants lacking the K^+ transport system. Potassium loss in yeast cells treated with mercury (236) was shown to be an "all or none" effect (see above).

Various cell types.—In ascites tumor cells Haller (116) found the half-times of net sodium outward transport to depend on the medium: 21.8 min. in saline, 10.6 min in serum, and 5 min in ascites fluid. Potassium strophantoside inhibition required high concentrations of 10^{-5}–10^{-4} g per ml and was abolished in serum.

Potassium accumulation in brain cortex slices requires Ca to reach a maximal rate (103) and is inhibited by ouabain (102). K-strophanthin also inhibits K accumulation in the retina (114). In the perfused rat liver, insulin inhibits K loss (219). Calf lens accumulates K and extrudes Na, inhibited by ouabain (170).

Invertebrate spermatozoa (295) and *Tetrahymena* (87) were also found to accumulate K^+ and to extrude Na against the gradients.

Intestine.—Clarkson *et al.* (51) find Na, but not Cl, to be absorbed from isolated small intestine of the rat against the electrochemical gradient. Based on Ussing's flux ratio criterion, however, Curran (69) finds both Na and Cl absorption from the rat ileum *in vitro* to be "active" in the presence of glucose whereas, as in the rat colon (72), the flux ratios depart from those expected for diffusion only for Na, not for Cl. A carrier mechanism is suggested. Calcium and Sr increase Na flux below 1 mm and inhibit in higher concentrations (85). The authors assume two separate effects, one acting on a carrier, the second being a general "stiffening" of the membrane. Another possible interpretation might be competitive activation turning into inhibition at higher concentration, in accordance with prediction for carrier systems.

Electrical potential differences across the intestinal wall were measured by several authors. In the rat small intestine (12, 51) in the presence of glucose, differences of 4 to 9 mv were found, reduced by phlorizin; in the rat colon (72) 5 to 15 mv and in the colon of the Greek tortoise (11) 20 to 50 mv (positive on the serosal side).

Kidney tubules.—The subject has been reviewed by Ullrich (308). Measurements of electrical potential differences across the tubular cells of *Necturus* (transtubular PD) and across their external cell membranes (membrane PD) were reported in several papers (106, 326, 328, 329). The transtubular PD is about 20 mv, positive outside. For the membrane PD, 65 mv (106) and 73 mv (326) were given (external surface positive). High K lowers both values. The membrane PD was approximately halved by ouabain (106) and by DNP (329).

Sodium reabsorption and K secretion (after K injection) in the chicken is reduced by strophanthidin (227). In the dog a corresponding effect was demonstrated and analyzed by Tanabe *et al.* (300).

In dogs the stop-flow technique (299) revealed the site of maximal K secretion regularly distal to that of maximal Na absorption [according to Vander (314) and Hierholzer (130) it is located in the collecting duct]; the site of maximal K absorption immediately proximal to the secretory site (also in the distal tubule); the site of ouabain action on Na resorption identical with that of maximal Na reabsorption (338).

Maximal distal Na absorption, normally independent of plasma Na, is lowered at high plasma Na concentrations in adrenalectomized animals (this change is reversed by aldosterone) and after treatment with the aldosterone antagonist SC-8109 (315). Graphical evaluation of this dependence yielded a linear Lineweaver-Burke plot indicating a value for k_M of about 3 mM (316). Aldosterone increased the rate of reabsorption without changing this value.

In experiments on kidney cortex slices, Lassen & Thaysen (187), taking the difference of sodium efflux at 0°C and 37°C as "active sodium transport", find the ratio Na transported: O_2 consumed to be 25. This ratio compares to 16-20 as found by Zerahn and to 19 as reported by Leaf & Dempsey (189) both working with the frog skin.

Frog's and toad's skin and bladder.—According to Ussing's interpretation of the membrane asymmetry in the epithelial cell of the frog's skin (309), the external membrane is sodium permeable and the internal membrane potassium permeable. Furthermore, a Na-K exchange pump is assumed to be located in the internal membrane. The first experimental evidence for this view was the demonstration that the two membranes behaved like a sodium electrode and a potassium electrode, respectively (175). New support was now furnished by measurements of osmotic volume changes of the epithelium cells carried out with a special microscopic method. Under conditions of varied ionic environment at the two boundaries of the epithelium (205), these measurements agreed with predictions based on Ussing's concept.

Inhibition of skin potential or short-circuit current (or both) or Na transport was observed in the present of Ca (70), ethylenediaminetetraacetic acid (73), cholera toxin (100), and ouabain (222, 330). The latter agent had no effect on the toad skin (330). N-dodecylpyridine-2-aldoxime and N-methylpyridine-2-aldoxime exerted a stimulating effect (304) which in the case of the former was followed by inhibition (competitive activation?).

The effect of neurohypophyseal hormones on the toad bladder was to increase permeability for thiourea (206), and to increase water flow (124, 264, 265) and Na transport (28, 189). Hays & Leaf (124) argue that a mere enlargement of pore sizes cannot be the common basis for all these actions since values for pore sizes incompatible with impermeability for thiourea are calculated from the observed net water flux in the presence of an osmotic gradient. Aldosterone was shown to enhance the short-circuit current in the toad bladder (58a). Hypophysectomy (220) increased Na outflux; destruction of the interrenal tissue decreased (26) the sodium transport in the frog skin.

Gastric mucosa.—Harris & Edelman report that in the frog gastric mucosa, potassium concentrations higher than 40 mM reverse the sign of the PD (121) and that potassium is moved across the mucosa against the electrochemical potential difference (120). Stimulation of H$^+$ secretion by histamine did not elicit increased P^{32} incorporation into phosphatidic acid (91), indicating that no phospholipid effect is involved in the H$^+$ secretion. It is concluded that in the salt gland, where a phospholipid effect occurs (cf. above), Na secretion is not preceded by H$^+$ secretion.

DIVALENT CATIONS

Shanes and co-workers (21, 283, 284, 285, 340) continued their work on calcium exchange in muscle. Calcium-45 release from frog sartorius is accelerated during accumulation by about 0.2 pmole per cm^2 per impulse, independent of the rate of stimulation (285). Caffein, in resting sartorius muscle, enhances both influx and outflux (21). In K contracture in the rectus abdominis, influx rises tenfold transitorily and fourfold permanently (284).

K-strophantin lowers the potassium threshold both for contracture and for increased Ca influx. In guinea pig atria (340), Ca influx rises by 0.55 pmole per cm² per contraction, without increase in total Ca content, or, curiously, in calcium efflux. Sekul & Holland (279) find inhibition of Ca influx by ouabain only in beating, not in quiescent, rabbit atria.

In smooth muscle (*Taenia coli*) Schatzmann (271) reports the following results for Ca exchange: 2.8 mmole per kg is nonexchangeable; exchange occurs in three fractions with half-times of <3, 3, and 300 min, respectively: the intracellular concentration of exchangeable Ca is about one third of the extracellular, indicating a pump. A Ca pump (ATP- and Mg-dependent) was also shown by Hasselbach & Makinose (122, 123, 221) to operate, in muscle, across the membrane of the grana of relaxing factor which store large amounts of calcium.

Magnesium uptake in frog sartorius (107) indicated that 70 to 80 per cent of total Mg is nonexchangeable, and indicated three exchanging compartments containing 0.21, 0.71, and 0.67 mmole Mg per kg and exchanging with half-times of 0.5, 3.0, and 300 min, respectively. Only the third fraction is interpreted to be intracellular. Its concentration is 0.6 mM (external 2 mM) indicating the operation of a pump.

Schachter *et al.* (266, 267, 268) note that intestinal Ca absorption occurs uphill (267), displays a maximal transport rate and specificity as compared to Mg, Sr, Ba (266), and is controlled by vitamin D (268) in a manner suitable for practical use in the bioassay of vitamin D.

In the kidney of dogs, Samiy *et al.* (263) report a reabsorption mechanism common for Ca and Mg (competition) in the distal tubule. The uptake of magnesium by yeast cells was studied by Netter & Sachs (225). It appears to be driven by metabolism (inhibition by cyanide, N_3, iodoacetic acid, F) to follow saturation kinetics (k_M equal $0.5.10^3$ M) and to be partially inhibited by K. According to kinetic analysis, the inhibition is competitive with $k_M = 2.8.10^{-3}$ M or K.

INORGANIC ANIONS

Chloride, in frog muscle, appears to be in equilibrium (3); probably the same is true for cardiac muscle (38). Influx and efflux for chloride in muscle were "tentatively concluded" not to be independent (3). Also NO_3 and thiocyanate reduced Cl permeability.

In the isolated small intestine of the rat, the monovalent anions all moved down the gradient (50). Those of weak acids moved faster in the jejunum than in the ileum, presumably in the undissociated form.

In the eye, iodide is accumulated in and secreted out of the eye by the ciliary body (16, 18). The mechanism resembles closely that operating in the thyroid. It appears not to transport Br (17).

In the thyroid the inhibition of iodide accumulation by various cardiac glycosides and their aglucones is antagonized by K (343). Quinidine 10⁻⁴ to 10⁻³ also inhibits iodide accumulation in the thyroid. The iodide-transporting mechanism of mouse submaxillary and rat mammary gland (344) is less potent but qualitatively similar to that of the thyroid (K-dependent, inhibited by cardiac glycosides). The same mechanism accumulates TcO_4 and ReO_4 (homologues of MnO_4) in the thyroid (345).

Phosphate transport by a specific system in the red cell membrane is questioned. The distribution ratio of $H_2PO_4^-$ appears to be related to that of Cl by a constant factor (318). Enzyme inhibitors did not affect total P uptake and decreased the specific activity of internal organic phosphate (239).

Systems transporting sulfate uphill were described in the stomach mucosa by Hogben (132); in the micro-organism *Desulphovibrio desulphuricans* (101) by Furusaka (O_2-dependent and inhibited by selenate); and in the kidney cortex mitochondria in the rat (accumulating several hundred fold) by Davies *et al.* (75). Renal tissue accumulates sulfate even at 0°C (80) (inhibited by phlorizin which enhances at 38°C!).

In the tunicate *Ciona intestinalis*, vanadium increased fivefold the sulfate uptake by the organism (22).

Various Solutes

Using the stop-flow technique, Pena & Malvin (238) studied the permeability of tubular cells to various organic molecules. Urea and glycerol penetrated along the entire nephron, D-arabinose only after administration of Pitressin, mannitol not at all. Oxygen appears to be transported in the swim bladder of fish in the molecular form since $O^{18}-O^{18}$, $O^{18}-O^{16}$, and $O^{16}-O^{16}$ maintain their isotope ratio (341). The transport is inhibited competitively by CO (342). Iron absorption in the intestine can occur against the gradient (83) and is enhanced by Fe-complexing agents (98).

The uptake of vitamin B_{12} in mouse ascites tumor cells and HeLa cells is increased twentyfold by ascites fluid and by human serum (58). Absorption of B_{12} in everted sacs of guinea pig intestine is enhanced by intrinsic factor, but only under aerobic conditions and at high temperature (297).

Water, Total Solutes

Water transport across the frog skin is increased by D-tubocurarine (302) and by atropine and pilocarpine (303). Burck & Netter (32) described a medium in which liver slices maintain constant water content over 45 minutes. Curran & Macintosh (69, 71) suggest a mechanism of water shift coupled to active solute transport in a system consisting of a wide pore membrane in series with a small pore membrane. Experiments on a macroscopic model agree with the prediction.

Total intracellular concentration of solutes in yeast cells and various plant cells, according to Conway & Armstrong (55), is amazingly high: 0.59 M in yeast cells and as high as 1.42 M in sugar beet cells.

LITERATURE CITED

1. Abrams, A., McNamara, P., and Johnson, J. B., *J. Biol. Chem.*, 235, 3659–62 (1960)
2. Adrian, R. H., *J. Physiol. (London)*, 151, 154–85 (1960)
3. Adrian, R. H., *J. Physiol. (London)*, 156, 623–32 (1961)
4. Akedo, H., and Christensen, H. N., *J. Biol. Chem.*, 237, 113–17 (1962)
5. Akedo, H., and Christensen, H. N., *J. Biol. Chem.*, 237, 118–22 (1962)
6. Akedo, H., Sugawa, T., Yoshikawa, S., and Suda M., *J. Biochem. (Tokyo)*, 47, 124–30 (1960)
7. Allfrey, V. G., Meudt, R., Hopkins, J. W., and Mirsky, A. E., *Proc. Natl. Acad. Sci. US*, 47, 907–32 (1961)
8. Alvarado, F., and Crane, R. K., *Biochim. Biophys. Acta*, 56, 170–72 (1962)
9. Aschheim, E., *Experientia*, 16, 305 (1960)
10. Baillien, M., and Schoffeniels, E., *Biochim. Biophys. Acta*, 53, 521–36 (1961)
11. Baillien, M., and Schoffeniels, E., *Biochim. Biophys. Acta*, 53, 537–748 (1961)
12. Barry, R. J. C., Dikstein, S., Matthews, J., and Smyth, D. H., *J. Physiol. (London)*, 155, 17–18P (1960)
13. Battaglia, F. C., Manchester, K. L., and Randle, P. J., *Biochim. Biophys. Acta*, 43, 50–54 (1960)
14. Battaglia, F. C., and Randle, P. J., *Biochem. J.*, 75, 408–16 (1960)
15. Becker, B., *Am. J. Ophthalmol.*, 50, 862/192–867/197 (1960)
16. Becker, B., *Arch. Ophthalmol.*, 65, 832–36 (1961)
17. Becker, B., *Arch. Ophthalmol.*, 65, 837–39 (1961)
18. Becker, B., *Am. J. Physiol.*, 200, 804–6 (1961)
19. Becker, B., and Forbes, M., *Am. J. Physiol.*, 200, 461–64 (1961)
20. Bhattacharya, G., *Biochem. J.*, 79, 369–77 (1961)
21. Bianchi, C. P., *J. Gen. Physiol.*, 44, 845–58 (1961)
22. Bielig, H. J., Pfleger, K., Rummel, W., and Seifen, E., *Z. Physiol. Chem.*, 327, 35–40 (1961)
23. Bihler, I., and Crane, R. K., *Biochim. Biophys. Acta*, 59, 78–93 (1962)
24. Bihler, I., Hawkins, K. A., and Crane, R. K., *Biochim. Biophys. Acta*, 59, 94–102 (1962)

25. *Biochem. Aktiven Transports, Colloq. German Biochem. Soc.*, 12 (Springer, Berlin, 1961)
26. Bishop, W. R., Mumbach, M. W., and Scheer, B. T., *Am. J. Physiol.*, 200, 451–53 (1961)
27. Boezi, J. A., and de Moss, R. D., *Biochim. Biophys. Acta*, 49, 471–84 (1961)
27a. Bonting, S. L., Simon, K. A., and Hawkins, N. M., *Arch. Biochem. Biophys.*, 95, 416–23 (1961)
28. Bourgnet, J., and Maetz, J., *Biochim. Biophys. Acta*, 52, 552–65 (1961)
29. Bozler, E., and Lavine, D., *Am. J. Physiol.*, 195, 45–49 (1958)
30. Bozler E., *Am. J. Physiol.*, 200, 651–55 (1961)
31. Bülbring, E., *Arch. Ges. Physiol.*, 273, 1–17 (1961)
32. Burck, H. C., and Netter, H., *Klin. Wochschr.*, 38, 359–66 (1960)
33. Burg, M. B., and Orloff, J., *Am. J. Physiol.*, 202, 565–71 (1962)
34. Cadenas, E., Ko, H., Park, C. P., and Rasmussen, H., *J. Biol. Chem.*, 236, Pc63–Pc64 (1961)
35. Caldwell, P. C., *J. Physiol. (London)*, 152, 545–60 (1960)
36. Caldwell, P. C., Hodgkin, A. L., Keynes, R. D., and Shaw, T. I., *J. Physiol. (London)*, 152, 561–90 (1960)
37. Caldwell, P. C., and Keynes, R. D., *J. Physiol. (London)*, 154, 177–89 (1960)
38. Carmeliet, E. E., *J. Physiol. (London)*, 156, 375–88 (1961)
39. Carmeliet, E. E., *Chloride and Potassium Permeability in Cardiac Purkinje Fibers* (Arscia, S. A., Ed., Bruxelles, 1961)
40. Chapman-Andresen, C., *Lunds Univ. Arsskr.*, 2, No. 15 (1960)
41. Chapman-Andresen, C., and Holtzer, H., *J. Biophys. Biochem. Cytol*, 8, 288–91 (1960)
42. Christensen, H. N., *Symp. Membrane Transport Metab.*, 470–78 (Czechoslov. Acad. Sci., Prague, 1961)
43. Christensen, H. N., *Advan. Protein Chem.*, 15, 239–314 (1960)
44. Christensen, H. N., and Jones, J. C., *J. Biol. Chem.*, 236, 76–80 (1961)
45. Christensen, H. N., and Jones, J. C., *J. Biol. Chem.*, 237, 1203–6 (1962)
46. Christensen, H. N., and Oxender, D. L., *Am. J. Clin. Nutr.*, 8, 131–36 (1960)

47. Cirillo, V. P., *Ann. Rev. Microbiol.*, **15**, 197–218 (1961)
48. Cirillo, V. P., *Trans. N.Y. Acad. Sci.*, [II]**23**, 725–34 (1961)
49. Cirillo, V. P., *Symp. Membrane Transport Metab.*, 343–51 (Czechoslov. Acad. Sci., Prague, 1961)
50. Clarkson, T. W., Rothstein, A., and Cross, A. *Am. J. Physiol.*, **200**, 781–88 (1961)
51. Clarkson, T. W., Cross, A. C., and Toole, S. R., *Am. J. Physiol.*, **200**, 1233–35 (1961)
52. Conway, E. J., *Nature*, **187**, 394–96 (1960)
53. Conway, E. J., *Potassium Symp.*, *Ann. Meeting Intern. Potash Inst.*, 209–27 (1960)
54. Conway, E. J., *J. Gen. Physiol.*, **43**, 17–41 (1960)
55. Conway, E. J., and Armstrong, W. McD., *Biochem., J.*, **81**, 631–39 (1961)
56. Conway, E. J., Kernan, R. P., and Zadunaisky, J. A., *J. Physiol. (London)*, **155**, 263–79 (1961)
57. Conway, E. J., and Mullaney, M., *Symp. Membrane Transport Metab.*, 116–30 (Czechoslov. Acad. Sci., Prague, 1961)
58. Cooper, B. A., and Paranchych, W., *Nature*, **191**, 393–95 (1961)
58a. Crabbé, J., *J. Clin. Invest.*, **40**, 2103–10 (1961)
59. Crane, R. K., *Pharmacol. Rev.*, **40**, 789–825 (1960)
60. Crane, R. K., *Biochim. Biophys. Res. Commun.*, **4**, 436–40 (1961)
61. Crane, R. K., *Biochim. Biophys. Acta*, **45**, 477–82 (1960)
62. Crane, R. K., and Mandelstam, P., *Biochim. Biophys. Acta*, **45**, 460–76 (1960)
63. Crane, R. K., Miller, D., and Bihler, I., *Symp. Membrane Transport Metab.*, 439–49 (Czechoslov. Acad. Sci., Prague, 1961)
64. Csaky, T. Z., *Biochem. Pharmacol.*, **8**, 38–38 (1961)
65. Csaky, T. Z., *Am. J. Physiol.*, **201**, 999–1001 (1961)
66. Csaky, T. Z., and Fernald, G. W., *Am. J. Physiol.*, **198**, 445–48 (1960)
67. Csaky, T. Z., and Thale, M., *J. Physiol. (London)*, **151**, 59–65 (1960)
68. Csaky, T. Z., and Zollicoffer, L., *Am. J. Physiol.*, **198**, 1056–58 (1960)
69. Curran, P. F., *J. Gen. Physiol.*, **43**, 1137–48 (1960)
70. Curran, P. F., and Gill, J. R., Jr., *J. Gen. Physiol.*, **45**, 625–41 (1962)
71. Curran, P. F., and Macintosh, J. R., *Nature*, **193**, 347–48 (1962)
72. Curran, P. F., and Schwartz, G. F., *J. Gen. Physiol.*, **43**, 555–71 (1960)
73. Curran, P. F., Zadunaisky, J., and Gill, J. R., Jr., *Biochim. Biophys. Acta*, **52**, 392–95 (1961)
74. Dahlqvist, A., and Borgström, B., *Biochem. J.*, **81**, 411–18 (1961)
75. Davies, R. E., Delluva, A. M., Deyrup, I. J., and Winters, R. W., *Symp. Membrane Transport Metab.*, 285–95 (Czechoslov. Acad. Sci., Prague, 1961)
76. Despopoulos, A., *Proc. Intern. Congr. Nephrol., Geneva and Evian, 1st, 1960*, 706–8 (Karger, Basel, 1961)
77. Despopoulos, A., *Am. J. Physiol.*, **198**, 230–32 (1960)
78. Despopoulos, A., *Am. J. Physiol.*, **200**, 163–66 (1961)
79. Deul, D. H., and McIlwain, H. J., *J. Neurochem.*, **8**, 246 (1961)
80. Deyrup, I. J., and Davies, R. E., *J. Gen. Physiol.*, **44**, 555–69 (1960/61)
81. Diedrich, D. F., *Biochim. Biophys. Acta*, **47**, 618–20 (1961)
82. Dobbing, J., *Pharmacol. Rev.*, **41**, 130–88 (1961)
83. Dowdle, E. B., Schachter, D., and Schenker, H., *Am. J. Physiol.*, **198**, 609–13 (1960)
84. Duchâteau-Bosson, Gh., and Florkin, M., *Comp. Biochem. Physiol.*, **3**, 245–49 (1961)
85. Dumont, P. A., Curran, P. F., and Solomon, A. K., *J. Gen. Physiol.*, **43**, 1119–36 (1960)
86. Dunham, E. T., and Glynn, I. M., *J. Physiol. (London)*, **156**, 274–93 (1961)
87. Dunham, P. B., and Child, F. M., *Biol. Bull.*, **121**, 129–40 (1961)
88. Durbin, R. P., *J. Gen. Physiol.*, **44**, 315–26 (1960)
89. Durham, N. N., and Hubbard, J. S., *J. Bacteriol*, **80**, 225–31 (1960)
90. Eddy, A., and Indge, K. J., *Biochem. J.*, **82**, 15P–16P (1962)
91. Eggman, L. D., and Hokin, L. E., *Biochim. Biophys. Acta*, **47**, 600–1 (1961)
92. Emmelot, P., and Bos, C. J., *Biochim. Biophys. Acta*, **58**, 374–75 (1962)
93. Faust, R. G., *J. Cellular Comp. Physiol.*, **56**, 103–21 (1960)
94. Finch, L. R., and Hird, F. J. R., *Biochim. Biophys. Acta*, **43**, 268–77 (1960)
95. Finch, L. R., and Hird, F. J. R., *Biochim. Biophys. Acta*, **43**, 278–87 (1960)

96. Fisher, R. B., *Ciba Found. Symp. Enzymes Drug Action*, 83–94 (Churchill, London, 1961)
97. Forbes, M., and Becker, B., *Am. J. Ophthalmol.*, **50**, 867/197–873/203 (1960)
98. Forth, W., and Seifen, E., *Arch. Exptl. Pathol. Pharmakol.*, **241**, 556 (1961)
99. de la Fuente, G., and Sols, A., *Biochim. Biophys. Acta*, **56**, 49–62 (1962)
100. Fuhrman, G. J., and Fuhrman, F. A., *Nature*, **188**, 71–72 (1960)
101. Furusaka, C., *Nature*, **192**, 427–29 (1961)
102. Gardos, G., *J. Neurochem.*, **5**, 199–201 (1960)
103. Gardos, G., *Acta Physiol. Acad. Sci. Hung.*, **18**, 265–69 (1961)
104. Giebel, O., and Passow, H., *Arch. Ges. Physiol.*, **271**, 378–88 (1960)
105. Giebel, O., and Passow, H., *Naturwissenschaften* **48**, 721–22 (1961)
106. Giebisch, G., *J. Gen. Physiol.*, **44**, 659–78 (1960/61)
107. Gilbert, D. L., and MacCann, J., *J. Gen. Physiol.*, **43**, 1103–18 (1960)
108. Glynn, I. M., *J. Physiol.* (*London*), **160**, 18–19P (1962)
109. Goldacre, R. J., in ref. 112, 633–43 (1961)
110. Goldstein, D. A., and Solomon, A. K., *J. Gen. Physiol.*, **44**, 1–17 (1960)
111. Goodford, P. J., and Hermansen, K., *J. Physiol.* (*London*), **153**, 29P (1960)
112. Goodwin, T. W., and Lindberg, Eds., *Biol. Structure Function*, *Proc. IUB/IUBS Intern. Symp. 1st, Stockholm, 1960* (1961)
114. Greeff, K., *Verhandl. Deut. Ges. Kreislaufforsch.*, **26**, Tagung 127–32 (1960)
115. Hagihira, H., Ogata, M., Takedatsu, N., and Suda, M., *J. Biochem.* (*Tokyo*), **47**, 139–43 (1960)
116. Haller, J. St., *Sodium and Potassium Transport in Mouse Ascites Tumor Cells* in vitro: *Effects of Different Media and of Cardiac Glycosides and Steroid Hormones* (Doctoral Thesis, Univ. of Berne (MD), 1961)
117. Halvorson, H. D., and Cowie, D. B., *Symp. Membrane Transport Metab.*, 479–87 (Czechoslov. Acad. Sci., Prague, 1961)
118. Hancock, R., *Biochim. Biophys. Acta*, **37**, 47–55 (1960)
119. Harris, G., and Thompson, C. C. *Biochim. Biophys. Acta*, **52**, 176–83 (1961)
120. Harris, J. B., and Edelman, I. S., *Am. J. Physiol.*, **198**, 280–84 (1960)
121. Harris, J. B., and Edelman, I. S., *Am. J. Physiol.*, **198**, 285–88 (1960)
122. Hasselbach, W., and Makinose, M., *Biochem. Z.*, **333**, 518–28 (1961)
123. Hasselbach, W., and Makinose, M., *Biochem. Biophys. Res. Commun.*, **7**, 132–36 (1962)
124. Hays, R. M., and Leaf, A., *J. Clin. Invest.*, **39**, 995–96 (1960)
125. Heinz, E., *Biochem. Aktiven Transports, Colloq. German Biochem. Soc.*, 167–85 (Springer, Berlin, 1961)
126. Heinz, E., and Patlak, C. S., *Biochim. Biophys. Acta*, **44**, 324–34 (1960)
127. Hempling, H. G., *Federation Proc.*, **20**, 139 (1961)
128. Hempling, H. G., and Hare, D., *J. Biol. Chem.*, **236**, 2498–502 (1961)
129. Henderson, M. J., Morgan, H. E., and Park, C. R., *J. Biol. Chem.*, **236**, 237–77 (1961)
130. Hierholzer, K., *Am. J. Physiol.*, **201**, 318–24 (1961)
131. Hoffman, J. F., Tosteson, D. C., and Whittam, R., *Nature*, **185**, 186–87 (1960)
132. Hogben, C. A. M., *Federation Proc.*, **20**, 139–39 (1961)
133. Hokin, L. E., and Hokin, M. R., *J. Gen. Physiol.*, **44**, 61–85 (1960)
134. Hokin, L. E., and Hokin, M. R., *Nature*, **189**, 836–37 (1961)
135. Hokin, L. E., and Hokin, M. R., *Symp. Membrane Transport Metab.*, 204–18 (Czechoslov. Acad. Sci., Prague, 1961)
136. Hokin, M. R., and Hokin, L. E., *Nature*, **190**, 1016–17 (1961)
137. Hokin, M. R., and Hokin, L. E., *Lab. Invest.*, **10**, 1151–61 (1961)
138. Holter, H., and Ottolenghi, P., *Compt. Rend. Lab. Carlsberg*, **31**, 409–22 (1960)
139. Holtzer, H., and Holtzer, S., *Compt. Rend. Lab. Carlsberg*, **31**, 373–408 (1960)
140. Horecker, B. L., Osborn, M. J., McLellan, W. L., Jr., Avigad, G., and Asensio, C., *Symp. Membrane Transport Metab.*, 378–87 (Czechoslov. Acad. Sci., Prague, 1961)
141. Horecker, B. L., Thomas, J., and Monod, J., *J. Biol. Chem.*, **235**, 1580–85 (1960)
142. Horecker, B. L., Thomas, J., and Monod, J., *J. Biol. Chem.*, **235**, 1586–90 (1960)
143. Huang, K. C., Moore, K. B., and Campbell, P. D., *Am. J. Physiol.*, **199**, 5–8 (1960)

144. Jacobs, F. A., Coen, L. J., and Hillman, R. S. L., *J. Biol. Chem.*, **235**, 1372–75 (1960)
145. Jacobs, F. A., Flaa, R. C., and Belk, W. F., *J. Biol. Chem.*, **235**, 3224–27 (1960)
146. Jacquez, J. A., *Am. J. Physiol.*, **200**, 1063–68 (1961)
147. Jacquez, J. A., *Proc. Nat. Acad. Sci. US*, **47**, 153–63 (1961)
148. Jacquez, J. A., *Cancer Res.*, **17**, 890–96 (1957)
149. Jacquez, J. A., and Hutchinson, D. J., *Cancer Res.*, **19**, 397–401 (1959)
150. Janke, J., Gerlach, E., Fleckenstein, A., and Mathé, G., *Arch. Ges. Physiol.*, **270**, 286–307 (1960)
151. Järnefelt, J., *Biochim. Biophys. Acta*, **48**, 104 (1961)
152. Jeuniaux, C., Bricteux-Grégoire, S., and Florkin, M., *Cahier Biol. Marine*, **II**, 373–79 (1961)
153. Jeuniaux, C., Bricteux-Grégoire, S., and Florkin, M., *Arch. Intern. Physiol. Biochim.*, **70**, 155–56 (1962)
154. Jeuniaux, C., Duchâteau-Bosson, G., and Florkin, M., *Biochem. J.*, **79**, 24–25 P (1961)
155. Jeuniaux, C., Duchâteau-Bosson, G., and Florkin, M., *J. Biochem.*, **49**, 527–31 (1961)
156. Johnstone, R. M., and Quastel, J. H., *Biochim. Biophys. Acta*, **46**, 514–26 (1961)
157. Johnstone, R. M., and Quastel, J. H., *Biochim. Biophys. Acta*, **46**, 527–32 (1961)
158. Joseph, N. R., Engel, M. B., and Catchpole, H. R., *Nature*, **191**, 1175–78 (1961)
159. Kahn, J. B., Jr., *J. Pharmacol. Exptl. Therap.* **136**, 197–204 (1962)
160. Katchalsky, A., *Symp. Membrane Transport Metab.*, 69–86 (Czechoslov. Acad. Sci., Prague, 1961)
161. Kedem, O., *Symp. Membrane Transport Metab.*, 87–93 (Czechoslov. Acad. Sci., Prague, 1961)
162. Kedem, O., and Katchalsky, A., *J. Gen. Physiol.*, **45**, 143–79 (1961)
163. Kempner, E. S., and Cowie, D. B., *Biochim. Biophys. Acta*, **42**, 401–8, (1960)
164. Kepes, A., *Biochem. Aktiven Transports, Colloq. German Biochem. Soc.*, 100–11 (Springer, Berlin, 1961)
165. Kepes, A., *Biochim. Biophys. Acta*, **40**, 70–84 (1960)
166. Kernan, R. P., *Nature*, **193**, 986–87 (1962)
167. Kessel, D., and Lubin, M., *Biochim. Biophys. Acta*, **57**, 32–43 (1962)
168. Keynes, R. D., *Symp. Membrane Transport Metab.*, 131–39 (Czechoslov. Acad. Sci., Prague, 1961)
169. Keynes, R. D., *Biochem. Aktiven Transports, Colloq. German Biochem. Soc.*, 145–66 (Springer, Berlin, 1961)
170. Kinoshita, J. H., Kern, H. L., and Merola, L. O., *Biochim. Biophys. Acta*, **47**, 458–66 (1961)
171. Kinsey, V. E., *Circulation*, **21**, 968–87 (1960)
172. Kinter, W. B., and Cline, A. L., *Am. J. Physiol.*, **201**, 309–17 (1961)
173. Kleinzeller, A., and Kotyk, A., Eds., *Symp. Membrane Transport Metabol.* (Publ. House Czechoslov. Acad. Sci., Prague, 1961)
174. Kleinzeller, A., and Kotyk, A., *Biochim. Biophys. Acta.*, **54**, 367–69 (1961)
175. Koefoed-Johnsen, V., and Ussing, H. H., *Acta Physiol. Scand.*, **42**, 298–308 (1958)
176. Krane, S. M., and Crane, R. K., *J. Biol. Chem.*, **234**, 211–16 (1959)
177. Kuchler, R. L., and Grauer, R. C. *Biochim. Biophys. Acta*, **57**, 534–42 (1962)
178. Kurella, G. A., *Biofizika*, **5**, 260–69 (1960)*
179. Kurella, G. A., ref. **173**, 54–68 (1961)
180. Lacko, L., and Burger, M., *Nature*, **191**, 881–82 (1961)
181. Larralde, J., Giraldez, A., and Ron-Noya, J., *Rev. Espan. Fisiol.*, **17**, 193–201 (1961)
182. Lassen, U. V., *Biochim. Biophys. Acta*, **53**, 557–69 (1961)
183. Lassen, U. V., *Biochim. Biophys. Acta*, **57**, 123–29 (1961)
184. Lassen, U. V., and Overgaard-Hansen, K., *Biochim. Biophys. Acta*, **57**, 111–17 (1962)
185. Lassen, U. V., and Overgaard-Hansen, K., *Biochim. Biophys. Acta*, **57**, 118–22 (1962)
186. Lassen, U. V., and Overgaard-Hansen, K., *Scand. J. Clin. Lab. Invest.*, **14**, 157–62 (1962)
187. Lassen, U. V., and Hess-Thaysen, J. H., *Biochim. Biophys. Acta*, **47**, 616–18 (1961)
188. Leach, F. R., and Snell, E. E., *J. Biol. Chem.*, **235**, 3523–31 (1960)
189. Leaf, A., and Dempsey, E., *J. Biol. Chem.*, **235**, 2160–63 (1960)
190. Lee, J. E., and Lifson, N., *Biochim. Biophys. Acta*, **54**, 284–87 (1961)
191. LeFèvre, P. G., *Pharmacol. Rev.*, **13**, 39–70 (1961)

192. LeFèvre, P. G., *Nature*, **191**, 970–72 (1961)

193. LeFèvre, P. G., and McGinniss, G. F., *J. Gen. Physiol.*, **44**, 87–103 (1960)

194. Lepke, S., and Passow, H., *Arch. Ges. Physiol.*, **271**, 389–96 (1960)

195. Lepke, S., and Passow, H., *Arch. Ges. Physiol.*, **271**, 473–87 (1960)

196. Lin, E. C. C., and Wilson, T. H., *Am. J. Physiol.*, **199**, 127–30 (1960)

197. Lindemann, B., and Passow, H., *Arch. Ges. Physiol.*, **271**, 497–510 (1960)

198. Lindemann, B., and Passow, H., *Arch. Ges. Physiol.*, **271**, 488–96 (1960)

199. Lindemann, B., and Solomon, A. K., *J. Gen. Physiol.*, **45**, 801–10 (1962)

200. Ling, G., *J. Gen. Physiol.*, **43**, Suppl., 149–74 (1960)

201. Lluch, M., and Ponz, F., *Rev. Espan. Fisiol.*, **16**, Suppl. I, 309–16 (1960)

202. Lluch, M., and Ponz, F., *Rev. Espan. Fisiol.*, **16**, 327–36 (1961)

203. Lubin, M., and Kessel, D., *Biochim. Biophys. Res. Commun.*, **2**, 249 (1960)

204. Lubin, M., Kessel, D. H., Budreau, A., and Gross, J. D., *Biochim. Biophys. Acta* **42**, 535–38 (1960)

205. MacRobbie, A. C., and Ussing, H. H., *Acta Physiol. Scand.*, **53**, 348–65 (1961)

206. Maffly, R. H., Hays, R. M., Lamdin, E., and Leaf, A., *J. Clin. Invest.*, **39**, 630–41 (1960)

207. Matthews, J., and Smyth, D. H., *J. Physiol. (London)*, **154**, 63–64 P (1960)

208. McDougal, D. B., Little, K. D., and Crane, R. K., *Biochim. Biophys. Acta*, **45**, 483–89 (1960)

209. Miller, D., and Crane, R. K., *J. Lab. Clin. Med.*, **56**, 928–28 (1960)

210. Miller, D., and Crane, R. K., *Biochim. Biophys. Acta*, **52**, 281–93 (1961)

211. Miller, D., and Crane, R. K., *Biochim. Biophys. Acta*, **52**, 293–98 (1961)

212. Miller, D., and Crane, R. K., *Anal. Biochem.*, **2**, 284–86 (1961)

213. Mitchell, P., *Biochem. Aktiven Transports, Colloq. German Biochem. Soc.*, 581–603 (Springer, Berlin, 1961)

214. Mitchell, P., *Nature*, **191**, 144–48 (1961)

215. Mitchell, P., *Symp. Membrane Transport Metab.*, 22–34 (Czechoslov. Acad. Sci., Prague, 1961)

216. Morgan, H. E., Cadenas, D. M., Regen, D. M., and Park, C. R., *J. Biol. Chem.*, **236**, 262–68 (1961)

217. Morgan, H. E., Henderson, M. J., Regen, D. M., and Park, C. R., *J. Biol. Chem.*, **236**, 253–61 (1961)

218. Morgan, H. E., Post, R. L., and Park, C. R., *Symp. Membrane Transport Metab.*, 423–30 (Czechoslov. Acad. Sci., Prague, 1961)

219. Mortimore, G. E., *Am. J. Physiol.*, **200**, 1315–19 (1961)

220. Myers, R. M., Bishop, W. R., and Scheer, B. T., *Am. J. Physiol.*, **200**, 444–50 (1961)

221. Nagai, T., Makinose, M., and Hasselbach, W., *Biochim. Biophys. Acta*, **43**, 223–38 (1960)

222. Nakajima, S., and Takashi, H., *Japan. J. Physiol.*, **11**, 457–65 (1961)

223. Nathans, D., Tapley, D. F., and Ross, J. E., *Biochim. Biophys. Acta*, **41**, 271–82 (1960)

224. Netter, H., *Biochem. Aktiven Transports, Colloq. German Biochem. Soc.*, 15–44 (Springer, Berlin, 1961)

225. Netter, H., and Sachs, L., *Biochem. Z.*, **334**, 18–36 (1961)

226. Noall, M. W., *Biochim. Biophys. Acta*, **40**, 180–81 (1960)

227. Orloff, J., and Burg, M., *Am. J. Physiol.* **199**, 49–54 (1960)

228. Osborn, M. J., McLellan, W. L., Jr., and Horecker, B. L., *J. Biol. Chem.*, **236**, 2585–89 (1961)

229. Overgaard-Hansen, K., and Lassen, U. V., *Nature*, **184**, 553–54 (1959)

230. Oxender, D. L., and Royer, M., *Federation Proc.*, **20**, 140 (1961)

231. Page, E.. and Solomon, A. K., *J. Gen. Physiol.*, **44**, 327–44 (1960)

232. Paine, C. M., and Heinz, E., *J. Biol. Chem.*, **235**, 1080–85 (1960)

233. Pappenheimer, J. R., Heisey, S. R., and Jordan, E. F., *Am. J. Physiol.*, **200**, 1–10 (1961)

234. Park, C. R., Reinwein, D., Henderson, M. J., Cadenas, E., and Morgan, H. E., *Am. J. Med.*, **26**, 647–84 (1959)

235. Passow, H., *Biochem. Aktiven Transports, Colloq. German Biochem. Soc.*, 54–99 (Springer, Berlin, 1961)

236. Passow, H., and Rothstein, A., *J. Gen. Physiol.*, **43**, 621–33 (1960)

237. Passow, H., Rothstein, A., and Clarkson T. W., *Pharmacol. Rev.* **13**, 185–224 (1961)

238. Pena, J. C., and Malvin, R. L., *J. Gen. Physiol.*, **45**, 643–49 (1962)

239. Pfleger, K., and Seifen, E., *Biochem. Z.*, **335**, 595–605 (1962)

240. Pfleger, K., Rummel, W., Seifen, E., and Baldauf, J., *Med. Exptl.*, **5**, 473–79 (1961)

241. Platts, M. M., and Mudge, G. H., *Am. J. Physiol.*, **200**, 387–92 (1961)

242. Ponz, F., *VIes Journées Biochim. Latines*, 1–25 (Genève, 1961)

243. Ponz, F., and Lluch, M., *Rev. Espan. Fisiol.*, **16**, Suppl. I, 297–308 (1960)

244. Post, R. L., and Albright, C. D., *Symp. Membrane Transport Metab.*, 219–27 (Czechoslov. Acad. Sci., Prague, 1961)

245. Post, R. L., Merritt, C. R., Kinsolving, C. R., and Albright, C. D., *J. Biol. Chem.*, **235**, 1796–802 (1960)

246. Post, R. L., Morgan, H. E., and Park, C. R., *J. Biol. Chem.*, **236**, 269–72 (1961)

247. Post, R. L., and Rosenthal, A. S., *J. Gen. Physiol.*, **45**, 614 A (1962)

248. Quastel, J. H., *Can. Cancer Conf.*, **4**, 3–27 (1961)

249. Quastel, J. H., *Am. J. Clin. Nutr.*, **8**, 137–46 (1960)

250. Randle, P. J., *Symp. Membrane Transport Metab.*, 431–38 (Czechoslov. Acad. Sci., Prague, 1961)

251. Reiner, J. M., *Experientia*, **17**, 457–57 (1961)

252. Renkin, E. M., *J. Gen. Physiol.*, **44**, 1159–64 (1960/61)

253. Rickenberg, H., and Maio, J. J., *Symp. Membrane Transport Metab.*, 409–22 (Czechoslov. Acad. Sci., Prague, 1961)

254. Riggs, T. R., and Walker, L. M., *J. Biol. Chem.*, **235**, 3603–7 (1960)

255. Riklis, E., and Quastel, J. H., *Can. J. Biochem. Physiol.*, **36**, 363–71 (1958)

256. Roche, M., Ed., *Symp. Cell Membrane Physiol.*, *Caracas, 1959*, *J. Gen. Physiol.*, **43**, II, (1961)

257. Rosenberg, L. E., Blair, A., and Segal, S., *Biochim. Biophys. Acta*, **54**, 479–88 (1961)

258. Rosenberg, T., *Pathol. Biol.*, **9**, 795–802 (1961)

259. Rotman, B., and Guzman, R., *Pathol. Biol.*, **9**, 806–10 (1961)

260. Rudolph, G., *Verhandl. Deut. Ges. Kreislaufforsch.*, 93–114, 27. Tagung (1961)

261. Rummel, W., and Stupp, H. F., *Med. Exptl.*, **3**, 303–8 (1960)

262. Salomon, L. L., Allums, J. A., and Smith, D. E., *Biochem. Biophys. Res. Commun.*, **4**, 123–26 (1962)

263. Samiy, A. H. E., Brown, J. L., Globus, D. L., Keisler, R. H., and Thompson, D. D., *Am. J. Physiol.*, **198**, 599–602 (1960)

264. Sawyer, W. H., *Endocrinology*, **66**, 112–20 (1960)

265. Sawyer, W. H., and Schisgall, R. M., *Am. J. Physiol.*, **187**, 312–17 (1960)

266. Schachter, D., Dowdle, E. B., and Schenker, H., *Am. J. Physiol.*, **198**, 263–68 (1960)

267. Schachter, D., Dowdle, E. B., and Schenker, H., *Am. J. Physiol.*, **198**, 275–79 (1960)

268. Schachter, D., Kimberg, D. V., and Schenker, H., *Am. J. Physiol.*, **200**, 1263–71 (1961)

269. Schanker, L. S., and Tocco, D. J., *Biochim. Biophys. Acta*, **56**, 469–73 (1962)

270. Scharff, T. G., *Arch. Biochem. Biophys.*, **95**, 329–35 (1961)

271. Schatzmann, H. J., *Arch. Ges. Physiol.*, **274**, 295–310 (1961)

272. Schoffeniels, E., *Arch. Intern. Physiol. Biochim.*, **70**, 160–61 (1962)

273. Scholefield, P. G., and Abadom, P. N., *Proc. Can. Fed. Biol. Soc.*, **4**, 56 (1961)

274. Schreiber, S. S., Oratz, M., and Rothschild, M. A., *Am. J. Physiol.*, **198**, 89–93 (1960)

275. Schultz, S. G., and Solomon, A. K., *Nature*, **187**, 802–4 (1960)

276. Schultz, S. G., and Solomon, A. K., *J. Gen. Physiol.*, **45**, 355–69 (1961)

277. Schultz, S. G., and Solomon, A. K., *J. Gen. Physiol.*, **44**, 1189–99 (1961)

278. Segal, S., Blair, A., and Rosenberg, L. E., *Nature*, **192**, 1085–86 (1961)

279. Sekul, A. A., and Holland, W. C., *Am. J. Physiol.*, **199**, 457–59 (1960)

280. Sen, A. K., and Widdas, W. F., *J. Physiol. (London)*, **160**, 392–403 (1962)

281. Sen, A. K., and Widdas, W. F., *J. Physiol. (London)*, **160**, 404–16 (1962)

282. Shanes, A. M., Ed., *Biophys. Physiol. Pharmacol. Actions*, *New York, 1960* (Am. Assoc. Advan. Sci., Washington, 1961)

283. Shanes, A. M., in ref. 282, 309–16 (1961)

284. Shanes, A. M., *J. Cellular Comp. Physiol.*, **57**, 193–202 (1961)

285. Shanes, A. M., and Bianchi, C. P., *J. Gen. Physiol.*, **43**, 481–93 (1960)

286. Skou, J. C., *Biochim. Biophys. Acta*, **42**, 6–23 (1960)

287. Smyth, D. H., *Symp. Membrane Transport Metab.*, 488–99 (Czechoslov. Acad. Sci., Prague, 1961)

288. Solomon, A. K., *Sci. Am.*, **203**, 146–56 (1960)

289. Solomon, A. K., *Symp. Membrane Transport Metab.*, 94–99 (Czechoslov. Acad. Sci., Prague, 1961)

290. Solomon, A. K., *Biophys. J.*, **2**, 79–95 (1962)

291. Sols, A., and de la Fuente, G., *Symp. Membrane Transport Metab.*, 361–77 (Czechoslov. Acad. Sci., Prague, 1961)

292. Spencer, R. P., and Samiy, A.H., *Am. J. Physiol.*, **199**, 1033–36 (1960)

293. Stein, W. D., *Nature*, **191**, 352–55 (1961)

293a. Stein, W. D., *Biochem. Biophys. Acta*, **59**, 66 (1962)

294. Steinbach, H. B., *J. Gen. Physiol.*, **44**, 1131–42 (1961)

295. Steinbach, H. B., and Dunham, P. B., *Biol. Bull.*, **120**, 411–19 (1961)

296. Stolkowski, J., *Potassium Symp.*, *Proc. Congr. Intern. Potash Inst.*, *6th*, 635–768 (1960)

297. Strauss, E. W., and Wilson, T. H., *Am. J. Physiol.*, **198**, 103–7 (1960)

298. Sugiki, S., Constant, M. A., and Becker, B., *J. Cellular Comp. Physiol.*, **58**, 181–84 (1961)

299. Sullivan, L. P., Wilde, W. S., and Malvin, R. L., *Am. J. Physiol.*, **198**, 244–54 (1960)

300. Tanabe, T., Tsunemi, I., Abiko, Y., and Iida, S., *Biochem. Pharmacol.*, **8**, 38–38 (1961)

301. Tenenhouse, A., and Quastel, J. H., *Can. J. Biochem. Physiol.*, **38**, 1311–25 (1960)

302. Tercafs, R. R., and Schoffeniels, E., *Science*, **133**, 1706 (1961)

303. Tercafs, R. R., and Schoffeniels, E., *Arch. Intern. Physiol. Biochim.*, **69**, 604–5 (1961)

304. Tercafs, R. R., and Schoffeniels, E., *Arch. Intern. Physiol. Biochim.*, **70**, 129–30 (1962)

305. Tosteson, D. C., and Hoffman, J. F., *J. Gen. Physiol.*, **44**, 169–94 (1960)

306. Troshin, A. S., *Symp. Membrane Transport Metab.*, 45–53 (Czechoslov. Acad. Sci., Prague, 1961)

307. Tzur, R., and Shapiro, B., *Biochim. Biophys. Acta*, **42**, 325–33 (1960)

308. Ullrich, K. J., *Ergeb. Physiol.*, **50**, 433–89 (1959)

309. Ussing, H. H., *J. Gen. Physiol.*, **43**, 135–47 (1960)

310. Ussing, H. H., *Symp. Biol. Approaches to Cancer Chemotherapy, Louvain,* 89–99 (Academic, London, 1960)

311. Ussing, H. H., *Potassium Symp.*, *Proc. Congr. Intern. Potash Inst.*, *6th*, 229–39 (1960)

312. Ussing, H. H., *Biochem. Aktiven Transports, Colloq. German Biochem. Soc.*, 1–14 (Springer, Berlin, 1961)

313. Ussing, H. H., Kruhøffer, P., Hess-Thaysen, J., and Thorn, N. A., *Handbuch Exptl. Pharmakol.*, **13**, (1960)

314. Vander, A. J., *Am. J. Physiol.*, **201**, 505–10 (1961)

315. Vander, A. J., Wilde, W. S., and Malvin, R. L., *Proc. Soc. Exptl Biol. Med.*, **103**, 525–27 (1960)

316. Vander, A. J., Wilde, W. S., and Malvin, R. L., *J. Theoret. Biol.*, **2**, 236–43 (1961)

317. Vardanis, A., and Quastel, J. H., *Can. J. Biochem. Physiol.*, **39**, 1811–27 (1961)

318. Vestergaard-Bogind, B., and Hesselbo, T., *Biochim. Biophys. Acta*, **44**, 117–30 (1960)

319. Villegas, R., and Barnola, F. V., *Nature*, **188**, 762–63 (1960)

320. Villegas, R., and Barnola, F. V., *J. Gen. Physiol.*, **44**, 963–77 (1961)

321. Weatherall, M., *Proc. Royal Soc. (London)*, B, **156**, 57–82 (1962)

322. Weatherall, M., *Proc. Royal Soc. (London)*, B, **156**, 83–95 (1962)

323. Weidmann, S., *Am. Heart J.*, **61**, 298–302 (1961)

324. Whittam, R., *Biochem. J.*, **84**, 110–18 (1962)

325. Whittam, R., and Wheeler, K. P., *Biochim. Biophys. Acta*, **51**, 622 (1961)

326. Whittembury, G., *J. Gen. Physiol.*, **43**, 43–56 (1960)

327. Whittembury, G., Sugino, N., and Solomon, A. K., *Nature*, **187**, 699–701 (1960)

328. Whittembury, G., Sugino, N., and Solomon, A. K., *J. Gen. Physiol.*, **44**, 689–712 (1961)

329. Whittembury, G., and Windhager, E. E., *J. Gen. Physiol.*, **44**, 679–87 (1961)

330. Widdas, W. F., *Biochem. Pharmacol.*, **8**, 123–24 (1961)

331. Widdas, W. F., *Brit. Med. Bull.*, **17**, 107–11 (1961)

332. Wiesmeyer, H., and Cohn, M., *Biochim. Biophys. Acta*, **39**, 440–47 (1960)

333. Wilbrandt, W., *Fortschr. Zool.*, **12**, 28–127 (1960)

334. Wilbrandt, W., *Biochem. Aktiven Transports, Colloq. German Biochem. Soc.*, 112–36 (Springer, Berlin, 1961)

335. Wilbrandt, W., *Intern. Rev. Cytol.*, 203–20 (1961)

336. Wilbrandt, W., *Ciba Found. Symp. Enzymes Drug Action*, 43–57 (Churchill, London, 1962)

337. Wilbrandt, W., and Rosenberg, T., *Pharmacol. Rev.*, **13**, 109–83 (1961)

338. Wilde, W. S., and Howard, P. J., *J. Pharmacol. Exptl. Therap.*, **130**, 232–38 (1960)

338a. Wilson, T. H., *Intestinal Absorption* (Saunders, London, 1962)

339. Wilson, T. H., and Landau, B. R., *Am. J. Physiol.*, **198**, 99–102 (1960)

340. Winegrad, S., and Shanes, A. M., *J. Gen. Physiol.*, **45**, 371–94 (1962)

341. Wittenberg, J. B., *J. Gen. Physiol.*, **44**, 521–26 (1960/61)

342. Wittenberg, J. B., and Wittenberg, B. A., *J. Gen. Physiol.*, **44**, 527–42 (1960/61)

343. Wolff, J., *Biochim. Biophys. Acta*, **38**, 316–24 (1960)

344. Wolff, J., and Maurey, J., *Biochim. Biophys. Acta*, **47**, 467–74 (1961)

345. Wolff, J., and Maurey, J. R., *Biochim. Biophys. Acta*, **57**, 422–26 (1962)

346. Yoshida, H., and Nukada, T., *Biochim. Biophys. Acta*, **46**, 408–10 (1961)

347. Zierler, K. L., *Bull. Johns Hopkins Hosp.*, **109**, 35–48 (1961)

* English translation will be announced in *Technical Translations*, issued by the Office of Technical Services, U. S. Department of Commerce, and will be made available by the Photoduplication Service, Library of Congress, and by the SLA Translation Center at the John Crerar Library, Chicago, Illinois.

INVERTEBRATE MECHANISMS FOR DILUTING AND CONCENTRATING THE URINE[1]

By Bodil Schmidt-Nielsen

Departments of Zoology and Physiology, Duke University, Durham, North Carolina

IN COLLABORATION WITH

Donald F. Laws

Department of Zoology, University of Adelaide, Adelaide, South Australia

INTRODUCTION

The present review deals with the function of excretory organs in a number of invertebrate phyla. For a few of these phyla the volume of available information is considerable; for others it is virtually nil. The only reason for this gap in knowledge appears to be lack of interest since the physiology and anatomy can easily be investigated with modern techniques. For this reason, one of the primary purposes of this review is to stimulate interest in the unexplored phyla by demonstrating the considerable structural and functional similarities between the excretory organs of different phyla and between invertebrates and vertebrates.

The ability to produce a urine that is hypoosmotic to the "plasma" is found in the fresh-water and terrestrial forms of almost every phylum in the animal kingdom. The ability to make a hyperosmotic urine is much more confined and is, according to our present knowledge, found only in insects, birds, and mammals, and to a slight degree in crustaceans. In birds and mammals the urine is concentrated through the countercurrent multiplier system, which has been comprehensively treated in recent excellent reviews by Scholander (161), Ullrich *et al.* (193), and Morel & Guinnebault (108). The concentration mechanism of insects and crustaceans which is not completely understood will be discussed here.

The specialization of the countercurrent multiplier mechanism in the mammalian kidney is based on the existing ability of distal tubular cells of invertebrates and lower vertebrates to dilute the fluid inside the tubule by reabsorbing electrolytes and leaving water behind. For this reason the diluting mechanism as it has evolved in lower animals is of considerable interest for the understanding of the mammalian kidney function.

The kidney plays an important role in the osmoregulation of fresh-water animals where its major function appears to be the excretion of excess water. Since fresh-water animals are hyperosmotic to their environment, there is a net influx of water by diffusion through their gills and body surface. To avoid dilution of the body fluids, excess water must be excreted with a minimum of salt.

[1] The survey of literature pertaining to this review was concluded in July 1962.

In marine invertebrates and lower vertebrates the kidney assumes a different role. The majority of these animals are isosmotic to their environment. There is no osmotic influx of water, and the kidney does not serve an osmoregulatory function. In some of these animals urine flow may be reduced to one tenth, or less, that of related fresh-water forms, while others may have no excretory organs at all (67, 86). It appears that the excretory organs, when present in marine forms, serve mainly in ion and volume regulation (173).

Some marine organisms are hypoosmoregulators; i.e., their body fluids have a lower osmotic concentration than the surrounding sea water. In some hypoosmotic regulators, such as most crustaceans, the urine is not more concentrated than the blood and the kidney's role in osmoregulation is negligible. Excess sodium chloride is excreted by such organs as the gills and rectal gland (20, 85), while divalent ions are frequently excreted by the kidneys (134).

In brackish water, estuaries, and saline pools, animals must often adapt to a great variety of environmental concentrations. Some forms are always in osmotic equilibrium with their environment. Others show hyperosmotic but not hypoosmotic regulation. Still others show both hyper- and hypoosmotic regulation and are able to maintain a fairly constant osmotic concentration of the body fluids over a wide range of salinities (77, 78, 164, 173). *Artemia salina* is a beautiful example of an animal belonging to this latter group (28).

In terrestrial animals the need for water conservation makes it advantageous to excrete solutes with a minimum of water. Many terrestrial insects, for example, excrete a urine that is practically dry (202). The role of osmoregulation in terrestrial insects is taken over entirely by the excretory organs. The mechanisms for urine production vary greatly among insects as do the composition and osmolality of this urine (26).

The various renal structures associated with the production of urines with different osmolalities relative to the blood appear to be characteristic and to show certain similarities when compared in widely different groups of animals. Hence, even in animals where physiological data are lacking, the structure of the kidney may reveal basic information concerning its function.

PROTOZOA

Structure.—Contractile vacuoles are characteristic of fresh-water Protozoa and parasitic and marine ciliates but are lacking in other marine and parasitic groups. The primary function of the vacuole is believed to be that of removing water entering the cell by osmosis (85), but there is considerable uncertainty as to how the vacuole functions.

In most protozoans the vacuole appears to be an impermanent structure, formed anew after each contraction. In the ciliates, however, it occupies a fixed position with one or several canals leading to it. In the amoeba the vacuole is surrounded by a membrane which according to Mercer (106) is identical to the external membrane of the animal. Electron micrographs show that the membrane consists of two dense zones about 20 A thick separated by a light zone (total thickness 50 to 70 A). The mature vacuole is surrounded by a crowd of mitochondria which is not yet present in the small growing vacuole (119). A vast number of tiny vesicles, which presumably burst into the main vacuole, are found between the layer of mitochondria and the membrane. Bairati & Lehmann (3) observed in addition an intermediate fibrillar layer between the mitochondria and vacuolar membrane. They suggest that this layer may be the contractile part of the vacuole.

The fixed contractile vacuole of the ciliates frequently has a permanent canal or elaborate structure connecting it with the outside (135, 156). Surrounding the vacuole are vesicles, a dense reticulum of anastomosing tubules, and mitochondria (36, 156).

Function.—Considerable interest is beginning to center around the function of the contractile vacuole. It is generally agreed that it is osmoregulatory, and until recently it was believed that water was actively secreted into the vacuole (79, 85). However, the improbability of active water transport on thermodynamic grounds (15) as well as from a comparative physiological point of view makes this unlikely.

Fresh-water protozoans are distinctly hyperosmotic to their environment and there is suggestive evidence that even some marine forms are slightly hyperosmotic. The osmotic pressure of protozoans has been estimated by various indirect methods, such as disintegration in distilled water (95), osmotic pressure at which the contractile vacuole ceases to function (145), and volume changes at various concentrations of the medium (65). The results differ widely. This may result partly from variation between species but also partly from erroneous assumptions. Thus, Hopkins (65), disregarding the lag in function of the contractile vacuole (79), has argued:

When the amoebae are placed in dilute sea water of a given strength with a resulting decrease in volume, we can safely conclude that the osmotic pressure is higher externally than internally. If, on the other hand, the volume of the amoebae increases the osmotic pressure of the protoplasm is greater than that of the medium.

On this basis he found the osmotic pressure of the protoplasm of amoebae to be close to that of the medium. Lövtrup & Pigón (95), on the other hand, found the osmotic pressure of the amoeboid *Pelomyxa* to be about 90 mOs.

The ionic composition of protozoans has been determined by direct analysis and by equilibration with radioisotopes (22, 33, 82). In *Tetrahymena* in very dilute media, potassium and a small amount of sodium are maintained intracellularly (33). Chloride concentration is much lower than the cation concentration. Increases in cellular potassium or sodium are not accompanied by increases in chloride. In more concentrated media the intracellular potassium concentration is always higher than that of the medium while intracellular sodium is lower. Thus, in a medium of 4.75 mM potassium and 36.5 mM sodium the cellular concentrations were 32 mM potassium and 12.7 mM sodium. The authors suggest that potassium is specifically accumulated and retained by a system of internal binding sites with a saturation level, while sodium is extruded by an active mechanism. An adenosine triphosphate-splitting enzyme has been found to be localized in the cellular membrane of *Amoeba proteus* (65), which may be involved in the ion transport.

Klein (82) similarly found in *Acanthamoeba* a higher intracellular concentration of potassium than of sodium. Carter (22) measured the concentrations of potassium, sodium, and bromide in the ciliate *Spirostomum ambiguum* by equilibration with radioactive media. He found much lower sodium and potassium concentrations inside the cell than did the other authors, 10 to 12 mM potassium and about 1 mM sodium. These concentrations are probably too low because of the inexchangeability of a large fraction of the intracellular potassium (82). Carter (22) determined the time of half exchange for potassium to be two to three hours in *Spirostomum*. Klein (82) found that only 40 per cent of the potassium in *Ancanthamoeba* is exchangeable and that the exchangeable fraction consists of a rapid and slow component. The half lives of the fast and slow components are three minutes and forty-six minutes, respectively. In *Spirostomum*, sodium is exchanged in a matter of a few minutes (22). In *Acanthamoeba* (82), sodium exchange was found to be similar to potassium exchange with approximately the same half lives for the fast and slow components.

Since fresh-water protozoans are hyperosmotic to their environment and highly permeable to water (37, 65, 81), it is obvious that water continuously diffuses into them. The finding that the rate of vacuolar output varies inversely with the salinity of the medium (25, 51, 65) agrees with the notion that the vacuole serves the function of bailing out inflowing water. The rate of output, however, also varies with the rate of catabolism (65) and with temperature (80).

Cosgrove & Kessel (25) found a linear relation between the estimated osmotic gradient across the cellular wall and the rate of output of the vacuole in media concentrations ranging from 10 to 100 mM sodium chloride. The water must be removed as a solution that is either isosmotic or hypoosmotic to the protoplasm of the cell. Disregarding active water transport as a possible mechanism, we are left with the following possibilities. A solute could be transported into the vacuole with water following passively. The solute could either remain in the vacuole and be expelled to the outside when the vacuole empties, or it could be reabsorbed into the cell leaving a hypoosmotic solution behind. It is conceivable that the fluid in the vesicles surrounding the main vacuole is isosmotic to the protoplasm while solutes are actively reabsorbed in the main vacuole. This, however, would require an exceedingly low degree of water permeability of the vacuolar wall, since the small size of the vacuole (0.0001 mμl) gives a very large surface-to-volume ratio.

COELENTERATA

Most of the coelenterates are marine, but fresh- and brackish-water species are known (116, 152). No excretory organs are known in these animals. The ionic composition of marine forms differs from that of the sea water; and fresh-water forms are distinctly hyperosmotic to their environment. Lenhoff & Bovaird (89) found that a trace amount of sodium is essential for the growth of fresh-water hydra. They have essentially no extracellular fluid, and the body potassium-to-sodium ratio is about 9.8. Kinne (77, 78) found the optimum salt concentration for maximal growth of hydra to be 1.67 per cent.

The osmolality of the fresh-water medusa *Craspedacusta sowerbyi* corresponds to about 3 per cent sea water and is more than fifteen times that of the river water in which it lives (116). How water gained by osmosis is excreted is unknown.

ECHINODERMATA

All echinoderms are aquatic; none can live in fresh water and only a few in brackish water (12, 191). They have no special excretory organs and are unable to osmoregulate (134). Ion exchange takes place through tube feet, respiratory tree, etc.

PLATYHELMINTHES

Structure.—The phylum includes parasitic as well as free-living fresh-water and marine species. The excretory system comprises a pair of longitudinal, long coiled tubules, one on each side of the body. These are connected near the posterior end by a transverse tube or by a large bladder (115). The longitudinal tubes give off numerous branches ramifying through the entire body and ending in flame cells. The animals have no coelom, anus, circulatory, or respiratory system. The flame cells and tubules are thus surrounded by connective tissue and not by spaces containing fluid (124). There are some rather interesting reports on the structure of the flame cells in trematodes. Willey (205) examined the flame cells with a light microscope and found the flame to be longitudinally striated and composed of long cilia with a canal extending through the center of the flame. Electron microscopy (166) revealed that the flame cells consist of bundles of about eighty cilia enclosed by a single double-layered membrane with a series of stiffening members arranged in stockade fashion around the bundle of cilia. The development of the excretory system in a parasitic trematode has been described by Kuntz (88).

Kromhout (86) has made a very interesting comparison of the protonephridial system of fresh-water, brackish-water, and marine forms of the Turbellarian *Gyratrix hermaphroditus* which clearly demonstrates the importance of various parts of the excretory system in osmoregulation. In the fresh-water form the protonephridial system is most extensive and complex. The parts of the tubules closest to flame cells are enveloped by paranephrocytes, cells measuring from 50 to 60 μ each. After many convolutions the tubule runs into a contractile region, the "ampulla", which is a continuation of the main tubule surrounded by an enlargement of the syncytial tissue. The posterior end of the tubule enlarges into a bladder which opens to the outside through the nephridiopore.

In the brackish-water form the ampulla is entirely lacking, as are the paranephrocytes. In the marine form neither ampullae, paranephrocytes, nor tubules are found; i.e., the marine form has no excretory system.

Function.—The actual function of the flame cells is unknown. Senft *et al.* (167) postulated that the membrane surrounding the flame is freely permeable to water. They found no specialized secretory cells in the flame cell system and suggested, in agreement with Martin (104) and Kümmel (87), that the beating action of cilia causes a distal movement of fluid within the flame cell lumen. This motion is thought to produce enough pressure differential to allow filtration through the flame cell membrane. However, since there are no fluid spaces around them (124), this seems somewhat unlikely. Coil (24) has found a relatively high activity of alkaline phosphatase in the flame cells and in the fine tubules leading from them, which may suggest active sodium transport possibly followed by diffusion of water and solutes into the tubules, Beaver (9) found that the flame cells can be stimulated by saline. No work has been done on the function of the rest of the tubule or the paranephrocytes.

Kromhout's findings (86) that the ampulla is found only in fresh-water forms strongly suggest that it is concerned with the production of hypoosmotic fluid through reabsorption of salt. This is also supported by Hyman's observation (66) that ampullae seem to occur only in fresh-water representatives of marine Turbellaria.

ASCHELMINTHES

Structure.—The more recent experimental work done on animals from this phylum is almost exclusively limited to the nematodes. However, despite the lack of physiological data, certain deductions concerning the function of the excretory organs can be made by correlating their structure (49, 67) with the habitat of the animals.

In the class Rotifera there are both fresh-water and marine forms. While the fresh-water forms have long, coiled protonephridia with flame cells and urinary bladder, the marine forms lack excretory organs. The same is true of the class Gastrotricha.

It appears quite general, according to Goodrich's (49) description, that the protonephridia of fresh-water Aschelminthes are differentiated into a posterior glandular region opening at the excretory pore and an anterior "capillary" region ending in the flame cells.

The class Kinorhyncha is exclusively marine (67). Here there is an excretory organ, but as in other marine animals (compare annelids, crustaceans, fish, etc.) the excretory tube is very short. The protonephridium is described as a multinucleated flame cell, the flame of which consists of one long flagellum. A short tube provided with driving flagella leads directly from each flame cell to its own nephridiopore. In *Priapulida* the protonephridial part of the urogenital system consists of large clusters of solenocytes (protonephridial bulbs provided with flagella instead of tufts of cilia) opening into the urogenital duct by short collecting canals.

The Nematoda have a peculiar excretory system, entirely different from that of other classes of the phylum. Although the class includes marine, fresh-water, and parasitic forms, the primitive stem nematode was evidently marine (21, 39, 67, 162). The excretory system appears to have originated *de novo* (199) from the renette cell found in marine nematodes and not from a protonephridial system as suggested by Chitwood & Chitwood (23). Two types of excretory organs, glandular and tubular, have developed. In the marine nematodes (Adenophorea) the excretory system consists of a single glandular renette cell provided with a short duct which opens through the excretory pore. In the fresh-water and parasitic forms (Secernentea) a lateral canal system is attached to the renette gland cell (1, 64). Some authors say that the excretory canals are simply channels within what appears to be a single gland cell (199). Others (64) claim that they are composed of numerous cells. It is of particular interest that the terminal duct which leads to the excretory pore is lined by cuticle in the fresh-water forms but not in the marine forms (64). This cuticle-lined duct is acidophilic (199). A cuticle-lined terminal duct of the excretory organs appears to be present in a number of fresh-water animals.

Function.—In all the fresh-water forms we shall assume that the excretory system serves in an osmoregulatory capacity, excreting the water entering the body through the water-permeable cuticle (14). In the fresh-water forms, which all have long, differentiated protonephridia, it seems likely that a hypoosmotic fluid is produced by solute reabsorption in the posterior glandular region of the protonephridium. Experimental data are entirely lacking, but should be rather easy to obtain through micropuncture studies.

In the fresh-water nematodes it has been shown that the renette gland cell has an excretory function (200) and that it participates in osmoregulation. An inverse relation between pulsation rate of the excretory ampulla and the solute concentration of the media was shown by Weinstein (198). In a larva of *Nippostrongylus muris* placed in distilled water, 530 μ^3 per min were discharged from the excretory pore, whereas when it was placed in saline the rate of discharge decreased to 246 μ^3 per min.

It is possible that the cuticle-lined, acidophilic portion of the terminal duct is the part in which the fluid is made hypoosmotic since the terminal duct is not cuticle-lined in the marine forms (compare Annelida and Insecta).

The function of the excretory organs in the marine forms is not well understood. Since the organs are missing in several species, they do not seem to be essential. The solenocytes in *Priapulida* (107) have been shown to concentrate ammoniacal carmine. The results of dye studies on the excretory cells of nematodes have been reviewed by Weinstein (199); in *Ascaridina* (five species studied) the potassium salts of fluorescein and erythrosin were concentrated and excreted through the excretory pore after oral injection.

Injected ammoniacal carmine concentrated in the lateral lines adjacent to the canal. Nitrogenous compounds are apparently excreted through this organ but it is also quite possible that they play an important part in ion regulation.

ANNELIDA

Structure.—This phylum includes fresh-water, marine, and terrestrial forms. The excretory system consists of sets of paired excretory tubules, or nephridia, located in each body segment. Each nephridium opens into the coelomic cavity by means of a ciliated funnel, or nephridiostome. In some annelids the nephridium forms a long coiled tubule, differentiated into several parts, which opens at an external nephridiopore. In others it is short and undifferentiated. Grobben (54) pointed out that the length of the nephridial canal in annelids and crustaceans varies with habitat, being short in marine forms and long in fresh-water and terrestrial forms.[2]

The nephridium of the polychaete *Nereis vexillosa* has been described in detail by Jones (71). It is a long, convoluted tubule the outer surface of which is covered by a single thin layer of squamous coelomic epithelium. Interestingly enough, at the terminal end of the nephridial canal, the wall of the lumen thins and becomes lined with invaginated cuticle [cf. cestodes (94), nematodes, and insects]. The mean diameter of the nephridium is 24 μ and the over-all length 1.7 mm. According to Jones (71) no blood vessels occur within the nephridial mass, and in only two places is the nephridial system approached by vascular elements. In contrast to this, Krishnan (84) has indicated that in *Lycastis indica*, *Nereis chilkaensis*, and *Perinereis nuntia*, blood vessels are found in close association with the distal part of the nephridium. He also has pointed out that the extent of nephridial vascularization, as well as the length of the nephridium, is inversely related to the salinity of the environment. Furthermore, he found that the blood supply to the nephridia undergoes a diminution when *Lycastis* is acclimatized to sea water.

Young *Nereis* have small short protonephridia. During growth some of these degenerate while others acquire a coiled canal and a nephridiostome (49). Thus, the originally marine polychaetes appear to be able to adapt their excretory system for osmoregulation in fresh water. It is interesting that the viviparous *Neanthes* can reproduce in fresh water, while *Nereis diversicolor*, which is oviparous, cannot (179). It may be that the nephridia of young *Neanthes* are more fully developed at birth and therefore are able to produce a hypoosmotic urine. This, then, could explain the success of fresh-water reproduction of *Neanthes*.

A description of the nephridium of the earthworm *Lumbricus terrestris* has been given by Meisenheimer (105). The nephridium is differentiated into several parts. Following the nephridiostome is a narrow tube ciliated in the first part, then a wider middle tube, and finally a wide tube which is further

---

[2] Terrestrial annelids are essentially fresh-water forms, since they live in moist soil.

differentiated into three parts before it finally opens into a muscular duct or bladder. The nephridium is very richly vascularized.

Function.—Osmoregulation has been shown for some Nereid polychaetes (72, 179). *Nereis diversicolor* can tolerate fresh water with 1 to 2 meq Cl per liter, and *Nereis virens* can also tolerate lowered salinities, although only to 67 meq Cl per liter (72). The permeability to water and chloride is not the same in the two species. In *N. virens* 50 per cent of the body chloride is exchanged per hour in a medium containing 65 meq Cl per liter, while in *N. diversicolor* the exchange is only 25 per cent per hour. It is not known whether the ability to dilute the urine differs in these two species. Smith (179) found that the effect of temperature on adaption to low salinities by *N. diversicolor* and *Neanthes litthi* differs somewhat. *Nereis* osmoregulates below 1.5°C, while at this temperature the osmoregulation in *Neanthes* breaks down.

Ramsay (136) determined the osmotic pressure and chloride concentrations of coelomic fluid, blood, and urine of earthworms kept in various saline media. The blood was slightly hypoosmotic to the coelomic fluid. As the concentration of the medium was increased, the osmotic pressure of the two body fluids also increased and was always greater than that of the medium. The urine was always strongly hypoosmotic to the body fluids except in the most concentrated media, where the osmotic pressure of coelomic fluid corresponded to a salt solution of 1.4 per cent and that of the urine to 1.37 per cent. This finding shows that the nephridium of the earthworm, like the distal tubule of a vertebrate, can produce either a hypoosmotic urine or a urine that is essentially isosmotic to the blood. Other fresh-water annelids have been shown to tolerate higher salinities, e.g., two species of leech (97, 154) tolerate salinities up to 1.3 to 1.5 per cent. No measurements of urine osmolality were made.

By means of micropuncture studies together with microdeterminations of freezing point, Ramsay (137) was able to locate the tubular zone in which the fluid becomes hypoosmotic. This proved to be the so-called middle tube. Samples from the more distal part of the nephridium where the tube becomes wider were still more hypoosmotic. Apparently, solute reabsorption takes place against an osmotic gradient over an extended zone stretching from the end of the thin tubule to the muscular duct or bladder. Whether or not reabsorption takes place in the bladder cannot be seen from Ramsay's data.

The sipunculids, a marine group closely related to the Annelida, apparently have no ability to osmoregulate, but they do show volume control. The volume increases initially in dilute sea water (80 to 90 per cent), then gradually returns to normal. The worm is permeable to salt mostly through the gut or nephridiopores or both, while the body wall is highly permeable to water. When the nephridiopores were plugged, volume control failed (55), indicating to us that any excess salt is normally eliminated with water by the nephridia.

Experiments by Greif (53) have shown that excised nephridia from the sipunculid *Phascolosoma gouldi* accumulate far more Hg_2O_3 from a solution of labeled chlormerodrin than do other tissues of this animal. The uptake of mercury could be inhibited by cyanide, penicillin, and cyanine dye and partly inhibited by probenecid.

In the annelids another tissue in addition to the nephridia, the chlorogocytes, had been considered as a kidney of storage. However, these cells, which appear to be modified peritoneal cells (48), have no such function (48, 194, 195). Their primary function is to store lipids and glycogen (153).

MOLLUSCA

Structure.—Aquatic as well as terrestrial forms are found among the Mollusca. The aquatic molluscs were originally marine, but many have invaded brackish and fresh water and have become secondarily adapted to these environments. From the existing literature we have not been able to detect any characteristic structural variations of the excretory organs in molluscs from different habitats.

The molluscan excretory system consists of a central cavity, the pericardium, surrounding the heart and intestine and of either one or two kidneys (often called Bojanus organs) into which the pericardial cavity opens through a narrow aperture. Each kidney is basically a tube connecting the pericardium with the exterior, but its structure may be complicated in various ways (49, 187). Frequently it consists of a glandular spongy section followed by a thin-walled, nonglandular part called the bladder or posterior renal coelom. The bladder opens to the exterior by a small aperture.[3]

In the oyster (40, 41) the paired kidneys seem to consist mostly of "bladder", bordered medially and posteriorly by blind tubules which diminish in size with distance from the bladder. These tubules are bathed in blood from the adductor muscle region, which, in turn, is supplied by a blood vessel coming directly from the ventricle.

In the garden snail the wall of the glandular portion of the kidney forms many permanent folds. The cells are tall and columnar, containing coarse acidophilic granules and many crystalline concretions. In the bladder portion there are low columnar cells showing vertical striations from the luminal surface to the basement membrane (118). Electron microscopy of the kidney of the snail *Helix pomatia* (13) has shown that the wall of the bladder consists of two cell types. Certain cells, small and few in number, are ciliated and located in the luminal corners between the other, more numerous cells. The other cells are described as follows: "Practically the entire height of the cell is occupied by a system of cytomembranes, between which lie intercalated numerous oval mitochondria. These cells are also ciliated at their apical end." As Bouillon himself points out, these cells, except for the ciliation, are

---

[3] Another structure called Keber's organ, which consists of specialized cells lining the anterior part of the pericardium, had been thought to have an excretory function and to discharge its products into the pericardial cavity. Kato (76), working on certain lamellibranchs, has shown that the excreta from this organ are discharged from the mantle and gills and not through the Bojanus organ.

remarkably similar in ultrastructure to those of the mammalian renal distal tubule.

Function.—Most molluscs can tolerate wide variations in the salinity of their environment (40, 41, 46, 207). This tolerance appears to be mostly on the cellular level since they remain isosmotic to their environment over a wide range of salinities and only become hyperosmotic in fresh water or very dilute brackish water (31, 40, 41, 45, 46, 109, 111, 114, 129, 155, 197, 207). When mussels are exposed to sudden changes in salinity they close their valves and thus delay the exchange with the environment (45, 109).

Weak osmoregulatory ability appears to be widespread among molluscs (197). It is found in bivalves (40, 41, 43, 45, 46, 117, 126, 130, 146, 155) as well as in snails (13, 104, 111, 126, 157). Kidneys of bivalves and snails can elaborate a hypoosmotic urine and it is possible that active uptake of salt by the gills also plays a role in hyperosmotic regulation.

The osmotic concentration of the body fluids in fresh-water forms is extremely low. In the mussel *Anodonta* the plasma chloride concentration ranges from 3 to 20 meq per liter when the surrounding water has a total salt concentration of 1 meq per liter (43). Potts (129) determined the sodium concentration in *Anodonta* plasma to be about 15.5 meq per liter and Picken (126) found that the osmotic concentration corresponded to 0.10 per cent sodium chloride which is about 34 mOs. All these values agree essentially.

The snail *Theodoxus fluviatilis* is hyperosmotic in fresh water and maintains a blood concentration of 80 to 90 mOs (111). In another snail *Viviparus fasciatus*, the blood concentration was 113 mOs in fresh water (114).

The renal function has been most carefully investigated in *Anodonta*. A filtrate of the blood accumulates in the pericardium. This fluid was found to be isosmotic (126) and to have the same chloride, phosphate, and calcium concentration as the blood (43), and thus it appears to be a true ultrafiltrate. During the passage of the filtrate through the two parts of the Bojanus organ, salt is reabsorbed and protein and nonprotein nitrogenous waste products are added. The chloride concentration of the urine collected from the bladder is about one half that of the blood, and the nitrogen concentration is about three- to fourfold higher (43). The urine osmolality is about 0.6 that of the blood (126). This means that an osmotic gradient of about 15 mOs is created across the membrane of the bladder. From data obtained by Potts (130) it appears that the filtration rate approximately equals the urine flow, being about 1 to 2 ml per hr per 100 g; thus water does not appear to be reabsorbed along with the salt.

Snails are likewise able to produce a hypoosmotic urine. In the African snail *Achatina fulica*, the osmolality of the blood was 250 mOs and that of the urine 153 mOs (104). Terrestrial snails apparently can adapt to water conservation as well as to excretion of excess water (13, 157). During estivation the vector snail *Oncomelania nosophora* can tolerate a 40 per cent loss of body water (83). Kidney function continues during estivation, and nitrogenous waste (uric acid) is stored in the bladder. During such periods water is probably reabsorbed along with salt from the bladder (13). To our knowledge no determinations of the osmolality of the "stored urine" have been made. Bouillon suggests that the highly specialized cells with many "cytomembranes" and mitochondria found in the wall of the bladder of the snail *Helix pomatia* are characteristic of adaptation to terrestrial life, i.e., to water conservation. To the present authors it seems likely that their specialized structure is related to their function of producing a hypoosmotic as well as an isosmotic urine similar to the cells in the vertebrate distal tubule.

Investigations by Jullien *et al.* (73, 74, 75) indicate that a sodium load is not readily excreted in the snail *Helix pomatia*. Injections of NaCl, KCl, or CaCl$_2$ resulted in marked increases of these ions in the hemolymph. Injected calcium disappeared from the hemolymph quite rapidly in about two days. Sodium or potassium injection resulted in a compensatory fall in the calcium concentration while the hemolymph concentration of sodium or potassium remained elevated for up to seven days. Apparently the kidney conserves sodium and excretes divalent ions (cf. crustaceans, fish, and birds).

The ionic regulation in marine molluscs has been little investigated. In the bivalve *Mytilus edulis* the ionic composition of the blood closely resembles that of sea water, but shows somewhat greater concentrations of calcium, postassium, and total carbon dioxide. The ionic composition of the urine of the octopus has been determined and compared with sea water, but not with the blood (35). Potassium and sulfate concentrations appear to be significantly higher in the urine than in sea water.

Three independent facts suggested that the ability to osmoregulate in fresh water may not be present in young bivalves. (*a*) The embryos of *Anodonta* after hatching in the fall remain in the gills of the mother all winter. The following spring they attach themselves to the gills of fish and lead a parasitic life for 3 to 12 weeks (63). (*b*) In the fresh-water mussel *Lamellidens marginalis*, the osmotic pressure of the blood increases with age, rising from about 20 to 35 mOs (117). (*c*) In the Japanese marsh clam *Corbicula japonica*, it has been shown that the adults osmoregulate but the young do not (207). It is possible that the kidney in the young bivalve has not developed to the point where it can produce a hypoosmotic urine, and that this is related to the fact that bivalves have invaded fresh water from a marine habitat.

Finally, it should be mentioned that Potts (132) has made determinations of sodium fluxes in the muscle fibers of the marine mussel *Mytilus* and the fresh-water mussel *Anodonta*. From these measurements he calculated the energy required for sodium extrusion, assuming that it is entirely an active process. The values he arrived at were 0.26 cal per g per hr for *Mytilus* and 0.046 cal per g per hr for *Anodonta*. He suggests on this basis that a fresh-water animal, with a low osmotic concentration of its tissues,

may perform less ionic work than a marine animal; for although it has to perform a certain amount of ionic work at the body surface it may be saved a large amount of ionic work at the surface of each cell. Conversely, the many marine animals which maintain a salt concentration in the blood which is less than that of sea water, for example: teleosts, selachians, lampreys, sturgeons, grapsoid crabs and many shrimps, may be more efficient than otherwise appears.

These considerations may explain the observation (96, 180) that the oxygen consumption of certain molluscs increases when the salinity of their environment is increased; i.e., the increased energy demand for ionic regulation may more than balance the decreased energy demand for osmoregulatory purposes.

ARTHROPODA

This phylum is the largest in the animal kingdom, but of its eight classes only two, the crustaceans and the insects, have been studied in any detail. These two classes will therefore occupy all of the present discussion.

CRUSTACEA

Structure.—Fresh-water, brackish-water, marine, and terrestrial forms are found. In the majority of crustaceans the excretory organs consist of a pair of "antennary glands" or "green glands" located in the head (54, 125). Each gland has (*a*) a closed coelomic sac; (*b*) a canal, the "labyrinth" or "green body"; (*c*) a nephridial canal (absent in marine and brackish-water forms); and (*d*) a bladder.

A single layer of epithelial cells surrounds the coelomic sac, which is richly supplied with hemolymph through small vessels or lacunae. The labyrinth is a highly involuted canal, composed of a single layer of large cells in contact with a thin basement membrane. The cells, like those of the vertebrate proximal tubule, show basal striation and an apical brush border (2, 98, 99, 100). Electron microscopy (2) has shown simple basal infoldings of the plasma membrane and mitochondria scattered throughout the cytoplasm. Cytoplasmic inclusions of unknown derivation were also observed.

The cells in the nephridial canal have much in common with the distal tubular cells of vertebrates (8). Electron micrographs demonstrate a series of lamellae or infoldings of the plasma membrane at the base of the cells. The cytoplasmic compartments between the lamellae contain rows of mitochondria (cf. mollusca). Maluf (99) noted large apical vacuoles, which he associated with water secretion; however, these were not mentioned by Beams, Anderson & Press (8).

It is of interest that distinct morphological and functional differences are found between the kidneys of fresh-water crustaceans on the one hand, and secondary invaders of fresh or brackish water and marine forms, on the other hand. Grobben (54) noticed that the nephridial canal is present only in fresh-water forms. Peters (125) found that the lobster, which lacks the nephridial canal, can make isosmotic urine, while the crayfish, which possesses a long nephridial canal, can make hypoosmotic urine. He further showed that the fluid in the coelomic sac and labyrinth has the same chloride concentration as the hemolymph, but that the fluid along the nephridial canal becomes progressively more dilute as it approaches the bladder. Schwabe (163) found that the fresh-water crustacean *Palaemonites varians microgenitor* does not have a nephridial canal. It was later shown (121, 122) that the urine is always isosmotic to the hemolymph in various species of *Palaemonites* adapted to fresh water. In other cases also, where fresh-water crustaceans have been found to lack a nephridial canal, it has been shown that they lack the ability to produce a hypoosmotic urine (158). The degree to which the urine can be made hypoosmotic appears to be related to the length of the nephridial canal in *Gammarus* (68, 92).

It is quite evident that the nephridial canal is essential for the production of a hypoosmotic urine. However, the significance of this ability is not clear, since successful adaptation to fresh water has frequently been accomplished without it (121, 158, 163).

Osmoregulation.—The crustaceans show a wide range of osmoregulatory ability (85). Some, like the crayfish *Asellus aquaticus* (91) and the shore crab *Carcinus maenas* (174), are hyperosmotic in dilute sea water but are not able to maintain a lower osmotic concentration than the medium. Others show hypo- as well as hyperosmotic regulation (4, 56, 57, 134, 148), the most extreme example being *Artemia salina*, which can osmoregulate successfully in salinities ranging from 0.25 per cent sodium chloride to crystallizing salt brine (27, 28, 127). Still others may have no osmoregulation (57).

Three factors are involved in crustacean osmoregulation: (*a*) the active uptake or secretion of sodium and chloride by the gills, (*b*) the permeability of the body surface (gills primarily) to salt and water, and (*c*) the excretion of salt and water by the kidneys. Potts (131) estimated the theoretical minimum osmotic work required by a crustacean in fresh water to produce an isosmotic or a hypoosmotic urine. His calculations were based on the assumption that the animal is permeable to water but not to electrolytes. They showed that an animal producing a urine hypoosmotic to the hemolymph and isosmotic to the medium can maintain its body salt concentration with only 10 per cent of the osmotic work required by an animal making a urine isosmotic to the hemolymph.

That this conclusion is based on incomplete assumptions was shown by several investigators (16, 17, 18, 28, 29, 121, 168 to 172, 174, 175) who found high rates of sodium and chloride in- and outfluxes in various crustaceans. Shaw (175), on the basis of flux determinations, suggested that adaptation to fresh water is not primarily a renal matter, but involves two main factors: (*a*) a gradual reduction in permeability of the body surface to salt, and (*b*) the acquisition of an active uptake mechanism with a high affinity for the ions which it is transporting.

Shaw's suggestions are supported by good experimental evidence. The mechanism in the gills for active uptake of sodium and chloride ions is fully saturated at lower external concentrations in fresh-water forms than in brackish-water forms (175, 176). Also, the rate of sodium loss, measured as the ^{22}Na outflux, was much lower in fresh- than in brackish-water forms. In

Carcinus maenas (174) it was 890 μM per hr per 50 g, while it was only 7.5 μM per hr per 50 g in the fresh-water crayfish *Astacus papillipes* (168), indicating a reduced permeability in the fresh-water form.

The urinary sodium loss is quite low compared to the over-all loss even in *Carcinus maenas* whose urine is isosmotic to the blood and whose urine flow increases up to tenfold when it is adapted to fresh water (174). This loss ranges from only 2.7 per cent of the total loss, when the animal is in sea water, to 21.1 per cent when it is in 40 per cent sea water (174). Loss of sodium in the urine, however, may be a little more significant than appears at first sight, since part of the total outflux might be accounted for by "exchange diffusion", and therefore might not represent actual loss of sodium. Bryan (17) estimates that under normal conditions 30 per cent of the sodium outflux in *Astacus fluviatilis* is caused by exchange diffusion in connection with the active uptake of sodium by the gills. Similarly, Croghan (29) found extremely high sodium fluxes between the hemolymph of *Artemia salina* and the medium, with a marked increase in more concentrated media where active excretion of salt by the gills takes place. He concluded that rapid exchange diffusion of sodium and chloride takes place across the gills.

Kidney function.—The question of filtration into the coelomic sac has been reinvestigated in the lobster (19) and in the crayfish (150). Both studies indicate that filtration does indeed occur here. The argument is based on the facts that inulin is excreted, that glucosuria can be induced by increasing the plasma glucose concentration, and that phlorizin poisoning causes glucose to appear in the urine. Maluf (101) earlier arrived at the conclusion that inulin is actively secreted in the coelomic sac of the crayfish because he found that the U/B (urine:blood) ratios decreased toward unity when the inulin concentration of the blood was increased. However, Riegel & Kirschner (150) suggest that this conclusion is erroneous, because in their experiments the inulin U/B ratios remained nearly constant when the range of blood concentrations was extended down to less than one milligram per cent inulin. Maluf's data may, furthermore, be differently interpreted (104).

The function of the labyrinth can best be dealt with through a discussion of the marine and brackish-water crustaceans which do not possess a nephridial canal. In all of these the urine is either isosmotic or slightly hyperosmotic to the blood. In the lobster, the inulin U/B ratio is unity (19). In *Carcinus maenas* and in other crabs, the inulin U/B ratio may be as high as 2 to 3 (151), indicating that water is reabsorbed in the labyrinth.

In the lobster, the sodium concentrations in the urine and hemolymph are equal, but in various crabs, namely, *Uca pugnax* and *U. pugilator* (52), *Carcinus maenas* (151), *Pachygrapsus crassipes* (60, 133), *Palaemon serratus* (120), and *Potamon niloticus* (169), the sodium concentration in the urine is lower than in the hemolymph, and sodium must therefore be actively reabsorbed in the labyrinth.

Changes in sodium and magnesium excretion in the urine are both involved in adaptation of crustaceans to varying salinities of their environment, and, in many, an inverse relationship between the excretion of these two ions is found. Magnesium is usually present in the urine in considerably greater concentrations than in the hemolymph and must be actively secreted (59). When a lobster (19) is placed in dilute sea water, the magnesium U/B ratio decreases to values below unity indicating reabsorption of magnesium, while in full strength sea water, magnesium is secreted, giving a U/B ratio of 2 to 3. In *Palaemon serratus* (120) the urinary magnesium concentration is always higher than that of the hemolymph and increases considerably with increasing salinity of the medium, even though the hemolymph concentration of magnesium remains almost unchanged. The hemolymph sodium concentration, on the other hand, increases with increasing salinity. In the lobsters (19) *Palaemon serratus* (120) and *Potamon niloticus* (169), the urine sodium concentration varies in the same direction as the hemolymph sodium concentration, and the sodium U/B ratio remains constant. In others, *Uca pugnax* (52), *Carcinus maenas* (151), *Pachygrapsus crassipides* (58, 133), however, the sodium concentration in the urine decreases significantly with increasing salinity of the medium or with dehydration. Thus, in *Pachygrapsus* (133) the sodium U/B ratio was 1.1 when the animal was in 50 per cent sea water, 0.68 in 100 per cent sea water, and 0.38 in 170 per cent sea water. In these same crabs the magnesium concentration increased considerably with increasing salinity.

It has further been shown that the concentration of magnesium in the urine is dictated by the salinity of the medium and not by the magnesium content (60) because during brief periods of submersion in salt solutions corresponding to 50 per cent, 100 per cent, and 175 per cent sea water the magnesium concentration of urine of *Pachygrapsus* reflected the salinity of the medium regardless of whether magnesium was present or absent in abnormally high concentrations, while the urine sodium concentration decreased with increasing salinity. Prosser *et al.* (133), who submerged the crabs for longer periods of time, found that, in the absence of $MgSO_4$ in the medium, urine sodium increased with increasing salinity. The difference in findings could be a result of the difference in lengths of submersion.

Another extremely interesting finding in the crustaceans is that a urine slightly hyperosmotic to the hemolymph has been observed independently by several investigators in various crabs. In *Carcinus* the urine osmolality exceeded the hemolymph osmolality by about 3 per cent after the crab had been dehydrated for four days (151). In *Uca* (52), hyperosmotic urine (10 to 20 per cent) was produced when the crab was placed in 175 per cent sea water. In *Ocypode albicans* and *Goniopsis cruentatus* the chloride U/B ratio reached values of 1.6 to 1.8 when the crabs were placed in full strength sea water (42). Flemister suggests active water reabsorption, but it seems more likely to us that the hyperosmolality is brought about by the secretion of magnesium, perhaps in the most distal, and possibly relatively water-impermeable part of the labyrinth. The secretion of divalent ions such as magnesium and sulfate into the urine and the conservation of sodium are found in many other groups of animals.

As mentioned earlier, the nephridial canal is necessary for the production of a hypoosmotic urine and is present only in true fresh-water forms. Its function appears to be similar to that of the vertebrate distal tubule. From Peter's (125) finding that chloride concentration decreases along the canal and from analogy with the mammalian tubule, we can assume that active reabsorption of electrolytes takes place against an osmotic gradient leaving water behind. The urinary osmotic concentration may be as low as 4 to 5 mM sodium chloride. Some water reabsorption, however, also takes place in the nephridal canal. The average inulin U/B ratio in the crayfish is 3 to 4 but values as high as 28 have been recorded (150). Such high values have so far not been recorded for crustaceans without a nephridial canal.

The renal response to a salt load is quite different in the fresh-water crayfish with a nephridial canal from that in crabs without a nephridial canal. Thus, when the sodium concentration in the hemolymph of the crayfish *Astacus* (18) was increased by placing the animal in saline media exceeding 200 mM per liter, the urine sodium concentration increased almost to the level of the hemolymph. The urine flow, moreover, increased. An increase in the sodium concentration in the urine could in theory be brought about either by a decreased sodium reabsorption in the nephridial canal or an increased permeability to (hence reabsorption of) water, but the increase in urine volume may suggest that the first explanation is correct. The renal response to water loads of another species of crayfish *Orconectes virilis* was studied by Riegel (149), who found that severe water loads caused large and pronounced increases in the inulin clearance, urine flow, and total sodium excretion. Urine flow nearly doubled and sodium excretion increased fourfold while the inulin U/B ratios decreased.

INSECTA

Structure.—Insects have been adapted to a terrestrial life since the early Pennsylvanian Period. Some have secondarily become adapted to fresh water in the larval stage or in the larval and adult stages. A few have migrated to salt marshes and some inhabit the crystallizing brine of salt lakes (188).

Because of their unique ability to produce not only a hypoosmotic urine but also a highly hyperosmotic urine, the excretory organs in insects play a much more important role in osmoregulation than they do in other invertebrates. In the majority of insects they consist of the Malpighian tubules and the hindgut.[4] These parts are intimately concerned with the formation of urine.

The Malpighian tubules vary greatly in number, from two to over one hundred, in the different orders of insects. They are long, slender, blind tubules derived as an outgrowth from the intestine. One end opens into the

---

[4] The Collembola and Aphids are exceptions in that they do not have Malpighian tubules. In the primitive wingless Collembola, excretion takes place through labial nephridia, middle intestinal epithelium, hypodermis, and fat bodies (38).

junction between midgut and hindgut; the other, the blind end, either lies free in the hemocoele or is "cryptonephric", i.e., attached to the wall of the posterior hindgut (69) and enveloped in the peritoneal membrane. Lison (90) has given a detailed description of this attachment in *Tenebrio* (the flour beetle). The surface of the Malpighian tubules toward the intestine is smooth, while the surface toward the hemocoele is swollen. Openings in the membrane of the swollen surface have been postulated, but according to Lison, the membrane is continuous. Poll (128) has suggested filtration through this surface.

The Malpighian tubules consist of several histologically distinct segments which vary in number and structure in the different orders of insects. In some a segment is concerned with mucous secretion (47) or secretion of silk (70) or brochosomes (30, 177). Only two segments appear to be present in most orders. Wiggleworth (201) has described these parts in *Rhodnius prolixus* which possesses four tubules, each of which consists of an upper segment (including the closed end) with granular epithelium and with clear fluid in the lumen, and a lower segment with almost granular-free epithelium and with crystalline spheres of uric acid filling the lumen. The description for *Corcyra cephalonica* (182) is almost identical except that the tubules of *Corcyra* are cryptonephric which they are not in *Rhodnius*. For this reason Srivastava (182) divides the tubule into three segments. However, the cryptonephric and the middle segments are histologically identical to the upper segment as described in *Rhodnius*. Both upper and lower segments have a striated border toward the lumen. The striated border of the upper segment is of the honey-comb type, while in the lower segment it is a brush border with well separated filaments (201). Electron micrographs of these segments in *Rhodnius* (204), in *Macrosteles* (178), in *Melanoplus* (7), and in *Gryllus* (10, 11) have shown that in the upper segment the mitochondria are most conspicuous in the apical part of the cells. The prominent honeycomb border is 3 to 4 μ long, each filament being about 1 μ wide and sometimes densely packed with mito-chondria. The basal zone of the cells has only a few mitochondria. Crystals of uric acid are found in the cells (182, 204). The cells of the lower segment differ in that the maximum density of mitochondria is found between the invagi-nated cytomembranes at the base of the cells. Crystalline spheres of uric acid are found in the lumen between the filaments of the brush border.

The hindgut with the rectum and rectal gland constitutes an important part of the excretory system because the fluid emerging from the Malpighian tubules is modified as it passes through this part. Wigglesworth (202) made a detailed comparison of the hindgut in all main orders of insects and suggested that the rectal gland and the rectal epithelium reabsorb water from the urine before it is discharged. In most orders the hindgut consists of two or three main segments: (*a*) a long thin region with comparatively small epithelial cells; (*b*) a capacious sac, "the rectum", surrounded by a muscular coat and, in some, following the rectum; (*c*) a muscular canal with low epithelium. The rectum and anal canal are usually lined with cuticle. The "rectal glands", usually six in number, are situated in the anterior part of the rectum. They are composed of large cuboidal cells, very richly supplied by tracheae. Often the terminal tracheoles can be seen ramifying throughout the cells. Electron microscopy of the hindgut of insects reveals some interesting structures (113, 178). In *Macrosteles fascifrons* Stal (Homoptera) (178), the entire rectum is lined by a uniform columnar epithelium which, according to Wigglesworth (202), is of the same type as that composing the rectal gland. These cells possess lamellae filled with mitochondria on the luminal side. Similar cells have been described in the rectum of termites by Noirot & Noirot-Timothee (113) who state, "At the apical part of the cells the membrane folds irregularly toward the interior forming cytoplasmic compartments with many mitochondria, giving a striated appearance to the cell which is visible in the light microscope." According to the authors, these cells are remarkably similar to the cells of the distal tubule of mammals, but with the polarity reversed, since in the distal tubule it is the basal part of the cell which exhibits the cytoplasmic compartments filled with mitochondria.

Ramsay (138) has studied the structure and function of the hindgut in two species of mosquito larvae *Aedes aegypti* and *Aedes detritus*. The first inhabits fresh water and can produce a urine hypoosmotic or isosmotic to the hemolymph. The other, *A. detritus*, lives in brackish water and can, in addition, make a hyperosmotic urine. He associates the ability to form a hyperosmotic urine with a region in the anterior part of the rectum lined with an epithelium distinctly different from that in the remainder of the rectum. This anterior region was not found in *A. aegypti*. It is not clear from Ramsay's description whether or not this anterior region in *A. detritus* is identical to the "rectal glands" described by Wigglesworth (202). Further investigations comparing cellular specialization in the rectum with ability or inability to produce a hyperosmotic urine in various insects would be highly desirable.

Osmoregulation.—Some aquatic insects are able to osmoregulate successfully in fresh (110) and salt water (93, 112), maintaining the hemolymph osmotic concentration relatively constant over wide ranges of salinities. Thus, in *Chironomus salinarius* (112) the freezing point depression of the hemolymph is $\Delta = 0.63°C$ (350 mOs) when the larvae are in a medium of $\Delta = 0.05°C$ and rises to only $\Delta = 0.94°C$ when the medium is $\Delta = 1.5°C$. A relatively large fraction of the total osmotic concentration of insect hemolymph is attributable to amino acids (32, 203). When the larvae of *Libellula* and *Aeschna* are placed in distilled water, the osmotic concentration of the hemolymph is maintained through a rise in amino acid concentration in spite of a fall in the chloride concentration (159, 160). In caddis larvae (Trichoptera) (190), the regulation is of a different type. The salt concentration of the hemolymph is maintained at a relatively constant level, lower than that of the medium, while the total osmotic concentration of the hemolymph remains equal to that of the medium over a wide range of media concentrations.

Insects are not impermeable to salt and water. The permeability of the cuticle of a number of aquatic insect larvae and terrestrial insects has been determined by Beament and others (5, 6, 102). A considerable variation in permeability of the cuticle is found among the aquatic insects. The greatest permeability is evident in the anal papillae or "gills". The exchange of labeled sodium between the external medium and the hemolymph and whole body in *Aedes aegypti* was found to be half complete in 60 hours (184, 192) with 90 per cent of the exchange taking place through the anal papillae (184). The function of the anal papillae apparently is that of active uptake of ions from a dilute medium (141, 184, 185). As in the crustaceans, it is quite possible that such exchange studies do not indicate the true permeability since "exchange diffusion" may take place at the site of active ion uptake.

When insect larvae are placed in dilute media or in media having extreme deficiencies of chloride, alkali, or cations (186), the papillae hypertrophy, whereas when the larvae are placed in more concentrated media the papillae atrophy (62). Thus, the papillae appear to be of no importance in hypo-osmoregulation. Insect larvae in hyperosmotic environments osmoregulate primarily with the excretory organs.

Function of Malpighian tubules and hindgut.—It was suggested by Wigglesworth (201) on the basis of his experiments with *Rhodnius* that potassium and urate ions are secreted into the upper segment of the Malpighian tubules, the segment in which the cells were later found to contain urate crystals (204). Ramsay (140) confirmed these findings and showed that the fluid in the upper segment is slightly hyperosmotic to the hemolymph and has a potassium concentration around 120 meq per liter while that of the hemolymph has only 5 to 10 meq per liter. The sodium concentration, on the other hand, was lower in the upper segment than in the hemolymph. Electrical potential measurements also indicated active potassium secretion in this segment (142). Not all insects, however, secrete uric acid in the upper segment of the Malpighian tubule. In *Sitophilus granarius* (L.) (61) and in *Periplaneta americana* (183), uric acid and urates are secreted in the hindgut. In many insects a large fraction or all of the uric acid is stored in the fat bodies (181, 183).

Patton & Craig (123) and Srivastava (182) on the basis of their findings from insects with cryptonephric tubules, *Tenibrio molitor* (L.) (123) and *Corcyra cephalonica* Stainton (182), suggest that filtration takes place in the so-called middle tube, the part of the upper segment immediately following the cryptonephric part. The hemolymph apparently moves into this middle portion leaving only larger molecules behind. Thus, glycogen has been shown to enter the lumen. Such a movement into the tubule is quite likely in view of the findings by Ramsay (140) that the tubular fluid is hyperosmotic to the hemolymph. Ramsay and Riegel (144) have recently confirmed these findings and shown that inulin as well as glucose, fructose, and sucrose enters the urine of the stick insect *Dixippus morosus* through the wall of the Malpighian tubule. However, the U/B ratio for inulin is much lower (0.046) than the ratios for the sugars (0.75, 0.58, and 0.58 respectively).

The function of the lower segment is, according to Wigglesworth (201), that of reabsorption of alkali and water, thus acidifying the content of the tubule with resulting precipitation of uric acid. The results by Ramsay (140) have confirmed this hypothesis. In the lower segment the osmotic concentration is slightly (6 to 39 mM) lower than that of the hemolymph (143). On the basis of this finding Ramsay (140) suggested that water is secreted into the tubule; however, it is much more likely that the hypoosmolality is brought about through active salt reabsorption. Ramsay (140) showed that the potassium concentration decreases in the lower segment while the sodium concentration increases. Presumably some passive water reabsorption also takes place in this segment.

The fluid entering the hindgut from the Malpighian tubules is thus always slightly hypoosmotic to the hemolymph regardless of the final concentration of the urine (139, 140, 141). Final changes in osmotic concentration take place in the hindgut where the urine may remain isosmotic or become hypoosmotic or hyperosmotic to the hemolymph.

As mentioned earlier, the fresh-water insect larva *Aedes aegypti* can produce a hypoosmotic urine when placed in a dilute medium, whereas the urine becomes isosmotic to the hemolymph when the larva is placed in a concentrated medium. In contrast to this, the brackish-water mosquito larva *A. detritus* can, in addition, produce a hyperosmotic urine in concentrated media (138). The same is true of the fly larva *Coelopa frigida* which can concentrate the urine up to six times the concentration of hemolymph (189). Another brackish-water fly larva *Ephydra riparia* cannot make the urine hypoosmotic but can make it either isosmotic or highly hyperosmotic, up to ten times the concentration of the hemolymph (189). Hyperosmotic urine has also been demonstrated in the adult bloodsucking insect *Rhodnius* (140). Most adult insects and terrestrial insect larvae make a urine that is practically dry (202). The osmolality of this urine has, to our knowledge, not been determined.

The mechanisms through which the osmolality of the urine is changed are still quite obscure. The production of hypoosmotic urine is probably accomplished by active electrolyte reabsorption by epithelium with a low permeability to water. The epithelium concerned with this operation presumably can change permeability to water since the urine can also be made isosmotic. Thus, the insect hindgut in certain respects appears to function much the same as the bladder of molluscs, the nephridium of the earthworm, or the distal tubule of vertebrates.

The "dry urine", if isosmotic to the hemolymph, could likewise be made through passive water reabsorption, secondary to electrolyte reabsorption. Wigglesworth (202) associated the presence of a well-developed rectal gland with the ability to reabsorb water from the urine but he also points out that part of the solidification takes place in the elongated thin region of the hindgut.

Hyperosmolality of the urine could be brought about through two possible mechanisms, ion secretion into the hindgut fluid or active water reabsorption. The unlikelihood of the latter leaves us with the first possibility. In *Rhodnius* (140) it seems likely that potassium is secreted in the rectum since Ramsay (140) found the osmolality of the urine to increase in direct proportion to the potassium concentration but to be independent of the sodium concentration.

Whether or not sodium is secreted in the rectum of brackish-water species is not known. In the fresh-water larvae of *Aedes aegypti* the sodium concentration of the intestinal fluids is only about one half the sodium concentration of the hemolymph; however, when the larvae are kept in solutions with high sodium chloride concentrations, the sodium concentration in intestinal fluid never exceeds that of the hemolymph. To our knowledge the urine of brackish-water species has not been analyzed for sodium.

The correlation between structure and function in the excretory system of the insects is particularly intriguing, but needs to be explored much further. It appears that ions are secreted in the upper segment of the Malpighian tubule as well as in the rectum and reabsorbed in the lower segment and in some unidentified part of the hindgut. The epithelial cells in the upper segment and rectal gland are peculiar in that they have lamellae with many mitochondria in the apical part of the cell. We would suggest that this particular feature may be characteristic for ion secretion. The cells of the lower segment resemble the cells of the proximal tubule of most other species in that the mitochondria are situated more in the basal and middle parts of the cell. They also appear to function like those of a proximal tubule.

A COMPARISON BETWEEN INVERTEBRATE AND VERTEBRATE KIDNEYS

The excretory mechanism of invertebrates (except insects) is in many ways quite similar to that of vertebrates. The functional renal unit in vertebrates and in most invertebrates consists of (*a*) a part into which secretion or filtration takes place, (*b*) a proximal tubule with a high permeability to water, and (*c*) a distal tubule in which the permeability to water is usually low but can increase in response to the need for water conservation.

Filtration or secretion.—In most vertebrate nephrons an ultrafiltrate of the blood is formed by filtration through the glomerular capillaries. In the aglomerular fish the tubular fluid apparently is formed through secretion of solutes into the tubule with water following passively (103).

In many of the invertebrates the question of whether the tubular fluid is formed by secretion or filtration has not yet been answered. In the Malpighian tubules of insects a combination of the two seems to be involved: solute is secreted into the tubule, creating an osmotic gradient which causes bulk flow into the tubule of an ultrafiltrate of the hemolymph (123, 182). The function of the flame cells in Platyhelminthes and Aschelminthes may be of a similar nature, with the beating action of the cilia enhancing the flow through the tubules (167). Filtration is evident in molluscs, crustaceans, and annelids.

In the latter the coelomic fluid entering through the nephrostome is also an ultrafiltrate of the blood.

Proximal tubule.—The proximal tubular cells of the vertebrate nephron are characteristically cuboidal with brush borders on the luminal side. At the basal end of the cell, the membrane is thrown into folds which reach a short distance into the cell, giving it a striated appearance. Mitochondria are scattered throughout the cytoplasm with a few being found between the cytomembranes.

For most invertebrates electron-microscopical studies of the renal unit have not been made. In crustaceans, however, the description given by Anderson & Beams (2) of the cells of the labyrinth is almost identical to the description of mammalian proximal cells.

In vertebrates the proximal tubule shows a high permeability to water, and the fluid inside the tubule remains essentially isosmotic to the blood. This has been shown by micropuncture in amphibians (196) and mammals (50, 206). Marine teleosts which have only a proximal tubule (34) excrete a urine that is isosmotic or slightly hypoosmotic to the blood (44).

Although the fluid in the proximal tubule remains isosmotic to the blood, changes in its composition and volume are brought about through secretion and reabsorption of organic and inorganic solutes. In the mammalian kidney under normal conditions, the sodium concentration in the proximal tubule remains identical to that of the plasma. In the healthy marine teleost the sodium chloride concentration in the tubule decreases practically to zero as it is replaced by divalent ions, principally magnesium (44).

In the invertebrates the part of the excretory organ which corresponds to the proximal tubule appears to be permeable to water as it is in the vertebrates. Direct experimental evidence from annelids, crustaceans, and molluscs has shown that the fluid in this "proximal" part is isosmotic to the blood or hemolymph. Furthermore, it is evident that marine and brackish-water forms which presumably make an isosmotic urine have no "distal tubule" but only what corresponds to a proximal tubule. This has been found in Platyhelminthes, Aschelminthes, annelids, and crustaceans. In the crustaceans in which renal function has been most thoroughly investigated, it has been found that in some species sodium reabsorption and magnesium secretion are important functions of the proximal tubule as they are in marine teleosts.

Distal tubule.—Vertebrate distal tubular cells have no brush border although they do have a few microvilli. They differ from the proximal cells particularly in that the basal plasma membrane makes deep elaborate folds which reach deeper into the cell than do those of the proximal tubule. Mitochondria are densely packed between these cytomembranes while only a few are scattered throughout the cytoplasm (147).

Remarkably similar descriptions are given for the distal part of various invertebrate kidneys, e.g., the cells of the so-called bladder of snails (13) and the nephridial canal of the crayfish (8). Cellular specialization in the distal tubule of Platyhelminthes, Aschelminthes, and annelids has been described but until electron-microscopical studies of these structures become available it is not possible to say whether this specialization is similar to that of the vertebrates. The cuticle lining of the distal parts of the excretory canal of many fresh-water forms, i.e., nematodes, annelids, and insects, may possibly serve in reducing the permeability of these parts to water.

The characteristic function of the vertebrate distal tubule is that of electrolyte reabsorption against an osmotic gradient. When a dilute urine is being produced, the permeability to water is low, making the tubular fluid strongly hypoosmotic to the blood (206). The permeability of the tubule to water can, however, increase and the tubular fluid can then become essentially isosmotic to the blood (206). The increase in permeability to water is effected through the release of a neurohypophyseal hormone (ADH) in response to dehydration or osmotic loading.

The distal tubular fluid of certain invertebrates, such as the earthworm (137), the fresh-water clam (126), and the crayfish (125), has been shown to be hypoosmotic to the blood or hemolymph. It has also been shown in the earthworm (136) and in the crayfish (18) that the osmolality of the urine will increase toward that of the blood if the animals are exposed to osmotic loads. It seems possible that the permeability of the distal tubule of invertebrates may be regulated by hormones as it is in vertebrates.

In the phyla Platyhelminthes and Aschelminthes, no measurements of urine osmolality have been made so far as we know. The presence of a long, differentiated tubule in all the fresh-water forms, as well as the need for eliminating water, strongly indicates that members of these phyla may possess the ability to produce a hypoosmotic urine.

As discussed under insects, the structural and functional characteristics of the excretory system of insects differ fundamentally from those of vertebrates and other invertebrates. No further comparisons with vertebrates will be made here. From the foregoing discussion it is evident not only that excellent work has been done in the field of invertebrate kidney physiology, but also that many areas remain open for further investigations.

LITERATURE CITED

1. Allen, M. W., in *Nematology* (Sasser, J. N., and Jenkins, W. R., Eds., Univ. of North Carolina Press, Chapel Hill, N.C., 480 pp., 1960)
2. Anderson, E., and Beams, H. W., *Proc. Iowa Acad. Sci.*, **63**, 681–85 (1956)
3. Bairati, A., and Lehmann, F. E., *Protoplasma*, **45**, 525–39 (1956)
4. Beadle, L. C., *Biol. Rev.*, **18**, 172–83 (1943)
5. Beament, J. W. L., *J. Exptl. Biol.*, **38**, 277–90 (1961)
6. Beament, J. W. L., *Biol. Rev.*, **36**, 281–320 (1961)
7. Beams, H. W., Tahmisian, T. N., and Devine, R. L., *J. Biophys. Biochem. Cytol.*, **1**, 197–202 (1955)
8. Beams, H. W., Anderson, E., and Press, N., *Cytologia*, **21**, 50–57 (1956)
9. Beaver, P. C., *J. Parasitol.*, **16**, 13–23 (1929)
10. Berkaloff, A., *Ann. Sci. Nat.*, **2**, 869–947 (1960)

11. Berkaloff, A., *Compt. Rend. Acad. Sci.*, **248**, 466–69 (1959)

12. Binyon, J., *J. Marine Biol. Assoc. U. K.*, **41**, 161–74 (1961)

13. Bouillon, J., *Ann. Sci. Nat.*, **2**, 719–49 (1960)

14. Brand, Theodore Von, in *Nematology*, 249–66 (Sasser, J. N., and Jenkins, W. R., Eds., Univ. North Carolina Press, Chapel Hill, N. C., 480 pp., 1960)

15. Brodsky, W. A., Rehm, W. S., Dennis, W. H., and Miller, D. G., *Science*, **121**, 302–3 (1955)

16. Bryan, G. W., *J. Exptl. Biol.*, **37**, 83–99 (1960)

17. Bryan, G. W., *J. Exptl. Biol.*, **37**, 100–12 (1960)

18. Bryan, G. W., *J. Exptl. Biol.*, **37**, 113–28 (1960)

19. Burger, J. W., *Biol. Bull.*, **113**, 207–23 (1957)

20. Burger, J. W., and Hess, W. N., *Science*, **131**, 670–71 (1960)

21. Capstick, C. K., *J. Animal Ecol.* **28**, 189–210 (1959)

22. Carter, L., *J. Exptl. Biol.*, **34**, 71–84 (1957)

23. Chitwood, B. G., and Chitwood, M. B., *An Introduction to Nematology*, 11 (Monumental Printing Co., Baltimore, Md., 1950)

24. Coil, W. H., *Proc. Helminthol. Soc., Wash., D. C.*, **25**, 137–38 (1958)

25. Cosgrove, W. B., and Kessel, R. G., *J. Protozool.* **5**, 296–98 (1958)

26. Craig, R., *Ann. Rev. Entomol.*, **5**, 53–68 (1960)

27. Croghan, P. C., *J. Exptl. Biol.*, **35**, 213–18 (1958)

28. Croghan, P. C., *J. Exptl. Biol.*, **35**, 219–33 (1958)

29. Croghan, P. C., *J. Exptl. Biol.*, **35**, 425–36 (1958)

30. Day, M. F., and Briggs, M., *J. Ultrastruct. Res.*, **2**, 239–44 (1958)

31. Diskus, A., *Protoplasma*, **49**, 187–96 (1958)

32. Duchâteau, G., and Florkin, M., *Arch. Intern. Physiol. Biochim.*, **66**, 573–91 (1958)

33. Dunham, P. B., and Child, F. M., *Biol. Bull.*, **121**, 129–40 (1961)

34. Edwards, J. G., *Anat. Record*, **63**, 263–72 (1935)

35. Emanuel, C. P., and Martin, A. W., *Z. Vergleich. Physiol.*, **39**, 226–34 (1956)

36. Fauré-Fremiet, E., and Rouiller, C., *J. Protozool.*, **6**, 29-37 (1959)

37. Faust, R. G., and Filosa, M. F., *J. Cellular Comp. Physiol.*, **54**, 297–98 (1959)

38. Feustel, H., *Z. Wiss. Zool.*, **161**, 209–38 (1958)

39. Filipjev, I. N., *Smithsonian Inst. Misc. Collections*, **89**, No. 34 (1934)

40. Fingerman, M., and Fairbanks, L. D., *Com. Fisheries Rev.*, **19**, 10 (1957)

41. Fingerman, M., and Fairbanks, L. D., *Proc. Natl. Shellfisheries Assoc.*, **48**, 125–33 (1958)

42. Flemister, L. J., *Biol. Bull.*, **115**, 180–200 (1958)

43. Florkin, M., and Duchâteau, G., *Physiol. Comp. Oecol.*, **1**, 29–45 (1948)

44. Forster, R. P., *J. Cell. Comp. Physiol.*, **42**, 487–509 (1953)

45. Freeman, R. F. H., and Rigler, F. H., *J. Marine Biol. Assoc. U. K.*, **36**, 553–67 (1957)

46. Fuji, A., *Bull. Fac. Fisheries, Hokkaido Univ.*, **8**, 163–77 (1957)

47. Gagnepain, J., *Compt. Rend. Acad. Sci.*, **242**, 2777–79 (1956)

48. Gansen, P. Semal-van, *Enzymologia*, **20**, 98–108 (1958/59)

49. Goodrich, E. S., *Quart. J. Microscop. Sci.*, **86**, 113–392 (1945)

50. Gottschalk, C. W., and Mylle, M., *Am. J. Physiol.*, **196**, 927–36 (1959)

51. Green, J., *Nature*, **179**, 432 (1957)

52. Green, J. W., Harsch, M., Barr, L., and Prosser, C. L., *Biol. Bull.*, **116**, 76–87 (1959)

53. Greif, R. L., *Federation Proc.*, **19**, 362 (1960)

54. Grobben, C., *Arb. Zool. Inst. Wein*, **3**, 93–110 (1880)

55. Gross, W. J., *J. Exptl. Biol.*, **31**, 402–23 (1954)

56. Gross, W. J., *Biol. Bull.*, **121**, 290–301 (1961)

57. Gross, W. J., *Biol. Bull.*, **112**, 43–62 (1957)

58. Gross, W. J., *Biol. Bull.*, **116**, 248–57 (1959)

59. Gross, W. J., and Holland, P. V., *Physiol. Zool.*, **33**, 21–28 (1960)

60. Gross, W. J., and Marshall, L. A., *Biol. Bull.*, **119**, 440–53 (1960)

61. Gupta, P. D., *Ann. Entomol. Soc. Am.*, **53**, 632–38 (1960)

62. Haas, H., and Strenzke, K., *Biol. Zentr.*, **76**, 513–28 (1957)

63. Hegner, R. W., *Invertebrate Zoology*, 363 (MacMillan, New York, 570 pp., 1933)

64. Hirschmann, H., in *Nematology*, 125–80 (Sasser, J. N., and Jenkins, W. R., Eds., Univ. North Carolina

Press, Chapel Hill, N. C., 480 pp., 1960)

65. Hopkins, D. L., *Biol. Bull.*, **90**, 158–76 (1946)

66. Hyman, L. H., *The Invertebrates: Plate-helminthes and Rhynohocoela*, **II** (McGraw-Hill, New York, 1940)

67. Hyman, L. H., *The Invertebrates: Acanthocephala, Aschelminthes, and Entoprocta*, **III**, 94–243 (McGraw-Hill, New York, 572 pp., 1951)

68. Hynes, H. B. N., *J. Animal Ecol.*, **23**, 38–84 (1954)

69. Imms, A. D., *A General Textbook of Entomology*, 161–67 (Methuen, London, 886 pp., 1957)

70. Ishihara, R., *Nippon Sanshigaku Zasshi*, **27**, 374–81 (1958)

71. Jones, M. L., *Biol. Bull.*, **113**, 407–13 (1957)

72. Jørgensen, C. B., and Dales, R. P., *Physiol. Comp. Oecol.*, **4**, 357–74 (1957)

73. Jullien, A., Ripplinger, J., and Cardot, J., *J. Physiol. (Paris)*, **50**, 338–42 (1958)

74. Jullien, A., Ripplinger, J., and Cardot, J., *Comp. Rend. Soc. Biol.*, **152**, 634–36 (1958)

75. Jullien, A., Ripplinger, J., Cardot, J., Duvernoy, J., and Jolly, M., *Compt. Rend. Soc. Biol.*, **151**, 1214–17 (1957)

76. Kato, K., *Sci. Rept. Saitama Univ.*, **3**, 233–44 (1960)

77. Kinne, O., *Zool. Jahrb. Abt. Allgem. Zool. Physiol. Tiere*, **66**, 565–638 (1956)

78. Kinne, O., *Ann. Biol.*, **61**, 87–92 (1957)

79. Kitching, J. A., *Symp. Soc. Exptl. Biol.*, **8**, 63–75 (1954)

80. Kitching, J. A., *J. Exptl. Biol.*, **31**, 68–75 (1954)

81. Kitching, J. A., and Padfield, J. E., *J. Exptl. Biol.*, **37**, 73–82 (1960)

82. Klein, R. L., *J. Cellular Comp. Physiol.*, **53**, 241–58 (1959)

83. Komiya, Y., and Hashimoto, I., *Japan. J. Med. Sci. Biol.*, **11**, 339–46 (1958)

84. Krishnan, G., *Proc. Natl. Inst. Sci. India*, **18**, 241–55 (1953)

85. Krogh, A., *Osmotic Regulation in Aquatic Animals*, 10–27, 65–98 (Cambridge, 242 pp., 1939)

86. Kromhout, G. A., *J. Morphol.*, **72**, 167–81 (1943)

87. Kümmel, G., *Z. Naturforsch.*, **13b**, 677–79 (1958)

88. Kuntz, R. E., *Trans. Am. Microscop. Soc.* **76**, 269–74 (1957)

89. Lenhoff, H. M., and Bovaird, J., *Exptl. Cell Res.*, **20**, 384–94 (1960)

90. Lison, L., *Bull. Classe Sci., Acad. Roy. Belg.*, **23**, 317–27 (1937)

91. Lockwood, A. P. M., *J. Exptl. Biol.*, **36**, 546–55 (1959)

92. Lockwood, A. P. M., *J. Exptl. Biol.*, **38**, 647–58 (1961)

93. Lockwood, A. P. M., and Croghan, P. C., *Nature*, **184**, Suppl. 6, 370–71 (1959)

94. Logachev, E. D., *Doklady Akad. Nauk SSSR*, **123**, 958–60 (1958)*

95. Lövtrup, S., and Pigón, A., *Compt. Rend. Lab. Carlsberg, Ser. Chim.*, **28**, 1–36 (1951)

96. Lumbye, J., *Hydrobiologia*, **10**, 245–62 (1958)

97. Madanmohanrao, G., *Proc. Indian Acad. Sci., Sect. B*, **51**, 211–18 (1960)

98. Maluf, N. S. R., *Zool. Jahrb., Allgem. Zool. Physiol. Tiere*, **59**, 515–34 (1938–1939)

99. Maluf, N. S. R., *Biol. Bull.*, **81**, 127–33 (1941)

100. Maluf, N. S. R., *Biol. Bull.*, **81**, 134–48 (1941)

101. Maluf, N. S. R., *Biol. Bull.*, **81**, 235–60 (1941)

102. Marcuzzi, G., and Santoro, V., *Ric. Sci.*, **29**, 2576–81 (1959)

103. Marshall, E. K., and Grafflin, A. L., *J. Cellular Comp. Physiol.*, **1**, 161–76 (1932)

104. Martin, A. W., *Ann. Rev. Physiol.*, **20**, 225–42 (1958)

105. Meisenheimer, J., *Ergeb. Zool.*, **2**, 275 (1910)

106. Mercer, E. H., *Proc. Roy. Soc. (London), B*, **150**, 216–32 (1959)

107. Moltschanov, L., *Bull. Acad. Imp. Sci. St.-Pétersbourg, Ser. 6*, **2**, 957–67 (1908)

108. Morel, F., and Guinnebault, M., *J. Physiol. (Paris)*, **53**, 75–130 (1961)

109. Motwani, M. P., *Proc. Natl. Inst. Sci. India, B*, **21**, 227–46 (1955)

110. Nemenz, H., *J. Insect Physiol.*, **4**, 38–44 (1960)

111. Neumann, D., *Biol. Zentr.*, **79**, 585–605 (1960)

112. Neumann, D., *Biol. Zentr.*, **80**, 693–715 (1961)

113. Noirot, M. C., and Noirot-Timothee, C., *Compt. Rend. Acad. Sci.*, **251**, 2779–81 (1960)

114. Obuchowicz, L., *Bull. Soc. Amis Sci. Lettres Poznan, Ser. B*, **14**, 367–70 (1958)

115. Odening, K., *Biol. Zentr.*, **79**, 91–97 (1960)

116. Okuda, Y., *J. Biochem.* (*Tokyo*), **44**, 243–48 (1957)

117. Padmanabhanaidu, B., and Ramamurthy, R., *J. Exptl. Biol.*, **38**, 35–41 (1961)

118. Pan, C., *Bull. Museum Comp. Zool. Harvard Coll.*, **119**, 237–99 (1958)

119. Pappas, G. D., and Brandt, P. W., *J. Biophys. Biochem. Cytol.*, **4**, 485–87 (1958)

120. Parry, G., *J. Exptl. Biol.*, **31**, 601–13 (1954)

121. Parry, G., *J. Exptl. Biol.*, **32**, 408–22 (1955)

122. Parry, G., *J. Exptl. Biol.*, **34**, 417–23 (1957).

123. Patton, R. L., and Craig, R., *J. Exptl. Zool.*, **81**, 437–57 (1939)

124. Pedersen, K. J., *Z. Zellforsch. Mickroskop. Anat.* **53**, 609–28 (1961)

125. Peters, H., *Z. Morphol. Ökol. Tiere*, **30**, 355–81 (1935)

126. Picken, L. E. R., *J. Exptl. Biol.*, **14**, 20–34 (1937)

127. Plattner, F., *Arch. Ges. Physiol.*, **261**, 172–82 (1955)

128. Poll, M., *Rec. Inst. Zool. Torley-Rousseau*, **5**, 74 (1934)

129. Potts, W. T. W., *J. Exptl. Biol.*, **31**, 376–85 (1954)

130. Potts, W. T. W., *J. Exptl. Biol.*, **31**, 614–17 (1954)

131. Potts, W. T. W., *J. Exptl. Biol.*, **31**, 618–30 (1954)

132. Potts, W. T. W., *J. Exptl. Biol.*, **36**, 676–89 (1959)

133. Prosser, C. L., Green, J. W., and Chow, T. J., *Bicl. Bull.*, **109**, 99–107 (1955)

134. Prosser, C. L., and Brown, I. A., *Comparative Animal Physiology*, 60, 76 (Saunders, Philadelphia, 688 pp., 1961)

135. De Puytorac, P., *Arch. Anat. Microscop. Morphol. Exptl.*, **49**, 241–56 (1960)

136. Ramsay, J. A., *J. Exptl. Biol.*, **26**, 46–56 (1949)

137. Ramsay, J. A., *J. Exptl. Biol.*, **26**, 65–75 (1949)

138. Ramsay, J. A., *J. Exptl. Biol.*, **27**, 145–57 (1950)

139. Ramsay, J. A., *J. Exptl. Biol.*, **28**, 62–73 (1951)

140. Ramsay, J. A., *J. Exptl. Biol.*, **29**, 110–26 (1952)

141. Ramsay, J. A., *J. Exptl. Biol.*, **30**, 79–89 (1953)

142. Ramsay, J. A., *J. Exptl. Biol.*, **30**, 358–69 (1953)

143. Ramsay, J. A., *J. Exptl. Biol.*, **31**, 104–13 (1954)

144. Ramsay, J. A., *Nature*, **191**, 1115 (1961)

145. Rao, K. P., *J. Animal Morphol. Physiol.* **5**, 79–83 (1958)

146. Rao, K. P., and Ramachandra, R., *J. Exptl. Biol.*, **38**, 29–34 (1961)

147. Rhodin, J., *Am. J. Med.*, **24**, 661–75 (1958)

148. Riegel, J. A., *Biol. Bull.*, **116**, 272–84 (1959)

149. Riegel, J. A., *J. Exptl. Biol.*, **38**, 291–99 (1961)

150. Riegel, J. A., and Kirschner, L. B., *Biol. Bull.*, **118**, 296–307 (1960)

151. Riegel, J. A., and Lockwood, A. P. M., *J. Exptl. Biol.*, **38**, 491–99 (1961)

152. Robson, E. A., *Nature*, **179**, 787–88 (1957)

153. Roots, B. I., *Comp. Biochem. Physiol.*, **1**, 218–26 (1960)

154. Rosca, D. I., Wittenberger, C., and Rusdea, D., *Acad. Rep. Populare Romine, Filiala Cluj, Studii Cercetari Biol.*, **9**, 113–36 (1958)

155. Rotthauwe, H. W., *Veroeffentl. Inst. Meeresforsch. Bremerhaven*, **5**, 143–59 (1958)

156. Rudzinska, M. A., *J. Protozool.*, **4**, Suppl., 9 (1957)

157. Saxena, B. B., *J. Animal Morphol. Physiol.*, **2**, 87–95 (1955)

158. Schlieper, C., and Herrmann, F., *Zool. Jahrb., Abt. Anat. Ontog. Tiere*, **52**, 624–30 (1930)

159. Schoffeniels, E., *Arch. Intern. Physiol.*, **58**, 1–4 (1950)

160. Schoffeniels, E., *Arch. Intern. Physiol.*, **68**, 507–8 (1960)

161. Scholander, P. F., *Hvalradets Skrifter* (*Sci. Results Marine Biol. Res.*), **44**, 1–24 (1958)

162. Schuurmans Stekhoven, J. H., Jr., *Interrelations Between Free-Living and Parasitic Nematodes*, in *Papers on Helminth, 30-year Jubileum*, 637–39 (K. J. Skrjabin, Moscow, 1937)

163. Schwabe, E., *Z. Vergleich. Physiol.*, **19**, 183–236 (1933)

164. Seck, C., *Kiel. Meeresforsch.*, **13**, 220–43 (1957)

165. Sells, B. H., Six, N., and Brachet, J., *Exptl. Cell Res.*, **22**, 246–55 (1961)

166. Senft, A. W., *Biol. Bull.*, **117**, 387 (1959)

167. Senft, A. W., Philpott, D. E., and Pelofsky, A. H., *J. Parasitol.*, **47**, 217–29 (1961)

168. Shaw, J., *J. Exptl. Biol.*, **36**, 126–44 (1959)

169. Shaw, J., *J. Exptl. Biol.*, **36**, 157-76 (1959)

170. Shaw, J., *J. Exptl. Biol.*, **37**, 534-47 (1960)
171. Shaw, J., *J. Exptl. Biol.*, **37**, 548-56 (1960)
172. Shaw, J., *J. Exptl. Biol.*, **37**, 557-72 (1960)
173. Shaw, J., in *Comparative Biochemistry*, **2**, 471-518 (Florkin, M., Ed., Academic, New York, 685 pp., 1960)
174. Shaw, J., *J. Exptl. Biol.*, **38**, 135-52 (1961)
175. Shaw, J., *J. Exptl. Biol.*, **38**, 153-62 (1961)
176. Shaw, J., and Sutcliffe, D. W., *J. Exptl. Biol.*, **38**, 1-16 (1961)
177. Smith, D. S., and Littau, V. C., *J. Histochem. Cytochem.*, **8**, 312 (1960)
178. Smith, D. S., and Littau, V. C., *J. Biophys. Biochem. Cytol.*, **8**, 103-33 (1960)
179. Smith, R. I., *Publ. Union Intern. Sci. Biol.*, *Paris*, *Ser. B*, **24**, 93-107 (1958)
180. Soldatova, I. N., and Turpaeva, E. P., *Doklady Akad. Nauk SSSR*, **130**, 126-27 (1960)*
181. Spiegler, P. E., *J. Insect Physiol.*, **8**, 127-32 (1962)
182. Srivastava, P. N., *J. Insect Physiol.*, **8**, 223-32 (1962)
183. Srivastava, P. N., and Gupta, P. D., *J. Insect Physiol.*, **6**, 163-67 (1961)
184. Stobbart, R. H., *J. Exptl. Biol.*, **36**, 641-53 (1959)
185. Stobbart, R. H., *J. Exptl. Biol.*, **37**, 594-605 (1960)
186. Strenzke, K., and Neumann, D., *Biol. Zentr.*, **79**, 199-225 (1960)
187. Strohl, J., *Die Exkretion (Mollusken)*, *Hans Winterstein Handbuch Vergleich. Physiol.*, 443-607 (Jena, Verlag von Gustav Fischer, 1924)
188. Survorow, E. K., *Zool. Anz.*, **32**, 674-76 (1908)

189. Sutcliffe, D. W., *Nature*, **187**, 331-32 (1960)
190. Sutcliffe, D. W., *J. Exptl. Biol.*, **38**, 501-19 (1961)
191. Thomas, L. P., *Bull. Marine Sci. Gulf Carib.*, **11**, 158-60 (1961)
192. Treherne, J. E., *J. Exptl. Biol.*, **31**, 386-401 (1954)
193. Ullrich, K. J., Kramer, K., and Boylan, J. W., *Progr. Cardiovascular Diseases*, **3**, 395-431 (1961)
194. Urich, K., *Naturwissenschaften*, **44**, 356-57 (1957)
195. Urich, K., *Z. Vergleich. Physiol.*, **41**, 342-63 (1958)
196. Walker, A. M., Hudson, C. L., Findley, T., and Richards, A. N., *Am. J. Physiol.*, **118**, 121 (1937)
197. Weel, P. B. van, *Z. Vergleich. Physiol.*, **39**, 492-506 (1957)
198. Weinstein, P. P., *Exptl. Parasitol.*, **1**, 363-76 (1952)
199. Weinstein, P. P., *Host Influence on Parasite Physiology*, 65-92 (Stauber, L. E., Ed., Rutgers Univ. Press, New Brunswick, N. J., 96 pp., 1960)
200. Weinstein, P. P., and Haskins, W. T., *Exptl. Parasitol.*, **4**, 226-43 (1955)
201. Wigglesworth, V. B., *J. Exptl. Biol.*, **8**, 428-42 (1931)
202. Wigglesworth, V. B., *Quart. J. Microscop. Sci.*, **75**, 131-50 (1932-33)
203. Wigglesworth, V. B., *J. Exptl. Biol.*, **15**, 235-47 (1938)
204. Wigglesworth, V. B., and Salpeter, M. M., *J. Insect Physiol.*, **8**, 299-307 (1962)
205. Willey, C. H., *Anat. Record*, **60**, 84-85 (1934)
206. Wirz, H., *Helv. Physiol. Acta*, **14**, 353-62 (1956)
207. Yamamoto, G., *Bull. Marine Biol. Sta. Asamushi, Tohoku Univ.*, **9**, 141-44 (1959)

* English translation will be announced in *Technical Translations*, issued by the Office of Technical Services, U. S. Department of Commerce, and will be made available by the Photoduplication Service, Library of Congress, and by the SLA Translation Center at the John Crerar Library, Chicago, Illinois.

AUTHOR INDEX

SUBJECT INDEX

108, 113, 619
muscle effects of, 621
myosin binding of, 256
phosphorylation and, 108
sodium transport and, 616-20
thyroid actions of, 363, 621
venous system and, 222

E

Eclampsia
review on, 263
Elastin
chemistry of, 46
connective tissue and, 46
Electroencephalography
see Brain, electrical
activity of
Electrolytes
absorption of, 186, 187
age changes and, 124
cellular exchanges of, 108, 109, 113, 114
cell metabolism and, 108, 123
endocrine regulation of
review on, 91
kidney handling of, 102-9
metabolism of, 91-132
microsome binding of, 27, 28
neurohypophyseal
responses and, 413-15
parathyroid effects on, 343
stomach secretion and, 178, 179
tissue content of, 123, 124
transport of, 102-9
ADH and, 405, 413
weak
excretion of, 114-18
Emotion
ADH secretion and, 401
Emphysema
airway resistance in, 150
Endocrines
biological rhythms and, 593, 594
cell permeability and, 292
cyclic AMP and, 292
general mechanism of
action of, 291
metabolism controlled by, 291-317
see also individual
endocrine glands and
hormones
Endotoxins
shock from, 225
Enterogastrone
stomach secretion and, 178
Enzymes
biliary, 184
diuretic actions and, 129

kidney content of, 126
leukocytic, 203
pancreatic, 182-84
pepsin, 180
reproductive tissues and, 269
Epileptic seizures
thresholds for, 282
Erythropoiesis
see Red corpuscles,
erythropoiesis
Esophagus
motility of, 169-71
gastroesophageal reflux, 171
heartburn and, 170, 171
normal pressures in, 169
review on, 171
nervous control of, 170
secondary peristalsis in, 170
sphincter of, 170
Estrogens
adrenal cortex effects of, 282
adrenal secretion of, 278
atherosclerosis and, 282
biosynthesis of, 278
bone actions of, 282
calcium metabolism and, 350
congeners of, 272, 283
conjugation of, 276, 278, 283
coronary anastomoses and, 249
determination of, 283, 284
erythropoiesis and, 282
excretion of, 265, 278
gonadotropin secretion and, 264-68
goitrogenesis and, 282
hypophyseal actions of, 280, 282
hypothalamic effect of, 264
17-ketosteroid excretion
and, 279
lactation and, 276
mammary gland and, 276, 281
mast cells and, 45
mechanism of action of, 279, 280
membrane transport and, 611
metabolism of, 277, 278, 284
mucopolysaccharides and, 56, 280
ovarian effects of, 272, 273, 279
ovarian secretion of, 273
oviduct action of, 279
oxytocin and, 397
placental action of, 280

placental content of, 274, 275
plasma proteins and, 279
progesterone interaction
with, 269
prolactin synthesis and, 268
purification of, 283
secretion of
abortion and, 277
gonadotropins and, 265, 266, 269
polycystic ovaries and, 284
seizure thresholds and, 282
separation of, 284
steroidogenesis and, 282
thyroxin secretion and, 282
uterine effects of, 67, 269, 270, 273, 279, 280, 415
vaginal effects of, 270
Estrous cycle
diurnal rhythms and, 594
enzyme changes and, 269, 270
hysterectomy and, 270
mucoproteins and, 270
oxytocin effects on, 419
periodicity of, 270
uterine changes in, 269
vaginal changes in, 270
Estrus
hypothalamus and, 264
testosterone and, 267
Excretion, invertebrate, 631-54
annelid, 638-40
arthropod, 643-52
aschelminthic, 636-38
coelenterate, 634, 635
contractile vacuoles and, 632-34
crustacean, 643-47
crystonephric tubules and, 650, 651
echinoderm, 635
flame cells and, 635, 636, 652
gills and, 650
green glands and, 643
hindgut and, 648-52
insect, 647-52, 654
invertebrate-vertebrate
relations, 652-54
kidneys and, 640, 641, 645-47, 650-54
labyrinth and, 645, 653
Malpighian tubules and, 647, 648, 650-52
molluscan, 640-43
nephridia and, 638, 639, 643, 644, 647
platyhelminthic, 635, 636
protonephridia and, 636-38
protozoan, 632-34

CUMULATIVE INDEX

VOLUMES 21 TO 25

INDEX OF CONTRIBUTING AUTHORS

INDEX OF CHAPTER TITLES

VOLUMES 21 TO 25